p.178

6.60

Principles of Advanced Mathematics

BRUCE E. MESERVE
Montclair State College
Upper Montclair, New Jersey

ANTHONY J. PETTOFREZZO
Montclair State College
Upper Montclair, New Jersey

DOROTHY T. MESERVE
Upper Montclair, New Jersey

Principles of

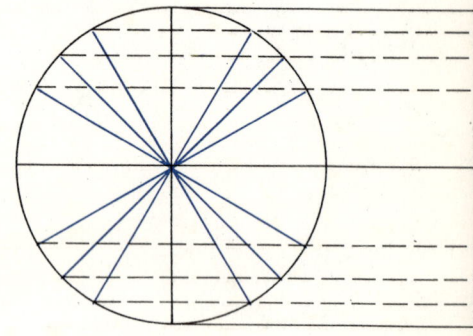

Advanced Mathematics

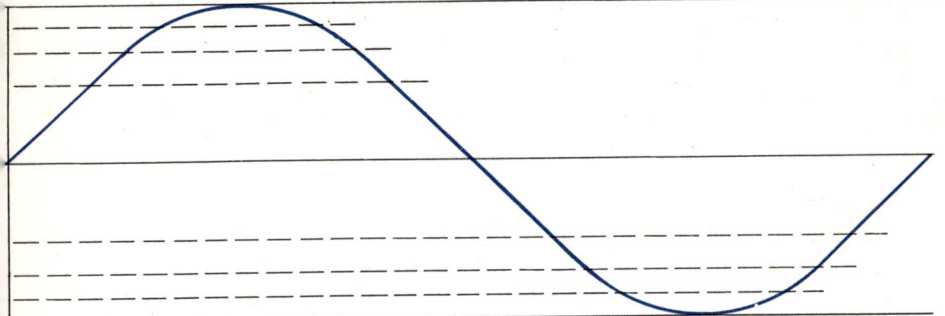

THE L. W. SINGER COMPANY
A DIVISION OF RANDOM HOUSE, INC.
Syracuse · Atlanta · Burlingame · Chicago · Dallas

Copyright © 1964 by The L. W. Singer Company, Inc.
All rights reserved. No part of this book may be reproduced in any form without permission from the publisher.
264.2   *Manufactured in the United States of America*   71233

PREFACE

Principles of Advanced Mathematics is designed to prepare students for a course in analytic geometry and calculus as their next course in mathematics. Students who master most of the material in this book may acquire sufficient background in analytic geometry to proceed directly into a course in calculus.

This book is intended for students who have a mathematical background comparable to that which may be obtained from *A First Course in Geometry* and *Second Course in Algebra* in this series. Some teachers may feel that their students have already mastered some topics such as:

    sets, relations, and functions—Chapter 1;

    measurements in geometry—Chapter 3;

    trigonometry and circular functions—Chapters 4 and 5.

In each such case the Keyed Practice at the end of the appropriate chapter may be used to identify any aspects of the topic deserving class discussion; the tests at the end of the chapter may be used to check the student's mastery of these prerequisites for future work in mathematics. Basically, the end-of-chapter materials for each chapter of the book enable the teacher:

    to identify the major topics from the summary;

    to identify the most important mathematical terms from the list of words at the end of the summary;

    to identify topics on which additional class work is needed from the Keyed Practice; and

    to check the student's mastery of the mathematical content of the chapter using the chapter tests.

There is also a separate booklet of Achievement Tests which may be used to check the student's mastery of indicated chapters and, when the chapters are taken in order, his mastery of the cumulative material at major stages of the course.

Throughout *Principles of Advanced Mathematics* there is an emphasis upon the underlying mathematical structure and the use of proven pedagogical approaches to the subject matter. There is ample material for students who have had accelerated courses in algebra and geometry and for students who have studied supplementary topics either in experimental programs or in special sections of algebra and geometry.

The mathematical content of Chapters 1 through 8, §§ 9–1 through 9–5, and §§ 10–1 through 10–9 is considered by the authors to be essential in the preparation of students for calculus. The rest of the book includes highly desirable and useful supplementary material which may be selected

PREFACE

according to the needs of the students and the time available. The mathematical content of Chapter 1 should be mastered before Chapters 2, 3, 4, and 6 are considered; any one of these chapters may be considered immediately after Chapter 1. The rational, real, and complex number systems are systematically developed in Chapter 6 and considered to be part of the essential background for calculus. Chapters 4 and 5 should precede Chapters 9 and 11; Chapters 2, 6, 7, and 8 should precede Chapters 9 and 10; Chapter 11 should precede Chapter 12. The minimal mathematical content prerequisite to calculus may be supplemented to whatever extent time and interest allow with work on probability density functions and other statistical concepts in Chapter 9, limits (the basic concept of calculus) in Chapter 10, vectors in Chapter 11, and abstract algebra with an emphasis upon the algebra of matrices in Chapter 12.

The varying interests and abilities of students have been recognized by the flexible mathematical structure of the book, the wide variety of material which provides an opportunity to select topics, and the careful gradation of the sets of exercises. As in the other books of this series, the exercises are divided into three levels of difficulty: simple applications of the principles are developed first, down to a point marked by three blue dots • • •; then follow more difficult exercises requiring more than a routine application of the principles just considered; finally there are exercises (each preceded by a blue dot •) which will challenge the thinking of the superior students.

Careful attention has been given to readability. New terms are defined; accuracy and precision are considered; topics are related to the student's experience in algebra and geometry. Selected examples illustrate new concepts. *Test Yourself* exercises with answers at the end of each chapter provide the student with an immediate check on his understanding. Ample practice material is provided so that skills and understandings will become fixed.

The authors have had many years of experience teaching high school students and have had a special interest in the preparation of students for college. One author has made an extensive survey of the expectations of colleges regarding the mathematical preparation of their incoming students. All authors are well acquainted with the Report of the Commission on Mathematics appointed by the College Entrance Examination Board, the work of the School Mathematics Study Group, and the current curricular changes in secondary schools and colleges. The authors gratefully acknowledge the helpful advice which they have received from many teachers and students.

B. E. M.   A. J. P.   D. T. M.

CONTENTS

1 Sets of Elements   1

1. Sets and subsets
2. Operations with sets
3. The algebra of sets
4. Sets of numbers
5. Statements and their graphs
6. Sets of ordered pairs
7. Numbers as distances
8. Relations
9. Inverse relations
10. Functions

2 Permutations, Combinations, and Probability   45

1. Permutations
2. Special permutations
3. Combinations
4. The binomial theorem
5. Mathematical probability
6. Sample spaces
7. The addition law of probability
8. Conditional probability
9. Mathematical expectation

3 Measurements of Geometric Figures   97

1. Units of measure
2. Approximate computation
3. Linear measurements
4. Distance formulas
5. Angular measurements
6. Geometric figures
7. Areas
8. Volumes
9. Solids of revolution (Supplementary)

4 Circular Functions and Their Graphs   147

1. Trigonometric functions
2. Solution of special triangles
3. Circular functions
4. Quadrantal and negative angles
5. Line values of circular functions
6. Graphs of sines and cosines
7. Graphs of tangents and cotangents
8. Graphs of secants and cosecants
9. Special methods of graphing
10. Inverses of sines and cosines
11. Inverses of tangents and cotangents
12. Inverses of secants and cosecants
13. Polar coordinates

CONTENTS

5 Statements Involving Circular Functions — 205

1. Identities
2. Values of circular functions
3. Solution of right triangles
4. Law of sines
5. Law of cosines
6. Law of tangents (Supplementary)
7. Area
8. Multiple-angle formulas
9. Identities involving multiple-angles
10. Equations

6 Systems of Numbers — 259

1. Mathematical systems
2. Groups
3. Integers
4. Rational numbers
5. Integral domains and fields
6. Real numbers
7. Complex numbers
8. Representations of complex numbers
9. Products and quotients
10. De Moivre's theorem

7 Linear and Quadratic Expressions — 327

1. Equations of lines on a plane
2. Graphs of linear relations
3. Systems of linear relations
4. Linear equations in several variables
5. Quadratic functions of one variable
6. Circles and spheres
7. Parabolas
8. Ellipses
9. Hyperbolas
10. Quadratic expressions in two variables
11. Systems of relations
12. Variation

8 Polynomials — 415

1. Polynomial expressions
2. Remainder and factor theorems
3. Synthetic division
4. Number of roots of a polynomial equation
5. Descartes' Rule of Signs
6. Rational roots
7. Location principle
8. Roots and coefficients
9. Polynomial inequalities
10. Rational functions
11. Formula for $\sqrt[r]{N}$ (Supplementary)

9 Special Functions — 473

1. Power functions
2. Exponential and logarithmic functions
3. Exponential and logarithmic equations
4. Parametric equations

viii

5. Absolute value and other functions
6. Probability density functions
7. Mean, variance, standard deviation
8. Probability distribution functions
9. Binomial density functions
10. Other density functions (Supplementary)
11. Probability for continuous variables (Supplementary)

10 Sequences, Series, and Limits 531

1. Limits
2. Sequences of numbers
3. Null sequences
4. Limit of a sequence of numbers
5. Theorems on limits
6. Finite series
7. Infinite series
8. The binomial series
9. Mathematical induction
10. Area
11. Limits of functions
12. Rates of change

11 Vectors 595

1. Numbers and vectors
2. Addition and subtraction of vectors
3. Multiplication of a vector by a scalar
4. Linear functions
5. Rectangular cartesian coordinates
6. Division of a line segment in a given ratio
7. Scalar product
8. Direction cosines
9. Vector product
10. Equation of a plane
11. Equations of a line
12. Applications

12 The Algebra of Matrices 661

1. Matrices
2. Multiplication of matrices
3. Special matrices
4. Special complex matrices
5. Rank of a matrix
6. Inverse of a matrix
7. Systems of matrices
8. Translations
9. Rotations
10. Rigid motions and dilations

Tables 730

Index 749

Chapter 1

Sets of Elements

§ 1-1 Sets and subsets

The concept of a set is fundamental to the study of mathematics and at least intuitively familiar to you. In this chapter we briefly consider the notation, definitions, and properties of sets so that these may be used freely throughout the following chapters.

The word "set" will not be defined; however we shall describe a **set** as a collection of clearly identified objects or ideas such as numbers, persons, figures, and so on. A given set is **well-defined** if it is always possible to determine whether any particular object or idea does or does not belong to the set; that is, is or is not a **member** of the set. In mathematics we are only concerned with well-defined sets. Objects or ideas which are members of a set are called the **elements** of the set. It is customary to use capital letters to designate specific sets. The elements of a set are usually represented by small letters. The relation of **membership** is the only important relation between a given object and a given set. We use the notation

$b \in A$ for "b is a member of A";
$b \notin A$ for "b is not a member of A."

The entire membership of a set may be specified in various ways. In the **roster** or **listing** method braces are used to enclose a list of the names of elements of the set. Thus, if D stands for the set of positive integers less than 5, we write

$$D = \{1, 2, 3, 4\}.$$

We read this as, "D is the set whose elements are 1, 2, 3, and 4." If E represents the set of positive even integers, then we may write

$$E = \{2, 4, 6, 8, \cdots\}.$$

The array of three dots is used to indicate that there are more elements in the set than those actually shown. The three dots may be used whenever there can be no doubt as to the identity of the missing elements.

If the elements of a set such as D may be counted, the set is called a **finite set**. A set having an unlimited number of elements such as the set E of positive even integers, the set of real numbers, or the set of points

1

SETS OF ELEMENTS

on a line is called an **infinite set.** Notice that the roster method is useful only for finite sets or for such infinite sets as have a pattern which is obvious to the reader. In other cases we may define a set by a verbal rule. For example, we may define a set R as the set of all real numbers.

The most common relations among sets are summarized in the following array:

NOTATION	READ AS	DEFINITION
$A \subseteq B$	A is a **subset** of B.	If $x \in A$, then $x \in B$.
$A \not\subseteq B$	A is not a subset of B.	There exists an $x \in A$, $x \notin B$.
$A = B$	A is **equal** to B.	$A \subseteq B$ and $B \subseteq A$.
$A \neq B$	A is not equal to B.	$A \not\subseteq B$ or $B \not\subseteq A$.
$A \subset B$	A is a **proper subset** of B.	$A \subseteq B$ and $A \neq B$.
$A \not\subset B$	A is not a proper subset of B.	$A = B$ or $A \not\subseteq B$.

Notice that A is a subset of B if and only if each element of A is an element of B; A is equal to B if and only if the two sets have the same elements; A is a proper subset of B if and only if each element of A is an element of B and there is at least one element of B that is not an element of A.

Illustrations. Let $C = \{1, 2, 3\}$, $D = \{3, 1, 2\}$, $E = \{1, 2, 3, 4, 5\}$, and $F = \{3, 4, 5\}$. Then $C \subseteq D$, $D \subseteq C$, $C = D$, $C \subseteq E$, $E \not\subseteq C$, $C \neq E$, $C \subset E$, $C \not\subseteq F$, and $C \neq F$.

Frequently we wish to discuss sets of elements which are subsets of some fixed reference set. Such a reference set is called the **universe** or the **universal set** under discussion and is denoted by U. For example, if U is the set of real numbers x, then the set of solutions (that is, the **solution set** or **truth set**) of the equation $x^2 = 9$ has two elements, 3 and -3. We write in **set-builder notation**

$$\{x \mid x^2 = 9\}$$

for "the set of all x such that $x^2 = 9$." Then

$$\{x \mid x^2 = 9\} = \{3, -3\}.$$

Notice that $\{x \mid x^2 = 9\}$ is another way of writing the solution set $\{3, -3\}$ of the statement $x^2 = 9$. Whenever you are asked to find the solution set of a statement, the second form (that is, the simpler one) should be used for the answer.

When U is the set of real numbers, the set $\{x \mid x^2 + 2 = 0\}$ has no elements. Such a set is called the **null set** or **empty set.** Either $\emptyset$ or $\{\ \}$ may be used to denote the null set. By definition the null set is a subset of every set.

§ 1-1 SETS AND SUBSETS

Example 1. Find the solution set for each statement (i) when U is the set of positive integers; (ii) when U is the set of all integers (positive, negative, and zero): (a) $x + 2 = 2 + x$; (b) $x - 2 = 2 - x$; (c) $x + 2 = x$; (d) $x^2 = 9$; (e) $x^2 < 9$.

(i) The solution sets are: (a) U; (b) $\{2\}$; (c) $\emptyset$; (d) $\{3\}$; (e) $\{1, 2\}$.

(ii) The solution sets are: (a) U; (b) $\{2\}$; (c) $\emptyset$; (d) $\{3, -3\}$; (e) $\{-2, -1, 0, 1, 2\}$.

Example 2. List all the subsets of the set $S = \{a, b, c\}$.

$\emptyset, \{a, b, c\}, \{a\}, \{b\}, \{c\}, \{a, b\}, \{a, c\}, \{b, c\}$.

TEST YOURSELF

Identify each statement as true or false if $A = \{1, 2, 3\}$ and $B = \{2, 3, 4\}$:

1. $1 \in A$. 2. $1 \in B$. 3. $2 \notin A$. 4. $A \subseteq B$.

Give the solution set for each statement when U is the set of positive integers:

5. $x + 2 = 7$.
6. $x + 2 = 0$.
7. $x + 5 = 5 + x$.
8. $|x - 5| = 1$.

Answers to Test Yourself Exercises may be found at the end of each chapter.

EXERCISES

Let $D = \{0, 1, 2, 3, \cdots, 9\}$, $E = \{0, 2, 4, 6, 8\}$, and $P = \{2, 3, 5, 7\}$. Identify the statements in Exercises 1 through 12 as true or false:

1. $3 \in D$.
2. $3 \in E$.
3. $E \subseteq D$.
4. $E \subset D$.
5. $E \subset P$.
6. $5 \notin E$.
7. $5 \notin D$.
8. $\{2, 3, 4\} \subset D$.
9. $\{2, 3, 4\} \subset E$.
10. $\{2, 3, 4\} \not\subset P$.
11. $15 \in D$.
12. $3 + 4 \in P$.

• • •

13 through 22. Write each of the statements in Exercises 1 through 10 in words.

The three blue dots between Exercises 12 and 13 and the single dot in front of parts (f) and (g) of Exercise 25 are used throughout the book to indicate grouping of exercises according to difficulty. The exercises before the three dots are relatively easy; the exercises after the dots are of moderate difficulty except for the exercises or parts of exercises which are preceded by single dots and are included for students who can do superior work.

SETS OF ELEMENTS

23. List all the subsets of $\{q, p, r\}$.
24. List all the subsets of $\{1, 3, 5, 7\}$.
25. State the number of subsets for a set having: **(a)** one element; **(b)** two elements; **(c)** three elements; **(d)** four elements; **(e)** five elements; ●**(f)** ten elements; ●**(g)** n elements.

In Exercises 26 through 29 give the solution set for each statement when U is **(a)** *the set of positive integers;* **(b)** *the set of all integers:*

26. $x + 5 = 11$. **28.** $|x| \leq 3$.
27. $2x - 4 = 13$. **29.** $|x - 2| \leq 2$.

30. Use the roster method to describe: **(a)** the set of vowels in the word *Ticonderoga;* **(b)** the set of prime numbers less than 25; **(c)** the set of all Americans born on the moon.

31. Use a verbal statement to describe each of the following sets: **(a)** $\{2, 4, 6, 8\}$; **(b)** $\{1, 4, 9, 16, 25\}$; **(c)** $\{\sqrt{2}, \sqrt{3}, \sqrt{5}, \sqrt{6}, \sqrt{7}, \sqrt{8}, \sqrt{10}, \cdots\}$; ●**(d)** {January, March, May, July, August, October, December}.

§ 1–2 Operations with sets

We now represent the elements of a universal set U as the points of a **rectangular region,** that is, the points interior to and on a rectangle. However, the region determined by any simple closed curve may be used (Figure 1–1).

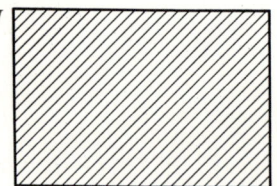
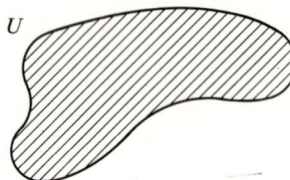

Figure 1–1

The elements of any set $A \subseteq U$ may be represented as points of the rectangular region U. Normally we use an oval or circular region to represent $A \subset U$ (Figure 1–2).

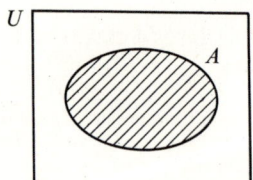
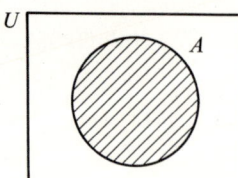
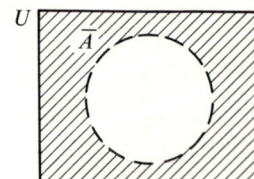

Figure 1–2 Figure 1–3

§ 1-2 OPERATIONS WITH SETS

The set of elements of U which are not elements of A is called the **complement** of A and denoted by $\bar{A}$ (Figure 1-3). Sometimes the symbol A' or $\sim A$ is used instead of $\bar{A}$. In Figure 1-3 notice that the circle is shown by a broken line since the points on the circle are points of A rather than $\bar{A}$. Also note that the complement of $\bar{A}$ is A; that is, $\bar{\bar{A}} = A$. Diagrams such as those in Figures 1-2 and 1-3 are useful in visualizing operations with sets and relations among sets. These figures are called **Venn diagrams**.

The operation (**complementation**) of finding $\bar{A}$ for a given set A and a given universe U is an example of a **unary operation** since it is an operation on a single element, a set such as A. Any operation (such as addition, subtraction, multiplication, and division) which involves two elements is called a **binary operation.** We now consider two binary operations on sets.

Given two sets A and B, the set of all elements x such that $x \in A$ and $x \in B$ is the **intersection** of A and B. We write $A \cap B$ (read as "A cap B") for this intersection. The four basic ways in which non-empty sets A and B can intersect are shown in Figure 1-4. The case $A \cap B = B$ we consider to be in principle the same as $A \cap B = A$. Notice that in each case $A \cap B \subseteq A$ and $A \cap B \subseteq B$. In the second diagram where $A \cap B = \emptyset$ the sets A and B are called **disjoint** sets.

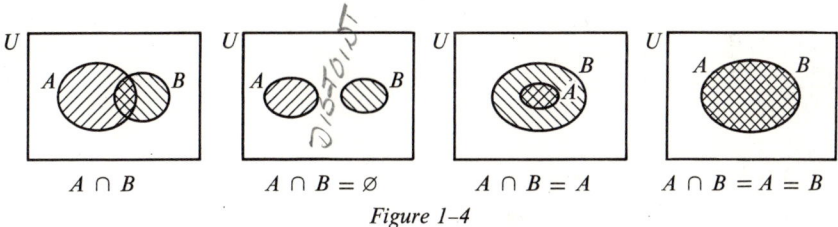

$A \cap B \qquad A \cap B = \emptyset \qquad A \cap B = A \qquad A \cap B = A = B$

Figure 1-4

Given two sets A and B, the set of elements x such that $x \in A$ or $x \in B$ (that is, x is a member of at least one of the sets A, B) is called the **union** of A and B. We write $A \cup B$ (read as "A cup B") for this union. The four basic ways in which nonempty sets A and B can form unions are shown in Figure 1-5. The case $A \cup B = A$ is considered to be in principle the same as $A \cup B = B$. Notice that in all four cases $A \subseteq A \cup B$ and $B \subseteq A \cup B$.

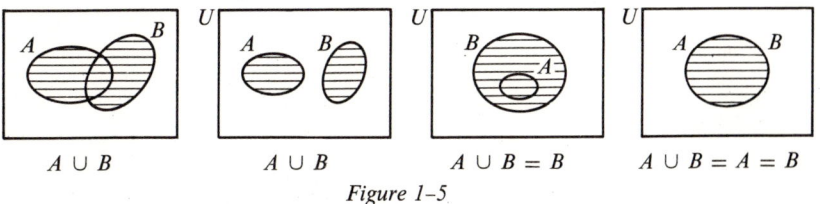

$A \cup B \qquad A \cup B \qquad A \cup B = B \qquad A \cup B = A = B$

Figure 1-5

5

SETS OF ELEMENTS

TEST YOURSELF

Let $A = \{1, 2, 3\}$, $B = \{2, 3, 4\}$, and $U = \{1, 2, 3, 4, 5\}$. In each exercise identify the specified set by the roster method or as one of the given sets:

1. $\bar{A}$.
2. $\bar{B}$.
3. $A \cap B$.
4. $A \cup B$.
5. $A \cup \emptyset$.
6. $A \cap \emptyset$.
7. $B \cup U$.
8. $B \cap U$.

EXERCISES

Let $R = \{1, 3, 5\}$, $S = \{2, 4\}$, $T = \{1, 2, 3, 5\}$, and $U = \{1, 2, 3, 4, 5\}$. In Exercises 1 through 16 identify the specified set by the roster method or as one of the given sets:

1. $\bar{R}$.
2. $\bar{U}$.
3. $R \cap T$.
4. $S \cap T$.
5. $S \cap R$.
6. $S \cap U$.
7. $U \cap \emptyset$.
8. $R \cup S$.

9. $\overline{R \cup T}$.
10. $S \cup T$.
11. $S \cup \emptyset$.
12. $\overline{S \cap \emptyset}$.
13. $\overline{S} \cup S$.
14. $T \cap T$.
15. $\overline{\emptyset \cap \emptyset}$.
16. $\overline{S \cup T}$.

- 17. If $A = \{2, 3, 5\}$ and $B = \{2, 3, 7\}$, express in terms of A and B for 30 and 42: (a) the L. C. M.; and (b) the G. C. D.
- 18. Find sets A and B and repeat Exercise 17 for 858 and 210.
- 19. Find sets A and B and repeat Exercise 17 for 1015 and 2310.

§ 1-3 The algebra of sets

The operations of union and intersection of sets have many of the properties of addition and multiplication in ordinary algebra. The laws in the following array are now postulated for sets. They may be used to prove statements as in ordinary algebra and geometry.

Commutative Laws

ORDINARY ALGEBRA	ALGEBRA OF SETS
$a + b = b + a$	$A \cup B = B \cup A$
$a \times b = b \times a$	$A \cap B = B \cap A$

Associative Laws

ORDINARY ALGEBRA	ALGEBRA OF SETS
$a + (b + c) = (a + b) + c$	$A \cup (B \cup C) = (A \cup B) \cup C$
$a \times (b \times c) = (a \times b) \times c$	$A \cap (B \cap C) = (A \cap B) \cap C$

§ 1-3 THE ALGEBRA OF SETS

Distributive Laws

ORDINARY ALGEBRA   ALGEBRA OF SETS

$a \times (b + c) = a \times b + a \times c$ $A \cap (B \cup C) = (A \cap B) \cup (A \cap C)$
 $A \cup (B \cap C) = (A \cup B) \cap (A \cup C)$

Notice that there are two distributive laws in the algebra of sets but only one in ordinary algebra. Each law may be illustrated by means of Venn diagrams.

Example 1. Use Venn diagrams to illustrate the statement that

$$A \cup (B \cup C) = (A \cup B) \cup C.$$

Three sets A, B, C are required. We use three regions for A, B, C, copy the figure twice, shade the part that is specified in each member of the equation, and observe that the totality (union) of shaded portions is the same for each figure (member of the equation).

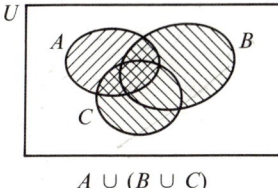
$A \cup (B \cup C)$

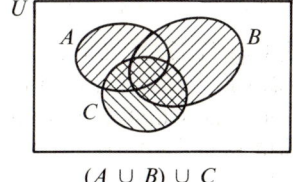
$(A \cup B) \cup C$

Figure 1-6

The properties of the **additive identity element** 0 and the **multiplicative identity element** 1 in ordinary algebra are very similar to those of the empty set $\varnothing$ and the universal set U respectively in the algebra of sets:

$$a + 0 = a, \qquad A \cup \varnothing = A;$$
$$a \times 1 = a, \qquad A \cap U = A;$$
$$a \times 0 = 0, \qquad A \cap \varnothing = \varnothing$$

The properties

$$\overline{\overline{A}} = A, \quad \varnothing \subseteq A, \quad A \subseteq U, \quad A \cap B \subseteq A, \quad A \subseteq A \cup B$$

were considered in the preceding section. The property

$$A \cup A = A \cap A = A$$

is often called the **idempotent law**.

7

SETS OF ELEMENTS

Example 2. Prove: $A \cap (A \cup B) = A \cup (A \cap B) = A$.

$A \cap (A \cup B) = (A \cap A) \cup (A \cap B)$	Distributive law.
$= A \cup (A \cap B)$	Idempotent law.
$= A \cup C$ where $C \subseteq A$	$A \cap B \subseteq A$.
$= A$	Definition of $\cup$.

Example 3. Use Venn diagrams to illustrate the truth of the statement: $\overline{A \cup B} = \overline{A} \cap \overline{B}$.

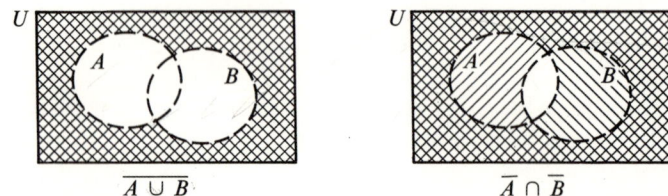

Figure 1-7

It is evident that in the two diagrams the regions shaded in both directions are equivalent, therefore $\overline{A \cup B} = \overline{A} \cap \overline{B}$.

Example 4. Use Venn diagrams to illustrate the truth of the statement: $(A \cap B) \cup C \neq A \cap (B \cup C)$.

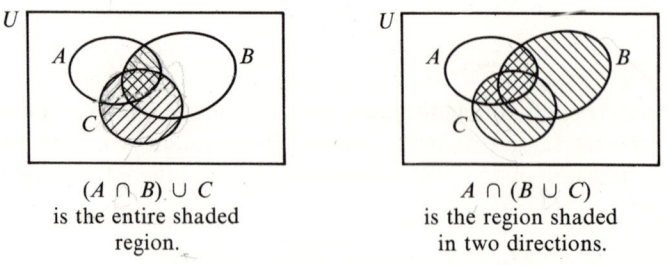

$(A \cap B) \cup C$ is the entire shaded region.

$A \cap (B \cup C)$ is the region shaded in two directions.

Figure 1-8

Since the desired shaded regions of the two diagrams are not equivalent, it is apparent that $(A \cap B) \cup C \neq A \cap (B \cup C)$.

Each finite set A has an associated nonnegative integer $n(A)$ which represents the number of elements in the set A. The integer $n(A)$ is called the **cardinal number** of the set A. The use of sets, their cardinal numbers, and Venn diagrams to solve problems is shown in Example 5.

§ 1-3   THE ALGEBRA OF SETS

Example 5. In the Washington High School there are:

(i)   25 seniors in the mathematics class,
(ii) 19 seniors in the physics class,
(iii) 12 seniors in the German class,
(iv) 13 seniors studying both mathematics and physics,
(v)   8 seniors studying both mathematics and German,
(vi) 9 seniors studying both physics and German, and
(vii) 5 seniors studying mathematics, physics, and German.

How many different seniors are studying at least one of these courses?

There are three classes under consideration so three regions M, P, and G are needed (Figure 1-9). The given statements may be expressed in the form:

(i) $n(M) = 25$,
(ii) $n(P) = 19$,
(iii) $n(G) = 12$,
(iv) $n(M \cap P) = 13$,
(v) $n(M \cap G) = 8$,
(vi) $n(P \cap G) = 9$,
(vii) $n[(M \cap P) \cap G] = 5$.

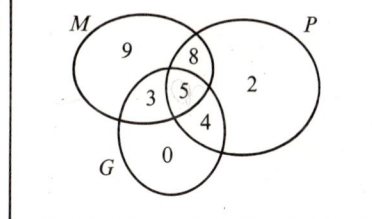

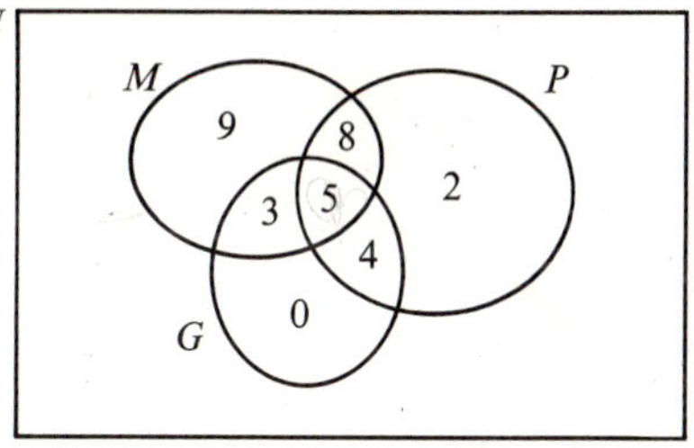

Figure 1-9

Thus, as in the figure, we may label the region $(M \cap P) \cap G$ with 5; the region $(M \cap P) \cap \overline{G}$ with $13 - 5$, that is, 8; the region $(M \cap G) \cap \overline{P}$ with $8 - 5$, that is, 3; the region $(P \cap G) \cap \overline{M}$ with $9 - 5$, that is, 4; the region $M \cap \overline{(P \cup G)}$ with $25 - (8 + 5 + 3)$, that is, 9; the region $P \cap \overline{(M \cup G)}$ with $19 - (8 + 5 + 4)$, that is, 2; and the region $G \cap \overline{(M \cup P)}$ with $12 - (3 + 5 + 4)$, that is, 0. Then we may read from the Venn diagram that there are 9 of these seniors studying only mathematics, 2 only physics, and none only German. The total number of different seniors studying these courses is $(9 + 8 + 2 + 3 + 5 + 4 + 0)$; that is, 31.

TEST YOURSELF

Let $A = \{1, 2, 3, 4\}$, $B = \{2, 3, 4, 5\}$, and $C = \{3, 4, 5, 6\}$. Show that each of the following statements is true for these sets:

1. $A \cup B = B \cup A$.
2. $(A \cap B) \cap C = A \cap (B \cap C)$.
3. $(A \cup B) \cup C = A \cup (B \cup C)$.
4. $A \cap (B \cup C) = (A \cap B) \cup (A \cap C)$.

9

SETS OF ELEMENTS

EXERCISES

Let $U = \{1, 2, 3, 4, 5, 6, 7, 8, 9, 10\}$, $A = \{1, 2, 3, 4, 5, 6, 7\}$, $B = \{1, 3, 5, 7, 9\}$, and $C = \{2, 3, 4, 6\}$. Show that each of the following statements is true for these sets:

1. $A \cup B = B \cup A$.
2. $A \cap B = B \cap A$.
3. $A \cup (B \cup C) = (A \cup B) \cup C$.
4. $B \cap C \neq A \cap B$.
5. $A \cap (B \cap C) = (A \cap B) \cap C$.
6. $A \cap (B \cup C) = (A \cap B) \cup (A \cap C)$.
7. $A \cup (B \cap C) = (A \cup B) \cap (A \cup C)$.

• • •

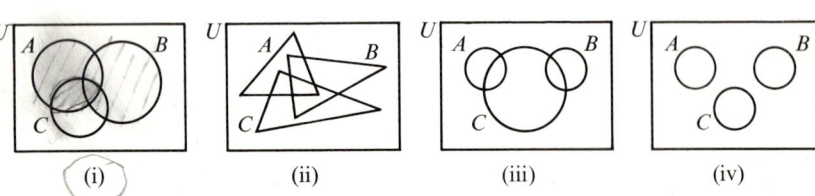

(i) (ii) (iii) (iv)

In each of the Exercises 8 through 11 copy each of the four figures given above and shade the specified region:

8. $(A \cap B) \cup (A \cap C)$.
9. $(A \cup B) \cap (A \cup C)$.
10. $A \cap (\overline{B} \cup \overline{C})$.
11. $(\overline{A \cup B}) \cap \overline{C}$.

12. If $U = \{a, b, c, d, e, f, g, h, i, j, k, l\}$, $A = \{b, d, e, f, g, h\}$, $B = \{e, g, h\}$, and $C = \{a, b, c, d, e, f, g, h, i\}$, (a) state the relationships among A, B, C, and U; (b) show in general how these relationships could be represented in a single Venn diagram.

• 13. Draw a Venn diagram with U as the set of plane quadrilaterals, A as the set of trapezoids, B as the set of parallelograms, C as the set of rhombuses, and D as the set of rectangles. Determine and identify the set $C \cap D$.

• 14. If U is the set of plane triangles, A is the set of isosceles triangles, B is the set of equilateral triangles, and C is the set of right triangles, (a) draw a Venn diagram showing the relationships among U, A, B, and C; (b) identify D, the set of scalene triangles, relative to your Venn diagram.

§ 1-4 SETS OF NUMBERS

15. A survey was made to determine the magazine reading habits of 100 high school students. The following data were collected:

   41 percent read magazine A,
   51 percent read magazine B,
   43 percent read magazine C,
   11 percent read both A and B,
   17 percent read both A and C,
   16 percent read both B and C,
   9 percent read A, B, and C.

(a) Draw a Venn diagram showing these data. (b) How many of the students surveyed did not read any of these magazines?

SUPPLEMENTARY EXERCISES

1. Show that $A \cup B = A \cup C$ for the sets $A = \{1, 2, 4\}$, $B = \{1, 2, 3\}$, and $C = \{3, 4\}$. Note that in this case $B \neq C$; thus $A \cup B = A \cup C$ is not in general a sufficient condition for $B = C$.

2. Use Venn diagrams to show that $\overline{A \cap B} = \overline{A} \cup \overline{B}$. This statement along with that of Example 3 are called **De Morgan's Laws** after the English mathematician and logician, Augustus De Morgan.

3. Show that $n(A \cup B) = n(A) + n(B) - n(A \cap B)$.

Use De Morgan's Laws $\overline{A \cup B} = \overline{A} \cap \overline{B}$ and $\overline{A \cap B} = \overline{A} \cup \overline{B}$ and prove:

4. $\overline{A} \subseteq \overline{A \cap B}$.
5. $\overline{A \cup B} \subseteq \overline{B}$.
6. $A \cap (\overline{A \cup B}) = \emptyset$.
7. $A \cup (\overline{A \cap B}) = U$.
8. $(\overline{A \cap B}) \cup \overline{C} = \overline{(A \cup B) \cap C}$.

§ 1-4 Sets of numbers

You have studied several different sets of numbers and their properties. For example, you have used the set of **natural numbers,**

$$\{1, 2, 3, 4, 5, \cdots\},$$

for counting and observed that for any natural numbers a and b there is a unique (one and only one) natural number $a + b$. There is also a unique natural number $a \times b$. In other words, the set of natural numbers is **closed** under addition and multiplication. The set of natural numbers is not closed under subtraction and division since differences such as $3 - 5$ and quotients such as $3 \div 5$ do not represent natural numbers.

11

SETS OF ELEMENTS

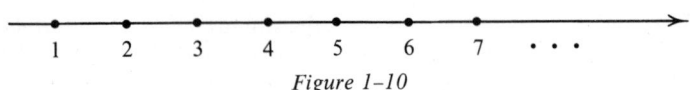
Figure 1-10

As in Figure 1-10 the set of natural numbers may be represented by points on a line. The numbers provide a scale for the line; a line with a scale is a **number line.** The number associated with a point on a number line is the **coordinate** of the point; the point is the **graph** of the number.

The order of the natural numbers may be considered either algebraically or in terms of a number line. On the number line in Figure 1-10 the graphs A and B of any two natural numbers represented by a and b must satisfy exactly one of three conditions: (i) A and B coincide (that is, are the same point), (ii) A is on the left of B, (iii) A is on the right of B. In algebra we have (i) a **equals** b ($a = b$) when a and b stand for the same number, (ii) a **is less than** b ($a < b$) when there exists a natural number c such that $a + c = b$, (iii) a **is greater than** b ($a > b$) when $b < a$. We say that the set of natural numbers is linearly **ordered** to indicate that exactly one of these three conditions must hold. The symbols $<$ and $>$ are often called **inequality symbols.**

You have also studied the set of **integers,**

$$\{\cdots, -4, -3, -2, -1, 0, 1, 2, 3, 4, \cdots\}.$$

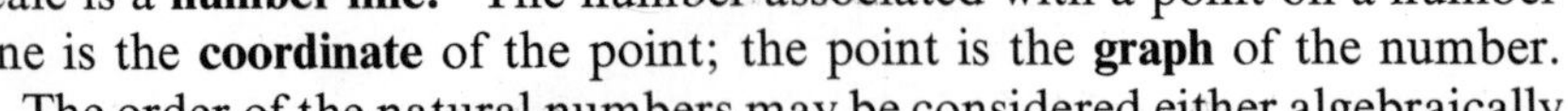

$$\cdots -4 \quad -3 \quad -2 \quad -1 \quad 0 \quad 1 \quad 2 \quad 3 \quad 4 \quad 5 \cdots$$
Figure 1-11

Each integer may be graphed on a number line as in Figure 1-11. The integer zero may be introduced as a difference of natural numbers since for any natural number a we have

$$0 = a - a.$$

Then for any positive integer a

$$a = a - 0; \qquad 0 < a$$

since $0 + a = a$; there is a negative integer $-a$ such that

$$a + (-a) = 0; \qquad -a = 0 - a; \qquad -a < 0.$$

For any negative integer b, there is a positive integer $-b$;

$$b < 0; \qquad 0 < -b.$$

On the number line the point with coordinate 0 is called the **origin.** Each point with a negative integer b as its coordinate is at a distance $-b$

§ 1-4 SETS OF NUMBERS

from the origin. Thus on a number line the distance from the origin of each point different from the origin is positive. The distance of the origin from the origin is defined to be zero. Then the **absolute value** of any integer is defined to be the distance of its graph from the origin;

$$|a| = a \text{ if } 0 < a \text{ or } 0 = a;$$
$$|a| = -a \text{ if } a < 0.$$

Since exactly one of the three conditions must hold, the definition is complete.

The set of integers may be **ordered algebraically** according to their graphs as in Figure 1-11. The set of integers may also be **ordered numerically** according to the order of their absolute values. When two numbers with the same absolute value are to be ordered numerically, we adopt the convention of listing the positive number first. Thus $-5, -3, -1, 0, 3$ are listed in their algebraic order; their numerical order would be $0, -1, 3, -3, -5$. Any list of numbers is a **sequence**. A sequence of distinct numbers is finite if the set of numbers listed is finite; a sequence is infinite if the set of numbers listed is infinite. The elements of any finite sequence of integers may be placed in either algebraic order or numerical order.

You have studied rational numbers. When rational numbers are considered, division by any number different from zero is possible. If a and b represent integers and $b \neq 0$, then $\frac{a}{b}$ represents a **rational number.** Each rational number has a graph on the number line. Rational numbers may be ordered either algebraically or numerically. The set of rational numbers is closed under addition, subtraction, and multiplication. The set of rational numbers different from zero is closed under division.

You have studied real numbers. Real numbers may be used to obtain a coordinate for each point on a number line. There is a one-to-one correspondence between the points on a number line and the **real numbers.** Some of the points have rational numbers as coordinates, others do not. In this sense the set of real numbers is often considered to be the union of the set of rational numbers and the set of irrational numbers. When the set of real numbers is the universal set, the set of **irrational numbers** is the complement of the set of rational numbers. The existence of irrational numbers is often explained in terms of a line segment of length $\sqrt{2}$. For example, by the Pythagorean Theorem if a square has a side of length 1 unit, then each of its diagonals has length $\sqrt{2}$ units. As in Example 1 we may prove that $\sqrt{2}$ does not represent a rational number. Then, under the assumption that each point on a number line has a real number as its coordinate, $\sqrt{2}$ represents an irrational number.

13

SETS OF ELEMENTS

Example 1. Prove that $\sqrt{2}$ does not represent a rational number.

This proof is based upon the properties of equations and the following facts which you have studied previously:

(i) Any integer is either even or odd.

(ii) An integer is even if and only if it may be represented by $2k$ for some integer k.

(iii) If the square of an integer is even, the integer is even.

(iv) Any rational number may be represented by $\dfrac{a}{b}$ where a and b are not both even.

Suppose that $\sqrt{2}$ represents a rational number, then $\sqrt{2} = \dfrac{a}{b}$ where $b \neq 0$ and a and b are not both even.

$\sqrt{2}\,b = a$ Multiply both members by b.
$2b^2 = a^2$ Square both members.

Since a^2 is even, a must be even. Let $a = 2k$, thus

$a^2 = 4k^2$
$2b^2 = 4k^2$ Substitution.
$b^2 = 2k^2$ Divide both members by 2.

Then b^2 is even, and b must be even contrary to the assumption that a and b are not both even. Since our assumption that $\sqrt{2}$ represents a rational number has led to a contradiction, $\sqrt{2}$ does not represent a rational number.

Example 2. Prove that $k\sqrt{2}$ for any integer $k \neq 0$ does not represent a rational number.

Suppose that $k\sqrt{2} = \dfrac{a}{b}$ for some rational number $\dfrac{a}{b}$. Then $\sqrt{2} = \dfrac{a}{bk}$ and $\sqrt{2}$ represents a rational number which is impossible (Example 1). Since our assumption that $k\sqrt{2}$ represents a rational number has led to a contradiction, the assumption must be false; that is, $k\sqrt{2}$ does not represent a rational number.

Other sets of numbers will be considered in future chapters. In each chapter, and indeed each problem, it is essential that the set of numbers (universe) under consideration be clearly recognized.

§ 1-4 SETS OF NUMBERS

TEST YOURSELF

Identify each statement as true or false:

1. On a number line the set of points with positive integers as coordinates is a subset of the set of points with rational numbers as coordinates.

2. The set of irrational numbers is a subset of the set of rational numbers.

3. Zero is an integer.

4. The union of the set of integers and the set of rational numbers is the set of integers.

Express without using the absolute value symbol:

5. $-|3|$. **6.** $|-3|$. **7.** $-|-3|$.

Insert the proper inequality symbol between:

8. -5 and -9. **9.** $\frac{5}{2}$ and $\frac{9}{4}$. **10.** $|-2|$ and $|-3|$.

EXERCISES

In Exercises 1 through 8 let P represent the set of positive integers; N, the set of negative integers; I, the set of integers; Q, the set of rational numbers; T, the set of irrational numbers; and R, the set of real numbers. Identify each statement as true or false:

1. $P \cup N = I$.
2. $P \cap N = \emptyset$.
3. $N \cup Q = \emptyset$.
4. $Q \cap T = R$.

5. $N \subseteq I$.
6. $(P \cup N) \subset Q$.
7. $I \subset T$.
8. $(Q \cap R) \cup T = R$.

• • •

9. Find a number such that only one number has that number as its absolute value. Are there any others?

10. Find a number such that no number has that number as its absolute value. Are there any others?

11. List the numbers $2, 1.62, -\frac{5}{3}, -\frac{7}{3}, \frac{3}{2}$; (a) in algebraic order; and (b) in numerical order.

12. Insert the proper inequality symbol between:
(a) x and $x + 1$ when x represents a positive number;
(b) x and $\frac{1}{x}$ when $x > 1$; (c) x and $\frac{1}{x}$ when $0 < x < 1$.

15

SETS OF ELEMENTS

13. Prove that $\frac{a}{b}\sqrt{2}$ does not represent a rational number for any rational number $\frac{a}{b} \neq 0$.

• **14.** Use number lines and graph the points with coordinate r such that (a) $3r > r$; (b) $3r = r$; (c) $3r < r$; (d) $|r| = r$.

• **15.** Assume that if the square of an integer is a multiple of 3, then the integer is a multiple of 3. (a) Prove that $\sqrt{3}$ does not represent a rational number. (b) Choose a convenient unit segment and construct a line segment of length $\sqrt{3}$.

§ 1-5 Statements and their graphs

We have been using symbols such as 1, 5, -3, and $\sqrt{2}$ for specific numbers. We have also used letters such as a, b, and k to represent any integers. Since a number is an abstraction and does not have a physical existence, we cannot write numbers. Rather we write symbols for numbers. Symbols for specific numbers are called **numerals**; symbols which may represent any element or elements of a set of numbers are called **variables**. If the given set of numbers is the set of real numbers, the variable is called a **real variable**. In general, the given set of numbers is called the **domain** of the variable.

Each statement involving only a variable x with domain D, numbers, and operations (that is, involving only expressions in x) has a solution set S where $S \subseteq D$. This terminology may be used to summarize the types of statements that are considered in algebra. A statement of equality of expressions in x is:

(i) an **identity**   if $S = D$;
(ii) a **conditional equation** with at least   if $S \subset D$ and $S \neq \emptyset$;
one solution
(iii) an **impossible equation**   if $S = \emptyset$.

A statement of inequality of expressions in x is:

(i) an **absolute inequality**   if $S = D$;
(ii) a **conditional inequality**   if $S \subset D$ and $S \neq \emptyset$;
(iii) a **false statement of inequality**   if $S = \emptyset$.

Thus all statements of equality or inequality in terms of expressions in x may be *classified* in terms of their solution sets, that is, the sets of replacements for the variable such that the statements are true. If the domain

16

§ 1-5 STATEMENTS AND THEIR GRAPHS

of the variable is a subset of the set of real numbers, each conditional statement has a graph on a number line.

Example 1. Graph $\{x \mid |x| < 2\}$.

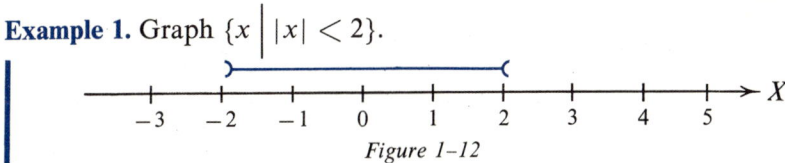

Figure 1-12

Example 2. Graph $\{x \mid |x - 2| = x - 2\}$.

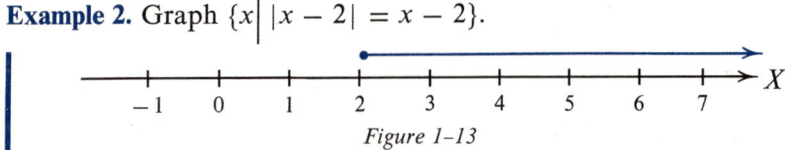

Figure 1-13

Note that by definition $|x - 2| = x - 2$ if and only if $0 < x - 2$ or $0 = x - 2$, that is, $x - 2 \geq 0$.

Intersections of solution sets are used when a variable is to satisfy two or more conditional statements simultaneously. *Unions of solution sets* are used when a variable is to satisfy at least one of two or more conditional statements. From this point of view the intersection $A \cap B$ may be considered as "A and B"; the union $A \cup B$ may be considered as "A or B" where "or" is used to show that at least one of the conditional statements is satisfied.

Example 3. Graph (a) $\{x \mid |x| \leq 2\} \cap \{x \mid x > -1\}$.

(b) $\{x \mid |x| \leq 2\} \cup \{x \mid x > -1\}$.

$|x| \leq 2$.

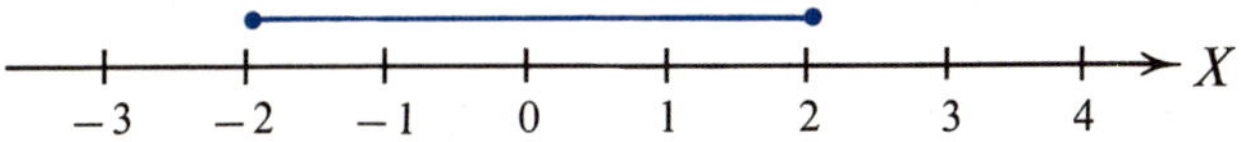

$x > -1$.

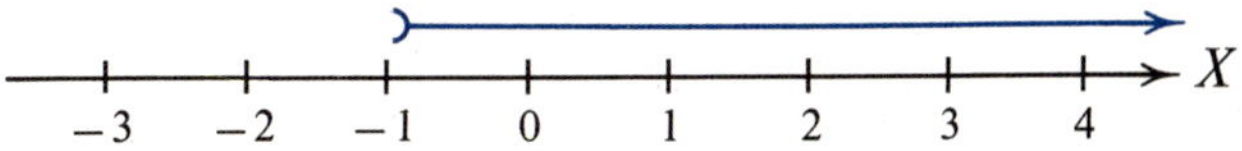

(a) $|x| \leq 2$ and $x > -1$.

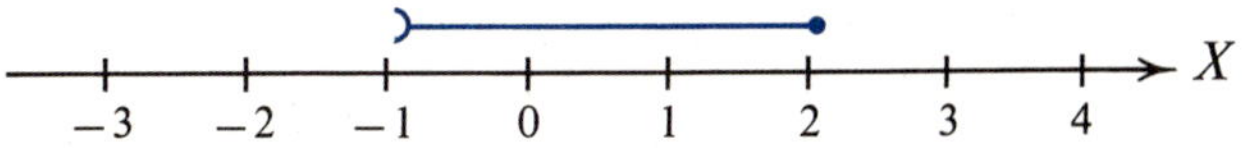

(b) $|x| \leq 2$ or $x > -1$.

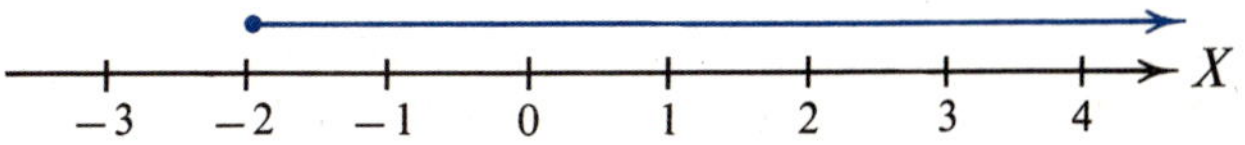

Figure 1-14

17

SETS OF ELEMENTS

TEST YOURSELF

Graph each set on a number line:

1. $\{x \mid x + 2 = 4\}$.
2. $\{x \mid x > -1\}$.
3. $\{x \mid |x| \neq 2\}$.
4. $\{x \mid |x + 1| = 3\}$.
5. $\{x \mid x > 3\} \cap \{x \mid x < 5\}$.
6. $\{x \mid x > 3\} \cup \{x \mid x < 5\}$.
7. $\{x \mid x > 1\} \cap \{x \mid x < -1\}$.
8. $\{x \mid x > 1\} \cup \{x \mid x < -1\}$.

EXERCISES

Graph each set on a number line:

1. $\{x \mid x \leq 1\}$.
2. $\{x \mid x + |3| = 5\}$.
3. $\{x \mid x > x - 1\}$.
4. $\{x \mid x - 6 = 3 - x\}$.
5. $\{x \mid x \neq 0\}$.
6. $\{x \mid x + 3 < x + 5\}$.
7. $\{x \mid |x| \geq 2\}$.
8. $\{x \mid |x - 1| = 1\}$.
9. $\{x \mid |x - 2| \leq 3\}$.
10. $\{x \mid |x| \neq 3\}$.
11. $\{x \mid x^2 - 1 = 15\}$.
12. $\{x \mid x^2 + 3x - 4 = 0\}$.

• • •

13. $\{x \mid |x| = 2\} \cap \{x \mid x < 0\}$.
14. $\{x \mid x > 0\} \cap \{x \mid x < 5\}$.
15. $\{x \mid x > 0\} \cap \{x \mid x = 3\}$.
16. $\{x \mid x = 1\} \cup \{x \mid x = 2\}$.
17. $\{x \mid x > 0\} \cup \{x \mid x = 2\}$.
18. $\{x \mid x < 0\} \cup \{x \mid x = 2\}$.
19. $\{x \mid x < 0\} \cap \{x \mid x > 0\}$.
20. $\{x \mid |x| < 2\} \cup \{x \mid x^2 > 1\}$.

Use your graphs for the preceding exercises and specify by the roster method the solution set for the statement in the specified exercise when the universal set is restricted to the set of (a) natural numbers and zero; (b) integers:

21. Exercise 8.
22. Exercise 9.
23. Exercise 13.
24. Exercise 14.
25. Exercise 17.
26. Exercise 18.

§ 1-6 Sets of ordered pairs

In previous courses you have graphed statements such as $x + y = 5$ and $x^2 + y^2 \leq 4$ on a **coordinate plane** (Figure 1-15). Each point (x, y) on the plane corresponds to an ordered pair of real numbers. They are called **ordered pairs** since there are two numbers and their order is important, that is, in general $(x, y) \neq (y, x)$.

Let $S = \{a, b\}$ and $T = \{p, q, r\}$. The set of ordered pairs (x, y) where $x \in S$ and $y \in T$ is denoted by $S \times T$;

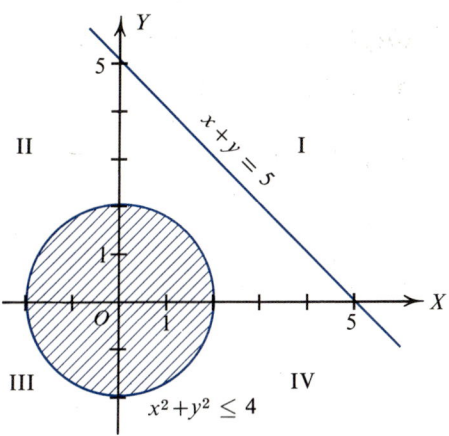

Figure 1-15

$$S \times T = \{(a, p), (a, q), (a, r), (b, p), (b, q), (b, r)\}.$$

The set $S \times T$ is called the **Cartesian set** (or **Cartesian product**) of S and T. When the cardinal numbers of each set are considered, note that $n(S \times T) = [n(S)][n(T)]$.

The Cartesian set $R \times R$ where R is the set of real numbers has infinitely many elements and has the **Cartesian plane,** that is, the coordinate plane (Figure 1-15), as its graph. The plane has four quadrants (I, II, III, IV) as numbered in the figure. In this case the first element of the ordered pair (x, y) is the **x-coordinate** or **abscissa;** the second element is the **y-coordinate** or **ordinate** of the point $P: (x, y)$. The set of pairs $(x, 0)$ has the **x-axis** $\overleftrightarrow{OX}$ as its graph; the set of pairs $(0, y)$ has the **y-axis** $\overleftrightarrow{OY}$ as its graph. Unless otherwise specified we assume that all graphs of statements involving two variables are to be made on a Cartesian plane.

Example 1. Graph the equation $y = x^2 - 4$ and represent the points as a set of ordered pairs.

Each point of the graph of $y = x^2 - 4$ is a member of the set of ordered pairs $\{(x, x^2 - 4)\}$; that is, the set of all ordered pairs of the form $(x, x^2 - 4)$. Notice that we graph an equation by plotting enough points to determine the shape of the curve and then draw a "smooth" curve through these points as the graph.

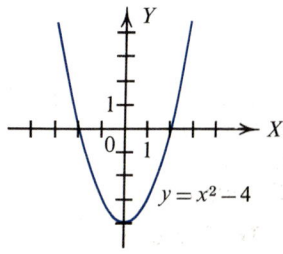

Figure 1-16

19

SETS OF ELEMENTS

Whenever $A \subset R$ and $B \subset R$ where R is the set of real numbers, $A \times B$ has a subset of the Cartesian plane as its graph. When A and B are subsets of the set of integers, the graph is called a **lattice** and each point of the graph is called a **lattice point**.

Example 2. Graph $A \times B$ where $A = \{0, 1, 2\}$ and $B = \{2, 3, 4\}$.

The elements of $A \times B$ are:

(0, 2,), (1, 2), (2, 2),

(0, 3), (1, 3), (2, 3),

(0, 4), (1, 4), (2, 4).

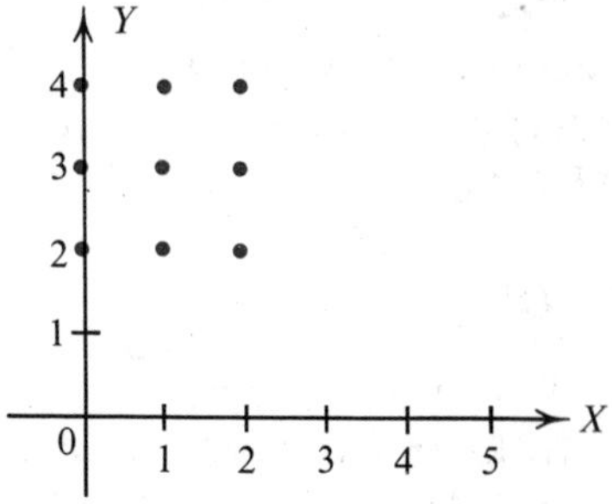

Figure 1-17

Ordered pairs of numbers may also be used to introduce new types of numbers. For example, let S represent the set of natural numbers and zero:

$$S = \{0, 1, 2, 3, 4, \cdots\}.$$

Each difference $a - b$ where $a \in S$ and $b \in S$ represents an integer. Note that $a - a = 0$, $a - 0 = a$, and $0 - a = -a$. Since in general $a - b \neq b - a$, each difference $a - b$ may be thought of as an ordered pair (a, b). Since any integer may be represented in several ways, for example,

$$5 - 3 = 2 - 0 = 9 - 7 = 2,$$

we must define the conditions under which two ordered pairs represent the same number:

$$(a, b) = (c, d) \text{ if and only if } a + d = b + c. \tag{1}$$

You may check that this definition is consistent with what you already know about differences of numbers by thinking of

$$a - b = c - d \text{ if and only if } a + d = b + c$$

and the closure property of integers under addition. Also since $(a - b) + (c - d) = (a + c) - (b + d)$ and $(a - b) \times (c - d) = (ac + bd) -$

20

§ 1-6 SETS OF ORDERED PAIRS

$(bc + ad)$, we define sums and products of our ordered pairs of elements of S as:

$$(a, b) + (c, d) = (a + c, b + d), \text{ and} \qquad (2)$$

$$(a, b) \times (c, d) = (ac + bd, bc + ad). \qquad (3)$$

Order relations are defined by

$$(a, b) < (c, d) \text{ if and only if } a + d < b + c. \qquad (4)$$

The four definitions (1), (2), (3), and (4) and the properties of the elements of S determine completely the properties of the new numbers (integers) which we have represented as ordered pairs (a, b). This manner of using ordered pairs will be considered further in later chapters.

TEST YOURSELF

1. List the elements of $A \times A$ where $A = \{1, 3\}$.
2. Graph the Cartesian set $A \times B$ where $A = \{1, 2\}$ and $B = \{3, 4\}$.
3. Graph $x^2 - y = 1$ and represent the points as a set of ordered pairs.

EXERCISES

1. Graph the Cartesian set $A \times A$ where $A = \{1, 2, 3\}$.
2. List the elements of $A \times B$ and $B \times A$ where: (a) $A = \{r, s, t\}$ and $B = \{m, n\}$; (b) $A = \{-2, -1, 0, 1\}$ and $B = \{3, 4, 5\}$.
3. What is the sign of (a) the ordinate; and (b) the abscissa of any point on the Cartesian plane in quadrant I? Quadrant II? Quadrant III? Quadrant IV?
4. Graph $x - y = 2$ and represent the points as a set of ordered pairs.
5. Repeat Exercise 4 for $y - x^2 = 2$.

• • •

6. For any real number k the set of points (x, k) has a line as its graph. The set of lines obtained by considering all possible values of k is called a **one-parameter family** of lines. The lines have the common property of being parallel to the x-axis; each line of the family may be identified by the **parameter** k. Describe the graphs of the set of points (k, y) and explain why they may be called a one-parameter family of lines.
7. Repeat Exercise 6 for the sets of points $(x, k - x)$.
8. Describe the graphs of the sets of points $x^2 + y^2 = r^2$ as a one-parameter family of curves (Exercise 6).
9. Let $A = \{1, 2, 3, 4\}$ and graph the subset of $A \times A$ such that (a) the first and second elements are equal; (b) the second element is greater than the first.

SETS OF ELEMENTS

10. Let A: $(0, 4)$ and B: $(0, 10)$ be the end points of the base of an isosceles triangle. Express the coordinates of the possible positions of the third vertex C as a set of ordered pairs.

• **11.** Repeat Exercise 10 with A: $(3, 0)$ and B: $(0, -3)$.

• **12.** Think of each rational number $\frac{p}{q}$ as an ordered pair (p, q) where p and q represent integers and $q \neq 0$. Then define equality, addition, and multiplication of these ordered pairs (p, q).

The concept of ordered pairs and Cartesian products $A \times B$ with elements (a, b) may be extended to ordered triples and Cartesian products $A \times B \times C$ with (a, b, c) where $a \in A$, $b \in B$, and $c \in C$.

• **13.** Let $A = \{1, 2\}$, $B = \{1, 2, 3\}$, and $C = \{0, 1\}$. List the elements of $A \times B \times C$.

• **14.** Give a geometric interpretation of $R \times R \times R$ where R is the set of real numbers.

• **15.** The points on the plane $x - y = 0$ satisfy the equation $x - y + 0z = 0$ and may be expressed as a set of ordered triples (x, x, z) for any real numbers x and z. Express the points on each of these figures as a set of ordered triples: **(a)** the plane $x + y = 0$; **(b)** the plane $x + y - 3 = 0$; **(c)** the plane $x - y + 2 = 0$; **(d)** the line of intersection of planes $x + y - 3 = 0$ and $x - y + 2 = 0$.

§ 1-7 Numbers as distances

Two distinct points A and B determine a line AB for which we use the notation $\overleftrightarrow{AB}$. These points also determine a line segment AB with the given points as end points. We denote this by $\overline{AB}$. The **distance** between the points, that is, the length of the line segment, is a number of units. When the points are on a number line, the line segment with end points at the origin, 0, and the unit point, 1, is taken as the unit of length. Then the distance $\overline{AB}$ may be expressed in several ways where A has coordinate a and B has coordinate b:

$$\overline{AB} = |a - b| = |b - a| = \sqrt{(a - b)^2} = \sqrt{(b - a)^2}. \qquad (5)$$

The distance $\overline{AB}$ also may be expressed in terms of the coordinates of A and B when the points are on a plane or in space. We think of a coordinate plane as the graph of $R \times R$ where R is the set of real numbers. Then each point is the graph of an ordered pair (x, y). We use two perpendicular lines, the x-axis $(y = 0)$ and the y-axis $(x = 0)$, as reference lines. We use the intersection of the axes as the origin $(0, 0)$. Whenever we are concerned with distances, we assume that the unit points $(1, 0)$ and $(0, 1)$ on the axes are at the same distance from the origin.

§ 1-7 NUMBERS AS DISTANCES

Let $A: (x_1, y_1)$ and $B: (x_2, y_2)$ be any two points on a coordinate plane. If $y_1 = y_2$, then $\overleftrightarrow{AB}$ is the line $y = y_1$ parallel to the x-axis and $\overline{AB} = |x_2 - x_1|$ (Figure 1-18). If $x_1 = x_2$, then $\overleftrightarrow{AB}$ is the line $x = x_1$ parallel to the y-axis and $\overline{AB} = |y_2 - y_1|$ (Figure 1-19). If $y_1 \neq y_2$ and $x_1 \neq x_2$, then $\overline{AB}$ is the hypotenuse of a right triangle ABC with the right angle at $C: (x_2, y_1)$ (Figure 1-20), $\overline{AC} = |x_2 - x_1|$, $\overline{BC} = |y_2 - y_1|$, and by the Pythageorean Theorem

$$\overline{AB} = \sqrt{(x_2 - x_1)^2 + (y_2 - y_1)^2}. \tag{6}$$

This **distance formula** may be used for any points A and B on a coordinate plane whether or not they are distinct points and whether or not $\overleftrightarrow{AB}$ is parallel to a coordinate axis (Exercise 21).

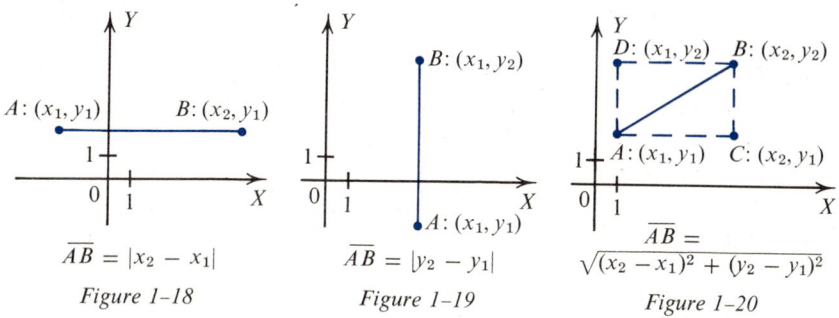

Figure 1-18   Figure 1-19   Figure 1-20

Example 1. Find the distance between (a) $A: (4, -1)$ and $B: (7, -1)$; (b) $A: (4, -1)$ and $C: (7, 3)$.

(a) $\overline{AB} = \sqrt{(7-4)^2 + (-1+1)^2} = \sqrt{(7-4)^2} = 3.$
(b) $\overline{AC} = \sqrt{(7-4)^2 + (3+1)^2} = \sqrt{9 + 16} = 5.$

The coordinate plane may be visualized as based upon a square $OABC$ (Figure 1-21) with $\overleftrightarrow{OA}$ as the x-axis, $\overleftrightarrow{OC}$ as the y-axis, and coordinates for the points as $O: (0, 0)$, $A: (1, 0)$, $B: (1, 1)$, and $C: (0, 1)$. Then any point $P: (x, y)$ on the coordinate plane but not on a coordinate axis (that is, $x \neq 0$ and $y \neq 0$) is a vertex of a rectangle $OQPR$ where $\overline{OQ} = \overline{RP} = x$, the distance of P from the y-axis, and $\overline{OR} = \overline{QP} = y$, the distance of P from the x-axis. Any point $P: (x, y)$ is at a distance x from the y-axis, y from the x-axis, and $\sqrt{x^2 + y^2}$ from the origin.

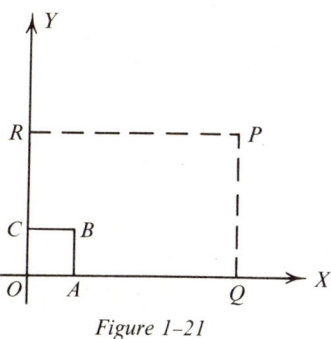

Figure 1-21

23

SETS OF ELEMENTS

A coordinate system for three-dimensional space may be visualized as based upon a cube $OABCDEFG$ (Figure 1–22) with $\overleftrightarrow{OA}$ as the x-axis, $\overleftrightarrow{OC}$ as the y-axis, $\overleftrightarrow{OG}$ as the z-axis, the plane $OABC$ as the xy-plane, the plane $OCFG$ as the yz-plane, the plane $OADG$ as the xz-plane, and coordinates for the points as $O: (0, 0, 0)$, $A: (1, 0, 0)$, $B: (1, 1, 0)$, $C: (0, 1, 0)$, $D: (1, 0, 1)$, $E: (1, 1, 1)$, $F: (0, 1, 1)$, and $G: (0, 0, 1)$. Then any point $P: (x, y, z)$ in space but not on a coordinate plane, (that is, $x \neq 0$, $y \neq 0$, $z \neq 0$) is a vertex of rectangular solid (prism) $OHIJKPLM$ where $\overline{OH} = \overline{JI} = \overline{MK} = \overline{LP} = x$, the distance of P from the yz-plane; $\overline{OJ} = \overline{HI} = \overline{ML} = \overline{KP} = y$, the distance of P from the xz-plane; and $\overline{OM} = \overline{HK} = \overline{JL} = \overline{IP} = z$, the distance of P from the xy-plane.

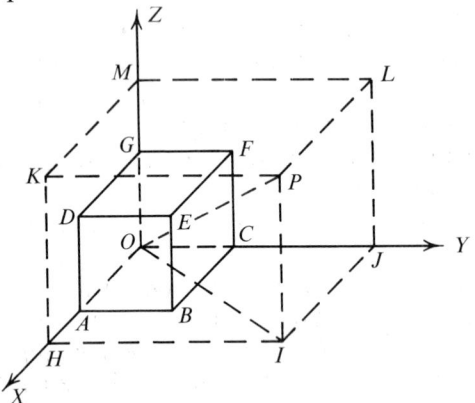

Figure 1–22

If $z = 0$, then P is on the xy-plane and may be located as in Figure 1–21 if $x \neq 0$ and $y \neq 0$. If $z = 0$ and $y = 0$, then P is on the x-axis and may be located as in § 1–4. Any point $P: (x, y, z)$ is at a distance x from the yz-plane, y from the xz-plane, z from the xy-plane and $\sqrt{x^2 + y^2 + z^2}$ from the origin. Notice in Figure 1–22 that I has coordinates $(x, y, 0)$; in right triangle OHI, $\overline{OI} = \sqrt{x^2 + y^2}$; hence in right triangle OIP, $\overline{OP} = \sqrt{(\sqrt{x^2 + y^2})^2 + z^2} = \sqrt{x^2 + y^2 + z^2}$.

On a plane the statement $\overline{OP}^2 = x^2 + y^2$ provides the basis for an equation of the form

$$x^2 + y^2 = r^2$$

for any **circle** with center at the origin and radius r (Figure 1–23). In space the statement $\overline{OP}^2 = x^2 + y^2 + z^2$ provides the basis for an equation of the form

$$x^2 + y^2 + z^2 = r^2$$

for any **sphere** with center at the origin and radius r (Figure 1–24).

§ 1-7 NUMBERS AS DISTANCES

$x^2 + y^2 = r^2$

Figure 1-23

$x^2 + y^2 + z^2 = r^2$

Figure 1-24

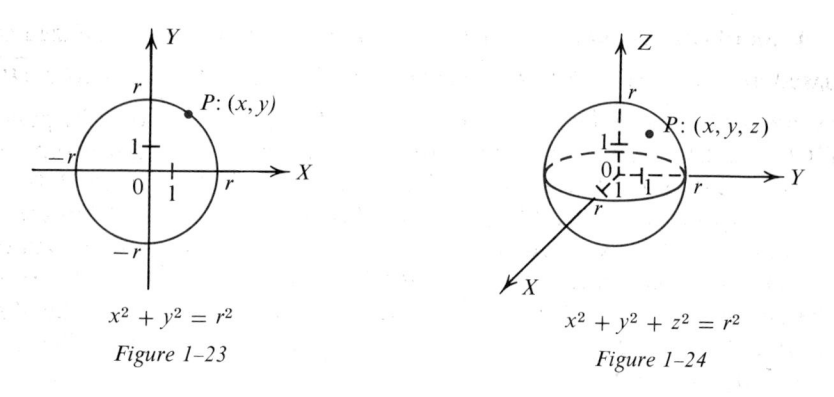

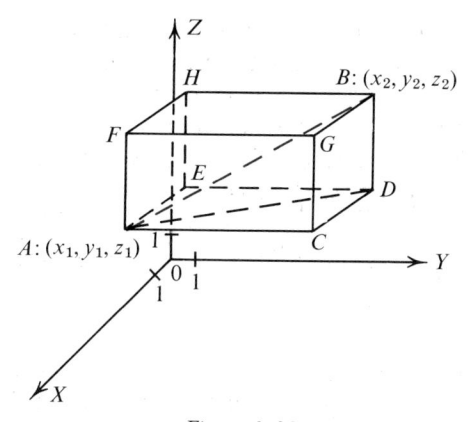

The distance $\overline{AB}$ between any two points $A: (x_1, y_1)$ and $B: (x_2, y_2)$ on a coordinate plane may be visualized as the length of a line segment parallel to a coordinate axis (if $x_1 = x_2$ as in Figure 1-19 or $y_1 = y_2$ as in Figure 1-18) or as the length of the diagonal of a rectangle $ACBD$ (Figure 1-20). In space any two points $A: (x_1, y_1, z_1)$ and $B: (x_2, y_2, z_2)$ are on a plane $z = z_1$ parallel to the xy-plane if $z_1 = z_2$; they are on a plane $y = y_1$ parallel to the xz-plane if $y_1 = y_2$; they are on a plane $x = x_1$ parallel to the yz-plane if $x_1 = x_2$. If $x_1 \neq x_2, y_1 \neq y_2$, and $z_1 \neq z_2$, then the distance $\overline{AB}$ is the length of the diagonal of a rectangular prism $ACDEFGBH$ as in Figure 1-25 where $A, C, G,$ and F are on the plane $x = x_1$; $E, D, B,$ and H are on the plane $x = x_2$; $A, E, H,$ and F are on the plane $y = y_1$; $C, D, B,$ and G are on the plane $y = y_2$; $A, C, D,$ and E are on the plane $z = z_1$; and $F, G, B,$ and H are on the plane $z = z_2$. In other words, the vertices

Figure 1-25

of the rectangular prism are $A: (x_1, y_1, z_1)$, $C: (x_1, y_2, z_1)$, $D: (x_2, y_2, z_1)$, $E: (x_2, y_1, z_1)$, $F: (x_1, y_1, z_2)$, $G: (x_1, y_2, z_2)$, $B: (x_2, y_2, z_2)$, and $H: (x_2, y_1, z_2)$.

SETS OF ELEMENTS

Then $\overline{AE} = \overline{CD} = \overline{GB} = \overline{FH} = |x_2 - x_1|$; $\overline{AC} = \overline{ED} = \overline{FG} = \overline{HB} = |y_2 - y_1|$; $\overline{AF} = \overline{CG} = \overline{DB} = \overline{EH} = |z_2 - z_1|$; in right triangle ACD, $\overline{AD} = \sqrt{(x_2 - x_1)^2 + (y_2 - y_1)^2}$; and in right triangle ADB,

$$\overline{AB} = \sqrt{(x_2 - x_1)^2 + (y_2 - y_1)^2 + (z_2 - z_1)^2}. \tag{7}$$

This distance formula may be used for any points A and B in space whether or not they are distinct points and whether or not $\overleftrightarrow{AB}$ is parallel to a coordinate plane (Exercise 22).

The coordinates of any point on a line, on a plane, or in space are real numbers. The square of any real number is either positive or zero, that is, **nonnegative**. Thus from our formulas (5), (6), and (7) all distances are nonnegative numbers of units.

Example 2. Find the distance from $A: (1, -3, 5)$ to $B: (2, 4, -1)$.

Think of A as (x_1, y_1, z_1), B as (x_2, y_2, z_2) and use formula (7);
$$\overline{AB} = \sqrt{(2-1)^2 + (4+3)^2 + (-1-5)^2}$$
$$= \sqrt{1 + 49 + 36} = \sqrt{86}.$$

On a coordinate plane the formula (6) provides the basis for an equation of the form

$$(x - x_1)^2 + (y - y_1)^2 = r^2 \tag{8}$$

for any circle with center (x_1, y_1) and radius r since the circle is the set of all points (x, y) at a distance r from its center (x_1, y_1). In space the formula (7) provides the basis for an equation of the form

$$(x - x_1)^2 + (y - y_1)^2 + (z - z_1)^2 = r^2 \tag{9}$$

for any sphere with center (x_1, y_1, z_1) and radius r since the sphere is the set of all points (x, y, z) at a distance r from its center (x_1, y_1, z_1).

Example 3. Find an equation for the sphere with center at $(2, -3, 7)$ and radius 5.

Use the formula (9) to obtain
$$(x - 2)^2 + (y + 3)^2 + (z - 7)^2 = 25.$$

The distance formulas (6) and (7) have been introduced in this section so that they can be used throughout this book. These formulas will be applied to the usual topics of analytic geometry in Chapter 7.

§ 1-7 NUMBERS AS DISTANCES

TEST YOURSELF

Find the distance between the points:

1. (5, 7) and (−3, 7).
2. (−1, 3) and (2, −1).
3. (1, −2, 3) and (4, −2, 7).
4. (3, 2, 1) and (5, −2, 3).

Find an equation for the circle with:

5. Center (0, 0) and radius 7.
6. Center (3, −2) and radius 1.

Find an equation for the sphere with:

7. Center (0, 0, 0) and radius 7.
8. Center (−2, 3, 1) and radius 5.

EXERCISES

Find the distance between the points:

1. (7, 11) and (7, −2).
2. (3, 8) and (8, 20).
3. (−1, −2) and (3, −5).
4. (1, 7, 5) and (1, 3, 2).
5. (2, −1, 3) and (−5, 3, 2).
6. (1, 5, −7) and (−1, 2, 7).

Find an equation for the circle with:

7. Center (3, −7) and radius 10.
8. Center (−5, 2) and radius 15.

Find an equation for the sphere with:

9. Center (2, −3, 5) and radius 7.
10. Center (−1, 2, −7) and containing (2, 1, −3).

• • •

Find an equation for the set of points P: (x,y) where the distance of P from:

11. (3, 5) is the same as the distance of (3, 5) from (−1, 5).
12. (3, 5) is the same as the distance of P from (−1, 5).
13. (1, 4) is the same as the distance of P from (4, 1).
14. (6, −8) is one-half the distance of P from (0, 0).

In Exercises 15 through 20 find an equation for the set of points P: (x, y, z) such that the distance of P from:

15. (1, 3, −5) is 2.
16. (2, −1, 4) is the same as the distance of (3, −2, 5) from (2, 1, 4).

27

SETS OF ELEMENTS

17. $(1, -3, 7)$ is the same as the distance of P from $(2, 5, 1)$.
18. $(5, -2, 3)$ is the same as the distance of P from $(1, 5, -2)$.
19. $(2, -3, 1)$ is one-half the distance of P from $(0, 0, 0)$.
20. $(3, 5, -6)$ is one-half the distance of P from $(-5, 3, 2)$.
21. Explain why formula (6) may be used for any points $A: (x_1, y_1)$ and $B: (x_2, y_2)$ whether or not they are distinct and whether or not $\overleftrightarrow{AB}$ is parallel to a coordinate axis.
22. Explain why formula (7) may be used for any points $A: (x_1, y_1, z_1)$ and $B: (x_2, y_2, z_2)$ whether or not they are distinct and whether or not $\overleftrightarrow{AB}$ is parallel to a cooordinate plane.
23. Find an equation for the line which is the perpendicular bisector of $\overline{AB}$ where $A: (x_1, y_1)$ and $B: (x_2, y_2)$.
24. Find an equation for the plane which is the perpendicular bisector of $\overline{AB}$ where $A: (x_1, y_1, z_1)$ and $B: (x_2, y_2, z_2)$.
• 25. Prove that the point (a) with coordinate $\dfrac{x_1 + x_2}{2}$ on a line is equidistant from the points with coordinates x_1 and x_2; (b) with coordinates $\left(\dfrac{x_1 + x_2}{2}, \dfrac{y_1 + y_2}{2}\right)$ on a plane is equidistant from the points with coordinates (x_1, y_1) and (x_2, y_2); (c) with coordinates $\left(\dfrac{x_1 + x_2}{2}, \dfrac{y_1 + y_2}{2}, \dfrac{z_1 + z_2}{2}\right)$ in space is equidistant from the points with coordinates (x_1, y_1, z_1) and (x_2, y_2, z_2). In a later section we shall observe that the points considered here are the mid-points of the line segments with the given end points.

§1-8 Relations

The set of all ordered pairs of real numbers (x, y) is the Cartesian set $R \times R$ and has the Cartesian plane as its graph (§ 1–6). Any conditional statement such as

$$y = x + 2, \qquad y \geq x^2, \qquad x^2 + y^2 = 25, \tag{10}$$

has a subset of $R \times R$ as its solution set and a subset of the Cartesian plane as its graph. The set of ordered pairs (x, y) which satisfy a conditional statement in x and y is called a **relation** in x and y. For example, the three conditional statements (10) determine respectively these three relations:

$$\{(x, y) \mid y = x + 2\}, \quad \{(x, y) \mid y \geq x^2\}, \quad \{(x, y) \mid x^2 + y^2 = 25\}$$

where it is assumed that x and y stand for real numbers.

§ 1-8 RELATIONS

The first member x of the ordered pair (x, y) is the **independent variable**; the set of possible values of x is the **domain** of the relation. The second member y of the ordered pair is the **dependent variable**; the set of possible values of y is the **range** of the relation. The domain and range of the particular relation may be specified. They may also be restricted by the particular relation under discussion. For example, both the domain and the range of $\{(x, y) \mid y = x + 2\}$ may be taken as the set of real numbers. If the domain of $\{(x, y) \mid y \geq x^2\}$ is the set of real numbers, then the range is the set of nonnegative real numbers.

In general, although we think of a relation as a set of ordered pairs, a relation may be expressed in several ways such as:

(i) the solution set of a conditional statement such as $y \geq x^2$ or $\{(x, y) \mid y \geq x^2\}$ where x and y stand for real numbers;

(ii) as a set of ordered pairs such as $\{(1, 3), (2, 3), (1, 4), (2, 4), (1, 5), (2, 5)\}$ with $\{1, 2\}$ as its domain and $\{3, 4, 5\}$ as its range;

(iii) a table of values such as a table of the squares of integers from 1 to 99 inclusive;

(iv) a graph (Figure 1–26) where the points of the graph have ordered pairs of real numbers (x, y) as their coordinates;

(v) a verbal rule such as: If x is a rational number, y is the set of integers less than 1; if x is irrational, $y = 2$.

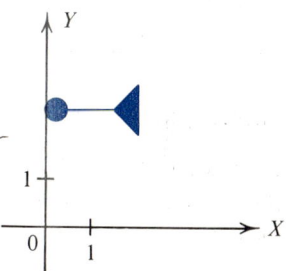

Figure 1–26

Example 1. Determine the elements of the relation $T = \{(x, y) \mid y = x^2\}$ on the Cartesian set $A \times A$ where $A = \{0, 1, 2, 3, 4\}$. Graph the relation. State the domain and range of the relation.

The conditional statement $y = x^2$ is satisfied by only three of the twenty-five ordered pairs in the Cartesian set $A \times A$; the set $T = \{(0, 0), (1, 1), (2, 4)\}$. A graph of the Cartesian set $A \times A$ is shown in Figure 1–27. The graph of the set T consists of the points indicated by the three heavy dots. The domain of the relation T is the set $\{0, 1, 2\}$; the range is the set $\{0, 1, 4\}$.

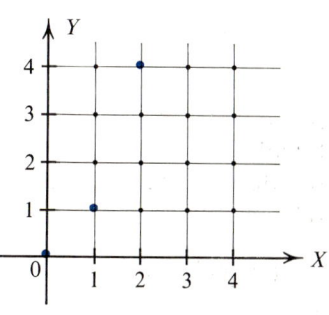

Figure 1–27

29

SETS OF ELEMENTS

Example 2. Determine the elements of the relation $S = \{(x, y) \mid y$ is a factor of $x\}$ on the Cartesian set $A \times B$ where $A = \{1, 2, 3, 4, 5, 6\}$ and $B = \{1, 2, 3\}$. Graph the relation. State the domain and the range of the relation.

The number 1 is a factor of every element of A; 2 is a factor of 2, 4, and 6; 3 is a factor of 3 and 6. Hence $S = \{(1, 1), (2, 1), (3, 1), (4, 1), (5, 1), (6, 1), (2, 2), (4, 2), (6, 2), (3, 3), (6, 3)\}$. The graph of S is shown in Figure 1–28. The domain of S is $\{1, 2, 3, 4, 5, 6\}$, that is, A. The range of S is $\{1, 2, 3\}$, that is, B.

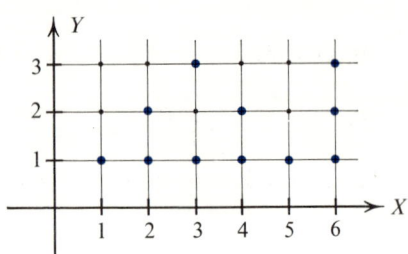

Figure 1–28

TEST YOURSELF

1. State the domain and the range of the relation $S = \{(0, 1), (3, 2), (3, 4), (5, 6)\}$.

2. List the elements of the relation $T = \{(x, y) \mid y = 2x\}$ on the Cartesian set $A \times A$ where $A = \{0, 1, 2, 3, 4\}$.

3. Graph T in Exercise 2.

EXERCISES

Determine the elements of the following relations on the Cartesian set $A \times A$. Graph each relation. State the domain and the range of each relation:

1. $S = \{(x, y) \mid y = x\}$; $A = \{-2, 0, 2, 4, 6\}$.

2. $R = \{(x, y) \mid y > x\}$; $A = \{-1, 0, 1\}$.

3. $S = \{(x, y) \mid y < x - 1\}$; $A = \{1, 2, 3\}$.

4. $S = \{(x, y) \mid y \neq x\}$; $A = \{0, 1, 2, 3\}$.

5. $T = \{(x, y) \mid y = |x|\}$; $A = \{-3, -2, -1, 0, 1, 2, 3\}$.

§ 1-9 INVERSE RELATIONS

6. $T = \{(x, y) \mid y > |x|\}$; $A = \{-3, -2, -1, 0, 1, 2, 3\}$.
7. $D = \{(x, y) \mid x + y \text{ is even}\}$; $A = \{-3, -2, -1, 0, 1, 2, 3\}$.
8. $E = \{(x, y) \mid x^2 + y^2 = 25\}$; $A = \{-5, -4, -3, -2, -1, 0, 1, 2, 3, 4, 5\}$.
9. $G = \{(x, y) \mid xy = 4\}$; $A = \{-4, -3, -2, -1, 0, 1, 2, 3, 4\}$.
10. $S = \{(x, y) \mid x^2 + y^2 \leq 16\}$; $A = \{-4, -3, -2, -1, 0, 1, 2, 3, 4\}$.
11. $G = \{(x, y) \mid |y| = |x|\}$; $A = \{-2, -1, 0, 1, 2\}$.

• • •

Write a conditional statement which is satisfied by the pairs (x, y) of the relation:

12. $\{(-2, -2), (-1, -1), (3, 3)\}$. $x = y$
13. $\{(1, 3), (2, 6), (3, 9)\}$. $3x = y$
14. $\{(0, 5), (0, 2), (0, 7), (0, 1)\}$. $x = 0$
15. $\{(2, 3), (4, 3), (-2, 3), (6, 3)\}$. $y = 3$
16. $\{(1, 1), (2, 8), (3, 27)\}$. $y = x^3$
• 17. $\{(-1, 1), (-3, 3), (0, 0), (4, 4)\}$. $y = |x|$

§ 1-9 Inverse relations

Given any set R of ordered pairs, we may find a set R' by interchanging the elements of each ordered pair in R. Thus if $R = \{(1, 3), (1, 5), (1, 7), (2, 2), (2, 4)\}$, then $R' = \{(3, 1), (5, 1), (7, 1), (2, 2), (4, 2)\}$. The relation R' is the **inverse** of R. The range of R becomes the domain of R', and the domain of R becomes the range of R'.

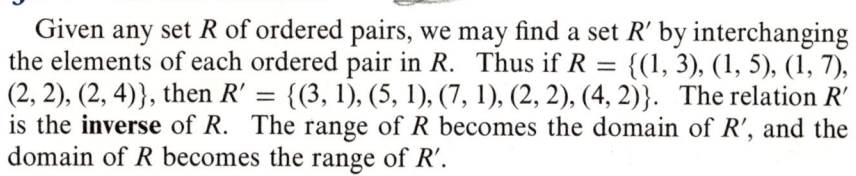

If a relation R is given as the solution set of a conditional statement, then the interchange of elements of the ordered pairs is accomplished by the interchange of the dependent and independent variables. It is desirable, but not theoretically essential, to solve the resulting statement for the new dependent variable.

31

SETS OF ELEMENTS

Example 1. Find the inverse of the relation S when $S = \{(x, y) \mid y = x + 2\}$.

$$S = \{(x, y) \mid y = x + 2\} = \{(x, x + 2)\}$$
$$S' = \{(x + 2, x)\} = \{(y, x) \mid y = x + 2\}$$

Since it is customary to call the first elements of the ordered pairs x and to solve for the dependent variable, we

(i) interchange x and y, and
(ii) solve for y;

$$S' = \{(x, y) \mid x = y + 2\} = \{(x, y) \mid y = x - 2\}.$$

The two steps used in Example 1 may be reversed. Then we

(i) solve for the independent variable, x, and
(ii) interchange the variable x and y;

$$S' = \{(y, x) \mid x = y - 2\} = \{(x, y) \mid y = x - 2\}.$$

Example 2. Find the inverse of the relation expressed by the equation $2x - 3y = 4$.

The given relation has equation $2x - 3y = 4$; the inverse relation has equation $2y - 3x = 4$. This inverse may also be expressed as $\left\{(x, y) \mid y = \dfrac{3x + 4}{2}\right\}$ or as the set of ordered pairs $\left(x, \dfrac{3x + 4}{2}\right)$.

The inverse of a relation may also be visualized graphically. Consider the graphs of $S = \{(x, y) \mid y = x + 2\}$ and $S' = \{(x, y) \mid y = x - 2\}$ in

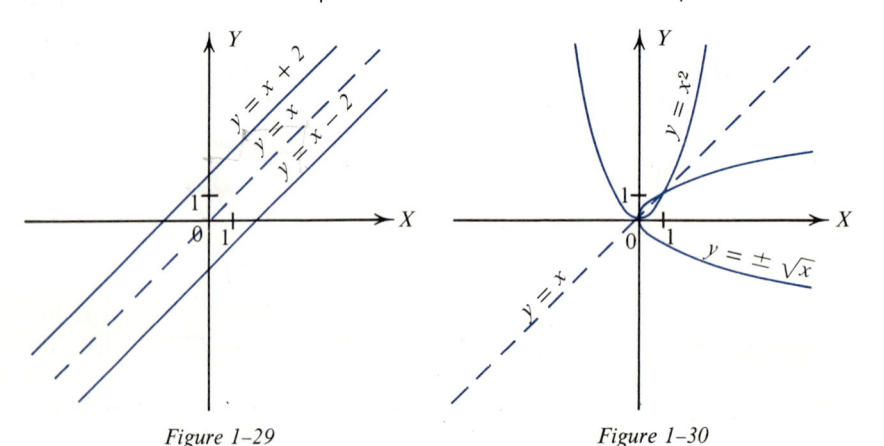

Figure 1–29

Figure 1–30

32

§ 1-9 INVERSE RELATIONS

Figure 1-29 and the graphs of $T = \{(x, y) \mid y = x^2\}$ and $T' = \{(x, y) \mid y = \pm\sqrt{x}\}$ in Figure 1-30. In each case the graph of the inverse may be obtained by "reflecting" the graph of the given relation in the line $y = x$. In other words, the new graph is the "mirror image" of the original graph with the line $y = x$ acting as the "mirror." This is true for all relations and their inverses; the line segments joining corresponding points (x_1, y_1) and (y_1, x_1) have the line $y = x$ as their perpendicular bisector. We describe this situation by saying that the graph of any relation is **symmetric** to the graph of its inverse with the line $y = x$ as the **axis of symmetry**.

Example 3. Find the inverse of the relation A where $A = \{(1, 2), (3, 1), (4, 2)\}$. Graph A and A'.

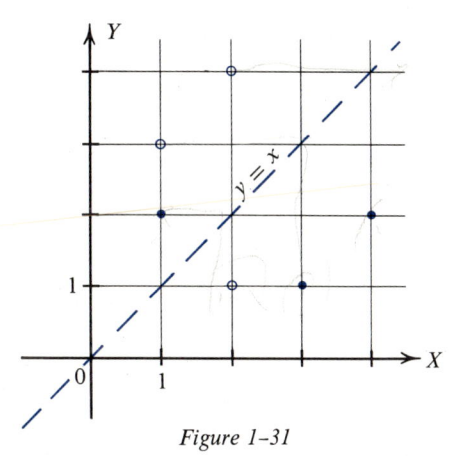

Figure 1-31

$A' = \{(2, 1), (1, 3), (2, 4)\}$. In Figure 1-31 the points of the graph of A are indicated by the heavy dots. The points of the graph of A' are indicated by the hollow dots. Note that the graph of A is a reflection of the graph of A' in the line $y = x$ and conversely.

TEST YOURSELF

1. Find the inverse of the relation $T = \{(1, 3), (2, 5), (1, 7)\}$.

2. Find the inverse of the relation expressed by the equation $y = 3x + 7$.

3. Graph the inverse of the relation whose graph is given in the figure.

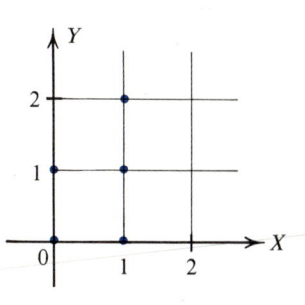

33

SETS OF ELEMENTS

EXERCISES

Find the inverse of each relation:

1. $\{(-1, 7), (0, 5), (3, 2)\}$.
2. $\{(2, -3), (2, 1), (2, 0), (2, 5)\}$.
3. $\{(4, 0), (5, 0), (-3, 0), (-2, 0)\}$.
4. $\{(-1, 2), (-1, 3), (2, 2), (2, 1)\}$.

5. In Exercises 1 through 4 state the domain and the range for each (a) relation; (b) inverse.

Graph the inverse of the relation whose graph is:

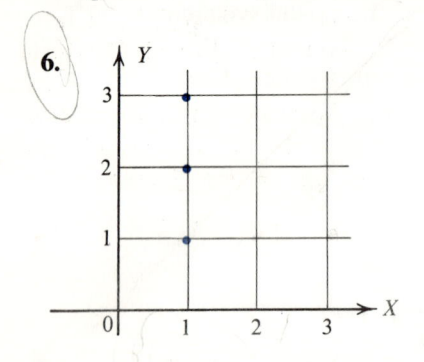

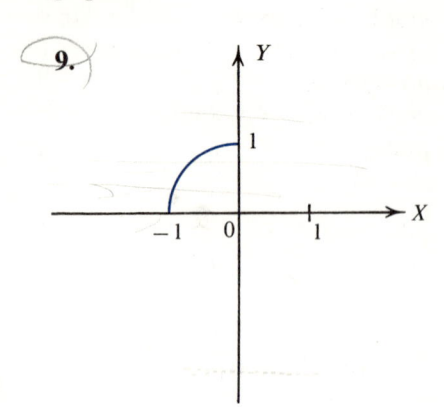

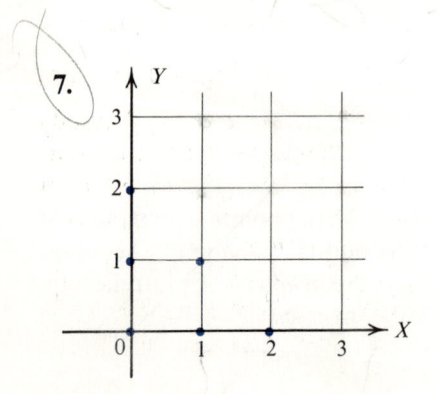

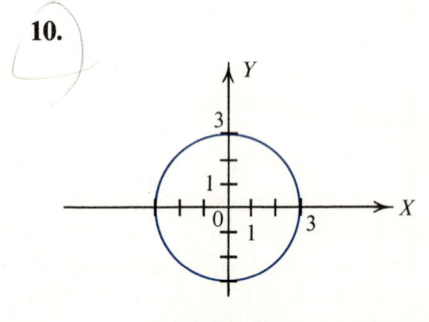

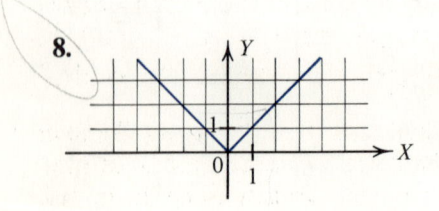

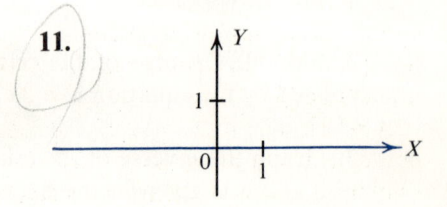

6.

7.

8.

9.

10.

11.

34

In Exercises 12 through 19 find the inverse of the relation expressed by the given statement:

12. $3x + y = 12$.
13. $xy = 4$.
14. $x^2 + y^2 \leq 9$.
15. $y = x^3$.
16. $y \geq x + 1$.
17. $y = x^2 + 2x - 3$.
18. $y = |x|$.
- 19. $y = x + |x|$.

- 20. A relation R is **symmetric** if it is identical with its inverse. In other words, whenever $(x, y) \in R$ and $(y, x) \in R$ then $R = R'$ and R is a symmetric relation. Identify the relations in Exercises 12 through 19 which are symmetric.

- 21. A relation R is **reflexive** if for each x in the domain of R, the ordered pair $(x, x) \in R$. In other words, if the graph of R on $A \times A$ includes all the points of the graph of $y = x$ on $A \times A$, then R is reflexive. Is the relation R reflexive when $R = \{(x, y) \mid y = |x|\}$ on the set $A \times A$ where $A = \{-1, 0, 1\}$?

§ 1-10 Functions

Consider the relation $S = \{(x, y) \mid y = x + 2\}$ graphed in Figure 1-29 and the relation $T' = \{(x, y) \mid y = \pm\sqrt{x}\}$ graphed in Figure 1-30. For each value of the independent variable in the relation S there is exactly one value of the dependent variable; that is, each line parallel to the y-axis intersects the graph of S in at most one point. For the positive values of the independent variable of T' there are two values of the dependent variable; each line $x = k$ where $k > 0$ intersects the graph in two points. For example, $(4, 2)$ and $(4, -2)$ are both elements of the relation T'. Basically, the relation T' differs from the relation S in that there exists in T' at least one value of the independent variable such that there are at least two corresponding values of the dependent variable.

A relation in which there is at most one value of the dependent variable for each value of the independent variable is a **function**. Thus a function is a set of ordered pairs such that no two pairs have the same first element and different second elements. For example, the relation $\{(1, 2), (3, 4), (6, 9), (7, 10)\}$ is a function; the relation $\{(1, 2), (1, -2), (2, 3), (3, 6)\}$ is not a function.

A relation in x and y is a function if and only if every line parallel to or coincident with the y-axis intersects the graph of the relation in at most one point. This is called the **straight line test**. To determine the inverse

SETS OF ELEMENTS

R' of any relation R we interchange the variables. Accordingly, there is also a straight line test to determine whether or not R' is a function: lines parallel to or coincident with the y-axis are used for R; the graph of R and lines parallel to or coincident with the x-axis may be used for R'. The relation graphed in Figure 1-32 is a function, but its inverse is not a function. Neither the relation graphed in Figure 1-33 nor its inverse is a function. The relations graphed in Figures 1-34 and 1-35 and their inverses are functions.

Figure 1-32

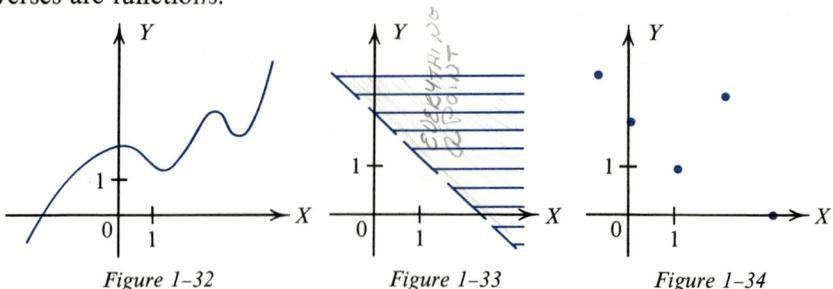

Figure 1-33

Figure 1-34

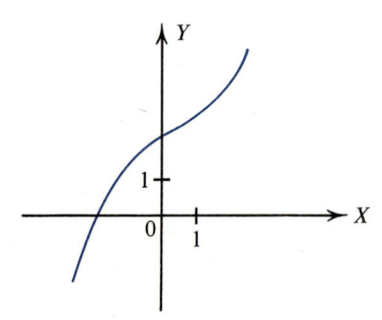

Figure 1-35

The word *function* is used in several ways. We have defined a function as a set of ordered pairs (x, y). Sometimes we call the dependent variable y **a function of** x. For instance, in connection with the relation $\{(x, y) \mid y = x + 2\}$ which is also a function, we may speak of either y or $x + 2$ as a function of x. Frequently we write $f(x)$, read as "f of x," or $g(x)$ for specific functions of x. For example, if $f(x) = x^2 + 2x - 3$, then $f(0) = 0^2 + 2(0) - 3 = -3$; $f(1) = 1^2 + 2(1) - 3 = 0$; and $f(a) = a^2 + 2a - 3$ for any number or expression a. Special relations and functions will be discussed in later chapters.

TEST YOURSELF

Tell whether the given relation is or is not a function:

1. $R = \{(0, 1), (2, 1), (3, 7)\}$.

2. $T = \{(-2, 0), (1, 4), (-2, 3)\}$.

3. $\{(x, y) \mid y^2 = x\}$.

4. $\{(x, y) \mid y = |x - 1|\}$.

Given $f(x) = 3x^2 + 7$, find:

5. $f(3)$. **6.** $f(-1)$. **7.** $f(b)$. **8.** $f(2a)$.

36

SUMMARY OF CHAPTER 1

EXERCISES

In Exercises 1 through 4 graph each relation and use the straight line test to determine whether or not the relation is a function:

1. {(1, 1), (2, 2), (3, 3), (4, 4)}.
2. {(1, 2), (2, 2), (3, 2), (4, 2)}.
3. {(3, 1), (3, 3), (3, 4), (3, 6)}.
4. {(1, 1), (3, 1), (4, 5), (3, 7)}.

5. For each relation in Exercises 1 through 4 **(a)** find the inverse; and **(b)** tell whether or not the inverse is a function.

• • •

State whether or not the equation represents a function:

6. $2x + y = 10$.
7. $y = x^2 + 2$.
8. $y^2 = x$.
9. $x^2 + y^2 = 4$.
10. $y = |2x - 1|$.
11. $\dfrac{3}{x+2} = y$.

In Exercises 12 through 16 use $f(x) = x^2 - 3x + 2$ and find:

12. $f(-2)$.
13. $f(0)$.
14. $f(a)$.
15. $f(a + h)$.
16. $\dfrac{f(a+h) - f(a)}{h}$.

• **17 through 22.** Use the relations given in Exercises 6 through 11 and **(a)** find the inverse of the relation; **(b)** determine whether or not the inverse is a function.

SUMMARY OF CHAPTER 1

1. In this chapter you have studied the uses and properties of sets. You have learned that the basic concept of a set involves membership. The language of sets employs many new symbols:

$$a \in A, \quad p \notin A, \quad A \subseteq B, \quad D \not\subseteq B, \quad A = C, \quad A \neq D, \quad A \subset E,$$
$$A \not\subseteq H, \quad \emptyset \subset A, \quad A \subseteq U. \quad (\S\ 1\text{-}1)$$

2. The elements of a set may be represented by the points interior to and on the boundary of a plane region, that is, by Venn diagrams. Given a universal set U, the complement $\overline{A}$ of any given set A may be found; also the intersection $A \cap B$ and the union $A \cup B$ of any given sets A and B may be found. (§ 1–2)

37

SETS OF ELEMENTS

3. The union and intersection of sets satisfy most of the laws of algebra. (§ 1-3)

4. The sets of natural, integral, rational, irrational, and real numbers may be graphed on a number line. (§ 1-4)

5. Statements about an unspecified member of a set of numbers may be made using a variable and may be graphed on a number line. (§ 1-5)

6. The set of all ordered pairs (a, b) where $a \in A$ and $b \in B$ form the Cartesian set $A \times B$. Such sets are used to find solution sets for statements in two variables and in the development of the number system. (§ 1-6)

7. The distance $\overline{AB}$ between two points A and B with coordinates a and b on a number line may be expressed as

$$\overline{AB} = |a - b| = |b - a| = \sqrt{(a - b)^2} = \sqrt{(b - a)^2}. \qquad (5)$$

For $A: (x_1, y_1)$ and $B: (x_2, y_2)$ on a coordinate plane

$$\overline{AB} = \sqrt{(x_2 - x_1)^2 + (y_2 - y_1)^2}. \qquad (6)$$

For $A: (x_1, y_1, z_1)$ and $B: (x_2, y_2, z_2)$ in space

$$\overline{AB} = \sqrt{(x_2 - x_1)^2 + (y_2 - y_1)^2 + (z_2 - z_1)^2}. \qquad (7)$$

On a coordinate plane any circle with center (x_1, y_1) and radius r has equation

$$(x - x_1)^2 + (y - y_1)^2 = r^2; \qquad (8)$$

in space any sphere with center (x_1, y_1, z_1) and radius r has equation

$$(x - x_1)^2 + (y - y_1)^2 + (z - z_1)^2 = r^2. \quad \text{(§ 1-7)} \qquad (9)$$

8. A relation is a set of ordered pairs which satisfy a conditional statement. Each relation shows a pairing of values of an independent variable (first element) and a dependent variable. (§ 1-8)

9. The inverse of any relation is a relation and may be found either algebraically or geometrically. (§ 1-9)

10. A relation in which any given first element corresponds to one and only one second element is a function. (§ 1-10)

11. The words on the following page have been introduced or used extensively in this chapter:

SUMMARY OF CHAPTER 1

abscissa (§ 1–6)
absolute value (§ 1–4)
additive identity element (§ 1–3)
associative (§ 1–3)
axis of symmetry (§ 1–9)
binary operation (§ 1–2)
cardinal number (§ 1–3)
Cartesian plane (§ 1–6)
Cartesian product (§ 1–6)
Cartesian set (§ 1–6)
circle (§ 1–7)
closed (§ 1–4)
commutative (§ 1–3)
complement (§ 1–2)
complementation (§ 1–2)
conditional statement (§ 1–5)
coordinate (§ 1–4)
coordinate plane (§ 1–6)
dependent variable (§ 1–8)
disjoint sets (§ 1–2)
distance (§ 1–7)
distance formula (§ 1–7)
distributive (§ 1–3)
domain (§§ 1–5, 1–8)
element (§ 1–1)
empty set (§ 1–1)
equal sets (§ 1–1)
equation (§ 1–5)
finite sets (§ 1–1)
function (§ 1–10)
graph (§ 1–4)
idempotent (§ 1–3)
independent variable (§ 1–8)
inequality (§§ 1–4, 1–5)
infinite sets (§ 1–1)
integers (§ 1–4)
intersection (§ 1–2)
inverse (§ 1–9)
irrational number (§ 1–4)
lattice (§ 1–6)
lattice point (§ 1–6)
member (§ 1–1)

multiplicative identity element (§ 1–3)
natural number (§ 1–4)
nonnegative (§ 1–7)
null set (§ 1–1)
number line (§ 1–4)
numeral (§ 1–5)
ordered algebraically (§ 1–4)
ordered numerically (§ 1–4)
ordered pairs (§ 1–6)
ordinate (§ 1–6)
origin (§ 1–4)
parameter (§ 1–6)
proper subset (§ 1–1)
range (§ 1–8)
rational number (§ 1–4)
real number (§ 1–4)
real variable (§ 1–5)
rectangular region (§ 1–4)
relation (§ 1–8)
roster method (§ 1–1)
sequence (§ 1–4)
set (§ 1–1)
set-builder notation (§ 1–1)
solution set (§ 1–1)
sphere (§ 1–7)
statements (§ 1–5)
subset (§ 1–1)
symmetric (§ 1–9)
truth set (§ 1–1)
unary operation (§ 1–2)
union (§ 1–2)
unit point (§ 1–7)
universal set (§ 1–1)
universe (§ 1–1)
variable (§ 1–5)
Venn diagram (§ 1–2)
well-defined (§ 1–1)
x-axis (§ 1–6)
x-coordinate (§ 1–6)
y-axis (§ 1–6)
y-coordinate (§ 1–6)

SETS OF ELEMENTS

KEYED PRACTICE ON CHAPTER 1 *

1. List all the proper subsets of {1, 3, 5}. (§ 1–1)
2. Let $U = \{0, 1, 2, 3, 4, 5, 6, 7, 8, 9\}$, $A = \{1, 3, 5, 7, 9\}$, $B = \{2, 4, 6, 8\}$, and $C = \{2, 3, 5, 7\}$. Identify by the roster method: (a) $A \cap C$; (b) $\overline{C}$; (c) $B \cup C$; (d) $\emptyset \cup \overline{A}$. (§ 1–2)
3. Copy the figure and shade the region representing $B \cap (A \cup C)$. (§ 1–3)
4. List 3, $-\frac{10}{3}$, $\frac{7}{2}$, and $-\frac{16}{5}$, in (a) algebraic order; (b) numerical order. (§ 1–4)
5. Graph on a number line: $x < 2$ or $x \geq 5$. (§ 1–5)
6. (a) Graph $y + x - 1 = 0$ on a coordinate plane; (b) represent the points as a set of ordered pairs. (§ 1–6)
7. Find an equation for a sphere with center at $(1, 5, -3)$ and containing $(2, -1, 2)$. (§ 1–7)
8. List the elements of the relation $R = \{(x\ y) \mid y \geq |2x|\}$ in the Cartesian set $A \times A$ where $A = \{-1, 0, 1, 2, 3\}$. State the domain and the range of the relation. (§ 1–8).
9. Find the inverse R' of the relation R expressed by the equation $2x - 3y = 6$. (§ 1–9)
10. Let $f(x) = x^2 + 6x$ and state (a) whether or not $f(x)$ defines a function; (b) $f(-2)$; (c) the inverse of $f(x)$; (d) whether or not the inverse of the relation $(x, f(x))$ is a function. (§ 1–10)

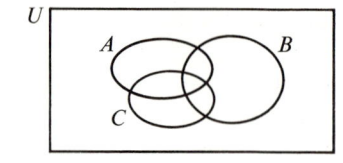

TESTS ON CHAPTER 1

A

1. Let $U = \{0, 1, 2, 3, 4, 5, 6, 7, 8, 9\}$, $A = \{1, 3, 5, 7\}$, $B = \{1, 2, 3, 4, 5, 6, 7\}$, and $C = \{2, 3, 4, 6\}$. Identify each statement as true or false: (a) $A \subseteq B$; (b) $A \subseteq C$; (c) $\overline{A} = C$; (d) $A \cap C = \emptyset$; (e) $A \cap B = A$.
2. List two positive real numbers less than 1 that are not rational.
3. Graph on a number line: $|x - 3| \leq 2$.
4. Graph the Cartesian set $A \times B$ where $A = \{1, 3\}$ and $B = \{2, 3\}$.
5. Find an equation for the circle with center $(1, 2)$ and containing $(3, 5)$.

* Answers to Keyed Practice Exercises may be found at the end of each chapter.

TESTS ON CHAPTER 1

6. Find an equation for the set of points $P: (x, y)$ where the distance of P from $(1, 5)$ is the same as the distance of P from $(3, 7)$.

7. Let $R = \{(1, 3), (2, 5), (1, -3), (4, 7)\}$ and state **(a)** the inverse of R; **(b)** whether or not R is a function; **(c)** whether or not the inverse of R is a function.

8. On a coordinate plane graph $x^2 + y^2 = 9$ and state whether or not the relation which has this graph is a function.

9. Find the inverse of the relation expressed by the equation $y = 3 - x$.

10. Let $f(x) = x^3 - 4x$. **(a)** Find $f(2)$. **(b)** Tell whether or not the inverse of the set of ordered pairs $(x, f(x))$ is a function.

B

1. Let P be the set of positive integers, R the set of rational numbers, U the set of real numbers, and identify $P \cap (\overline{P \cup R})$.

2. List five irrational numbers.

3. Graph on a number line: $x > 1$ and $|x - 2| \leq 2$.

4. Graph $x \geq y$ on the set $A \times B$ of elements (x, y) where $A = \{2, 4, 5\}$ and $B = \{1, 3, 4\}$.

5. Find an equation for the sphere with center $(2, 1, -3)$ and through $(5, -1, 2)$.

6. Find an equation for the set of points $P: (x, y)$ such that P is equidistant from $(2, 7)$ and $(1, 5)$.

7. Let $g(x) = x^2 - 3x + 5$ and find **(a)** $g(3)$; **(b)** $g(2b)$; **(c)** $g(d + 1)$.

8. If possible give an example of **(a)** a real number that is not rational; **(b)** a function that is not a relation.

9. Find the inverse of the relation expressed by the equation $y = x^2 - 1$.

10. Find an equation for the set of points $P: (x, y, z)$ such that the distance of P from $(1, -2, 5)$ is the same as the distance of $(2, 1, 3)$ from $(1, -1, 5)$.

C

1. Let U be the set of real numbers, R the set of rational numbers, I the set of integers; identify $I \cup (\overline{I \cap R})$.

2. Prove that $3\sqrt{2}$ does not represent a rational number.

3. Let I be the set of integers and graph $x^2 + y^2 \leq 25$ in $I \times I$.

4. Find an equation for the set of points $P: (x, y, z)$ such that the distance of P from $(2, 5, 1)$ is the same as the distance of P from $(-1, 3, 4)$.

SETS OF ELEMENTS

5. Find an equation for the sphere with center $(-2, 3, -4)$ and containing $(3, 7, -11)$.

6. (a) On a coordinate plane graph $x^2 + y^2 = 4$. **(b)** Tell whether or not the relation which has this graph is its own inverse.

7. Let $h(x) = x^2 - 2x - 1$ and find **(a)** $h(5)$; **(b)** $h(-2)$; **(c)** $h(k)$; **(d)** $h(k + 1)$; **(e)** $h(x + 1)$.

8. (a) Find the inverse of the relation expressed by the equation $y = x^2 + 1$. **(b)** State the domain and the range of the inverse relation.

9. Graph the relation $y = |x - 2|$.

10. Find an equation for the set of points $P: (x, y, z)$ such that the distance of P from $(3, 0, 2)$ is twice the distance of P from $(4, 1, 9)$.

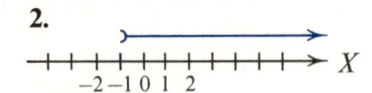

ANSWERS TO TEST YOURSELF EXERCISES

§ 1-1. **1.** True. **2.** False. **3.** False. **4.** False. **5.** {5}. **6.** Ø. **7.** U. **8.** {4, 6}.

§ 1-2. **1.** {4, 5}. **2.** {1, 5}. **3.** {2, 3}. **4.** {1, 2, 3, 4}. **5.** A. **6.** Ø. **7.** U. **8.** B.

§ 1-3. **1.** $A \cup B = \{1, 2, 3, 4, 5\} = B \cup A$.
2. $(A \cap B) \cap C = \{3, 4\} = A \cap (B \cap C)$.
3. $(A \cup B) \cup C = \{1, 2, 3, 4, 5, 6\} = A \cup (B \cup C)$.
4. $A \cap (B \cup C) = \{2, 3, 4\} = (A \cap B) \cup (A \cap C)$.

§ 1-4. **1.** True. **2.** False. **3.** True. **4.** False. **5.** -3. **6.** 3.
7. -3. **8.** $-5 > -9$. **9.** $\frac{5}{2} > \frac{9}{4}$. **10.** $|-2| < |-3|$.

§ 1-5. **1.** [graph on number line, point at 1, marks $-2, -1, 0, 1, 2$]

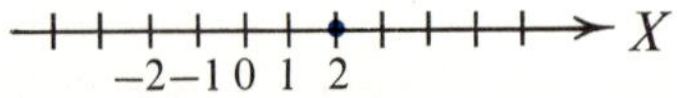

5. [graph on number line, interval from just after 2 to just before 4, marks $0, 1, 2, 3, 4, 5$]

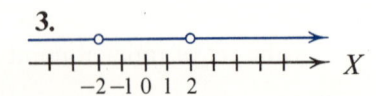

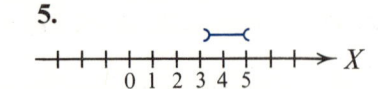

2. [graph on number line, ray starting just after 0 extending right, marks $-2, -1, 0, 1, 2$]

6. [graph on number line, entire line, marks $-1, 0, 1$]

3. [graph on number line, open interval between -1 and 1, marks $-2, -1, 0, 1, 2$]

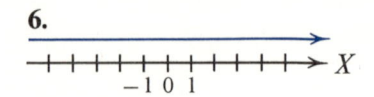

7. [graph on number line, Ø at 0, marks $-1, 0, 1$]

4. [graph on number line, points at -4 and 1, marks $-4, -1, 0, 1, 2$]

8. [graph on number line, exterior of interval between -1 and 1, marks $-1, 0, 1$]

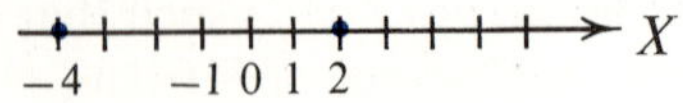

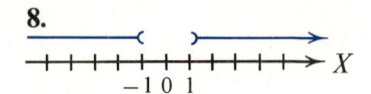

ANSWERS TO TEST YOURSELF EXERCISES

§ 1-6. **1.** $\{(1, 1), (1, 3), (3, 1), (3, 3)\}$.

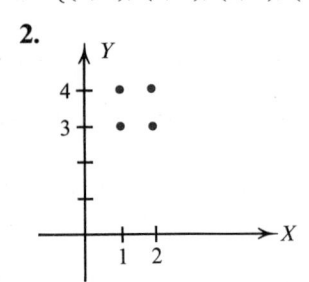

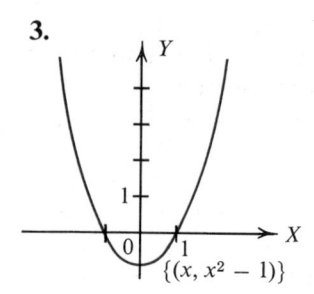

2.

3. $\{(x, x^2 - 1)\}$

§ 1-7. **1.** 8. **2.** 5. **3.** 5. **4.** $2\sqrt{6}$. **5.** $x^2 + y^2 = 49$.
6. $(x - 3)^2 + (y + 2)^2 = 1$. **7.** $x^2 + y^2 + z^2 = 49$.
8. $(x + 2)^2 + (y - 3)^2 + (z - 1)^2 = 25$.

§ 1-8. **1.** Domain, $\{0, 3, 5\}$; range, $\{1, 2, 4, 6\}$.
2. $T = \{(0, 0), (1, 2), (2, 4)\}$.
3.

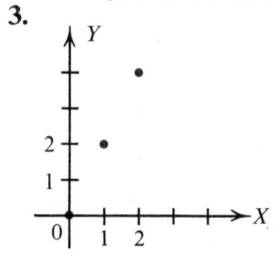

§ 1-9. **1.** $T' = \{(3, 1), (5, 2), (7, 1)\}$.

2. $y = \frac{1}{3}x - \frac{7}{3}$.

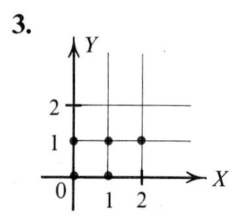

3.

§ 1-10. **1.** Function. **2.** Not a function. **3.** Not a function.
4. Function. **5.** 34. **6.** 10. **7.** $3b^2 + 7$. **8.** $12a^2 + 7$.

43

SETS OF ELEMENTS

ANSWERS TO KEYED PRACTICE ON CHAPTER 1

1. $\{1\}, \{3\}, \{5\}, \{1, 3\}, \{1, 5\}, \{3, 5\}, \emptyset$.

2. (a) $\{3, 5, 7\}$; (b) $\{0, 1, 4, 6, 8, 9\}$; (c) $\{2, 3, 4, 5, 6, 7, 8\}$;
(d) $\{0, 2, 4, 6, 8\}$.

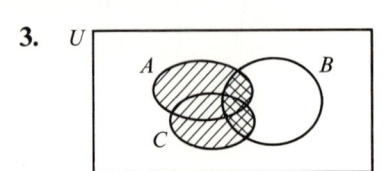

3.

Drawing 1–13

4. (a) $-\frac{10}{3}, -\frac{16}{5}, 3, \frac{7}{2}$; (b) $3, -\frac{16}{5}, -\frac{10}{3}, \frac{7}{2}$.

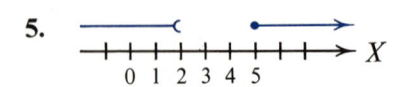

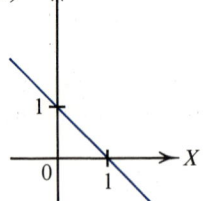

5.

6. (a) (b) $\{(x, -x + 1)\}$.

7. $(x - 1)^2 + (y - 5)^2 + (z + 3)^2 = 62$.

8. $\{(-1, 2), (-1, 3), (0, 0), (0, 1), (0, 2), (0, 3), (1, 2), (1, 3)\}$. Domain is $\{-1, 0, 1\}$; range is $\{0, 1, 2, 3\}$.

9. $y = \frac{3}{2}x + 3$.

10. (a) Function; (b) -8; (c) $y = -3 \pm \sqrt{x + 9}$;
(d) not a function.

Chapter 2

Permutations, Combinations, and Probability

§ 2–1 Permutations

We often are interested in arranging the elements of a set or arranging the elements of a subset. For example, consider the problem of arranging four books on a shelf. Let a, b, c, and d represent the four books. The possible arrangements of the elements of the set $\{a, b, c, d\}$ are:

a, b, c, d;	b, a, c, d;	c, a, b, d;	d, a, b, c;
a, b, d, c;	b, a, d, c;	c, a, d, b;	d, a, c, b;
a, c, b, d;	b, c, a, d;	c, b, a, d;	d, b, a, c;
a, c, d, b;	b, c, d, a;	c, b, d, a;	d, b, c, a;
a, d, b, c;	b, d, a, c;	c, d, a, b;	d, c, a, b;
a, d, c, b;	b, d, c, a;	c, d, b, a;	d, c, b, a.

Suppose that we had room for only two books on the shelf. Then we would have to consider the arrangements of the elements of all the subsets containing two books which could be selected from the original set of four books. These arrangements of the elements in the subsets $\{a, b\}$, $\{a, c\}$, $\{a, d\}$, $\{b, c\}$, $\{b, d\}$, and $\{c, d\}$ are:

a, b;	a, c;	a, d;	b, c;	b, d;	c, d;
b, a;	c, a;	d, a;	c, b;	d, b;	d, c.

An **arrangement** or **permutation** is a selection in a definite order of a specified number of elements from a given set. In the case of the permutations of the four books we only needed to consider ordering the elements of one selection of the books; that is, $\{a, b, c, d\}$. In the case of the permutations of two books from the set of four we had to consider ordering the elements of the six subsets. Note that $\{a, b\}$ and $\{b, a\}$ are symbols for the same subset; thus we think of these as notations for the same selection when the order of the elements is not important. A selection without regard to order of a number of elements from a set is called a **combination** (§ 2–3); a selection in a definite order is a *permutation*. Thus a permutation may be considered as an ordering of the elements of a combination.

In this section we shall be concerned primarily with determining the number of permutations or combinations that can be formed from a set

45

PERMUTATIONS, COMBINATIONS, AND PROBABILITY

of n distinguishable elements (that is, unlike elements) taking r at a time. Occasionally we may find it convenient to list the individual permutations or combinations, but this is usually too cumbersome to be a desirable method for determining the number of selections involved in a particular problem. In order to establish a method which is generally applicable we first need to understand the fundamental principle of enumeration of such selections. Example 1 illustrates this concept.

Example 1. There are three routes $\{A, B, C\}$ from town X to town Y and four routes $\{a, b, c, d\}$ from town Y to town Z. How many routes are there from town X to town Z by way of town Y?

We need to select one member from a set of three and one from a set of four. In selecting the two routes which we unite to form our final route from X to Z, we first select a route from X to Y and then a route from Y to Z.

The possible routes may be shown on a **tree diagram** as in Figure 2-1. We may count the end *branches* of the tree diagram to determine the number of possible routes from X to Z. The tree diagram shows us clearly that each of the three routes from X to Y can be followed by any one of the four routes from Y to Z, thus there are 3×4, that is, 12, possible different routes from X to Z by way of Y.

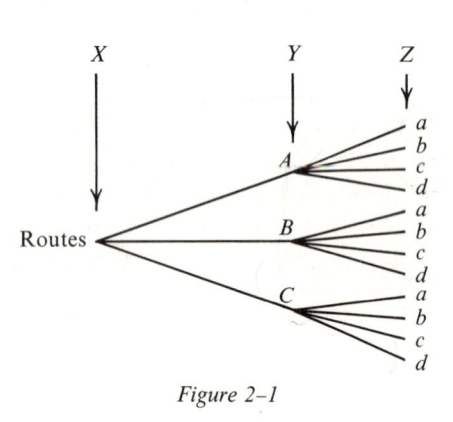

Figure 2-1

In Example 1 we could have determined the number of routes from X to Z by representing each of the routes as an element of the Cartesian set $\{A, B, C\} \times \{a, b, c, d\}$ on a lattice (or grid) as in Figure 2-2. Then selecting a route from X to Y may be thought of as selecting one of the three vertical columns; selecting a route from Y to Z may be thought of as selecting one of the four horizontal rows. There is a one-to-one correspondence between the routes from X to Z and the points of intersection of these rows and columns. Therefore this method, too, gives the number of routes as 12.

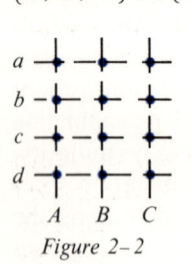

Figure 2-2

§ 2–1 PERMUTATIONS

Example 1 illustrates the **fundamental principle of enumeration:** <u>If a selection can be made in any one of m ways, and if after this selection has been made a second selection can be made in any one of n ways, then the two selections can be made in the order stated in any one of mn ways.</u> This principle can be extended for any finite sequence of selections.

Example 2. There are five routes $\{A, B, C, D, E\}$ from town T to town U, two routes $\{N, S\}$ from town U to town V, and three routes $\{a, b, c\}$ from town V to town W. How many routes are there from T to W by way of U and V in that order?

We can use a tree diagram as in Figure 2–3 and count thirty routes.

It is more convenient to apply the fundamental principle of enumeration to find that there are 5×2, that is, 10, routes from T to V, and then apply the principle again to find that there are 10×3, that is, 30, routes from T to W. Notice that we might have written this as $5 \times 2 \times 3$ to obtain the same result.

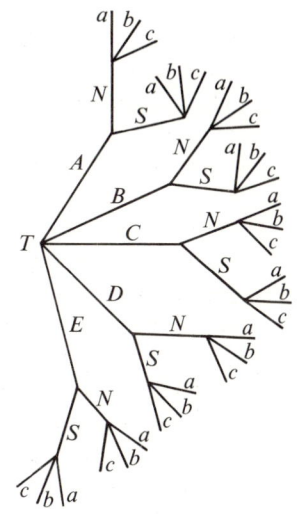

Figure 2–3

Example 3. A football coach needs to choose 1 of 5 boys to play quarterback, 1 of 3 boys to play left halfback, 1 of 2 boys to play right halfback, and 1 of 3 boys to play fullback. How many different backfields (one player in each of the four positions) can the coach assemble for use on the field?

By applying the fundamental principle of enumeration the coach may assemble 5×3, that is, 15, different sets of quarterbacks and left halfbacks. To go with each of these sets he must select 1 of 2 right halfbacks. Hence, the coach may assemble 15×2, that is, 30, different

47

PERMUTATIONS, COMBINATIONS, AND PROBABILITY

sets of players for the three positions so far considered. To complete his possible sets of backfields the coach can apply the fundamental principle again to include the fullbacks. Thus, the coach can assemble 30 × 3, that is, 90, different sets of backfields.

Notice that the fundamental principle of enumeration was applied three times and thus, in a sense, was extended to give 5 × 3 × 2 × 3, that is, 90 sets of backfields.

In general, the problem of determining the number of permutations from a set of n distinguishable elements taken r at a time is essentially a matter of applying the fundamental principle of enumeration. The first element may be selected in any one of n ways. After the selection has been made, the second element may be selected in any one of $(n - 1)$ ways. We continue in this manner; thus subsequent selections may be made in any one of $(n - 2), (n - 3), (n - 4), \cdots$ ways until r selections have been made. The rth selection can be made in $(n - r + 1)$ ways. If we denote the number of permutations of n elements, r at a time, by $_nP_r$, we have

$$_nP_r = n(n - 1)(n - 2) \cdots (n - r + 1). \tag{1}$$

We can arrange four distinct books on a shelf selecting four at a time in $_4P_4$ ways. We can arrange two books from a set of four on a shelf by selecting two at a time; that is, in $_4P_2$ ways. By formula (1),

$$_4P_4 = 4(4 - 1)(4 - 2)(4 - 3) = 4 \times 3 \times 2 \times 1 = 24;$$
$$_4P_2 = 4(4 - 1) = 4 \times 3 = 12.$$

These results are consistent with the results obtained in the first two paragraphs of this section.

Factorial notation is convenient when we need to express the product of successive positive integers. We define for all positive integers n

$$n! = n(n - 1)(n - 2)(n - 3) \cdots (3)(2)(1)$$

where $n!$ is read "n factorial." For example,

$$1! = 1;$$
$$2! = 2 \times 1 = 2;$$
$$3! = 3 \times 2 \times 1 = 6;$$
$$4! = 4 \times 3 \times 2 \times 1 = 24;$$
$$5! = 5 \times 4 \times 3 \times 2 \times 1 = 120;$$
$$\cdots$$

If we multiply $_nP_r$ in (1) by $\dfrac{(n - r)!}{(n - r)!}$, we have

§ 2-1   PERMUTATIONS

$$_nP_r = \frac{n(n-1)(n-2)\cdots(n-r+1)(n-r)!}{(n-r)!};$$

$$_nP_r = \frac{n!}{(n-r)!}. \qquad (2)$$

Notice that $_nP_n = n!$. However, if we substitute n for r in the formula (2) we obtain

$$_nP_n = \frac{n!}{(n-n)!} = \frac{n!}{0!}.$$

Since $n! = \frac{n!}{0!}$ if and only if $0! = 1$, we *define* **0! = 1** so that the formula (2) will have meaning for all nonnegative integral values of r less than or equal to n.

Example 4. How many different signals can be made by placing three of eleven different flags on a flagpole, one above the other?

This problem involves the arrangement of a selection of elements from a set; that is, a permutation. The number of permutations of 11 elements taken 3 at a time is $_{11}P_3$;

$$_{11}P_3 = \frac{11!}{(11-3)!} = \frac{11!}{8!} = 11 \times 10 \times 9 = 990.$$

Example 5. In ordinary decimal notation how many three digit positive even integers can be written using the digits 1, 3, 4, and 6 with no digit repeated?

This is not a simple problem of finding $_4P_3$ since the units' digit is subject to the condition of evenness. For our three-digit number to be even, the units' digit must be 4 or 6; that is, there are two choices for the units' place. Digits for the remaining two places, the tens' and hundreds' places, may be chosen from the remaining three. This choice can be made in $_3P_2$ ways. Therefore, we can choose our three digits in $2 \times {_3P_2}$ ways;

$$2 \times {_3P_2} = 2 \times \frac{3!}{(3-2)!} = 2(3)(2) = 12.$$

Hence, there are 12 possible three-digit positive even integers using the digits 1, 3, 4, and 6 with no digit repeated.

If repetition of the digits were permissible, it would be possible to form 4(4)(2), that is, 32, three-digit positive even integers.

PERMUTATIONS, COMBINATIONS, AND PROBABILITY

In your supplementary reading or future study you may encounter other common symbols for the permutation of n elements taken r at a time. Among these symbols are: P_r^n, $P_{n,r}$, and $P(n, r)$.

TEST YOURSELF

Evaluate:

1. $6!$ 2. $\dfrac{8!}{3!\,5!}$.   3. $\dfrac{10!}{2!\,3!\,4!}$.   4. $_5P_2$.   5. $_4P_4$.

EXERCISES

In Exercises 1 through 9 evaluate:

1. $5!$
2. $7!$
3. $(2n)!$ for $n = 3$.
4. $\dfrac{13!}{10!}$.
5. $\dfrac{12!}{4!\,6!\,2!}$
6. $_7P_3$.
7. $_{25}P_1$.
8. $_5P_5$.
9. $_{12}P_4$.

10. At a certain high school there are four candidates for senior class president, five candidates for vice-president, three candidates for secretary, and six candidates for treasurer. In how many ways can the offices be filled?

11. A basketball coach has three candidates on his squad for each of the five positions. In how many ways can he form a team?

12. A person buying an automobile from the *NOGO* company has a choice of five body styles, a choice of two motors, and a choice of eight body colors. In how many ways can he choose a car different in at least one of these three features?

13. To open a particular type of lock requires three different settings on a dial consisting of sixty numbers. How many possible sequences of settings can the manufacturer choose?

14. In how many ways can a president, a vice-president, a secretary, a treasurer, and an historian of a club be selected from among twenty-five members if no member holds more than one office?

15. Find the number of three-digit positive even integers that can be written using the digits 1, 2, 3, 4, and 5 **(a)** if repetition of the digits is not permitted; **(b)** if repetition of the digits is permitted.

16. Find how many three-digit positive odd integers can be written using the digits 2, 5, 6, and 8 **(a)** if repetition of the digits is not permitted; **(b)** if repetition of the digits is permitted.

§ 2-2 SPECIAL PERMUTATIONS

• • •

17. Prove: $\dfrac{1}{n!} + \dfrac{1}{(n+1)!} = \dfrac{n+2}{(n+1)!}$.

18. Prove that $\dfrac{n \times (n+1)!}{(n+1) \times (n-1)!}$ is a perfect square.

19. Find n if $_nP_2 = 20$.

20. Find n if $_nP_5 = 6 \times {_nP_3}$.

21. Find n if $7 \times {_nP_2} = 12 \times {_{n-2}P_2}$.

22. Prove: $_nP_r = n \times {_{n-1}P_{r-1}}$.

• 23. How many basketball teams can be formed from a squad of sixteen players if three can play center, eight can play either of the two forward positions, and five can play either of the two guard positions?

• 24. The automobile license plates for a particular state are identified by two letters from the English alphabet followed by a three-digit number greater than 99. Find how many different license plates are possible (a) if repetition of letters and digits is permitted; (b) if repetition of the letters only is permitted.

• 25. In how many ways can two different physics texts, three different mathematics texts, and five different biology texts be arranged on a shelf if all books on the same subject are to be together?

§ 2-2 Special permutations

In every case the n elements used in the permutations in the preceding section were distinguishable (different). We now turn our attention to permutations where k of the n elements are indistinguishable (alike). For example, consider finding the number of possible permutations of the letters in the word *SYSTEMS*, using all the letters. We first subscript the S's so as to make them distinguishable. That is, the letters of the word *SYSTEMS* are considered as S_1, S_2, S_3, Y, T, E, and M. The number of permutations of these seven distinguishable letters taken seven at a time is $_7P_7$, that is, $7!$. One of these arrangements is

$$S_1TS_2EMS_3Y$$

where the S's may be considered as occupying positions one, three, and six. If we hold T, E, M, and Y in their present positions, we may arrange the three S's in positions one, three, and six in

$$_3P_3 = 3! = 6$$

ways. Notice that, if the subscripts on the S's were not present, these six arrangements would be indistinguishable. Hence, for every permutation in which the S's are indistinguishable there exist $3!$ permutations when

51

PERMUTATIONS, COMBINATIONS, AND PROBABILITY

the S's are distinguishable. If N represents the number of permutations of the letters S, Y, S, T, E, M, S where the S's are indistinguishable, then $3! \, N$ represents the number of permutations for which the S's are distinguishable. Since the number of permutations of the seven letters with distinguishable S's is $7!$, we have

$$3! \, N = 7!; \quad \text{hence} \quad N = \frac{7!}{3!}$$

where N represents the number of permutations with indistinguishable S's.

In general, the number N of permutations of n elements taken n at a time where k of the elements are indistinguishable and the remaining $(n - k)$ elements are distinguishable from each other and from the k elements may be expressed as

$$N = \frac{n!}{k!}. \tag{3}$$

The k indistinguishable elements are often described by saying that one of these elements has **multiplicity** k.

Example 1. How many arrangements of the letters of the word *PULL* are possible?

Since two letters are alike, there are $\frac{4!}{2!}$, that is, 12, ways of arranging the letters of the word *PULL*. They are:

PULL;	UPLL;	LLUP;	LLPU;
PLUL;	ULPL;	LULP;	LPLU;
PLLU;	ULLP;	LUPL;	LPUL.

We may extend the argument concerned with permutations of n elements of which k are alike to the number N of permutations of n elements of which k_1 are alike, k_2 others are alike, k_3 others are alike, $\cdots$, and k_t others are alike. Then

$$N = \frac{n!}{k_1! \, k_2! \, k_3! \, \cdots \, k_t!}. \tag{4}$$

Example 2. How many arrangements of the letters of the word *MISSISSIPPI* are possible?

The word *MISSISSIPPI* has eleven letters. The letters I and S are each of multiplicity 4 and the letter P is of multiplicity 2. Hence there are

$$\frac{11!}{4! \, 4! \, 2!}, \text{ that is, } 34{,}650,$$

ways of arranging the letters of the word *MISSISSIPPI*.

§ 2-2 SPECIAL PERMUTATIONS

We have considered thus far the permutations of elements in a row or along a line. Such permutations are called **linear permutations.** Unless otherwise specified all permutations and arrangements are assumed to be linear. Let us now consider the possible arrangements of elements on a circle; that is, **circular permutations.** There are two types of circular permutations depending on whether one element's "being on the right" of another has significance or does not have significance. When people are seated around a circular table, it is customary to attach significance to "being on a person's right." When keys are carried on a key ring, it is possible to turn the key ring over (rotate it about a diameter) and thus "being on the right" of a certain key is equivalent to "being on the left" of that key. In either case, if one arrangement on a circle can be obtained from another arrangement by rotating the circle about its center, the two arrangements are equivalent as in Figure 2-4. If "being on the right" is not significant, then a rotation about any diameter, as in Figure 2-5, also produces an equivalent arrangement. Note that the points A, B, C, D, E on the two circles of Figure 2-4 read in clockwise order; the points A, B, C, D, E on the two circles of Figure 2-5 read clockwise on one circle and counterclockwise on the other. Thus the significance of the orientation (clockwise or counterclockwise) of the circle is equivalent to the significance of "being on the right."

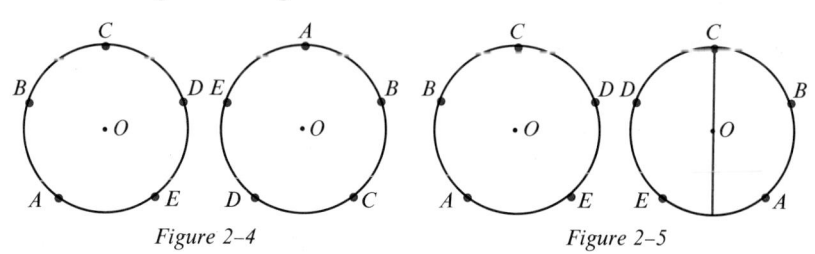

Figure 2-4   Figure 2-5

In a circular permutation the position of one element, such as A in Figure 2-4, provides a reference point but does not otherwise affect the arrangement. Thus if we assume that the orientation of the circle has significance, each circular permutation of n distinguishable elements taken r at a time corresponds to r linear permutations. If $_nP_r^*$ denotes the number of circular permutations of n distinguishable elements taken r at a time, then

$$r \times {_nP_r^*} = {_nP_r} \quad \text{hence} \quad {_nP_r^*} = \frac{_nP_r}{r}. \tag{5}$$

When $r = n$, we obtain a variation of this formula so that $_nP_n^* = \frac{_nP_n}{n} = \frac{n!}{n} = (n-1)!$. If we impose the further condition that orientation shall not be significant (as in the case of the keys on a ring), then we

PERMUTATIONS, COMBINATIONS, AND PROBABILITY

must divide the number of circular permutations indicated by the formula (5) by 2.

Example 3. In how many ways could King Arthur and seven of his knights have been seated at the round table?

> The number of circular permutations of eight elements is 7!, that is, 840. Hence King Arthur and seven of his knights could have been arranged in 840 ways at the round table.

It is often convenient to leave answers in a simplified factored form without multiplying the factors. (See Test Yourself, Exercise 1.)

TEST YOURSELF

1. Evaluate: $\dfrac{12!}{4!\,3!\,5!}$.

2. How many arrangements of the letters in the word *LETTER* are possible if all of the letters are used?

3. Find the number of circular permutations which include all of the four elements a, b, c, and d when orientation is significant.

4. List the circular permutations of the elements in Exercise 3.

EXERCISES

Evaluate:

1. $\dfrac{11!}{7!\,2!\,2!}$.   2. $\dfrac{15!}{11!\,3!\,2!\,1!}$.

In Exercises 3 through 8 how many arrangements using all the letters of the letters in the given word are possible?

3. *ALGEBRA*.
4. *MAXIMUM*.
5. *MINIMUM*.
6. *CALCULUS*.
7. *MATHEMATICS*.
8. *STATISTICS*.

9. In how many ways can seven flags be displayed on a vertical pole if three flags are red, two flags are blue, and two flags are yellow?

10. In how many ways can seven people be seated at a round table?

11. In how many ways can seven keys be placed on a key chain?

• • •

12. Find the number of ways in which five boys and five girls can be seated alternately **(a)** in a row; **(b)** in a circle.

• 13. Find the number of ways in which three pupils can be seated **(a)** in a row containg five seats; **(b)** in a circle containing five seats.

54

§ 2-3 COMBINATIONS

● 14. (a) How many three-digit numbers (that is, integers which in decimal notation must be expressed using three digits) are there? (b) How many have no two digits alike? (c) How many have all three digits alike? (d) How many have exactly two digits alike?

§ 2-3 Combinations

A selection of a number of elements in a specified order is a *permutation;* a selection of a number of elements without regard to order is a *combination*. In either case we are selecting subsets of some given set of elements. These subsets may be, but are not necessarily, proper subsets of the given set. Thus if we are asked to give the number of combinations of n elements taken r at a time, we are really being asked to find the number of subsets containing r elements that can be formed from a set of n elements.

Consider the problem of determining the number of combinations of five elements taken three at a time. Let the elements be represented by a, b, c, d, and e. We wish to find the number of subsets containing three elements when the subsets must be formed from the set $\{a, b, c, d, e\}$. A simple enumeration yields the following subsets with cardinal number three:

$$\{a, b, c\}, \quad \{a, b, d\}, \quad \{a, b, e\}, \quad \{a, c, d\}, \quad \{a, c, e\},$$
$$\{a, d, e\}, \quad \{b, c, d\}, \quad \{b, c, e\}, \quad \{b, d, e\}, \quad \{c, d, e\}.$$

There are ten subsets, therefore the number of combinations of five elements taken three at a time is ten.

We can also solve this same problem by considering permutations. The number of permutations of five elements taken three at a time is $_5P_3$, that is, 60. Each combination such as the set $\{a, b, d\}$ corresponds to six permutations since there are 3! permutations of these three elements. Hence, every subset of three elements from the given set of five elements yields six permutations. If we denote the number of combinations of five elements taken three at a time by $_5C_3$, then $6 \times {_5C_3} = {_5P_3} = 60$; that is, $_5C_3 = 10$.

In general, every subset of r elements of a set of n elements yields $r!$ permutations of the r elements. If we denote the number of combinations of n elements taken r at a time by $_nC_r$, then

$$r! \times {_nC_r} = {_nP_r} \quad \text{and} \quad {_nC_r} = \frac{_nP_r}{r!}.$$

Since $_nP_r = \dfrac{n!}{(n-r)!}$, we may write

$$_nC_r = \frac{n!}{r!\,(n-r)!}. \tag{6}$$

55

PERMUTATIONS, COMBINATIONS, AND PROBABILITY

Example 1. Find **(a)** the number of different committees of three persons which can be chosen from a group of eight persons; **(b)** the number of different committees possible if one of the eight persons must be on the committee.

(a) The number of subsets of three elements that can be formed from a set of eight elements is $_8C_3$; that is,

$$_8C_3 = \frac{8!}{3!\,(8-3)!} = \frac{8!}{3!\,5!} = \frac{(8)(7)(6)}{(3)(2)} = 56.$$

Therefore fifty-six different committees of three persons can be chosen from a group of eight persons.

(b) If a particular person must be a committee member, then the remaining two committee positions must be filled by two of the remaining seven persons. This can be done in $_7C_2$ ways;

$$_7C_2 = \frac{7!}{2!\,(7-2)!} = \frac{7!}{2!\,5!} = \frac{(7)(6)}{2} = 21.$$

Hence, if a particular person must be on the committee, there are twenty-one different committees possible.

Example 2. A bag contains five red beads and three white beads. In how many ways can a set of two red beads and two white beads be selected from the bag?

This is not the simple problem of finding the combinations of eight elements taken four at a time. The number of such combinations would include the possible sets of four red beads, three red beads and one white bead, two read beads and two white beads, and one red bead and three white beads. We need to consider the ways in which we can select two red beads from the set of five red beads and the ways in which we can select two white beads from the set of three white beads. We can select the two red beads in $_5C_2$ ways; we can select the two white beads in $_3C_2$ ways. Using the fundamental principle of enumeration we can select two red beads and two white beads in $_5C_2 \times {_3C_2}$ ways;

$$_5C_2 \times {_3C_2} = \frac{5!}{2!\,3!} \times \frac{3!}{2!\,1!} = (10)(3) = 30.$$

There are thirty ways of selecting two red beads and two white beads from a bag containing five red beads and three white beads.

Notice that when we select a subset of three elements from a set of five elements, such as $\{a, b, d\}$ from $\{a, b, c, d, e\}$, that selection leaves out a particular set of two elements, in this case $\{c, e\}$. Indeed every selection of r elements from a set of n elements has associated with it a selection of $(n - r)$ elements from the set of n elements; that is, the set of omitted elements can be considered a selection. Thus it appears that

$$_nC_r = {_nC_{n-r}}. \tag{7}$$

This statement may be proved for all positive integers n and r where $r < n$:

$$_nC_r = \frac{n!}{r!\,(n-r)!};$$

$$_nC_{n-r} = \frac{n!}{(n-r)!\,[n-(n-r)]!} = \frac{n!}{(n-r)!\,r!} = {_nC_r}.$$

The number of subsets containing n elements which can be formed from a set of n elements is one, the set itself. Thus $_nC_n = 1$. Then by (7) for $r = n$ we have

$$_nC_n = {_nC_0} = 1.$$

We define the number of combinations of n elements taken zero at a time to be one. This is consistent with our interpretation of combinations by means of sets since the number of subsets with no elements which can be formed from a set of n elements is one set, the empty set.

Example 3. Use the notation of combinations, $_nC_r$, to find the total number of subsets of a set containing five elements.

> The number of subsets containing r elements of a set with five elements is $_5C_r$. Thus the total number of subsets of a set of five elements is
>
> $_5C_0 + {_5C_1} + {_5C_2} + {_5C_3} + {_5C_4} + {_5C_5}$; that is,
>
> $1 + 5 + 10 + 10 + 5 + 1 = 32.$

Any set of five elements has thirty-two subsets. (We shall prove in the next section that the total number of subsets of any set of n elements is 2^n.)

In your supplementary reading or future study you may encounter other common symbols for the combinations of n elements taken r at a time. Among these symbols are C_r^n, $C_{n,r}$, $C(n, r)$, and $\binom{n}{r}$.

PERMUTATIONS, COMBINATIONS, AND PROBABILITY

TEST YOURSELF

In Exercises 1 and 2 evaluate:

1. $_7C_3$.   **2.** $_3C_0 + {_3C_1} + {_3C_2} + {_3C_3}$.

3. How many committees of four members can be selected from a group of ten persons?

4. In Exercise 3 how many committees can be selected if two particular persons must be on the committee?

EXERCISES

In Exercises 1 through 6 evaluate:

1. $_5C_4$.   **3.** $_{40}C_3$.   **5.** $_{15}C_{10}$.

2. $_6C_6$.   **4.** $_{15}C_5$.   **6.** $_7C_0$.

7. In how many ways can a committee of three students be selected from a group of nine students?

8. In how many ways can your instructor assign eight problems for homework from a set of eighteen problems?

9. An English instructor announces that on the following day each student will be asked to recite two of ten poems. Hap Hazard decides to study only two poems. In how many ways can he select the two poems to study?

10. How many straight lines are determined by a set of seven points if no three of the set are collinear?

• • •

11. From an ordinary deck of fitfy-two cards find the number of different hands that can be dealt containing (a) five cards; (b) seven cards; (c) thirteen cards.

12. How many different committees consisting of two boys and three girls can be formed from a group of five boys and eight girls?

13. In how many ways can a bridge hand of thirteen cards contain exactly eight spades?

14. Find n if (a) $_nC_{12} = {_nC_3}$; (b) $_nC_{16} = {_nC_4}$.

15. Find n if (a) $_nC_2 = 45$; (b) $_nC_{n-2} = 28$.

§ 2-4 THE BINOMIAL THEOREM

16. Evaluate $_0C_0$. Interpret the results in terms of the number of subsets of a set.

17. Consider five horizontal and eight vertical lines on a plane. How many rectangles are formed by these lines?

18. Find the number of diagonals of a regular polygon which has (a) six sides; (b) eight sides; (c) n sides.

19. In a league of four high school baseball teams, how many league games will be played if each team plays two games with every other team?

20. Find the number of ways in which a committee of twelve persons can be divided into (a) two equal subcommittees; (b) three equal subcommittees; (c) four equal subcommittees.

● 21. Prove that $_nC_r = {_{n-2}C_r} + 2{_{n-2}C_{r-1}} + {_{n-2}C_{r-2}}$.

● 22. Prove that $_{2n}C_n = {_{2n-1}C_n} + {_{2n-1}C_{n-1}}$.

● 23. In a deck of fifty-two cards find how many five card hands are possible which contain (a) four aces; (b) four aces or four kings; (c) four aces, four kings, or four queens.

● 24. If a committee of six members is to be chosen from among five Democrats and three Republicans such that at least two members of each party serve on the committee, how many committees are possible?

● 25. A bag contains four red and seven white beads. If three beads are selected, find how many selections are possible if (a) they may be of any color; (b) there must be exacty two white beads; (c) there must be at least two white beads; (d) they must be of the same color.

● 26. (a) How many different mixed doubles teams (one boy and one girl) can be formed by a tennis club consisting of eight girls and nine boys? (b) How many mixed doubles matches can be arranged?

● 27. A committee of four people is to be chosen from a group of nine people. In how many ways can a committee be selected if two particular people agree to serve only if both are selected?

● 28. In how many ways can a bridge hand of thirteen cards contain seven cards of one suit, three cards of another, two cards of a third, and one card of the fourth?

§ 2-4 The binomial theorem

In this section we shall consider methods of finding the terms of the expansion of the nth power of a binomial expression $(a + b)$ where n is a positive integer; that is, the expansion of $(a + b)^n$ for a positive integral value of n.

PERMUTATIONS, COMBINATIONS, AND PROBABILITY

The powers of a binomial form several patterns. Consider these powers:

$$(a + b)^0 = 1$$
$$(a + b)^1 = a + b$$
$$(a + b)^2 = a^2 + 2ab + b^2$$
$$(a + b)^3 = a^3 + 3a^2b + 3ab^2 + b^3$$
$$(a + b)^4 = a^4 + 4a^3b + 6a^2b^2 + 4ab^3 + b^4$$
$$(a + b)^5 = a^5 + 5a^4b + 10a^3b^2 + 10a^2b^3 + 5ab^4 + b^5$$
$$\ldots$$

You can check each of these by multiplication. Can you see any patterns?

Each power is of the form $(a + b)^n$. Can you find a pattern for the number of terms? For the first terms? For the last terms? For the powers of a in successive terms? For the powers of b in successive terms? For the coefficients?

Write just the coefficients:

```
                1
              1   1
            1   2   1
          1   3   3   1
        1   4   6   4   1
      1   5  10  10   5   1
    1   6  15  20  15   6   1
  1   7  21  35  35  21   7   1
                ...
```

Do you see any pattern here? What would be the first number on the next row? The second number? Write down a few more rows until you feel well acquainted with the pattern. This array is called **Pascal's triangle** after the French mathematician Blaise Pascal (1623–1662). However, it had appeared earlier in both Europe and China. On each row of the array, the first and last elements are 1's; each of the other numbers is equal to the sum of the two closest numbers (one on the left and one on the right) in the row above it.

Here are a few other patterns that you should see in the list of powers of $(a + b)$. For each positive integer n:

(i) The expansion of $(a + b)^n$ has $(n + 1)$ terms.

(ii) The literal factors of the terms of the expansion are

$$a^n,\ a^{n-1}b,\ a^{n-2}b^2,\ \ldots,\ ab^{n-1},\ b^n.$$

§ 2-4 THE BINOMIAL THEOREM

(iii) The sum of the exponents in each term is n.

(iv) As we look from one term to the next (left to right) the exponent of a is decreased by 1 and the exponent of b is increased by 1.

(v) The coefficients of the first and last terms are each 1.

(vi) The coefficients of the second and the next to last terms are each n.

(vii) The coefficients of any two terms equidistant from the ends of their row are the same.

(viii) For any given n, the coefficients of each of the terms of $(a + b)^n$ may be found in their proper order on the $(n + 1)$ row of Pascal's triangle.

These patterns enable us to find the terms of the expansion of $(a + b)^n$ for any relatively small value of n. However, the information gained by studying the patterns helps us to understand the binomial theorem, a theorem which makes it possible for us to write the expansion of any positive integral power of a binomial expression.

The **binomial theorem:** *For every positive integer n,*

$$(a + b)^n = {}_nC_0 a^n + {}_nC_1 a^{n-1}b + {}_nC_2 a^{n-2}b^2 + \cdots$$
$$+ {}_nC_k a^{n-k}b^k + \cdots + {}_nC_{n-1} ab^{n-1} + {}_nC_n b^n.$$

PROOF: Consider the expression $(a + b)^n$ written as the product of its n factors:

$$(a + b)^n = \underbrace{(a + b)(a + b)(a + b) \cdots (a + b)}_{n \text{ factors}}.$$

Each term of the expression obtained by multiplying the n factors of the right hand member of the equation may be obtained by choosing either an a or a b from each factor. There are n choices (one from each factor) for each term. Therefore the terms of the expanded expression are of the form a^n, $a^{n-1}b$, $a^{n-2}b^2$, $\cdots$, $a^{n-r}b^r$, $\cdots$, ab^{n-1}, and b^n. The problem is to determine how many of each of these terms we have. Consider the terms containg the factor $a^{n-r}b^r$. Each of these terms is found by selecting b's from r of the n factors and a's from the remaining $(n - r)$ factors. According to the fundamental principle of enumeration this can be done in ${}_nC_r \times {}_{n-r}C_{n-r}$, that is, ${}_nC_r$, ways. Hence, there are ${}_nC_r$ terms of the form $a^{n-r}b^r$. The number of terms of the form a^n, $a^{n-1}b$, $a^{n-2}b^2$, $\cdots$, or b^n may be obtained by letting $r = 0, 1, 2, \cdots, n$ respectively. Therefore

$$(a + b)^n = {}_nC_0 a^n + {}_nC_1 a^{n-1}b + {}_nC_2 a^{n-2}b^2 + \cdots$$
$$+ {}_nC_r a^{n-r}b^r + \cdots + {}_nC_{n-1} ab^{n-1} + {}_nC_n b^n.$$

61

PERMUTATIONS, COMBINATIONS, AND PROBABILITY

Notice in the theorem that:

(i) The rth term involves b^{r-1}.
(ii) The term involving b^r is the $(r + 1)$ term.
(iii) The $(r + 1)$ term is ${}_nC_r a^{n-r} b^r$.

The theorem holds for powers of a difference such as $(a - b)^n$ since

$$(a - b)^n = [a + (-b)]^n.$$

These properties are particularly useful when one specific term of the expansion of a power of a binomial expression is desired.

Example 1. Find the seventh term of $(x - 2)^{10}$.

Write $(x - 2)^{10}$ as $[x + (-2)]^{10}$; thus $a = x$, $b = -2$, and $n = 10$. Each term of $(x - 2)^{10}$ has the form ${}_{10}C_r x^{10-r}(-2)^r$. The terms may be obtained by taking $r = 0, 1, 2, 3, 4, 5, 6, 7, 8, 9, 10$. The seventh term is found by taking $r = 6$, since the values of r start with 0. The seventh term is ${}_{10}C_6 x^4(-2)^6$, that is, $\dfrac{10!}{6!\,4!} x^4 (-2)^6$;

$$\frac{10!}{6!\,4!} x^4 (-2)^6 = \frac{(10)(9)(8)(7)}{(4)(3)(2)(1)} x^4(64) = 210x^4(64) = 13{,}440x^4.$$

The binomial theorem is often useful in finding powers of decimals.

Example 2. Use the binomial theorem to find 1.1^5 to three decimal places.

$1.1^5 = (1 + 0.1)^5$
$= {}_5C_0(1)^5 + {}_5C_1(1)^4(0.1) + {}_5C_2(1)^3(0.1)^2 + {}_5C_3(1)^2(0.1)^3$
$\qquad + {}_5C_4(1)(0.1)^4 + {}_5C_5(0.1)^5$
$= 1^5 + 5(1)^4(0.1) + 10(1)^3(0.1)^2 + 10(1)^2(0.1)^3$
$\qquad + 5(1)(0.1)^4 + (0.1)^5$
$= 1 + 0.5 + 0.1 + 0.01 + 0.0005 + 0.00001$
$= 1.61051$
$1.1^5 \approx 1.611$

Notice that when 1.61051 is rounded off (§ 3-2) to three decimal places, the symbol $\approx$ is used for "is approximately equal to."

Let us consider the coefficients ${}_nC_r$ and ${}_nC_{r+1}$ of two consecutive terms of any positive integral power of a binomial $(a + b)$;

$${}_nC_r \times \frac{n-r}{r+1} = \frac{n!}{(n-r)!\,r!} \times \frac{n-r}{r+1} = \frac{n!}{(n-r-1)!\,(r+1)!} = {}_nC_{r+1}.$$

In other words, the coefficient of a term may be multiplied by the exponent

§ 2-4   THE BINOMIAL THEOREM

of a and divided by 1 more than the exponent of b to obtain the coefficient of the next term. This property is often useful when only the first few terms of an expansion of a binomial are desired. However, notice in Example 3 that the numerical factors of the terms of the binomial must not be included when this procedure is followed.

Example 3. Find the first four terms of $(a - 2b)^{20}$.

$$(a - 2b)^{20} = a^{20} + \frac{20}{1}a^{19}(-2b) + \frac{(20)(19)}{2}a^{18}(-2b)^2$$
$$+ \frac{(20)(19)(18)}{(2)(3)}a^{17}(-2b)^3 + \cdots$$
$$= a^{20} + 20a^{19}(-2b) + 190a^{18}(-2b)^2$$
$$+ 1140a^{17}(-2b)^3 + \cdots$$
$$= a^{20} - 40a^{19}b + 760a^{18}b^2 - 9120a^{17}b^3 + \cdots$$

Example 3 of § 2–3 involved the total number N of subsets of a set of five elements. As before

$$N = {}_5C_0 + {}_5C_1 + {}_5C_2 + {}_5C_3 + {}_5C_4 + {}_5C_5.$$

Consider now the expansion of $(1 + 1)^5$ by the binomial theorem:

$$(1 + 1)^5 = {}_5C_0 + {}_5C_1 + {}_5C_2 + {}_5C_3 + {}_5C_4 + {}_5C_5 = N.$$

Thus, as before, $N = 2^5 = 32$. In general, if we let $a = b = 1$ in the expansion of $(a + b)^n$, we obtain

$$(1 + 1)^n = 2^n = {}_nC_0 + {}_nC_1 + {}_nC_2 + \cdots + {}_nC_{n-1} + {}_nC_n.$$

The terms of the right hand member of this equation represent the number of subsets of r elements which can be formed from a set of n elements when $r = 0, 1, 2, 3, \cdots, n - 1, n$. Their sum represents the total number of possible subsets of a set of n elements, that is, 2^n.

Example 4. A shop specializing in gift baskets of fruit has seven kinds of fruit available. How many different assortments of one or more kinds of fruit can the shop provide?

Let N represent the total number of possible assortments.

$$N = {}_7C_1 + {}_7C_2 + {}_7C_3 + {}_7C_4 + {}_7C_5 + {}_7C_6 + {}_7C_7;$$
$$= (1 + 1)^7 - {}_7C_0, \text{ since the null set must be excluded;}$$
$$= 2^7 - 1 = 127.$$

There are 127 different assortments of fruit possible.

63

PERMUTATIONS, COMBINATIONS, AND PROBABILITY

TEST YOURSELF

1. Find the first four terms of $(x - 1)^9$.
2. Find 2.1^7 to three decimal places.
3. Find the eighth term of $(2x + y^2)^{14}$.

EXERCISES

A

Expand:

1. $(a + b)^6$.
2. $(a - b)^6$.
3. $(x - 3)^4$.
4. $(2x - y)^5$.
5. $(x - 2y)^5$.
6. $(2x + 3)^4$.

Find the first four terms of:

7. $(x - 1)^{20}$.
8. $\left(x - \dfrac{3}{2}\right)^{10}$.
9. $(2x + 3y)^{12}$.
10. $\left(x + \dfrac{1}{x^2}\right)^8$.
11. $(x^2 - 2y^3)^{17}$.
12. $\left(xy - \dfrac{3}{x}\right)^{12}$.

In Exercises 13 through 26 find:

13. The fourth term of $(a - 3)^4$.
14. The third term of $\left(2x^2 - \dfrac{3}{4x}\right)^{12}$.
15. The rth term of $(x - 2y)^n$.
16. The middle term of $(a + 1)^{16}$.
17. The middle term of $(x - y)^{12}$.
18. 1.1^{10} to three decimal places.
19. 1.2^{12} to three decimal places.

• • •

20. The term of $(x - y)^{10}$ with the factor y^4.
21. The term of $(x - y^2)^{12}$ with the factor y^6.
22. The constant term of $\left(x - \dfrac{1}{x}\right)^{18}$.
23. 0.99^{12} to three decimal places.
24. 0.98^{10} to three decimal places.
25. The constant term of $\left(x - \dfrac{1}{x^2}\right)^6$.
26. The constant term of $\left(2x^2 - \dfrac{1}{x}\right)^{12}$.
27. Prove that ${}_nC_r = {}_{n-1}C_r + {}_{n-1}C_{r-1}$. Interpret this equation in terms of the entries in a Pascal triangle.

§ 2–4 THE BINOMIAL THEOREM

● 28. In how many ways can a committee be formed from a group of twelve people if the committee must have at least three people on it?

B

Expand:

1. $(x + 2y)^4$.
2. $(1 - 2x^3)^4$.
3. $(2x - 3y)^5$.
4. $(3x + 2y)^4$.
5. $(2x^2 - 3y^3)^3$.
6. $(5y + 2x^2)^4$.

Find:

7. The fifth term of $\left(x - \dfrac{2}{x^2}\right)^{11}$.
8. The seventh term of $\left(3x^2 + \dfrac{2}{y}\right)^{10}$.
9. 1.1^{11} to three decimal places.
10. 1.01^7 to five decimal places.

Evaluate:

11. $_4C_0 + {_4C_1} + {_4C_2} + {_4C_3} + {_4C_4}$.
12. $_6C_2 + {_6C_3} + {_6C_4} + {_6C_5} + {_6C_6}$.

● ● ●

In Exercises 13 through 15 find the first four terms of:

13. $\left(\dfrac{2a}{b} + \dfrac{b^2}{4a^2}\right)^{16}$.
14. $\left(2 + \dfrac{1}{n}\right)^n$.
15. $\left(2 - \dfrac{1}{6x}\right)^{24}$.

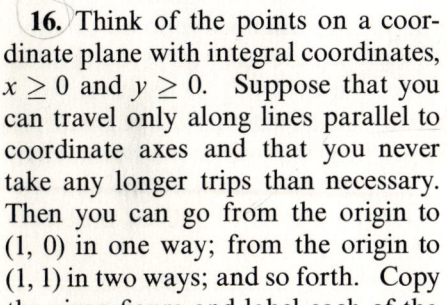

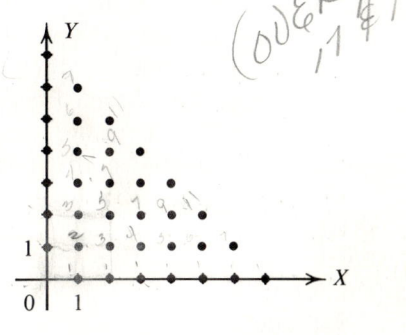

16. Think of the points on a coordinate plane with integral coordinates, $x \geq 0$ and $y \geq 0$. Suppose that you can travel only along lines parallel to coordinate axes and that you never take any longer trips than necessary. Then you can go from the origin to $(1, 0)$ in one way; from the origin to $(1, 1)$ in two ways; and so forth. Copy the given figure and label each of the points with the number of ways of traveling from the origin to that point. Compare this array of figures with the binomial coefficients.

65

PERMUTATIONS, COMBINATIONS, AND PROBABILITY

17. (a) Expand $(a + b)^5$. (b) If $a = \frac{1}{2}$ and $b = \frac{1}{2}$, find the value of each term of the expansion. (c) Find the value of each term if $a = \frac{2}{3}$ and $b = \frac{1}{3}$.

18. Let $a = 1$ and $b = -1$ in the expansion of $(a + b)^n$ and use the binomial theorem to show that

$$_nC_0 + {_nC_2} + \cdots + {_nC_n} = {_nC_1} + {_nC_3} + \cdots + {_nC_{n-1}}$$

if n is even. Determine a comparable relationship if n is odd.

19. Expand $(a + b + c)^4$.
20. The terms of the expansion of $(a + b + c)^n$ may be considered in the general form $Aa^{n-r}b^{r-k}c^k$ for some constant A. Express the coefficient A in terms of n, r, and k.

§ 2-5 Mathematical probability

Games of chance in one form or another are common to the experience of almost everyone. Certainly, from the beginning of time, people have had to deal with the problem of making a decision in the face of uncertainty about the occurrence of some future event. If we use a broad interpretation of what we mean by a "game of chance," the making of such a decision might be characterized as part of a game of chance. The problem of evaluating the chance that one decision is more likely to succeed than another leads quite naturally into the theory of probability.

Formal mathematical consideration of the theory of probability began during the seventeenth century when the French gentleman and gambler, Chevalier de Méré, proposed the following problem to the mathematician Pascal. Consider a game of chance between two players in which a score of n points wins, and each player has an equal chance of making a point. If the game is abandoned when one player has obtained a points and the second player has obtained b points, how should the stakes be divided between them? The answer to the question involved the calculation of the chance (probability) that each player had of winning the game at the time it was stopped. Pascal sent the problem to another mathematician, Fermat. Both Pascal and Fermat solved the problem independently by different methods. They extended their study to other related problems and in so doing developed the theory of probability.

Suppose you are given a box which contains seven beads of the same size and shape; that is, they are indistinguishable to the touch. However, five of the beads are colored red, and two of the beads are colored white. Consider an experiment in which one bead is to be chosen **at random** (that

§ 2–5   MATHEMATICAL PROBABILITY

is, without any basis for selecting one bead rather than another) from the box. What is the chance that the bead chosen is white? With no more information than this it seems reasonable to assume that each bead is equally likely to be chosen. Since there are two white beads among the seven beads, we would say that a white bead has two chances out of seven of being chosen. In other words, the probability that a white bead is chosen is $\frac{2}{7}$.

Consider another experiment, that of throwing a **die,** that is, a cube whose six faces are marked respectively with one, two, three, four, five, and six dots. We shall consider the outcomes of this experiment to be the number of dots on the top face of the die when the die comes to rest. What is the probability that an odd number occurs? If we agree that there are only six possible outcomes to our experiment and that these outcomes are equally likely, then the probability that the desired event occurs is $\frac{3}{6}$, that is, $\frac{1}{2}$, since three of the six face values are odd numbers.

Throughout this book we assume that, unless otherwise specified, all dice are unbiased (not loaded); all coins are unbiased; and all dice and coins fall with a face up.

Consideration of problems of the type we have just discussed helps us to frame an elementary definition of what is called mathematical probability. In order to state this definition we shall employ the terminology of sets. It will be convenient to label the set of all possible equally likely outcomes of an experiment as a **sample space** S. A sample space for a particular probability problem plays the role of the universal set in that problem. Each outcome of an experiment is called a **sample point** or, more briefly, a **point.** The total number of points in a sample space is denoted by $n(S)$. That is, $n(S)$ is the cardinal number of the sample space S.

The various outcomes of an experiment may be grouped according to their properties. In this way subsets of a sample space may be obtained. Any subset of a sample space is called an **event.** The number of elements in an event A is denoted by $n(A)$. In our experiment with the beads in a box a sample space was the set of colored beads. That is, $S = \{\text{red}_1, \text{red}_2, \text{red}_3, \text{red}_4, \text{red}_5, \text{white}_1, \text{white}_2\}$ and $n(S) = 7$. If we called the choosing of a white bead event A, then $A = \{\text{white}_1, \text{white}_2\}$ and $n(A) = 2$. The **mathematical probability** of an event A may be represented by $P(A)$ and expressed as

$$P(A) = \frac{n(A)}{n(S)}. \qquad (8)$$

PERMUTATIONS, COMBINATIONS, AND PROBABILITY

This mathematical probability $P(A)$ is a **probability function** and is a special type of function called a set function. A **set function** is a function whose domain is one or more sets and whose range is a set of numbers. The domain of $P(A)$ consists of the possible sets A and S. If $A = S$, then the event A is certain to occur and its probability is 1; $\frac{n(S)}{n(S)} = 1$. If $A = \emptyset$, the empty set, then the occurrence of event A is impossible and its probability is 0; $\frac{n(\emptyset)}{n(S)} = 0$. Formally, we have

$$\emptyset \subseteq A \subseteq S;$$
$$n(\emptyset) \leq n(A) \leq n(S);$$
$$\frac{n(\emptyset)}{n(S)} \leq \frac{n(A)}{n(S)} \leq \frac{n(S)}{n(S)};$$
$$0 \leq P(A) \leq 1.$$

Note that the cardinal number of a set may be considered as a set function according to our definition of a set function.

The occurrence of an event is a **success**; the nonoccurrence of an event is a **failure**. For any event A we may think of the set S as the universe. Then $A \cup \overline{A} = S$; $A \cap \overline{A} = \emptyset$; $n(A) + n(\overline{A}) = n(S)$; $\frac{n(A)}{n(S)} + \frac{n(\overline{A})}{n(S)} = \frac{n(S)}{n(S)}$; $P(A) + P(\overline{A}) = 1$. In other words, for any event the probability of success plus the probability of failure is 1.

The definition we have just given of mathematical probability is intuitively clear and has found wide acceptance as an elementary definition. However, it is somewhat circular in that it depends upon the concept of equally likely outcomes which really means equally probable outcomes. In Chapter 9 we shall give for mathematical probability a more rigorous definition which will avoid this difficulty.

Example 1. Ten beads are numbered 1 to 10 and placed in a box. If two beads are selected at random and simultaneously from the box, what is the probability that their sum is 10?

> Consider the two beads selected as ordered pairs of numbers (x, y). Since x may be assigned one of ten values and y may be assigned one of nine values, there are ninety ordered pairs of numbers in our sample space S. We may represent S geometrically by the points in Figure 2–6. If A is the event that $x + y = 10$, then $A = \{(1, 9), (2, 8), (3, 7), (4, 6), (6, 4), (7, 3), (8, 2), (9, 1)\}$. In Figure 2–6 the elements of A are

§ 2-5 MATHEMATICAL PROBABILITY

represented by the colored dots. Thus, $P(A) = \dfrac{n(A)}{n(S)} = \dfrac{8}{90} = \dfrac{4}{45}$.

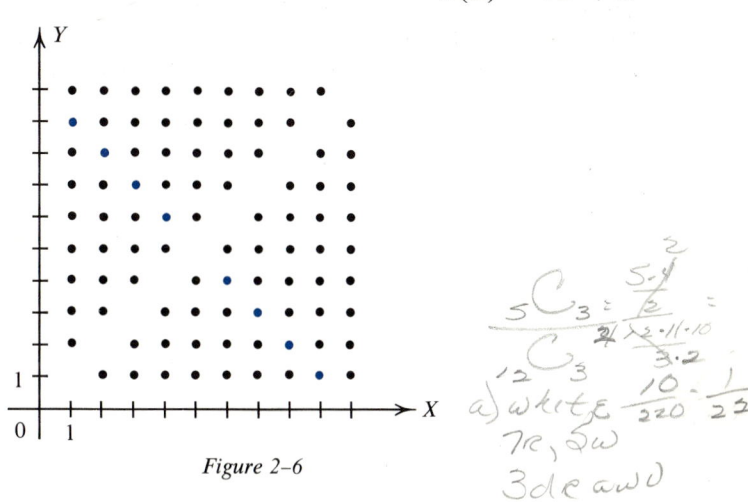

Figure 2-6

Example 2. A bag contains seven red balls and five white balls. If three balls are drawn at random at one time, (a) what is the probability that they are all white? (b) What is the probability that they are not all white?

(a) A sample space S for this problem consists of the different sets of three balls which can be selected without regard to order from the twelve balls in the bag; $n(S) = {}_{12}C_3$. Let A be the event that three white balls are selected; then $n(A) = {}_5C_3$ and

$$P(A) = \frac{{}_5C_3}{{}_{12}C_3} = \frac{\frac{5!}{3!\,2!}}{\frac{12!}{3!\,9!}} = \frac{1}{22}.$$

(b) $P(\overline{A}) = 1 - P(A) = 1 - \dfrac{1}{22} = \dfrac{21}{22}$.

In some experiments it may not be convenient or possible to enumerate a set of equally likely outcomes. In such cases we must refer to a second definition of probability based upon observed evidence. If in a number of trials an event has occurred m times and failed n times, then the **empirical,** or **statistical, probability** of the event occurring is defined as equal to $\dfrac{m}{m+n}$. For example the probability of a man age x living to age y based upon past observations of men of the same age x living to age y as recorded in a mortality table such as those used by life insurance companies (see

69

PERMUTATIONS, COMBINATIONS, AND PROBABILITY

Example 3) is an empirical probability. Note that the reliability of an empirical probability measure depends in part upon the number $m + n$ of previous trials.

Example 3. According to the American Experience Mortality Tables of 100,000 Americans alive at age 10 there will be 92,637 alive at age 20 and 78,106 alive at age 40. (a) Find the probability that an American alive at age 10 will be alive at age 20. (b) Find the probability that an American alive at age 20 will be alive at age 40.

(a) The probability that an American alive at age 10 will be alive at age 20 is $\frac{92,637}{100,000}$, that is, approximately 0.93.

(b) The probability that an American alive at age 20 will be alive at age 40 is $\frac{78,106}{92,637}$, that is, approximately 0.84.

TEST YOURSELF

A die has two faces colored red and four faces colored blue. Find the probability of obtaining on a single throw:

1. A red face.
2. A blue face.
3. Either a red or a blue face.
4. A green face.

EXERCISES

1. Find the probability of selecting at random a white marble from a bag containing three white marbles and five red marbles.
2. If two beads are selected at random from a bag containing six red beads and four white beads, what is the probability that both are red?
3. A tag is drawn at random from a set of twenty tags numbered from 1 to 20. What is the probability that its number is divisible by 3?
4. Find the probability of the face value of an ordinary die being greater than 1 and less than 6 in a single toss of the die.

• • •

5. If a die is thrown twice, what is the probability that the face value of the die on the first throw is less than 3 and the face value of the die on the second throw is 4?

70

§ 2-6 SAMPLE SPACES

6. A boy's pocket contains five dimes and ten pennies. If he selects at random four coins and simultaneously, what is the probability that he will get two dimes and two pennies?

7. An urn contains five white, four black, and six red balls of indistinguishable size and shape. If three balls are drawn at random and simultaneously, what is the probability that two are red and one is white?

8. A factory produces a certain type of light bulb. If on the average 5% of the bulbs are defective, what is the probability that a bulb selected at random is defective?

9. What is the probability that an American alive at age 10 will be alive at age 40? (Use the data from Example 3.)

10. What is the probability that an American alive at age 10 will not be alive at age 40? (Use the data from Example 3.)

11. A bag contains five red, four white, and three blue beads. If two beads are selected at random, without replacement, what is the probability that both are of the same color?

12. A three-digit number is to be written using digits from the set of digits 1 through 9 inclusive. Find the probability that the number will be odd (a) if repetition of digits is permitted; (b) if repetition of digits is not permitted.

§ 2-6 Sample spaces

The problem of finding the mathematical probability $P(A)$ of any event A is basically a problem of identifying an appropriate sample space S of equally likely outcomes such that all possible outcomes are included in S and A is a subset of S. Then $n(A)$ and $n(S)$ must be found. Frequently some agreement must be reached *a priori* (in advance) on what constitutes a particular sample space. For this reason mathematical probability is sometimes called **a priori probability.** In most elementary problems common sense and a reasonable understanding of the properties of the experiment in which we are interested allow us to agree upon a sample space.

A very important property to bear in mind in selecting a sample space S for an experiment is that the points of S must be equally likely to occur. Let us consider a classical experiment. If two coins are tossed, what is the probability that two heads appear? The mathematician D'Alembert argued that three outcomes were possible: (1) two heads, (2) one head and one tail, and (3) two tails. Since only one of these three outcomes may be associated with the event of obtaining two heads, he concluded, incorrectly, that the probability of obtaining two heads when two coins are tossed is $\frac{1}{3}$. His error lay in the fact that he failed to recognize that the

71

PERMUTATIONS, COMBINATIONS, AND PROBABILITY

outcomes he associated with the experiment of tossing the two coins were not equally likely. To illustrate the equally likely outcomes consider the two coins to be of different denominations, a nickel and a dime. Let h stand for heads and t for tails. Then a sample space S for this experiment may be defined as

$$S = \{(h, h), (h, t), (t, h), (t, t)\}$$

where the first letter of each ordered pair represents the outcome for the nickel and the second letter represents the outcome for the dime. Each ordered pair represents a single outcome within the experiment. There are four, not three, equally likely outcomes. If A is the event that two heads appear, then $A = \{(h, h)\}$ and

$$P(A) = \frac{n(A)}{n(S)} = \frac{1}{4}.$$

Example 1. Find a sample space for the experiment of tossing three coins.

Since we are interested in whether each coin falls heads or tails, we may reason that each coin must fall in one of two ways; therefore the number of points in our sample space is $2 \times 2 \times 2$, that is, 8, by the fundamental principle of enumeration. If we denote the points by ordered triples of h's (heads) and t's (tails) where each position in a triple is associated with a specific coin, then our sample space S may be defined as

$$S = \{(h, h, h), (h, h, t), (h, t, h), (t, h, h),$$
$$(h, t, t), (t, h, t), (t, t, h), (t, t, t)\}.$$

Example 2. A pair of dice are thrown simultaneously. Find the probability that the sum of the face values is 8.

The possible sums of the face values are 2, 3, 4, 5, 6, 7, 8, 9, 10, 11 and 12. However, since these outcomes are not equally likely, they do not form a sample space. In order to determine a sample space it is necessary for us to distinguish one die from the other. Consider one die painted red and the other die white. Since there are six equally likely outcomes for each die, by the fundamental principle of enumeration there are 6×6, that is, 36, equally likely ways in which the pair of dice may fall. Consider the thirty-six equally likely outcomes as ordered pairs (r, w) where r represents the face value of the red die and w represents the face value of the white die. That is, each ordered pair of numbers (r, w) is a point in our sample space S and $n(S) = 36$. The points of S are in the array:

$$(1, 1), (1, 2), (1, 3), (1, 4), (1, 5), (1, 6),$$
$$(2, 1), (2, 2), (2, 3), (2, 4), (2, 5), (2, 6),$$
$$(3, 1), (3, 2), (3, 3), (3, 4), (3, 5), (3, 6),$$
$$(4, 1), (4, 2), (4, 3), (4, 4), (4, 5), (4, 6),$$
$$(5, 1), (5, 2), (5, 3), (5, 4), (5, 5), (5, 6),$$
$$(6, 1), (6, 2), (6, 3), (6, 4), (6, 5), (6, 6).$$

If A is the event that the sum of the face values is 8, then $A = \{(2, 6), (3, 5), (4, 4), (5, 3), (6, 2)\}$ and $n(A) = 5$. Therefore $P(A) = \dfrac{n(A)}{n(S)} = \dfrac{5}{36}$.

We have spoken of "a" sample space rather than "the" sample space for an experiment. There may be many possible sample spaces for an experiment. The one which we choose depends upon the questions we desire to answer about the experiment. For example, consider an experiment in which a card is chosen at random from an ordinary deck of bridge cards. Such a deck contains thirteen cards in each of four suits: spades, hearts, diamonds, and clubs. Customarily the spade and club suits are black in color while the hearts and diamonds are red. Each suit contains ten "number" cards, 1 (ace), 2, 3, 4, $\cdots$, 10; and three "face" cards, jack, queen, and king which we shall denote by J, Q, and K respectively. If we are interested in the suit of the card chosen at random, we may consider a sample space S_1 consisting of four points. That is,

$$S_1 = \{\text{spade, heart, diamond, club}\}$$

since each of the suits is equally likely to occur. If we are interested in the color of the card chosen, we may consider a sample space S_2 consisting of two points; that is,

$$S_2 = \{\text{red, black}\},$$

since either color is equally likely to occur. If we are interested in the denomination of the card chosen, an appropriate sample space S_3 would consist of thirteen points. That is,

$$S_3 = \{1, 2, 3, 4, 5, 6, 7, 8, 9, 10, J, Q, K\}$$

since each value is equally likely to occur. If we are interested in the suit and the denomination of the card chosen, we would have to consider a sample space S_4 where $n(S_4) = 52$. Some examples of points in S_4 are the seven of hearts, the ace of spades, the two of clubs, and so on.

PERMUTATIONS, COMBINATIONS, AND PROBABILITY

Certain sample spaces give more information than others. For example, S_4 would give more information than either S_1 or S_3. We speak of S_4 as being a more *fundamental* sample space than S_1 or S_3.

TEST YOURSELF

1. Give a sample space for two-digit numbers using digits from the set {3, 4, 5, 6} **(a)** allowing repetition of digits; **(b)** not allowing repetition of digits.
2. A coin is tossed and a die is thrown. State a sample space for this experiment.
3. Find a sample space for the experiment of tossing four coins.

EXERCISES

1. Three cards, an ace, a king, and a queen, are face down on a table. If two cards are selected at random, what is the probability that one of them is the ace?
2. If two coins are tossed, what is the probability of not obtaining two heads?
3. If three coins are tossed, find the probability that **(a)** exactly two of them will come up heads; **(b)** at least two of them will come up heads.
4. A boy has four coins, a penny, a nickel, a dime, and a quarter, in his pocket. If he selects two coins at random and simultaneously **(a)** give a sample space to describe the possible coins selected. **(b)** What is the probability that the sum of the values of the coins selected is less than twenty cents?
5. What is the probability that the total face value of a pair of dice will be greater than nine on a single toss?

• • •

6. If a pair of dice are thrown, find the probability that the face value of one die is less than four and the face value of the other die is equal to three.
7. Five cards are selected at random from an ordinary deck of bridge cards. Find the probability that the five cards are four queens and the ace of spades.
8. Given a deck of ordinary bridge cards, what is the probability that five cards dealt at random from the deck will contain four aces?
9. From a deck of ordinary bridge cards one card is selected at random. What is the probability that the card selected is not a queen?

74

§ 2-7 THE ADDITION LAW OF PROBABILITY

10. Find the probability of being dealt a thirteen card bridge hand containing six spades, four hearts, two diamonds, and one club.

11. Find the probability of being dealt a thirteen card bridge hand containing exactly two aces.

12. Toss two coins sixty times and record the number of times no, one, and two heads appear. Compare your results with the expected results according to D'Alembert's analysis of this experiment. Compare your results with the expected results according to our analysis of this experiment.

13. A committee consists of five men and three women. If a chairman and a secretary are selected at random, and if one person may not hold both positions, find the probability that both are of the same sex.

14. What is the probability of obtaining seven as the sum of the face values if three dice are thrown?

15. If six dice are thrown simultaneously, what is the probability that each of the numbers from one through six will appear on the top faces?

§ 2-7 The addition law of probability

There are problems in which we are interested in determining the probability that at least one of two events occurs in an experiment. We shall use set notation to describe this situation. If A and B are two events of a sample space S, then the probability that A or B occurs will be denoted by $P(A \cup B)$ where $P(A \cup B) = \dfrac{n(A \cup B)}{n(S)}$ by the definition of mathematical probability. In a similar manner the probability that both of two events A and B occur is denoted by $P(A \cap B)$ where $P(A \cap B) = \dfrac{n(A \cap B)}{n(S)}$.

If we throw a pair of dice, what is the probability that the sum of the values of the faces will be either less than five or a multiple of four? By examination of the sample space which was discussed for this experiment in Example 2 of § 2-6 we can determine the points associated with event A, the sum is less than five, or event B, the sum is a multiple of four. We find that

$$A \cup B = \{(1, 1), (1, 2), (1, 3), (2, 1), (2, 2), (2, 6),$$
$$(3, 1), (3, 5), (4, 4), (5, 3), (6, 2), (6, 6)\};$$

and $n(A \cup B) = 12$. Thus

$$P(A \cup B) = \frac{12}{36} = \frac{1}{3}.$$

PERMUTATIONS, COMBINATIONS, AND PROBABILITY

It is often desirable in more difficult probability problems to determine $P(A \cup B)$ in terms of $P(A)$, $P(B)$, and $P(A \cap B)$. The following theorem is called the **addition law of probability** and relates these four probability functions.

Theorem: $P(A \cup B) = P(A) + P(B) - P(A \cap B).$ (9)

PROOF: The relationship among the cardinal numbers of the sets A, B, $A \cup B$, and $A \cap B$ is given by the equation

$$n(A \cup B) = n(A) + n(B) - n(A \cap B).$$

If we divide by $n(S)$, we have

$$\frac{n(A \cup B)}{n(S)} = \frac{n(A)}{n(S)} + \frac{n(B)}{n(S)} - \frac{n(A \cap B)}{n(S)}$$

which, by the definition of mathematical probability, may be interpreted as

$$P(A \cup B) = P(A) + P(B) - P(A \cap B).$$

Example 1. If a card is chosen at random from a deck of bridge cards, what is the probability that it is a heart or a seven?

Consider the suit and denomination of each of the fifty-two cards as the points of our sample space S. Let A be the event that a heart of any denomination is chosen and B be the event that a seven of any suit is chosen. The set $A \cap B$ contains a point, the seven of hearts. Now that we have identified S, A, B, and $A \cap B$, we know that $n(S) = 52$, $n(A) = 13$, $n(B) = 4$, and $n(A \cap B) = 1$. Thus $P(A) = \frac{13}{52}$, $P(B) = \frac{4}{52}$, $P(A \cap B) = \frac{1}{52}$, and

$$P(A \cup B) = P(A) + P(B) - P(A \cap B)$$
$$= \frac{13}{52} + \frac{4}{52} - \frac{1}{52} = \frac{16}{52} = \frac{4}{13}.$$

Two or more events are called **mutually exclusive** events if they have no points in common; that is, if their intersection is the empty set. For example, in throwing a die the six possible outcomes in terms of their face values represent six mutually exclusive events. In determining a sample space for an experiment we always consider a set of mutually exclusive events, that is, mutually exclusive possible outcomes.

§ 2-7 THE ADDITION LAW OF PROBABILITY

Corollary: If events A and B are mutually exclusive, then

$$P(A \cup B) = P(A) + P(B). \tag{10}$$

The proof of this corollary follows directly from the addition law and the definition of mutually exclusive events. Accordingly, the proof is left as an exercise for the student.

Example 2. A box contains eight red beads and five white beads. If an experiment consists of choosing at random four beads from the box, what is the probability that not more than one bead will be white?

Think of the beads as marked in some way so that any two beads of the same color may be distinguished. An appropriate sample space consists of the sets of four beads which can be selected from the thirteen beads in the box. Thus $n(S) = {}_{13}C_4$. Let A be the event that four red beads are selected, and let B be the event that three red beads and one white bead are selected. The probability that not more than one white bead is selected is the probability that A or B occurs. Events A and B are mutually exclusive; that is, $P(A \cap B) = 0$. Thus $P(A \cup B) = P(A) + P(B)$.

Since $n(A) = {}_8C_4$, then $P(A) = \dfrac{{}_8C_4}{{}_{13}C_4} = \dfrac{14}{143}$. If we can select three red beads in ${}_8C_3$ ways and one white bead in ${}_5C_1$ ways, we can do both in ${}_8C_3 \times {}_5C_1$ ways. Thus

$$n(B) = {}_8C_3 \times {}_5C_1, \quad \text{and} \quad P(B) = \frac{{}_8C_3 \times {}_5C_1}{{}_{13}C_4} = \frac{56}{143}.$$

Therefore $P(A \cup B) = \dfrac{14}{143} + \dfrac{56}{143} = \dfrac{70}{143}.$

In a sample space S all points which do not belong to event A belong to the **complementary event** $\overline{A}$. In other words, in the universe S all elements which are not members of set A are members of set $\overline{A}$. (See § 1–2.) As we stated in § 2–5, $P(\overline{A}) = 1 - P(A)$ since $n(A) + n(\overline{A}) = n(S)$.

This relationship is useful in calculating the probability of an event in any problem where it is more convenient to calculate the probability of the complementary event.

Example 3. A committee of three people is to be chosen at random from a group of six boys and four girls. What is the probability that at least one girl is on the committee?

PERMUTATIONS, COMBINATIONS, AND PROBABILITY

Our sample space S consists of all the committees of three which can be selected from the group of ten, thus $n(S) = {}_{10}C_3 = 120$. If we let A represent the event that a committee has at least one girl as a member, then $\overline{A}$ must be the event that a committee has no girls as members; that is, a committee composed entirely of boys. Since $n(\overline{A}) = {}_6C_3 = 20$, then $P(\overline{A}) = \dfrac{n(\overline{A})}{n(S)} = \dfrac{20}{120} = \dfrac{1}{6}$, and

$$P(A) = 1 - P(\overline{A})$$
$$= 1 - \frac{1}{6} = \frac{5}{6}.$$

Therefore the probability is $\dfrac{5}{6}$ that there will be at least one girl on the committee.

This problem could have been solved by applying an extension of our corollary. In that case we would have had the more laborious task of calculating

$$ {}_6C_2 \times {}_4C_1 + {}_6C_1 \times {}_4C_2 + {}_4C_3 $$

to obtain $n(A)$.

The complementary event $\overline{A}$ also is used to define odds. The **odds** in favor of the occurrence of an event A are defined to be the ratio $\dfrac{P(A)}{P(\overline{A})}$. The odds against the occurrence of an event A are defined to be the ratio $\dfrac{P(\overline{A})}{P(A)}$.

Example 4. Find the odds in favor of obtaining three heads in three tosses of a coin.

Let A be the event of obtaining three heads; thus $P(A) = \dfrac{1}{8}$, $P(\overline{A}) = 1 - P(A) = \dfrac{7}{8}$. Therefore the odds in favor of A are $\dfrac{P(A)}{P(\overline{A})} = \dfrac{1}{7}$.

TEST YOURSELF

1. Given $P(A) = \dfrac{2}{5}$, $P(B) = \dfrac{1}{2}$, and $P(A \cap B) = \dfrac{1}{5}$, find $P(A \cup B)$.

2. If A and B are mutually exclusive events with $P(A) = \dfrac{1}{6}$ and $P(B) = \dfrac{2}{3}$, find $P(A \cup B)$.

§ 2-7 THE ADDITION LAW OF PROBABILITY

3. Given $P(A) = \frac{1}{2}$, $P(A \cup B) = \frac{5}{6}$, and $P(A \cap B) = \frac{1}{3}$, find $P(B)$.

4. Given $P(A) = \frac{2}{9}$, find $P(\overline{A})$.

EXERCISES

1. Find the probability of obtaining a seven or an eleven on a single throw of a pair of dice.

2. Show that if $P(A) = \frac{3}{4}$ and $P(B) = \frac{2}{3}$, then A and B cannot be mutually exclusive events.

3. Find $P(A \cup B \cup C)$ if for any pair of the given events the events are mutually exclusive.

4. Find $P(A \cup B \cup C)$.

5. A man approaching a $0.25 toll booth on the Garden State Parkway selects at random three coins from his pocket. If he had one quarter, two dimes, and four nickels in his pocket, what is the probability that he selects an insufficient amount to cover the toll?

• • •

6. What is the probability that five cards dealt from an ordinary deck of bridge cards will contain at least three aces?

7. If a team's leading batter has probabilities of $\frac{1}{8}$ of getting a single, $\frac{1}{12}$ of getting a double, $\frac{1}{24}$ of getting a triple, and $\frac{1}{12}$ of getting a homer on every time at bat, what is the probability that he does not get a hit in one time at bat? Assume that he either gets a hit or is out.

8. Three players each throw a pair of dice. What is the probability that at least one of them will throw a seven?

9. From a group of four lawyers, three doctors, and five teachers a committee of three is chosen at random. What is the probability that there will be a majority of one profession on the committee?

10. Consider events A, B, and C such that $P(A) = P(B) = P(C) = \frac{1}{4}$, $P(A \cap B) = P(B \cap C) = 0$, and $P(A \cap C) = \frac{1}{8}$. What is the probability that at least one of the events A, B, C occurs?

11. Given three mutually exclusive events A, B, C which exhaust the sample space, $P(\overline{A}) = \frac{5}{7}$, and $P(B) = \frac{3}{10}$; find $P(C)$.

79

PERMUTATIONS, COMBINATIONS, AND PROBABILITY

12. Find the odds on a single throw of a pair of dice against obtaining (**a**) an eight; (**b**) a seven; (**c**) a four.

• **13.** A cube has three faces lettered with an A, two faces lettered with a B, and one face lettered with a C. Find the odds in favor of (**a**) throwing an A in a single throw; (**b**) throwing an A and then a C on two successive throws.

• **14.** What are the odds against getting a seven or an eleven on a single throw of a pair of dice?

§ 2-8 Conditional probability

Given two events, A and B, of a sample space, the probability that event A will occur given that event B has occurred is called the **conditional probability of A given B** and is denoted by $P(A \mid B)$.

The following example illustrates the fact that, in general, the calculation of the conditional probability of one event given another event may be thought of as restricting an appropriate sample space S to a subset of S. Bear in mind that in a sample space S, $A \cap B = B \cap A$ thus $n(A \cap B) = n(B \cap A)$ and $P(A \cap B) = P(B \cap A)$.

Example 1. Find the probability that, in a single throw of a die, the face value is greater than three given that the face value is an odd number.

> Let A be the event that the face value of the die is greater than three and B the event that the face value is an odd number. Thus $A = \{4, 5, 6\}$ and $B = \{1, 3, 5\}$. An appropriate initial sample space for our experiment is the set S of equally likely outcomes;
>
> $$S = \{1, 2, 3, 4, 5, 6\}.$$
>
> However, since we are given the fact that event B has occurred, we must restrict our consideration to a reduced sample space of three equally likely outcomes; in this case, B. Our new sample space $S_1 = B = \{1, 3, 5\}$; so $n(S_1) = n(B) = 3$. The set of points in S_1 which are favorable to event A is the set of points in $A \cap B$; that is, $A \cap B = \{5\}$, and $n(A \cap B) = 1$. Hence
>
> $$P(A \mid B) = \frac{n(A \cap B)}{n(B)} = \frac{1}{3}.$$
>
> Notice that $P(A \mid B) \neq P(A)$ in this problem since
>
> $$P(A) = \frac{n(A)}{n(S)} = \frac{3}{6} = \frac{1}{2}.$$

§ 2-8 CONDITIONAL PROBABILITY

In the preceding example we found that $P(A \mid B) = \dfrac{n(A \cap B)}{n(B)}$. This is true in general provided $n(B) \neq 0$. Since A and B are subsets of some sample space S, the ratio $\dfrac{n(A \cap B)}{n(B)}$ may be written as

$$\dfrac{\dfrac{n(A \cap B)}{n(S)}}{\dfrac{n(B)}{n(S)}}, \text{ that is, } \dfrac{P(A \cap B)}{P(B)}.$$

The preceding discussion gives rise to the following formal definition of conditional probability:

Given two events A and B of a sample space, the **conditional probability of A given B**, $P(A \mid B)$, is defined by

$$P(A \mid B) = \dfrac{P(A \cap B)}{P(B)}, \text{ where } P(B) \neq 0. \tag{11}$$

Example 2. Assume that each child born is equally likely to be either a boy or a girl. If a family has two children, find the probability that both children are boys if (a) the older child is a boy; (b) at least one of the children is a boy.

> Let b represent a boy and g represent a girl. An appropriate sample space S for all possible sets of two children born in a family may be represented by
> $$S = \{(b, b), (b, g), (g, b), (g, g)\}$$
> where the first letter of each ordered pair represents the older child and the second letter represents the younger child. Let A represent the event that the older child is a boy and B represent the event that the younger child is a boy. Then $A = \{(b, b), (b, g)\}$, $B = \{(b, b), (g, b)\}$, $A \cup B = \{(b, b), (b, g), (g, b)\}$, and $A \cap B = \{(b, b)\}$; thus $n(A) = 2$, $n(B) = 2$, $n(A \cup B) = 3$, $n(A \cap B) = 1$, and $n(S) = 4$.
>
> (a) The probability that both children are boys given that the older child is a boy is
> $$P(A \cap B \mid A) = \dfrac{P([A \cap B] \cap A)}{P(A)}.$$
> Since $[A \cap B] \cap A = A \cap B$, then
> $$P(A \cap B \mid A) = \dfrac{P(A \cap B)}{P(A)} = \dfrac{\frac{1}{4}}{\frac{1}{2}} = \dfrac{1}{2}.$$

81

PERMUTATIONS, COMBINATIONS, AND PROBABILITY

(b) The probability that both children are boys given that at least one child is a boy is

$$P(A \cap B \mid A \cup B) = \frac{P([A \cap B] \cap [A \cup B])}{P(A \cup B)}.$$

Since $[A \cap B] \cap [A \cup B] = A \cap B$, then

$$P(A \cap B \mid A \cup B) = \frac{P(A \cap B)}{P(A \cup B)} = \frac{\frac{1}{4}}{\frac{3}{4}} = \frac{1}{3}.$$

Note that Example 3 illustrates the fact that we may have $P(A \mid B) \neq P(B \mid A)$.

Example 3. If ten tags marked respectively 1, 2, 3, 4, 5, 6, 7, 8, 9, 10 are placed in a container and one tag is chosen at random, find the probability that the tag chosen is **(a)** less than or equal to five given that it is greater than three; **(b)** greater than three given that it is less than or equal to five.

Our sample space $S = \{1, 2, 3, 4, 5, 6, 7, 8, 9, 10\}$ and $n(S) = 10$. Let A be the event that the tag chosen is less than or equal to five and B be the event that the tag chosen is greater than three. Then $A = \{1, 2, 3, 4, 5\}$, $B = \{4, 5, 6, 7, 8, 9, 10\}$, $A \cap B = \{4, 5\}$, $n(A) = 5$, $n(B) = 7$, and $n(A \cap B) = 2$.

(a) The probability that the tag chosen is less than or equal to five given that it is greater than three is

$$P(A \mid B) = \frac{P(A \cap B)}{P(B)} = \frac{\frac{2}{10}}{\frac{7}{10}} = \frac{2}{7}.$$

(b) The probability that the tag chosen is greater than three given that it is less than or equal to five is

$$P(B \mid A) = \frac{P(B \cap A)}{P(A)} = \frac{P(A \cap B)}{P(A)} = \frac{\frac{2}{10}}{\frac{5}{10}} = \frac{2}{5}.$$

Consider two events A and B where $P(A) \neq 0$ and $P(B) \neq 0$. The probability $P(A \cap B)$ that the events A and B both occur satisfies both

82

§ 2-8 CONDITIONAL PROBABILITY

of these equations from the definition of conditional probability:

$$P(A \mid B) = \frac{P(A \cap B)}{P(B)}; \qquad P(B \mid A) = \frac{P(A \cap B)}{P(A)}.$$

Thus

$$P(A \cap B) = P(B) \times P(A \mid B) = P(A) \times P(B \mid A). \qquad (12)$$

This statement is called the **multiplication law of probability.** It states that the probability of the compound event A and B is the product of the probability of event B and the conditional probability of event A given event B. The probability of A and B is also equal to the product of the probability of event A and the conditional probability of event B given event A.

The multiplication law of probability is especially useful when two events occur in succession and the possible outcomes of the second event depend upon the possible outcomes of the first event. A set of equally likely outcomes for both events may be difficult to enumerate while sample spaces for the first event and for the second event given the first event may be easily identified. This situation is shown in Example 4.

Example 4. If a box contains three red beads and three white beads, what is the probability of selecting at random a white bead and then a red bead if the bead drawn first is not replaced?

Let A represent the drawing of a white bead and B the drawing of a red bead. Then $P(B \mid A)$ is the probability of drawing a red bead after a white bead. Since there are three white beads among the six beads in the box, $P(A) = \frac{3}{6}$. After a white bead has been removed, there are three red beads among the five remaining beads; thus $P(B \mid A) = \frac{3}{5}$.

Then

$$P(A \cap B) = P(A) \times P(B \mid A) = \frac{3}{6} \times \frac{3}{5} = \frac{3}{10}.$$

If we try to find a sample space for the two events, we might be tempted to consider $S = \{(r, r), (r, w), (w, r), (w, w)\}$ where each point would represent an ordered selection from among the red beads r and the white beads w. However, the set of points in S does not satisfy the definition of a sample space as we have it in this chapter since the points are not equally likely to occur. For example, consider the points (w, r) and (w, w). The probability of selecting a white bead first is

83

PERMUTATIONS, COMBINATIONS, AND PROBABILITY

the same in each case; but after a white bead has been selected, the probability of selecting a second white bead would be $\frac{2}{5}$ while the probability of selecting a red second bead is $\frac{3}{5}$. Thus we see that these two outcomes are not equally likely.

Conditional probabilities are also used to define independent events. An event A is **independent** of an event B if the occurrence of B does not affect the occurrence of A; that is, $P(A \mid B) = P(A)$. The multiplication law can be used to prove that if A is independent of B, then B is independent of A. (See Exercise 17.) Accordingly, we consider A and B to be independent events if $P(A \mid B) = P(A)$.

Example 5. If a card is drawn at random from an ordinary deck of bridge cards, find the probability that the card is a seven given that it is a spade.

Consider the sample space S to be the set of fifty-two cards identified by suit and denomination. Thus $n(S) = 52$. Let A represent the event that the card is a seven and B represent the event that the card is a spade. Thus $n(A) = 4$, $P(A) = \frac{4}{52} = \frac{1}{13}$, $n(B) = 13$, $P(B) = \frac{13}{52} = \frac{1}{4}$, $n(A \cap B) = 1$, and $P(A \cap B) = \frac{1}{52}$. By the multiplication law

$$P(A \cap B) = P(B) \times P(A \mid B);$$

$$\frac{1}{52} = \frac{13}{52} \times P(A \mid B); \; P(A \mid B) = \frac{1}{13}.$$

Since $P(A) = \frac{1}{13} = P(A \mid B)$, the events A and B are independent events.

Example 6. If a coin is tossed five times, find the probability that two heads and three tails appear.

The occurrence of a head has a probability equal to $\frac{1}{2}$ on each toss and is an event independent of the outcomes of other tosses; thus the probability that two tosses yield two heads is $\left(\frac{1}{2}\right)^2$. The occurrence of a tail has a probability equal to $\frac{1}{2}$ on each toss and is an event independent of the outcomes of other tosses; thus the probability that three

84

tosses yield three tails is $\left(\frac{1}{2}\right)^3$. The probability that a particular sequence of five tosses yields two heads and three tails is $\left(\frac{1}{2}\right)^2\left(\frac{1}{2}\right)^3$, that is, $\left(\frac{1}{2}\right)^5$. However, the two heads could have occurred on any two of the five tosses. In other words, there are $_5C_2$, that is, 10, such sequences of five tosses yielding two heads and three tails; and each of these sequences has probability $\left(\frac{1}{2}\right)^5$. Since these are mutually exclusive events, we have the probability of obtaining two heads and three tails in five tosses equal to $10 \times \left(\frac{1}{2}\right)^5$, that is, $\frac{5}{16}$.

TEST YOURSELF

In Exercises 1 through 3, given $P(A) = \frac{1}{2}$, $P(B) = \frac{2}{3}$, and $P(A \cap B) = \frac{5}{12}$, find:

1. $P(A \mid B)$.   **2.** $P(B \mid A)$.   **3.** $P(A \cup B)$.

4. If A and B are independent events with $P(A) = \frac{1}{3}$ and $P(B) = \frac{1}{3}$, find $P(A \cap B)$.

5. If two boys each toss two coins, what is the probability that they both get two heads?

EXERCISES

1. Given $P(A \cap B) = \frac{1}{3}$ and $P(A \mid B) = \frac{2}{5}$, find $P(B)$.

2. If A and B are independent events and $P(A) = \frac{1}{2}$ and $P(B) = \frac{1}{3}$, find $P(A \cap B)$.

3. Two students work independently on a problem. The probability that the first one will solve it is $\frac{3}{4}$, and the probability that the second one will solve it is $\frac{2}{3}$. What is the probability that at least one of the students will solve the problem?

PERMUTATIONS, COMBINATIONS, AND PROBABILITY

4. A pair of dice are thrown. Find the probability that the sum of the face values is greater than ten given **(a)** that one and only one of the faces is a six; **(b)** that at least one of the faces is a six; **(c)** that none of the faces is a six.

5. An urn contains five green balls, seven red balls, and four white balls. Find the probability of **(a)** drawing a red, a white, and a green ball in that order without replacement; **(b)** drawing a red or a white ball followed by a green ball without replacement.

6. Each of three boxes contains nine pieces of paper numbered respectively 1, 2, 3, $\cdots$, 9. If one piece of paper is selected at random from each box, what is the probability that the sum of the numbers on the three pieces is odd?

7. Find the probability that a card drawn at random from an ordinary deck of bridge cards is a four given that **(a)** it is a two, three, four, or five; **(b)** it is a spade.

8. The probability that at least one of the events A or B occurs is $\frac{4}{5}$. The probability that A occurs is $\frac{1}{2}$, and the probability that B occurs is $\frac{2}{5}$. Find the probability that A occurs if B is known to occur.

• • •

9. If a teacher gives a true-false test with only five questions, find the probability of a student getting five correct answers if **(a)** he is only guessing; **(b)** he knows that there are more true answers than false; **(c)** he knows that there are more true answers than false and that the answer to the fourth question is false.

10. If two people each toss three coins, what is the probability that they each get the same number of heads?

11. If the probability of team A defeating team B is $\frac{2}{3}$ in each baseball game they play, what is the probability that team A will win four games before team B can win four games?

12. An urn contains four white marbles and two black marbles. If three marbles are drawn at random in succession and without replacement, what is the probability that the third marble is a black one?

13. Find the probability that the ace of spades lies next to the ace of hearts in an ordinary deck of fifty-two cards.

14. Given $P(A)$ the probability of an event A for an experiment, explain why the probability of A occuring at least once in n repetitions of the experiment is $1 - [P(\overline{A})]^n$.

§ 2-9   MATHEMATICAL EXPECTATION

15. What is the probability of throwing a seven with a pair of dice at least once in four tosses?

16. On the average on a certain machine five percent of the total number of parts produced are defective. If a sample of n parts is taken from the production of that machine, what is the probability that at least one part is defective?

17. Prove that if A is independent of B, then B is independent of A.

18. The mortality rate for a certain disease is one per hundred. Find a numerical expression for the probability of exactly five deaths from this disease in a group of 400.

19. An urn contains two white, one black, and four red balls. A second urn contains one white, three black, and three red balls. If an urn is chosen at random and then three balls are selected at random from that urn, find the probability that the three balls will be **(a)** red; **(b)** black; **(c)** all the same color.

● **20.** **(a)** Find the probability that no two people in a group of r people have the same birthday with regard to month and day. **(b)** What is the probability that at least two people in a group of r people celebrate their birthdays on the same date? Assume a year of 365 days.

● **21.** If one die of a pair of dice is biased so that the chance of throwing each face value is proportional to that value, what is the probability of throwing a nine in a single throw of the pair of dice?

● **22.** If the probability of a torpedo hitting a ship is $\frac{1}{3}$, how many torpedos must be fired at a ship to give a probability greater than $\frac{9}{10}$ for at least one hit?

● **23.** A game is played in which A and B take turns drawing a bead from a box which contains five red beads and three white beads. If the beads are not replaced after each drawing and the winner is the player who first draws a white bead, what is the probability that A wins if he has the first turn?

● **24.** A bag contains three white and five red balls. Two balls selected at random are withdrawn simultaneously and replaced by two red balls. Then two balls are again selected at random and withdrawn simultaneously. Find the probability that these two balls are alike in color.

§ 2-9   Mathematical expectation

A set of events $A_1, A_2, A_3, \cdots, A_n$ is **exhaustive** in a sample space S if the complement of the union of the sets is the empty set; that is, $\overline{A_1 \cup A_2 \cup A_3 \cup \cdots \cup A_n} = \emptyset$. In an experiment or game in which

PERMUTATIONS, COMBINATIONS, AND PROBABILITY

numerical values $v_1, v_2, v_3, \cdots, v_n$ may be attached to each member of an exhaustive set of mutually exclusive events $A_1, A_2, A_3, \cdots, A_n$ respectively, then the **mathematical expectation** E of the experiment or game is defined as

$$E = P(A_1) \times v_1 + P(A_2) \times v_2 + P(A_3) \times v_3 + \cdots + P(A_n) \times v_n. \quad (13)$$

Example 1. Find the expected face value when a single die is thrown.

The possible face values, 1, 2, 3, 4, 5, 6, are equally likely to occur. Thus the probability associated with each outcome is $\frac{1}{6}$. Therefore, the expected value E is

$$E = \frac{1}{6} \times 1 + \frac{1}{6} \times 2 + \frac{1}{6} \times 3 + \frac{1}{6} \times 4 + \frac{1}{6} \times 5 + \frac{1}{6} \times 6 = 3.5.$$

Note that the expected value is not necessarily one of the possible outcomes.

Example 2. Find the expected sum of the face values of a pair of dice on a single throw.

The possible sums of the face values are 2, 3, 4, $\cdots$, 12. Let $A_2, A_3, A_4, \cdots, A_{12}$ represent respectively the event of obtaining the indicated sum. The sums of the face values are the numerical values attached to the respective events. We can refer to the sample space S for this experiment as shown in the array in Example 2 of § 2–6. We find that $P(A_2) = \frac{1}{36}$, $P(A_3) = \frac{2}{36}$, $P(A_4) = \frac{3}{36}$, $P(A_5) = \frac{4}{36}$, $P(A_6) = \frac{5}{36}$, $P(A_7) = \frac{6}{36}$, $P(A_8) = \frac{5}{36}$, $P(A_9) = \frac{4}{36}$, $P(A_{10}) = \frac{3}{36}$, $P(A_{11}) = \frac{2}{36}$, and $P(A_{12}) = \frac{1}{36}$. The expected sum E of the face values is

$$E = \frac{1}{36} \times 2 + \frac{2}{36} \times 3 + \frac{3}{36} \times 4 + \frac{4}{36} \times 5 + \frac{5}{36} \times 6 + \frac{6}{36} \times 7$$
$$+ \frac{5}{36} \times 8 + \frac{4}{36} \times 9 + \frac{3}{36} \times 10 + \frac{2}{36} \times 11 + \frac{1}{36} \times 12 = 7.$$

Example 3. A man pays one dollar for a raffle ticket on a car worth $3500. If 10,000 raffle tickets are sold, what is the expected value of the man's purchase?

§ 2-9   MATHEMATICAL EXPECTATION

The man either wins the car or he does not. Let A be the event that he wins the car. Since each raffle ticket is equally likely to be the winning ticket, $P(A) = \frac{1}{10,000}$; and the value $3499 associated with winning is the value of the car minus the cost of his ticket. Since $P(\overline{A}) = \frac{9999}{10,000}$ and the value associated with not winning is $(-\$1)$, the man's expected gain, that is, the mathematical expectation E of this raffle, is

$$E = \frac{1}{10,000} \times 3499 + \frac{9999}{10,000} \times (-1) = -0.65.$$

Therefore the value E is $(-\$0.65)$, a loss of sixty-five cents.

Mathematical expectation is also used in measuring the fairness of games of chance. A game is said to be **fair** if each player has a mathematical expectation of zero. (See Exercise 9.)

TEST YOURSELF

A single tag is selected at random from a set of four tags marked 1, 3, 5, *and* 7 *respectively. Let x be the number marked on the tag selected. Find:*

1. The expected value of x.
2. The expected value of x^2.

EXERCISES

1. A bag contains four dollar bills and six play dollar bills. What is the mathematical expectation of a single random selection?

2. An American twenty years old purchases an insurance policy for which the insurance company will pay his wife $10,000 in the event of his death before age forty. What is the value of the wife's expectation? Use the data in Example 3 of § 2–5.

3. If x is the number of heads obtained when four coins are tossed, find the expected value of (**a**) x; (**b**) x^2.

4. A church raffle sells 4000 tickets at one dollar each for an automobile worth $2000. If you buy a ticket, what is your mathematical expectation?

5. A box contains five red beads and three white beads. If three beads are selected at random in a single draw, find the expected number of red beads.

PERMUTATIONS, COMBINATIONS, AND PROBABILITY

• • •

6. The probability that a marksman will hit a certain target is 0.1. Find the value of his expectation if he has three trials and will receive ten points for each hit.

7. Bob and Dick bet on the face value of a die. If each throws the die once and Bob wagers $1.00 against Dick's $1.20 that he can get a higher face value than Dick can get, what is Bob's expectation?

8. A container holds four red chips and one white chip. Each red chip is worth a dime, and the white chip is worth a nickel. If a boy is allowed to select one chip at a time, without replacement, until the white chip is selected, what is his expectation?

9. Player A throws a die and receives two cents for each dot on the face of the die from player B. How much should player A pay player B per throw for the game to be fair?

• **10.** A gambling house quotes the following odds against the roll of a pair of dice: 1 to 1 for less than seven, 4 to 1 for seven, and 1 to 1 for more than seven. What is the house's expectation on each roll of the dice if a player wagers one dollar on each of the three events stated?

SUMMARY OF CHAPTER 2

1. In this chapter you have studied permutations, combinations, and elementary probability. A permutation is a selection in a definite order of a number of elements from a set. Factorial notation was introduced and defined; that is, $n! = n(n-1)(n-2) \cdots (3)(2)(1)$.

The number $_nP_r$ of permutations of n things taken r at a time can be derived using the fundamental principle of enumeration:

> If a selection can be made in any one of m ways, and if after this selection has been made a second selection can be made in any one of n ways; then the two selections can be made in the order stated in any one of mn ways.

This principle can be extended for any finite sequence of selections; then

$$_nP_r = n(n-1)(n-2) \cdots (n-r+1) \tag{1}$$

$$= \frac{n!}{(n-r)!} . \quad (\S\ 2\text{-}1) \tag{2}$$

2. The number N of permutations of n elements taken n at a time where k of the elements are indistinguishable (alike) and the $(n-k)$ remaining

SUMMARY OF CHAPTER 2

elements are distinguishable (different) from each other and from the k elements may be expressed as

$$N = \frac{n!}{k!} \tag{3}$$

This procedure may be extended for k_1 alike, k_2 others alike, $\cdots$, and k_t others alike to obtain

$$N = \frac{n!}{k_1!\, k_2!\, k_3! \cdots k_t!}. \tag{4}$$

In circular permutations the first element chosen merely determines a reference point;

$$_nP_r^* = \frac{_nP_r}{r}. \quad (\S\, 2\text{-}2) \tag{5}$$

3. A combination is a selection without regard to order of a number of elements from a set. If $_nC_r$ is the number of combinations of n elements taken r at a time, then

$$_nC_r = \frac{n!}{r!\,(n-r)!} \tag{6}$$

$$_nC_r = {}_nC_{n-r}. \quad (\S\, 2\text{-}3) \tag{7}$$

4. The binomial theorem may be stated in the form:

$$(a+b)^n = {}_nC_0 a^n + {}_nC_1 a^{n-1}b + {}_nC_2 a^{n-2}b^2 + \cdots$$
$$+ {}_nC_k a^{n-k}b^k + \cdots + {}_nC_{n-1} ab^{n-1} + {}_nC_n b^n. \quad (\S\, 2\text{-}4)$$

5. The mathematical probability $P(A)$ of an event A may be expressed as

$$P(A) = \frac{n(A)}{n(S)} \tag{8}$$

where $n(A)$ is the cardinal number of the event A and $n(S)$ is the cardinal number of the sample space S. The probability $P(A)$ of the success of the event plus the probability $P(\overline{A})$ of the failure of the event is 1. (§ 2-5)

6. Sample spaces are used in solving probability problems. A given experiment may have different sample spaces. (§ 2-6)

7. The addition law of probability may be stated as

$$P(A \cup B) = P(A) + P(B) - P(A \cap B). \tag{9}$$

If A and B are mutually exclusive events, then

$$P(A \cup B) = P(A) + P(B). \tag{10}$$

The odds in favor of A are $\dfrac{P(A)}{P(\overline{A})}$. (§ 2-7)

PERMUTATIONS, COMBINATIONS, AND PROBABILITY

8. The conditional probability $P(A \mid B)$ of A given B where $P(B) \neq 0$ may be expressed as

$$P(A \mid B) = \frac{P(A \cap B)}{P(B)}. \tag{11}$$

The basic property of a conditional probability is that the sample space of the event A may be different after the occurrence of the event B from what it was before the event B.

The multiplication law of probability may be stated as

$$P(A \cap B) = P(B) \times P(A \mid B) = P(A) \times P(B \mid A). \quad (\S\ 2\text{-}8) \tag{12}$$

9. The mathematical expectation E of an experiment or a game involving mutually exclusive events $A_1, A_2, \cdots, A_n$ with numerical values $v_1, v_2, \cdots, v_n$ respectively is defined as

$$E = P(A_1) \times v_1 + P(A_2) \times v_2 + \cdots + P(A_n) \times v_n. \quad (\S\ 2\text{-}9) \tag{13}$$

10. The following words have been introduced or used extensively in this chapter:

a priori probability (§ 2–6)	mathematical expectation (§ 2–9)
arrangement (§ 2–1)	mathematical probability (§ 2–5)
binomial theorem (§ 2–4)	multiplicity (§ 2–2)
circular permutation (§ 2–2)	mutually exclusive (§ 2–7)
combination (§§ 2–1, 2–3)	odds (§ 2–9)
complementary event (§ 2–7)	ordered selection (§ 2–1)
conditional probability (§ 2–8)	Pascal's triangle (§ 2–4)
empirical probability (§ 2–5)	permutation (§ 2–1)
event (§ 2–5)	point (§ 2–5)
exhaustive (§ 2–9)	probability (§ 2–5)
factorial notation (§ 2–1)	probability function (§ 2–5)
failure (§ 2–5)	sample space (§§ 2–5, 2–6)
fair game (§ 2–9)	selection (§ 2–1)
fundamental principle of enumeration (§ 2–1)	set function (§ 2–5)
	sets (§ 2–1)
game of chance (§ 2–5)	statistical probability (§ 2–5)
independent events (§ 2–8)	subsets (§ 2–1)
lattice (§ 2–1)	success (§ 2–5)
linear permutation (§ 2–2)	tree diagram (§ 2–1)

KEYED PRACTICE ON CHAPTER 2

1. A baseball coach has to decide upon a batting order for his nine players. (a) How many possible batting orders are there? (b) If the pitcher bats last, how many possible batting orders are there? (§ 2–1)

TESTS ON CHAPTER 2

2. How many arrangements of the letters of the word *TENNESSEE* are possible if all of the letters are used? (§ 2–2)

3. In how many ways can six keys be arranged on a key ring? (§ 2–2)

4. Find n if $12\,_nC_4 = \,_nC_5$. (§ 2–3)

5. In how many ways can a bridge hand of thirteen cards be dealt which contains seven spades, three hearts, three clubs, and no diamonds? (§ 2–3)

6. Find the third term of $\left(2x - \dfrac{3}{x}\right)^{10}$. (§ 2–4)

7. If two beads are selected at random from a bag containing seven red beads and five green beads, what is the probability that both are red? (§ 2–5)

8. On a single throw of a pair of dice find the probability of getting a nine. (§ 2–6)

9. If a card is chosen at random from an ordinary deck of bridge cards, what is the probability that it is an ace or a spade? (§ 2–7)

10. Consider a set of twenty tags having the pair of letters *ac* marked on eight tags, *ad* on five tags, *bc* on three tags, and *bd* on the remaining four tags. Let A, B, C, and D denote the event that a tag is chosen on which the letter $a, b, c,$ or d respectively appears. Find: **(a)** $P(B)$; **(b)** $P(B|C)$; **(c)** $P(C|B)$; **(d)** $P(C \cap D)$. (§ 2–8)

11. A bag contains five quarters, seven dimes, and forty-nine pennies. What is the mathematical expectation of a single random selection of a coin from the bag? (§ 2–9)

TESTS ON CHAPTER 2

A

1. Evaluate: $_{12}P_5$.

2. How many arrangements of the letters of the word *ALABAMA* are possible if all the letters are used?

3. If an examination contains sixteen questions and each student is required to answer the first five questions and any five others, how many different selections of problems to answer may a student make?

4. Find the first four terms of $(3a - b)^9$.

5. A tag is drawn at random from a set of thirty tags numbered respectively $1, 2, 3, \cdots, 30$. What is the probability that the number on the tag is divisible by 5?

6. What is the probability that the total face value of a pair of dice will be less than seven on a single throw?

PERMUTATIONS, COMBINATIONS, AND PROBABILITY

7. John may take a qualifying test for a certain position three times. If his chance of passing each test is sixty percent, what is his chance of qualifying for the position?

8. If one card is selected at random from each of three different decks of ordinary bridge cards, what is the probability that all three cards will be spades?

9. Find the probability that the sum of the face values of a pair of dice is eight if we are told that the sum is an even number.

10. Sixty lottery tickets are sold and a man is given one of them. If there is a first prize of ten dollars and a second prize of five dollars, what is his ticket's expected value to the nearest cent?

B

1. In how many ways can five keys be arranged on a key ring?

2. In how many ways can six flags be displayed all at once on a vertical pole if three flags are red, two flags are white, and one flag is blue?

3. Evaluate: $_6C_2 + {}_6C_3 + {}_6C_4 + {}_6C_5 + {}_6C_6$.

4. A bag contains six red balls and four white balls. If two balls are drawn at random at one time, what is the probability that they are not both white?

5. How many different sums of money can be made from a penny, a nickel, a dime, a quarter, and a half-dollar taking one or more coins at a time?

6. Six cards are dealt at random from a deck of ordinary bridge cards. What is the probability that the four aces are among the six cards?

7. At a certain spot on a busy street the probability of a jaywalker being hit by an automobile is 0.01. Find to the nearest hundredth the probability that a jaywalker can cross that street at that spot twice a day for thirty days without being hit.

8. If, on the average, two out of every three people have had measles and one out of every four people has had mumps, find the probability that a person has had **(a)** both; **(b)** neither.

9. If a die is thrown five times, what is the probability that it will come up six exactly twice?

10. A civic organization sold 1000 raffle tickets at one dollar each. The prize is a color television set worth $450. What is the mathematical expectation of the purchaser of a single ticket?

ANSWERS TO TEST YOURSELF EXERCISES

C

1. If only the digits 1, 2, 4, 6, and 7 are used and no digits may be repeated, find the number of positive integers which may be written that are **(a)** less than 500; **(b)** greater than 500.

2. Find how many ways six boys and six girls can be seated alternately **(a)** in a row; **(b)** in a circle.

3. In how many ways can a bridge hand of thirteen cards contain exactly seven hearts? (Leave your answer in combination notation.)

4. Find 0.98^{12} to three decimal places.

5. A factory produces a certain type of light bulb. On the average, ninety-six percent of the bulbs meet acceptable standards; the rest are defective. If six bulbs are selected at random, find to the nearest hundredth the probability that none of these are defective.

6. What is the probability of obtaining five as the sum of the face values in one throw of three dice?

7. What is the smallest number of throws of a single die such that the probability of throwing an odd number is at least eighty percent?

8. For a certain type of seed the probability of a single seed germinating is 0.7. If five seeds are planted, find the probability that **(a)** exactly three seeds will germinate; **(b)** at least three seeds will germinate.

9. A box contains one straw of each of these lengths: two, three, four, five, six, seven, eight, nine, ten, twelve, and thirteen inches. If three straws are drawn at random, what is the probability that they may be used to represent the sides of a right triangle?

10. In a certain game the player pays five cents for the privilege of drawing a card from an ordinary bridge deck. In return he receives ten cents if he draws an ace, king, queen, or jack; five cents if he draws a ten or a two; two cents if he draws a seven; and nothing if he draws any other card. What is his mathematical expectation?

ANSWERS TO TEST YOURSELF EXERCISES

§ 2-1. **1.** 720. **2.** 56. **3.** 12,600. **4.** 20. **5.** 24.

§ 2-2. **1.** $(11)(10)(9)(7)(4)$, that is, 27,720. **2.** 180. **3.** 6. **4.** (a, b, c, d), $(a, b, d, c), (a, d, b, c), (a, c, b, d), (a, c, d, b), (a, d, c, b)$.

§ 2-3. **1.** 35. **2.** 8. **3.** 210. **4.** 28.

§ 2-4. **1.** $x^9 - 9x^8 + 36x^7 - 84x^6$. **2.** 180.109. **3.** $(13)(11)(8)(3)(128)x^7y^{14}$, that is, $439{,}296 x^7 y^{14}$.

§ 2-5. **1.** $\frac{1}{3}$. **2.** $\frac{2}{3}$. **3.** 1. **4.** 0.

95

PERMUTATIONS, COMBINATIONS, AND PROBABILITY

§ 2-6. 1. (a) $S = \{33, 34, 35, 36, 43, 44, 45, 46, 53, 54, 55, 56, 63, 64, 65, 66\}$;
(b) $S = \{34, 35, 36, 43, 45, 46, 53, 54, 56, 63, 64, 65\}$.
2. Let the first element of each ordered pair represent the outcome, h for a head and t for a tail, for the coin; and let the second element be the face value on the top face of the die. Then $S = \{(h, 1), (h, 2), (h, 3), (h, 4), (h, 5), (h, 6), (t, 1), (t, 2), (t, 3), (t, 4), (t, 5), (t, 6)\}$.
3. Let h and t represent heads and tails as in Exercise 2; and let the outcomes for the first, second, third, and fourth coins be represented respectively by the first, second, third, and fourth positions in each ordered quadruple. Then $S = \{(h, h, h, h), (h, h, h, t), (h, h, t, h), (h, t, h, h), (t, h, h, h), (h, h, t, t), (h, t, h, t), (h, t, t, h), (t, h, t, h), (t, h, h, t), (t, t, h, h), (h, t, t, t), (t, h, t, t), (t, t, h, t), (t, t, t, h), (t, t, t, t)\}$.

§ 2-7. 1. $\frac{7}{10}$. 2. $\frac{5}{6}$. 3. $\frac{2}{3}$. 4. $\frac{7}{9}$.

§ 2-8. 1. $\frac{5}{8}$. 2. $\frac{5}{6}$. 3. $\frac{3}{4}$. 4. $\frac{1}{9}$. 5. $\frac{1}{16}$.

§ 2-9. 1. 4. 2. 21.

ANSWERS TO KEYED PRACTICE ON CHAPTER 2

1. (a) 9!, that is, 362,880.   (b) 8!, that is, 40,320.
2. 3780.
3. 60.
4. $n = 64$.
5. $(13)^3(11)^3(3)(2)^4$; that is, 140,361,936.
6. $103,680x^6$.
7. $\frac{7}{22}$.
8. $\frac{1}{9}$.
9. $\frac{4}{13}$.
10. (a) $\frac{7}{20}$; (b) $\frac{3}{11}$; (c) $\frac{3}{7}$; (d) 0.
11. 4 cents.

96

Chapter 3

Measurements of Geometric Figures

§ 3-1 Units of measure

Any measure is a number. The number tells us "how many" or "how much" of a certain kind of unit is under consideration.

A **linear measurement** (distance, length of a line segment) may be expressed as a number of units. Among the common units of linear measure are:

> inches, feet, yards, centimeters,
> meters, kilometers, miles, Angstrom
> units, furlongs, rods, and light years.

Conversion factors are used to express a measurement which is given in terms of a number of one kind of unit as a number of another kind of unit. These conversion factors are given as statements of equality. The conversion factors for the units listed in the preceding paragraph are:

> 1 foot = 12 inches;
> 1 yard = 3 feet;
> 1 inch = 2.54 centimeters;
> 1 meter $\approx$ 39.37 inches;
> 1 kilometer = 1000 meters;
> 1 mile = 5280 feet;
> 1 meter = 1×10^{10} Angstrom units;
> 1 mile = 8 furlongs;
> 1 rod = 16.5 feet;
> 1 light year $\approx 5.9 \times 10^{12}$ miles.

Any **angular measurement** may be expressed as a number of units such as:

> revolutions, degrees, straight angles,
> right angles, radians, minutes,
> and seconds.

As in linear measure, conversion factors may be used to change angular

MEASUREMENTS OF GEOMETRIC FIGURES

measurements from one kind of unit to another. Some of these conversion factors are:

$$1 \text{ revolution} = 360°;$$
$$1 \text{ straight angle} = 180°;$$
$$1 \text{ right angle} = 90°;$$
$$1 \text{ radian} \approx 57.2958°;$$
$$1 \text{ revolution} = 2\pi \text{ radians};$$
$$1 \text{ degree} = 60 \text{ minutes};$$
$$1 \text{ minute} = 60 \text{ seconds}.$$

Areas are measured in terms of units of area. These units may be square units derived from one of the linear units, or they may be special units. Thus any **area measurement** may be expressed as a number of units such as:

square inches, square feet, square miles,
square centimeters, square meters, and
special units such as acres, and hectares.

Conversion factors for these special units are:

$$1 \text{ acre} = 4840 \text{ square yards};$$
$$1 \text{ hectare} = 10{,}000 \text{ square meters}.$$

Volumes are measured in terms of units of volume. These units may be cubic units derived from one of the linear units or they may be special units. Thus any **volume measurement** may be expressed as numbers of units such as:

cubic inches, cubic feet, cubic miles, cubic centimeters
and special units such as cords, and liters.

Conversion factors for these special units are:

$$1 \text{ cord} = 128 \text{ cubic feet};$$
$$1 \text{ liter} = 1000 \text{ cubic centimeters}.$$

Any measurement is a number of units. Usually any one of several units may be used and there are conversion factors which may be used to express measurements of the same types of quantities in terms of the same units. For example:

$$30 \text{ miles per hour} = 44 \text{ feet per second};$$
$$1 \text{ knot} = 1.1516 \text{ miles per hour};$$
$$1 \text{ pound} = 16 \text{ ounces};$$
$$1 \text{ gallon} = 32 \text{ gills};$$
$$1 \text{ gill} = 32 \text{ drams}.$$

§ 3-1 UNITS OF MEASURE

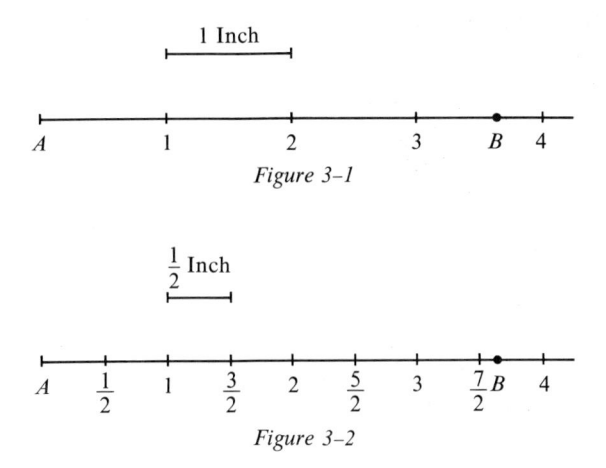

Figure 3-1

Figure 3-2

The length of the line segment AB in Figure 3-1 may be given as four inches. This statement means simply that when the line segment AB is measured to the nearest inch, the length is four inches. If the line segment AB were measured to the nearest half inch, as in Figure 3-2, the length would be seven halves of an inch; that is, three and one-half inches. Notice that in each case the measurement is a number of units where the number (four in the first case and seven in the second case) expresses a comparison between the quantity measured and the unit of measure. Since in each case the comparison is an *observed* comparison, it is in fact an *estimate*.

Suppose, for instance, that you wish to consider the measurement of $\overline{AB}$ in terms of eighths of an inch. Do you consider $\overline{AB}$ to be twenty-nine or thirty eighths of an inch long? In other words, does your observation lead you to believe that the length of $\overline{AB}$ is three and five-eighths or three and six-eighths inches? Although you may have confidence in the accuracy of your observed estimate when the units are inches, halves of an inch, and even eighths of an inch, you have had to make an arbitrary decision in each case; and for some units (perhaps sixteenths of an inch) such a decision is not an easy one to make. For this reason <u>all measurements are treated as approximations.</u> We may emphasize that a measurement such as that of $\overline{AB}$ in Figure 3-1 is an approximation by using the symbol $\approx$ meaning "is approximately equal to"; then $\overline{AB} \approx 4$. In other words, the length of the line segment AB is approximately four inches.

The **precision** of the measurement is determined by the unit used; the smaller the unit, the more precise the measurement. Thus seven halves of an inch is a more precise measurement than four inches. This also means that ten halves of an inch is a more precise measurement than five

99

MEASUREMENTS OF GEOMETRIC FIGURES

inches. Often the manner in which a number is written indicates the unit of measure. For example:

$\frac{10}{2}$ inch = 10 halves of an inch (to the nearest half inch);

5 inches = 5 inches (to the nearest inch).

There are also special procedures for computations involving measurements as we shall see in the next section. Since these procedures are due to the approximate nature of the measurements, they are frequently called **approximate computations.** Sometimes the numbers so used are called **approximate numbers.**

TEST YOURSELF

Express the given measurement in terms of the specified unit:

1. 25 inches; feet.
2. π radians; revolutions.

Select the most precise measurement:

3. 2 hours, 65 minutes, $\frac{1}{4}$ week.
4. 7.5 feet, 235 inches, 2 meters.
5. 3.052 yards, 26 feet, 38 centimeters.

EXERCISES

Express the given measurement in terms of the specified unit:

1. 1 meter; feet (to the nearest hundredth).
2. 3 rods; yards.
3. 6 right angles; radians (as a multiple of π).
4. 2 cubic yards; cubic feet.

Select the most precise measurement:

5. 2 yards, 10 feet, 75 inches.
6. 4 inches, 25 centimeters, 2 rods.

• • •

Express the given measurement in terms of the specified unit:

7. 75 miles per hour; feet per second.
8. 1 mile; meters.

§ 3-2   APPROXIMATE COMPUTATION

Select the most precise measurement:

9. 754 Angstrom units, 2 furlongs, 37 meters.
10. 1.50 yards, 2.3 feet, 9 inches.
11. 4.125 revolutions, 5 degrees, 1.2 right angles.
- 12. 5 acres, 2.7 square miles, 25 square kilometers.
- 13. 1.2 rods, 5.73 furlongs, 17.254 miles.

§ 3-2   Approximate computation

The convention of using the manner in which a measurement is expressed to imply the unit of measure used makes scientific notation desirable. In ordinary decimal notation zeros are often needed solely to indicate the location of the decimal point. For example, sixty-two thousands is written as 62,000; and 620 hundreds is also written as 62,000. Thus the numeral 62,000 does not indicate whether the measurement is to the nearest thousand or the nearest hundred. Indeed, this same numeral would be used when the unit of measure is to the nearest ten or the nearest one. In scientific notation each digit has a meaning (is significant). For example,

$$6.2 \times 10^4 = 62{,}000 \text{ to the nearest thousand;}$$
$$6.20 \times 10^4 = 62{,}000 \text{ to the nearest hundred;}$$
$$6.2000 \times 10^4 = 62{,}000 \text{ to the nearest unit.}$$

In **scientific notation** any number may be written as 1×10^k or as $b \times 10^k$ for some number b between 1 and 10 and some integer k (positive, negative, or zero). Under this convention 4.50×10^3 and 4.5×10^3 have different interpretations as to precision. In general zeros following the last non-zero digit after the decimal point are not used unless they have meaning, that is, are **significant**. All other digits are always assumed to be significant whenever they are used. Any zero between two significant digits is significant; for example, the zero in 503 is significant. In ordinary notation zeros must be used as in 62,000 to the nearest thousand or 0.0053 simply to locate the decimal point and thus are considered not significant. The number of significant decimal digits used to express an approximate number is taken as a measure of the **accuracy** of the number.

You have probably used these rules for approximate computation in previous courses:

(i) A sum or difference of approximate numbers is no more *precise* than one of the least precise given numbers.

(ii) A product, quotient, power, or root is no more *accurate* than one of the least accurate given numbers.

MEASUREMENTS OF GEOMETRIC FIGURES

Consider two boards with their lengths: $\overline{AB} \approx 14$ feet and $\overline{CD} \approx 15$ inches. The length $\overline{AB}$ is known to the nearest foot; the length $\overline{CD}$ is known to the nearest inch. As stated in Rule (i), the total length of the two boards is known only to the nearest foot ($\overline{AB} + \overline{CD} \approx 15$ feet). Also if a board $\overline{BE} = \overline{CD}$ were cut from the board $\overline{AB}$, the length of the remaining piece would be expressed only to the nearest foot ($\overline{AE} \approx 13$ feet). Note that actually

$$13 \text{ feet } 6 \text{ inches} \leq \overline{AB} \leq 14 \text{ feet } 6 \text{ inches,}$$
$$14\tfrac{1}{2} \text{ inches} \leq \overline{CD} \leq 15\tfrac{1}{2} \text{ inches,}$$
$$14 \text{ feet } 8\tfrac{1}{2} \text{ inches} \leq \overline{AB} + \overline{CD} \leq 15 \text{ feet } 9\tfrac{1}{2} \text{ inches,}$$
$$12 \text{ feet } 2\tfrac{1}{2} \text{ inches} \leq \overline{AE} \leq 13 \text{ feet } 3\tfrac{1}{2} \text{ inches.}$$

Thus $\overline{AB} + \overline{CD}$ might be measured as either fifteen feet or sixteen feet and $\overline{AE}$ might be measured as either twelve feet or thirteen feet depending upon the given lengths.

Accordingly, the results of approximate computations must be interpreted merely as the best possible estimates from the given information. These results may or may not be the same as could be obtained by measurements. These results cannot be expected to be (even though they may actually be) any more precise or accurate than the least precise or accurate of the given information.

Counting numbers are assumed to be exact; that is, they are assumed to have as many significant digits as the other numbers in any problem. For example, if $\overline{AB} \approx 173$ centimeters, then $2\overline{AB}$ is considered the same as $2.00\overline{AB}$ and $2\overline{AB} \approx 346$ centimeters where there are three significant digits in the answer even though the counting number 2 is expressed with only one significant digit. The need for this special treatment of counting numbers is evident from the statement:

$$2\overline{AB} = \overline{AB} + \overline{AB} \approx 346 \text{ centimeters.}$$

If a computation appears to give a number with more significant digits than the accuracy of its given information justifies, the number should be **rounded off.** To round off a number consider the digit which is in the last decimal position which is to be kept:

(i) Keep this digit if the digit following it is less than 5.

(ii) Increase this digit by 1 if the following digit is greater than 5, or is a 5 which is followed by at least one digit which is different from 0.

(iii) Replace this digit with the nearest even digit if the following digit is a 5 followed only by zeros.

There is a simpler rule for rounding off, but our rule is recommended by the American Standards Association and is considered to be the better one to use in preparation for future technical work.

Example 1. Round off each number to three significant digits: (a) 21.53; (b) 375.7; (c) 126.5; (d) 437.5.

(a) 21.5;   (b) 376;   (c) 126;   (d) 438.

Example 2. Consider the given numbers to be approximate numbers, and perform the indicated operations:

(a) $1.5 + 3.72 + 5.17$;
(b) $524 + 27 + 0.05$;
(c) 1.2×45.234.

```
(a)   1.5              (b)   524              (c)   45.234
      3.72                    27                  × 1.2
      5.17                     0.05               90468
     10.39 ≈ 10.4           551.05 ≈ 551         45234
                                                 54.2808 ≈ 54
```

Notice that in each case in Example 2 the answers have been expressed according to the rules (i) and (ii) for computations with approximate numbers. As in Example 2, it is customary to round off after completing the operation. When several operations are to be performed on a given set of information, one additional digit is usually retained until the final answer is found. Under special circumstances two or even more digits may be retained.

TEST YOURSELF

1. Round off each number to three significant digits:

(a) 127.500;   (b) 436.500.

2. Consider the given numbers to be approximate numbers, and perform the indicated operations:

(a) $25.37 + 37.125$;   (b) 2.1×237.

EXERCISES

Round off each number to four significant digits:

1. 2.3527.   **3.** 12.645.   **5.** 27.355.
2. 12.64501.   **4.** 0.13723.   **6.** 1298.5.

MEASUREMENTS OF GEOMETRIC FIGURES

Consider the given numbers to be approximate numbers, and perform the indicated operations:

7. $0.023 + 5.13 + 2.01$.
8. $10.5 - 7.23 + 5.009$.

9. $1.10 \times 2.3 \div 4.000$.
10. $(2.0)^2 \times 5.36$.

• • •

11. $(5.63 + 17.2) \times 1.2$.

12. $(15.7 - 14.2) \times 2.46$.

§ 3-3 Linear measurements

Any two points A and B determine: a line; a ray with end point A; a ray with end point B; a line segment with end points A and B; a vector with initial point A and terminal point B; and a vector with initial point B and terminal point A. Notations for these figures have not yet been standardized among mathematicians; but the notations that we shall use in this book are shown in Figure 3–3.

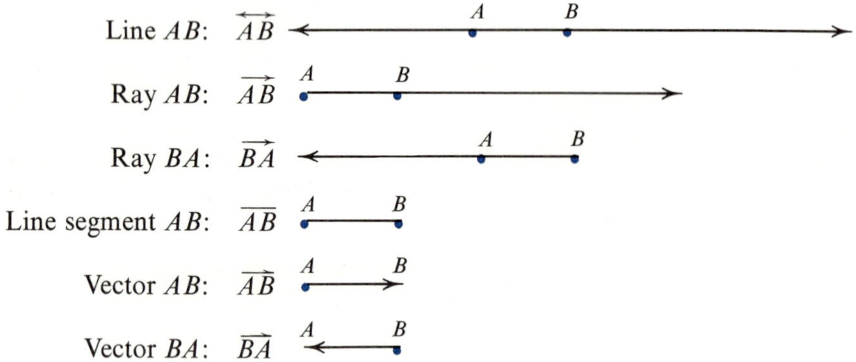

Line AB: $\overleftrightarrow{AB}$

Ray AB: $\overrightarrow{AB}$

Ray BA: $\overrightarrow{BA}$

Line segment AB: $\overline{AB}$

Vector AB: $\overrightarrow{AB}$

Vector BA: $\overrightarrow{BA}$

Figure 3–3

The notation $\overline{AB}$ is used for both the line segment and the length of the line segment. For any points A, B, C we have:

(i) $\overline{AB} = \overline{BA} \geq 0$;
(ii) $\overline{AB} = 0$ if and only if $A = B$, that is, A and B are two names for the same point;
(iii) $\overline{AB} + \overline{BC} \geq \overline{AC}$;
(iv) $\overline{AB} + \overline{BC} = \overline{AC}$ if and only if C is on $\overleftrightarrow{AB}$.

Linear measurements arise in many ways. They may represent lengths of given line segments (§ 1–7); they may represent distances of given points from given **geometric figures** (that is, any sets of points). The **distance of a point A from a line m** is $\overline{AB}$ where B is on m and $\overleftrightarrow{AB}$ is perpendicular

104

§ 3-3 LINEAR MEASUREMENTS

to m. If C is any point different from B on m and $\overrightarrow{AB}$ is perpendicular to m, then $\overline{AB} < \overline{AC}$. In other words, the distance of a point A from a line m is the length of the shortest line segment joining A to a point of m. Similarly, the **distance of a point A from a plane** α is measured along a line AB where $\overrightarrow{AB}$ is perpendicular to α and B is on α; that is, the distance is the length of the shortest line segment joining A to a point of α. In general, the **distance of a point A from any geometric figure** is the length of the shortest possible line segment with A as one end point and a point of the figure as the other end point. (See Figure 3-4).

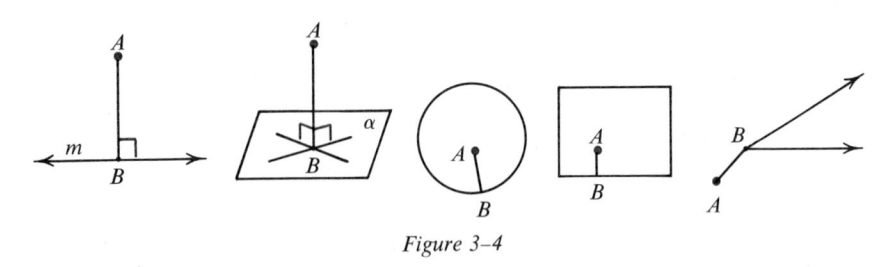

Figure 3-4

The **distance between any two geometric figures** is the length of the shortest possible line segment having a point of one figure as one end point and a point of the other figure as the other end point.

The basic figures are points, lines, and planes. Other figures consist of unions of points, parts of lines, and parts of planes. A line is determined by any two of its points. A plane is determined by:

> three points that are not on the same line;
> a line and a point that is not on the line;
> two intersecting lines;
> two parallel lines.

Any two distinct lines on a plane are either intersecting or parallel. Two distinct lines in space may be intersecting, parallel, or skew lines. Two lines are called **skew lines** if they are not on the same plane (**coplanar**). Thus skew lines do not intersect and are not parallel. However, two skew lines do have a common perpendicular; that is, there exists a line which is perpendicular to each of two given skew lines. Indeed, there is one and only one such perpendicular line for any given pair of skew lines. For example, in the case of the line determined by the intersection of the ceiling and front wall of an ordinary classroom and the line determined by the back wall and a side wall, the line determined by the ceiling and that side wall will be perpendicular to each of the first two lines.

Two lines a and b may: intersect (distance 0); be parallel (distance between them may be measured along any coplanar line which is perpen-

MEASUREMENTS OF GEOMETRIC FIGURES

dicular to them); be skew lines (distance between them is measured along their common perpendicular). These three cases are illustrated in Figure 3–5.

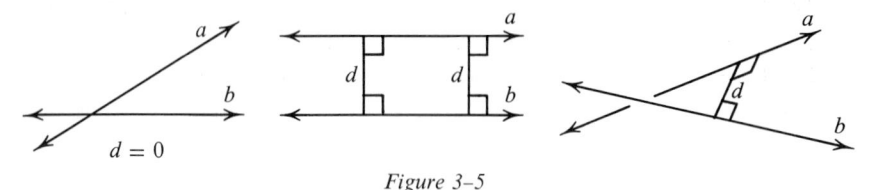

Figure 3–5

Example 1. Find the distance on a coordinate plane of the point A: (5, 7) from:

(a) the x-axis; (b) the line $x = 3$; (c) the circle $x^2 + y^2 = 64$.

(a) The point (5, 7) is located five units from the y-axis and seven units from the x-axis. Thus the distance from A to the x-axis is 7 units.

(b) The distance of A from the line $x = 3$ will be measured along the line through A and perpendicular to the line $x = 3$. Thus the distance is measured along the line $y = 7$ and is the distance from (5, 7) to (3, 7); that is, 2 units.

(c) The distance of A from the circle with center at the origin and radius eight units long must be measured along the line determined by A and the center of the circle. The distance from A to the origin is $\sqrt{5^2 + 7^2}$; that is, $\sqrt{74}$ units. Therefore the distance from A to the circle is $(\sqrt{74} - 8)$ units.

Example 2. Find the distance from the point (2, −5) to the figure consisting of the set of points (2, 6), (−1, −1), (−3, −5), (6, −2), and (14, 0).

The distances from (2, −5) to the points in the order listed are: 11 units, 5 units, 5 units, 5 units, and 13 units. Therefore the distance from (2, −5) to the figure is 5 units.

TEST YOURSELF

Find the distance on a coordinate plane of the point (3, 7) from the given figure:

1. The y-axis.
2. The line $x = 11$.
3. The point (−1, 4).
4. {(3, 1), (0, 7), (1, 1)}.

§ 3-3 LINEAR MEASUREMENTS

EXERCISES

Find the distance on a coordinate plane of the point $(-5, 7)$ from the given figure:

1. The y-axis.
2. The line $x = -2$.
3. The line $y = 3$.
4. The point $(1, -1)$.
5. $\{(1, 15), (0, 0), (4, 7), (2, 11)\}$.
6. $\{(x, y) \mid x^2 + y^2 - 16 = 0\}$.

• • •

7. $\{(x, y) \mid x^2 + y^2 + 2x - 4 = 0\}$.
8. $\{(x, y) \mid x^2 + y^2 - 2y - 9 = 0\}$.
9. $\{(x, y) \mid (x, y) \in A \times A\}$ where $A = \{-1, 0, 1\}$.
10. $\{(x, y) \mid (x, y) \in A \times B\}$ where $A = \{1, 2, 3\}$ and $B = \{1, 3, 5\}$.

* SUPPLEMENTARY EXERCISES

These statements are provided as a summary of the common properties of lines and planes in space. Many of them are useful in measuring geometric figures. Each of the statements is true. Try to visualize a figure for each statement. Sketch a figure illustrating each statement. If you have difficulty accepting any statement, draw other sketches and try to find a sketch of a figure for which the statement does not hold.

1. If two points of a line are on a plane, then every point of the line is on the plane.
2. If two planes intersect (that is, have at least one point in common), they have (a) at least two points in common; (b) a line in common.
3. A plane may be determined by (a) three points that are not on the same line; (b) a line and a point that is not on the line; (c) two intersecting lines; (d) two parallel lines.
4. Three distinct planes in space may have in common (a) no points; (b) exactly one point; (c) a line.
5. If a line m is perpendicular to each of two intersecting lines at their point P of intersection, then the line m is perpendicular to the plane determined by the other two lines (that is, the line m is perpendicular to each line which is on the plane and passes through the point P).

*The supplementary exercises are designed to provide background information for those students who have not previously studied the properties of lines and planes in space.

MEASUREMENTS OF GEOMETRIC FIGURES

6. All lines perpendicular to a line *m* at a point *P* on *m* are on the plane which is perpendicular to the line *m* at the point *P*.

7. There is one and only one plane perpendicular to a line **(a)** at a given point of the line; **(b)** through a given point that is not on the line.

8. There is one and only one line perpendicular to a plane **(a)** at a given point of the plane; **(b)** through a given point that is not on the plane.

9. The locus of points equidistant from the ends of a line segment is a plane which is perpendicular to the line segment at its mid-point.

10. A line *OA* is perpendicular to a plane at *O*. Oblique lines (that is, lines which are not perpendicular to the plane) are drawn through *A* and intersecting the plane in points *B* and *C* respectively. **(a)** If $\overline{OB} = \overline{OC}$, then $\overline{AB} = \overline{AC}$. **(b)** If $\overline{OB} > \overline{OC}$, then $\overline{AB} > \overline{AC}$.

11. The locus of points equidistant from the points of a circle is a line which is perpendicular to the plane of the circle and passes through the center of the circle.

12. If two lines are perpendicular to the same plane, then they are parallel.

13. If a line *m* is parallel to a plane *α*, then *m* is parallel to the intersection of the plane *α* with any plane which contains *m*.

14. If two lines are parallel, then every plane which contains one of the lines is either parallel to the other line or contains the other line.

15. If a line *m* is parallel to a plane *α*, then any line through a point of *α* and parallel to *m* must be a line of the plane *α*.

16. One and only one plane may be drawn containing one of two skew lines and parallel to the other line.

17. One and only one plane may be drawn through a point which is not on either of two skew lines and parallel to each of the skew lines.

18. If each of two intersecting planes contains one of two parallel lines, then the line of intersection of the planes either is one of the given parallel lines or is parallel to each of these parallel lines.

19. If a line and a plane that does not contain the line are each perpendicular to a given line, then they are parallel.

20. If one of two parallel lines is perpendicular to a plane, then the other line is also perpendicular to the plane.

21. If each of two lines is parallel to a third line, then they are parallel to each other.

22. If a plane intersects two parallel planes, then the lines of intersection are parallel.

23. If two planes are perpendicular to the same line, then they are parallel.

24. If a line is perpendicular to one of two parallel planes, then the line is perpendicular to the other plane.

25. If each of two intersecting lines is parallel to a plane α, then the plane of these lines is parallel to the plane α.

26. If two angles on different planes have their sides parallel each to each, then the angles are either equal or supplementary and the planes of the angles are parallel.

27. If two straight lines intersect three or more parallel planes, then the corresponding segments cut off by the planes are proportional.

28. If three or more parallel planes intercept equal segments on one transversal, then they intercept equal segments on every transversal.

29. Two parallel planes are everywhere equidistant.

30. The locus of points equidistant from two parallel planes is the plane parallel to them and halfway between them.

31. If a line is perpendicular to a given plane α, then every plane which contains this line is perpendicular to the plane α.

32. If two planes are perpendicular, then any line drawn on one of the planes and perpendicular to their intersection is perpendicular to the other plane.

33. If two planes are perpendicular, then a line perpendicular to one of them at any point of their intersection lies on the other plane.

34. If two planes are perpendicular, then a line perpendicular to one of them from any point on the second plane lies on the second plane.

35. One and only one plane may be drawn parallel to a given plane and through a point that is not on the given plane.

36. One and only one line may be drawn perpendicular to a plane and through a point **(a)** on the plane; **(b)** not on the plane.

37. If two intersecting planes are each perpendicular to a third plane, then their line of intersection is perpendicular to that plane.

38. One and only one plane may be drawn perpendicular to a given plane and containing a given line that is not perpendicular to the given plane.

39. Between two skew lines one and only one common perpendicular may be drawn.

40. The projection onto a plane of a straight line which is not perpendicular to the plane is a straight line.

§ 3-4 Distance formulas

The use of numbers as distances in terms of the scale on a coordinate line, plane, or space was considered in § 1-7. For example, if R and S have coordinates r and s on a number line, then

$$\overline{RS} = |r - s| = \sqrt{(r - s)^2}.$$

MEASUREMENTS OF GEOMETRIC FIGURES

If R and S have coordinates (r_1, r_2) and (s_1, s_2) on a coordinate plane, then
$$\overline{RS} = \sqrt{(r_1 - s_1)^2 + (r_2 - s_2)^2}.$$
If R and S have coordinates (r_1, r_2, r_3) and (s_1, s_2, s_3) in a coordinate space, then
$$\overline{RS} = \sqrt{(r_1 - s_1)^2 + (r_2 - s_2)^2 + (r_3 - s_3)^2}.$$
The coordinate of the **mid-point** of $\overline{RS}$ is $\frac{r+s}{2}$ on a number line; the coordinates are $\left(\frac{r_1 + s_1}{2}, \frac{r_2 + s_2}{2}\right)$ on a coordinate plane, and $\left(\frac{r_1 + s_1}{2}, \frac{r_2 + s_2}{2}, \frac{r_3 + s_3}{2}\right)$ in a coordinate space.

Example 1. Consider $P: (1, -3, 5)$ and $Q: (2, 4, 3)$ and: (a) express $\overline{PQ}$ in simplest radical form; (b) find the coordinates of the mid-point M of $\overline{PQ}$.

(a) $\overline{PQ} = \sqrt{(1-2)^2 + (-3-4)^2 + (5-3)^2}$
$= \sqrt{1 + 49 + 4} = \sqrt{54} = 3\sqrt{6}$; that is, $3\sqrt{6}$ units.

(b) $M: \left(\frac{1+2}{2}, \frac{-3+4}{2}, \frac{5+3}{2}\right)$; that is, $M: \left(\frac{3}{2}, \frac{1}{2}, 4\right)$.

```
   O        R        T      S
   +--------+--------+------+----->
   0   1    r        t      s
```
Figure 3-6

On a coordinate line consider a point T on a line segment RS as in Figure 3-6. If $\overline{RT}:\overline{TS} = 2:1$, then
$$\overline{RT} = \frac{2}{3}\overline{RS};$$
$$\overline{OT} = \overline{OR} + \frac{2}{3}\overline{RS};$$
$$t = r + \frac{2}{3}(s - r) = \frac{2}{3}s + \frac{1}{3}r = \frac{2s + r}{3}.$$

On a coordinate plane with $R: (r_1, r_2)$, $S: (s_1, s_2)$, $T: (t_1, t_2)$ on $\overline{RS}$, and $\overline{RT}:\overline{TS} = 2:1$, the corresponding relations are
$$t_1 = \frac{2s_1 + r_1}{3}, \quad t_2 = \frac{2s_2 + r_2}{3}.$$

In a coordinate space with $R: (r_1, r_2, r_3)$, $S: (s_1, s_2, s_3)$, $T: (t_1, t_2, t_3)$ on $\overline{RS}$, and $\overline{RT}:\overline{TS} = 2:1$, the corresponding relations are
$$t_1 = \frac{2s_1 + r_1}{3}, \quad t_2 = \frac{2s_2 + r_2}{3}, \quad t_3 = \frac{2s_3 + r_3}{3}.$$

§ 3-4   DISTANCE FORMULAS

The basic similarity of the relations among the coordinates for the three cases of points on a line, on a plane, and in space should be clear. The reasons for this similarity are not hard to find. If three parallel lines (or planes) intersect two transversals, they intercept proportional segments on those transversals. Thus, on a plane the parallel lines $x = r_1$, $x = t_1$, $x = s_1$ divide the segment RS in the ratio of $2:1$ if and only if they intersect the x-axis to form segments in the ratio $2:1$; that is, if and only if $t_1 = \dfrac{2s_1 + r_1}{3}$. A similar statement may be made concerning the lines $y = r_2$, $y = t_2$, and $y = s_2$. In space the parallel planes $x = r_1$, $x = t_1$, $x = s_1$ divide the segment RS in the ratio $2:1$ if and only if they intersect the x-axis to form segments in the ratio $2:1$; that is, if and only if $t_1 = \dfrac{2s_1 + r_1}{3}$. Similar statements may be made for the planes $y = r_2$, $y = t_2$, $y = s_2$ and also for the planes $z = r_3$, $z = t_3$, $z = s_3$. Note that in each case T is two-thirds of the way from R to S, and each coordinate of T is two-thirds of the corresponding coordinate of S plus one-third of the corresponding coordinate of R.

In general, if T is on a line segment RS and divides the line segment so that $\overline{RT}:\overline{TS} = p:q$, then on a number line

$$t = \frac{ps + qr}{p + q};$$

on a coordinate plane

$$t_1 = \frac{ps_1 + qr_1}{p + q}, \quad t_2 = \frac{ps_2 + qr_2}{p + q};$$

and in a coordinate space

$$t_1 = \frac{ps_1 + qr_1}{p + q}, \quad t_2 = \frac{ps_2 + qr_2}{p + q}, \quad t_3 = \frac{ps_3 + qr_3}{p + q}.$$

Example 2. Find the coordinates of the point T on $\overline{RS}$ where $R: (2, -3, 5)$, $S: (9, 4, -9)$, and (a) $\overline{RT}:\overline{TS} = 3:4$; (b) $\overline{RT}:\overline{TS} = 4:3$.

(a) $t_1 = \dfrac{4r_1 + 3s_1}{7} = \dfrac{4(2) + 3(9)}{7} = \dfrac{35}{7} = 5;$

$t_2 = \dfrac{4r_2 + 3s_2}{7} = \dfrac{4(-3) + 3(4)}{7} = \dfrac{0}{7} = 0;$

$t_3 = \dfrac{4r_3 + 3s_3}{7} = \dfrac{4(5) + 3(-9)}{7} = \dfrac{-7}{7} = -1;$

T has coordinates $(5, 0, -1)$.

(b) $t_1 = \dfrac{3r_1 + 4s_1}{7} = \dfrac{3(2) + 4(9)}{7} = \dfrac{42}{7} = 6;$

$t_2 = \dfrac{3r_2 + 4s_2}{7} = \dfrac{3(-3) + 4(4)}{7} = \dfrac{7}{7} = 1;$

$t_3 = \dfrac{3r_3 + 4s_3}{7} = \dfrac{3(5) + 4(-9)}{7} = \dfrac{-21}{7} = -3;$

T has coordinates $(6, 1, -3)$.

TEST YOURSELF

1. Find the length of the line segment AB for A: $(1, 2, -2)$ and B: $(5, 2, 1)$.

2. Find the coordinates of the mid-point of the line segment with end points at $(2, -5, 7)$ and at $(6, 3, 5)$.

3. Find the coordinates of the point T on $\overline{RT}$ such that $\overline{RT}:\overline{TS} = 3:1$ for R: $(-3, 1, -2)$ and S: $(5, 9, 6)$.

EXERCISES

1. Consider the points A: $(1, -3)$ and B: $(7, 9)$ and find **(a)** $\overline{AB}$; **(b)** the coordinates of the mid-point of $\overline{AB}$; **(c)** the coordinates of the point T on $\overline{AB}$ such that $\overline{AT}:\overline{TB} = 1:2$; **(d)** the coordinates of the point S on $\overline{AB}$ such that $\overline{AS}:\overline{SB} = 5:1$.

2. Repeat Exercise 1 for the points A: $(7, 11)$ and B: $(13, -1)$.

3. Repeat Exercise 1 for the points A: $(2, 5, -4)$ and B: $(4, -1, 8)$.

4. Repeat Exercise 1 for the points A: $(17, -5, 13)$ and B: $(5, 7, -11)$.

• • •

5. In plane geometry you learned that a point on the plane of a circle is inside, on, or outside the circle according as the distance of the point from the center of the circle is less than, equal to, or greater than the radius of the circle. Tell whether each point is inside, on, or outside the circle with center at $(3, 5)$ and radius 12: **(a)** $(3, -7)$; **(b)** $(11, -3)$; **(c)** $(12, 13)$.

6. Tell whether each point is inside, on, or outside the circle with center at $(-2, 3)$ and radius 13: **(a)** $(6, 12)$; **(b)** $(-12, 5)$; **(c)** $(10, 8)$.

7. Tell whether each point is inside, on, or outside the circle with center at $(3, -5)$ and radius 17: **(a)** $(15, 7)$; **(b)** $(11, 10)$; **(c)** $(13, 8)$.

8. Tell whether each point is inside, on, or outside the sphere with center at $(1, -2, 3)$ and radius 11: **(a)** $(2, 4, 12)$; **(b)** $(9, 6, 8)$; **(c)** $(5, 5, -7)$.

9. Tell whether each point is inside, on, or outside the sphere with center at $(3, -5, -7)$ and radius 15: **(a)** $(4, 9, -7)$; **(b)** $(10, 0, 5)$; **(c)** $(-5, -5, 6)$.

§ 3-5 Angular measurements

Any point B of a line separates the line into two **half-lines**. The point B is the common **end point** of the two half-lines but is not considered to be a point of either half-line. Any line m on a plane separates the plane into two **half-planes**. The line m is the common **edge** of the two half-planes but is not considered to be on either half-plane. (See Figure 3-7.)

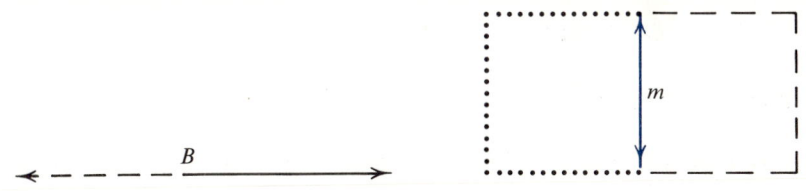

Figure 3-7

Any two half-lines having a common end point B when taken with that end point form a **plane angle** with B as **vertex** and the half-lines as **sides**. Any two half-planes having a common edge m when taken with that edge form a **dihedral angle** with m as **edge** and the half-planes as **faces**. If the two half-lines coincide, the plane angle has measure 0°; if the two half-planes coincide, the dihedral angle has measure 0°. If the two half-lines are on the same line but do not coincide, the plane angle has measure 180°; if the two half-planes are on the same plane but do not coincide, the dihedral angle has measure 180°.

The figure consisting of a half-line and its end point is a *ray* (§ 3-3). A plane angle may also be defined as the union of two rays with a common end point. Any two line segments with a common end point determine unique rays with a common end point; that is, unique half-lines with the common end point included. For example, $\overline{BA}$ and $\overline{BC}$ in Figure 3-8

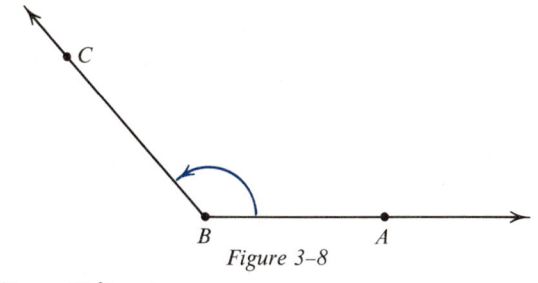

Figure 3-8

determine $\overrightarrow{BA}$ and $\overrightarrow{BC}$. Accordingly, even though two line segments with a common end point (such as $\overline{AB}$ and $\overline{BC}$) do not, by definition, form an angle, they determine the rays (such as $\overrightarrow{AB}$ and $\overrightarrow{BC}$) which do satisfy the definition of an angle; thus we may speak of angle ABC when $\overline{AB}$ and $\overline{BC}$ are known.

MEASUREMENTS OF GEOMETRIC FIGURES

We have seen that the measure of a line segment on a number line may be expressed as a nonnegative number such as $|r - s|$ in terms of the coordinates of the end points of the line segment. In Figure 3-6 the coordinates of the points depended upon the selection of an origin O, a unit of distance, and the position of the unit on the right or the left of the origin. The last choice determined the positive sense and the negative sense along the line. The absolute value of the coordinate p of each point P is the magnitude of $\overline{OP}$; the sign of p indicates whether the direction from O to P along the line is in the positive sense or the negative sense.

Angles such as ABC in Figure 3-8 may also be associated with numbers which serve as coordinates of $\overrightarrow{BC}$ relative to $\overrightarrow{BA}$. Usually the ray BA is taken as the origin, one degree where $360° = 1$ revolution is taken as the unit of angle measure, and a counter-clockwise sense of rotation is taken as the positive sense of rotation. Then $\angle ABA = 0°$, and if D is on $\overrightarrow{AB}$ and not on $\overline{AB}$, then $\angle ABD = 180°$ as previously mentioned. If arbitrary rotations clockwise and counter-clockwise are allowed, then any angle has an associated real number of degrees and there is an angle associated with any real number of degrees (Figure 3-9). If only the

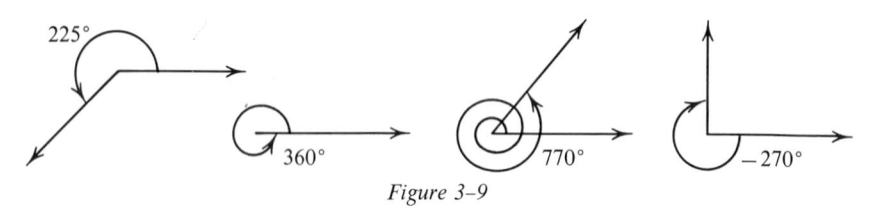

Figure 3-9

numerical measures (that is, their absolute values) of angles are desired and numbers of revolutions are disregarded, then each angle RST where R, S, and T are not on a straight line has a measure in degrees between 0 and 180 (Figure 3-10).

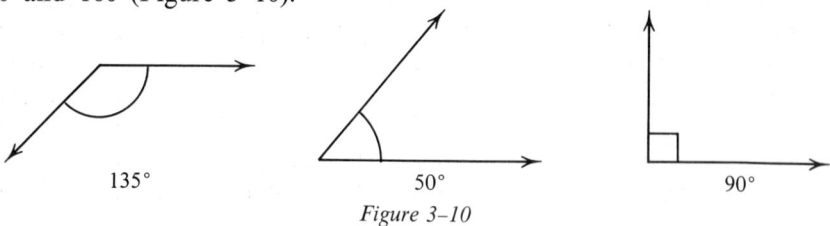

Figure 3-10

The restriction of angle measures in degrees to numbers between 0 and 180 is sometimes made in elementary courses. It is not desirable at this level where the measures of angles need to be considered in a manner very similar to that of the measure of line segments. Each angle ABC may be associated with a point P on a circle with radius 1 and center B

§ 3-5 ANGULAR MEASUREMENTS

as in Figure 3–11. Also each point P on the circle may be associated with a number p as in Figure 3–12.

The "wrapping" of the number line around the **unit circle** (a circle with radius 1) in Figure 3–12 associates each point on the circle with a number from 0 to 2π. Then as the line wraps around again each point P which was previously associated with p is

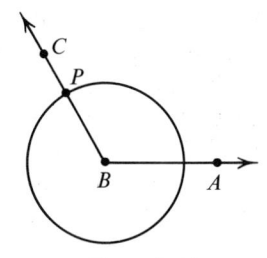

Figure 3–11

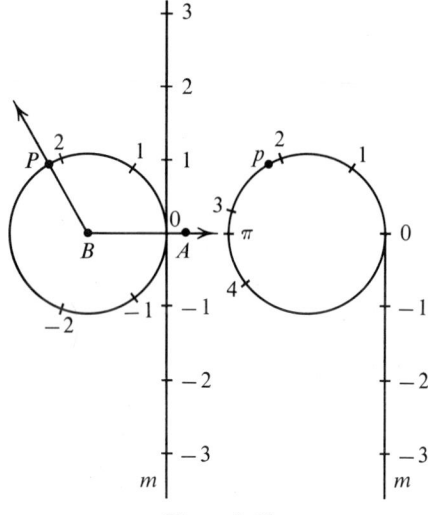

Figure 3–12

now associated with $p + 2\pi$; it is associated on the next wrap around with $p + 4\pi$, on the next wrap around with $p + 6\pi$, and so forth. This matching of real numbers with points P and thus with angles ABP is sometimes called a **wrapping function**. When the negative portion of the number line is wrapped around the circle, the point P is associated with $p - 2\pi$, then $p - 4\pi$, then $p - 6\pi$, and so forth. These numbers ($p + 2k\pi$ for any integer k) identify the point P and also the angle ABP; the numbers are the measures of the angles in radians rather than degrees. An angle of one **radian** intercepts an arc whose length is equal to the length of the radius of the circle. An angle of $\frac{\pi}{2}$ radians intercepts an arc which is one-fourth of the circle; that is, this angle has a measure of 90°. In general,

$$2\pi \text{ radians} = 360°;$$
$$1 \text{ radian} \approx 57.2958°.$$

115

MEASUREMENTS OF GEOMETRIC FIGURES

One advantage to be found in the use of radian measure of angles may be observed in Figure 3–13. The angle ABC has measure p radians; the arc TVP of the unit circle is p units long; the arc HNQ of the circle of radius r is pr units long. In general, any central angle HBQ of p radians in a circle of radius r intercepts an arc HNQ of length pr; that is,

$$s = r\theta$$

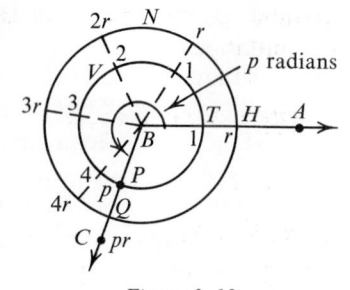

Figure 3–13

where s is the arc length, r is the radius of the circle, and θ is the measure of the central angle in radians. Radian measure also offers other advantages in advanced mathematics courses.

Example. In a circle of radius 3 units find the length of an arc which is intercepted by a central angle of 240°.

To find θ in radians we make use of the relationship

$$\frac{240}{180} = \frac{\theta}{\pi}.$$

Thus θ in radians is $\frac{4\pi}{3}$; therefore

$$s = r\theta = 3 \times \frac{4\pi}{3} = 4\pi.$$

The length of the arc is 4π units.

Any plane angle may be measured in terms of degrees, radians, or other units of angular measure. Any dihedral angle may be associated with a plane angle by selecting a point B on its edge m, drawing $\overrightarrow{BA}$ in one face and perpendicular to m, and drawing $\overrightarrow{BC}$ in the other face and perpendicular to m. In any given dihedral angle any two plane angles obtained in this way have the same measure. This measure is defined to be the measure of the dihedral angle. In other words, any dihedral angle may be measured by measuring one of its plane angles. (See angle ABC in Figure 3–14.)

When angles are to be expressed as numbers of radians and π is involved, it is customary to use the number π rather than any of its approxi-

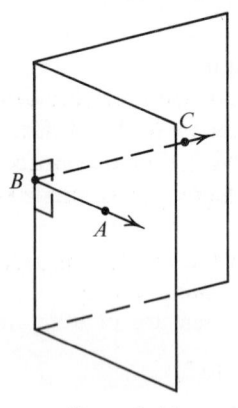

Figure 3–14

mations unless otherwise instructed or a decimal value is needed for computation.

TEST YOURSELF

1. Express each angle measure in radians:

(a) 90°; (b) 225°; (c) 810°.

2. A circle of radius 7 inches has an arc AC and a central angle ABC. If $\angle ABC = 2$ radians, how long is $\widehat{AC}$?

EXERCISES

A

Express each angle measure in radians:

1. 180°.
2. 270°.
3. 45°.
4. 30°.
5. 210°.
6. 330°.
7. 150°.
8. 450°.
9. 405°.
10. 570°.
11. 750°.
12. 1485°.

Consider each number as an angle measure in radians and express in degrees:

13. π.
14. $\frac{3}{2}\pi$.
15. $\frac{1}{6}\pi$.
16. $\frac{1}{4}\pi$.
17. $\frac{7}{8}\pi$.
18. 3π.
19. 2.
20. 2.5.
21. 3.
22. 5.
23. 0.25.
24. 0.05.

B

1. In a circle of radius 5.0 inches find the length of an arc which is intercepted by a central angle of (a) 1.2 radians; (b) 2.6 radians; (c) 5.0 radians.

2. In a circle of radius 24 feet find the length of an arc which is intercepted by a central angle of (a) 1.5 radians; (b) 2.25 radians; (c) 3.6 radians.

In Exercises 3 through 10 assume that an angle ABP as in Figure 3–12 is matched under the wrapping function with the given number and give four other numbers with which this angle is matched.

3. π.
4. $\frac{\pi}{2}$.
5. 2π.
6. 2.
7. 3.5.
8. -2.6.
9. -10.5.
10. 25.

MEASUREMENTS OF GEOMETRIC FIGURES

• • •

11. Use 3.14 for π and repeat Exercise 7 expressing your answers in decimal notation.
12. Repeat Exercise 11 for Exercise 8.
13. Repeat Exercise 11 for Exercise 9.
14. Find the radius of a circle if an arc 12 inches long is intercepted by a central angle of (a) 0.5 radians; (b) 2 radians; (c) 45°.

§ 3-6 Geometric figures

Any *geometric figure* is a set of points. If the points are on a plane (*coplanar*), the figure is a **plane figure;** if the points are not coplanar, the figure is a **space figure (three-dimensional figure).** In this section we introduce some of the general concepts and definitions which are needed for the discussion of areas (§ 3-7) and volumes (§ 3-8).

A few terms such as **point, line, curve, surface, area,** and **volume** are accepted without definition. Since these undefined terms are intuitively understood, they are used to provide a basis for defining other terms. Lines and polygons are considered to be special kinds of curves. Thus a plane curve may be composed in part or entirely of line segments.

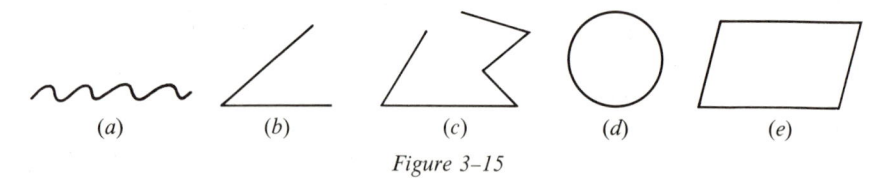

(a)   (b)   (c)   (d)   (e)

Figure 3-15

Curves such as those in Figure 3-15 are called **simple.** Notice that simple curves do not intersect themselves. If you copied any one of the curves (*a*), (*b*), or (*c*) in Figure 3-15, the path which you followed with your pencil did not bring the pencil back to its starting point. Such curves are said to be **open curves.** The curves in (*d*) and (*e*) are not open and are said to be **closed curves.** Curves such as those in (*b*), (*c*), and (*e*) which are composed of line segments are called **broken lines.** The curve (*e*) is a simple, closed, broken line. Any simple, closed, broken line is a **polygon.**

Any simple closed curve on a plane divides the plane into two parts (regions) called the **interior** (the bounded region) and the **exterior** (the unbounded region) of the curve. Any polygon is **convex** if every line segment having points of the polygon as its end points either lies along an edge of the polygon or has only its end points as points of the polygon; that is, each line segment joining points of the polygon lies entirely on or inside the polygon.

§ 3-6 GEOMETRIC FIGURES

A circle and its interior form a circular region. When we speak of the area of a circle, we mean the area of its circular region. A rectangle and its interior form a rectangular region. When we speak of the area of a rectangle, we mean the area of its rectangular region. In general, any simple closed curve and its interior form a bounded region; the area of this bounded region is called the area of the curve.

Certain plane curves may be thought of as *generated* by a moving point. For example, a ray AB may be generated by a point which starts at A and moves in the direction from A through B. A line AB may be generated by a point which moves in each of the two opposite directions from A through B and from B through A. A circle may be generated by a point which moves at a given distance (the radius) from a fixed point (the center).

Certain surfaces may be generated by a moving line. For example, a plane may be generated by a line m moving parallel to itself along a line t which is not parallel to m (Figure 3-16). The surface generated by a line m moving parallel to itself along a plane curve (**directrix**) which is not coplanar with m is a **cylindrical surface**. The line m may be thought of as *tracing* a given path, the directrix. Any plane curve may be used as directrix. For example, a circle, a parabola, and a sine curve (§ 4-6) are used in Figure 3-17. Notice that each of these surfaces is unbounded.

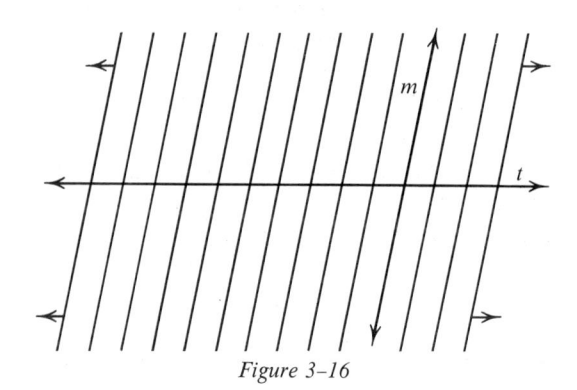

Figure 3-16

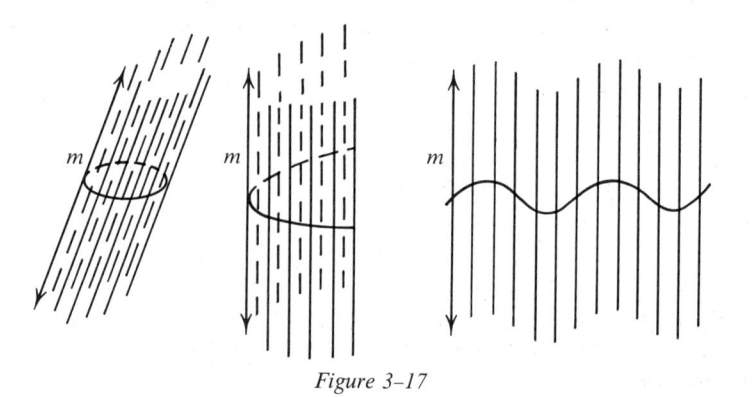

Figure 3-17

119

MEASUREMENTS OF GEOMETRIC FIGURES

The surface generated by a line *m* moving so that it always passes through a point *O* while it traces a plane curve (directrix) which is not coplanar with *O* is a **conical surface**. When the directrix is a simple closed curve, we obtain the two **nappes** of a conical surface; that is, the surface appears to be a double cone without bases (Figure 3–18). The directrix may be any plane curve and in particular may be a triangle (Figure 3–19).

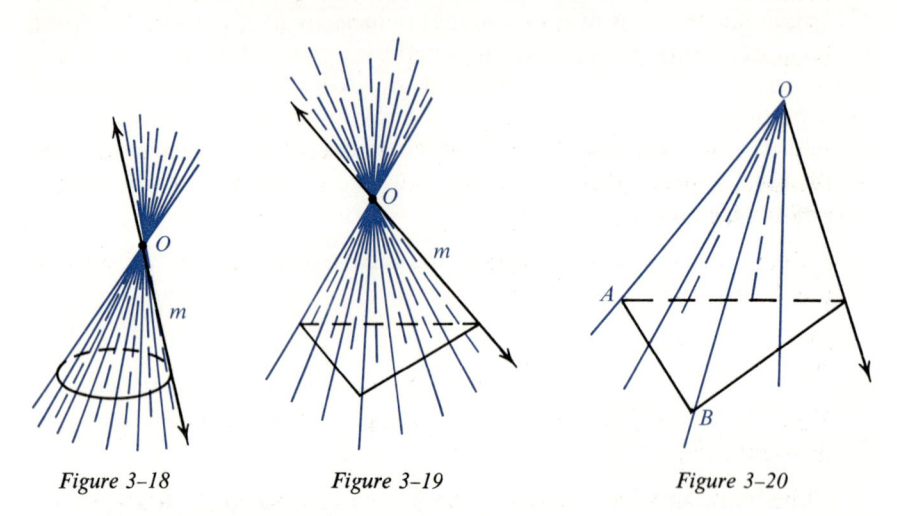

Figure 3–18   *Figure 3–19*   *Figure 3–20*

The surface generated by a ray with a fixed end point *O* and tracing a triangle *ABC* which is not coplanar with *O* is a **trihedral angle** *O-ABC* with **vertex** *O* (Figure 3–20) and appears to be "half" of the conical surface in Figure 3–19. In fact, it is one nappe of that surface. The plane angles *AOB*, *BOC*, and *COA* are the **face angles** of the trihedral angle. The lengths of the sides $\overline{AB}$, $\overline{BC}$, and $\overline{CA}$ of triangle *ABC* must be such that the sum of any two sides is greater than the third side; the face angles of the trihedral angle must be such that the sum of any two face angles is greater than the third face angle. If *O* were an interior point of triangle *ABC*, the sum of the angles *AOB*, *BOC*, and *COA* would be 360°; since *O* is not on the plane of the triangle, the sum of the face angles must be less than 360°.

The surface generated by a ray with a fixed end point *O* and tracing a convex polygon which is not coplanar with *O* is a convex **polyhedral angle**. Face angles are defined as for the trihedral angle, and the sum of the face angles must be less than 360°. If the polyhedral angle has *n* face angles, the sum of any (*n* − 1) face angles must be greater than the remaining face angle.

120

§ 3-6 GEOMETRIC FIGURES

Example 1. The measures of the face angles of a trihedral angle are 115°, 127°, and x degrees. What is the range of possible values for x?

Since the sum of the three face angles must be less than 360°, $115 + 127 + x < 360$. Since the sum of any two face angles must be greater than the third, $115 + x > 127$. Thus $x < 360 - 115 - 127$, that is, $x < 118$; also $x > 127 - 115$, that is, $x > 12$; therefore $12 < x < 118$. In other words, the measure of the third face angle is greater than 12° and less than 118°.

Example 2. A given polyhedral angle has four faces. If the measures of the face angles are 28°, 37°, 74°, and x degrees, what is the range of possible values for x?

Since the sum of any three of the face angles must be greater than the fourth face angle, then

$28 + 37 + 74 > x$, $139 > x$, $x < 139$; and
$28 + 37 + x > 74$, $x > 74 - 28 - 37$, $x > 9$, $9 < x$.

Thus $9 < x < 139$; that is, the measure of the fourth face angle is greater than 9° and less than 139°.

Cylindrical surfaces, conical surfaces, and polyhedral angles do not have areas or volumes since they are unbounded and thus infinite in extent. We now consider a few figures which are bounded, have areas (§ 3-7), and have volumes (§ 3-8). Any figure which has a volume is sometimes called a **solid.**

A **cube** (Figure 3-21) is a space figure with square regions as its faces. A cube is a simple closed figure since it has a single interior and a single exterior. Any simple closed space figure with polygons (each polygon is a simple closed plane curve) and their interiors as faces is a **polyhedron.** For example, each of the solids in Figure 3-22 is a polyhedron.

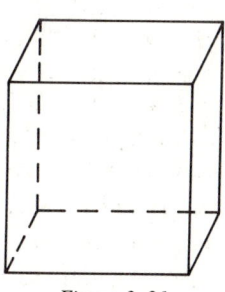

Figure 3-21

The vertices of the polygonal faces of a polyhedron are the **vertices** of the polyhedron; the sides of the polygons are the **edges** of the polyhedron. A line segment having two vertices of the polyhedron as end points is: an edge of the polyhedron if the vertices are consecutive vertices of a face of the polyhedron; a **diagonal of a face** of the polyhedron if it is not an edge and the vertices are vertices of the same face; a **diagonal of the polyhedron** if the vertices are not vertices of the same face.

MEASUREMENTS OF GEOMETRIC FIGURES

A polyhedron is **convex** if each line segment whose end points are points of the polyhedron lies entirely on or within the polyhedron. Each of the solids in Figure 3-22 is a convex polyhedron.

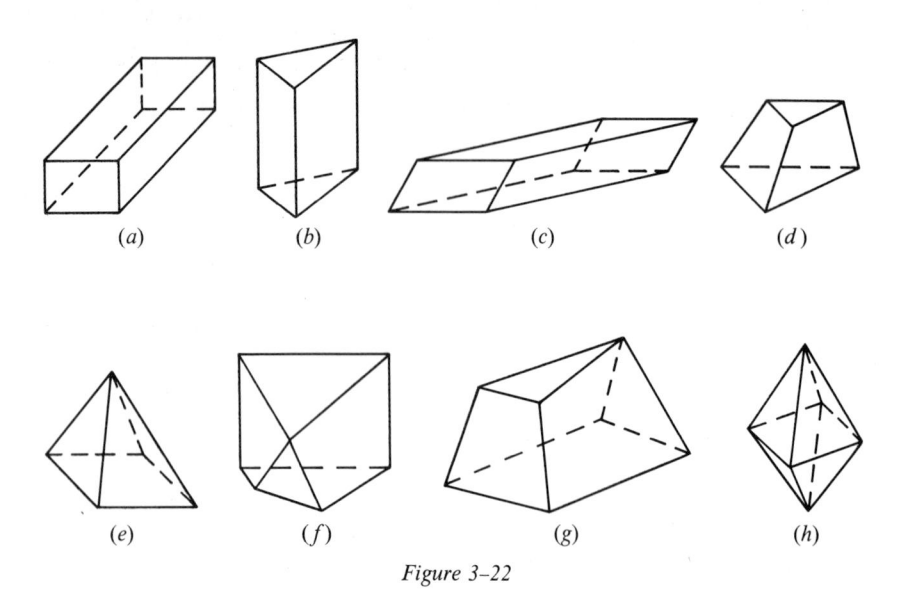

Figure 3-22

All of the vertices of each of the solids except (*f*) and (*h*) in Figure 3-22 lie in two parallel planes. Any polyhedron with all of its vertices in two parallel planes is a **prismatoid**. In a prismatoid the faces which are in the two parallel planes are the **bases** of the prismatoid; the edges which are not edges of the bases are **lateral edges** of the prismatoid.

If the two bases of a prismatoid have the same number of sides, the prismatoid is a **prismoid**. In Figure 3-22 the solids (*a*), (*b*), (*c*), and (*d*) are prismoids. If the lateral edges of the prismoid are parallel, the prismoid is a **prism**. In Figure 3-22 the solids (*a*), (*b*), and (*c*) are prisms. When the lateral edges are perpendicular to the plane of the base as in (*a*) and (*b*), the prism is a **right prism;** in all other cases the prisms are **oblique prisms** as in (*c*). Prisms are classified as triangular, quadrangular, hexagonal, and so forth according as the bases are triangles, quadrangles, hexagons, and so forth.

If one base of a prismatoid consists of a single point *V*, the prismatoid is a **pyramid** with vertex *V* and the other base of the prismatoid as the **base** of the pyramid. Pyramids are classified by their bases in the same manner as prisms. For example, the prismatoid (*e*) in Figure 3-22 is a quadrangular pyramid.

TEST YOURSELF

1. Sketch a broken line that is (**a**) simple and not closed; (**b**) closed and not simple; (**c**) simple and closed.

2. Sketch a quadrangular prismoid that is not a prism.

3. If the measures of the face angles of a trihedral angle are 90°, 60°, and x degrees, find the range of possible values for x.

EXERCISES

A

The measures of the face angles of a polyhedral angle are given. Find the range of possible values for x:

1. 137°, 156°, x degrees.
2. 114°, 121°, x degrees.
3. 38°, 61°, x degrees.
4. 25°, 49°, x degrees.
5. 12°, 177°, x degrees.
6. 56°, 163°, x degrees.

• • •

7. 87°, 92°, 106°, x degrees.
8. 35°, 51°, 72°, x degrees.
9. 55°, 67°, 164°, x degrees.
10. 52°, 73°, 185°, x degrees.

B

Sketch:

1. A curve that is (**a**) simple and not closed; (**b**) closed and not simple; (**c**) simple and closed.
2. A rectangular prism and its diagonals.
3. A polygon that is convex.
4. A polygon that is not convex.
5. A polyhedron that is convex.
6. A polyhedron that is not convex.
7. A triangular prism.
8. An hexagonal prism.

MEASUREMENTS OF GEOMETRIC FIGURES

• • •

*A plane curve obtained as the intersection of a plane and a space figure is called a **plane section** of the space figure. Sketch figures showing:*

9. A square as a plane section of a cube.

10. A rectangle as a plane section of a cube.

11. A triangle as a plane section of a cube.

• 12. A circle as a plane section of (**a**) a right circular cone; (**b**) an oblique circular cylinder.

• 13. An ellipse as a plane section of (**a**) a right circular cone; (**b**) an oblique circular cylinder.

§ 3-7 Areas

Any simple closed curve has an area, the area of the bounded region of the curve. Any figure composed of a finite number of simple closed curves and their interiors has an area.

You have previously used the formulas for the area A in square units of many common figures including:

square of side s	$A = s^2$;
circle of radius r	$A = \pi r^2$;
rectangle of base b and height h	$A = bh$;
parallelogram of base b and height h	$A = bh$;
trapezoid of height h and bases b and b'	$A = \dfrac{h}{2}(b + b')$;
triangle of base b and height h	$A = \dfrac{1}{2}bh$.

Probably you also studied **Hero's formula** for the area of a triangle whose sides are a, b, c and where $2s = a + b + c$:

$$A = \sqrt{s(s - a)(s - b)(s - c)}.$$

A polygon with all of its sides equal and all of its angles equal is a **regular polygon**. A circle may be inscribed in any regular polygon;

§ 3-7 AREAS

the center of this circle is the **center** of the polygon; the radius of this circle is the **apothem** of the polygon. Any regular polygon with perimeter p and apothem a has area A where $A = \frac{1}{2}ap$.

The formulas for the areas of plane curves are also used to obtain the areas (surfaces) of three-dimensional figures. For example, four points which are not on the same plane determine a **tetrahedron**. In Figure 3-23 the tetrahedron $ABCD$ has the four points A, B, C, and D as **vertices**; the six line segments AB, BC, AC, AD, BD, and CD as **edges**; and the four triangular regions ABC, ABD, BCD, and ACD as **faces**. The area of the tetrahedron is the sum of the areas of its faces. The tetrahedron is **regular** if all its faces are equilateral triangles.

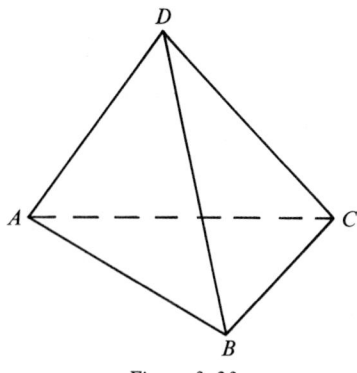

Figure 3-23

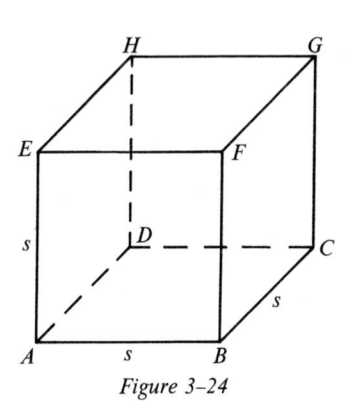

Each face of a cube (Figure 3-24) is a square. There are eight vertices, twelve edges, and six faces. If the length of each edge is s units, then the area of each face is s^2 square units and the area of the cube is $6s^2$ square units. The cube may be visualized as having a square lower base $ABCD$ and a square upper base $EFGH$ with each of the edges $\overline{AE}$, $\overline{BF}$, $\overline{CG}$, and $\overline{DH}$ perpendicular to the parallel planes of the bases. Thus a cube is a special case of a right prism with square bases.

Figure 3-24

A right prism with rectangular bases is called a **rectangular prism**. As in Figure 3-25 each face is a rectangle and the area A of the prism may be found as the sum of the areas of its faces:

$$A = 2lw + 2lh + 2wh.$$

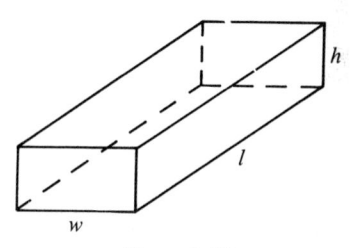

Figure 3-25

125

MEASUREMENTS OF GEOMETRIC FIGURES

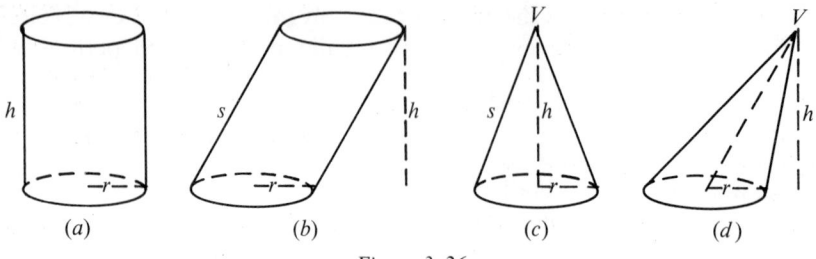

Figure 3-26

Each of the solids in Figure 3-26 has an altitude h and a circular base of radius r. The **lateral surface** (curved surface) of each of the solids (a) and (b) may be generated by a line segment (**element**) moving parallel to itself and around the circular base. In (a) the line segments are perpendicular to the base and the solid is a **right circular cylinder**.

If you had a paper model of the solid (a) in Figure 3-26, you might cut off each base by cutting along the circumference of each circle, then cut along a line perpendicular to the planes of the bases. This last cutting operation would make it possible for you to flatten out the curved surface and observe that it becomes a rectangle with length $2\pi r$ and width h. Thus you should expect the area of the curved surface to be $2\pi rh$ square units.

Since both bases are circles of radius r, the area of each base is πr^2 square units; the circumference of each base is $2\pi r$ units thus the **lateral area** (the area of the curved surface) is $2\pi rh$ square units; and the **total area** is $2\pi r^2 + 2\pi rh$, that is, $2\pi r(r + h)$ square units.

The line segment s used to generate the curved surface of the solid (b) in Figure 3-26 is not perpendicular (that is, is **oblique**) to the plane of the base, so the solid is an **oblique circular cylinder**. The length of the line segment s is the **slant height** of the cylinder. The lateral area of this cylinder is $2\pi rs$; the total area is $2\pi r^2 + 2\pi rs$, that is, $2\pi r(r + s)$ square units.

The lateral surface of the solid (c) in Figure 3-26 may be generated by a line segment (**element**) s with one end point fixed at V and the other end point tracing the circle which determines the base. The lateral surface of the solid (d) requires line segments (elements) of different lengths. If you had a paper model of the solid (c), cut the curved surface free from the base, and cut along one of the elements to the **vertex** V; you could flatten this surface out and observe that it becomes a sector of a circle with radius s and arc $2\pi r$.

The line segment joining the vertex V of the solid (c) to the center of the base is perpendicular to the base, so the solid is a **right circular cone**.

§ 3–7   AREAS

In (d) the line segment joining V to the center of the base is not perpendicular to the base, so the solid is an **oblique circular cone**. The length of an element s is the **slant height** of the right circular cone. The lateral area of this cone is πrs square units; and the total area is $\pi r^2 + \pi rs$, that is, $\pi r(r + s)$ square units. Since the elements of the lateral surface of the oblique circular cone are of different lengths, we do not have a simple formula for its area.

If each lateral edge of a prism (or each element of a cylinder) is cut by a plane, the two new solids formed are prisms (or cylinders) if the intersecting plane is parallel to the plane of the base (Figure 3–27a). The two new solids are called **truncated prisms** (or **truncated cylinders**) if the intersecting plane is not parallel to the plane of the base (Figure 3–27b).

(a)   (b)

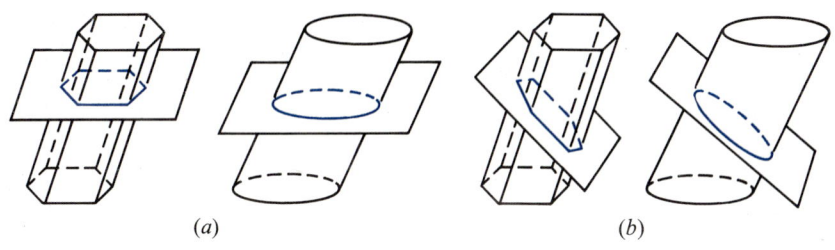

Figure 3–27

If each lateral edge of a pyramid (or each element of a cone) is cut by a plane which does not pass through the vertex of the pyramid (or cone), the new solid formed containing the vertex is a pyramid (or cone) and the other new solid is a **frustum** of a pyramid (or cone) if the intersecting plane is parallel to the plane of the base (Figure 3–28a). If the intersecting plane is not parallel to the plane of the base, the solid containing the base of the original pyramid (or cone) is a **truncated pyramid** (or **truncated cone**) (Figure 3–28b).

(a)   (b)

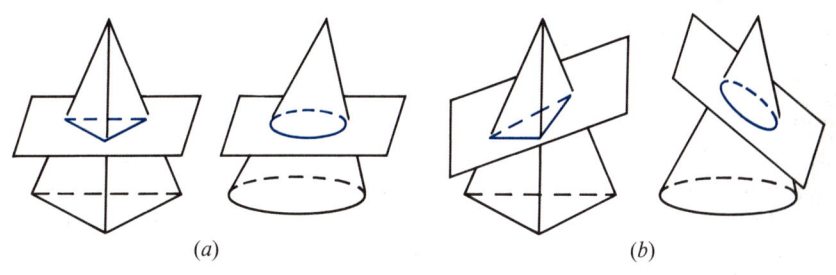

Figure 3–28

If a plane intersects a sphere, the intersection is a circle. The circle is a **great circle of the sphere** if the plane contains the center of the sphere; the

127

MEASUREMENTS OF GEOMETRIC FIGURES

circle is a **small circle of the sphere** if the plane does not contain the center of the sphere. The part of a sphere between two parallel planes which intersect the sphere is a **zone**. If one of the planes is tangent to the sphere, the part of the sphere is a **zone of one base**.

These definitions will be used as we summarize and extend the formulas for total area A and lateral area L of several common space figures:

regular tetrahedron with edge e	$A = e^2\sqrt{3}$;
cube with edge e	$A = 6e^2$;
rectangular prism with edges l, w, and h	$A = 2lw + 2lh + 2wh$;
right prism with height h and perimeter of base p	$L = hp$;
right circular cylinder with radius r and height h	$L = 2\pi rh$ $A = 2\pi r(r + h)$;
oblique circular cylinder with radius r and slant height s	$L = 2\pi rs$ $A = 2\pi r(r + s)$;
right circular cone with radius r and slant height s	$L = \pi rs$ $A = \pi r(r + s)$;
frustum of a right circular cone with radii R and r and slant height s	$L = \pi s(R + r)$ $A = \pi(R^2 + r^2 + sR + sr)$;
sphere of radius r	$A = 4\pi r^2$;
zone of height h of sphere of radius r	$A = 2\pi rh$.

Any two figures of the same *shape* are **similar** ($\sim$); any two figures of the same *shape* and *size* are **congruent** ($\cong$). These descriptions of similar and congruent figures may be treated formally in a more extensive course in geometry. As in your study of plane geometry if triangle ABC is similar to triangle RST, then

$$\angle A = \angle R, \quad \angle B = \angle S, \quad \angle C = \angle T;$$
$$\frac{AB}{RS} = \frac{BC}{ST} = \frac{AC}{RT} = \frac{k}{1}.$$

The ratio $k:1$ is called the **ratio of similitude**. The corresponding sides of the similar triangles are in the ratio of $k:1$ and are said to be **proportional**. Any two corresponding linear dimensions (angle bisectors, medians, perimeters, and the like) of the similar triangles are in this same ratio. Since the areas of the triangles may be expressed as products of lengths of two linear dimensions, the ratio of the areas of the triangles is $k^2:1$.

If two figures on a plane or in space are similar, then: corresponding plane and dihedral angles are equal; corresponding linear dimensions are in a constant ratio, $k:1$; corresponding areas are in the ratio $k^2:1$.

Example. A can is in the shape of a right circular cylinder of radius 1 inch and height 3 inches. A similar can is to be made with height 6 inches. Find its **(a)** radius; **(b)** lateral area.

(a) The ratio of similitude is 6:3 and any two corresponding linear dimensions have this ratio. Thus $r:1 = 6:3$; r is 2 inches. The same result might have been obtained by taking $k = \frac{6}{3} = 2$ and $r = k(1) = 2$.

(b) The lateral area ($2\pi rh$) of the smaller can is $2\pi(1)(3)$, that is, 6π square inches. The ratio of the lateral areas of the cans is $k^2:1$, that is, 4:1. Thus the lateral area of the larger can is 24π square inches. Notice that $2\pi(kr)(kh) = k^2(2\pi rh)$.

TEST YOURSELF

1. Find the total area of a cube with edge 2 inches long.
2. Find **(a)** the lateral area, and **(b)** the total area of a right circular cylinder with radius 4 inches and height 10 inches.

EXERCISES

A

In Exercises 1 through 6 find the total area of the given figure:

1. A rectangular prism 3 inches by 5 inches by 7 inches.
2. An equilateral triangle with side e using Hero's formula.
3. A regular hexagon with side e.
4. A right triangular prism with height 8 inches and an equilateral triangle with side 3 inches as base.
5. A right hexagonal prism with height 10 inches and a regular hexagon with side 2 inches as base.
6. A right circular cone with height 12 inches and radius of base 5 inches.

• • •

7. The altitudes of two right circular cylinders are equal. The radius of the first cylinder is twice the radius of the second. Find the ratio of the lateral area of the first cylinder to that of the second.
• **8.** A right circular cone has height 12 inches and radius of base 6 inches. How far from the base should a plane parallel to the base be passed through the cone so that the lateral areas of the two parts will be equal?
• **9.** Repeat Exercise 8 for a cone of height h and radius r.

129

MEASUREMENTS OF GEOMETRIC FIGURES

• **10.** Repeat Exercise 9 so that the lateral area of the remaining cone will be one-third of the area of the original cone.

B

1. Find the least number of faces that (a) a polyhedron can have; (b) a prism can have.

2. Describe the change in the area of a cube when its edge is (a) doubled; (b) tripled; (c) halved.

3. Describe the change in the area of a sphere when its radius is (a) doubled; (b) tripled; (c) halved.

4. Find the area of a sphere with (a) radius 5 inches; (b) diameter 1.2 feet.

5. Find the ratio of the areas of two regular tetrahedrons if the ratio of their edges is 1:2.

6. Find the ratio of the lateral areas of two similar hexagonal prisms if the ratio of their heights is 3:1.

• • •

7. A great circle of a sphere has area 9π square feet. Find (a) the radius of the sphere; (b) the area of the sphere.

8. Use 3.1416 for π and find the cost to the nearest dollar at $2.00 per square yard of painting a hemispherical dome whose diameter is 30.0 feet.

• **9.** Find how far from the center of a sphere with radius 10 inches a plane should pass through the sphere if (a) the ratio of the areas of the two parts of the sphere is to be 1:3; (b) the area of the circle in which the plane intersects the sphere is to be 50π square inches.

§ 3-8 Volumes

A cube with an edge 1 unit long is defined to have a volume of 1 cubic unit. In previous courses you have used the formulas for the volume V in cubic units of many common figures such as:

cube with edge e	$V = e^3$;
rectangular prism with edges l, w, and h	$V = lwh$;
right circular cylinder with radius r and height h	$V = \pi r^2 h$;
right prism with height h and area of base B	$V = Bh$;
pyramid with height h and area of base B	$V = \frac{1}{3} Bh$;
circular cone with radius r and height h	$V = \frac{1}{3} \pi r^2 h$;
sphere with radius r	$V = \frac{4}{3} \pi r^3$.

§ 3-8 VOLUMES

Volumes of many solids may be approximated by using regular polygons to approximate circles and regular polyhedrons to approximate spheres.

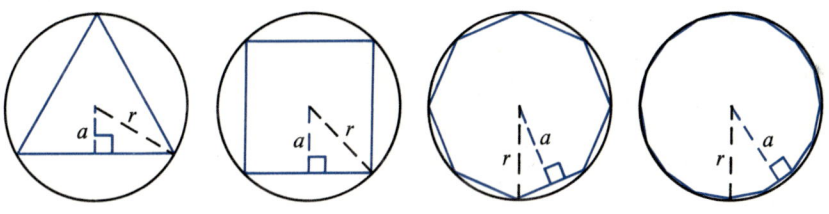

Figure 3–32

Regular polygons of three, four, eight, and sixteen sides are shown in Figure 3–32. Notice that as the number of sides increases:

(i)   The polygon approaches its circumscribed circle.
(ii) The apothem a approaches the radius r.
(iii) The perimeter p approaches the circumference.
(iv) The area $\frac{1}{2}ap$ approaches $\frac{1}{2}r(2\pi r)$, that is, πr^2.

Thus as the number of sides increases, the areas of the polygons approach the area of the circumscribed circle and each area may be used as an approximation for the area of the circle. If the number of sides of the polygon is allowed to increase without bound, we obtain a derivation of the formula $A = \pi r^2$ for the area of a circle.

Example 4. Use a sequence of regular polygons to approximate the area of the base of a right circular cylinder of radius r and height h. Then use the volumes of prisms with height h and the polygons as bases to obtain a formula for the volume of the cylinder.

The areas $\frac{1}{2}ap$ of the polygons approach $\frac{1}{2}r(2\pi r)$ and the volumes $\frac{1}{2}aph$ of the prisms approach $\pi r^2 h$. Thus the volume of the cylinder is given by the formula $V = \pi r^2 h$.

The method used in Example 4 may also be used to obtain formulas for the volumes of oblique circular cylinders, right circular cones, and oblique circular cones.

Approximations may also be used to extend our understanding of volumes. Think of a rectangular prism as a stack of cards such as a deck

133

MEASUREMENTS OF GEOMETRIC FIGURES

of bridge cards. The total volume of the cards is the same whether the stack is straight, twisted, or slanted (Figure 3-33).

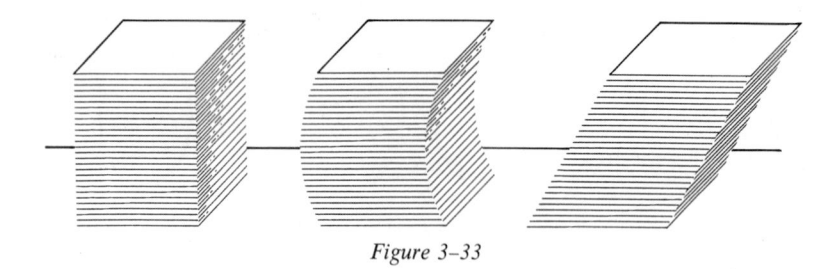

Figure 3-33

If we had a square, a triangle, and a circle of the same area B, we could construct a square pyramid, a triangular pyramid, and a circular cone of the same height as in Figure 3-34. The midsections A of the three figures are equal since each is equal to one quarter of the base. At any distance

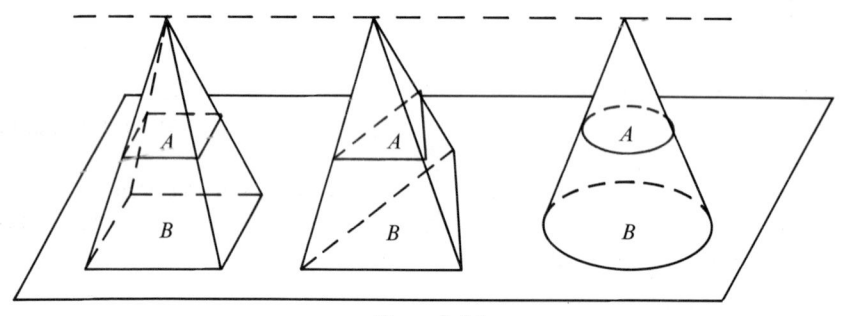

Figure 3-34

h above the base the plane sections of the three figures have the same area. If the three figures are visualized as consisting of stacks of cards such that at each level the cards have the same thickness and the same area, then we may expect the three figures to have the same volume. This expectation is usually stated as **Cavalieri's theorem:**

<u>If two space figures lie between two parallel planes and if on each plane parallel to these planes the plane sections of the space figures have equal areas, then the space figures have equal volumes.</u>

The proof of Cavalieri's theorem may be based upon approximations such as those that we have considered. However, we shall assume Cavalieri's theorem without proof.

TEST YOURSELF

Find the volume of:

1. A sphere inscribed in a cube of edge 8 inches.

2. A pyramid with altitude 12 inches and a square base with side 6 inches.

3. A frustum of a circular cone with height 7 inches and radii 2 inches and 8 inches.

EXERCISES

In Exercises 1 through 4 find the volume of:

1. A prism with height 18 inches and a square base with side 3 inches.
2. A pyramid with height 5 feet and a rectangular base 2 feet by 3 feet.
3. A cylinder inscribed in a cube with edge 10 inches.
4. A cube with surface 96 square inches.
5. As in the illustrative Example 4 use approximations to find a formula for the volume of a cone.

Use 3.14 *for* π. *In Exercises 6 through 8 assume that iron weighs* 450 *pounds per cubic foot, and find:*

6. The length to the nearest inch of a 25 pound iron bar with a square cross-section of side 1 inch.
7. The weight of a spherical iron ball 4 inches in diameter.
8. The weight to the nearest pound of a cylindrical iron rod 15 inches long and 6 inches in diameter.

• • •

9. A cylindrical tank 12 inches in diameter is resting on its circular base and is partly filled with water. When an iron casting is submerged, the water level is raised 5.2 inches. What is the volume of the casting?

Use 3.14 *for* π. *In Exercises 10 through 14 assume that* 1 *gallon occupies* 231 *cubic inches, and find:*

10. The height of a 30 gallon cylindrical water tank with diameter 12 inches.
11. The number of gallons of water needed to fill a tank 5 feet square and 3 feet high.
12. The number of gallons per minute flowing through a cylindrical pipe 4 inches in diameter at a rate of 15 miles per hour.
13. The height of a quart can if it is **(a)** a cylinder with inside diameter 3 inches; **(b)** a square prism with inside edge 3 inches.

135

MEASUREMENTS OF GEOMETRIC FIGURES

14. The number of gallons of water needed to fill a swimming pool 60 feet long, 12 feet wide, and with a depth varying uniformly from 2 feet at one end to 10 feet at the other end.

15. A roll of 0.12 inch diameter wire weighs 100 pounds. The material of which the wire is made weighs 120 pounds per cubic foot. How long is the wire?

• **16.** The base of a pyramid is a regular hexagon with edge 8 inches. The height of the pyramid is 25 inches. Find the volume of the frustum of the pyramid determined by a plane intersecting the pyramid 15 inches from its base.

§ 3–9 Solids of revolution (Supplementary)

Many common space figures may be obtained (generated) by rotating plane figures about a fixed line (**axis**). For example, a sphere may be generated by rotating a circle about one of its diameters. However notice that the circle needs to rotate through only 180°.

If a circle of radius r is rotated a complete revolution about an axis in the plane of the circle but outside the circle (that is, t units from the center of the circle where $t > r$), then a **torus** (doughnut) is generated (Figure 3–35). The volume of the torus is equal to the product of the area πr^2 of the circle and the distance $2\pi t$ traversed by the center of the circle: $V = 2\pi^2 r^2 t$. The area of the torus is equal to the product of the circumference $2\pi r$ of the circle and the distance $2\pi t$ traversed by the center of the circle: $A = 4\pi^2 rt$.

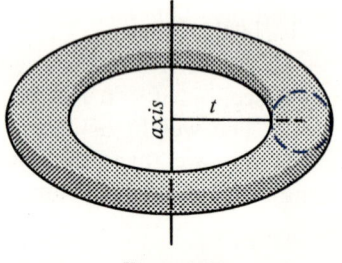

Figure 3–35

The center of any circle is the center of gravity (**centroid**) of the circle. The centroid of any regular polygon or rectangle is the center of the circle through its vertices. The centroid of any triangle is the point of intersection of its medians.

The results just obtained for a torus are special cases of the theorems of Pappus. The **theorems of Pappus** may be stated as follows:

If a surface S of revolution is generated by revolving a simple plane curve of length c about a line which is in the plane of the curve but does not cut the curve, then the area of the surface of revolution is equal to the

§ 3-9 SOLIDS OF REVOLUTION

product of the length of the generating curve and the circumference of the circle of radius t described by the centroid of the curve; that is, $S = 2\pi t c$.

If a solid of revolution is generated by revolving a simple curve and its interior about a line in the plane of the curve but not cutting the curve, then the volume V of the solid is equal to the product of the area A of the curve and the circumference of the circle of radius t described by the centroid of the area; that is, $V = 2\pi t A$.

Example. Consider a triangle ABC with altitudes of lengths h_a, h_b, and h_c. Use the theorem of Pappus for volumes to find the distance of the centroid of the triangle from each side of the triangle.

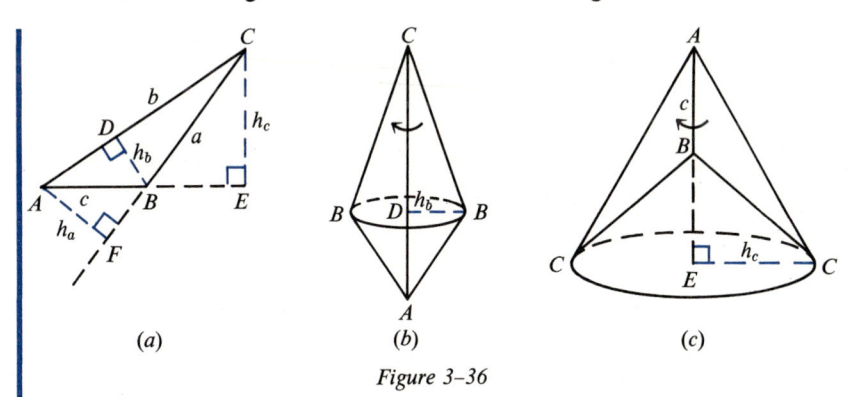

Figure 3-36

If the triangle is revolved about $\overleftrightarrow{AC}$, two cones are generated as in (b) of Figure 3-36. Each cone has a circular base with center D and radius h_b. The volumes of the cones are $\frac{1}{3}\pi h_b^2 \overline{CD}$ and $\frac{1}{3}\pi h_b^2 \overline{AD}$. The total volume of the solid generated by revolving the triangle about $\overleftrightarrow{AC}$ is the sum of the volumes of the cones;

$$\frac{1}{3}\pi h_b^2 \overline{CD} + \frac{1}{3}\pi h_b^2 \overline{AD} = \frac{1}{3}\pi h_b^2 (\overline{CD} + \overline{AD}) = \frac{1}{3}\pi h_b^2 \overline{AC}.$$

By the theorem of Pappus for volumes the total volume of the solid generated is given by the formula

$$V = 2\pi R_b \left(\frac{1}{2} b h_b\right) = \pi R_b h_b \overline{AC}$$

where R_b is the distance of the centroid from $\overleftrightarrow{AC}$. Thus $\frac{1}{3}\pi h_b^2 \overline{AC} = \pi R_b h_b \overline{AC}$ and $R_b = \frac{1}{3} h_b$.

137

MEASUREMENTS OF GEOMETRIC FIGURES

If the triangle is revolved about $\overrightarrow{AB}$, the volume of the solid of revolution may be visualized as the difference of two cones as in (c) of Figure 3-36:

$$V = \frac{1}{3}\pi h_c^2 \overline{AE} - \frac{1}{3}\pi h_c^2 \overline{BE} = \frac{1}{3}\pi h_c \overline{AB}.$$

By the theorem of Pappus the volume of the solid generated is $2\pi R_c \left(\frac{1}{2} ch_c\right)$ and thus $R_c = \frac{1}{3} h_c$. In a similar manner, $R_a = \frac{1}{3} h_a$.

If a right triangle is revolved about its hypotenuse, two cones are generated as in (b) of Figure 3-36. If a right triangle is revolved about a side that is not the hypotenuse, a single cone is generated.

In all cases the centroid of the triangle is one-third of the way from each side to the opposite vertex. This is consistent with and provides a means of proving the statement that the centroid of a triangle is at the intersection of the medians.

TEST YOURSELF

1. A circle of radius 1 inch is revolved about a line in the plane of the circle and 5 inches from its center. Find the surface of the figure (torus) generated.

2. Find the volume of the torus generated in Exercise 1.

EXERCISES

1. A circle of radius $\frac{1}{2}$ inch is revolved about a line in the plane of the circle and 2 inches from its center. Find (a) the surface; (b) the volume of the solid generated.

2. A square of side three inches is revolved about a line in the plane of the square and 6 inches from its center. Find (a) the surface; (b) the volume of the solid generated.

3. A rectangle 4 inches by 6 inches is revolved about a line in the plane of the rectangle and parallel to the longer sides. If the line is 5 inches from the center of the rectangle, find (a) the surface; (b) the volume of the solid generated.

4. Repeat Exercise 3 when the line is parallel to the shorter sides of the rectangle.

5. A rectangle is revolved about one of its longer sides. Use the theorem of Pappus to derive the formula for the volume of the right circular cylinder generated.

6. A rhombus with an angle of 60° and sides of 5 inches is revolved about a line in the plane of the rhombus and 12 inches from its center. Find **(a)** the surface; **(b)** the volume of the solid generated.

• **7.** Use 3.14 for π, disregard the volume of the glass and electrical connections, and find the volume to the nearest cubic inch of a circular fluorescent lamp with inner radius 5.0 inches and outer radius 6.0 inches.

SUMMARY OF CHAPTER 3

1. In this chapter you have studied measurements, geometric figures, and measurements of geometric figures. Any measurement is a number of units. There are conversion factors which may be used to express measurements of the same types of quantities in terms of the same units. All measurements are treated as approximations. (§ 3–1)

2. When numbers are written in scientific notation, all digits are significant. The number of significant decimal digits provides a measure of the accuracy of the number. A sum or difference of approximate numbers is no more *precise* than one of the least precise given numbers; a product, quotient, power, or root is no more *accurate* than one of the least accurate given numbers. (§ 3–2)

3. Linear measurements often arise as distances. The distance of a point A from any geometric figure is the length of the shortest possible line segment with A as one end point and a point of the figure as the other end point. (§ 3–3)

4. The length of a line segment RS is given on a number line by $|r - s|$; on a coordinate plane by $\sqrt{(r_1 - s_1)^2 + (r_2 - s_2)^2}$; in a coordinate space by $\sqrt{(r_1 - s_1)^2 + (r_2 - s_2)^2 + (r_3 - s_3)^2}$. The midpoint of $\overline{RS}$ has coordinates $\frac{r + s}{2}$ on a number line; $\left(\frac{r_1 + s_1}{2}, \frac{r_2 + s_2}{2}\right)$ on a coordinate plane; $\left(\frac{r_1 + s_1}{2}, \frac{r_2 + s_2}{2}, \frac{r_3 + s_3}{2}\right)$ in a coordinate space. If a point T is on $\overline{RS}$ and divides the line segment so that $\overline{RT} : \overline{TS} = p : q$, then on a number line

$$t = \frac{ps + qr}{p + q};$$

MEASUREMENTS OF GEOMETRIC FIGURES

on a coordinate plane

$$t_1 = \frac{ps_1 + qr_1}{p+q}, \quad t_2 = \frac{ps_2 + qr_2}{p+q};$$

and in a coordinate space

$$t_1 = \frac{ps_1 + qr_1}{p+q}, \quad t_2 = \frac{ps_2 + qr_2}{p+q}, \quad t_3 = \frac{ps_3 + qr_3}{p+q}. \quad (\S\ 3\text{-}4)$$

5. Plane angles may be formed by rays or by half-lines and their common end point; dihedral angles are formed by half-planes and their common edge. The wrapping function is used to associate plane angles with real numbers. Angles may be measured in either degrees or radians; 2π radians equal $360°$. The measure s of an arc intercepted by a central angle θ in a circle of radius r is given by the equation $s = r\theta$ where θ is measured in radians. The measure of a dihedral angle is the same as the measure of a plane angle having its vertex on the edge of the dihedral angle and each side on a face of the dihedral angle and perpendicular to the edge. (§ 3-5)

6. Any simple, closed, broken line is a polygon. A ray and a line may be generated by moving points; a plane, by a line moving parallel to itself and tracing a nonparallel line as directrix; a cylindrical surface, by a line moving parallel to itself and tracing a plane curve as directrix; a conical surface, by a line through a fixed point and tracing a plane curve not coplanar with the fixed point as directrix; a trihedral angle, by a ray with its end point fixed and tracing a triangle which is not coplanar with the end point as directrix; a convex polyhedral angle, by a ray with its end point fixed and tracing a convex plane polygon which is not coplanar with the end point as directrix. Any simple closed space figure with plane polygons and their interiors as faces is a *polyhedron*. If all the vertices of the polyhedron are in two parallel planes, the polyhedron is a *prismatoid* with the faces in the parallel planes as bases and the edges which are not edges of the bases as lateral edges. If one base of the prismatoid consists of a single point, the prismatoid is a *pyramid*. If the bases of the prismatoid have the same number of sides, the polyhedron is a *prismoid*. If the lateral edges of a prismoid are parallel, the polyhedron is a *prism*. (§ 3-6)

7. The lateral areas and the total areas of most of the common solids can be found from the formulas for the areas of common plane curves. Similar plane or space figures with ratio of similitude $k:1$ have areas in the ratio $k^2:1$. (§ 3-7)

SUMMARY OF CHAPTER 3

8. The volume V of any common solid may be found from the prismoidal formula

$$V = \frac{h}{6}(B_1 + 4M + B_2)$$

where h is the distance between the parallel bases of the solid considered as a prismatoid, B_1 and B_2 are the areas of the bases, and M is the area of the midsection. Similar solids with ratio of similitude $k:1$ have volumes in the ratio of $k^3:1$. Cavalieri's theorem provides a general approach for volumes:

If two space figures lie between two parallel planes and if on each plane parallel to these planes the plane sections of the space figures have equal area, then the space figures have equal volumes. (§ 3-8)

9. The areas and volumes of solids of revolution may be expressed in terms of the centroids, perimeters, and areas of the generating curves. The general statements of these relationships are given in the theorems of Pappus:

If a surface S of revolution is generated by revolving a simple plane curve of length c about a line which is in the plane of the curve but does not cut the curve, then the area of the surface of revolution is equal to the product of the length of the generating curve and the circumference of the circle of radius t described by the centroid of the curve; that is, $S = 2\pi t c$.

If a solid of revolution is generated by revolving a simple curve and its interior about a line in the plane of the curve but not cutting the curve, then the volume V of the solid is equal to the product of the area A of the curve and the circumference of the circle of radius t described by the centroid of the area; that is, $V = 2\pi t A$. (§ 3-9)

10. The following words have been introduced or used extensively in this chapter:

accuracy (§ 3-2)
altitude (§ 3-7)
angular measurement (§ 3-1)
apothem (§ 3-7)
approximate computations (§ 3-1)
approximate numbers (§ 3-1)
arc length (§ 3-5)
area measurement (§§ 3-1, 3-7)
axis of revolution (§ 3-9)
base (§ 3-6)
bounded region (§ 3-6)

broken line (§ 3-6)
Cavalieri's theorem (§ 3-8)
centroid (§ 3-9)
closed curve (§ 3-6)
congruent figures (§ 3-7)
conical surface (§ 3-6)
conversion factor (§ 3-1)
convex (§ 3-6)
coordinate plane (§ 3-3)
coplanar (§§ 3-3, 3-6)
cube (§§ 3-6, 3-7)

MEASUREMENTS OF GEOMETRIC FIGURES

curve (§ 3–6)
cylinder (§ 3–7)
cylindrical surface (§ 3–6)
diagonal (§ 3–6)
dihedral angle (§ 3–5)
directrix (§ 3–6)
distance (§§ 3–3, 3–4)
edge (§§ 3–5, 3–6, 3–7)
element (§ 3–7)
end point (§ 3–5)
exterior (§ 3–6)
face (§§ 3–5, 3–7)
face angle (§ 3–6)
frustum (§ 3–7)
generator (§ 3–6)
geometric figure (§§ 3–3, 3–6)
great circle (§ 3–7)
half-line (§ 3–5)
half-plane (§ 3–5)
Hero's formula (§ 3–7)
interior (§ 3–6)
lateral area (§ 3–7)
lateral edge (§ 3–6)
lateral surface (§ 3–7)
linear measurement (§§ 3–1, 3–3)
measurement (§ 3–1)
mid-point (§ 3–4)
midsection (§ 3–8)
nappe (§ 3–6)
oblique circular cone (§ 3–7)
oblique circular cylinder (§ 3–7)
oblique line (§ 3–7)
oblique prism (§ 3–6)
open curve (§ 3–6)
Pappus' theorems (§ 3–9)
plane angle (§ 3–5)
plane figure (§ 3–6)
plane section (§ 3–8)
polygon (§ 3–6)
polyhedral angle (§ 3–6)
polyhedron (§ 3–6)
precision (§ 3–1)

prism (§ 3–6)
prismatoid (§ 3–6)
prismoid (§ 3–6)
prismoidal formula (§ 3–8)
proportional (§ 3–7)
pyramid (§ 3–6)
radian (§ 3–5)
ratio of similitude (§ 3–7)
ray (§ 3–3)
rectangular prism (§ 3–7)
region (§ 3–6)
regular polygon (§ 3–7)
right circular cone (§ 3–7)
right circular cylinder (§ 3–7)
right prism (§ 3–6)
round off (§ 3–2)
scientific notation (§ 3–2)
side (§ 3–5)
significant (§ 3–2)
similar figures (§ 3–7)
simple curve (§ 3–6)
skew lines (§ 3–3)
slant height (§ 3–7)
small circle (§ 3–7)
solid (§ 3–6)
solid of revolution (§ 3–9)
space figure (§ 3–6)
sphere (§ 3–7)
surface (§ 3–6)
tetrahedron (§ 3–7)
torus (§ 3–9)
total area (§ 3–7)
trihedral angle (§ 3–6)
truncated (§ 3–7)
unbounded region (§ 3–6)
unit circle (§ 3–5)
vector (§ 3–3)
vertex (§§ 3–5, 3–6, 3–7)
volume measurement
   (§§ 3–1, 3–8)
wrapping function (§ 3–5)
zone (§ 3–7)

KEYED PRACTICE ON CHAPTER 3

1. Three measurements are given: 7 feet, 9.1 yards, and 253 inches. (a) Select the most precise of the given measurements. (b) Express each of the given measurements in terms of inches (to the nearest inch). (§ 3–1)

2. Round off each number to three significant digits: (a) 57.329; (b) 624.503; (c) 624.500. (§ 3–2)

3. Consider the given numbers to be approximate numbers and perform the indicated operations:
(a) $2.56 + 23.7 - 0.341$; (b) $(2.78 - 1.95) \times 3.11$. (§ 3–2)

4. Find the distance on a coordinate plane of the point $(3, -4)$ from
(a) $\{(x, y) \mid y = 2\}$; (b) $\{(x, y) \mid x^2 + y^2 + 2x = 3\}$. (§ 3–3)

5. Find the coordinates of the point C on $\overline{AB}$ such that $\overline{AC}:\overline{CB} = 2:3$ for $A: (-3, 1, 7)$ and $B: (7, 6, 2)$. (§ 3–4)

6. Express each angle measure in radians: (a) $120°$; (b) $780°$. (§ 3–5)

7. Consider each number as an angle measure in radians and express in degrees: (a) $\frac{4\pi}{3}$; (b) 1.5. (§ 3–5)

8. In a circle of radius 4.2 inches find the length of an arc which is intercepted by a central angle of 2.0 radians. (§ 3–5)

9. If the measures of the face angles of a trihedral angle are $135°$, $157°$, and x degrees, find the range of possible values for x. (§ 3–6)

10. Sketch a figure that is a prismatoid but is not a prismoid. (§ 3–6)

11. A right circular cylinder has radius 2 inches and height 7 inches. Find (a) the lateral area; (b) the total area. (§ 3–7)

12. Find the ratio of the lateral areas of two similar prisms with regular octagons as bases if the ratio of the edges of their bases is $6:4$. (§ 3–7)

13. Find the weight of a solid iron rectangular prism 6 inches by 3 inches by 4 inches if the iron used weighs 480 pounds per cubic foot. (§ 3–8)

14. If an equilateral triangle has edge 3 inches and is revolved about a line in the plane of the triangle and 4 inches from the centroid of the triangle, find: (a) the surface of the solid of revolution; (b) the volume of the solid of revolution. (§ 3–9)

TESTS ON CHAPTER 3

A

1. Select the most precise measurement: 35 feet, 2.5 yards, 7 centimeters.

2. Round off each number to three significant digits: (a) 0.01214; (b) 25.250.

MEASUREMENTS OF GEOMETRIC FIGURES

3. Find the distance on a coordinate plane of the point $(-12, 5)$ from
(a) $\{(x, y) \mid y = 3\}$; (b) $\{(x, y) \mid x^2 + y^2 = 4\}$.

4. Find the coordinates of the point T on $\overline{RS}$ such that $\overline{RT}:\overline{TS} = 1:3$ for R: $(2, 9, -3)$ and S: $(6, 1, 9)$.

5. Express each angle measure in radians: (a) 300°; (b) 930°.

6. Sketch a plane curve that is closed, simple, and convex.

7. Find the total area of a regular tetrahedron with an edge 4 inches long.

8. Find the volume of a rectangular pyramid with height 5 inches and base 2 inches by 3 inches.

9. Use 3.14 for π, and find the weight of a solid iron right circular cylinder 12 inches high with radius 6.0 inches if the iron used weighs 450 pounds per cubic foot.

10. Find the volume of a pyramid with vertices at A: $(2, 3, 5)$, B: $(-1, 3, 5)$, C: $(2, 7, 5)$, and D: $(3, 4, 9)$.

B

1. Select the most precise measurement: 5.12 miles, 2538 feet, 1256 kilometers.

2. Consider the given numbers to be approximate, and perform the indicated operations: (a) $137.25 - 3.4782$; (b) $(1.5 - 0.80) \times 1.31$.

3. Find the coordinates of the point Q on $\overline{MN}$ such that $\overline{MQ}:\overline{QN} = 4:3$ for M: $(25, 11, -4)$ and N: $(-3, 18, 17)$.

4. Find the distance on a coordinate plane of the point $(7, 11)$ from $\{(x, y) \mid x^2 + y^2 - 2x + 6y = 0\}$.

5. Consider each number as an angle measure in radians and express in degrees: (a) $\dfrac{5\pi}{6}$; (b) 4.5.

6. Sketch a space figure that is closed, simple, and convex.

7. Find the total area of a right hexagonal prism with height 12 inches and a regular hexagon with side 4 inches as base.

8. A rectangular tank which is a right prism with base 4.0 inches by 6.0 inches is partly filled with water. When an aluminum casting is submerged, the water level is raised 3.15 inches. What is the volume of the casting?

9. Assume that water weighs 62.4 pounds per cubic foot, and find the weight of the water in a full cylindrical pail with radius 4 inches and height 12 inches. Use 3.14 for π.

10. If the measures of the face angles of a trihedral angle are 93°, 102°, and x degrees, find the range of possible values for x.

ANSWERS TO TEST YOURSELF EXERCISES

C

1. Consider the given numbers to be approximate numbers and perform the indicated operations: (a) $(27.3 + 125 - 148) \times 1.13$; (b) $0.03 \times (12,000 + 2750)$.

2. Find the coordinates of the point H on $\overline{RS}$ such that $\overline{RH}:\overline{HS} = 3:5$ for $R: (6, -17, 41)$ and $S: (-10, 7, -15)$.

3. Tell whether each point is inside, on, or outside the circle with equation $x^2 + y^2 - 6x + 4y - 237 = 0$: (a) $(15, 10)$; (b) $(-5, 13)$; (c) $(13, -11)$.

4. Find the radius of a circle if an arc 14 inches long is intercepted by a central angle of (a) 3.5 radians; (b) 225°.

5. If the measures of the face angles of a polyhedral angle of four faces are 18°, 84°, 105°, and x degrees, find the range of possible values for x.

6. Find the total area of a frustum of a right circular cone if the slant height of the frustum is 10 inches and the radii of the bases are 5 inches and 3 inches.

7. How far from the base of a pyramid with an altitude of 12 inches should a plane parallel to the base be passed if it is to cut off a pyramid whose lateral area is one-fourth that of the given pyramid?

8. A roll of wire having diameter 0.080 inches weighs 90 pounds. The material of which the wire is made weighs 150 pounds per cubic foot. Express the length of the wire in terms of π.

9. How far from the base of a cone with an altitude of 56 inches should a plane parallel to the base be passed to divide the cone into parts whose volumes are in the ratio of $1:7$ where the newly formed cone is the smaller solid?

10. Use 3.14 for π, disregard the volume of the glass and the electrical connections, and find to the nearest cubic inch the volume of a circular fluorescent lamp with an inner radius of 3.0 inches and an outer radius of 4.0 inches.

ANSWERS TO TEST YOURSELF EXERCISES

§ 3-1. 1. $2\frac{1}{12}$ feet.   2. $\frac{1}{2}$ revolution.   3. 65 minutes.   4. 235 inches.

5. In order to determine how precise each measurement is we must compare the magnitudes of the units in which the measurements are given: $\frac{1}{1000}$ yard $= 0.036$ inch, 1 foot $= 12$ inches, 1 centimeter ≈ 0.3937 inch; thus 3.052 yards is given in terms of the smallest unit and is the most precise of the given measurements.

§ 3-2. 1. (a) 128.   (b) 436.   2. (a) 62.50.   (b) 5.0×10^2.

MEASUREMENTS OF GEOMETRIC FIGURES

§ 3-3. 1. 3 units. **2.** 8 units. **3.** 5 units.
4. The distance from (3, 7) to (3, 1) is 6 units; to (0, 7) is 3 units; to (1, 1) is $2\sqrt{10}$ units; therefore the distance from (3, 7) to {(3, 1), (0, 7), (1, 1)} is 3 units.

§ 3-4. 1. 5 units. **2.** (4, −1, 6). **3.** (3, 7, 4).

§ 3-5. 1. (a) $\frac{\pi}{2}$; (b) $\frac{5\pi}{4}$; (c) $\frac{9\pi}{2}$. **2.** 14 inches.

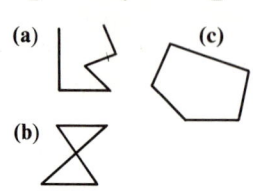

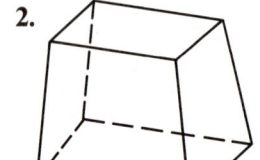

§ 3-6. 1. (a) (c) **2.**
(b)
3. $30 < x < 150$.

§ 3-7. 1. 24 square inches. **2.** (a) 80π square inches. (b) 112π square inches.

§ 3-8. 1. $r = 4$; $V = \frac{4}{3}\pi 64$; volume is $\frac{256}{3}\pi$ cubic inches.
2. $B = 36$; volume is 144 cubic inches.
3. $h = 7$; $B_1 = 64\pi$; $B_2 = 4\pi$; $M = 25\pi$; volume is 196π cubic inches.

§ 3-9. 1. $C = 2\pi$; $t = 5$; the surface of the torus is $20\pi^2$ square inches.
2. $A = \pi$; $t = 5$; the volume of the torus is $10\pi^2$ cubic inches.

ANSWERS TO KEYED PRACTICE ON CHAPTER 3

1. (a) 253 inches. (b) 7 feet = 84 inches; 9.1 yards = 328 inches; 253 inches.
2. (a) 57.3; (b) 625; (c) 624.
3. (a) 25.9; (b) 2.6.
4. (a) 6 units; (b) $(4\sqrt{2} - 2)$ units.
5. C: (1, 3, 5).
6. (a) $\frac{2\pi}{3}$; (b) $\frac{13\pi}{3}$.
7. (a) 240°; (b) $\left(\frac{270}{\pi}\right)°$.
8. 8.4 inches.
9. $22 < x < 68$.
10.

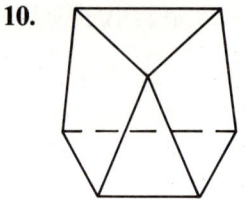

11. (a) 28π square inches; (b) 36π square inches.
12. 36:16, that is, 9:4.
13. 20 pounds.
14. (a) 72π square inches; (b) $18\pi\sqrt{3}$ cubic inches.

Chapter 4

Circular Functions and Their Graphs

§ 4-1 Trigonometric functions

Any triangle may be subdivided into right triangles. Any polygon may be subdivided into triangles. (See Figure 4–1.)

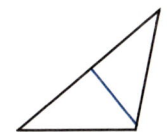

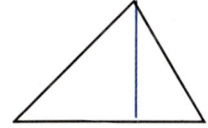

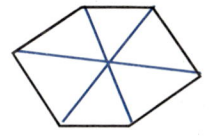

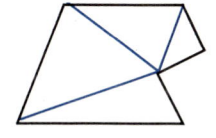

Figure 4–1

The sum of the angles of any triangle is 180°. If the angles of one triangle are equal to the angles of another triangle, the triangles are **similar.** For example, any two triangles with angles of 45°, 45°, and 90° are similar; any two triangles with angles 30°, 60°, 90° are similar.

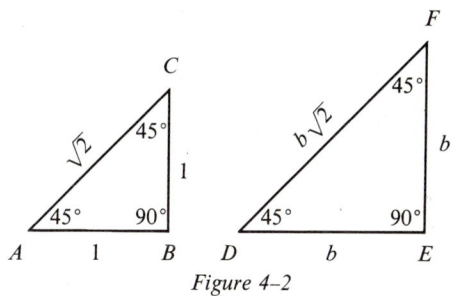

Figure 4–2

In Figure 4–2 we used the fact that triangle ABC is similar to triangle DEF (that is, $\triangle ABC \sim \triangle DEF$) in labeling the lengths of the sides of triangle DEF. Since the triangles are similar, $\overline{AB}:\overline{DE} = \overline{BC}:\overline{EF} = \overline{AC}:\overline{DF}$. Thus if $\overline{DE} = b$, then $\overline{EF} = b$ and $\overline{DF} = b\sqrt{2}$. Notice that each 45°-45°-90° triangle has two equal sides and a **hypotenuse** (the side opposite the right angle). The length of the hypotenuse is $\sqrt{2}$ times the length of each of the other two sides.

If you know the length of any side of a 45°-45°-90° triangle, you can find the lengths of the other two sides. If one of the short sides is 5 units long, then the lengths of the other two sides are 5 units and $5\sqrt{2}$ units. If the length of the hypotenuse is $7\sqrt{2}$ units, then each of the other sides is 7 units long.

CIRCULAR FUNCTIONS AND THEIR GRAPHS

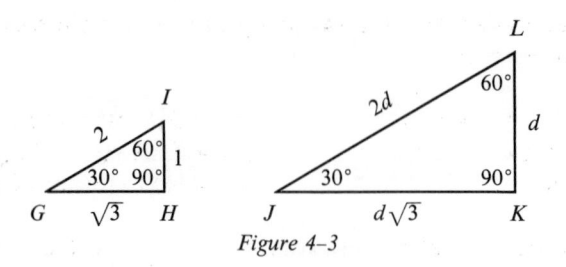

Figure 4-3

In Figure 4-3 we used the fact that triangle *GHI* is similar to triangle *JKL* in labeling the lengths of the sides of triangle *JKL*. The hypotenuse of each 30°-60°-90° triangle is twice as long as the side opposite the 30° angle. The length of the side opposite the 60° angle is $\sqrt{3}$ times the length of the side opposite the 30° angle.

If you know the length of any side of a 30°-60°-90° triangle, you can find the lengths of the other two sides. If the side opposite the 30° angle is 3 units long, then the length of the hypotenuse is 6 units and the length of the other side is $3\sqrt{3}$ units. If the length of the hypotenuse is 8 units, then the lengths of the other two sides are 4 units and $4\sqrt{3}$ units. If the length of the side opposite the 60° angle is $5\sqrt{3}$ units, then the length of the hypotenuse is 10 units and the length of the other side is 5 units.

You have seen that the ratios of the sides of 45°-45°-90° and 30°-60°-90° triangles can be used to find the lengths of all the sides if the length of any side is known. Such ratios have special names and may be used for any right triangle. As in Figure 4-4 we usually select one of the angles that is not a right angle and identify two of the sides of the triangle with reference to this acute angle. The side opposite the right angle is called the hypotenuse; the other two sides are identified as the **side opposite** and the **side adjacent** to the selected acute angle. For triangle *ABC* we say that $\overline{BC}$ is the side opposite angle *A* and $\overline{AC}$ is the side adjacent to angle *A*. Also, as in Figure 4-4, we may use the symbol ⌐ to show that an angle is a right angle.

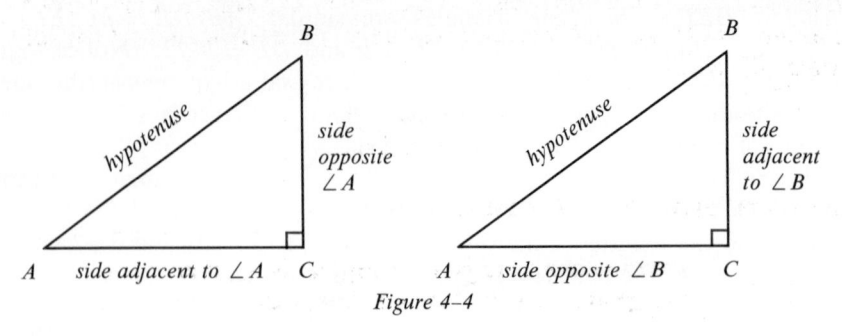

Figure 4-4

§ 4-1 TRIGONOMETRIC FUNCTIONS

We may define six ratios for any acute angle of a right triangle. These abbreviations are used:

sin A for sine of angle A;   cot A for cotangent of angle A;
cos A for cosine of angle A;   sec A for secant of angle A;
tan A for tangent of angle A;   csc A for cosecant of angle A.

The abbreviation ctn A also is frequently used for the cotangent of angle A. For any triangle ABC with $\angle C = 90°$, we have

$$\sin A = \frac{a}{c} \left(\text{that is, } \frac{\text{side opposite}}{\text{hypotenuse}}\right);$$

$$\cos A = \frac{b}{c} \left(\text{that is, } \frac{\text{side adjacent}}{\text{hypotenuse}}\right);$$

$$\tan A = \frac{a}{b} \left(\text{that is, } \frac{\text{side opposite}}{\text{side adjacent}}\right);$$

$$\cot A = \frac{b}{a} \left(\text{that is, } \frac{\text{side adjacent}}{\text{side opposite}}\right);$$

$$\sec A = \frac{c}{b} \left(\text{that is, } \frac{\text{hypotenuse}}{\text{side adjacent}}\right);$$

$$\csc A = \frac{c}{a} \left(\text{that is, } \frac{\text{hypotenuse}}{\text{side opposite}}\right).$$

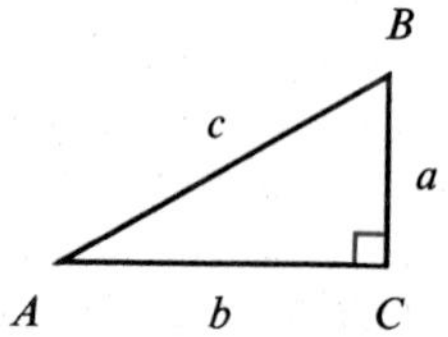

Figure 4-5

Each of the six ratios depends upon the shape of the triangle but not upon the size of the triangle. Since the ratios may be used in determining measures of sides of triangles, they are often called **trigonometric ratios** or **trigonometric functions.** The word trigonometry comes from the Greek words *trigonon* (triangle) and *metron* (measure). Thus **trigonometry** is based (at least historically) upon measures of triangles. For any given value of the angle A an expression such as "sin A" stands for a single ratio, that is, a single numerical value. Such expressions should not be confused with the multiplication of literal number symbols as in ab^2. Statements such as

$$\angle A = 30°, \text{ and}$$
$$b = 25 \text{ feet}$$

are abbreviations for statements such as

the measure of angle A in degrees is 30; and
the measure (length) of b in feet is 25.

CIRCULAR FUNCTIONS AND THEIR GRAPHS

TEST YOURSELF

Use the given figure:

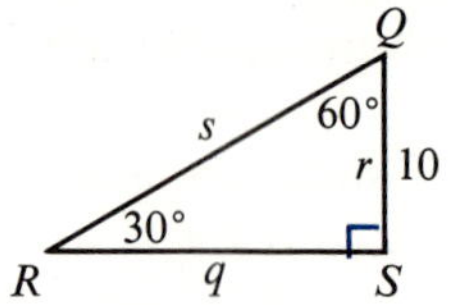

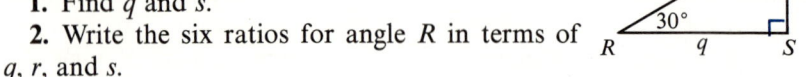

1. Find q and s.
2. Write the six ratios for angle R in terms of q, r, and s.
3. Use the results obtained in Exercise 1 and find a value for each of the six ratios for angle R.
4. Explain why the values for the six ratios for angle R are true for the 30° angle in any 30°-60°-90° right triangle. Then find a value for each of the six ratios for 30°.

EXERCISES

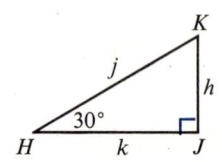

1. In triangle HJK, $\angle H = 30°$ and $\angle J = 90°$. How large is angle K?
2. In Exercise 1 if $j = 12$ inches, how long is h? How long is k?
3. In triangle XYZ, $\angle Y = 45°$ and $\angle Z = 90°$. How large is angle X? 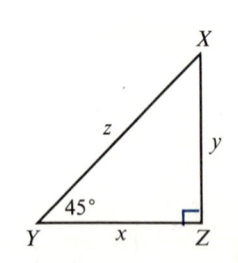
4. In Exercise 3 if $y = 8$ inches, how long is x? How long is z?
5. Find a value for each of the six ratios for an angle of 45°.
6. Find a value for each of the six ratios for an angle of 60°.

Use right triangle ABC with sides 3, 4, and 5 for Exercises 7 through 18. Find the values of:

7. $\sin A$ and $\cos B$.
8. $\cos A$ and $\sin B$.
9. $\tan A$ and $\cot B$.
10. $\cot A$ and $\tan B$.
11. $\sec A$ and $\csc B$.
12. $\csc A$ and $\sec B$.
13. $\sin^2 A + \cos^2 A$.
14. $\tan^2 A - \sec^2 A$.
15. $\cot^2 A - \csc^2 A$.
16. $\tan A \cot A$.
17. $\sin B \csc B$.
18. $\cos B \sec B$.

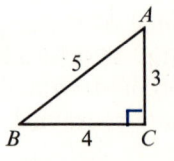

• • •

19. In Exercise 1 write the six ratios for angle H in terms of h, j, and k.
20. In Exercise 3 write the six ratios for angle X in terms of x, y, and z.
21. In Exercise 1 write the six ratios for angle K in terms of h, j, and k.

§ 4-2   SOLUTION OF SPECIAL TRIANGLES

● **22.** Prove that if an acute angle of one right triangle is equal to an acute angle of another right triangle, the triangles are similar.

§ 4–2 Solution of special triangles

Years ago the importance of trigonometry was due primarily to its use in surveying and thus to the measuring of triangles and other polygons. Examples of such applications are given in this section and in Chapter 5.

The importance of trigonometry and in particular the circular functions (§ 4–3) in modern mathematics is due primarily to the periodicity of the functions (§ 4–6). This periodicity makes it possible to use circular functions in approximating functions which represent sound waves and other periodic events. The resulting applications in advanced mathematics are, in general, beyond the scope of this text. Notice that modern trigonometry is concerned with much more than triangle measure and thus the name is in a sense a misnomer.

Any right triangle has a hypotenuse, two other sides, a right angle, and two acute angles. We *solve* a triangle by finding the measures of its angles and sides.

Example 1. Solve triangle ABC if $\angle C = 90°$, $\angle B = 30°$, and $c = 10$ inches.

Draw a figure (Figure 4–6). You know that the sum of the angles of the triangle must be 180°. Thus $\angle A = 180° - 90° - 30° = 60°$.

As in § 4–1 you know that the length of the hypotenuse of a 30°-60°-90° triangle is twice the length of the side opposite the 30° angle. In other words, $\sin B = \sin 30°$; $\dfrac{b}{10} = \dfrac{1}{2}$; $2b = 10$; $b = 5$ inches.

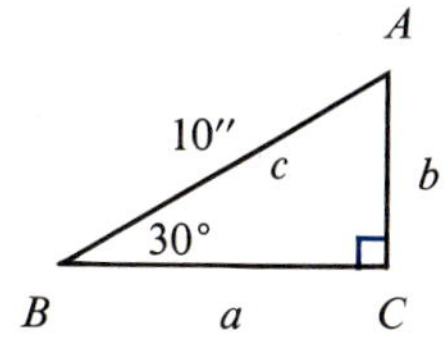

Figure 4–6

Similarly, $\cos B = \cos 30° = \dfrac{\sqrt{3}}{2}$ as in § 4–1. Then $\dfrac{a}{10} = \dfrac{\sqrt{3}}{2}$; $2a = 10\sqrt{3}$; $a = 5\sqrt{3}$ inches.

Notice how the ratios $\sin 30° = \dfrac{1}{2}$ and $\cos 30° = \dfrac{\sqrt{3}}{2}$ helped you solve the right triangle in Example 1. You also learned in § 4–1 that $\sin 45° = \dfrac{1}{\sqrt{2}}$, $\cos 45° = \dfrac{1}{\sqrt{2}}$, and $\tan 45° = 1$.

151

CIRCULAR FUNCTIONS AND THEIR GRAPHS

Example 2. Solve triangle DEF if $\angle D = 90°$, $\angle E = 45°$, and $e = 6$ feet.

Draw a figure; $\angle F = 180° - 90° - 45° = 45°$;
$\tan E = \dfrac{6}{f} = 1, f = 6$ feet;
$\sin E = \dfrac{6}{d} = \dfrac{1}{\sqrt{2}}, d = 6\sqrt{2}$ feet.

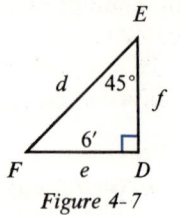

Figure 4-7

TEST YOURSELF

1. Solve triangle HIK if $\angle H = 90°$, $\angle I = 45°$, and $h = 10$ feet.
2. Solve triangle PMN if $\angle P = 90°$, $\angle M = 60°$, and $n = 3$ feet.

EXERCISES

Solve each triangle:

1.

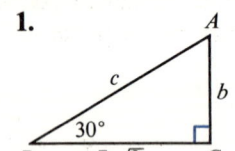

2.

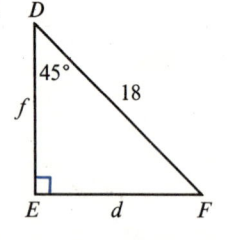

3.

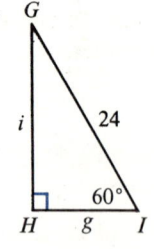

4. John wanted to measure the height h of a tree $\overline{RS}$. He first found a point T such that $\angle TRS = 90°$ and $\angle RTS = 45°$. Then he measured $\overline{RT}$ as 42 feet. Find the height of the tree.

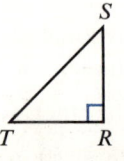

5. As in Exercise 4 if $\angle TRS = 90°$, $\angle RTS = 60°$, and $\overline{RT} = 50$ feet, find the height of the tree.

6. Find the length of an altitude of an equilateral triangle with side 24 inches.

7. Find the length of the side of an equilateral triangle with an altitude 10 inches.

8. Find the side of a square with diagonal 15 feet.

9. An airplane pilot flew 700 miles in a southeasterly direction. How far south did he fly?

• 10. The hypotenuse c of triangle ABC is equal to $2a$; $b = 6$ feet. Solve the triangle.

● **11.** Bill and Don each started walking at a rate of 4 miles per hour from the same place at the same time. Bill walked west and Don walked north on a level plane. How far apart were they after 3 hours?

● **12.** As in Exercise 11, how far apart would Bill and Don be after 3 hours if Bill walked in a northwesterly direction and Don walked north?

§ 4–3 Circular functions

We now consider angles on a coordinate plane and extend our definitions of the trigonometric functions to include functions of any angle, acute or otherwise. When the six ratios are defined for general angles, they are called **circular functions.** The reason for this name will be shown in § 4–4.

An angle is formed by two rays with a common end point. When we measure an angle, we think of one ray as the **initial side,** the other ray as the **terminal side.** We also may think of any angle AOB as placed on a coordinate plane with the vertex O at the origin and the initial side $\overrightarrow{OA}$ along the positive x-axis; that is, in **standard position** on the plane.

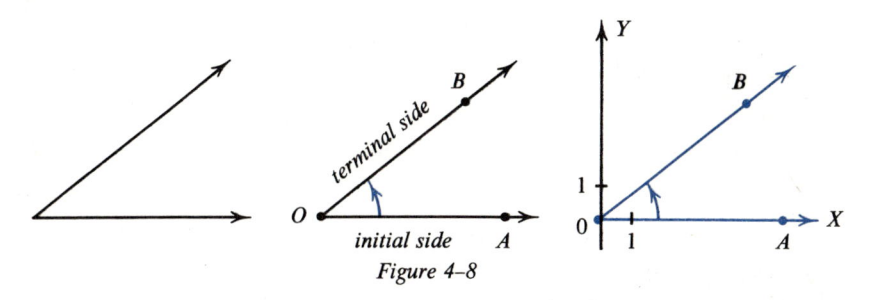

Figure 4–8

Angles of any size may be placed in standard position on a coordinate plane. In each case some point P with coordinates (x, y) is selected on the terminal side but not at the vertex. Then $\overline{PQ}$ is drawn perpendicular to the x-axis with Q on the axis. The length of $\overline{OP}$ is called r; since it is the length of a line segment, r is positive for all angles.

Any angle may be placed in standard position on a coordinate plane. Also any point P different from the origin O determines an angle XOP where X is on the positive x-axis. If P is not on the positive x-axis, we usually think of the initial side $\overrightarrow{OX}$ as rotating counterclockwise to $\overrightarrow{OP}$. Then angle XOP is called a **positive angle.** The Greek letter θ (theta) is often used to represent an angle as in Figure 4–9. The Greek letters α (alpha), β (beta), γ (gamma), ϕ (phi), and ω (omega) also are frequently used as names for angles.

CIRCULAR FUNCTIONS AND THEIR GRAPHS

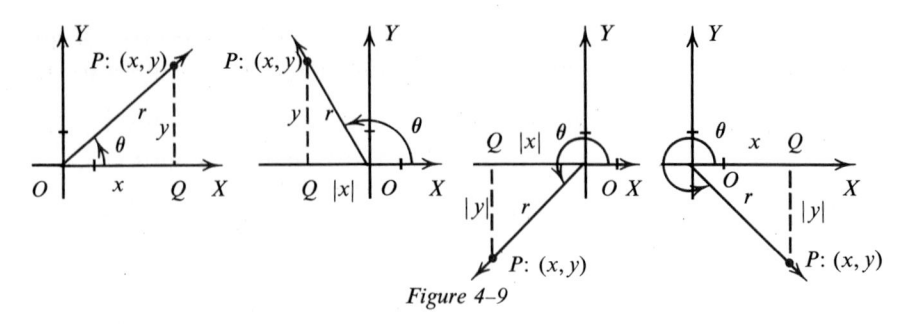

Figure 4-9

If P is not on one of the axes, triangle OPQ is a right triangle with hypotenuse r (see Figure 4-9). If the angle θ is acute, then as in § 4-1

$$\sin \theta = \frac{y}{r}; \qquad \csc \theta = \frac{r}{y};$$

$$\cos \theta = \frac{x}{r}; \qquad \sec \theta = \frac{r}{x};$$

$$\tan \theta = \frac{y}{x}; \qquad \cot \theta = \frac{x}{y}.$$

Figure 4-10

In Figure 4-10 notice that for any two choices P_1 and P_2 of the point P for the same angle θ, we obtain the same ratios since, as in Exercise 22 of § 4-1, $\triangle OP_1Q_1 \sim \triangle OP_2Q_2$. Thus we have

$$\frac{y_1}{r_1} = \frac{y_2}{r_2}; \quad \frac{x_1}{r_1} = \frac{x_2}{r_2}; \quad \frac{y_1}{x_1} = \frac{y_2}{x_2}, \quad \text{and so forth.}$$

For any acute angle in standard position the coordinates x and y of the point P (Figure 4-9) are also the lengths of $\overline{OQ}$ and $\overline{QP}$. Whenever P is not on a coordinate axis, the lengths of two sides of triangle OPQ are the absolute values of the coordinates of P. For any acute angle we have seen that the six trigonometric functions may be defined in terms of r and the coordinates of P. We now extend these definitions so that they apply for any angle for which the ratios are defined. In this way we define the circular functions of a general angle θ. Notice in Figure 4-9 that whenever P is not on an axis, a right triangle OPQ is formed. The acute angle POQ of this triangle is called the **reference angle** of the angle θ. Angles for which P is on a coordinate axis are considered in § 4-4.

The definitions of the circular functions are based upon trigonometric functions and thus upon angles. However, the use of angles is merely a custom and a convenience. The functions may be defined for all arcs of

§ 4-3 CIRCULAR FUNCTIONS

a unit circle and thus for all real numbers. In this sense we write, for example, "sin 30°" to mean "the sine of a number associated with an angle of 30°, that is, $\sin \frac{\pi}{6}$." (See § 3-5.)

The functions of angles greater than 90° can be expressed in terms of the ratios for their reference angles. Thus we may use the 30°-60°-90° and 45°-45°-90° triangles from §§ 4-1 and 4-2 to find functions of angles such as 120°, 135°, 150°, 240°, and 315°.

Example. Find the six circular functions of 150°.

The reference angle is 30° since $150° + 30° = 180°$. Take $\overline{OP} = 2$. Then $\overline{PQ} = 1$ and $\overline{OQ} = \sqrt{3}$ as in § 4-1. The x-coordinate of P is $-\sqrt{3}$; the y-coordinate is 1. Notice that the functions are expressed in terms of coordinates and r. Remember that in the reference triangle OPQ the hypotenuse is r, $r = \sqrt{x^2 + y^2}$ for any $P: (x, y)$, and r is always positive. Thus

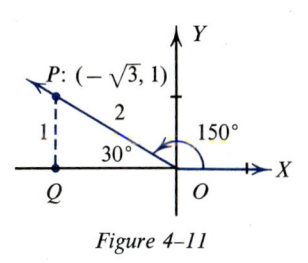

Figure 4-11

$$\sin 150° = \frac{y}{r} = \frac{1}{2}; \qquad \csc 150° = \frac{r}{y} = 2;$$

$$\cos 150° = \frac{x}{r} = \frac{-\sqrt{3}}{2}; \qquad \sec 150° = \frac{r}{x} = \frac{2}{-\sqrt{3}} = -\frac{2\sqrt{3}}{3};$$

$$\tan 150° = \frac{y}{x} = \frac{1}{-\sqrt{3}} = -\frac{\sqrt{3}}{3}; \qquad \cot 150° = \frac{x}{y} = -\sqrt{3}.$$

Each function of an angle XOP may be expressed in terms of x, y, and r where $\overline{OP} = r$ and the coordinates of P are (x, y). Since r is always positive, the sign of the function depends upon the signs of x and y; that is, upon the quadrant in which P is located. Many people use the array in Figure 4-12 to help them remember the signs of the functions. In the array "A" shows that all trigonometric functions are positive when P is in the first quadrant; "S" shows that the sine is positive in the second quadrant; "T" shows that the tangent is positive in the third quadrant; "C" shows that the cosine is positive in the fourth quadrant. In the second quadrant sine and cosecant are positive; all others are negative. In the third quadrant tangent and cotangent are positive; all others are negative. In the fourth quadrant cosine and secant are positive; all others are negative.

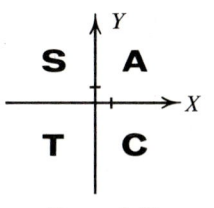

Figure 4-12

CIRCULAR FUNCTIONS AND THEIR GRAPHS

TEST YOURSELF

1. Find the six circular functions of 135°.
2. Use the results obtained in Exercise 1 to prove that (a) sin 135° = sin 45°; (b) cos 135° = −cos 45°.

EXERCISES

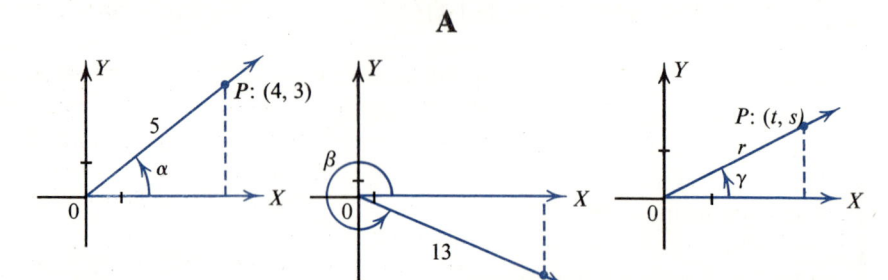

A

Use the given figures and find the six circular functions of each angle:

1. α.   **2.** β.   **3.** γ.

In Exercises 4 through 15 make a drawing for each angle as in the Example for this section. Then for each angle find the six circular functions. Give each value to the nearest thousandth.

4. 30°.　　**6.** 60°.　　**8.** 135°.　　**10.** 225°.
5. 45°.　　**7.** 120°.　　**9.** 210°.　　**11.** 240°.

• • •

12. 300°.　　**13.** 315°.　　**14.** 330°.　　• **15.** 390°.

16. Compare the values of each function: (a) of 30° and 150°; (b) of 45° and 135°; (c) of 60° and 120°.

17. Compare the values of each function: (a) of 30° and 210°; (b) of 45° and 225°; (c) of 60° and 240°; (d) of 120° and 300°.

18. Use the general definitions of circular functions and prove:

(a) $\csc \phi = \dfrac{1}{\sin \phi}$;　(b) $\sec \phi = \dfrac{1}{\cos \phi}$;　(c) $\cot \phi = \dfrac{1}{\tan \phi}$.

• **19.** See the given figure and prove:

(a) $\cos \theta = \sin (90° + \theta)$;
(b) $\sec \theta = \csc (90° + \theta)$;
(c) $\cot \theta = -\tan (90° + \theta)$.

156

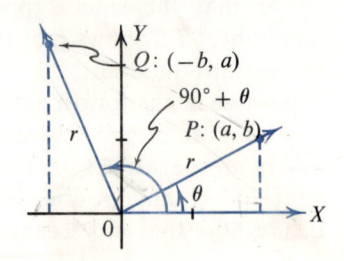

§ 4-3 CIRCULAR FUNCTIONS

B

Consider angles in standard position with $P: (x, y)$ on the terminal side. Consider the six circular functions and list those which are always positive when P is in the given quadrant.

1. I.   **2.** II.   **3.** III.   **4.** IV.

5 through 8. Repeat Exercises 1 through 4 listing the functions which are always negative when P is in the given quadrant.

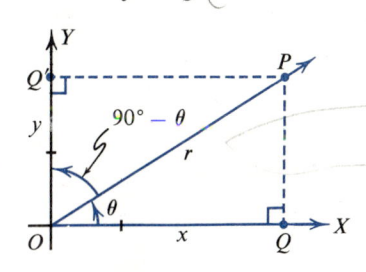

9. Use triangle QOP in the given figure and express each of the six circular functions of θ in terms of x, y, and r. Then use triangle $Q'OP$ and express each of the six functions of $(90° - \theta)$ in terms of x, y, and r.

10. Draw an acute angle θ in standard position with $\tan \theta = \frac{3}{4}$. Give the value of each of the other five circular functions.

11. Draw an obtuse angle (that is, take P in the second quadrant) in standard position with $\sin \theta = \frac{1}{2}$. Give the value of each of the other five circular functions.

• • •

Draw a figure in each case; find a set of values for x, y, and r. Make a table showing the values of the six circular functions of each angle θ with P in the quadrant specified.

12. $\cos \theta = \frac{1}{2}$, I.

13. $\tan \theta = 1$, III.

14. $\cot \theta = -1$, II.

15. $\sin \theta = -\frac{1}{2}$, IV.

16. $\sec \theta = 2$, IV.

17. $\csc \theta = \frac{2}{\sqrt{3}}$, II.

18. $\tan \theta = \frac{5}{12}$, I.

• **19.** $\tan \theta = -3$, II.

• **20.** An angle of 405° is shown in the figure. Find the values of the six circular functions of 405°.

• **21.** As in Exercise 20 draw a figure and find the six circular functions of 420°.

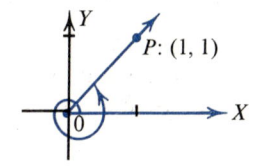

CIRCULAR FUNCTIONS AND THEIR GRAPHS

• 22 through 29. Explain why it was necessary to know the quadrant in Exercises 12 through 19.
• 30. Describe the range of possible values of each of the six circular functions.

§ 4–4 Quadrantal and negative angles

The six circular functions were defined in § 4–3 for any angle XOP in standard position where P is not on a coordinate axis. If P is on an axis, the angle is called a **quadrantal angle**. Thus $0°$, $90°$, $180°$, $270°$, $360°$, $450°$, and so forth are quadrantal angles. The definitions of the circular functions for quadrantal angles are the same as for other angles (§ 4–3) whenever the ratios have meaning. Since division by zero is not allowed, we say that a function is **undefined** whenever the ratio involves division by zero. In such cases the absolute values of the ratios for "nearby" angles are very large.

Example 1. Find the circular functions of $90°$.

> If $\theta = 90°$, then P has coordinates $(0, y)$ and Q coincides with the origin, O. Thus there is no triangle OQP; $x = 0$ and $y = r$. In any case r is always positive. We use the definitions for general angles:
>
> $\sin \theta = \dfrac{y}{r}$, so $\sin 90° = \dfrac{r}{r} = 1$.
>
> $\cos \theta = \dfrac{x}{r}$, so $\cos 90° = \dfrac{0}{r} = 0$.
>
> $\tan \theta = \dfrac{y}{x}$, $x = 0$; and $\tan 90°$ is undefined.
>
> $\cot \theta = \dfrac{x}{y}$, so $\cot 90° = \dfrac{0}{r} = 0$.
>
> $\sec \theta = \dfrac{r}{x}$, $x = 0$; and $\sec 90°$ is undefined.
>
> $\csc \theta = \dfrac{r}{y}$, so $\csc 90° = \dfrac{r}{r} = 1$.

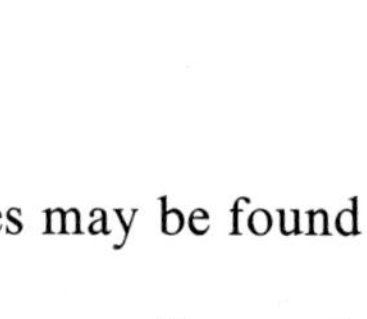

Figure 4–13

The circular functions of the other quadrantal angles may be found as in Example 1.

Any angle may be placed in standard position on a coordinate plane as angle XOP (§ 4–3). Each angle may be measured in terms of a rotation about O from the initial side $\overrightarrow{OX}$ to the terminal side $\overrightarrow{OP}$. If the rotation

§ 4-4 QUADRANTAL AND NEGATIVE ANGLES

is counterclockwise, the angle is a *positive angle*. In Figure 4–14 θ is a positive angle. If the rotation is clockwise, the angle is a **negative angle**. In Figure 4–14 ϕ is a negative angle.

Consider any positive angle θ with $P: (x, y)$ on its terminal side. Then, as in Figure 4–15, $P': (x, -y)$ is on the terminal side of the corresponding negative angle, $-\theta$. Check each of these statements using triangles POQ and $P'OQ$:

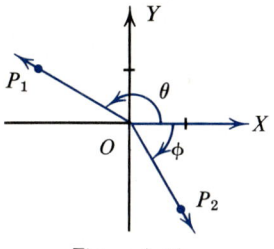

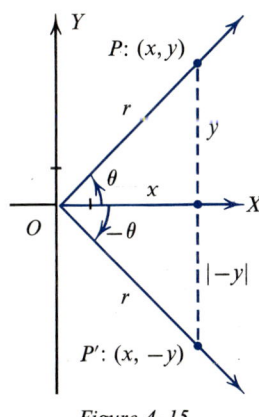

Figure 4–14

$$\sin(-\theta) = \frac{-y}{r} = -\frac{y}{r} = -\sin\theta;$$

$$\cos(-\theta) = \frac{x}{r} = \cos\theta;$$

$$\tan(-\theta) = \frac{-y}{x} = -\frac{y}{x} = -\tan\theta;$$

$$\cot(-\theta) = \frac{x}{-y} = -\frac{x}{y} = -\cot\theta;$$

$$\sec(-\theta) = \frac{r}{x} = \sec\theta;$$

$$\csc(-\theta) = \frac{r}{-y} = -\frac{r}{y} = -\csc\theta.$$

Figure 4–15

Each of these *formulas for functions of negative angles* is true for any angle θ for which the circular function is defined. Thus any circular function of a negative angle may be expressed in terms of that function of a positive angle.

Example 2. Find the six circular functions of $-30°$.

Draw a figure using $P: (\sqrt{3}, -1)$. Then $r = \overline{OP} = 2$; $x = \sqrt{3}, y = -1$, and

Figure 4–16

$$\sin(-30°) = \frac{-1}{2} = -\frac{1}{2}; \qquad \csc(-30°) = \frac{2}{-1} = -2;$$

$$\cos(-30°) = \frac{\sqrt{3}}{2}; \qquad \sec(-30°) = \frac{2}{\sqrt{3}} = \frac{2\sqrt{3}}{3};$$

$$\tan(-30°) = \frac{-1}{\sqrt{3}} = -\frac{\sqrt{3}}{3}; \qquad \cot(-30°) = \frac{\sqrt{3}}{-1} = -\sqrt{3}.$$

CIRCULAR FUNCTIONS AND THEIR GRAPHS

Example 2 may also be solved using the formulas for functions of negative angles and the values of the functions of 30° (§ 4-1):

$$\sin(-30°) = -\sin 30° = -\frac{1}{2}; \qquad \csc(-30°) = -\csc 30° = -2;$$

$$\cos(-30°) = \cos 30° = \frac{\sqrt{3}}{2}; \qquad \sec(-30°) = \sec 30° = \frac{2\sqrt{3}}{3};$$

$$\tan(-30°) = -\tan 30° = -\frac{\sqrt{3}}{3}; \qquad \cot(-30°) = -\cot 30° = -\sqrt{3}.$$

Given any angle θ in standard position on a coordinate plane, we have defined the six circular functions of θ. In § 4-3 we noticed that the ratios were the same for any two points P on the terminal side of the angle. We defined the distance $\overline{OP}$ as positive. Since division by r is required in two of the ratios, it is convenient to pick $r = 1$. That is, we pick P on the circle with radius 1 and center at the origin.

Note that if $r = 1$, $\sin \theta = \frac{y}{1} = y$ and $\cos \theta = \frac{x}{1} = x$. Then each $P: (x, y)$ has coordinates $(\cos \theta, \sin \theta)$ and may be called P_θ. In Figure 4-17 the points on the unit circle are labeled by the number of degrees of the angle in standard position with terminal side through P. The coordinates of $P_{30°}$ are $(\cos 30°, \sin 30°)$, that is, $\left(\frac{\sqrt{3}}{2}, \frac{1}{2}\right)$. The coordinates of $P_{45°}$ are $(\cos 45°, \sin 45°)$, that is, $\left(\frac{\sqrt{2}}{2}, \frac{\sqrt{2}}{2}\right)$; and so forth.

Each point P_θ on the *circle of radius 1 and center at the origin* has x-coordinate $\cos \theta$ and y-coordinate $\sin \theta$. For this reason the ratios for general angles are called *circular functions*. That is, these functions may be defined in terms of the points on the circle without any reference to angles.

For each point P on the unit circle there is an angle θ equal to angle XOP in standard position.

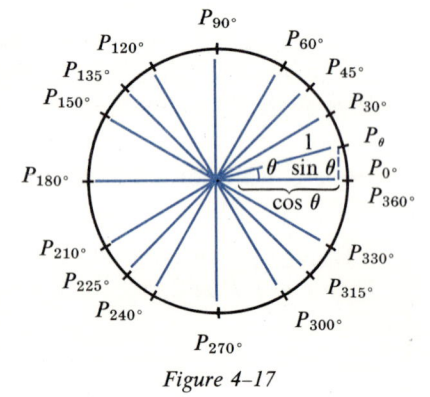

Figure 4-17

We see that the value of $\cos \theta$ is the x-coordinate of P. The value of $\sin \theta$ is the y-coordinate of P. If we plot the values of $\sin \theta$ relative to θ as in Figure 4-18, we have a graph of $y = \sin x$ where $0° \le x \le 360°$. Then we can estimate values of $\sin \theta$ either from the circle or from the graph.

§ 4-4 QUADRANTAL AND NEGATIVE ANGLES

Figure 4–18

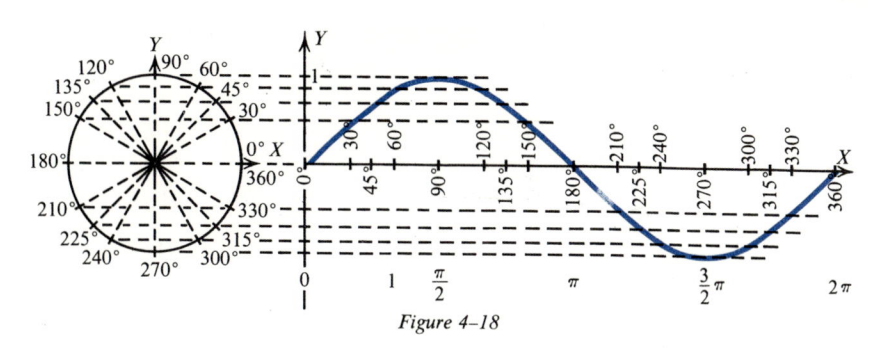

This graph should be the same as the one you obtain in A Exercise 15, using a table of values. Notice that for each value of θ, $|\sin \theta| \leq 1$. You should expect this since $\sin \theta = \dfrac{y}{r}$ and $|y| \leq r$.

TEST YOURSELF

1. For 180° take P at $(-1, 0)$; then $\overline{PQ} = 0$. Find, or identify as undefined, each of the six circular functions of 180°.

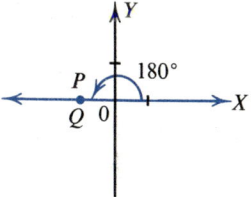

2. Take P: $(1, 1)$ on the terminal side of an angle of 45° in standard position. Take P': $(1, -1)$ on the terminal side of an angle of $-45°$. **(a)** Find the value of each of the six circular functions of 45° and of $-45°$. **(b)** For each function give an equation stating that function of $-45°$ in terms of that function of 45°.

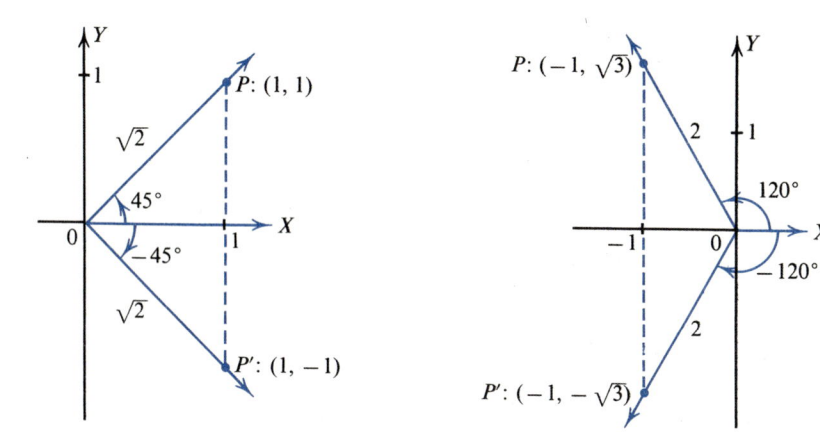

3. Use P: $(-1, \sqrt{3})$ and P': $(-1, -\sqrt{3})$ for angles of 120° and $-120°$. Then repeat Exercise 2 for these angles.

161

CIRCULAR FUNCTIONS AND THEIR GRAPHS

EXERCISES

A

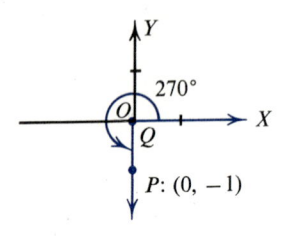

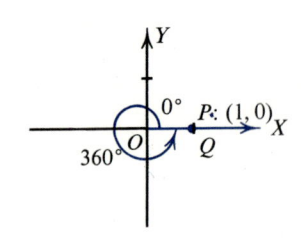

1. For 270° take P at $(0, -1)$; then $\overline{OQ} = 0$. Find, or identify as undefined, each of the six circular functions of 270°.

2. For 360° take P at $(1, 0)$; then $\overline{PQ} = 0$. Find, or identify as undefined, each of the six circular functions of 360°.

3. Repeat Exercise 2 for 0°.

• • •

List the circular functions that are undefined when θ has the given value:

4. 0°.   **5.** 90°.   **6.** 180°.   **7.** 270°.   **8.** 360°.

9. An angle of 450° is shown in the figure. Find the values for the circular functions that are defined for 450°.

10. Use the values obtained in Exercise 9 and show that $\sin^2 450° + \cos^2 450° = 1$.

• **11.** As in Exercise 9, make a drawing and find the values of the functions that are defined for 540°.
• **12.** Repeat Exercise 11 for 630°.
• **13.** Repeat Exercise 11 for 810°.
• **14.** Make a table of the values for $\sin \theta$ for θ equal 0°, 30°, 45°, 60°, 90°, 120°, 135°, 150°, 180°, 210°, 225°, 240°, 270°, 300°, 315°, 330°, and 360°.
• **15.** Use the table of values obtained in Exercise 14 and make a smooth curve as a graph of $y = \sin x$ where the values of θ are used for x. Make your graph for $0° \leq x \leq 360°$ and make 180° on your x-scale correspond to about 3.1 on your y-scale.
• **16 and 17.** Repeat Exercises 14 and 15 for $\cos \theta$ and $y = \cos x$.

§ 4–5 LINE VALUES OF CIRCULAR FUNCTIONS

B

Pick a point P, draw a figure, and find the values of the circular functions that are defined for each value of θ when θ is:
1. $-60°$.
2. $-90°$.
3. $-135°$.
4. $-150°$.
5. $-180°$.
6. $-210°$.
7. $-270°$.
8. $-315°$.
9. $-360°$.
10. $-390°$.

§ 4–5 Line values of circular functions

We have seen that the six trigonometric ratios are often called *circular functions* because of their dependence, in general cases, upon a circle. This section is concerned with the dependence of the circular functions upon a unit circle. We use a unit circle on a coordinate plane to find line segments equal in length to the magnitude of each function. We also use the position of each line segment on the coordinate plane to tell us the sign of the function. In other words we find **line values** of the circular functions.

Consider a point $P: (x, y)$ on the terminal side of an angle θ in standard position. If the point P is also on the unit circle with center at the origin, its coordinates may be expressed as $(\cos \theta, \sin \theta)$, that is, $x = \cos \theta$ and $y = \sin \theta$ as in § 4–4. Next consider any acute angle QOP in standard position with Q at $(1, 0)$ and P on the unit circle as in Figure 4–19. Construct the line segment PT perpendicular to the x-axis, where T is on the x-axis. Then, as in § 4–4,

$$\sin \theta = \frac{\overline{PT}}{\overline{OP}} = \frac{\overline{PT}}{1} = \overline{PT}, \text{ and}$$

$$\cos \theta = \frac{\overline{OT}}{\overline{OP}} = \frac{\overline{OT}}{1} = \overline{OT}.$$

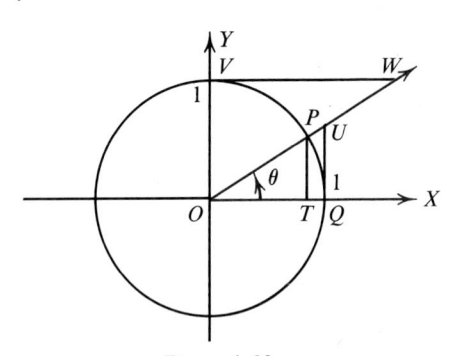

Figure 4–19

The bars are used, as in $\overline{PT}$, to show that lengths of line segments are under consideration.

Construct the line segment QU perpendicular to the x-axis at $Q: (1, 0)$ where U is on the line OP. Then $\angle OPT = \angle OUQ$ and

$$\tan \theta = \frac{\overline{PT}}{\overline{OT}} = \cot OPT = \cot OUQ = \frac{\overline{UQ}}{\overline{OQ}} = \frac{\overline{UQ}}{1} = \overline{UQ}. \text{ Also}$$

$$\sec \theta = \frac{\overline{OU}}{\overline{OQ}} = \frac{\overline{OU}}{1} = \overline{OU}.$$

163

CIRCULAR FUNCTIONS AND THEIR GRAPHS

Let V be the point $(0, 1)$. Construct the line segment VW perpendicular to the y-axis where W is on the line OP. Then $\angle \theta = \angle OWV$ and

$$\cot \theta = \cot OWV = \frac{\overline{VW}}{\overline{OV}} = \frac{\overline{VW}}{1} = \overline{VW}. \text{ Also}$$

$$\csc \theta = \csc OWV = \frac{\overline{OW}}{\overline{OV}} = \frac{\overline{OW}}{1} = \overline{OW}.$$

The line value of each of the circular functions of the acute angle θ may now be identified from the graph as in Figure 4–20:

$\sin \theta = \overline{PT}$;
$\cos \theta = \overline{OT}$,
$\tan \theta = \overline{QU}$;
$\cot \theta = \overline{VW}$;
$\sec \theta = \overline{OU}$;
$\csc \theta = \overline{OW}$.

Figure 4–20

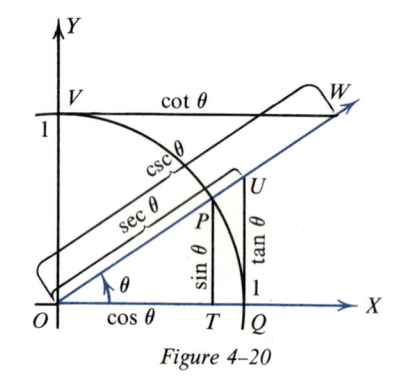

Notice that when angle θ is acute, all circular functions are positive and only the lengths of the line segments need to be considered. For a general angle θ the point $P: (x, y)$ may lie in any quadrant but the method of constructing the line values is precisely as before with the same points

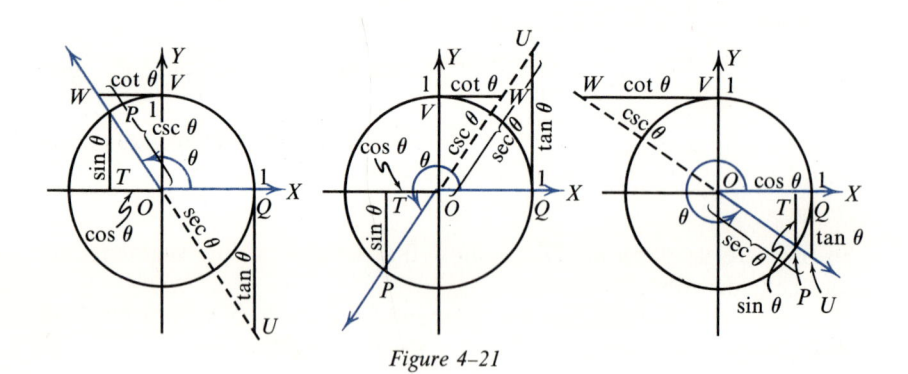

Figure 4–21

$Q: (1, 0)$ and $V: (0, 1)$. Furthermore, the coordinates of the points P, T, U, and W which are used to find the lengths of the line segments representing $\sin \theta$, $\cos \theta$, $\tan \theta$, and $\cot \theta$ also provide us with the appropriate signs

§ 4-5 LINE VALUES OF CIRCULAR FUNCTIONS

for these functions as shown in the array:

Circular function	Line value	Sign the same as
$\sin \theta$	$\overline{PT}$	y-coordinate of P
$\cos \theta$	$\overline{OT}$	x-coordinate of T
$\tan \theta$	$\overline{QU}$	y-coordinate of U
$\cot \theta$	$\overline{VW}$	x-coordinate of W

Finally, some basis is needed for selecting signs for $\overline{OU}$ and $\overline{OW}$; that is, for $\sec \theta$ and $\csc \theta$. Sec θ is positive when P is in the first or fourth quadrants, negative when P is in the second or third quadrants. Thus, we take $\overline{OU}$ as positive when U is on the ray OP and take $\overline{OU}$ as negative when U is not on the ray OP; that is, negative when U is on the extension of line PO through O. Similarly, the line value, $\overline{OW}$, of $\csc \theta$ is taken as positive when W is on the ray OP, negative when W is not on the ray OP.

TEST YOURSELF

Draw a unit circle using 2 inches as the unit for the radius and an angle of 120° in standard position:

1. Construct the line values for each of the six circular functions of 120°.

2. Use a ruler and your figure for Exercise 1 to estimate the values for the six functions of 120°.

3. Use the procedure for the construction for the line value for $\tan \theta$ to explain why $\tan 90°$ is undefined.

EXERCISES

Draw a unit circle using 2 inches as the unit radius:

1. Draw an angle of 210° in standard position and construct the line values for each of the six circular functions of this angle. Then use a ruler and estimate the values of the functions of 210°.

2. Repeat Exercise 1 for an angle of 315°.

CIRCULAR FUNCTIONS AND THEIR GRAPHS

• • •

Consider the procedure for the construction of the line values and identify the value or values of θ, $0° \leq \theta < 360°$, for which each statement is true:

3. $\sec \theta = 1$.
4. $\csc \theta = 1$.
5. $\sin \theta = \tan \theta$.
6. $\cos \theta = \cot \theta$.
7. $\sin \theta = \cos \theta$.
8. $\tan \theta = \cot \theta$.

Consider the procedure for the construction of the line values and give an intuitive argument to support each statement:

9. $|\sin \theta| \leq 1$.
10. $|\cos \theta| \leq 1$.
11. $|\sec \theta| \geq 1$.
12. $|\csc \theta| \geq 1$.
13. $|\sin \theta| \leq |\tan \theta|$.
14. $|\cos \theta| \leq |\cot \theta|$.
15. $|\csc \theta| > |\cot \theta|$.
16. $|\sec \theta| > |\tan \theta|$.
17. $\csc 270° = -1$.
• 18. $\cot 180°$ is undefined.
• 19. $\csc 180°$ is undefined.
• 20. $\sec 270°$ is undefined.

List the values of θ where $-360° \leq \theta \leq 720°$ for which the function is undefined:

• 21. $\sin \theta$.
• 22. $\cos \theta$.
• 23. $\tan \theta$.
• 24. $\cot \theta$.
• 25. $\sec \theta$.
• 26. $\csc \theta$.

§ 4–6 Graphs of sines and cosines

The line values of the functions of any angle θ in § 4–5 would be identical with those for any angle $(\theta + k \times 360°)$ where k is any integer since the same point P and the same line segments would be used. For sines and cosines we have

$$\sin(\theta + k \times 360°) = \sin \theta, \quad \cos(\theta + k \times 360°) = \cos \theta.$$

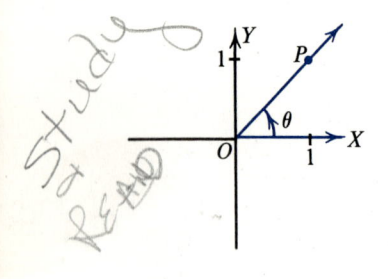

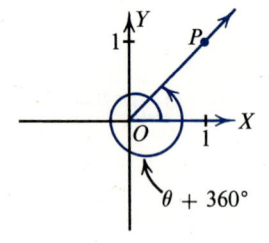

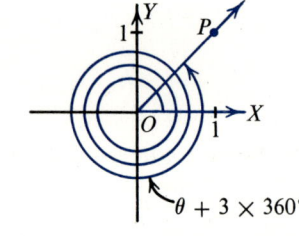

Figure 4–22

Formally, we say that $\sin x$ and $\cos x$ are **periodic functions** with period

§ 4-6 GRAPHS OF SINES AND COSINES

360°. In other words, their values for $x = \theta$ are the same as those for $(\theta + k \times 360°)$ for any value of θ and any integer k; that is, the values of sin x and cos x repeat themselves every 360°.

The period of sin x is 360°, that is, 2π, since 2π is the smallest positive number such that $\sin x = \sin (x + 2\pi)$ for all values of x. Similarly, the period of cos x is 2π since $\cos x = \cos (x + 2\pi)$ for all values of x and no positive number smaller than 2π will produce the desired equality. In general, the **period** of a periodic function $f(x)$ is the smallest positive number p such that $f(x) = f(x + p)$ for all values of x.

The graph of $y = \sin x$ for $0° \leq x \leq 360°$ was obtained in § 4–4 from the line values of sin x. The same graph is obtained when x is measured in radians, or any other unit of angular measure (Figure 4–23).

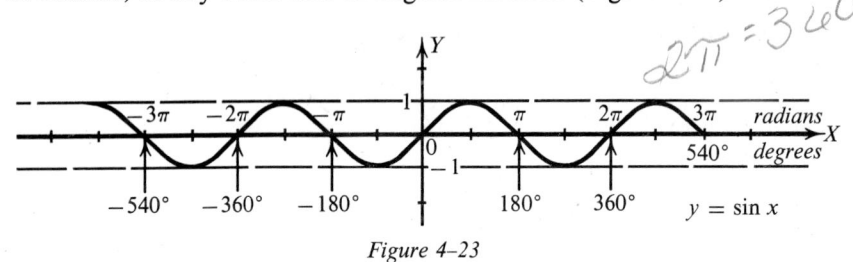

Figure 4-23

The graph of $y = \cos x$ may also be obtained from the line values. However, as shown in the sequence of figures, one easy way to find the graph of $y = \cos x$ is from the formula $\cos x = \sin (90° + x)$ from § 4-3, A Exercise 19; that is, by moving the x-scale and y-axis 90° to the right

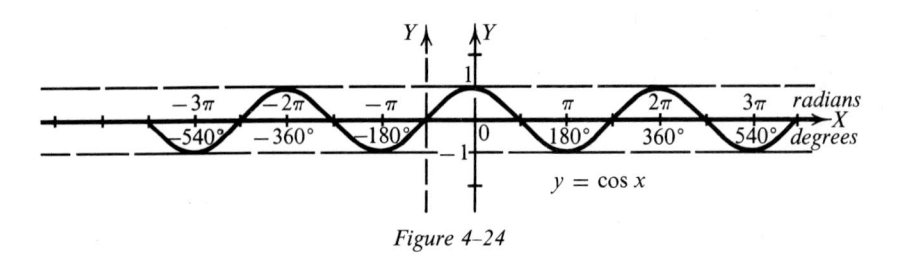

Figure 4-24

relative to the graph of $y = \sin x$. Note that the result obtained by leaving the curve fixed and moving the x-scale and y-axis 90° to the right is precisely the same as the result obtained by leaving the x-scale and y-axis fixed and moving the curve 90° to the left. Usually we think of moving the curve, but in trigonometry it is often easier to think of moving the axes. The graph of any equation of the form $y = \sin (x + b)$ for a given real number b may be obtained by moving the x-scale and the y-axis b units to the right. The two graphs are said to be different in **phase**. The graphs

CIRCULAR FUNCTIONS AND THEIR GRAPHS

of $y = \sin x$ and $y = \cos x$ differ in phase by 90° since $\cos x = \sin(x + 90°)$. The graphs of $y = \sin x$ and $y = \sin(x + b)$ differ in phase by b units. The graphs of $y = \cos x$ and $y = \cos(x + 30°)$ differ in phase by 30°.

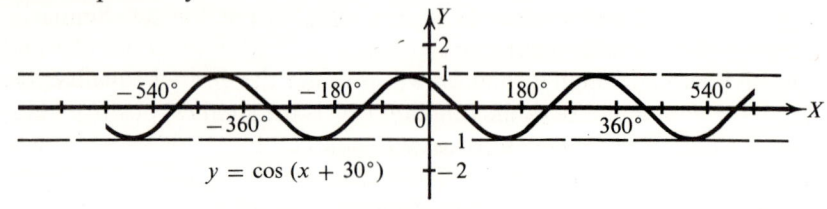

Figure 4–25

We need to establish a reasonable basis for a comparison between the scalar units on the x-axis and those on the y-axis. Each unit on the y-axis stands for a linear measure of one unit, the radius of the unit circle. In order to obtain a corresponding scale on the x-axis we note that 360° corresponds to 2π radians and that 2π is then the measure of the circumference in linear units equal to the radius. In order to compare distances along the x- and y-axes and thus to obtain the graphs in the proper shape, we take 1 unit on the y-axis equal to 1 radian on the x-axis. Accordingly, we take the length of π radians, that is 180°, on the x-axis approximately equal to three units on the y-axis. Then since most students in elementary trigonometry feel more at ease with angles measured in degrees than with angles measured in radians, we usually label the x-axis in degrees.

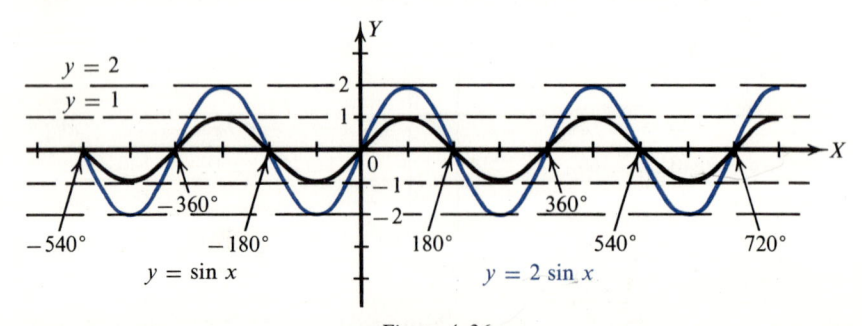

Figure 4–26

The graphs of equations of the form $y = k \sin x$ and $y = k \cos x$ may be obtained by multiplying the y-coordinates of the points on the graphs of $y = \sin x$ and $y = \cos x$ by k. For example, to graph $y = 2 \sin x$ we use broken lines $y = 2$ and $y = -2$ as guidelines as in Figure 4–26. Then for any given value of x the graph of $y = 2 \sin x$ is twice as far from the x-axis as the graph of $y = \sin x$.

§ 4-6 GRAPHS OF SINES AND COSINES

The graph of $y = \sin x$ is said to have *amplitude* 1 since the graph oscillates between -1 and 1. The graph of $y = 3 + \sin x$ oscillates between $3 - 1$ and $3 + 1$, that is, between 2 and 4; it also has amplitude 1. The graph of $y = 5 \sin x$ oscillates between -5 and 5; it has amplitude 5. In general, any bounded periodic function has half of the difference between those bounds as its **amplitude**.

Throughout this book the instruction "sketch the graph" is intended to imply that the student should present a freehand drawing of the graph with the appropriate shape and position but without plotting more than a few selected points precisely. It is assumed that precise plotting of points and graphing can be done whenever specifically requested for a particular portion of a graph. The steps involved in a precise plotting of points for the graph of an equation involving circular functions are shown in the example.

Example. Graph: $y = 3 \sin (x + 60°)$.

x	$x + 60°$	Form of $\sin (x + 60°)$	Value of $\sin (x + 60°)$	y, that is, $3 \sin (x + 60°)$
$-240°$	$-180°$	$\sin 0°$	0	0
$-210°$	$-150°$	$-\sin 30°$	-0.50	-1.50
$-195°$	$-135°$	$-\sin 45°$	-0.71	-2.13
$-180°$	$-120°$	$-\sin 60°$	-0.87	-2.61
$-150°$	$-90°$	$-\sin 90°$	-1.00	-3.00
$-120°$	$-60°$	$-\sin 60°$	-0.87	-2.61
$-105°$	$-45°$	$-\sin 45°$	-0.71	-2.13
$-90°$	$-30°$	$-\sin 30°$	-0.50	-1.50
$-60°$	$0°$	$\sin 0°$	0	0
$-30°$	$30°$	$\sin 30°$	0.50	1.50
$-15°$	$45°$	$\sin 45°$	0.71	2.13
$0°$	$60°$	$\sin 60°$	0.87	2.61
$30°$	$90°$	$\sin 90°$	1.00	3.00
$60°$	$120°$	$\sin 60°$	0.87	2.61
$75°$	$135°$	$\sin 45°$	0.71	2.13
$90°$	$150°$	$\sin 30°$	0.50	1.50
$120°$	$180°$	$\sin 0°$	0	0

CIRCULAR FUNCTIONS AND THEIR GRAPHS

Notice that the values for x have been selected so that $(x + 60°)$ will have related angles of $0°$, $30°$, $45°$, $60°$, or $90°$ for which the values of the sine are familiar to us from our knowledge of $30°$-$60°$-$90°$ triangles, $45°$-$45°$-$90°$ triangles, and quadrantal angles of $0°$ and $90°$. In this way we may plot a reasonably accurate curve without using a standard table of values of circular functions (§ 5–2). However, when a standard table of values is available, this kind of foresight in selecting values for x is not necessary. Also, additional points on the curve may be found when a standard table of values is used.

The values given in the table for $y = 3 \sin(x + 60°)$ range over the interval $-240°$ to $120°$ and thus cover one complete period, $360°$, of the graph. We may use the fact that $\sin \theta = \sin(\theta + k \times 360°)$ for any integer k to extend our graph as far as we wish. In such cases we usually do the computations mentally and do not extend the table.

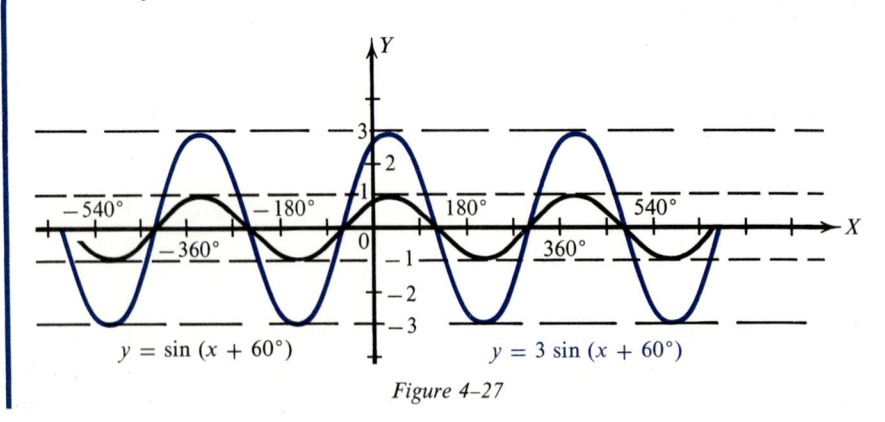

Figure 4–27

TEST YOURSELF

1. Sketch the graph of $y = 3 \sin x$ for $-360° \leq x \leq 720°$.

2. Use the graph in Exercise 1 to obtain a graph of $y = 3 \cos x$.

3. Sketch the graph of $y = \sin(x - 45°)$ for $-360° \leq x \leq 720°$.

EXERCISES

Sketch the graph for $-360° \leq x \leq 720°$:

1. $y = 2 \sin x$.
2. $y = 2 \cos x$.
3. $y = 4 \sin x$.
4. $y = 4 \cos x$.

§ 4-7 GRAPHS OF TANGENTS AND COTANGENTS

• • •

5. $y = -\sin x$.
6. $y = -\cos x$.
7. $y = -2 \sin x$.
8. $y = -2 \cos x$.
9. $y = \sin (x + 45°)$.
10. $y = \sin (x - 90°)$.
11. $y = \sin (x + 180°)$.
12. $y = \sin (x - 180°)$.
13. $y = \cos (x + 90°)$.

14. $y = 2 \cos (x - 90°)$.
15. $y = 2 \cos (x + 180°)$.
16. $y = 2 \sin (90° - x)$.
17. $y = -3 \cos (180° - x)$.
18. $y = -2 \sin (270° - x)$.
19. $y = \sin 2x$.
20. $y = 3 \sin 2x$.
21. $y = \sin \frac{x}{2}$.
22. $y = \sin \frac{x}{3}$.

Give **(a)** *the period and* **(b)** *the amplitude of the function indicated:*

23. Exercise 8.   25. Exercise 12.   27. Exercise 21.
24. Exercise 9.   26. Exercise 20.   28. Exercise 22.

§ 4-7 Graphs of tangents and cotangents

The graph (Figure 4-28) of $y = \tan x$ may be obtained either using line values (§ 4-6) or reference angles (§ 4-3) for which the values of the tangent are known from § 4-1.

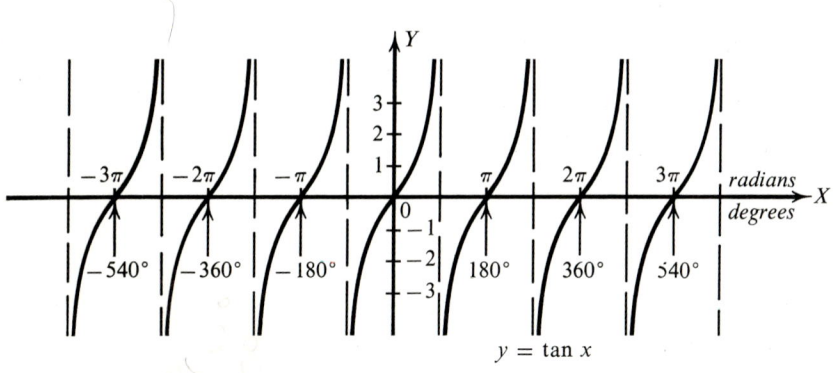

Figure 4-28

171

CIRCULAR FUNCTIONS AND THEIR GRAPHS

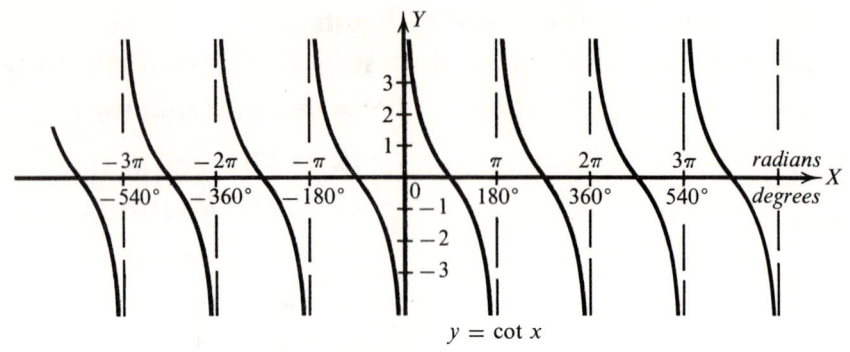

Figure 4-29

y = cot *x*

The graph (Figure 4-29) of $y = \cot x$ may be obtained directly or from the graph of $y = \tan x$ using the formula $\cot \theta = -\tan(90° + \theta)$ from § 4-3, A Exercise 19. The graphs of equations of the form $y = k \tan x$, $y = \tan(x + k)$, $y = k \cot x$, and $y = \cot(x + k)$ for real numbers $k \neq 0$ may be obtained as in § 4-6 for sin *x* and cos *x*. Notice that tan *x* and cot *x* do not have amplitudes since their values are not bounded. However, tan *x* and cot *x* are each periodic with period 180°.

TEST YOURSELF

Sketch the graph for $-360° \leq x \leq 720°$:

1. $y = 3 \cot x$. **2.** $y = -3 \cot x$. **3.** $y = \tan(x + 45°)$.

EXERCISES

Sketch the graph for $-360° \leq x \leq 720°$:

1. $y = 2 \tan x$.
2. $y = -2 \tan x$.
3. $y = 4 \cot x$.
4. $y = -4 \cot x$.
5. $y = \tan(x + 90°)$.
6. $y = \cot(x - 90°)$.

• • •

7. $y = \tan 2x$.
8. $y = \cot 2x$.
9. $y = 2 \tan 3x$.
10. $y = -2 \cot 3x$.
11. $y = \tan \frac{x}{2}$.
12. $y = \tan \frac{x}{3}$.

Give the period of the function indicated:

13. Exercise 3.
14. Exercise 5.
15. Exercise 8.
16. Exercise 9.
17. Exercise 11.
18. Exercise 12.

§ 4-8 Graphs of secants and cosecants

The graphs of $y = \sec x$ (Figure 4-30) and $y = \csc x$ (Figure 4-31) may be obtained using either line values (§ 4-5) or the formulas $\sec x = \dfrac{1}{\cos x}$, $\csc x = \dfrac{1}{\sin x}$ from § 4-3, A Exercise 18, and known values for $\sin x$ and $\cos x$.

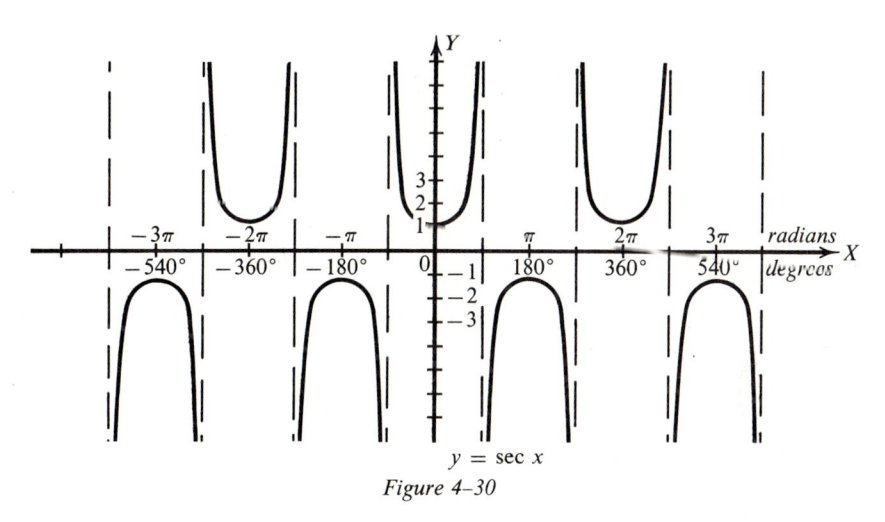

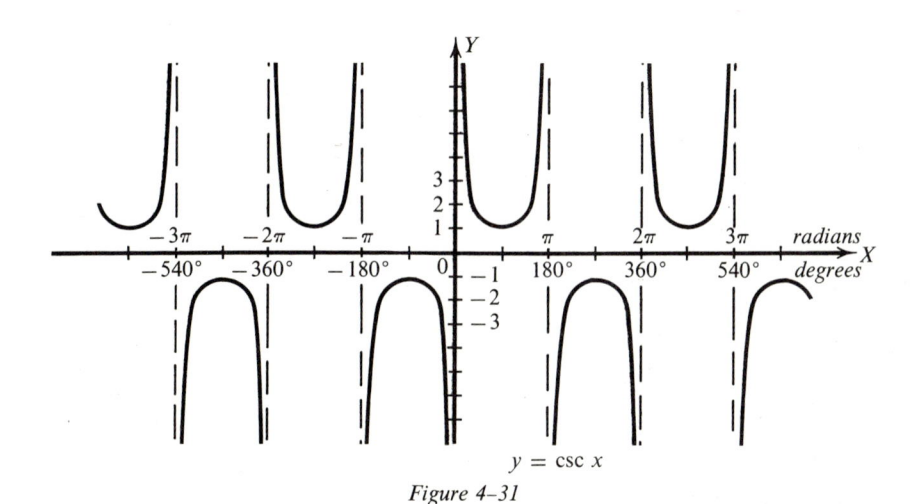

$y = \sec x$
Figure 4-30

$y = \csc x$
Figure 4-31

CIRCULAR FUNCTIONS AND THEIR GRAPHS

The graph of $y = \sec x$ may be obtained from that of $y = \csc x$ by a change of phase since $\sec x = \csc(x + 90°)$ from § 4-3, A Exercise 19. The graphs of equations of the form $y = k \sec x$, $y = k \csc x$, $y = \sec(x + k)$, and $y = \csc(x + k)$ for real numbers $k \neq 0$ may be obtained as in § 4-6 and § 4-7. Notice that $\sec x$ and $\csc x$ do not have amplitudes since their values, like those of $\tan x$ and $\cot x$, are not bounded. However, $\sec x$ and $\csc x$ are each periodic with period 360°, that is, 2π.

TEST YOURSELF

Sketch the graph for $-360° \leq x \leq 720°$:

1. $y = 3 \sec x$.
2. $y = \csc(x + 90°)$.

EXERCISES

Sketch the graph for $-360° \leq x \leq 720°$:

1. $y = 2 \sec x$.
2. $y = -2 \sec x$.
3. $y = 2 \csc x$.
4. $y = -3 \csc x$.
5. $y = \sec(x + 90°)$.
6. $y = \csc(x - 90°)$.

• • •

7. $y = \sec 2x$.
8. $y = \csc 2x$.
9. $y = 2 \sec 3x$.
10. $y = -2 \csc 3x$.
11. $y = \sec \dfrac{x}{2}$.
12. $y = \csc \dfrac{x}{3}$.

Give the period of the function indicated:

13. Exercise 2.
14. Exercise 6.
15. Exercise 8.
16. Exercise 10.
17. Exercise 11.
18. Exercise 12.

• **19.** Find the period of the function $y = \csc(kx + \theta)$ for any given constants k and θ. Find the difference in phase between this function and $y = \csc kx$.

§ 4-9 Special methods of graphing

The graph of an equation of the form $y = k \sin x$ may be obtained from the graph of $y = \sin x$ as in § 4-6. This method for using the graph of $y = f(x)$ to obtain the graph of $y = kf(x)$ for a real number k was also considered in §§ 4-7 and 4-8. In this section we consider sums and differences as well as products.

§ 4–9 SPECIAL METHODS OF GRAPHING

The y-coordinate of a point is sometimes called its ordinate. The method of graphing an equation such as $y = 3 + \sin x$ (Example 1) by adding the corresponding ordinates of the points on the graphs of $y = 3$ and $y = \sin x$ is called **graphing by composition of ordinates,** or simply *graphing by composition.*

Example 1. Graph by composition: $y = 3 + \sin x$.

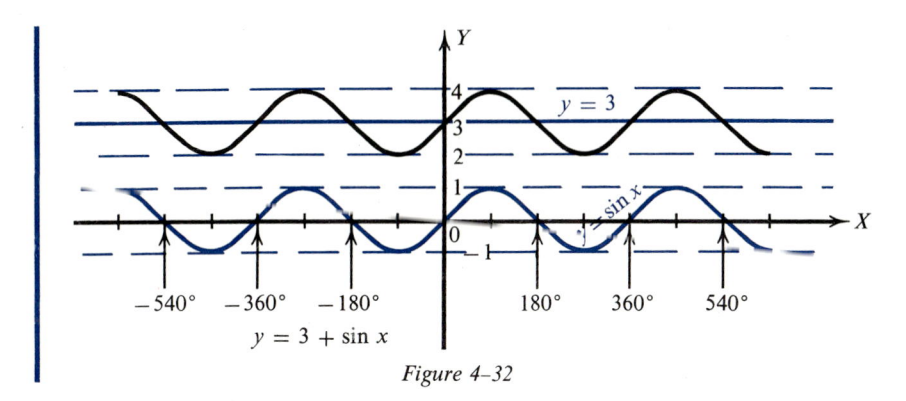

Figure 4–32

Graphs of functions such as $y = x \sin x$ may also be sketched after considering the graphs of the equations obtained when y is set equal to each factor. In this case special attention is given to the values of x for which each of the factors is zero. This method should not be confused with graphing by composition.

Example 2. Sketch the graph of $y = x \sin x$.

The graph of $y = x \sin x$ may be sketched quite effectively using only our knowledge of the graphs of $y = \sin x$ and $y = x$. Notice that when $x = -2\pi, -\pi, 0, \pi,$ or 2π, we have $\sin x = 0$ and therefore $x \sin x = 0$; when $x = -\frac{3\pi}{2}, \frac{\pi}{2},$ or $\frac{5\pi}{2}$, we have $\sin x = 1$ and $x \sin x = x$; when $x = -\frac{5\pi}{2}, -\frac{\pi}{2},$ or $\frac{3\pi}{2}$, we have $\sin x = -1$ and $x \sin x = -x$. Since $|\sin x| \leq 1$, it follows that $|x \sin x| \leq |x|$; and hence the lines $y = x$ and $y = -x$ are boundaries of the curve. Thus we may draw the guide lines $y = x$ and $y = -x$; plot the points $(-2\pi, 0), (-\pi, 0), (0, 0), (\pi, 0), (2\pi, 0), \left(-\frac{3\pi}{2}, -\frac{3\pi}{2}\right), \left(\frac{\pi}{2}, \frac{\pi}{2}\right),$ $\left(\frac{5\pi}{2}, \frac{5\pi}{2}\right), \left(-\frac{5\pi}{2}, \frac{5\pi}{2}\right), \left(-\frac{\pi}{2}, \frac{\pi}{2}\right),$ and $\left(\frac{3\pi}{2}, -\frac{3\pi}{2}\right)$; and sketch

175

CIRCULAR FUNCTIONS AND THEIR GRAPHS

the graph through these points. A table of values helps us draw the graph more precisely.

Degrees	\multicolumn{2}{c}{x}	sin x	y, that is, x sin x
	Radians	Use 3.14 for π		
0	0	0	0.00	0.0
30	$\frac{\pi}{6}$	0.52	0.50	0.3
45	$\frac{\pi}{4}$	0.79	0.71	0.6
60	$\frac{\pi}{3}$	1.05	0.87	0.9
90	$\frac{\pi}{2}$	1.57	1.00	1.6
120	$\frac{2\pi}{3}$	2.09	0.87	1.8
135	$\frac{3\pi}{4}$	2.36	0.71	1.7
150	$\frac{5\pi}{6}$	2.62	0.50	1.3
180	π	3.14	0.00	0.0
210	$\frac{7\pi}{6}$	3.67	−0.50	−1.8
225	$\frac{5\pi}{4}$	3.93	−0.71	−2.8
240	$\frac{4\pi}{3}$	4.19	−0.87	−3.6
270	$\frac{3\pi}{2}$	4.71	−1.00	−4.7
300	$\frac{5\pi}{3}$	5.24	−0.87	−4.6
315	$\frac{7\pi}{4}$	5.50	−0.71	−3.9
330	$\frac{11\pi}{6}$	5.76	−0.50	−2.9
360	2π	6.28	0.00	0.0
390	$\frac{13\pi}{6}$	6.81	0.50	3.4

Notice that for any value of x, sin (−x) = −sin x and x sin x = (−x) sin (−x). In other words, y has the same values for x as for −x

§ 4–9 SPECIAL METHODS OF GRAPHING

and we may use the same table of values of y for negative values of x as for positive values of x.

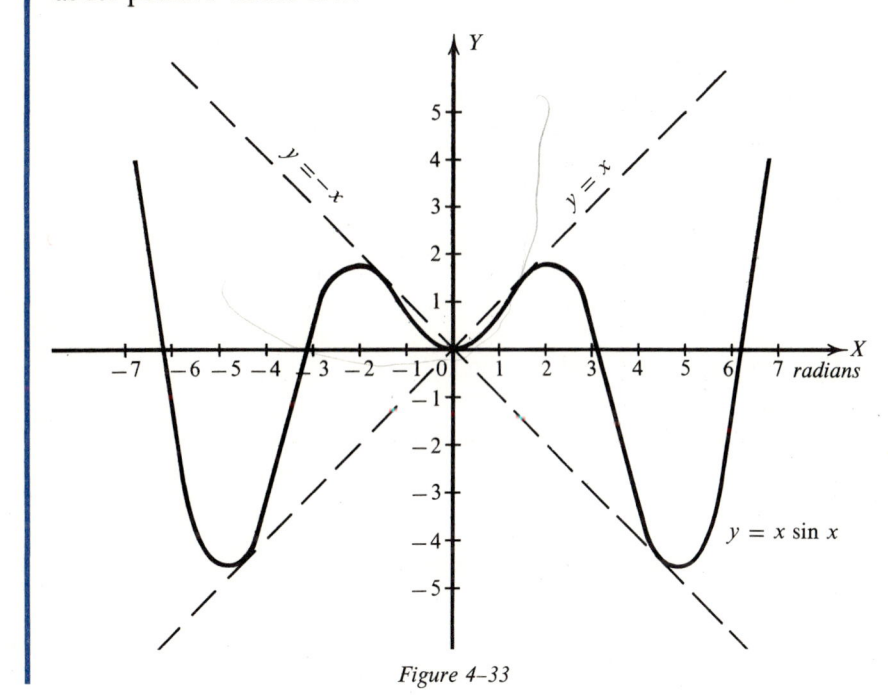

Figure 4–33

TEST YOURSELF

Sketch the graph for $-360° \leq x \leq 450°$:

1. $y = 2 - \sin x$.
2. $y = x + \sin x$.

EXERCISES

Sketch the graph for $-360° \leq x \leq 450°$:

1. $y = 2 + \sin x$.
2. $y = 3 - \sin x$.
3. $y = 2 - \cos x$.
4. $y = 1 + \tan x$.
5. $y = 1 + \csc x$.
6. $y = 1 - \csc x$.
7. $y = 2 - \tan x$.
8. $y = 2 + 2 \sin x$.

• • •

9. $y = x + \cos x$.
10. $y = x - \sin x$.
11. $y = \dfrac{2}{\sin x} + 1$.

177

CIRCULAR FUNCTIONS AND THEIR GRAPHS

- 12. $y = \dfrac{\frac{1}{2}}{\csc x} + 2.$

- 13. $y = \sin x + \cos x.$

- 14. $y = x \cos x.$

Sketch each pair of graphs on the same coordinate plane for $-2\pi \le x \le \dfrac{5\pi}{2}$:

- 15. $y = (\sin x) + \dfrac{\pi}{2}$ and $y = \sin\left(x + \dfrac{\pi}{2}\right).$

- 16. $y = (\tan x) + \pi$ and $y = \tan(x + \pi).$

§ 4–10 Inverses of sines and cosines

Relations and their inverse relations were considered in § 1–9. When it was possible to solve the equation representing a relation for the dependent variable, the equation representing the inverse relation was found by solving for the dependent variable and interchanging the dependent and independent variables. The domain of the relation becomes the range of the inverse relation and the range of the relation becomes the domain of the inverse relation.

In some cases it is not possible to obtain equations for the inverse relations without introducing new notations. Consider the equation $y = \sin x$. After interchanging x and y we cannot solve for y. Accordingly we introduce a new notation, $x = \arcsin y$, which, after interchanging the variables, becomes $y = \arcsin x$. Another way of writing this is $y = \sin^{-1} x$. Each of the last two equations is read as "y is an angle whose sine is x" and makes use of the original concepts of the circular functions for angles. We shall use the first notation at all times to avoid the confusion noted in this warning.

WARNING: In the notation $y = \sin^{-1} x$ for the inverse of $y = \sin x$, the symbol "-1" *is not an exponent* in the usual sense and the right member of the equation *does not equal* $\dfrac{1}{\sin x}.$

§ 4-10 INVERSES OF SINES AND COSINES

The graph (Figure 4-34) of $y = \text{arc sin } x$ can be obtained from the graph of $y = \sin x$ in the usual manner for graphing the inverse of a relation; that is, by reflecting the graph of $y = \sin x$ in the line $y = x$.

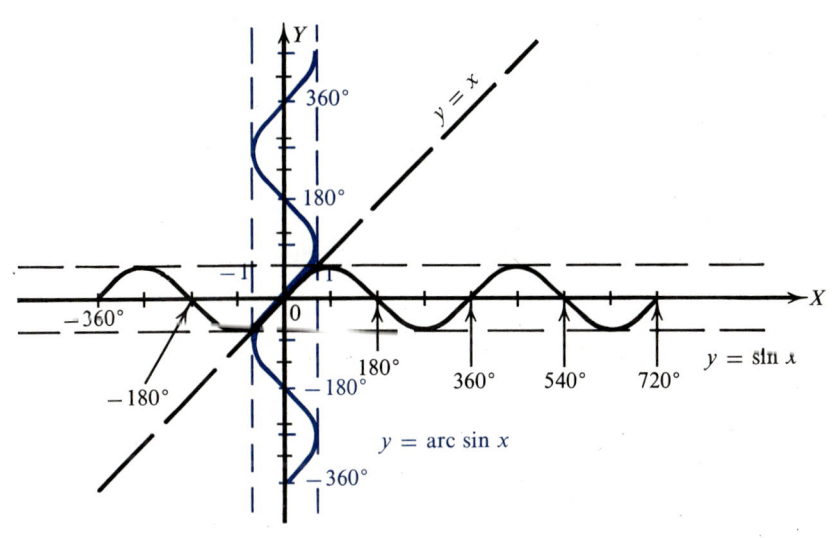

Figure 4-34

Notice that $y = \sin x$ is defined for any real number x and $|y| \leq 1$ for all x; $y = \text{arc sin } x$ is only defined when $|x| \leq 1$, but for any given value of x there are many possible values of arc sin x. That is, the inverse of the circular function $y = \sin x$ is a relation which is not a function.

In order to have a function, we must have at most one value of y for each value of x. Such will be the case for $y = \text{arc sin } x$ if we arbitrarily restrict the possible values of y to the interval $-\frac{\pi}{2} \leq y \leq \frac{\pi}{2}$ (that is, $-90° \leq y \leq 90°$). In other words we use only the part of the graph that is drawn with a heavy line. The values of y on this interval are called the **principal values** of $y = \text{arc sin } x$. It is customary to use capital "A" in $y = \text{Arc sin } x$, or capital "S" in $y = \text{Sin}^{-1} x$ to indicate that only the principal values of y are to be found.

The inverse of $y = \cos x$ is written $y = \text{arc cos } x$ and sometimes as $y = \cos^{-1} x$. In each case the equation is read as "y is an angle whose cosine is x"; and, as in the inverse of the sine function, capital letters are used when only principal values are sought. The graph (Figure 4-35) of $v = \text{arc cos } x$ can be obtained from the graph of $y = \cos x$ by reflecting

179

CIRCULAR FUNCTIONS AND THEIR GRAPHS

the graph of $y = \cos x$ in the line $y = x$; the principal values for $y = \text{arc cos } x$ are taken on the interval $0 \leq y \leq \pi$, that is, $0° \leq y \leq 180°$.

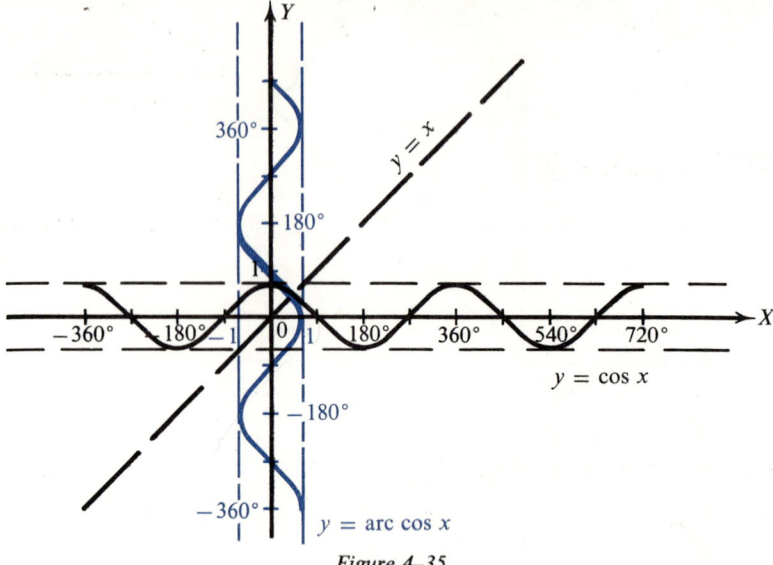

Figure 4–35

The graphs and tables of values may be used to solve the equations $y = \text{arc sin } x$ and $y = \text{arc cos } x$ for any values of x such that $|x| \leq 1$. We may also evaluate expressions such as $\cos\left(\text{Arc sin } \frac{1}{2}\right)$ using the principal value of the inverse relation.

Example 1. Find Arc sin $\frac{1}{2}$.

Since $\sin 30° = \frac{1}{2}$, the principal value of y is $30°$; that is, $\frac{\pi}{6}$. As in §4–6, the general values are $(30° + k \times 360°)$ and $(150° + k \times 360°)$, that is, $\frac{\pi}{6} + 2k\pi$ and $\frac{5\pi}{6} + 2k\pi$, where k stands for any integer.

Example 2. Simplify: $\cos\left(\text{Arc sin } \frac{1}{2}\right)$.

The principal value of arc sin $\frac{1}{2}$ is $30°$ as in Example 1. Thus
$$\cos\left(\text{Arc sin } \frac{1}{2}\right) = \cos 30° = \frac{\sqrt{3}}{2} \approx 0.866.$$

§ 4-10 INVERSES OF SINES AND COSINES

Example 3. Simplify: csc (Arc sin 0.3).

$\csc \theta = \dfrac{1}{\sin \theta}$; $\sin \theta = 0.3$, $\csc \theta = \dfrac{10}{3}$.

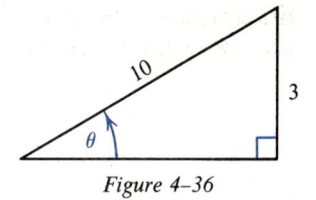

Figure 4–36

TEST YOURSELF

1. Simplify: $\sin \left(\text{Arc } \cos \dfrac{1}{2} \right)$. 2. Simplify: $\cos \left(\text{Arc } \cos \dfrac{1}{3} \right)$.

3. Find: $\text{Arc } \cos \left(-\dfrac{\sqrt{2}}{2} \right)$.

EXERCISES

State the correct way to read each symbol:

1. arc sin (-1).
2. arc cos $\dfrac{2}{3}$.
3. $\cos \left(\text{Arc sin } \dfrac{1}{3} \right)$.
4. $\csc \left(\text{Arc sin } \dfrac{1}{4} \right)$.

Find the value of:

5. Arc sin $\dfrac{\sqrt{3}}{2}$.
6. Arc cos $\dfrac{\sqrt{2}}{2}$.
7. Arc cos $\left(-\dfrac{\sqrt{3}}{2} \right)$.
8. Arc sin (-1).
9. Arc cos (-0.5).
10. Arc sin (-0.5).

In Exercises 11 through 20 simplify:

11. $\sin \left(\text{Arc sin } \dfrac{1}{4} \right)$.
12. cos (Arc cos 0.4).
13. $\sec \left(\text{Arc cos } \dfrac{1}{2} \right)$.
14. $\csc \left(\text{Arc sin } \dfrac{1}{5} \right)$.

• • •

15. sin (Arc cos 0.8).
16. cos (Arc sin 0.6).
17. sin (Arc sin x).
18. cos (Arc cos k).
19. cos (Arc sin x).
20. sin (Arc cos k).

CIRCULAR FUNCTIONS AND THEIR GRAPHS

- **21.** Graph $y = 2 \sin x$ and its inverse on the same coordinate plane.
- **22.** Graph $y = \cos \frac{1}{2} x$ and its inverse on the same coordinate plane.

§ 4-11 Inverses of tangents and cotangents

The inverse of $y = \tan x$ is written as $y = \text{arc tan } x$ and sometimes as $y = \tan^{-1} x$. In each case the equation is read as "y is an angle whose tangent is x" and principal values are designated by the use of capital letters. The graph (Figure 4-37) of $y = \text{arc tan } x$ can be obtained by reflecting the graph of $y = \tan x$ in the line $y = x$, the same method used in graphing $y = \text{arc sin } x$ and $y = \text{arc cos } x$ in § 4-10. In elementary mathematics the principal values for $y = \text{arc tan } x$ are usually taken on the interval $-\frac{\pi}{2} < y < \frac{\pi}{2}$, that is, $-90° < y < 90°$. In advanced mathematics courses the principal values may be taken on different intervals for special reasons.

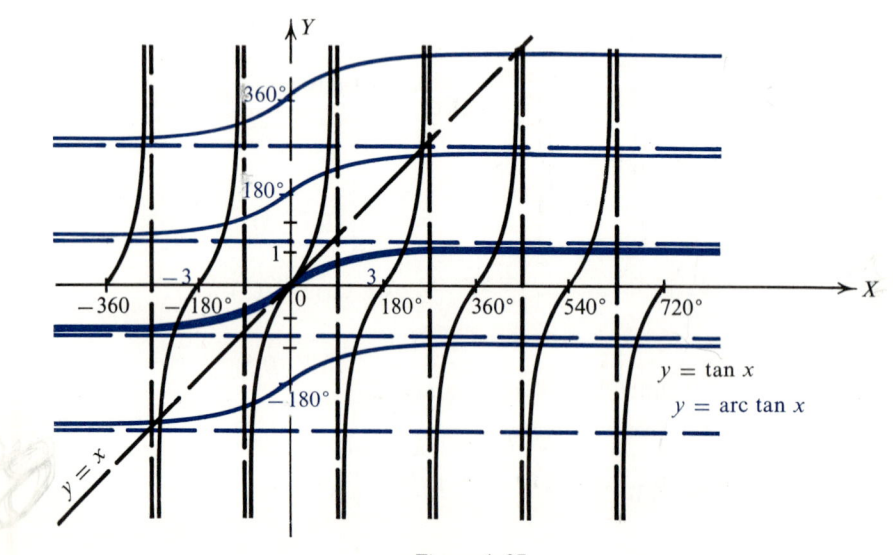

Figure 4-37

The inverse of $y = \cot x$ is written as $y = \text{arc cot } x$ and sometimes as $y = \cot^{-1} x$. In each case the equation is read as "y is an angle whose cotangent is x" and principal values are designated by capital letters. The graph (Figure 4-38) of $y = \text{arc cot } x$ can be obtained from the graph of

182

§ 4-11 INVERSES OF TANGENTS AND COTANGENTS

$y = \cot x$ by reflecting it in the line $y = x$. In elementary mathematics the principal values for $y = \text{arc cot } x$ are usually taken on the interval $0 < y < \pi$, that is, $0° < y < 180°$. Note that, as in the case of sin x and cos x, the inverses of tan x and cot x are relations rather than functions unless only principal values are considered.

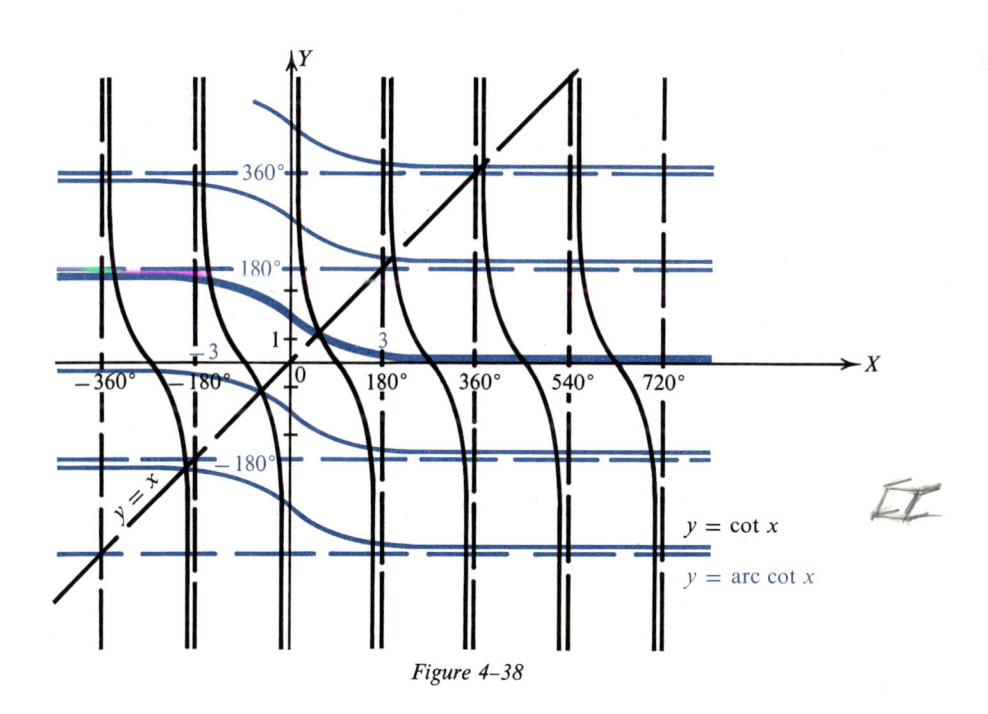

Figure 4-38

Example 1. Find the value of Arc tan (-1).

If $\tan \theta = -1$, then $\theta = (135° + k \times 360°)$ or $(-45° + k \times 360°)$ for some integer k. The principal value of arc tan (-1) is $-45°$.

Example 2. Find the value of csc (Arc tan $\sqrt{3}$).

Sketch a 30°-60°-90° triangle.
Arc tan $\sqrt{3} = 60°$;
csc 60° = $\frac{2}{3}\sqrt{3}$.

183

CIRCULAR FUNCTIONS AND THEIR GRAPHS

Example 3. Simplify: cos (Arc tan x) where $0 \leq x$.

If $\tan \theta = x$, then θ may be represented as angle A of triangle ABC where $\angle C = 90°$, $\overline{AC} = 1$, and $\overline{BC} = x$. Then $\overline{AB} = \sqrt{1 + x^2}$, $\tan A = x$, $\cos A = \dfrac{1}{\sqrt{1 + x^2}}$, and cos (Arc tan x) = $\dfrac{1}{\sqrt{1 + x^2}}$.

Figure 4–39

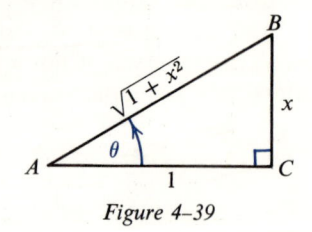

In all such future problems the condition $0 \leq x$ will be omitted since the result holds for all x for a suitable choice of signs for the radical.

TEST YOURSELF

Simplify:

1. $\tan \left(\text{Arc cot } \dfrac{1}{2} \right)$.   **2.** sin (Arc cot 3).   **3.** Find: Arc tan ($-\sqrt{3}$).

EXERCISES

Find the value of:

1. Arc tan $\sqrt{3}$.

2. Arc cot (-1).

3. Arc cot $(-\sqrt{3})$.

4. Arc tan $\left(-\dfrac{\sqrt{3}}{3} \right)$.

Simplify:

5. tan (Arc tan 3).
6. cot (Arc tan 2).
7. tan (Arc cot 0.5).

8. sec (Arc tan 2).
9. csc (Arc cot 3).
10. cos (Arc tan 4).

11. sin (Arc cot 2).
12. sin (Arc cot x).
13. cos (Arc cot x).

14. tan (Arc cos x).
15. cot (Arc sin x).
16. sin (Arc tan $\sqrt{x^2 - 1}$).

§ 4–12 Inverses of secants and cosecants

The inverse of $y = \sec x$ is written as $y = \text{arc sec } x$ and sometimes as $y = \sec^{-1} x$. In each case the equation is read as "y is an angle whose secant is x," and capital letters are used to designate the principal values. The graph (Figure 4–40) of $y = \text{arc sec } x$ can be obtained from the graph of $y = \sec x$ in the manner used for the other inverses of circular functions. The principal values for $y = \text{arc sec } x$ are usually taken on the interval $0 \leq y \leq \pi$, that is, $0° \leq y \leq 180°$.

184

§ 4-12 INVERSES OF SECANTS AND COSECANTS

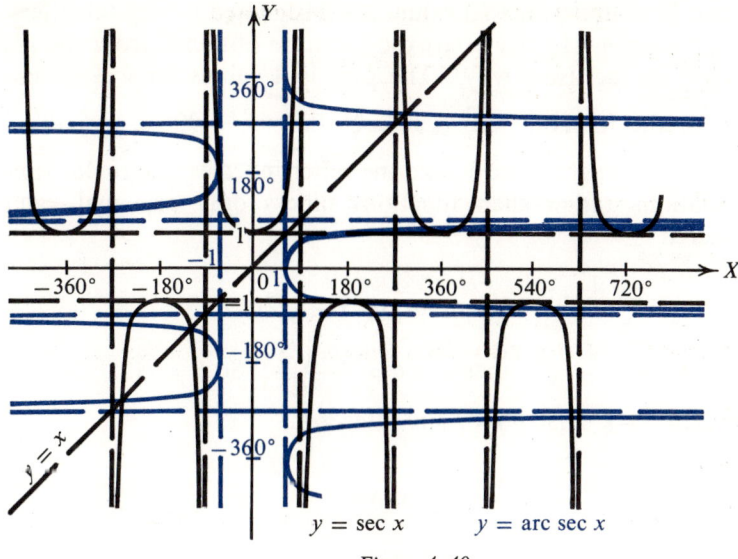

Figure 4-40

$y = \sec x \qquad y = \text{arc sec } x$

The inverse of $y = \csc x$ is written as $y = \text{arc csc } x$ and sometimes as $y = \csc^{-1} x$. In each case the equation is read as "y is an angle whose

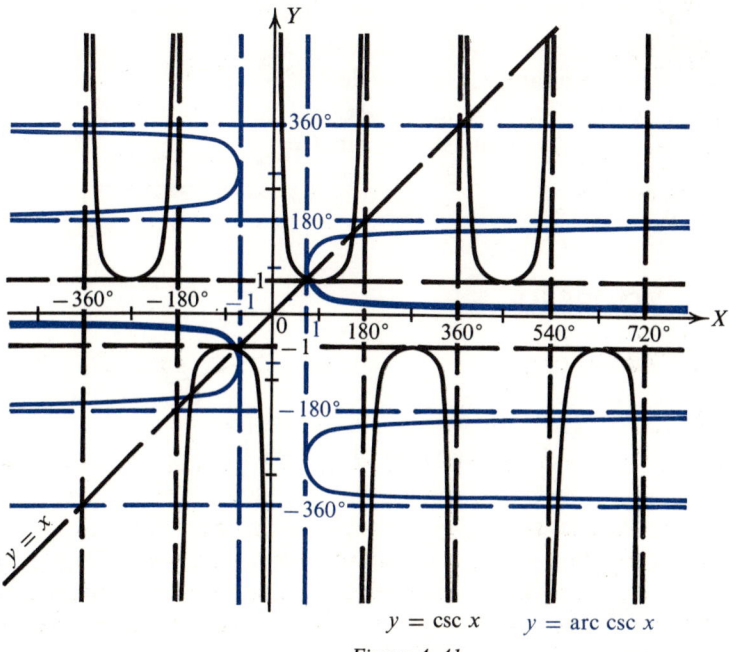

Figure 4-41

$y = \csc x \qquad y = \text{arc csc } x$

CIRCULAR FUNCTIONS AND THEIR GRAPHS

cosecant is x" and principal values are designated by capital letters. The graph (Figure 4–41) of $y = $ arc csc x can be obtained from the graph of $y = $ csc x in the usual way. The principal values for $y = $ arc csc x are taken on the interval $-\frac{\pi}{2} \leq y \leq \frac{\pi}{2}$, that is, $-90° \leq y \leq 90°$. Note that arc sec x and arc csc x, like the other inverses of circular functions, are relations rather than functions unless only principal values are considered.

Example 1. Find the value of arc sec $(-\sqrt{2})$.

If sec $\theta = -\sqrt{2}$, then cos $\theta = -\frac{\sqrt{2}}{2}$. So $\theta = (135° + k \times 360°)$ or $(225° + k \times 360°)$ for any integer k.

Example 2. Find the value of Arc csc 2.

If csc $\theta = 2$, then sin $\theta = \frac{1}{2}$ and $\theta = (30° + k \times 360°)$ or $(150° + k \times 360°)$ for any integer k. The principle value of θ is 30°.

Example 3. Simplify: sin (Arc sec x).

As in Example 3 of § 4–11 assume $0 \leq x$ and represent θ as angle A in triangle ABC where $\angle C = 90°$, $\overline{AB} = x$, and $\overline{AC} = 1$. Then $\overline{BC} = \sqrt{x^2 - 1}$ and sin $\theta = $ sin $A = \frac{\sqrt{x^2 - 1}}{x}$.

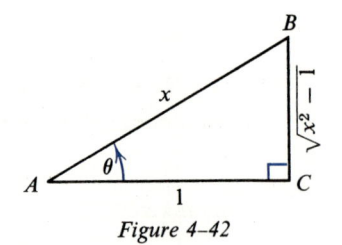

Figure 4–42

TEST YOURSELF

Simplify:

1. sin (Arc csc 17).
2. cos (Arc csc 3).
3. Find the value of Arc sec $\left(-\frac{2\sqrt{3}}{3}\right)$.

EXERCISES

Find the value of:

1. Arc sec 2.
2. Arc csc $(-\sqrt{2})$.

§ 4-13 POLAR COORDINATES

Simplify:

3. sec (Arc sec 25).
4. csc [Arc csc (−5)].
5. cos [Arc sec (−17)].
6. sin (Arc csc 7).

• • •

7. tan (Arc sec 2).
8. cot (Arc csc 3).
9. tan (Arc csc 2).
10. $\cot \left(\text{Arc sec } \frac{3}{2} \right)$.
11. cot (Arc csc x).
12. tan (Arc sec x).
13. cos (Arc csc x).
14. tan (Arc csc x).
15. cot (Arc sec x).
16. sin (2 Arc sec x).

§ 4-13 Polar coordinates

Any point on a plane may be represented by an ordered pair (x, y) of real numbers as in § 1-6. Any point A with rectangular coordinates (that is, Cartesian coordinates) (x, y) is at a distance r from the origin where $r = \sqrt{x^2 + y^2}$. If we denote the angle XOA by θ (Figure 4–43), and select the point P on $\overrightarrow{OA}$ such that $\overline{OP} = 1$, then P has Cartesian coordinates $(\cos \theta, \sin \theta)$. Since the right triangles OPQ and OAB are similar, the point A has Cartesian coordinates $(r \cos \theta, r \sin \theta)$. Indeed r and θ may be used to identify points $A: (x, y)$ on a plane. In each case $A: (x, y) = A: (r, \theta)$ where $\overline{OA} = r$ and $\angle XOA = \theta$ as in Figure 4–44. The numbers r and θ are called the **polar coordinates** of the point A. Equations of curves may be given either in terms of rectangular coordinates or polar coordinates.

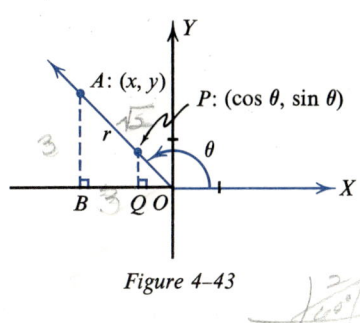

Figure 4–43

Figure 4–44

Example 1. Find polar coordinates for the point (a) $R: (5, 5)$; (b) $S: (-4\sqrt{3}, -4)$; (c) $T: (-5, 5)$.

(a) $R: (5, 5) = R: (5\sqrt{2}, 45°)$;
(b) $S: (-4\sqrt{3}, -4) = S: (8, 210°)$;
(c) $T: (-5, 5) = T: (5\sqrt{2}, 135°)$.

187

CIRCULAR FUNCTIONS AND THEIR GRAPHS

Example 2. Find rectangular coordinates for the point
(a) $M: (5\sqrt{2}, 135°)$; (b) $P: (8, 330°)$; (c) $Q: \left(6, \frac{2\pi}{3}\right)$.

(a) $M: (5\sqrt{2}, 135°) = M: (-5, 5)$;
(b) $P: (8, 330°) = P: (4\sqrt{3}, -4)$;
(c) $Q: (6, \frac{2\pi}{3}) = Q: (-3, 3\sqrt{3})$.

Example 3. Graph (a) $r = 2$; (b) $r \geq 0$ and $\theta = 2$; (c) $r \cos \theta = 2$.

(a) The equation $r = 2$ asserts that each point of the graph is at a distance of 2 units from the origin. Thus the graph is a circle with center at the origin and radius 2. The graph may also be identified in terms of rectangular coordinates:

$$r = \sqrt{x^2 + y^2} = 2; \qquad x^2 + y^2 = 4.$$

(b) The equation $\theta = 2$ where the number 2 is not indicated as a number of degrees or other units is assumed to mean 2 radians. Thus $\theta \approx 114.6°$ and since r is a positive number or zero, the graph is a ray with end point at the origin.

(c) The equation $r \cos \theta = 2$ is equivalent to the equation $x = 2$ in rectangular coordinates since $A: (x, y) = A: (r \cos \theta, r \sin \theta)$. Thus the graph is a line.

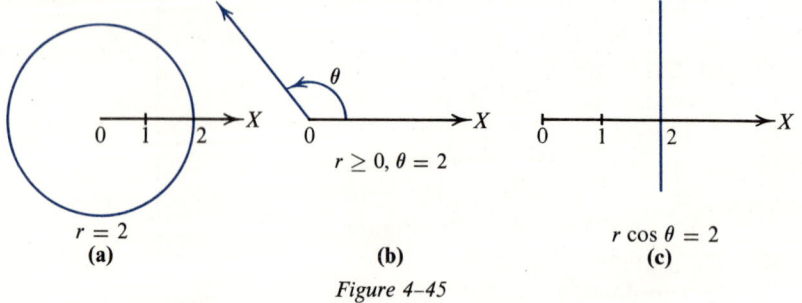

$r = 2$
(a)

$r \geq 0, \theta = 2$
(b)

$r \cos \theta = 2$
(c)

Figure 4–45

Example 4. Graph for $r \geq 0$ the equation $r(r - 2 \cos \theta) = 0$.

The graph may be drawn using either rectangular or polar coordinates.

$r(r - 2 \cos \theta) = 0$
$r^2 - 2r \cos \theta = 0$
$x^2 + y^2 - 2x = 0$
$(x - 1)^2 + y^2 = 1$

The graph is a circle of radius 1 and center $(1, 0)$.

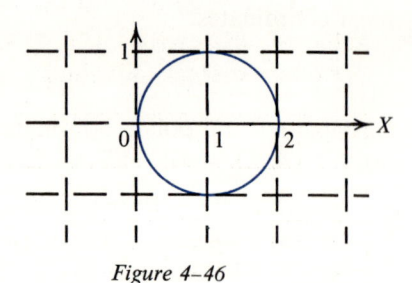

Figure 4–46

§ 4-13 POLAR COORDINATES

In graphing statements in terms of polar coordinates it is customary to extend the definition of r to include negative values. Then each point (r, θ) may be represented also by $(-r, \theta + \pi)$. For example, in Figure 4-47

$A: (2, 180°) = A: (-2, 0°);$
$B: (\sqrt{2}, 45°) = B: (-\sqrt{2}, 225°);$
$C: (2, 225°) = C: (-2, 45°);$
$D: (3, -30°) = D: (-3, 150°).$

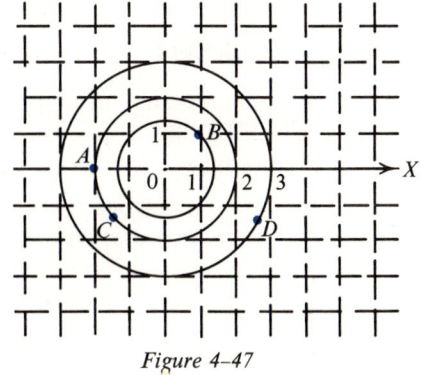

Unless otherwise stated we assume that r may represent any real number. If in Example 3(b) negative values of r are allowed, the graph is a line rather than a ray and that same line is also the graph of $\theta = \pi + 2$. The convenience of using negative values of r to indicate distances from the origin along the ray opposite the ray designated by θ is shown in Example 5.

Figure 4-47

Example 5. Graph $r = \sin 2\theta$ for all real values of r.

Notice that as θ varies from 0° to 90°, 2θ varies from 0° to 180° and $\sin 2\theta$ varies from 0 at 0° to 1 at 45° to 0 at 90°. As θ varies from 90° to 180°, 2θ varies from 180° to 360° and $\sin 2\theta$ varies from 0 at 90° to -1 at 135° to 0 at 180°. As θ varies from 180° to 270°, 2θ varies from 360° to 540°, and $\sin 2\theta$ varies from 0 at 180° to 1 at 225° to 0 at 270°. As θ varies from 270° to 360°, 2θ varies from 540° to 720° and $\sin 2\theta$ varies from 0 at 270° to -1 at 315° to 0 at 360°.

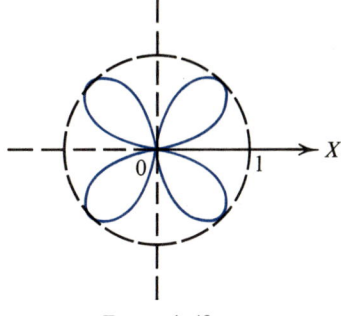

Figure 4-48

The points of each of the four "petals" may be plotted using this table of values for $0° \leq \theta \leq 90°$ and selecting appropriate signs for r for other intervals of values:

θ	0°	15°	22.5°	30°	45°	60°	67.5°	75°	90°
2θ	0°	30°	45°	60°	90°	120°	135°	150°	180°
r	0	0.5	0.7	0.87	1.0	0.87	0.7	0.5	0

CIRCULAR FUNCTIONS AND THEIR GRAPHS

The extension of polar coordinates to **cylindrical coordinates** is developed in the supplementary exercises. In cylindrical coordinates all real values of r are considered.

TEST YOURSELF

1. Find the rectangular coordinates for (a) P: (50, 135°); (b) Q: (−2, 180°).
2. Find polar coordinates for (a) R: (4, −4); (b) S: $(-2\sqrt{3}, 2)$.

Graph for all real values of r:

3. $r = 3$. 4. $r = \cos 2\theta$.

EXERCISES

Graph each point from its given polar coordinates:

1. A: (2, 45°).
2. B: (−1, 90°).
3. C: (3, 225°).
4. D: (1.5, 300°).
5. E: (−3, 0).
6. F: $\left(2, \dfrac{5\pi}{3}\right)$.

Find the rectangular coordinates for the point with the given polar coordinates:

7. G: (4, 135°).
8. H: (−4, 330°).
9. I: $\left(6, \dfrac{3\pi}{2}\right)$.

Find two pairs of polar coordinates for the point with the given rectangular coordinate:

10. J: (3, 3).
11. K: (3, −3).
12. L: (0, −2).
13. M: (−4, 2).
14. O: (0, 0).
15. P: (6, −8).

Graph for all real values of r:

16. $r = 1.5$.
17. $\theta = 30°$.
18. $r \sin \theta = 3$.
19. $r \cos \theta = -3$.
20. $r \sin \theta = -2$.
21. $r^2 = 2r \cos \theta$.

• • •

22. $r = 2 \cos 2\theta$.
23. $r = 3 \sin 2\theta$.
24. $r = \sin 3\theta$.
25. $r = \cos 3\theta$.
• 26. $r = \sin 4\theta$.
• 27. $r = \cos 4\theta$.

SUPPLEMENTARY EXERCISES

You have used rectangular coordinates on the xy-plane with a z-coordinate to locate a point (x, y, z) in space. Polar coordinates on a plane also may be used with a z-coordinate to locate a point (r, θ, z) in space. The three coordinates (r, θ, z) are called *cylindrical coordinates*. Graph each point from its given cylindrical coordinates:

1. $A: (2, 45°, 1)$.
2. $B: \left(1, \frac{\pi}{2}, 2\right)$.
3. $C: \left(-1, \frac{\pi}{2}, 1\right)$.
4. $D: (-2, \pi, 1)$.
5. $E: (\sqrt{2}, 0, 1)$.
6. $F: (-\sqrt{2}, 180°, 1)$.

• • •

Describe and give the equation in rectangular coordinates for the graph of each statement. The statements are given in terms of cylindrical coordinates.

7. $\theta = \frac{\pi}{4}$.
8. $z = 1$.
- 9. $r^2 + z^2 = 9$.
- 10. $r^2 = r \cos \theta$.
- 11. $r^2 = z^2$.
- 12. $r^2 - 2z^2 = 0$.

SUMMARY OF CHAPTER 4

1. In this chapter you have studied trigonometric and circular functions and their graphs. For any acute angle of a right triangle:

$\sin A = \frac{a}{c}$ $\left(\text{that is, } \frac{\text{side opposite}}{\text{hypotenuse}}\right)$;

$\cos A = \frac{b}{c}$ $\left(\text{that is, } \frac{\text{side adjacent}}{\text{hypotenuse}}\right)$;

$\tan A = \frac{a}{b}$ $\left(\text{that is, } \frac{\text{side opposite}}{\text{side adjacent}}\right)$;

$\cot A = \frac{b}{a}$ $\left(\text{that is, } \frac{\text{side adjacent}}{\text{side opposite}}\right)$;

$\sec A = \frac{c}{b}$ $\left(\text{that is, } \frac{\text{hypotenuse}}{\text{side adjacent}}\right)$;

$\csc A = \frac{c}{a}$ $\left(\text{that is, } \frac{\text{hypotenuse}}{\text{side opposite}}\right)$. (§ 4-1)

2. The six trigonometric functions may be used to solve any 30°-60°-90° or 45°-45°-90° right triangles which are determined by the given data. (§ 4-2)

CIRCULAR FUNCTIONS AND THEIR GRAPHS

3. The six circular functions may be defined for any angle in standard position on a coordinate plane:

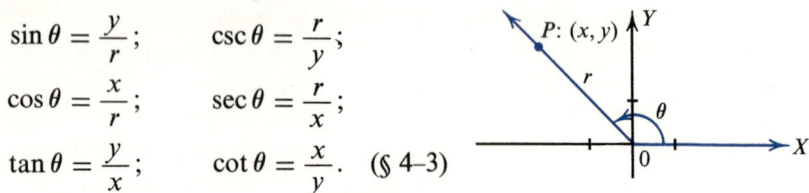

$$\sin \theta = \frac{y}{r}; \qquad \csc \theta = \frac{r}{y};$$
$$\cos \theta = \frac{x}{r}; \qquad \sec \theta = \frac{r}{x};$$
$$\tan \theta = \frac{y}{x}; \qquad \cot \theta = \frac{x}{y}. \qquad (\S \ 4\text{--}3)$$

4. The general definitions are true for quadrantal angles (90°, 180°, 270°, and so on) whenever the circular functions are defined (that is, do not involve division by zero). The circular functions may be defined for negative angles. These formulas hold:

$$\sin(-\theta) = -\sin \theta; \qquad \csc(-\theta) = -\csc \theta;$$
$$\cos(-\theta) = \cos \theta; \qquad \sec(-\theta) = \sec \theta;$$
$$\tan(-\theta) = -\tan \theta; \qquad \cot(-\theta) = -\cot \theta. \qquad (\S \ 4\text{--}4)$$

5. Each circular function that is defined for any given angle, θ, can be represented by a line segment taken with an appropriate sign. (§ 4–5)

6. The graph of $y = \sin x$ may be used to obtain the graphs of $y = \cos x$, $y = k \sin x$, $y = k \sin(x + b)$, $y = k \cos x$, and $y = k \cos(x + b)$ for any real numbers k and b. Each of these graphs has period 360°. The graphs of $y = k \sin(x + b)$ and $y = k \cos(x + b)$ have amplitude $|k|$ and differ in phase by 90°. (§ 4–6)

7. The equations $y = k \tan(x + b)$ and $y = k \cot(x + b)$ may be graphed for any given real numbers k and b; each graph has period 180°. (§ 4–7)

8. The equations $y = k \sec(x + b)$ and $y = k \csc(x + b)$ may be graphed for any given real numbers k and b; each graph has period 360°. (§ 4–8)

9. Sums and differences may be graphed by composition of ordinates; products may also be graphed. (§ 4–9)

10. The inverses of the circular functions are relations rather than functions unless only principal values are considered. Each inverse relation may be graphed. Many expressions involving inverse relations may be simplified. (§§ 4–10, 4–11, and 4–12)

11. The sine and cosine functions may be used to locate points on a plane by polar coordinates (r, θ) instead of rectangular coordinates (x, y);

$r \cos \theta = x;$
$r \sin \theta = y;$
$\quad r = \sqrt{x^2 + y^2};$
$(r, \theta) = (r, \theta + 2k\pi) = (-r, \theta + 2k\pi + \pi)$ for any integer k. (§ 4–13)

KEYED PRACTICE ON CHAPTER 4

12. The following words have been introduced or used extensively in this chapter:

acute angle (§ 4–1)
amplitude (§ 4–6)
arc cosecant (§ 4–12)
arc cosine (§ 4–10)
arc cotangent (§ 4–11)
arc secant (§ 4–12)
arc sine (§ 4–10)
arc tangent (§ 4–11)
circular function (§ 4–3)
composition of ordinates (§ 4–9)
cosecant (§ 4–1)
cosine (§ 4–1)
cotangent (§ 4–1)
cylindrical coordinates (§ 4–13)
domain (§ 4–10)
function (§ 4–10)
graph (§ 4–4)
graphing by composition (§ 4–9)
hypotenuse (§ 4–1)
initial side (§ 4–3)
inverse relation (§ 4–10)
line value (§ 4–5)
negative angle (§ 4–4)
ordinate (§ 4–9)

period (§ 4–6)
periodic function (§ 4–6)
phase (§ 4–6)
polar coordinates (§ 4–13)
positive angle (§ 4–3)
principal value (§ 4–10)
quadrantal angle (§ 4–4)
range (§ 4–10)
reference angle (§ 4–3)
relation (§ 4–10)
right triangle (§ 4–1)
secant (§ 4–1)
side adjacent (§ 4–1)
side opposite (§ 4–1)
similar triangles (§ 4–1)
sine (§ 4–1)
standard position (§ 4–3)
tangent (§ 4–1)
terminal side (§ 4–3)
trigonometric function (§ 4–1)
trigonometric ratio (§ 4–1)
trigonometry (§ 4–1)
undefined (§ 4–4)
unit circle (§ 4–5)

KEYED PRACTICE ON CHAPTER 4

1. Draw a triangle ABC with $\angle C = 90°$, $\overline{AB} = 13$, $\overline{AC} = 12$, and $\overline{BC} = 5$. Find each of the six ratios for angle B. (§ 4–1)

2. Find the side of a square with diagonal 8 inches. (§ 4–2)

3. Draw angle MOQ in standard position on a coordinate plane with Q at $(-3, 4)$. Find each of the six circular functions of angle MOQ. (§ 4–3)

4. For each of the four quadrants, consider the six circular functions and list those that are positive for each angle in standard position with its terminal side in that quadrant. (§ 4–4)

5. Construct the line values for each of the six circular functions of $300°$. (§ 4–5)

193

CIRCULAR FUNCTIONS AND THEIR GRAPHS

In Exercises 6 through 9 sketch the graph for $0° \leq x \leq 720°$:

6. $y = 2 \sin (x + 90°)$. (§ 4–6)
7. $y = 3 \tan x$. (§ 4–7)
8. $y = \sec (x - 90°)$. (§ 4–8)
9. $y = 1 + \sin x$. (§ 4–9)
10. Simplify: $\cos \left(\text{Arc } \sin \frac{2}{5} \right)$. (§ 4–10)
11. Simplify: $\sin (\text{Arc cot } 5)$. (§ 4–11)
12. Simplify: $\sin (\text{Arc sec } x)$. (§ 4–12)
13. Find two pairs of polar coordinates for the point with rectangular coordinates $(4\sqrt{3}, -4)$. (§ 4–13)

TESTS ON CHAPTER 4

A

1. Draw a right triangle with sides 3 inches, 4 inches, and 5 inches. Give the value of each of the six trigonometric ratios for the angle between the 4-inch and 5-inch sides.

In Exercises 2 through 5 evaluate:

2. $\text{Arc } \cos \left(-\frac{\sqrt{3}}{2} \right)$.

3. $\text{Arc } \tan \frac{\sqrt{3}}{3}$.

4. $\cos (\text{Arc sec } 3)$.

5. $\sin (\text{Arc tan } 2)$.

6. Give rectangular coordinates for the point with polar coordinates $\left(6, \frac{\pi}{6} \right)$.

7. For each of the quadrantal angles $0°, 90°, 180°,$ and $270°$, list the circular functions that are undefined for that angle.

8. Find the six circular functions of $-120°$.

Sketch the graph for $0° \leq x \leq 720°$:

9. $y = 3 \cos x$.
10. $y = -3 + \sin x$.

B

1. Take $P: (-7, 24)$ on the terminal side of an angle in standard position and give the value of each of the six circular functions of that angle.

2. Construct the line values for each of the six circular functions of $240°$.

3. Solve triangle ABC if $\angle B = 30°$, $\angle C = 90°$, and $a = 6\sqrt{3}$.

ANSWERS TO TEST YOURSELF EXERCISES

4. Evaluate: $\sec\left(\text{Arc } \cos \dfrac{\sqrt{2}}{2}\right)$.

5. Evaluate: $\tan\,[\text{Arc csc}\,(-2)]$.

6. Find the length of an altitude of an equilateral triangle with side 18 inches.

7. Find rectangular coordinates for the point with the given polar coordinates: **(a)** $(4, 60°)$; **(b)** $(10\sqrt{2}, 225°)$.

In Exercises 8 and 9 sketch the graph for $0° \leq x \leq 720°$:

8. $y = 2 \sin (x + 270°)$.
9. $y = \csc (x - 90°)$.
10. Graph on a plane: $r^2 = 2r \sin \theta$.

C

1. Construct the line values for each of the six circular functions of 315°.

2. Solve triangle ABC if $\angle A = 45°$, $\angle C = 90°$, and $c = 15$. (Leave your answer in simplest radical form.)

3. Find the six circular functions of 300° in terms of those of 60°.

4. Evaluate: **(a)** $\sin\left[\text{Arc csc}\left(-\dfrac{2\sqrt{3}}{3}\right)\right]$; **(b)** $\tan\left(\text{Arc sin }\dfrac{1}{2}\right)$.

5. For $-6 < x < 10$ list the values of x for which $\tan x$ is undefined.

6. For $0 \leq \theta \leq 2\pi$ state whether or not each expression is bounded:
(a) $5 \sin 2\theta$; **(b)** $\tan 5\theta$; **(c)** $\tan \dfrac{1}{5}\theta$.

7. For $-\pi \leq x \leq 3\pi$ graph $y = x - \cos x$.
8. Simplify: $\tan (\text{Arc sec } \sqrt{x})$.
9. Graph on a plane: $r = 2 \sin 3\theta$.
10. Use cylindrical coordinates and graph in space: **(a)** $r = 2$; **(b)** $r^2 + z^2 = 4$.

ANSWERS TO TEST YOURSELF EXERCISES

§ 4-1. **1.** $q = 10\sqrt{3}$; $s = 20$.

2. $\sin R = \dfrac{r}{s}$; $\cos R = \dfrac{q}{s}$; $\tan R = \dfrac{r}{q}$; $\cot R = \dfrac{q}{r}$; $\sec R = \dfrac{s}{q}$; $\csc R = \dfrac{s}{r}$.

3. $\sin R = \dfrac{1}{2}$; $\cos R = \dfrac{\sqrt{3}}{2}$; $\tan R = \dfrac{1}{\sqrt{3}} = \dfrac{\sqrt{3}}{3}$; $\cot R = \sqrt{3}$;

CIRCULAR FUNCTIONS AND THEIR GRAPHS

$\sec R = \dfrac{2}{\sqrt{3}} = \dfrac{2\sqrt{3}}{3}$; $\csc R = 2$.

4. For any 30°-60°-90° triangle the side opposite the 30° angle is half the hypotenuse; the side opposite the 60° angle is $\sqrt{3}$ times the side opposite the 30° angle. Thus if the side opposite the 30° angle is b, the hypotenuse is $2b$, and the other side is $b\sqrt{3}$. Then $\sin 30° = \dfrac{b}{2b} = \dfrac{1}{2}$; $\cos 30° = \dfrac{b\sqrt{3}}{2b} = \dfrac{\sqrt{3}}{2}$; $\tan 30° = \dfrac{b}{b\sqrt{3}} = \dfrac{1}{\sqrt{3}} = \dfrac{\sqrt{3}}{3}$; $\cot 30° = \dfrac{b\sqrt{3}}{b} = \sqrt{3}$; $\sec 30° = \dfrac{2b}{b\sqrt{3}} = \dfrac{2}{\sqrt{3}} = \dfrac{2\sqrt{3}}{3}$; $\csc 30° = \dfrac{2b}{b} = 2$.

§ 4-2. 1. $\angle K = 45°$, $i = 5\sqrt{2}$ feet, $k = 5\sqrt{2}$ feet.
2. $\angle N = 30°$, $p = 6$ feet, $m = 3\sqrt{3}$ feet.

§ 4-3. 1. The reference angle is 45°. Take P at $(-1, 1)$. Then $\overline{OP} = \sqrt{2}$;

$\sin 135° = \dfrac{1}{\sqrt{2}} = \dfrac{\sqrt{2}}{2}$;

$\cos 135° = \dfrac{-1}{\sqrt{2}} = -\dfrac{\sqrt{2}}{2}$;

$\tan 135° = -1$;

$\cot 135° = -1$; $\sec 135° = -\sqrt{2}$; $\csc 135° = \sqrt{2}$.

2. (a) $\sin 135° = \dfrac{1}{\sqrt{2}} = \sin 45°$; (b) $\cos 135° = \dfrac{-1}{\sqrt{2}} = -\cos 45°$.

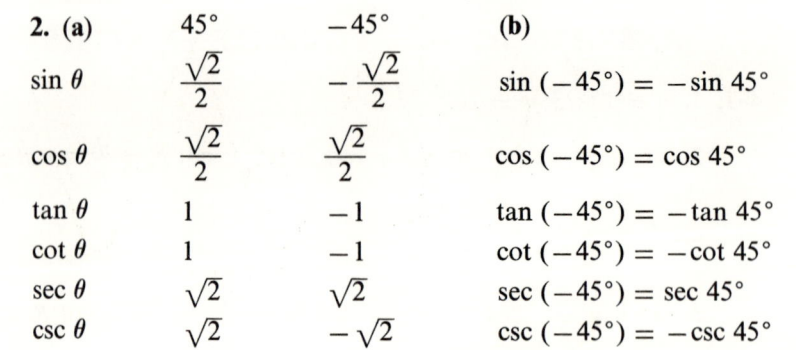

§ 4-4. 1. $\sin 180° = 0$; $\cos 180° = -1$; $\tan 180° = 0$; $\cot 180°$ is undefined; $\sec 180° = -1$; $\csc 180°$ is undefined.

2. (a)

	45°	−45°
$\sin \theta$	$\dfrac{\sqrt{2}}{2}$	$-\dfrac{\sqrt{2}}{2}$
$\cos \theta$	$\dfrac{\sqrt{2}}{2}$	$\dfrac{\sqrt{2}}{2}$
$\tan \theta$	1	−1
$\cot \theta$	1	−1
$\sec \theta$	$\sqrt{2}$	$\sqrt{2}$
$\csc \theta$	$\sqrt{2}$	$-\sqrt{2}$

(b) $\sin(-45°) = -\sin 45°$
$\cos(-45°) = \cos 45°$
$\tan(-45°) = -\tan 45°$
$\cot(-45°) = -\cot 45°$
$\sec(-45°) = \sec 45°$
$\csc(-45°) = -\csc 45°$

ANSWERS TO TEST YOURSELF EXERCISES

3. (a)

	120°	−120°
$\sin\theta$	$\dfrac{\sqrt{3}}{2}$	$-\dfrac{\sqrt{3}}{2}$
$\cos\theta$	$-\dfrac{1}{2}$	$-\dfrac{1}{2}$
$\tan\theta$	$-\sqrt{3}$	$\sqrt{3}$
$\cot\theta$	$-\dfrac{\sqrt{3}}{3}$	$\dfrac{\sqrt{3}}{3}$
$\sec\theta$	-2	-2
$\csc\theta$	$\dfrac{2\sqrt{3}}{3}$	$-\dfrac{2\sqrt{3}}{3}$

(b)

$\sin(-120°) = -\sin 120°$
$\cos(-120°) = \cos 120°$
$\tan(-120°) = -\tan 120°$
$\cot(-120°) = -\cot 120°$
$\sec(-120°) = \sec 120°$
$\csc(-120°) = -\csc 120°$

§ 4-5. 1.

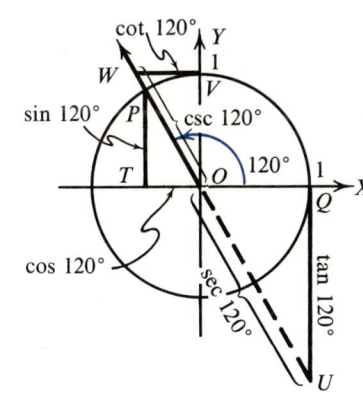

2. $\sin 120° \approx 0.87$; $\cos 120° \approx -0.50$; $\tan 120° \approx -1.73$; $\cot 120° \approx -0.58$; $\sec 120° \approx -2.00$; $\csc 120° \approx 1.15$. **3.** Whenever $\tan\theta$ is defined, the line value for $\tan\theta$ is $\overrightarrow{QU}$ where $\overline{QU}$ is perpendicular to the x-axis at Q and U is on $\overrightarrow{OP}$. When $\theta = 90°$, $\overrightarrow{OP}$ is along the positive y-axis and $\overleftrightarrow{QU}$ is parallel to $\overrightarrow{OP}$. These two distinct parallel lines cannot have a point U in common; thus there cannot be a line value for $\tan 90°$.

§ 4-6. 1 and 2.

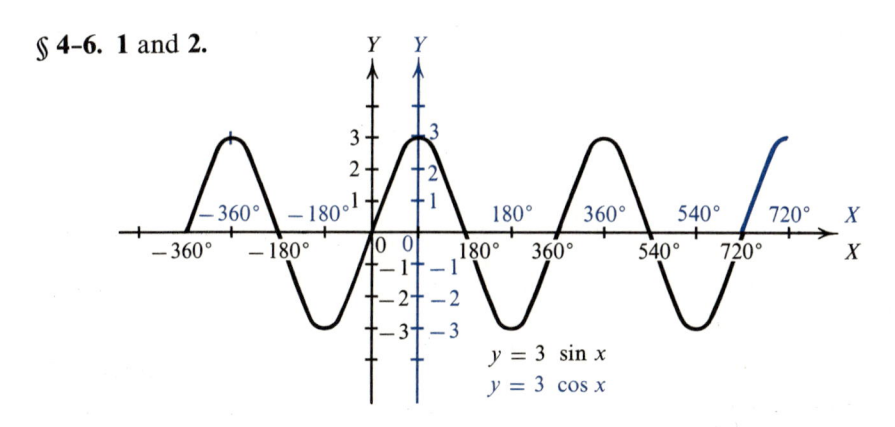

$y = 3 \sin x$
$y = 3 \cos x$

197

CIRCULAR FUNCTIONS AND THEIR GRAPHS

3.

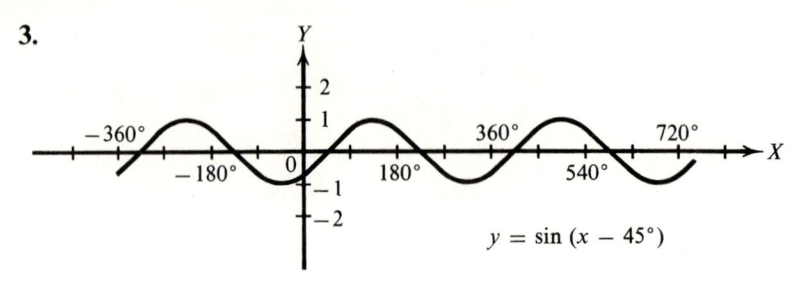

$y = \sin(x - 45°)$

Note that the graph of $y = \sin(x - 45°)$ may be obtained from the graph of $y = \sin x$ by moving the x-scale and the y-axis to the left 45°.

§ 4-7. 1 and 2.

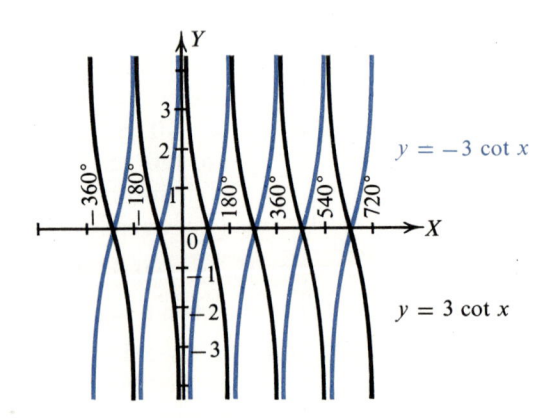

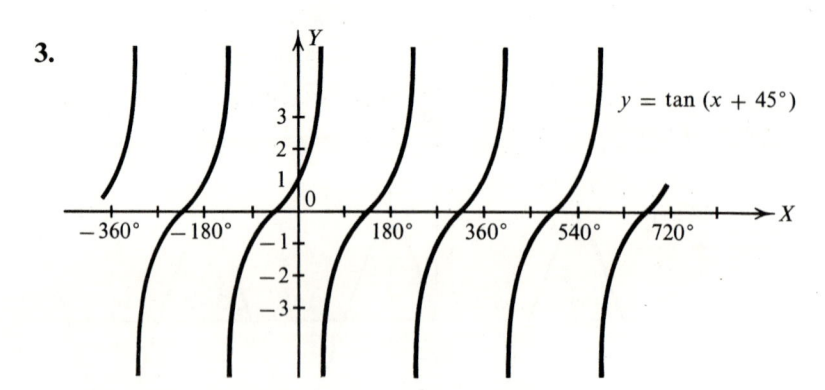

$y = -3 \cot x$

$y = 3 \cot x$

3.

$y = \tan(x + 45°)$

Note that the graph of $y = \tan(x + 45°)$ may be obtained from the graph of $y = \tan x$ by moving the x-scale and the y-axis to the right 45°.

… ANSWERS TO TEST YOURSELF EXERCISES

§ 4-8. 1.

$y = 3 \sec x$

2.

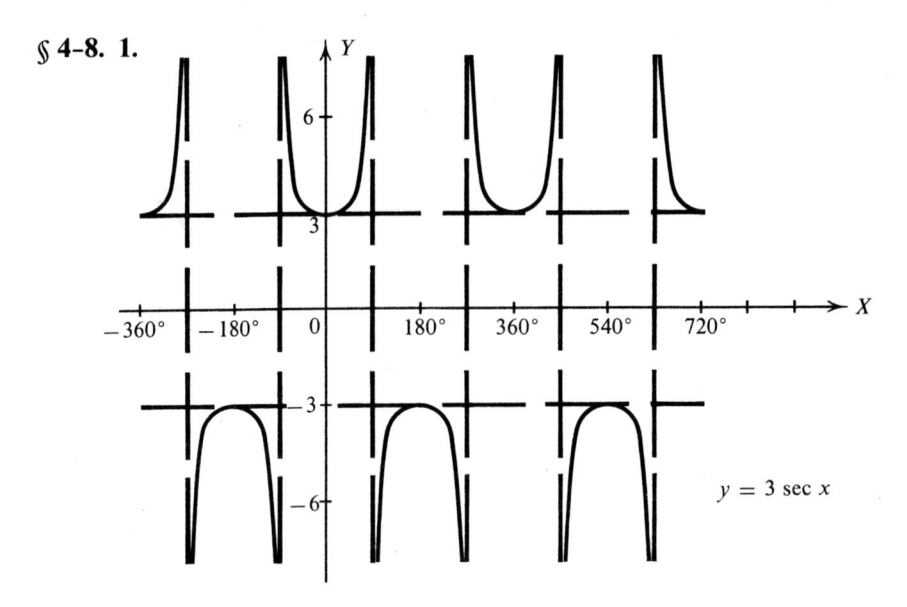

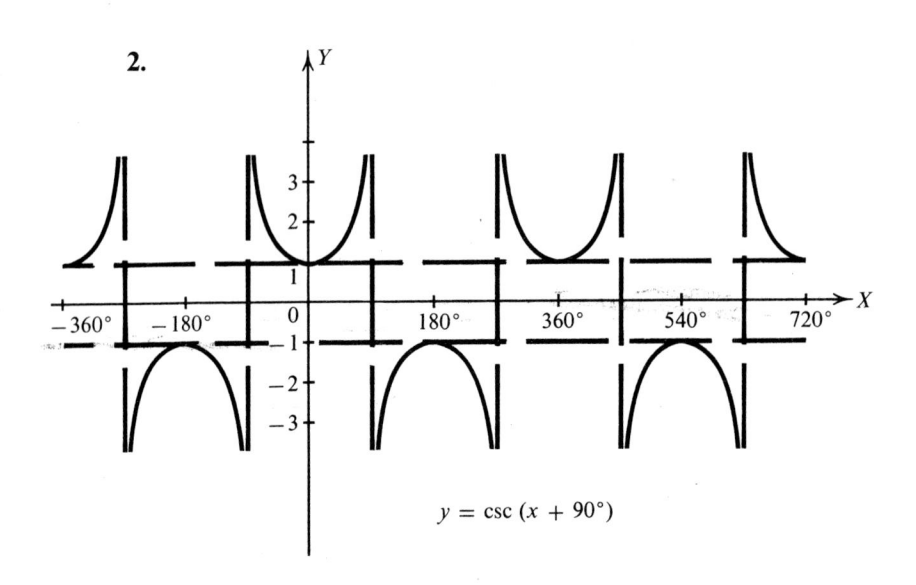

$y = \csc (x + 90°)$

Note that the graph of $y = \csc (x + 90°)$ is the graph of $y = \sec x$.

199

CIRCULAR FUNCTIONS AND THEIR GRAPHS

§ 4-9. **1.**

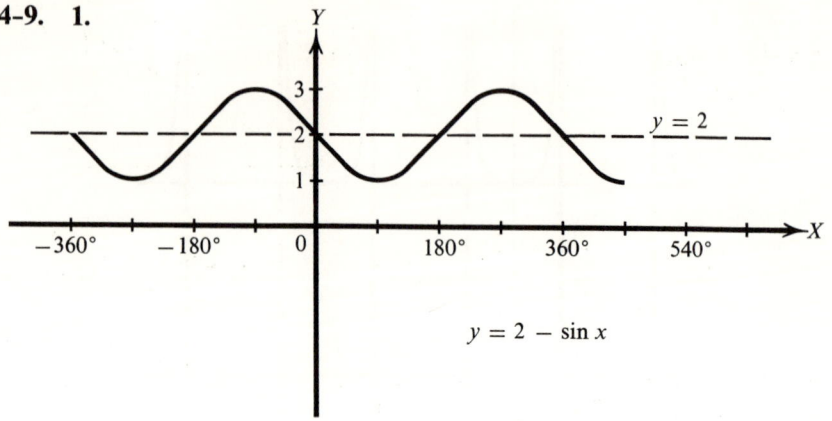

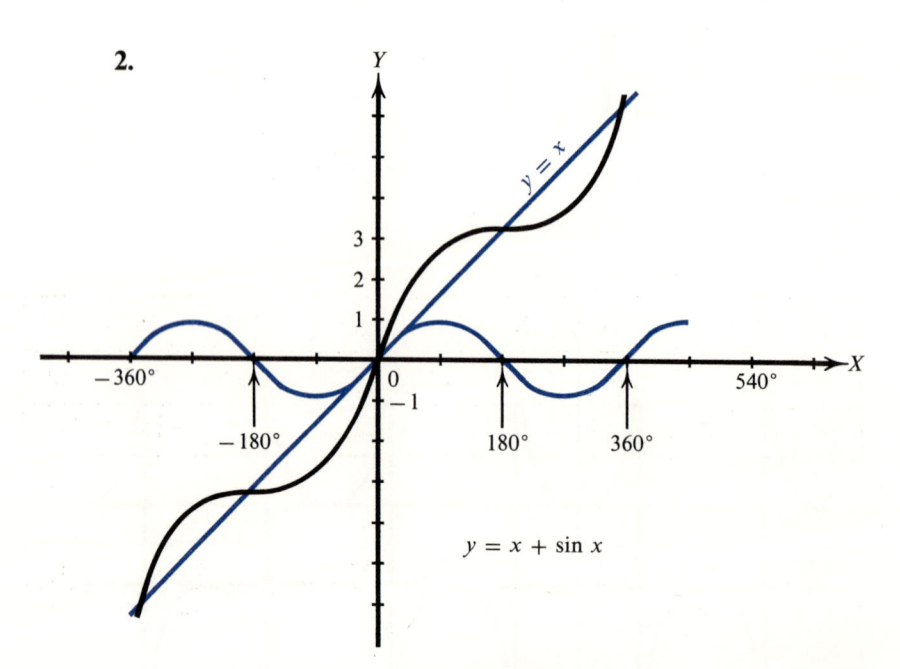

$y = 2 - \sin x$

2.

$y = x + \sin x$

§ 4-10. **1.** $\sin\left(\text{Arc}\cos\dfrac{1}{2}\right) = \sin 60° \approx 0.8660.$ **2.** $\dfrac{1}{3}.$ **3.** $\theta = 135°.$

§ 4-11. **1.** 2. **2.** $\dfrac{\sqrt{10}}{10}.$

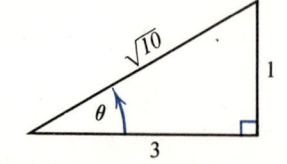

3. $\tan\theta = -\sqrt{3},\ \theta = -60°.$

200

ANSWERS TO KEYED PRACTICE ON CHAPTER 4

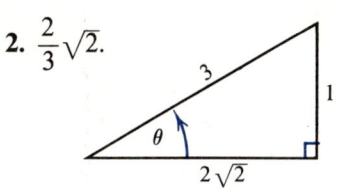

§ 4-12. 1. $\dfrac{1}{17}$. 2. $\dfrac{2}{3}\sqrt{2}$.

3. Arc sec $\left(-\dfrac{2\sqrt{3}}{3}\right)$ = Arc cos $\left(-\dfrac{\sqrt{3}}{2}\right)$, $\cos\theta = -\dfrac{\sqrt{3}}{2}$, $\theta = 150°$.

§ 4-13. 1. (a) $(-25\sqrt{2}, 25\sqrt{2})$; (b) $(2, 0)$.
2. (a) $(4\sqrt{2}, 315°)$; (b) $(4, 150°)$.

3. *(circle, $r = 3$)*

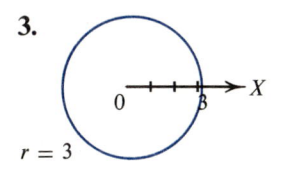

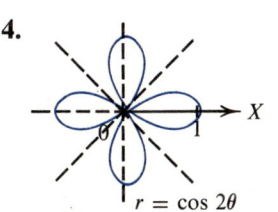

4. *(four-petal rose, $r = \cos 2\theta$)*

Table of values for $r = \cos 2\theta$:

θ	0°	15°	22½°	30°	45°	60°	67½°	75°	90°
2θ	0°	30°	45°	60°	90°	120°	135°	150°	180°
r	1	0.87	0.71	0.5	0	−0.5	−0.71	−0.87	−1

ANSWERS TO KEYED PRACTICE ON CHAPTER 4

1. $\sin B = \dfrac{12}{13}$; $\cos B = \dfrac{5}{13}$; $\tan B = \dfrac{12}{5}$; $\cot B = \dfrac{5}{12}$; $\sec B = \dfrac{13}{5}$; $\csc B = \dfrac{13}{12}$.

2. $4\sqrt{2}$ inches.

3. $\sin MOQ = \dfrac{4}{5}$; $\cos MOQ = -\dfrac{3}{5}$; $\tan MOQ = -\dfrac{4}{3}$; $\cot MOQ = -\dfrac{3}{4}$; $\sec MOQ = -\dfrac{5}{3}$; $\csc MOQ = \dfrac{5}{4}$.

4. In first quadrant all are positive; in second quadrant the sine and cosecant are positive; in third quadrant the tangent and cotangent are positive; in fourth quadrant the cosine and secant are positive.

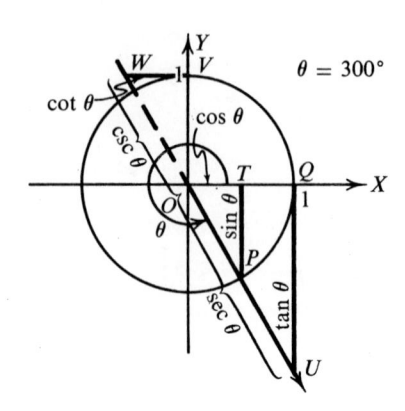

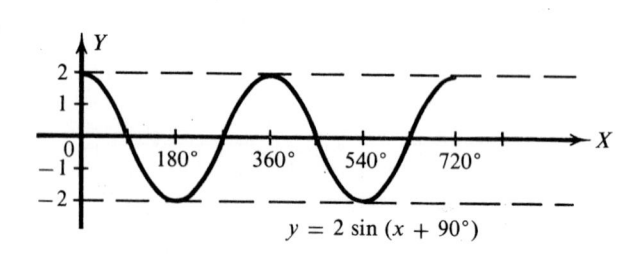

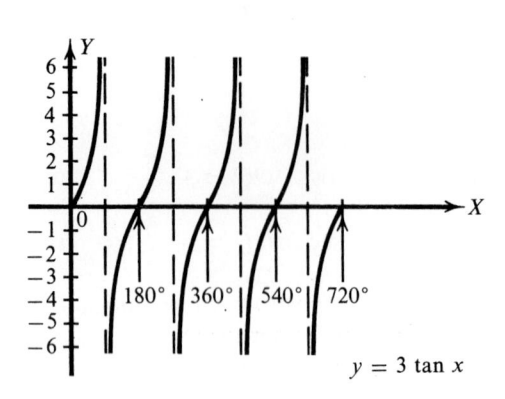

CIRCULAR FUNCTIONS AND THEIR GRAPHS

5. $\theta = 300°$

6. $y = 2 \sin(x + 90°)$

7. $y = 3 \tan x$

202

ANSWERS TO KEYED PRACTICE ON CHAPTER 4

8.

$y = \sec(x - 90°)$

9.

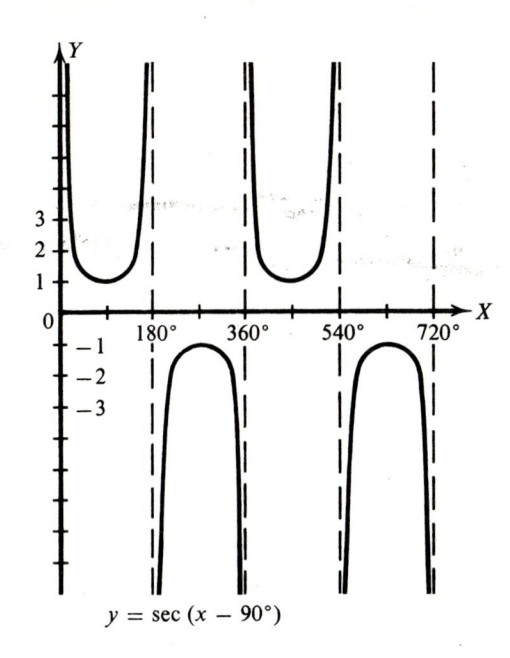

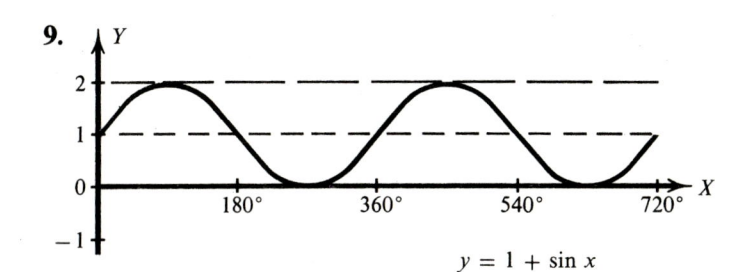

$y = 1 + \sin x$

10. $\dfrac{\sqrt{21}}{5}$.

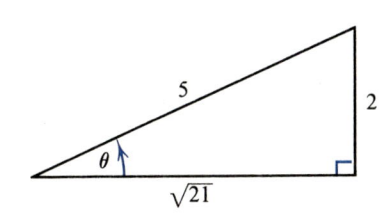

203

CIRCULAR FUNCTIONS AND THEIR GRAPHS

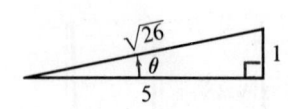

11. $\dfrac{\sqrt{26}}{26}$.

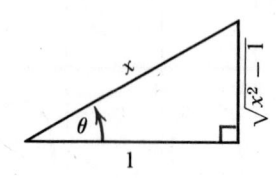

12. $\dfrac{\sqrt{x^2 - 1}}{x}$.

13. $(8, 330°), (-8, 150°)$ and in general for any integer k we may use $(8, \ 330° + k360°), \ (-8, \ 150° + k360°), \ (8, \ \dfrac{11}{6}\pi + 2k\pi),$ or $(-8, \ \dfrac{5}{6}\pi + 2k\pi)$.

Chapter 5

Statements Involving Circular Functions

§ 5-1 Identities

In the study of trigonometry the relations among the ratios are often considered more important than the solution of triangles. The ratios have been defined as circular functions for general angles in § 4–3:

$$\sin \theta = \frac{y}{r}; \quad \csc \theta = \frac{r}{y};$$

$$\cos \theta = \frac{x}{r}; \quad \sec \theta = \frac{r}{x};$$

$$\tan \theta = \frac{y}{x}; \quad \cot \theta = \frac{x}{y}.$$

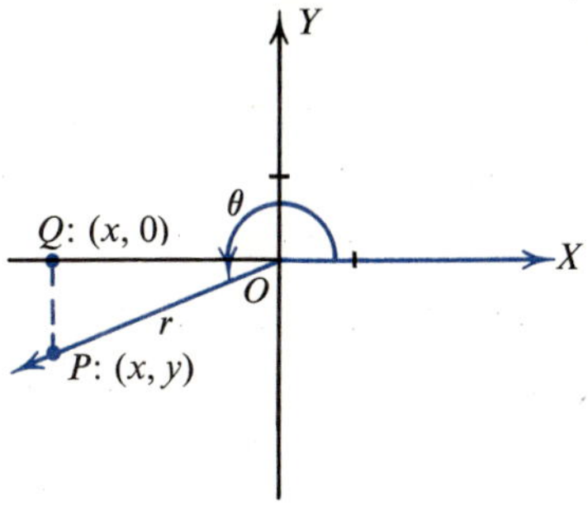

Figure 5–1

From this array we may observe the three **reciprocal relations** among the ratios:

$$\sin \theta = \frac{1}{\csc \theta}; \quad \cos \theta = \frac{1}{\sec \theta}; \quad \tan \theta = \frac{1}{\cot \theta}.$$

These relations may also be written as:

$$\sin \theta \csc \theta = 1; \quad \cos \theta \sec \theta = 1; \quad \tan \theta \cot \theta = 1. \tag{1}$$

Notice that the product $(\sin \theta)(\csc \theta)$ is written as $\sin \theta \csc \theta$ without parentheses. The parentheses are used only when necessary. For example, $\sin 2\theta$ is not the same as $2 \sin \theta$ as may be observed by comparing $\sin 60°$ and $2 \sin 30°$. However, $2 \sin \theta$ may also be written as $(\sin \theta)(2)$. If we wish to express the square of the circular function $\sin \theta$, we may write $\sin \theta \sin \theta$ or $(\sin \theta)^2$; but we customarily use the more convenient notation $\sin^2 \theta$. This is read "the sine squared of θ." Similarly, we may express the nth power of any circular function in the form $\sin^n \theta$.

For any point $P: (x, y)$ and $\overline{OP} = r$ as in Figure 5–1 we have $x^2 + y^2 = r^2$ by the distance formula (§ 1–7). If we divide both sides of

205

STATEMENTS INVOLVING CIRCULAR FUNCTIONS

this equation by r^2, x^2, and y^2 in turn, we have these equations:

$$\frac{x^2}{r^2} + \frac{y^2}{r^2} = \frac{r^2}{r^2}, \quad \text{that is,} \quad \sin^2\theta + \cos^2\theta = 1; \qquad (2)$$

$$\frac{x^2}{x^2} + \frac{y^2}{x^2} = \frac{r^2}{x^2}, \quad \text{that is,} \quad 1 + \tan^2\theta = \sec^2\theta; \qquad (3)$$

$$\frac{x^2}{y^2} + \frac{y^2}{y^2} = \frac{r^2}{y^2}, \quad \text{that is,} \quad \cot^2\theta + 1 = \csc^2\theta. \qquad (4)$$

These three relations are called the **Pythagorean relations.**

The Pythagorean and the reciprocal relations are called **identities** since they are true for all possible replacements of the variables for which the ratios are defined. We use identities to simplify expressions.

Example 1. Simplify: $\csc\theta\,(1 - \cos^2\theta)$.

Notice that $\sin^2\theta = 1 - \cos^2\theta$. Then
$\csc\theta\,(1 - \cos^2\theta) = \csc\theta\,\sin^2\theta = (\csc\theta\,\sin\theta)(\sin\theta) = \sin\theta$.

The general definitions $\sin\theta = \frac{y}{r}$, $\cos\theta = \frac{x}{r}$, $\tan\theta = \frac{y}{x}$, $\cot\theta = \frac{x}{y}$ may be used to derive these two additional identities:

$$\frac{\sin\theta}{\cos\theta} = \frac{\frac{y}{r}}{\frac{x}{r}} = \frac{y}{x} = \tan\theta, \quad \text{that is,} \quad \tan\theta = \frac{\sin\theta}{\cos\theta}; \qquad (5)$$

$$\frac{\cos\theta}{\sin\theta} = \frac{\frac{x}{r}}{\frac{y}{r}} = \frac{x}{y} = \cot\theta, \quad \text{that is,} \quad \cot\theta = \frac{\cos\theta}{\sin\theta}. \qquad (6)$$

You may *prove* these or any other identities by using reversible steps to simplify each member of the equation to the same expression; that is, by using the axiom:

<u>Expressions equal to the same expression are equal to each other.</u>

Many people think of this axiom in a slightly more general form as making it possible to substitute any quantity or expression for its equal. You may prove any identity by showing the steps needed

(a) to replace either member by the other as an equivalent expression, or

(b) to replace both members by the same equivalent expression (that is, "make both sides into the same expression").

§ 5-1 IDENTITIES

Example 2. Prove: $\cot \theta = \dfrac{\cos \theta}{\sin \theta}$.

$$\cot \theta = \frac{1}{\tan \theta} = \frac{1}{\frac{\sin \theta}{\cos \theta}} = \frac{\cos \theta}{\sin \theta}.$$

Example 3. Prove: $\sin^2 \theta \cot^2 \theta - 1 = -\sin^2 \theta$.

$$\sin^2 \theta \cot^2 \theta - 1 = \sin^2 \theta \times \frac{\cos^2 \theta}{\sin^2 \theta} - 1 = \cos^2 \theta - 1$$
$$= -(1 - \cos^2 \theta) = -\sin^2 \theta.$$

Trigonometric identities may be used to express each of the six circular functions of an angle θ in terms of any one of these functions, for instance $\cos \theta$:

$$\sin \theta = \pm\sqrt{1 - \cos^2 \theta}; \qquad \csc \theta = \frac{1}{\pm\sqrt{1 - \cos^2 \theta}};$$

$$\cos \theta = \cos \theta; \qquad \sec \theta = \frac{1}{\cos \theta};$$

$$\tan \theta = \frac{\pm\sqrt{1 - \cos^2 \theta}}{\cos \theta}; \qquad \cot \theta = \frac{\cos \theta}{\pm\sqrt{1 - \cos^2 \theta}}.$$

The sign of each circular function can be determined if the quadrant containing the terminal side when the angle is in standard position is known (§ 4-3). Thus for any given angle the signs of the radicals in the preceding equations can be easily determined.

The formulas for the circular functions of $(-\theta)$ in terms of functions of θ that you considered in § 4-4 are also identities:

$$\begin{aligned}
\sin(-\theta) &= -\sin \theta; & \csc(-\theta) &= -\csc \theta; \\
\cos(-\theta) &= \cos \theta; & \sec(-\theta) &= \sec \theta; \\
\tan(-\theta) &= -\tan \theta; & \cot(-\theta) &= -\cot \theta.
\end{aligned} \qquad (7)$$

Now study these figures:

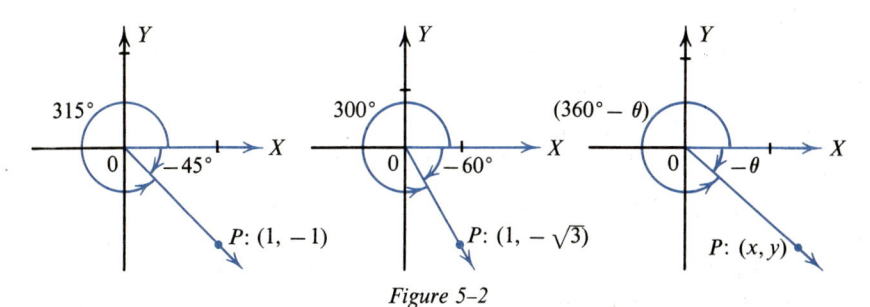

Figure 5-2

STATEMENTS INVOLVING CIRCULAR FUNCTIONS

Notice that if P is on the terminal side of an angle of $-45°$ in standard position, then P is on the terminal side of an angle of $315°$. If P is on the terminal side of $-60°$, then P is on the terminal side of an angle of $300°$. If P is on the terminal side of an angle of $(-\theta)$, then P is on the terminal side of an angle of $(360° - \theta)$. The circular functions of an angle of $(360° - \theta)$ can be defined in terms of the same point P as functions of an angle of $(-\theta)$; the same values of x, y, and r can be used. Check this statement for $315°$ and $-45°$ as in the figure; for $300°$ and $-60°$. Then the circular functions of $(360° - \theta)$ are the same as the functions of $(-\theta)$:

$$\sin(360° - \theta) = \sin(-\theta) = -\sin\theta;$$
$$\cos(360° - \theta) = \cos(-\theta) = \cos\theta;$$
$$\tan(360° - \theta) = \tan(-\theta) = -\tan\theta;$$
$$\cot(360° - \theta) = \cot(-\theta) = -\cot\theta;$$
$$\sec(360° - \theta) = \sec(-\theta) = \sec\theta;$$
$$\csc(360° - \theta) = \csc(-\theta) = -\csc\theta.$$

These formulas are true for all values of θ for which the functions are defined; that is, they are identities. Other formulas are developed in Examples 4 and 5 and the exercises.

Example 4. Find formulas for the six circular functions of $150°$ in terms of functions of $30°$.

Draw a figure with $P: (-\sqrt{3}, 1)$ and $Q: (\sqrt{3}, 1)$ on the terminal sides of the angles in standard position. Then

$$\sin 150° = \frac{y}{r} = \frac{1}{2} = \sin 30°;$$

$$\cos 150° = \frac{x}{r} = \frac{-\sqrt{3}}{2} = -\frac{\sqrt{3}}{2} = -\cos 30°;$$

$$\tan 150° = \frac{y}{x} = \frac{1}{-\sqrt{3}} = -\frac{1}{\sqrt{3}} = -\tan 30°;$$

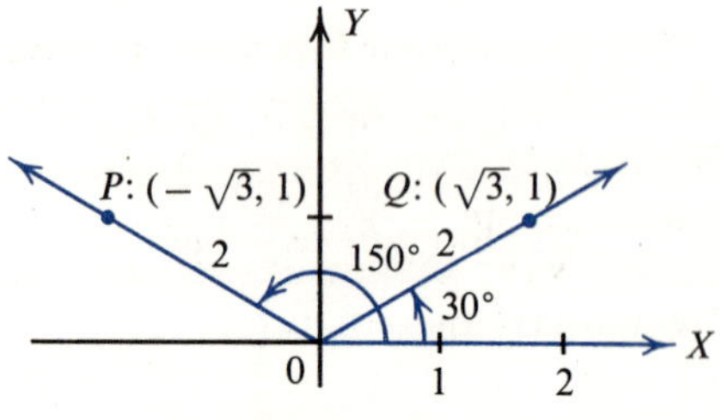

$$\cot 150° = \frac{x}{y} = \frac{-\sqrt{3}}{1} = -\frac{\sqrt{3}}{1} = -\cot 30°;$$

$$\sec 150° = \frac{r}{x} = \frac{2}{-\sqrt{3}} = -\frac{2}{\sqrt{3}} = -\sec 30°;$$

$$\csc 150° = \frac{r}{y} = \frac{2}{1} = \csc 30°.$$

Figure 5–3

§ 5-1 IDENTITIES

Example 5. Find formulas for the six circular functions of $(180° - \theta)$ in terms of functions of θ.

Draw a figure with $P: (x, y)$ on the terminal side of the angle $(180° - \theta)$ in standard position. Then if θ is acute, x is negative. In any case $Q: (-x, y)$ is on the terminal side of the angle θ in standard position. Then

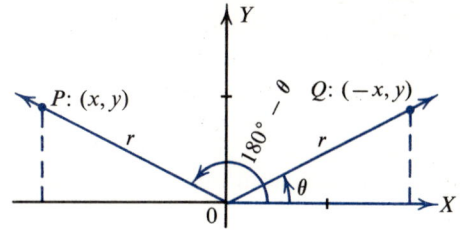

Figure 5-4

$$\sin (180° - \theta) = \frac{y}{r} = \sin \theta;$$

$$\cos (180° - \theta) = \frac{x}{r} = -\frac{-x}{r} = -\cos \theta;$$

$$\tan (180° - \theta) = \frac{y}{x} = -\frac{y}{-x} = -\tan \theta;$$

$$\cot (180° - \theta) = \frac{x}{y} = -\frac{-x}{y} = -\cot \theta;$$

$$\sec (180° - \theta) = \frac{r}{x} = -\frac{r}{-x} = -\sec \theta;$$

$$\csc (180° - \theta) = \frac{r}{y} = \csc \theta.$$

The six circular functions may be paired by reciprocals: sine and cosecant, cosine and secant, tangent and cotangent. They may also be paired in terms of their names: sine and *co*sine, tangent and *co*tangent, secant and *co*secant. We speak of sine and cosine as **cofunctions.** Then the cosine is the cofunction of sine; the sine is the cofunction of the cosine. Similar statements may be made for tangent and cotangent and for secant and cosecant. For acute angles each "cofunction" is "the function of the complement" of the angle (Figure 5-5):

$$\cos \theta = \frac{x}{r} = \sin (90° - \theta);$$

$$\cot \theta = \frac{x}{y} = \tan (90° - \theta);$$

$$\csc \theta = \frac{r}{y} = \sec (90° - \theta).$$

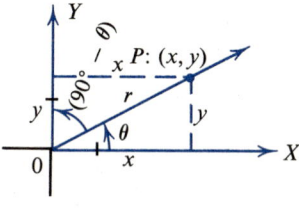

Figure 5-5

Another use of cofunctions is illustrated in Example 6.

209

STATEMENTS INVOLVING CIRCULAR FUNCTIONS

Example 6. Find formulas for the six circular functions of 150° in terms of functions of 60°.

Use Example 4 and the properties of cofunctions:

$$\sin 150° = \sin 30° = \cos 60°;$$
$$\cos 150° = -\cos 30° = -\sin 60°;$$
$$\tan 150° = -\tan 30° = -\cot 60°.$$

Then continue in this way or use the reciprocal relations:

$$\cot 150° = \frac{1}{\tan 150°} = \frac{1}{-\cot 60°} = -\tan 60°;$$

$$\sec 150° = \frac{1}{\cos 150°} = \frac{1}{-\sin 60°} = -\csc 60°;$$

$$\csc 150° = \frac{1}{\sin 150°} = \frac{1}{\cos 60°} = \sec 60°.$$

Notice in the exercises that frequently other letters have been used in place of θ and that both forms of the abbreviation for cotangent have been used. These variations have been introduced to help you become familiar with different notations which you may meet in other courses.

The instruction to *simplify* a trigonometric expression implies that, whenever possible, indicated operations should be performed and fractions should be reduced. It is often convenient to leave an answer in terms of sines, cosines, tangents, or cotangents since tables of values for these functions are readily available in most books dealing with elementary trigonometry.

TEST YOURSELF

1. Simplify: $\cos^2 \theta + \frac{1}{\sec^2 \theta}$.
2. Simplify: $\sqrt{\frac{1}{\cos^2 A} - 1}$.
3. Prove: $1 - \sin^2 x + \sin x \cot x = \cos^2 x + \cos x$.

EXERCISES

A

Simplify:

1. $\cos \theta \tan \theta$.
2. $\cos \theta \sec \theta$.
3. $\sin A \sec A$.
4. $\csc B \tan B$.
5. $\sec x \sqrt{1 - \sin^2 x}$.
6. $\csc \beta (1 - \cos^2 \beta)$.

§ 5-1 IDENTITIES

7. $\cos \alpha (1 + \tan^2 \alpha)$.
8. $(\sec^2 \alpha - 1) \cos^2 \alpha$.

9. $(\csc^2 c - 1) \tan c$.
10. $(1 - \sec^2 c) \cot c$.

• • •

11. $(1 - \cos^2 \theta)(1 + \cot^2 \theta)$.
12. $\cos A + \dfrac{\sin A}{\text{ctn } A}$.
13. $\dfrac{\cos \gamma \csc \gamma}{\cot \gamma}$.
14. $\dfrac{\sin \theta}{\cos \theta \tan^2 \theta}$.
15. $\sqrt{\dfrac{1 - \cos x}{1 + \cos x}}$.

16. $\dfrac{1}{\tan^2 x \sec^2 x} + \cos^2 x$.
17. $\tan^2 \beta \sec^2 \beta - \sec^2 \beta + 1$.
18. $\dfrac{\sin A}{1 - \cos A} + \dfrac{\sin A}{1 + \cos A}$.
19. $\dfrac{\sin x - 1}{\sin x + 1} - \dfrac{\sin x + 1}{\sin x - 1}$.
20. $\dfrac{\tan x + \text{ctn } y}{\text{ctn } x + \tan y}$.

B

1. Express each of the circular functions in terms of $\cos \theta$ as in this section. Select the proper sign for each radical when the terminal side of θ is in the second quadrant.
2. Repeat Exercise 1 for the third quadrant.
3. Repeat Exercise 1 for the fourth quadrant.

• • •

4. Express each of the circular functions in terms of $\sin \theta$ for any acute angle θ.
5. Repeat Exercise 4 when the terminal side of θ is in (a) the second quadrant; (b) the third quadrant; (c) the fourth quadrant.
6. Repeat Exercise 4 for $\tan \theta$.
7. Repeat Exercise 4 for $\cot \theta$.
8. Repeat Exercise 4 for $\sec \theta$.
9. Repeat Exercise 4 for $\csc \theta$.

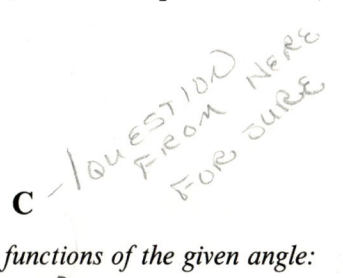

C

Find formulas for the six circular functions of the given angle:

1. $135°$ in terms of $45°$.
2. $210°$ in terms of $30°$.
3. $225°$ in terms of $45°$.
4. $210°$ in terms of $60°$.
5. $300°$ in terms of $30°$.
6. $300°$ in terms of $60°$.

STATEMENTS INVOLVING CIRCULAR FUNCTIONS

7. $(180° + \theta)$ in terms of θ.
8. $(90° + \theta)$ in terms of θ.
9. $(270° - \theta)$ in terms of θ.
10. $(270° + \theta)$ in terms of θ.
11. $30°$ in terms of $60°$.
12. $(90° - \theta)$ in terms of θ.

Explain each statement:

- 13. Cofunctions of complementary angles are equal.
- 14. For any specified circular function the absolute values of the functions of supplementary angles are equal.

D

Simplify:

1. $\sec \theta \sin (90° + \theta)$.
2. $\cos \theta \tan (90° + \theta)$.
3. $\tan \theta \cot (180° - \theta)$.
4. $\sec \theta \cot (-\theta)$.
5. $\sin (-\theta) \sec (-\theta)$.
6. $\sin (90° + \alpha) \cos (90° - \alpha)$.
7. $\tan (180° - \alpha) \sin (180° + \alpha)$.
8. $\sin (180° - \alpha) \sec (270° - \alpha)$.
9. $\cos (270° - \alpha) \cot (180° - \alpha)$.
10. $\sec (270° - \alpha) \tan (-\alpha)$.

11. $1 - \sin^2 (-\alpha)$.
12. $\sec^2 (90° - \alpha) - 1$.
13. $\dfrac{\sin (90° - \alpha)}{\cos (90° + \alpha)}$.
14. $\dfrac{1}{\tan^2 (90° + \alpha)} + 1$.
15. $1 - \dfrac{1}{\csc^2 (180° + \alpha)}$.

16. $\sin (-\alpha) \cos (90° - \alpha) - 1$.
17. $\tan (-\alpha) \cot (180° + \alpha) + 1$.
- 18. $\dfrac{\sec (-\alpha) \sin \alpha}{\csc (-\alpha) \cos \alpha} - 1$.
- 19. $\dfrac{\tan (90° + \alpha)}{\cot (90° - \alpha)} + \dfrac{\cot (180° + \alpha)}{\cot (180° - \alpha)}$.
- 20. $\dfrac{\sin (90° + \alpha)}{1 + \sin \alpha} + \dfrac{\sin (90° - \alpha)}{1 + \sin (-\alpha)}$.

E

Prove each of these identities:

1. $\csc \beta - \cos \beta \cot \beta = \sin \beta$.
2. $\sin \gamma \tan \gamma - \sec \gamma = -\cos \gamma$.
3. $\dfrac{\sin^2 x - \cos^2 x}{\tan^2 x - 1} = \cos^2 x$.

4. $\cos^2 \alpha - \sin^2 \alpha = 2\cos^2 \alpha - 1$.
5. $\tan^2 \theta \sin^2 \theta + \sin^2 \theta = \tan^2 \theta$.

§ 5-2 VALUES OF CIRCULAR FUNCTIONS

6. $(1 - \sin^2 x)(1 + \tan^2 x) = \cot x \tan x.$

7. $\dfrac{\sin x}{1 - \cos x} = \dfrac{1 + \cos x}{\sin x}.$

8. $\dfrac{\ctn x}{\csc x - 1} = \tan x(1 + \csc x).$

9. $\dfrac{1 + \tan^2 \beta}{1 + \cot^2 \beta} = \dfrac{1}{\cot^2 \beta}.$

• 10. $\dfrac{1}{\sec \alpha - \tan \alpha} + \dfrac{1}{\sec \alpha + \tan \alpha} = \dfrac{2 \tan \alpha}{\sin \alpha}.$

§ 5-2 Values of circular functions

The values of circular functions may be estimated from graphs as in § 4-5. Closer approximations for these values may be obtained from a table of values. Table II on pages 732 through 737 includes approximations for the sine, cosine, tangent, and cotangent ratios. All defined values are given for θ measured in degrees to the nearest 10′, $0° \leq \theta \leq 90°$. Approximations for secant and cosecant may be found using the relations

$$\sec \theta = \frac{1}{\cos \theta}, \quad \csc \theta = \frac{1}{\sin \theta}.$$

The table makes use of the fact that $\sin \theta = \cos(90° - \theta)$ and that $\tan \theta = \cot(90° - \theta)$. For example, you use the value of θ in the column at the left and the heading at the top of page 734 to find 0.3035 for $\sin 17° 40′$; you use the value of θ in the column at the right and the heading at the bottom of the page to find this 0.3035 for $\cos 72° 20′$.

You use the column at the left of each page of Table II and the headings at the top of each page for values of θ such that $0° \leq \theta \leq 45°$. You use the values of θ in the column at the right and headings at the bottom of each page for values of θ such that $45° \leq \theta \leq 90$.

To estimate values of ratios which are not in the table, interpolate as in the examples. Note that we use the symbol = for values from the table as a matter of custom even though $\approx$ would be appropriate. Practically all values in the table are approximations.

Example 1. Find $\sin 35° 17′$ from Table II.

$$10\left[7\begin{bmatrix}\sin 35° 20′ = 0.5783 \\ \sin 35° 17′ = \ ? \\ \sin 35° 10′ = 0.5760\end{bmatrix} x\right]23 \qquad \frac{7}{10} = \frac{x}{23}$$

Since $\dfrac{7}{10}$ of $23 \approx 16$, we add 16 ten-thousandths to $\sin 35° 10′$. The value for $\sin 35° 17′$ from the table is 0.5776.

STATEMENTS INVOLVING CIRCULAR FUNCTIONS

Example 2. Find cos 65° 23′ from Table II.

$$10\left[3\begin{bmatrix}\cos 65° 30' = 0.4147\\ \cos 65° 23' = ?\\ \cos 65° 20' = 0.4173\end{bmatrix}x\right]-26 \qquad \frac{3}{10}=\frac{x}{-26}$$

Since $\frac{3}{10}$ of $-26 \approx -8$, we subtract 8 ten-thousandths from cos 65° 20′. Then cos 65° 23′ = 0.4165.

Notice that cos 65° 23′ must be between cos 65° 20′ and cos 65° 30′. That is, 0.4147 < cos 65° 23′ < 0.4173. You can frequently avoid errors by checking that your answer is between the proper numbers. In doing this it is helpful to keep in mind that sine and tangent are increasing functions as θ increases from 0° to 90°; cosine is a decreasing function as θ increases from 0° to 90°. For other sequences of values of θ consider the graphs of the functions in Chapter 4.

Example 3. Find θ to the nearest minute if $\tan \theta = 1.3286$ where $0° < \theta < 90°$.

Find the numbers nearest 1.3286 in Table II.

$$10\left[x\begin{bmatrix}\tan 53° 10' = 1.3351\\ \tan \theta = 1.3286\\ \tan 53° 0' = 1.3270\end{bmatrix}16\right]81 \qquad \frac{x}{10}=\frac{16}{81}$$

Since $\frac{16}{81} \approx \frac{2}{10}$. $\theta \approx 53° 2'$.

Example 4. Solve for θ where $0° \leq \theta \leq 90°$: $9 \sin^2 \theta = 4$.

If $9 \sin^2 \theta = 4$, then $9 \sin^2 \theta - 4 = 0$;
$(3 \sin \theta - 2)(3 \sin \theta + 2) = 0$;

$$\sin \theta = \frac{2}{3} \quad \text{or} \quad -\frac{2}{3}.$$

That is, $\sin \theta = 0.6667$ or -0.6667.

When $0° < \theta \leq 90°$, $\sin \theta$ is positive. So we consider only the positive value.

$$10\left[x\begin{bmatrix}\sin 41° 50' = 0.6670\\ \sin \theta = 0.6667\\ \sin 41° 40' = 0.6648\end{bmatrix}19\right]22 \qquad \frac{x}{10}=\frac{19}{22}$$

Since $\frac{19}{22} \approx \frac{9}{10}$, $\theta \approx 41° 49'$.

214

§ 5–2 VALUES OF CIRCULAR FUNCTIONS

Logarithms of the values of circular functions are very useful whenever computations are involved. Table III on pages 738 through 743 gives the logarithms of the values in Table II. Notice that "−10" is assumed whenever characteristics appear to be 7, 8, or 9.

The values in Table III can be found from Tables I and II. For example,

$$\sin 30° = 0.5000 \qquad \text{Table II}$$
$$\log(\sin 30°) = \log 0.5000 = 9.6990 - 10 \qquad \text{Table I}$$

Note that we can save time by reading the value of log (sin 30°) directly from Table III. Notice in the examples that we drop the parentheses and write expressions such as log (sin 30°) in the form log sin 30°.

Example 5. Find log cos 68° 53′.

$$10 \left[3 \begin{bmatrix} \log \cos 69° 0' = 9.5543 - 10 \\ \log \cos 68° 53' = \quad ? \\ \log \cos 68° 50' = 9.5576 - 10 \end{bmatrix} x \right] - 33 \quad \frac{3}{10} = \frac{x}{-33}$$

Since $\frac{3}{10}$ of $-33 \approx -10$, we subtract 10;
log cos 68° 53′ = 9.5566 − 10.

Example 6. Find θ, $0° < \theta < 90°$, when log sin $\theta = 9.9762 - 10$.

$$10 \left[x \begin{bmatrix} \log \sin 71° 20' = 9.9765 - 10 \\ \log \sin \theta \quad = 9.9762 - 10 \\ \log \sin 71° 10' = 9.9761 - 10 \end{bmatrix} 1 \right] 4 \quad \frac{x}{10} = \frac{1}{4}$$

Since $\frac{1}{4}$ of $10 \approx 2$, θ is about 71° 12′.

Note in Example 2 that we only use interpolation to the nearest minute. Note also that we round off the change for θ by the usual rules (§ 3–2).

Values obtained by slide rule are sufficiently accurate for graphing and often for computations; they are especially useful in checking computations. Since sin θ and tan θ are approximately equal for small positive

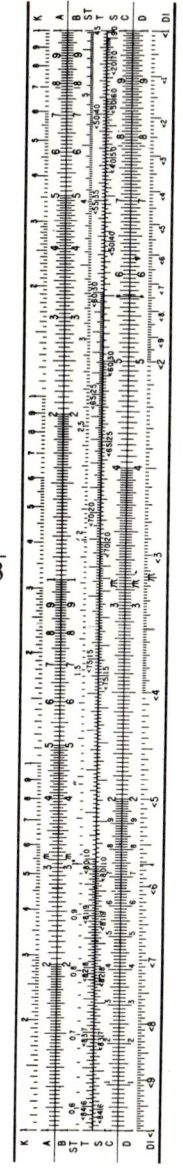

Figure 5–6

STATEMENTS INVOLVING CIRCULAR FUNCTIONS

values of θ, these values are often placed on the same scale. For angles from 34' to 5.7° the degrees are marked on the ST-scale; they match the common values of sine and tangent on the C-scale on the slide rule shown in Figure 5-6. For larger angles you use the values of θ in degrees marked on the S-scale and read $\sin \theta$ on the C-scale. You use values of θ up to 45° on the T-scale and read $\tan \theta$ on the C-scale. You use values of θ between 45° and 90° on the T-scale and read $\tan \theta$ on the DI (or CI) scale, since $\tan (90° - x) = \cot x = \dfrac{1}{\tan x}$. Remember that in all cases you determine the position of the decimal point. Values of $\cos \theta$ are found as $\sin (90° - \theta)$.

There are several types of slide rules. In each case you can quickly check which scales to use. For example, be sure that $\sin 30° = 0.5$ and that $\tan 45° = 1$.

TEST YOURSELF

Read on a slide rule and check in Table II:

1. sin 34°. 2. sin 67°. 3. tan 30°. 4. tan 70°.

Use Table II to find:

5. cos 35° 20'. 6. sin 64° 20'. 7. tan 64° 45'.

Use Table II to find θ where $0° < \theta < 90°$:

8. $\sin \theta = 0.1908$.
9. $\cos \theta = 0.2079$.
10. $\tan \theta = 1.4826$.
11. $\tan \theta = 0.4220$.

Use Table III to find:

12. log sin 20° 15'.
13. log cos 32° 19'.
14. log tan 65° 2'.
15. log cot 10° 4'.

Use Table III to find θ, $0° < \theta < 90°$, when:

16. $\log \sin \theta = 9.4130 - 10$.
17. $\log \cos \theta = 9.8968 - 10$.

EXERCISES

A

Read on a slide rule and check in Table II:

1. sin 25°. 4. tan 3°. 7. tan 68°. 10. sin 2°.
2. sin 35°. 5. tan 15°. 8. sin 75°. 11. tan 80°.
3. sin 4°.   6. sin 48°. 9. tan 50°. 12. sin 37°.

13. cos 38°. 16. cot 31°. • 19. sec 17°. • 22. sec 55°.
14. cos 87°. 17. cot 67°. • 20. csc 38°. • 23. sec 67°.
15. cos 20°. 18. cot 21°. • 21. csc 59°. • 24. csc 10°.

B

Use Table II to find:

1. sin 10° 20'.   3. tan 42° 10'.   5. cot 25° 23'.   7. cos 65° 53'.
2. cos 30° 30'.   4. tan 67° 20'.   6. sin 37° 37'.   8. tan 5° 1'.

Use Table II to find θ where $0° \leq \theta \leq 90°$:

9. $\sin \theta = 0.9613$.   13. $\sin \theta = 0.8360$.   • 17. $\csc \theta = 2.5$.
10. $\cos \theta = 0.9613$.   14. $\tan \theta = 2$.   • 18. $\sec \theta = \frac{4}{3}$.
11. $\tan \theta = 0.7720$.   • 15. $\sec \theta = 2$.
12. $\cot \theta = 0.8421$.   • 16. $\csc \theta = 3$.

C

Use Table III to find:

1. log sin 10° 10'.   3. log cos 65° 12'.   5. log cos 3° 1'.
2. log sin 70° 20'.   4. log tan 67° 15'.   6. log tan 5° 12'.

Use Table III to find θ, $0° < \theta < 90°$, when:

7. $\log \sin \theta = 9.6418 - 10$.   11. $\log \cot \theta = 1.0583$.
8. $\log \cos \theta = 9.9138 - 10$.   12. $\log \cot \theta = 9.0894 - 10$.
9. $\log \tan \theta = 8.5441 - 10$.   • 13. $\log \sec \theta = 0.9784$.
10. $\log \tan \theta = 1.4500$.   • 14. $\log \csc \theta = 0.2639$.

§ 5-3 Solution of right triangles

A triangle is *solved* when the length of each of its sides and the measure of each of its angles is known. Different cases arise according to the given information; that is, the way in which the triangle is *determined*. Any triangle is a **right triangle** if it has a 90° angle, an **oblique triangle** if it does not have a 90° angle. A right triangle ABC with $\angle C = 90°$ may be determined in any one of these ways:

1. Hypotenuse and leg, that is, c and a.
2. Hypotenuse and acute angle, that is, c and A.
3. Two legs, a and b.
4. Leg and acute angle, either a and A or a and B.

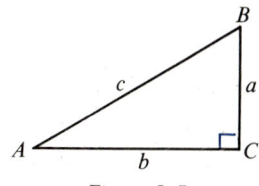

Figure 5-7

217

STATEMENTS INVOLVING CIRCULAR FUNCTIONS

In each case the trigonometric ratios, the equation $\angle A + \angle B + \angle C = 180°$, and the Pythagorean Theorem may be used to find the missing parts. The values for the trigonometric ratios may be found in tables, from their logarithms, or by the use of a slide rule (§ 5-2).

You should observe that the given facts are precisely the ones which you used in plane geometry when you proved two triangles congruent. Your concern there, as here, was to *determine* the triangle.

The following steps are suggested in solving triangles:

1. Draw a figure approximately to scale. This will help you to estimate the values of the required parts and thus avoid obvious errors.

2. Try to select one of the four trigonometric ratios (sine, cosine, tangent, and cotangent) listed in the table so that two of the given parts and one of the unknown parts which you wish to find are involved.

3. Arrange your work neatly following patterns such as those shown in the following examples. This will reduce the number of careless errors.

4. In finding any unknown part try to use only the given parts. Note that if an error is made in finding one unknown part, any other unknown parts found by using this one can be expected to be wrong also.

5. Check your work. If possible use a formula which involves all the parts that you have found.

Example 1. Solve triangle ABC if $\angle C = 90°$, $a = 23.50$, and $b = 18.00$.

Given:
$\angle C = 90°$
$a = 23.50$
$b = 18.00$

Find:
$\angle A$
$\angle B$
c

$\tan A = \dfrac{a}{b} = \dfrac{23.50}{18.00} \approx 1.3056,\ \angle A \approx 52°\ 33'.$

$\tan B = \dfrac{b}{a} = \dfrac{18.00}{23.50} \approx 0.7660,\ \angle B \approx 37°\ 27'.$

$c = \sqrt{a^2 + b^2} = \sqrt{552.25 + 324.00} \approx 29.60.$

CHECK: $\sin A = \dfrac{a}{c}$; $\sin 52°\ 33' = 0.7939.$

$\dfrac{a}{c} \approx \dfrac{23.50}{29.60} \approx 0.7939.$

$\angle A \approx 52°\ 33',\ \angle B \approx 37°\ 27',\ c \approx 29.60.$

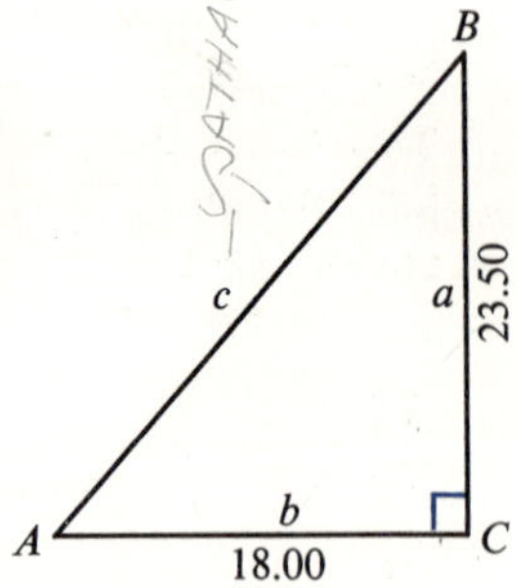

Figure 5–8

218

§ 5-3 SOLUTION OF RIGHT TRIANGLES

Example 2. Solve triangle ABC if $\angle A = 23°\,17'$, $\angle C = 90°$, $a = 0.1192$.

Given:
$\angle A = 23°\,17'$
$\angle C = 90°$
$a = 0.1192$

Find:
$\angle B$
b
c

$\angle B = 90° - \angle A = 90° - 23°\,17' = 66°\,43'$.
$b = a \cot A = 0.1192 \times 2.3239 \approx 0.2770$.
$c = \dfrac{a}{\sin A} = \dfrac{0.1192}{0.3953} \approx 0.3015$.

$\angle B = 66°\,43'$, $b \approx 0.2770$, $c \approx 0.3015$.

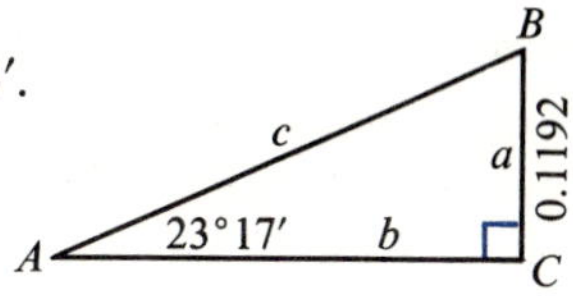

CHECK: $\sin B = \dfrac{b}{c}$; $\sin 66°\,43' = 0.9186$.

$\dfrac{b}{c} = \dfrac{0.2770}{0.3015} \approx 0.9187$.

Figure 5–9

Note that all computations based upon tables of values of trigonometric ratios should be expected to be approximate. Thus two methods for computing the same number may give results which differ slightly in the fourth significant digit. Accordingly the check for Example 2 is considered satisfactory.

Many applications of trigonometry involve angles measured up or down from a horizontal line. An angle measured up from a horizontal line is an **angle of elevation.** An angle measured down from a horizontal line is an **angle of depression.** For any given inclined line the angles of elevation and depression are equal.

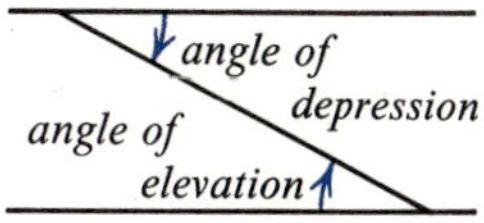

Figure 5–10

Example 3. A kite string 350 yards long has an angle of elevation of 33°. Assume that the string is a straight line and find the height of the kite.

The angle of elevation is measured from a horizontal line. The height of the kite is measured along the vertical line. These lines and the line along the kite string form a right triangle ABC; $\overline{AB} = 350$ yards; $\angle A = 33°$, $\angle C = 90°$.

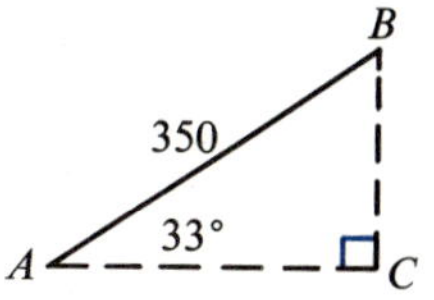

Figure 5–11

$\dfrac{BC}{AB} = \sin A$ Definition of $\sin A$ in triangle ABC.

$\dfrac{BC}{350} = \sin 33°$ Substitute given values.

219

STATEMENTS INVOLVING CIRCULAR FUNCTIONS

$\overline{BC} = 350 \sin 33°$ Multiply both members by 350.
$\overline{BC} = 350 \times 0.5446$ See Table II.
$\overline{BC} = 190.61$

The kite is about 191 yards high.

Several of the word problems in this chapter will involve compass directions. These will be given in the manner used by the armed forces. The given degrees are measured clockwise from north (000°). Thus east is 090°, south is 180°, and west is 270°.

TEST YOURSELF

In Exercises 1 and 2 solve and check triangle ABC if $\angle C = 90°$ and:

1. $\angle B = 47°, c = 21.5$.
2. $b = 172, c = 200$.
3. Find to the nearest foot the height of a kite with a string 300 feet long and an angle of elevation of 40°.

EXERCISES

A

Solve each triangle:

1. Triangle with $\angle A = 30°$, $AB = 4$, right angle at C, sides a, b.
2. Triangle DEF with $DF = 5$, $EF = 5$, right angle at D, side f.
3. Triangle GHI with $GH = 12$, $HI = 6$, right angle at I, side h.
4. Triangle KLJ with $KJ = 18$, $\angle J = 45°$, right angle at L, side j, k.

5. Triangle MNO with $\angle M = 40°$, $MO = 25$, right angle at O, sides o, m, N.
6. Triangle PQR with $PR = 17$, $\angle P = 53°$, right angle at R, side r, p, Q.
7. Triangle TWS with $TW = 3$, $TS = 5$, right angle at W, side t.
8. Triangle XYZ with $XZ = 42$, $YZ = 31$, right angle at Z, side z.

9. A 62-foot ladder leans against a wall with the base of the ladder 11 feet from the wall. Find the angle which the ladder makes with the wall. Assume level ground and a vertical wall.

220

§ 5-3 SOLUTION OF RIGHT TRIANGLES

10. An airplane flies in the direction 037° at 475 m.p.h. Find the distance north that it travels in 1 hour.
• 11. A chord has a central angle of 50° in a circle of radius 3.75 inches. Find the length of the chord.
• 12. How high would a car climb while driving 4 miles up a 5 percent grade?

B

In Exercises 1 through 6 give a set of formulas that may be used to solve any right triangle ABC with $\angle C = 90°$ when these parts are known:

1. c and a.
2. c and $\angle A$.
3. a and b.
4. a and $\angle A$.
5. a and $\angle B$.
6. b and $\angle A$.

7 through 12. Give for each triangle in Exercises 1 through 6 a formula which would be suitable for checking the solution.

• • •

Solve and check triangle ABC if $\angle C = 90°$ and:

13. $\angle A = 60° 00'$, $b = 150.0$.
14. $\angle B = 67° 00'$, $a = 260.0$.
15. $a = 24.00$, $b = 36.00$.
16. $b = 8.400$, $c = 10.00$.
17. $\angle B = 36° 00'$, $c = 500.0$.
18. $\angle A = 47° 30'$, $c = 98.00$.
19. $a = 1.025$, $c = 1.904$.
20. $\angle A = 73° 28'$, $a = 3000$.
21. $\angle B = 48° 42'$, $b = 410.3$.
22. $\angle A = 33° 33'$, $c = 0.1414$.

C

1. Find the hypotenuse of right triangle ABC if $\angle C = 90°$, $\angle A = 23° 17'$, and $a = 0.1192$.
2. Find the base and altitude of an isosceles triangle whose vertex angle is 80° 40' and whose equal sides each measure 80.00 feet.
3. An airplane flew 564 miles in a northeasterly direction. How far east did it fly?
4. How tall is a tree with a shadow 225 feet long on the level when the angle of elevation of the sun is 48° 30'?
5. Find the angle of elevation of the sun when a tree 113 feet tall has a shadow 157 feet long on the level.
6. A pilot flying 1000 feet above the ground sights an airport at an angle of depression of 13°. Find his horizontal distance from the airport sighted.

221

STATEMENTS INVOLVING CIRCULAR FUNCTIONS

• • •

7. From the top of a cliff 350 feet above sea level, a boat is seen at an angle of depression of 32°. How far is the boat from the foot of the cliff? How far is the boat from the top of the cliff?

8. Find the length of the longest possible runway on a rectangular field 1.5 miles by 0.75 miles. What angle would the runway make with the longer side of the field?

9. Find the length of chord AB in a circle with radius 18.00 inches if central angle AOB is 50° 30'.

10. Find the perimeter of a regular octagon inscribed in a circle with radius 25.00 inches.

11. Find the length of the apothem of a regular decagon inscribed in a circle with radius 20.00 inches.

12. A balloon carrying weather observation instruments is released at a point A. When the balloon passes over a point B, its angle of elevation from A is 40° 25'. The horizontal distance from A to B is 1200 feet. Find the height of the balloon as it passed over B.

13. A train is traveling due north along a straight track. When observed from a point 12,000 yards due west of the front end of the train, the train subtends an angle of 8° 30'. How long is the train?

14. A 12-foot pole stands vertically at the edge of a river. When seen from the opposite edge of the river the pole subtends an angle of 2° 16'. Find the width of the river.

15. A surveyor located points A and C at opposite ends of a lake. Then he located a point B such that $\angle ACB = 90°$. He measured $\overline{AB}$ as 550 yards; he measured $\angle BAC$ as 47°. Find the length of the lake.

16. A ship sails due south at 12 miles per hour. At noon the lookout sights a lighthouse at 132°. Two hours later, he sights the lighthouse at 042°. At what time was the ship nearest the lighthouse? How far was the ship from the lighthouse at that time?

17. A certain balloon is known to rise at the rate of 100 feet per minute. Due to the wind the angle of elevation of the balloon 6 minutes after it is released is 15° 30'. Find the velocity of the wind.

18. There is a flagpole on a tower in a level field. From a point 225 feet from the foot of the tower, the angle of elevation of the top of the tower is 12°; the angle of elevation of the top of the flagpole is 15°. How tall is the flagpole?

§ 5-4 Law of sines

The law of sines may be derived for any triangle ABC using some of the properties of figures on a coordinate plane. Consider triangle ABC with C at $(0, 0)$, B at $(a, 0)$, and A with a positive y-coordinate as in Figure 5-12. Draw the altitude $\overline{AD}$. Then $\overline{AD}$ is the y-coordinate of A and $\overline{AD} = b \sin C$.

Figure 5-12

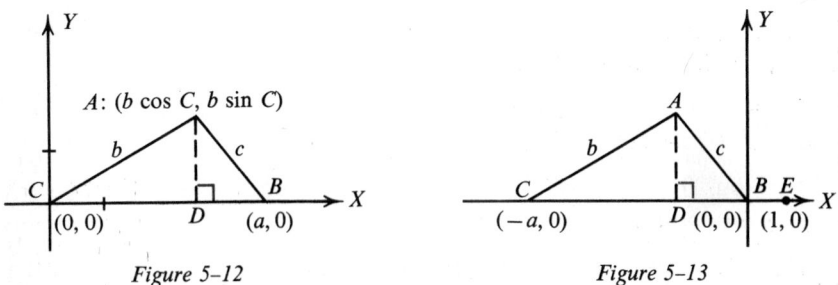

Figure 5-13

Next consider the same triangle ABC with C at $(-a, 0)$, B at $(0, 0)$, and A with a positive y-coordinate as in Figure 5-13. Draw the altitude $\overline{AD}$, and let E be at $(1, 0)$. Then A is at $(c \cos EBA, c \sin EBA)$. Notice that circular functions of angles such as $\angle EBA$ which are designated by three letters are written without the angle symbol in the same manner as functions of angles such as $\angle A$ which are designated by one letter. Since $\angle EBA = 180° - \angle ABC$, $c \sin EBA = c \sin ABC$. Since $\overline{AD}$, the y-coordinate of A, must be the same for each of the positions of triangle ABC on the coordinate plane, $b \sin C = c \sin B$ and

$$\frac{\sin C}{c} = \frac{\sin B}{b}.$$

Similarly, by placing $\overline{AC}$ along the x-axis we may prove that

$$\frac{\sin C}{c} = \frac{\sin A}{a}.$$

Thus for any triangle ABC we have the **law of sines**,

$$\frac{\sin A}{a} = \frac{\sin B}{b} = \frac{\sin C}{c}; \qquad (8)$$

the sines of the angles of any triangle must be proportional to the sides opposite the angles.

STATEMENTS INVOLVING CIRCULAR FUNCTIONS

Example 1. Solve triangle ABC if $\angle B = 100°$, $\angle C = 50°$, and $a = 20.3$ ft.

$$\angle A = 180° - \angle B - \angle C$$
$$\angle A = 180° - 100° - 50° = 30°$$

$$\frac{\sin A}{a} = \frac{\sin B}{b} \qquad\qquad \frac{\sin A}{a} = \frac{\sin C}{c}$$

$$b = \frac{a \sin B}{\sin A} \qquad\qquad c = \frac{a \sin C}{\sin A}$$

$$= \frac{20.3 \sin 100°}{\sin 30°} \qquad\qquad = \frac{20.3 \sin 50°}{\sin 30°}$$

$$= \frac{20.3 \sin 80°}{\sin 30°}$$

$\log 20.3 =$	1.3075		$\log 20.3 =$	1.3075
$\log \sin 80° =$	$9.9934 - 10$		$\log \sin 50° =$	$9.8843 - 10$
	$11.3009 - 10$			$11.1918 - 10$
$-\log \sin 30° =$	$-9.6990 + 10$		$-\log \sin 30° =$	$-9.6990 + 10$
$\log b =$	1.6019		$\log c =$	1.4928
$b =$	39.98		$c =$	31.10
$b \approx$	40.0 ft.		$c \approx$	31.1 ft.

Example 1 provides an illustration of the use of the law of sines in solving a triangle which is determined. The law of sines may also be used to find the two possible cases when two sides of a triangle and the angle opposite one of them is known. This situation in which there may be two possible answers is often called the **ambiguous case**.

Consider the possibilities for a triangle ABC when values for a, b, and acute angle B are given. Draw angle B; mark off $\overline{BC} = a$ on one side of angle B; draw $\overleftrightarrow{CD}$ where D is on the other side of angle B and $\overleftrightarrow{CD} \perp \overleftrightarrow{BD}$. Note that if $b < \overline{CD}$ there cannot exist a triangle ABC satisfying the given conditions; if $b = \overline{CD}$, there can exist one and only one triangle ABC, namely the right triangle DCB where A and D coincide and $\angle A = 90°$.

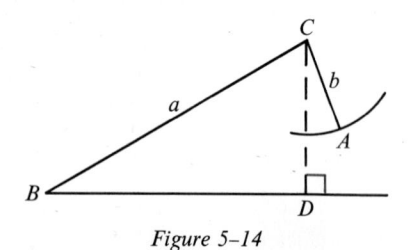

Figure 5-14

If $b > \overline{CD}$, there may be two possible triangles ABC. Specifically, if $a > b > \overline{CD}$, there will be triangle A_1BC and triangle A_2BC as in Figure 5-15. Note that since $\overline{A_1C} = b = \overline{A_2C}$, triangle A_1CA_2 is isosceles. Then $\angle CA_1A_2 = \angle CA_2A_1$, and $\angle CA_1B = 180° - \angle CA_2B$. Since

§ 5-4 LAW OF SINES

$\sin \theta = \sin(180° - \theta)$ for any θ, the sines of angles CA_1B and CA_2B are equal. Thus, when angle B is acute and $\sin A$ is known, there are cases in which angle A may be either obtuse or acute and these two possibilities give rise to two possible triangles. For example, if angle B is acute and $\sin A = \frac{1}{2}$, then when $a > b$ we may take either $\angle A = 30°$ or $\angle A = 150°$.

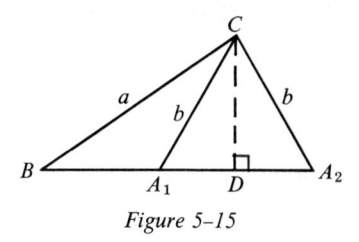

Figure 5-15

If $b > a > \overline{CD}$, there will be one and only one triangle ABC since any attempt to make the segment CA intersect the line BD in two points will cause one point to occur on the left of point B as in Figure 5-16. This construction forms triangle A_2BC in which the given angle B is an exterior angle of the triangle instead of an interior angle as required.

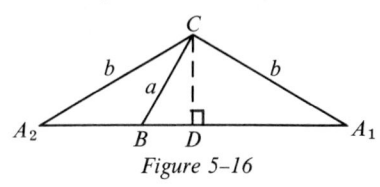

Notice that when the given angle equals 90° or is obtuse there can be only one possible triangle since the sum of the angles of the triangle is 180° and therefore each of the other angles must be acute.

Figure 5-16

This discussion of the ambiguous case may be summarized as in the following array in terms of the given angle, B, the opposite side, b, and the adjacent side, a. Notice that in each of the previous figures the altitude $\overline{CD} = a \sin B$.

Condition on a, b, and $\angle B$	Number of triangles
$b < a \sin B$	0
$b = a \sin B$	1
$a > b > a \sin B$	2
$a \leq b$	1

Before considering an example of the ambiguous case, we shall develop another formula which is particularly useful in checking answers. Since $\frac{\sin A}{a} = \frac{\sin C}{c}$ and $\frac{\sin B}{b} = \frac{\sin C}{c}$, we have

$$\frac{\sin A}{\sin C} = \frac{a}{c} \quad \text{and} \quad \frac{\sin B}{\sin C} = \frac{b}{c}.$$

225

STATEMENTS INVOLVING CIRCULAR FUNCTIONS

We add these equations to obtain the formula,

$$\frac{\sin A + \sin B}{\sin C} = \frac{a+b}{c}.$$

Two other forms may be derived in a similar manner:

$$\frac{\sin A + \sin C}{\sin B} = \frac{a+c}{b}; \quad \frac{\sin B + \sin C}{\sin A} = \frac{b+c}{a}.$$

Example 2. Solve triangle ABC if $\angle C = 42°15'$, $a = 380.0$, and $c = 324.0$.

Given:
$\angle C = 42°\ 15'$
$a = 380.0$
$c = 324.0$

Find:
$\angle A_1 \quad \angle BA_2C$
$\angle A_1BC \quad \angle A_2BC$
$\overline{A_1C} \quad \overline{A_2C}$

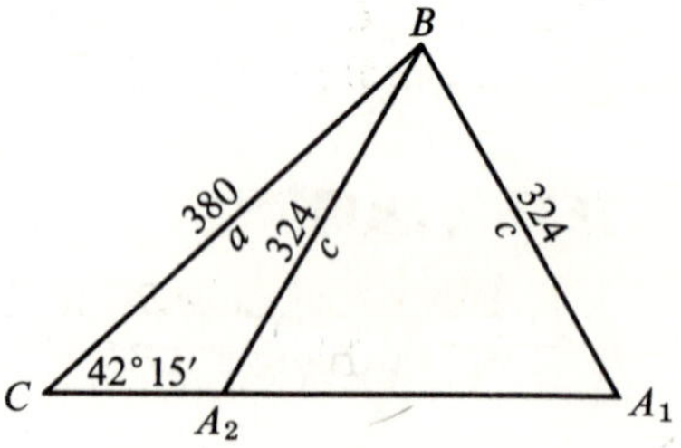

$$\sin A = \frac{a \sin C}{c}$$

$$\sin A = \frac{380.0 \times \sin 42°\ 15'}{324.0}$$

$\log \sin 42°\ 15' = \quad 9.8276 - 10$
$\log 380.0 = \quad \underline{2.5798}$
$\qquad\qquad\qquad\quad 12.4074 - 10$
$-\log 324.0 = \underline{-2.5105}$
$\log \sin A = \quad 9.8969 - 10$

Figure 5–17

$\angle A_1 \approx 52°\ 4'$
$\angle BA_2C = 180° - \angle A_1 = 180° - 52°\ 4' \approx 127°\ 56'$
$\angle A + \angle B + \angle C = 180°$
$\angle B + \angle A = 180° - \angle C = 137°\ 45'$
$\angle A_1BC \approx 137°\ 45' - 52°\ 4' = 85°\ 41'$
$\angle A_2BC \approx 137°\ 45' - 127°\ 56' = 9°\ 49'$

$$b = \frac{c \sin B}{\sin C}, \quad b = \frac{324.0 \times \sin 85°\ 41'}{\sin 42°\ 15'}$$

For triangle A_1BC:
$\log \sin 85°\ 41' = \quad 9.9988 - 10$
$\log 324.0 = \quad \underline{2.5105}$
$\qquad\qquad\qquad\quad 12.5093 - 10$
$-\log \sin 42°\ 15' = \underline{-9.8276 + 10}$
$\log \overline{A_1C} = \quad 2.6817$
$\overline{A_1C} \approx 480.6$

For triangle A_2BC:
$\log \sin 9°\ 49' = \quad 9.2317 - 10$
$\log 324.0 = \quad \underline{2.5105}$
$\qquad\qquad\qquad\quad 11.7422 - 10$
$-\log \sin 42°\ 15' = \underline{-9.8276 + 10}$
$\log \overline{A_2C} = \quad 1.9146$
$\overline{A_2C} \approx 82.15$

§ 5-4 LAW OF SINES

CHECK: Use $\dfrac{a+b}{c} = \dfrac{\sin A + \sin B}{\sin C}$.

$\angle A_1 \approx 52°\ 4'$, $\angle A_1BC \approx 85°\ 41'$, $\overline{A_1C} \approx 480.6$.
$\angle BA_2C \approx 127°\ 56'$, $\angle A_2BC \approx 9°\ 49'$, $\overline{A_2C} \approx 82.15$.

In any triangle the longest side is opposite the largest angle, and conversely. We shall use this statement, which is proved in most plane geometry courses, to tell us whether to choose an acute angle or an obtuse angle when the sine of the angle is known. For example, if $\angle B = 72°\ 10'$, $b = 9.00$, and $c = 8.19$ are given, then $\sin C = \dfrac{8.19 \times \sin 72°\ 10'}{9.00} =$ 0.8660, and $\angle C \approx 60°$ or $120°$. Since $c < b$, $\angle C < \angle B$; that is, $\angle C < 72°\ 10'$, therefore $\angle C \approx 60°$.

TEST YOURSELF

1. Solve triangle ABC if $\angle A = 55°$, $\angle B = 80°$, and $a = 12.5$.
2. Solve triangle ABC if $\angle B = 28°\ 30'$, $\angle C = 110°$, and $b = 215$.

EXERCISES

A

1. Give a set of formulas that may be used to solve triangle ABC when $\angle B$, $\angle C$, and a are given.
2. Give a set of formulas that may be used to solve triangle ABC when $\angle A$, $\angle C$, and c are given.

How many triangles having different shapes or sizes may be found satisfying the information given in each exercise? It is assumed that you will make use of facts you learned in this and other mathematics courses about the general properties of triangles. Notice that you are not asked to solve these triangles.

3. $\angle A = 26°$, $\angle B = 95°$, $c = 260$.
4. $\angle B = 72°\ 40'$, $\angle C = 55°\ 18'$, $a = 3.84$.
5. $\angle A = 53°$, $a = 284$, $b = 243$.
6. $\angle B = 105°$, $a = 15.8$, $b = 12.4$.
7. $\angle C = 46°\ 18'$, $a = 3.8$, $c = 2.9$.
8. $\angle B = 63°\ 26'$, $a = 521$, $b = 451$.
9. $\angle A = 89°$, $\angle C = 42°$, $a = 7.41$.
10. $\angle A = 58°$, $a = 68$, $b = 75$.

STATEMENTS INVOLVING CIRCULAR FUNCTIONS

• • •

11. $\angle A = 73° \ 10'$, $\angle B = 56° \ 31'$, $\angle C = 50° \ 19'$.
12. $\angle C = 17° \ 34'$, $a = 2.08$, $b = 3.71$.
13. $\angle A = 47°$, $a = 6.1$, $b = 8.9$.
14. $\angle B = 19° \ 34'$, $a = 17.4$, $b = 18.3$.
15. $\angle A = 84° \ 29'$, $b = 2.81$, $c = 4.73$.
16. $\angle A = 98°$, $\angle B = 45°$, $b = 27$.
17. $\angle B = 74° \ 35'$, $b = 279$, $c = 284$.
18. $\angle A = 53° \ 24'$, $\angle C = 64° 58'$, $a = 29.4$.
19. $\angle C = 67° \ 41'$, $b = 0.87$, $c = 0.95$.
20. $\angle C = 27° \ 43'$, $a = 0.74$, $c = 0.31$.
21. $a = 2540$, $b = 3318$, $c = 5953$.
22. $\angle A = 64° \ 58'$, $\angle B = 14° \ 26'$, $a = 0.411$.

B

Use Table II and solve triangle ABC given that:

1. $\angle A = 50°$, $\angle B = 60°$, and $c = 10$.
2. $\angle A = 45°$, $\angle C = 60°$, and $b = 20$.
3. $\angle B = 40° \ 40'$, $\angle C = 70° \ 30'$, and $a = 6$.

• • •

In Exercises 4 through 10 use Table III and solve triangle ABC given that:

4. $\angle A = 70° \ 10'$, $\angle B = 45° \ 20'$, and $a = 86.53$.
5. $\angle A = 48° \ 31'$, $\angle B = 75° \ 11'$, and $c = 284.8$.
6. $\angle A = 18° \ 24'$, $\angle C = 122° \ 15'$, and $a = 0.3189$.
7. $\angle B = 26° \ 16'$, $\angle C = 109° \ 37'$, and $b = 24.45$.
8. $\angle B = 115° \ 13'$, $\angle C = 41° \ 12'$, and $a = 16.48$.
9. $\angle C = 35° \ 10'$, $b = 31.50$, $c = 21.78$.
10. $\angle B = 28° \ 41'$, $a = 905.3$, and $b = 752.5$.

11. Construct a circle circumscribed about a given triangle ABC and prove that

$$\frac{a}{\sin A} = \frac{b}{\sin B} = \frac{c}{\sin C} = 2R$$

where R is the radius of the circumscribed circle.

HINT: Draw diameter $\overline{CE}$.

12. If a diagonal of a parallelogram is 232 units long and forms angles of 28° 10′ and 33° 10′ with the sides of the parallelogram, how long are the sides?

§ 5-5 Law of cosines

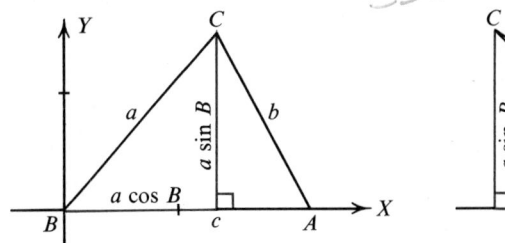

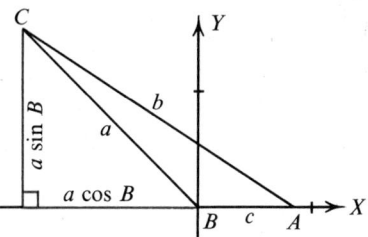

Figure 5-18

We now obtain another formula for the solution of any triangle. Consider triangle ABC with angle B in standard position and A on the x-axis. Then, as in Figure 5-18, C is in the first quadrant if angle B is acute; C is in the second quadrant if angle B is obtuse. In each case we have $A: (c, 0)$ and $C: (a \cos B, a \sin B)$. Then use the distance formula (§ 1-7) to obtain an expression for the square of the length b of $\overline{AC}$:

$$b^2 = (a \cos B - c)^2 + (a \sin B - 0)^2$$
$$= a^2 \cos^2 B - 2ac \cos B + c^2 + a^2 \sin^2 B$$
$$= a^2(\sin^2 B + \cos^2 B) - 2ac \cos B + c^2$$
$$= a^2 - 2ac \cos B + c^2, \text{ since } \sin^2 B + \cos^2 B = 1.$$

Usually we write the formula in the form $b^2 = a^2 + c^2 - 2ac \cos B$. Notice that sides a and c include angle B. This formula is true for any triangle ABC; it is called the **law of cosines.**

When two sides and the included angle of a triangle are given, we use one of these forms of the law of cosines to solve the triangle:

$$\begin{aligned} a^2 &= b^2 + c^2 - 2bc \cos A; \\ b^2 &= a^2 + c^2 - 2ac \cos B; \\ c^2 &= a^2 + b^2 - 2ab \cos C. \end{aligned} \tag{9}$$

When three sides of a triangle are given, we use one of these forms of the law of cosines to solve the triangle:

$$\cos A = \frac{b^2 + c^2 - a^2}{2bc};$$
$$\cos B = \frac{a^2 + c^2 - b^2}{2ac};$$
$$\cos C = \frac{a^2 + b^2 - c^2}{2ab}.$$

These formulas are used most easily with arithmetic or slide rule computation. They are not convenient for logarithmic computation since

STATEMENTS INVOLVING CIRCULAR FUNCTIONS

addition and subtraction are involved. The example illustrates the use of these formulas.

Example. Find the angles of triangle ABC to the nearest degree if $c = 8$, $b = 7$, and $a = 2$.

By the law of cosines:

$$\cos A = \frac{b^2 + c^2 - a^2}{2bc} = \frac{49 + 64 - 4}{112} = \frac{109}{112} \approx 0.973, \angle A \approx 13°;$$

$$\cos B = \frac{a^2 + c^2 - b^2}{2ac} = \frac{4 + 64 - 49}{32} = \frac{19}{32} \approx 0.594, \angle B \approx 54°;$$

$$\cos C = \frac{a^2 + b^2 - c^2}{2ab} = \frac{4 + 49 - 64}{28} = \frac{-11}{28}.$$

The fact that cos C is negative shows that $\angle C$ is obtuse. We use the formulas $\cos(180° - C) = -\cos C$. Then $\cos(180° - C) = \frac{11}{28} \approx 0.39$; $180° - \angle C \approx 67°$; and $\angle C \approx 113°$.

CHECK: $\angle A + \angle B + \angle C \approx 13° + 54° + 113° = 180°$.

TEST YOURSELF

Solve triangle ABC given that:

1. $\angle C = 60°$, $a = 7.00$, and $b = 9.00$.
2. $a = 2.00$, $b = 3.00$, and $c = 4.00$.

EXERCISES

1. Give a set of formulas that may be used to solve triangle ABC when $\angle B$, a, and c are given.
2. Give a set of formulas that may be used to solve triangle ABC when $\angle A$, b, and c are given.

In Exercises 3 through 7 solve triangle ABC given that:

3. $a = 4.00$, $b = 5.00$, and $c = 6.00$.
4. $\angle A = 45°$, $b = 100$, and $c = 300$.
5. $a = 1.20$, $b = 1.60$ and $c = 1.80$.
6. $a = 34.0$, $b = 39.0$, and $c = 47.0$.
7. $\angle C = 110°$, $a = 630$, and $b = 950$.

8. From the top of a cliff 120 feet above sea level the angles of depression of two swimmers are 46° and 39°. If one swimmer is directly behind the other relative to the observer, how far apart are the swimmers?

9. A boat 18 feet long is anchored off shore from a cliff. The boat is headed toward shore. The angles of elevation of the top of the cliff from the two ends of the boat are 67° and 77°. How high is the cliff?

10. Two fire lookout stations, A and B, are 23.6 miles apart. A fire was observed from A at an angle of 58° 12′ with line AB; a similar observation from B gave 47° 28′. Find the distance from each lookout to the fire.

• **11.** A pilot flying into New York found that Washington, D. C. was directly south and New York was 070°. If the direction from Washington to New York is 053° and the distance is 220 miles, how far was the pilot from New York?

• **12.** A pilot flying into Tulsa found that Dallas was at 280° and Tulsa was at 335°. If it is 280 miles from Dallas to Tulsa and the direction is 012°, how far was the pilot from Tulsa? How far was he from Dallas?

• **13.** A pilot flying into Kansas City found that St. Louis was at 060° and Kansas City was at 350°. If it is 250 miles from St. Louis to Kansas City, how far was the pilot from Kansas City? How far was he from St. Louis? Assume that the direction from St. Louis to Kansas City is 279°.

• **14.** The diagonal of a parallelogram is 24 feet long and makes angles of 54° 54′ and 24° 9′ with the sides. How long, to the nearest foot, is the other diagonal of the parallelogram?

§ 5-6 Law of tangents (Supplementary)

Any triangle may be determined uniquely by (*a*) three sides, (*b*) two sides and the included angle, or (*c*) two angles and a side. In the first two cases the triangle may be solved using the law of cosines; in the third case, using the law of sines. Thus any triangle that is uniquely determined may be solved.

The law of tangents provides a convenient formula when logarithms are to be used in solving the triangles where two sides and the included angle are known. This law may be derived by geometric methods. However, for the present treatment of trigonometry we shall postulate (assume without proof or derivation) the various forms of the **law of tangents**:

$$\frac{\tan\frac{1}{2}(A-B)}{\tan\frac{1}{2}(A+B)} = \frac{a-b}{a+b}; \quad \frac{\tan\frac{1}{2}(B-A)}{\tan\frac{1}{2}(B+A)} = \frac{b-a}{b+a}. \tag{10}$$

STATEMENTS INVOLVING CIRCULAR FUNCTIONS

Notice that the formula may be modified so that the right member is positive. For example, if $b > a$, then the second formula is used. Similar formulas may be used for B and C, and for A and C.

Example. Solve triangle ABC if $\angle A = 46° 24'$, $b = 31.60$, and $c = 52.70$.

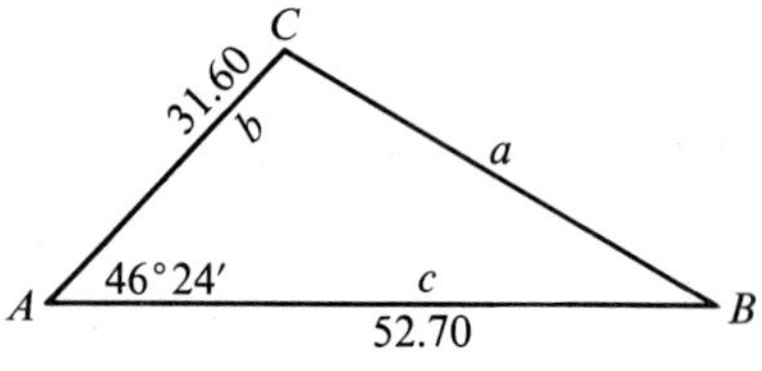

Given:
$\angle A = 46° 24'$
$b = 31.60$
$c = 52.70$
$\angle A + \angle B + \angle C = 180°$
$\angle C + \angle B = 180° - 46° 24'$
$= 133° 36'$
$\frac{1}{2}(\angle C + \angle B) = 66° 48'$

Find:
$\angle B$
$\angle C$
a

Figure 5–19

$c + b = 52.70 + 31.60 = 84.30$
$c - b = 52.70 - 31.60 = 21.10$

$$\frac{\tan \frac{1}{2}(C - B)}{\tan \frac{1}{2}(C + B)} = \frac{c - b}{c + b}, \quad \tan \frac{1}{2}(C - B) = \frac{21.10}{84.30} \tan 66° 48'$$

$\log \tan 66° 48' = \quad 10.3679 - 10$
$\log 21.10 = \quad \underline{1.3243}$
$\quad\quad\quad\quad\quad\quad\quad 11.6922 - 10$
$-\log 84.30 = \underline{-1.9258}$
$\log \tan \frac{1}{2}(C - B) = \quad 9.7664 - 10$

$\frac{1}{2}(C - B) \approx 30° 17'$

$\frac{1}{2}(C + B) \approx 66° 48'$

$\angle C \approx 97° 5'$, $\angle B \approx 36° 31'$

$\frac{a}{\sin A} = \frac{b}{\sin B}, \quad a = \frac{b \sin A}{\sin B} = \frac{31.60 \sin 46° 24'}{\sin 36° 31'}$

$\log \sin 46° 24' = \quad 9.8599 - 10$
$\log 31.60 = \quad \underline{1.4997}$
$\quad\quad\quad\quad\quad\quad\quad 11.3596 - 10$
$-\log \sin 36° 31' = \underline{-9.7746 + 10}$
$\log a = \quad 1.5850$
$a \approx 38.46$

CHECK: Use $\dfrac{a}{\sin A} = \dfrac{c}{\sin C}$.

$\angle B \approx 36° \ 31'$, $\angle C \approx 97° \ 5'$, $a \approx 38.46$.

EXERCISES

1. Give a list of formulas that may be used to solve triangle ABC using logarithms when angle B, a, and c are given with $a > c$.

2. Give a list of formulas that may be used to solve triangle ABC using logarithms when angle C, a, and b are given with $b > a$.

Solve triangle ABC given that:

3. $\angle B = 120°$, $a = 56.30$, and $c = 47.90$.
4. $\angle C = 43° \ 52'$, $a = 2360$, and $b = 3840$.
5. $\angle B = 99° \ 14'$, $a = 0.3280$, and $c = 0.7610$.
6. $\angle A = 100° \ 10'$, $b = 5.670$, and $c = 8.930$.

§ 5-7 Area

We assume that the area K in square units of any triangle is given by the formula

$$K = \frac{1}{2} bh$$

where b is the length of any side of the triangle and h is the length of the altitude drawn to that side. The purpose of this section is to obtain several other formulas for the area of a triangle.

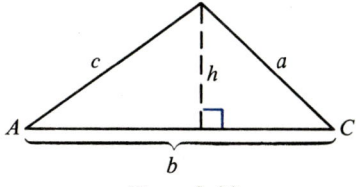

Figure 5-20

We may use $h = c \sin A$ to obtain

$$K = \frac{1}{2} bc \sin A. \tag{11}$$

In a similar manner we may obtain the formulas

$$K = \frac{1}{2} ac \sin B, \quad \text{and} \quad K = \frac{1}{2} ab \sin C.$$

From the law of sines (§ 5-4), $c = \dfrac{b \sin C}{\sin B}$. If we substitute for c in the formula (11), we obtain

$$K = \frac{b^2 \sin A \sin C}{2 \sin B}.$$

STATEMENTS INVOLVING CIRCULAR FUNCTIONS

Similarly, we may use $b = \frac{a \sin B}{\sin A}$ in the formula $K = \frac{1}{2} ab \sin C$ to obtain

$$K = \frac{a^2 \sin B \sin C}{2 \sin A}.$$

Finally, we may use $a = \frac{c \sin A}{\sin C}$ in the formula $K = \frac{1}{2} ac \sin B$ to obtain

$$K = \frac{c^2 \sin A \sin B}{2 \sin C}.$$

Given any triangle ABC, we know that the three angle bisectors all pass through a point O which is the center of a circle tangent to each of the three sides of the triangle. Call the radius of this circle r. Then we use the formula $K = \frac{1}{2} bh$; triangle OAB has area $\frac{1}{2} rc$; triangle OBC has area

Figure 5-21

$\frac{1}{2} ra$; triangle OCA has area $\frac{1}{2} rb$, and triangle ABC has area $\frac{1}{2} r(a + b + c)$; that is,

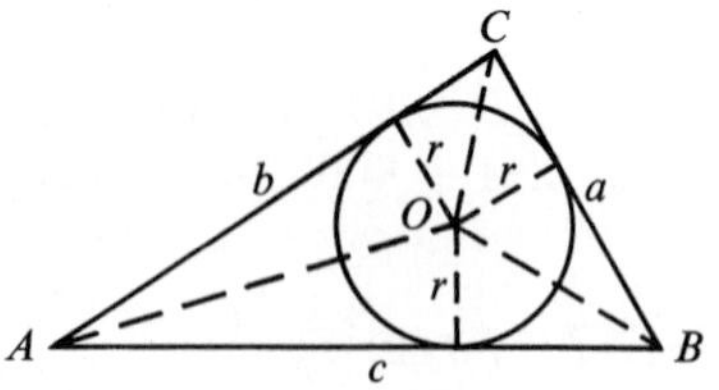

$$K = \frac{r}{2}(a + b + c). \tag{12}$$

Note that in this formula the area of the triangle is expressed in terms of the lengths of the radius of the inscribed circle and the sides of the triangle.

The formula is often expressed as $K = rs$ where

$$s = \frac{1}{2}(a + b + c)$$

and s is called the **semi-perimeter**. There is one other common formula for the area involving s,

$$K = \sqrt{s(s - a)(s - b)(s - c)}. \tag{13}$$

This is often called Hero's formula (§ 3–7); we shall assume it here without proof. The proof may be found in most geometry text books including the geometry book of this series.

The last two formulas for the area enable us to express r in terms of s and the sides of the triangle:

$$rs = \sqrt{s(s-a)(s-b)(s-c)},$$
$$r = \sqrt{\frac{(s-a)(s-b)(s-c)}{s}}. \tag{14}$$

Example. Find the area in acres of a triangular lot having two sides 68.34 rods and 89.16 rods and the included angle 57° 18′. 1 acre = 160 square rods.

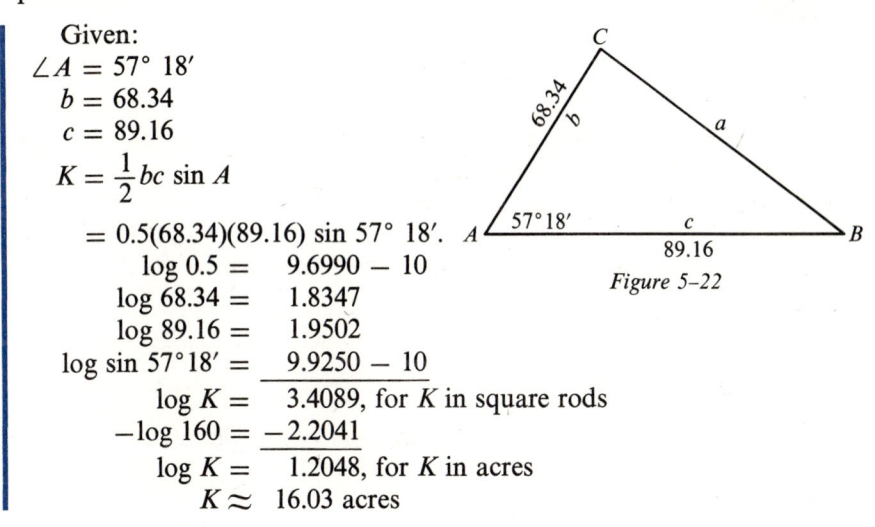

Given:
$\angle A = 57° 18'$
$b = 68.34$
$c = 89.16$

$K = \frac{1}{2} bc \sin A$

$= 0.5(68.34)(89.16) \sin 57° 18'$.

log 0.5 =	9.6990 − 10
log 68.34 =	1.8347
log 89.16 =	1.9502
log sin 57° 18′ =	9.9250 − 10
log K =	3.4089, for K in square rods
−log 160 =	−2.2041
log K =	1.2048, for K in acres
K ≈	16.03 acres

Figure 5–22

TEST YOURSELF

1. Find the area of a triangle with sides 2 inches, 3 inches, and 4 inches.
2. Find the area of triangle ABC if $\angle C = 65° 30'$, $a = 38.2$ and $b = 41.3$.
3. One angle of a parallelogram is 60°. Two of its sides are 15 and 25. Find its area.

EXERCISES

A

Give a formula or formulas that may be used to find the area of triangle ABC when you are given:

1. $\angle B$, a, and c.
2. $\angle A$, b, and c.
3. $\angle A$, $\angle B$, and b.
4. $\angle A$, $\angle B$, and c.
5. $\angle B$, $\angle C$, and a.
6. a, b, and c.

STATEMENTS INVOLVING CIRCULAR FUNCTIONS

In Exercises 7 through 12 find the area of triangle ABC given that:

7. $a = 100, b = 150, c = 200$.
8. $\angle B = 115°, a = 16.4$, and $c = 24.6$.
9. $s = 49.6$, and $r = 3.4$.
10. $a = 354.2, b = 416.8$, and $c = 624.6$.
11. $\angle B = 60° 20', \angle C = 45° 40'$, and $b = 24.14$.
12. $\angle A = 48° 15', \angle B = 69° 34'$, and $c = 613.4$.

• • •

13. One angle of a parallelogram is 55° 30'. Two of its sides are 20 inches and 30 inches. Find its area.

14. Prove that the area of any parallelogram in square units may be obtained by multiplying one-half the product of its diagonals by the sine of their included angle.

• 15. Prove that the area of any triangle may be expressed by the formula $K = \dfrac{abc}{4R}$ where R is the radius of the circumscribed circle.

B (Supplementary)

1. Consider any triangle ABC with inscribed circle O of radius r. Draw the radii perpendicular to the sides as in the figure. Label the segments of the sides x, y, z as in the figure since the two tangents to a circle from an external point must be equal. Prove each of these formulas: $x = s - a, y = s - b$, and $z = s - c$ where s is the semi-perimeter.

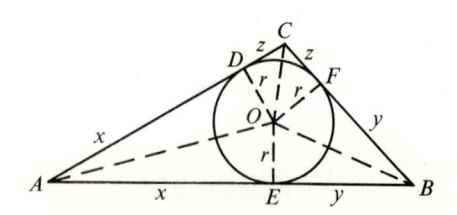

2. In the figure for Exercise 1 draw $\overline{OA}, \overline{OB}$, and $\overline{OC}$; note that each of these lines bisects an angle of the given triangle; use the results obtained in Exercise 1 and prove each of these formulas:

$$\tan \tfrac{1}{2} A = \frac{r}{s-a}; \quad \tan \tfrac{1}{2} B = \frac{r}{s-b}; \quad \tan \tfrac{1}{2} C = \frac{r}{s-c}. \qquad (15)$$

§ 5-8 MULTIPLE-ANGLE FORMULAS

3. Use the formula for r in terms of s, a, b, and c and derive each of these formulas:

$$\tan\frac{1}{2}A = \sqrt{\frac{(s-b)(s-c)}{s(s-a)}}; \qquad \tan\frac{1}{2}B = \sqrt{\frac{(s-a)(s-c)}{s(s-b)}};$$

$$\tan\frac{1}{2}C = \sqrt{\frac{(s-a)(s-b)}{s(s-c)}}.$$

NOTE: These formulas may be used instead of the law of cosines to solve triangles when three sides are known. They make it convenient to use logarithms in solving such triangles.

4. Find angle A in triangle ABC if $a = 4$, $b = 3$, and $c = 5$.
5. Find angle B in triangle ABC if $a = 2.97$, $b = 3.85$, and $c = 5.00$.
6. Solve triangle ABC if $a = 619$, $b = 749$, and $c = 583$.
7. Solve triangle ABC if $a = 55.61$, $b = 80.03$, and $c = 76.08$.

§ 5-8 Multiple-angle formulas

Draw a unit circle with center at the origin. Let $\angle QOP = \theta$ and $\angle QOR = \phi$ where Q has coordinates $(1, 0)$, and P and R are on the unit circle. Then $\overline{PO} = \overline{OR} = 1$, $\angle POR = \theta - \phi$, and by the law of cosines

$$\overline{PR}^2 = 1 + 1 - 2\cos(\theta - \phi)$$
$$= 2 - 2\cos(\theta - \phi).$$

The coordinates of P are $(\cos\theta, \sin\theta)$; the coordinates of R are $(\cos\phi, \sin\phi)$. Then by the distance formula

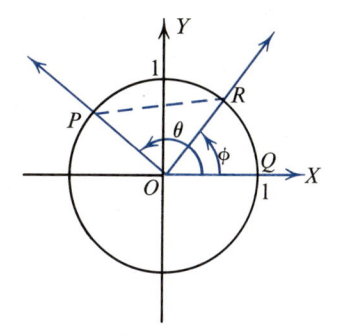

$$\overline{PR}^2 = (\cos\theta - \cos\phi)^2 + (\sin\theta - \sin\phi)^2$$
$$= \cos^2\theta - 2\cos\theta\cos\phi + \cos^2\phi$$
$$\quad + \sin^2\theta - 2\sin\theta\sin\phi + \sin^2\phi$$
$$= 1 - 2\cos\theta\cos\phi - 2\sin\theta\sin\phi + 1$$
$$= 2 - 2\cos\theta\cos\phi - 2\sin\theta\sin\phi.$$

Figure 5–23

Finally, we equate the two values of $\overline{PR}^2$ and obtain

$$2 - 2\cos(\theta - \phi) = 2 - 2\cos\theta\cos\phi - 2\sin\theta\sin\phi$$
$$\cos(\theta - \phi) = \cos\theta\cos\phi + \sin\theta\sin\phi. \qquad (16)$$

Note that in this derivation of the formula the magnitudes of θ and ϕ are unimportant. This is a general proof which holds for any real numbers θ and ϕ.

The formula for $\cos(\theta + \phi)$ may be obtained by replacing ϕ by $-\phi$

237

STATEMENTS INVOLVING CIRCULAR FUNCTIONS

in the formula (16). Then

$$\cos(\theta + \phi) = \cos[\theta - (-\phi)]$$
$$= \cos\theta\cos(-\phi) + \sin\theta\sin(-\phi)$$
$$\cos(\theta + \phi) = \cos\theta\cos\phi - \sin\theta\sin\phi. \quad (17)$$

The formula for $\sin(\theta + \phi)$ may be obtained by taking the sine as the cofunction of the complement;

$$\sin(\theta + \phi) = \cos[90° - (\theta + \phi)]$$
$$= \cos[(90° - \theta) - \phi]$$
$$= \cos(90° - \theta)\cos\phi + \sin(90° - \theta)\sin\phi$$
$$\sin(\theta + \phi) = \sin\theta\cos\phi + \cos\theta\sin\phi. \quad (18)$$

The formula for $\sin(\theta - \phi)$ may be obtained by replacing ϕ by $-\phi$ in the formula (18). Then

$$\sin(\theta - \phi) = \sin[\theta + (-\phi)]$$
$$= \sin\theta\cos(-\phi) + \cos\theta\sin(-\phi)$$
$$\sin(\theta - \phi) = \sin\theta\cos\phi - \cos\theta\sin\phi. \quad (19)$$

Formulas (16) through (19) may be used to derive many other formulas. Several of these are considered in the exercises; a few are used so frequently that a list of them is useful:

$$\sin 2\theta = 2\sin\theta\cos\theta; \quad (20)$$

$$\cos 2\theta = \cos^2\theta - \sin^2\theta; \quad (21)$$

$$\tan 2\theta = \frac{2\tan\theta}{1 - \tan^2\theta}; \quad (22)$$

$$\sin\frac{\theta}{2} = \pm\sqrt{\frac{1 - \cos\theta}{2}}; \quad (23)$$

$$\cos\frac{\theta}{2} = \pm\sqrt{\frac{1 + \cos\theta}{2}}; \quad (24)$$

$$\tan\frac{\theta}{2} = \pm\sqrt{\frac{1 - \cos\theta}{1 + \cos\theta}}. \quad (25)$$

In each case where the ambiguous $\pm$ sign is used the sign is to be selected according to the quadrant in which the terminal side falls for an angle of measure $\frac{\theta}{2}$ in standard position. Formulas (20), (21), and (22) are often called **double-angle formulas**. Formulas (23), (24), and (25) are often called **half-angle formulas**. All six formulas are **multiple-angle formulas.** Each formula can be derived, at least indirectly, from the formulas (16) through (19).

§ 5-8 MULTIPLE-ANGLE FORMULAS

Example 1. Derive a formula for (a) $\sin 2\theta$; (b) $\cos 2\theta$.

(a) $\sin 2\theta = \sin(\theta + \theta) = \sin \theta \cos \theta + \cos \theta \sin \theta$
$= 2 \sin \theta \cos \theta.$

(b) $\cos 2\theta = \cos(\theta + \theta) = \cos \theta \cos \theta - \sin \theta \sin \theta$
$= \cos^2 \theta - \sin^2 \theta.$

Notice also that $\cos 2\theta = 1 - 2 \sin^2 \theta;$
$$\cos 2\theta = 2 \cos^2 \theta - 1.$$

Example 2. Derive a formula for $\tan 2\theta$ in terms of (a) $\sin \theta$ and $\cos \theta$; (b) $\tan \theta$.

(a) $\tan 2\theta = \dfrac{\sin 2\theta}{\cos 2\theta} = \dfrac{2 \sin \theta \cos \theta}{\cos^2 \theta - \sin^2 \theta}.$

(b) $\tan 2\theta = \dfrac{2 \sin \theta \cos \theta}{\cos^2 \theta - \sin^2 \theta} = \dfrac{\dfrac{2 \sin \theta}{\cos \theta}}{\dfrac{\cos^2 \theta}{\cos^2 \theta} - \dfrac{\sin^2 \theta}{\cos^2 \theta}};$

$\tan 2\theta = \dfrac{2 \tan \theta}{1 - \tan^2 \theta}.$

The multiple-angle formulas for the other functions may be derived from those for sine and cosine as in Example 2. We shall consider primarily sines, cosines, and tangents, since formulas for cotangents, secants, and cosecants may be readily obtained in terms of their reciprocal functions.

Example 3. Derive a formula for $\sin \dfrac{\theta}{2}$ in terms of $\cos \theta$.

$\cos \theta = \cos\left(\dfrac{\theta}{2} + \dfrac{\theta}{2}\right)$

$\cos \theta = \cos^2 \dfrac{\theta}{2} - \sin^2 \dfrac{\theta}{2} = 1 - 2 \sin^2 \dfrac{\theta}{2}$

$\sin^2 \dfrac{\theta}{2} = \dfrac{1}{2}(1 - \cos \theta)$

$\sin \dfrac{\theta}{2} = \pm \sqrt{\dfrac{1 - \cos \theta}{2}} = \pm \dfrac{1}{2}\sqrt{2(1 - \cos \theta)}.$

The sign must be taken appropriate to the quadrant in which the terminal side of the angle $\dfrac{\theta}{2}$ is situated; that is, $\sin \dfrac{\theta}{2}$ is the positive

239

STATEMENTS INVOLVING CIRCULAR FUNCTIONS

square root when the terminal side of $\frac{\theta}{2}$ is in quadrant I or quadrant II; the negative square root when the terminal side of $\frac{\theta}{2}$ is in quadrant III or quadrant IV.

TEST YOURSELF

Derive a formula for tan $(\theta + \phi)$ in terms of:
1. sin θ, cos θ, sin ϕ, and cos ϕ.
2. tan θ and tan ϕ.

EXERCISES

1. Derive formulas for cot 2θ in terms of (a) sin θ and cos θ; (b) tan θ; (c) cot θ.
2. Derive a formula for sin 3θ in terms of sin θ and cos θ.
3. Derive a formula for cos 3θ in terms of sin θ and cos θ.

• • •

Derive a formula for the specified function in terms of sin θ, cos θ, sin ϕ, and cos ϕ:

4. sec 2θ.
5. tan $(\theta - \phi)$.
6. cot 2θ.
7. csc 3θ.
8. tan 3θ.
9. tan $\frac{\theta}{2}$.

Derive a formula for each function in terms of tan θ and tan ϕ:

10. tan $(\theta - \phi)$.
11. cot 2θ.
12. tan 3θ.
13. sec 2θ.
14. sin 2θ.
15. cos 2θ.

Derive a formula in terms of sin θ, cos θ, or sin θ and cos θ for:

16. cos $\frac{\theta}{2}$.
• 17. sin 4θ.
• 18. cos 5θ.

§ 5-9 Identities involving multiple-angles

A statement of equality which is true for all values of the variable(s) for which its members are defined is called an *identity* (§ 5-1). For example, each of the formulas that we have considered is an identity. The formulas may be used to replace expressions by equivalent expressions.

240

§ 5-9 IDENTITIES INVOLVING MULTIPLE-ANGLES

Example 1. Prove the identity:
$$\frac{\sin(\theta + \phi)}{\sin(\theta - \phi)} = \frac{\tan \theta + \tan \phi}{\tan \theta - \tan \phi}.$$

$$\frac{\tan \theta + \tan \phi}{\tan \theta - \tan \phi} = \frac{\dfrac{\sin \theta}{\cos \theta} + \dfrac{\sin \phi}{\cos \phi}}{\dfrac{\sin \theta}{\cos \theta} - \dfrac{\sin \phi}{\cos \phi}}$$

$$= \frac{\dfrac{\sin \theta \cos \phi + \cos \theta \sin \phi}{\cos \theta \cos \phi}}{\dfrac{\sin \theta \cos \phi - \cos \theta \sin \phi}{\cos \theta \cos \phi}}$$

$$= \frac{\sin \theta \cos \phi + \cos \theta \sin \phi}{\sin \theta \cos \phi - \cos \theta \sin \phi}$$

$$= \frac{\sin(\theta + \phi)}{\sin(\theta - \phi)}.$$

Proofs of identities provide practice in the same operations that are used in simplifying trigonometric expressions. The simplification of expressions is helpful in solving equations and in advanced mathematics. Usually a trigonometric expression is considered to be simplified when as many of the indicated operations as possible have been performed. The most desirable form of a simplified expression depends upon the way in which the expression is to be used. For computational purposes it is usually convenient to express all functions of multiple-angles in terms of single angles. Unless otherwise specified we shall assume that answers are to be suitable for computational purposes.

Example 2. Simplify: $\dfrac{\sin 2A}{1 - \cos 2A}$.

$$\frac{\sin 2A}{1 - \cos 2A} = \frac{2 \sin A \cos A}{1 - (\cos^2 A - \sin^2 A)}$$

$$= \frac{2 \sin A \cos A}{1 - [\cos^2 A - (1 - \cos^2 A)]}$$

$$= \frac{2 \sin A \cos A}{2 - 2 \cos^2 A} = \frac{\sin A \cos A}{1 - \cos^2 A}$$

$$= \frac{\sin A \cos A}{\sin^2 A} = \frac{\cos A}{\sin A}$$

$$= \cot A.$$

STATEMENTS INVOLVING CIRCULAR FUNCTIONS

TEST YOURSELF

1. Prove the identity: $\sin 2\theta = \dfrac{2 \tan \theta}{1 + \tan^2 \theta}$.

2. Simplify: $\dfrac{\sin 2\theta}{1 + \cos 2\theta}$.

EXERCISES

A

Prove each identity:

1. $\sin(A + B) + \sin(A - B) = 2 \sin A \cos B$.

2. $\cot A + \cot B = \dfrac{\sin(A + B)}{\sin A \sin B}$.

3. $\cot A \cot B - 1 = \dfrac{\cos(A + B)}{\sin A \sin B}$.

4. $\tan x + \cot x = 2 \csc x$.

5. $\sin 2x = \dfrac{2}{\tan x + \cot x}$.

6. $\dfrac{\sin(\theta + 45°)}{\cos(\theta - 45°)} = 1$.

7. $\dfrac{\cos^3 \theta + \sin^3 \theta}{\cos \theta + \sin \theta} = \dfrac{2 - \sin 2\theta}{2}$.

8. $\dfrac{\cos(x + y)}{\cos(x - y)} = \dfrac{1 - \tan x \tan y}{1 + \tan x \tan y}$.

9. $\sqrt{\dfrac{1 + \sin A}{1 - \sin A}} = \dfrac{\cos A}{1 - \sin A}$.

10. $\dfrac{\tan \theta - \sin \theta}{\tan \theta + \sin \theta} = \tan^2 \dfrac{\theta}{2}$.

B

Simplify:

1. $\sin(60° + \theta) - \sin(60° - \theta)$.
2. $\sin(\theta + 135°) - \cos(\theta - 45°)$.
3. $\dfrac{\cos 2A - 1}{\sin 2A}$.

242

§ 5-9 IDENTITIES INVOLVING MULTIPLE-ANGLES

4. $\dfrac{\sin 2x}{\sin x} - \dfrac{\cos 2x}{\cos x}$.

5. $\cos^4 \theta - \sin^4 \theta$.

6. $\cos 3x \cos 2x + \sin 3x \sin 2x$.

· · ·

7. $\cot \dfrac{\theta}{2} - \cot \theta$.

8. $\dfrac{1 - \cos 2\theta + \sin 2\theta}{1 + \cos 2\theta + \sin 2\theta}$.

9. $\csc 2x - \cot 2x$.

10. $\dfrac{\cos^3 \theta + \sin^3 \theta}{(2 - \sin 2\theta)(\cos \theta + \sin \theta)}$.

11. $\dfrac{2 \cos^2 \dfrac{\theta}{2}}{1 + \sec \theta}$.

12. $\dfrac{1 + \cos \theta}{\sin \theta} + \dfrac{\sin \theta}{1 + \cos \theta}$.

SUPPLEMENTARY EXERCISES

1. Use the formulas for $\sin(A + B)$ and $\sin(A - B)$ to derive the formulas:

$$\begin{aligned}\sin(A + B) + \sin(A - B) &= 2 \sin A \cos B, \\ \sin(A + B) - \sin(A - B) &= 2 \cos A \sin B.\end{aligned} \quad (26)$$

2. Let $A + B = \theta$ and $A - B = \phi$. Then $2A = \theta + \phi$ and $2B = \theta - \phi$; that is, $A = \dfrac{1}{2}(\theta + \phi)$ and $B = \dfrac{1}{2}(\theta - \phi)$. Make these substitutions in the formulas (26) to derive these formulas:

$$\begin{aligned}\sin \theta + \sin \phi &= 2 \sin \dfrac{1}{2}(\theta + \phi) \cos \dfrac{1}{2}(\theta - \phi), \\ \sin \theta - \sin \phi &= 2 \cos \dfrac{1}{2}(\theta + \phi) \sin \dfrac{1}{2}(\theta - \phi).\end{aligned} \quad (27)$$

3. Use the formulas for $\cos(A + B)$ and $\cos(A - B)$ to derive the formulas:

$$\begin{aligned}\cos(A + B) + \cos(A - B) &= 2 \cos A \cos B, \\ \cos(A + B) - \cos(A - B) &= -2 \sin A \sin B.\end{aligned} \quad (28)$$

STATEMENTS INVOLVING CIRCULAR FUNCTIONS

4. Use the substitution from (27) in the formulas (28) to derive the formulas:

$$\cos \theta + \cos \phi = 2 \cos \frac{1}{2}(\theta + \phi) \cos \frac{1}{2}(\theta - \phi),$$
$$\cos \theta - \cos \phi = -2 \sin \frac{1}{2}(\theta + \phi) \sin \frac{1}{2}(\theta - \phi).$$
(29)

Use the formulas (27) and (29) and express each of these as a product:

SAMPLE: $\sin 75° - \sin 15°$.

Let $\theta = 75°$ and $\phi = 15°$. Then $\theta + \phi = 90°$, $\theta - \phi = 60°$; $\frac{1}{2}(\theta + \phi) = 45°$, $\frac{1}{2}(\theta - \phi) = 30°$. By the second formula (27),

$$\sin 75° - \sin 15° = 2 \cos 45° \sin 30°.$$

Now the given expression can easily be evaluated:

$$\sin 75° - \sin 15° = 2 \times \frac{1}{\sqrt{2}} \times \frac{1}{2} = \frac{1}{\sqrt{2}} = \frac{\sqrt{2}}{2}.$$

5. $\sin 48° + \sin 32°$.
6. $\cos 83° + \cos 23°$.
7. $\sin 159° + \sin 59°$.
8. $\sin 65° - \sin 35°$.
9. $\cos 98° - \cos 8°$.

10. $\sin 5x + \sin 3x$.
11. $\cos 7x - \cos 5x$.
12. $\cos 4x + \cos 2x$.
13. $\cos 6x - \cos 2x$.
14. $\sin 3x - \sin 7x$.

Use the formulas (27) and (29) and simplify:

15. $\dfrac{\sin 75° + \sin 15°}{\sin 75° - \sin 15°}$.

16. $\dfrac{\sin 58° + \sin 32°}{\cos 58° - \cos 32°}$.

17. $\dfrac{\sin 40° - \sin 20°}{\sin 40° + \sin 20°}$.

18. $\dfrac{\cos 87° - \cos 33°}{\cos 87° + \cos 33°}$.

Use the formulas (27) and (29) and express as a sum or a difference of two functions:

19. $2 \sin 8x \cos 2x$.
20. $-2 \sin 3x \sin 8x$.
21. $\cos 6x \cos 2x$.
22. $\cos 2x \sin x$.

Use the formulas (27) and (29) and prove:

23. $\sin 8\theta + \sin 2\theta = 2 \cos 3\theta \sin 5\theta$.
24. $\sin 3x - \sin x + \sin 7x - \sin 5x = 4 \sin x \cos 2x \cos 4x$.

244

§ 5-10 Equations

An equation of the form $\sin x = k$ which is linear in "$\sin x$" may have many solutions or no solutions. Consider these examples: The equation $\sin x = 2$ has no solutions and thus is an impossible equation (§ 1-5) since $|\sin x| \leq 1$ for all x (§ 4-6). The equation $\sin x = 1$ is satisfied when $x = 90°, 450°, 810°, \cdots$ and when $x = -270°, -630°, \cdots$. Each of these roots may be expressed in the form $90° + (k \times 360°)$ for some integer k. Thus each of these roots arises from $90°$ and the periodicity of $\sin x$ (§ 4-6). The equation $\sin x = \frac{1}{2}$ has roots $30° + (k \times 360°)$ and $150° + (m \times 360°)$ for any integers k and m. Note that in this case the equation has two solutions, $30°$ and $150°$, which do not arise from one another due to the periodicity of $\sin x$.

Each of the circular functions has either period $360°$ or period $180°$. (See §§ 4-6, 4-7, and 4-8.) Thus if an equation in which the variable is expressed only in circular functions has a root θ, then it also has a root $(\theta + k \times 360°)$ for any integer k. Also all roots may be expressed in terms of the roots θ such that $0° \leq \theta < 360°$. Accordingly, in solving equations in terms of the circular functions we seek roots θ where $0° \leq \theta < 360°$ since each of the functions satisfies the equation $f(\theta) = f(\theta + k \times 360°)$ for all θ and any integer k. As in the examples we may solve equations involving circular functions using tables of values or we may estimate the roots from the graphs of the equations.

Example 1. Solve: $\cos x = \frac{1}{2}$ where $0° \leq x < 360°$.

Cos x is positive in the first and fourth quadrants; $\cos 60° = \frac{1}{2}$ and $\cos 300° = \frac{1}{2}$; $x = 60°$ or $300°$.

Example 2. Solve $\tan x = -\frac{1}{5}$ where $0° \leq x < 360°$.

Tan x is negative in the second and fourth quadrants; $\tan (180° - x) = -\tan x$ as in § 5-1; from the tables $\tan 11° 20' \approx \frac{1}{5}$; $x \approx 168° 40'$ or $348° 40'$.

Example 3. Solve: $\sin^2 x - \sin x - 6 = 0$ where $0° \leq x < 360°$.

Note that $\sin x$ stands for any one of a set of real numbers and thus is itself a variable. The given equation could be expressed as

STATEMENTS INVOLVING CIRCULAR FUNCTIONS

$y^2 - y - 6 = 0$ where $y = \sin x$. However, it seems best to recognize that circular functions may be treated the same as other variables and to solve the given equation directly for $\sin x$. In this particular example we solve by factoring.

If $\sin^2 x - \sin x - 6 = 0$, then $(\sin x - 3)(\sin x + 2) = 0$, and either $\sin x = 3$ or $\sin x = -2$. Since $|\sin x| \leq 1$ for all x, both of these equations are impossible and the given equation has no roots.

Example 4. Solve: $\cos^2 x = \sin 2x$ where $0° \leq x < 360°$.

If $\cos^2 x = \sin 2x$, then $\cos^2 x = 2 \sin x \cos x$, $\cos x (\cos x - 2 \sin x) = 0$ and either $\cos x = 0$ or $\cos x = 2 \sin x$. If $\cos x = 0$, then $x = 90°$ or $270°$. If $\cos x = 2 \sin x$, then $\cot x = 2$, $x \approx 26\frac{1}{2}°$ or $206\frac{1}{2}°$ using the table of values of $\cot \theta$ to estimate the value of x.

Example 5. Solve: $\sin^2 \frac{3}{2}x = \frac{1}{4}$ where $0° \leq x < 360°$.

If $\sin^2 \frac{3}{2}x = \frac{1}{4}$, then $\sin \frac{3}{2}x = \frac{1}{2}$ or $-\frac{1}{2}$. If $\sin \frac{3}{2}x = \frac{1}{2}$, then $\frac{3}{2}x = 30°, 150°, 390°$ or $510°$ and $x = 20°, 100°, 260°, 340°$. Note that values of $\frac{3}{2}x$ greater than $360°$ must be considered in order to find all positive values of x less than $360°$. If $\sin \frac{3}{2}x = -\frac{1}{2}$, then $\frac{3}{2}x = 210°$ or $330°$ and $x = 140°$ or $220°$.

Example 6. Solve graphically: $\sin x = \frac{\sqrt{2}}{2}$ where $0° \leq x \leq 360°$.

Sketch the graph of $y = \sin x$ and draw the line $y = \frac{\sqrt{2}}{2}$. Then estimate the x-coordinates of the intersections of the line and the curve; these occur when $x = 45°$ or $135°$.

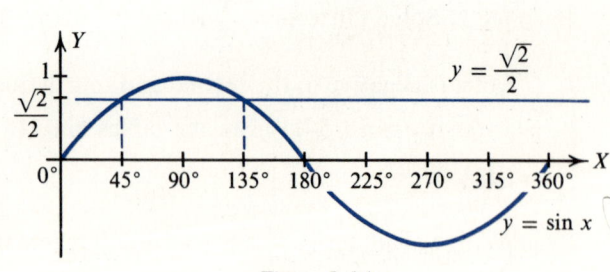

Figure 5–24

246

TEST YOURSELF

Solve for $0° \leq x < 360°$:

1. $\sin x = \cos 2x$.
2. $\sin x - \cos x = 1$.

EXERCISES

A

Solve for $0° \leq x < 360°$:

1. $\sin x = \sin 57°$.
2. $\cos x = -\cos 38°$.
3. $\sin^2 x = \frac{1}{2}$.
4. $4\cos^2 x = 1$.
5. $\sin^2 \frac{1}{2}x = \frac{3}{4}$.
6. $\tan^2 \frac{3}{4}x = 3$.
7. $\sin 2x - \cos x = 0$.
8. $\cot x = \tan x$.
9. $\tan x \cos x = 1$.
10. $\sin x \sec x = -1$.

11. $\cot x + \tan x = 2$.
12. $\sin x \csc 2x = -\frac{1}{3}\sqrt{3}$.
13. $\sqrt{3}\tan x + 2\sin x = 0$.
14. $2\cos^2 x + 7\sin x = 5$.
15. $6\sin^2 x + 5\sin x + 1 = 0$.
16. $3\tan^2 x + 17\tan x + 10 = 0$.
17. $5\sin x + 3 = 3\cos 2x$.
18. $\sin^2 x - \sin x - 1 = 0$.
19. $\cos^2 x + 2\cos x - 2 = 0$.
20. $2\tan 2x + \tan x = 0$.
- 21. $\cos 2x - \sin x = -1.5$.
- 22. $\sec x - 2\csc x = 0$.
- 23. $\sin x = 2 - \cos x$.

B

1. Graph the equation $y = \sin x$ where x is a number of degrees, $-360° \leq x \leq 720°$. Then relabel the horizontal scale for radians, $-2\pi \leq x \leq 4\pi$.

247

STATEMENTS INVOLVING CIRCULAR FUNCTIONS

Use your graph for Exercise 1 and solve each equation graphically:

2. $\sin x = \frac{1}{2}$.

3. $\sin x = -\frac{1}{2}$.

4. $\sin x = -1$.

5. $\sin x = \frac{\sqrt{3}}{2}$.

6. $\sin x = -\frac{\sqrt{3}}{2}$.

7. $y = \sin \frac{\pi}{6}$.

• • •

8. $y = \sin 1$.
9. $y = \sin 2$.
10. $y = \sin(-1)$.
11. $y = \sin(-3)$.

Use Table II where necessary and solve for θ where $0° \leq \theta \leq 90°$:

12. $\cos \theta = \sin \theta$.
13. $4 \cos^2 \theta - 1 = 0$.
• 14. $6 \sin^2 \theta - 5 \sin \theta + 1 = 0$.
• 15. $2 \cos^2 \theta - 3 \cos \theta + 1 = 0$.
• 16. $\sin^2 \theta - \cos^2 \theta = 1$.

SUMMARY OF CHAPTER 5

1. In this chapter you have studied statements involving trigonometric and circular functions. The reciprocal relations

$$\sin \theta = \frac{1}{\csc \theta}, \quad \cos \theta = \frac{1}{\sec \theta}, \quad \tan \theta = \frac{1}{\cot \theta}, \qquad (1)$$

and the Pythagorean relations

$$\sin^2 \theta + \cos^2 \theta = 1, \qquad (2)$$

$$1 + \tan^2 \theta = \sec^2 \theta, \qquad (3)$$

$$1 + \cot^2 \theta = \csc^2 \theta, \qquad (4)$$

are identities; that is, they are true for all values of θ for which the ratios are defined. There are also many other useful identities including

$$\tan \theta = \frac{\sin \theta}{\cos \theta}; \qquad (5) \qquad \cot \theta = \frac{\cos \theta}{\sin \theta}; \qquad (6)$$

$$\begin{array}{ll} \sin(-\theta) = -\sin \theta; & \csc(-\theta) = -\csc \theta; \\ \cos(-\theta) = \cos \theta; & \sec(-\theta) = \sec \theta; \\ \tan(-\theta) = -\tan \theta; & \cot(-\theta) = -\cot \theta; \end{array} \qquad (7)$$

248

SUMMARY OF CHAPTER 5

and the formulas for circular functions of $(90° - \theta)$, $(90° + \theta)$, $(180° - \theta)$, $(180° + \theta)$, $(270° - \theta)$, $(270° + \theta)$, $(360° - \theta)$ in terms of functions of θ. Any identities may be used in simplifying trigonometric expressions. (§ 5-1)

2. Approximate values of the circular functions may be obtained from a table of values (Table II), from a table of logarithms of values (Table III), or from a slide rule. (§ 5-2)

3. Any right triangle that is uniquely determined may be solved. (§ 5-3)

4. Any oblique triangle that is uniquely determined may be solved. If two angles and a side of any triangle are known, the law of sines,

$$\frac{\sin A}{a} = \frac{\sin B}{b} = \frac{\sin C}{c}, \tag{8}$$

may be used to solve the triangle. If two sides and the angle opposite one of them are known, there will be two, one, or no possible triangles (the ambiguous case). For example, if angle A, a, and b are given, there is no triangle if $a < b \sin A$, a right triangle if $a = b \sin A$, two possible triangles if $b > a > b \sin A$, and one triangle if $b < a$. (§ 5-4)

5. If three sides or if two sides and the included angle of any triangle are known, the law of cosines,

$$\begin{aligned} a^2 &= b^2 + c^2 - 2bc \cos A, \\ b^2 &= a^2 + c^2 - 2ac \cos B, \\ c^2 &= a^2 + b^2 - 2ab \cos C, \end{aligned} \tag{9}$$

may be used to solve the triangle. However, since addition and subtraction are involved, the computations cannot be done conveniently by logarithms. (§ 5-5)

6. If two sides and the included angle are known, the law of tangents,

$$\begin{aligned} \frac{\tan \frac{1}{2}(A - B)}{\tan \frac{1}{2}(A + B)} &= \frac{a - b}{a + b}, \\ \frac{\tan \frac{1}{2}(B - A)}{\tan \frac{1}{2}(B + A)} &= \frac{b - a}{b + a}, \end{aligned} \tag{10}$$

(and similar formulas for B and C, and A and C) may be used in place of the law of cosines to solve the triangle. In this case most of the computations are well adapted to the use of logarithms. (§ 5-6)

STATEMENTS INVOLVING CIRCULAR FUNCTIONS

7. The circular functions may be used to find the area K of a triangle. For example,
$$K = \frac{1}{2} bc \sin A. \tag{11}$$

Furthermore, if $s = \frac{1}{2}(a + b + c)$ and r is the radius of the inscribed circle, then the area may be expressed in terms of the sides and r as
$$K = \frac{r}{2}(a + b + c) \tag{12}$$

or, in terms of the sides alone, as
$$K = \sqrt{s(s - a)(s - b)(s - c)}. \tag{13}$$

The radius r may be expressed in terms of s and the sides as
$$r = \sqrt{\frac{(s - a)(s - b)(s - c)}{s}}. \tag{14}$$

The formulas for tangents of halves of angles may now be expressed as
$$\tan \frac{A}{2} = \frac{r}{s - a}, \quad \tan \frac{B}{2} = \frac{r}{s - b}, \quad \tan \frac{C}{2} = \frac{r}{s - c}. \quad (\S\ 5\text{-}7) \tag{15}$$

8. In this section and its related exercises these multiple-angle formulas were derived:
$$\cos(\theta - \phi) = \cos\theta \cos\phi + \sin\theta \sin\phi; \tag{16}$$
$$\cos(\theta + \phi) = \cos\theta \cos\phi - \sin\theta \sin\phi; \tag{17}$$
$$\sin(\theta + \phi) = \sin\theta \cos\phi + \cos\theta \sin\phi; \tag{18}$$
$$\sin(\theta - \phi) = \sin\theta \cos\phi - \cos\theta \sin\phi; \tag{19}$$
$$\sin 2\theta = 2 \sin\theta \cos\theta; \tag{20}$$
$$\cos 2\theta = \cos^2\theta - \sin^2\theta; \tag{21}$$
$$\tan 2\theta = \frac{2 \tan\theta}{1 - \tan^2\theta}; \tag{22}$$
$$\sin \frac{\theta}{2} = \pm \sqrt{\frac{1 - \cos\theta}{2}}; \tag{23}$$
$$\cos \frac{\theta}{2} = \pm \sqrt{\frac{1 + \cos\theta}{2}}; \tag{24}$$
$$\tan \frac{\theta}{2} = \pm \sqrt{\frac{1 - \cos\theta}{1 + \cos\theta}}. \quad (\S\ 5\text{-}8) \tag{25}$$

SUMMARY OF CHAPTER 5

9. Identities involving multiple angles may be used to prove other identities and to simplify expressions. In the supplementary exercises these formulas were derived:

$$\sin (A + B) + \sin (A - B) = 2 \sin A \cos B,$$
$$\sin (A + B) - \sin (A - B) = 2 \cos A \sin B; \qquad (26)$$

$$\sin \theta + \sin \phi = 2 \sin \tfrac{1}{2}(\theta + \phi) \cos \tfrac{1}{2}(\theta - \phi),$$
$$\sin \theta - \sin \phi = 2 \cos \tfrac{1}{2}(\theta + \phi) \sin \tfrac{1}{2}(\theta - \phi); \qquad (27)$$

$$\cos (A + B) + \cos (A - B) = 2 \cos A \cos B,$$
$$\cos (A + B) - \cos (A - B) = -2 \sin A \sin B; \qquad (28)$$

$$\cos \theta + \cos \phi = 2 \cos \tfrac{1}{2}(\theta + \phi) \cos \tfrac{1}{2}(\theta - \phi),$$
$$\cos \theta - \cos \phi = -2 \sin \tfrac{1}{2}(\theta + \phi) \sin \tfrac{1}{2}(\theta - \phi). \quad (\S \, 5\text{-}9) \qquad (29)$$

10. If an equation in which the variable occurs only in circular functions has a root θ, then it also has a root $(\theta + k \times 360°)$ for any integer k. Accordingly, in solving equations involving the circular functions we seek roots θ where $0° \leq \theta < 360°$. (§ 5-10)

11. The following words have been introduced or used extensively in this chapter:

ambiguous case (§ 5-4)
angle of depression (§ 5-3)
angle of elevation (§ 5-3)
area (§ 5-7)
circular function (§ 5-1)
cofunction (§ 5-1)
cosecant (§ 5-1)
cosine (§ 5-1)
cotangent (§ 5-1)
double-angle formulas (§ 5-8)
equation (§ 5-10)
half-angle formulas (§ 5-8)
Hero's formula (§ 5-7)
identity (§§ 5-1, 5-9)

interpolation (§ 5-2)
law of cosines (§ 5-5)
law of sines (§ 5-4)
law of tangents (§ 5-6)
multiple-angle formulas (§ 5-8)
oblique triangle (§ 5-3)
periodic function (§ 5-10)
Pythagorean relations (§ 5-1)
reciprocal relations (§ 5-1)
right triangle (§ 5-3)
secant (§ 5-1)
semi-perimeter (§ 5-7)
sine (§ 5-1)
tangent (§ 5-1)

STATEMENTS INVOLVING CIRCULAR FUNCTIONS

KEYED PRACTICE ON CHAPTER 5

1. Simplify: $\sin \theta \cot \theta$. (§ 5–1)

2. Simplify: $\sqrt{\dfrac{1 + \cos x}{1 - \cos x}}$. (§ 5–1)

3. Write as a single function of θ:

$$[\cos (90° + \theta)] \dfrac{\cos (-\theta)}{\sin (180° + \theta)}. \quad (\S\ 5\text{–}1)$$

4. Find: (a) $\sin 43° 4'$; (b) $\cos 39° 27'$; (c) $\tan 57° 53'$. (§5–2)
5. Find angle A if: (a) $\sin A = 0.5650$; (b) $\cos A = 0.8250$. (§ 5–2)
6. Use Table III and find the logarithm of each circular function in Exercise 4. (§ 5–2)
7. Solve triangle ABC if $\angle A = 42° 12'$, $\angle C = 90°$, and $a = 175.4$. (§ 5–3)
8. Solve triangle ABC if $\angle A = 34° 20'$, $\angle B = 75° 30'$, and $c = 17.38$. (§ 5–4)
9. Solve triangle ABC giving each angle to the nearest 10′ and each side to three significant digits if $\angle C = 30°$, $a = 8.00$, and $b = 10.0$. (§ 5–5)
• 10. Solve triangle ABC if $\angle C = 115°$, $a = 1560$, and $b = 2580$. (§ 5–6)
11. One angle of a parallelogram is $120°$. Two of its sides are 17 and 22. Find its area. (§ 5–7)
12. Express $\tan 4\theta$ in terms of $\tan \theta$. (§ 5–8)
13. Simplify:

$$\dfrac{2 \sin^2 \dfrac{\theta}{2}}{1 - \sec \theta}. \quad (\S\ 5\text{–}9)$$

14. Solve for $0° \leq x < 360°$: $4 \sin^2 x - 1 = 0$. (§ 5–10)

TESTS ON CHAPTER 5

A

1. Simplify: $(1 - \cos \theta)(1 + \cos \theta) \csc \theta$.
2. Derive a formula for $\csc 2\theta$ in terms of $\sin \theta$ and $\cos \theta$.
3. Simplify: $1 - \sec^2 \theta + \sec^2 \theta \tan^2 \theta$.
4. Simplify: $\dfrac{\sin (\theta - 135°)}{\cos (\theta - 45°)}$.

5. Solve for $0° \leq x < 360°$: $\sin x = \csc x$.
6. What is the area of triangle ABC if $\angle A = 30°$, $b = 16$, and $c = 21$?
7. Solve triangle ABC if $\angle A = 45°$, $\angle C = 90°$, and $c = 25$. (Leave your answers in simplest radical form.)
8. At a given instant an airplane is gliding to earth at a speed of 145 miles per hour. The angle of approach is $8° 25'$. What is the ground speed of the plane?
9. The angle of elevation of a tower is $31° 17'$, viewed from a point at a horizontal distance of 367.9 yards from its base. How high is the tower?
10. A triangle is formed by two radii and the chord joining their end points in a circle with radius 15.0 inches. The angle between the radii is $54° 30'$. Find the length of the chord and the area of the triangle.

B

1. Simplify: $\sec \theta - \dfrac{1}{\sec \theta}$.
2. Simplify: $\dfrac{\cot \theta + \tan \theta}{\sec \theta \csc \theta}$.
3. Derive a formula for $\cos 4\theta$ in terms of $\cos \theta$.
4. Simplify: $\tan^4 \theta + 3 \tan^2 \theta \sec^2 \theta - 4 \sec^4 \theta$.
5. Solve for $0° \leq x < 360°$: $4 \cos^2 x = 3$.
6. What is the area of triangle ABC if $a = 3$, $b = 7$, and $c = 8$?
7. Find the radius of the inscribed circle of triangle ABC if $a = 7$, $b = 8$, and $c = 11$.
8. Solve triangle ABC if $\angle A = 59°$, $a = 22$, and $b = 19$.
9. A vertical flagpole is made of two pieces of steel pipe held together by a metal band. The lower pipe extends 20 feet above the ground. From a point on the ground level with the ground at the bottom of the pole the angle of elevation of the joint between the two pipes is $28° 0'$ and the angle of elevation of the top of the flagpole is $51° 0'$. How tall is the flagpole?
10. A stay wire from 3 feet below the top of a telegraph pole to the ground is 117 feet long. If the inclination of the wire to the level ground is $43° 20'$, how high is the pole?

C

1. Simplify: $\dfrac{\sin(90° + \theta) \cos(-\theta)}{\cos(180° - \theta)}$.
2. Derive a formula for $\tan 2\theta$ in terms of $\sec \theta$.

STATEMENTS INVOLVING CIRCULAR FUNCTIONS

3. Simplify: $\sin^6 \theta + \cos^6 \theta + 3 \sin^2 \theta \cos^2 \theta$.
4. What is the area of triangle ABC if $a = 2.5$, $b = 3.4$, and $c = 5.1$?
5. Find the radius of the inscribed circle of triangle ABC if $a = 12$, $b = 13$, and $c = 15$.
6. Solve triangle ABC if $\angle C = 47°$, $b = 21$, and $c = 18$.
7. A tower stands on a level plain. When the sun is 18° 0' above the horizon, the shadow of the tower is 25 feet longer than when the sun is 36° 0' above the horizon. Find the height of the tower.
8. The rafters of a certain roof are 45 feet long. The span of the roof (distance between ends of opposite rafters) is 70 feet. Find the angle which the rafters make with the horizontal.
9. In order to calculate the height of a mountain a surveyor measured the angle of elevation of its top from a point A and found it to be 17° 18'. He then walked toward the mountain a distance of 3200 feet in the same horizontal plane and found the angle of elevation from this new point to be 22° 6'. How high was the mountain if A was 1000 feet above sea level?
10. Two observers A and B are on level ground 3697 feet apart and face toward each other. An airplane directly over the line joining A and B is observed to have an angle of elevation at A of 27° 49' and at B of 53° 37'. Find the height of the airplane above the plane of the observers.

ANSWERS TO TEST YOURSELF EXERCISES

§ 5-1. **1.** $2\cos^2 \theta$. **2.** $\tan A$. **3.** $1 - \sin^2 x + \sin x \cot x = (1 - \sin^2 x) + \sin x \dfrac{\cos x}{\sin x} = \cos^2 x + \cos x$.

§ 5-2. **1.** 0.56. **2.** 0.92. **3.** 0.58. **4.** 2.75.
5. 0.8158. **6.** 0.9013. **7.** 2.1203. **8.** 11°.
9. 78°. **10.** 56°. **11.** 22° 53'. **12.** 9.5392 − 10.
13. 9.9269 − 10. **14.** 0.3320. **15.** 0.7508.
16. 15°. **17.** 37° 57'.

§ 5-3. **1.** $90° - \angle B = \angle A$, $90° - 47° = 43°$, $\angle A = 43°$; $a = c \cos B$, $a = 21.5 \times 0.6820 \approx 14.7$; $b = c \sin B$, $b = 21.5 \times 0.7314 \approx 15.7$.
2. $\cos A = \dfrac{b}{c}$, $\cos A = \dfrac{172}{200} = 0.8600$, $\angle A \approx 30°\ 41'$; $\sin B = \dfrac{b}{c}$, $\sin B = \dfrac{172}{200} = 0.8600$, $\angle B \approx 59°\ 19'$; $a = \sqrt{c^2 - b^2}$, $a = \sqrt{200^2 - 172^2} \approx 102$.
3. 193 feet.

ANSWERS TO TEST YOURSELF EXERCISES

§ 5-4. **1.** $180° - \angle A - \angle B = \angle C$; $180° - 55° - 80° = 45°$, $\angle C = 45°$; $b = \dfrac{a \sin B}{\sin A}$, $c = \dfrac{a \sin C}{\sin A}$,

$$\begin{array}{ll}
\log 12.5 = & 1.0969 \\
\log \sin 80° = & 9.9934 - 10 \\ \hline
 & 11.0903 - 10 \\
-\log \sin 55° = & -9.9134 + 10 \\ \hline
\log b = & 1.1769 \\
b \approx 15.0 &
\end{array} \qquad \begin{array}{ll}
\log 12.5 = & 1.0969 \\
\log \sin 45° = & 9.8495 - 10 \\ \hline
 & 10.9464 - 10 \\
-\log \sin 55° = & -9.9134 + 10 \\ \hline
\log c = & 1.0330 \\
c \approx 10.8 &
\end{array}$$

2. $180° - \angle B - \angle C = \angle A$, $180° - 28° 30' - 110° = 41° 30'$, $\angle A = 41° 30'$; $a = \dfrac{b \sin A}{\sin B}$, $c = \dfrac{b \sin C}{\sin B}$,

$$\begin{array}{ll}
\log 215 = & 2.3324 \\
\log \sin 41° 30' = & 9.8213 - 10 \\ \hline
 & 12.1537 - 10 \\
-\log \sin 28° 30' = & -9.6787 + 10 \\ \hline
\log a = & 2.4750 \\
a \approx 299 &
\end{array}$$

$$\begin{array}{ll}
\log 215 = & 2.3324 \\
\log \sin 70° = & 9.9730 - 10 \\ \hline
 & 12.3054 - 10 \\
-\log \sin 28° 30' = & -9.6787 + 10 \\ \hline
\log c = & 2.6267 \\
c \approx 423 &
\end{array}$$

§ 5-5. **1.** $c^2 = a^2 + b^2 - 2ab \cos C = 49 + 81 - 2(7)(9)\left(\dfrac{1}{2}\right) = 67$, $c = 8.19$; $\dfrac{\sin A}{a} = \dfrac{\sin C}{c}$, $\sin A = \dfrac{7.00 \times 0.866}{8.19} \approx 0.7402$, $\angle A \approx 47° 50'$; $\angle B = 180° - \angle C - \angle A \approx 72° 10'$.

2. $\cos A = \dfrac{b^2 + c^2 - a^2}{2bc} = \dfrac{16 + 9 - 4}{24} = \dfrac{21}{24} = 0.8750$, $\angle A \approx 29° 0'$; $\cos B = \dfrac{a^2 + c^2 - b^2}{2ac} = \dfrac{4 + 16 - 9}{16} = \dfrac{11}{16} = 0.6875$, $\angle B \approx 46° 30'$; $\cos C = \dfrac{a^2 + b^2 - c^2}{2ab} = \dfrac{4 + 9 - 16}{12} = \dfrac{-3}{12} = -0.2500$, $\angle C \approx 104° 30'$.

255

STATEMENTS INVOLVING CIRCULAR FUNCTIONS

§ 5-7. 1. $K = \sqrt{s(s-a)(s-b)(s-c)}$, $\quad 2s = 2 + 3 + 4$, $\quad s = 4.5$,
$K = \sqrt{(4.5)(2.5)(1.5)(0.5)} = (0.5)^2 \sqrt{9 \times 5 \times 3 \times 1} = \frac{3}{4}\sqrt{15} \approx$
2.9 square inches.

2. $K = \frac{1}{2} ab \sin C = \frac{1}{2}(38.2)(41.3) \sin 65° 30' \approx 717.8$.

3. Area $ABCD$ = area $\triangle ABD$
+ area $\triangle BCD$ = 2(area $\triangle ABD$)
= $(2)\left(\frac{1}{2}\right)(15)(25) \sin 60°$
= $375 \times 0.8660 \approx 325$.

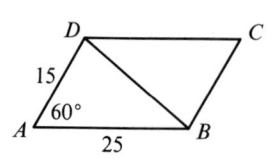

§ 5-8. 1. $\tan(\theta + \phi) = \dfrac{\sin(\theta + \phi)}{\cos(\theta + \phi)} = \dfrac{\sin\theta\cos\phi + \cos\theta\sin\phi}{\cos\theta\cos\phi - \sin\theta\sin\phi}$.

2. $\tan(\theta + \phi) = \dfrac{\sin(\theta + \phi)}{\cos(\theta + \phi)}$
$= \dfrac{(\sin\theta\cos\phi + \cos\theta\sin\phi) \div \cos\theta\cos\phi}{(\cos\theta\cos\phi - \sin\theta\sin\phi) \div \cos\theta\cos\phi}$
$= \dfrac{\tan\theta + \tan\phi}{1 - \tan\theta\tan\phi}$.

§ 5-9. 1. $\sin 2\theta = 2\sin\theta\cos\theta \times \dfrac{\sec^2\theta}{\sec^2\theta} = \dfrac{2\sin\theta\sec\theta}{\sec^2\theta} = \dfrac{2\tan\theta}{1 + \tan^2\theta}$.

2. $\dfrac{\sin 2\theta}{1 + \cos 2\theta} = \dfrac{2\sin\theta\cos\theta}{1 + (\cos^2\theta - \sin^2\theta)} = \dfrac{2\sin\theta\cos\theta}{1 + (2\cos^2\theta - 1)}$
$= \dfrac{2\sin\theta\cos\theta}{2\cos^2\theta} = \tan\theta$.

§ 5-10. 1. If $\sin x = \cos 2x$, then $\sin x = 1 - 2\sin^2 x$, $2\sin^2 x + \sin x - 1 = 0$, $(2\sin x - 1)(\sin x + 1) = 0$, $\sin x = \frac{1}{2}$ or -1, and $x = 30°$, $150°$, or $270°$.

2. If $\sin x - \cos x = 1$, then $\sin^2 x - 2\sin x\cos x + \cos^2 x = 1$, $2\sin x\cos x = 0$, and $x = 0°$, $90°$, $180°$, or $270°$. Since we have squared both members of the given equation each of these values for x must be checked. The given equation is satisfied when $x = 90°$ or $180°$.

ANSWERS TO KEYED PRACTICE ON CHAPTER 5

1. $\cos \theta$.

2. $\sqrt{\dfrac{1 + \cos \theta}{1 - \cos \theta}} = \sqrt{\dfrac{(1 + \cos \theta)^2}{1 - \cos^2 \theta}} = \dfrac{1 + \cos \theta}{\sin \theta} = \dfrac{1}{\sin \theta} + \dfrac{\cos \theta}{\sin \theta} = \csc \theta + \cot \theta$.

3. $[\cos (90° + \theta)]\dfrac{\cos (-\theta)}{\sin (180° + \theta)} = [-\cos (90° - \theta)]\dfrac{\cos \theta}{-\sin \theta} =$
$-\sin \theta \left(\dfrac{\cos \theta}{-\sin \theta}\right) = \cos \theta$.

4. (a) 0.6828; (b) 0.7722; (c) 1.5931.

5. (a) 34° 24'; (b) 34° 25'.

6. (a) 9.8343 − 10; (b) 9.8877 − 10; (c) 0.2022.

7. $\angle B = 47° \; 48'$; $b \approx 193.4$; $c \approx 261.1$.

8. $\angle C = 180° - \angle A - \angle B = 180° - 34° \; 20' - 75° \; 30' = 70° \; 10'$.

$a = \dfrac{c \sin A}{\sin C}$, $a = \dfrac{17.38 \times 0.5640}{0.9407} \approx 10.4$; $b = \dfrac{c \sin B}{\sin C}$,

$b = \dfrac{17.38 \times 0.9681}{0.9407} \approx 17.9$.

Answer: $\angle C = 70° \; 10'$; $a \approx 10.4$; $b \approx 17.9$.

9. $c^2 = a^2 + b^2 - 2ab \cos C$; $c^2 = 64 + 100 - 160(0.8660) = 25.44$,

$c \approx 5.04$; $\sin A = \dfrac{a \sin C}{c}$, $\sin A = \dfrac{8.00 \times 0.5}{5.04} \approx 0.7937$, $\angle A = 52°30'$;

$\sin B = \dfrac{b \sin C}{c}$, $\sin B = \dfrac{10.0 \times 0.5}{5.04} \approx 0.9921$, $\angle B \approx 82° \; 50'$, or 97° 10'.

The angle B required by our problem is 97° 10', since it is opposite the longest side of the triangle and since the smaller value for angle B does not give $\angle A + \angle B + \angle C = 180°$.
Answer: $\angle A \approx 52° \; 30'$; $\angle B \approx 97° \; 10'$; $c \approx 5.04$.

10. $\dfrac{\tan \frac{1}{2}(B - A)}{\tan \frac{1}{2}(B + A)} = \dfrac{b - a}{b + a}$, $B + A = 180° - 115° = 65°$,

$\tan \frac{1}{2}(B - A) = \dfrac{1020 \tan 32° \; 30'}{4140} = \dfrac{17 \tan 32° \; 30'}{69}$;

257

STATEMENTS INVOLVING CIRCULAR FUNCTIONS

$$\log 17 = 1.2304$$
$$\log \tan 32° 30' = \underline{9.8042 - 10}$$
$$= 11.0346 - 10$$
$$-\log 69 = \underline{-1.8388}$$
$$\log \tan \tfrac{1}{2}(B - A) = 9.1958 - 10$$

$\tfrac{1}{2}(B - A) \approx 8° 55';$ $B - A \approx 17° 50'$
$ \underline{B + A = 65°}$
$ 2B \approx 82° 50'$
$ B \approx 41° 25', A \approx 23° 35'.$

$$\frac{c}{\sin 65°} = \frac{1560}{\sin 23° 35'}; \; c = \frac{1560 \sin 65°}{\sin 23° 35'};$$

$$\log 1560 = 3.1931$$
$$\log \sin 65° = \underline{9.9573 - 10}$$
$$= 13.1504 - 10$$
$$-\log \sin 23° 35' = \underline{-9.6022 + 10}$$
$$\log c = 3.5482$$
$$c \approx 3533$$

Answer: $\angle A \approx 23° 35'; \; \angle B \approx 41° 25'; \; c \approx 3533.$

11. $K = 2\left(\tfrac{1}{2} bc \sin A\right),$

$K = 2\left(\tfrac{1}{2}\right)(17)(22) \sin 60°$

$= 374 \times 0.8660$

$\approx 324.$

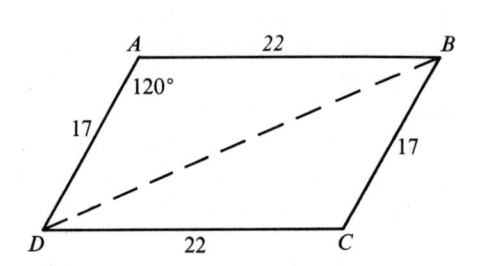

12. $\tan 4\theta = \tan(2\theta + 2\theta) = \dfrac{2 \tan 2\theta}{1 - \tan^2 2\theta} = \dfrac{2 \times \dfrac{2 \tan \theta}{1 - \tan^2 \theta}}{1 - \dfrac{4 \tan^2 \theta}{(1 - \tan^2 \theta)^2}} =$

$\dfrac{4 \tan \theta (1 - \tan^2 \theta)}{1 - 2 \tan^2 \theta + \tan^4 \theta - 4 \tan^2 \theta} = \dfrac{4 \tan \theta - 4 \tan^3 \theta}{1 - 6 \tan^2 \theta + \tan^4 \theta}.$

13. $\dfrac{2 \sin^2 \dfrac{\theta}{2}}{1 - \sec \theta} = \dfrac{\cos \theta \times 2 \times \left(\dfrac{1}{2}\right)^2 (2)(1 - \cos \theta)}{\cos \theta - 1} = -\cos \theta.$

14. $\sin^2 x = \tfrac{1}{4}; \; \sin x = \tfrac{1}{2} \text{ or } -\tfrac{1}{2}; \; x = 30°, 150°, 210°, \text{ or } 330°.$

Chapter 6

Systems of Numbers

§ 6-1 Mathematical systems

Mathematics is concerned with logical systems and thus with:

(i) sets of elements,
(ii) relations among the elements,
(iii) one or more operations defined over the set of elements, and
(iv) statements involving the elements, relations, and operations.

As in any logical system, some of the elements of any mathematical system must be accepted as undefined. Logical system, number, point, and line are usually included among the undefined elements in elementary courses. Other elements are defined in terms of the undefined elements.

The most common relation in algebra is the *equivalence relation* in which we state that one expression *equals* another; that is, that two expressions stand for the same number. Any equivalence relation determines a set of classes into which all of the elements under consideration may be placed such that any element of a particular class may be substituted for any other element of that class without altering the truth value of the statement in which the substitution has been made. Among the other types of relations that you have considered are the *order relations*: $<, \leq, >,$ and $\geq$.

A **relation R** is defined over a set S of elements if for any two elements a, b of S the statement

$$a \text{ is in the relation } \mathbf{R} \text{ to } b$$

can be determined to be true or false. If the statement is true, we write $a \mathbf{R} b$; if the statement is false, we write $a \not{\mathbf{R}} b$. For example, in algebra if **R** stands for the equivalence relation *equals*, we may write

$$2 + 3 = 5 \quad \text{as} \quad (2 + 3) \mathbf{R} 5;$$
$$3 + 1 \neq 2 \quad \text{as} \quad (3 + 1) \not{\mathbf{R}} 2.$$

We now use this notation for relations and the notation $a \in S$ for "a is a member of S" (§ 1–1) to give a formal definition of an equivalence relation. A relation **R** which is defined over a set S is an **equivalence relation**

259

SYSTEMS OF NUMBERS

for S if these three properties are satisfied for all possible selections of a, b, and c in S:

(i) If $a \in S$, then $a \mathbf{R} a$.
(ii) If $a, b \in S$ and if $a \mathbf{R} b$, then $b \mathbf{R} a$.
(iii) If $a, b, c \in S$ and if $a \mathbf{R} b$ and $b \mathbf{R} c$, then $a \mathbf{R} c$.

These three properties of an equivalence relation are called the **reflexive, symmetric,** and **transitive** properties respectively.

Example 1. Determine whether the relation $\geq$ is or is not an equivalence relation for the set of real numbers.

The relation $\geq$ is reflexive since $a \geq a$ for every real number a. The relation is transitive since if $a \geq b$ and $b \geq c$, then $a \geq c$. However, the relation is not symmetric (for instance, $5 \geq 3$ but $3 \not\geq 5$); hence it is not an equivalence relation.

Example 2. Determine whether the relation $\cong$ (is congruent to) is or is not an equivalence relation for the set of triangles on a plane.

Since every triangle is congruent to itself, the relation is reflexive. For every pair of triangles on a plane if one triangle is congruent to the second triangle, then the second triangle is congruent to the first; hence the relation $\cong$ is symmetric. Also, if one triangle is congruent to a second triangle and the second triangle is congruent to a third triangle, then the first triangle is congruent to the third triangle and the relation $\cong$ is transitive. Therefore the relation $\cong$ is an equivalence relation for the set of triangles on a plane.

The three properties of equivalence relations may be thought of as *patterns*. The search for and the study of patterns is an important characteristic of mathematics. We have already observed patterns as statements of relations among the elements of a set. Next we shall look for patterns as we consider the remaining ingredient of a mathematical system, namely, operations.

Let I stand for the set of integers. For any $a \in I$, $a^2 \in I$. The operation of squaring a number is uniquely defined over the set I since for each $a \in I$ there is one and only one a^2; the set I is closed under this operation since for each $a \in I$, $a^2 \in I$. The operation of squaring a number associates with each $a \in I$ an element $a^2 \in I$ and thus may be thought of as the function $a^2 = f(a)$. The domain of this function over I is I, and the range is the set of positive integers and zero. The operation of squaring a number is an example of a **unary operation** (§ 1-2) because it is defined for single elements $a \in I$.

§ 6-1   MATHEMATICAL SYSTEMS

Addition, subtraction, multiplication, and division are **binary operations** since each of these operations associates a unique number with an ordered pair of numbers. For example, if S is any subset of the set of real numbers, then each element of the Cartesian product $S \times S$ is associated under subtraction with a real number. In general we use $\odot$ to denote an arbitrary binary operation and read $a \odot b$ as "a op b." Any binary operation $a \odot b$ which associates exactly one element of S with an ordered pair of elements may be thought of as a function of the two elements in the ordered pair. For example, $a - b = f(a, b)$; $a + b = g(a, b)$. Similarly, **ternary operations,** and, in general, **n-ary operations** may be thought of as functions of ordered triples of elements and, in general, ordered n-tuples of elements. An illustration of a ternary operation may be found in § 11–10.

Consider any universal set U as in § 1–1 and let S be any subset of U. A binary operation $\odot$ is **defined** over S if each element $(a, b) \in S \times S$ is associated with an element $a \odot b \in T$ where $T \subseteq U$. If, also, $T \subseteq S$, then S is **closed** under the operation $\odot$. For example, relative to the set U of real numbers, the operations of addition, subtraction, and multiplication are defined over the set I of integers. Division is not defined over I since division by zero is not possible in the set U of real numbers. Division is defined over the set N of positive integers since zero is not an element of N and since any quotient of elements of N is an element of U although it may or may not be an element of N. The set N is closed under addition and multiplication; N is not closed under subtraction or division. For example, $3 - 5 \notin N$, and $5 \div 7 \notin N$.

A binary operation $\odot$ is **well-defined** over a set S if and only if for every $a, b, c, d \in S$ such that $a = b$ and $c = d$, then $a \odot c = b \odot d$. In the special cases where the binary operation is addition or multiplication over some subset of the real numbers, this definition of well-defined is equivalent to the statement that if equal expressions are added to, or multiplied by, equal expressions, then the sums, or products, are equal. However, not all binary operations are well-defined. As in Example 3, a single **counter-example** (that is, a single instance in which the general statement fails) is sufficient to prove that a general statement does not hold.

Example 3. Consider the set S of ordered pairs of positive integers (x_i, x_j). Define the equivalence relation,

$$(x_i, x_j) = (x_k, x_m) \text{ if and only if } x_i x_m = x_j x_k,$$

and a binary operation $\odot$,

$$(x_i, x_j) \odot (x_k, x_m) = (x_i, x_k).$$

Then prove that the operation $\odot$ is not well-defined.

261

SYSTEMS OF NUMBERS

We may prove that the operation $\odot$ is not well-defined by citing a counter-example; that is, by finding elements $a, b, c, d \in S$ such that $a = b, c = d$, and $a \odot c \neq b \odot d$.

Let $a = (8, 4)$, $b = (6, 3)$, $c = (3, 1)$, and $d = (6, 2)$. Then
$a = b$, $(8, 4) = (6, 3)$ since $8 \times 3 = 4 \times 6$;
$c = d$, $(3, 1) = (6, 2)$ since $3 \times 2 = 1 \times 6$;
$a \odot c = (8, 4) \odot (3, 1) = (8, 3)$;
$b \odot d = (6, 3) \odot (6, 2) = (6, 6)$;
$a \odot c \neq b \odot d$, $(8, 3) \neq (6, 6)$ since $8 \times 6 \neq 3 \times 6$.

Notice the use of the transitive property of the equivalence relation in the substitution of $(8, 3)$ for $(8, 4) \odot (3, 1)$ and the substitution of $(6, 6)$ in the last step.

In our familiar sets of numbers the usual operations are well-defined. Accordingly, unless otherwise specified, we shall assume that addition, subtraction, multiplication, and division (excluding division by zero) are well-defined.

We have just stated an "assumption" that operations are well-defined unless otherwise specified. Many statements involving the elements, relations, and operations of a mathematical system arise as *asssumed* statements. These statements may be called axioms, postulates, definitions, or simply assumptions. In ordinary algebra we usually assume that addition is commutative $(a + b = b + a)$; in Euclidean geometry we usually assume that any two distinct points determine a unique straight line. However, not all statements are assumptions. For example, in algebra we state word problems to be solved; in geometry we state theorems to be proved.

Our concepts of elements, relations, operations, and statements may now be used to form a definition of a mathematical system. A **mathematical system** consists of a set of elements, relations among the elements, one or more well-defined operations on the elements, and a set of axioms which the elements, relations, and operations satisfy. Different sets of elements, relations, operations, and axioms may define quite different mathematical systems. However, we assume that every mathematical system has an equivalence relation. All the properties of a particular mathematical system are inherent in the set of axioms for the system; but none of us can perceive all of the properties of the system as an immediate consequence of the set of axioms. Thus in a careful study of the structure of a particular mathematical system we need to state these properties in the form of theorems and exhibit the steps necessary to show that they are logical consequences of our assumptions. The structures of the common systems of numbers that we shall consider in the next few sections can be clearly understood in terms of the properties of mathematical systems.

Before we consider the properties of particular mathematical systems in more detail, we should notice that the terms we leave undefined, the definitions we use, and the axioms we use have been arbitrarily chosen by the mathematicians who propose the system. We tend to forget this privilege of selection because many mathematical systems are so familiar to us that we accept in them the usual undefined terms, definitions, and axioms as "right" without recognizing that when a particular system was first considered, arbitrary decisions were made regarding these assumptions. Often some external physical situation may motivate the choice of elements and axioms. Sometimes the axioms are pure inventions. However, the choice of axioms is not completely arbitrary; the mathematician must select his axioms so that the set he selects yields a "consistent" system.

We may think of a system as consistent if it does not involve any "contradictions." Thus a set of axioms is consistent if it does not imply any "contradictions." We first define an inconsistent set of axioms and then a consistent set of axioms. A set of axioms is **inconsistent** if their assumption implies two statements: one of the form "A is true," and another of the form "A is not true." A set of axioms is **consistent** if the set is not inconsistent. Unfortunately there is no valid general test for consistency. Usually the mathematician accepts the consistency of a set of axioms if he can find an interpretation of the undefined elements which leads to a consistent **model** (representation) of the system. Sometimes the consistency of the model can be proved in a system which is already known to be consistent. Often the consistency of the model is assumed by assuming that the physical universe is consistent.

We shall consider several models for some of the mathematical systems studied later in this chapter. A single contradiction in a model is sufficient to demonstrate the inconsistency of a set of axioms. Without the property of consistency a set of axioms is rather useless, so mathematicians usually are not interested in inconsistent sets of axioms.

TEST YOURSELF

Tell whether or not each relation is (a) *reflexive;* (b) *symmetric;* (c) *transitive;* (d) *an equivalence relation:*

1. "Is similar to" for the set of triangles on a plane.
2. "Is an integral divisor of" for the set $\{1, 2, 4, 6, 8\}$.

SYSTEMS OF NUMBERS

3. "Is east of" for the set of towns in the United States.
4. "Is the same age as" for the set of people in the world.

Tell which of the following sets are closed under the given operation:

5. The set of odd integers under addition.
6. The set of rational numbers under multiplication.
7. The set {0, 1} under addition.
8. The set of real numbers under the unary operation of taking the square root.

EXERCISES

Tell whether or not each relation is **(a)** *reflexive;* **(b)** *symmetric;* **(c)** *transitive;* **(d)** *an equivalence relation:*

1. "Is less than" for the set of positive integers.
2. "Is an integral multiple of" for the set of positive integers.
3. "Is not equal to" for the set of real numbers.
4. "Is perpendicular to" for the set of lines on a plane.
5. "Is parallel to" for the set of lines on a plane (assume that a line is considered to be parallel to itself).
6. "Is the supplement of" for the set of angles on a plane.
7. "Is prime to" (that is, the two numbers have no common integral factors greater than 1) for the set {2, 3, 4, 5, 6, 7}.
8. "Is the father of" for the set of people in the world.
9. "Is a student at the same high school as" for the set of all high school students.
10. "Lives within three miles of" for the set of people in the world.
11. "Is a subset of" for sets.
12. "Is a proper subset of" for sets.

In Exercises 13 through 24 tell which of the following sets are closed under the given operation:

13. The set of odd integers under multiplication.
14. The set of even integers under division.
15. The set of integers under subtraction.
16. The set of integers under division.
17. The set of rational numbers under division.
18. The set {0} under addition.
19. The set {1} under multiplication.
20. The set {0, 1} under subtraction.
21. The set of prime numbers under subtraction.

22. The set $\{1, -1, i, -i\}$ under multiplication where $i^2 = -1$.

23. The set S of ordered pairs of real numbers (x, y) under $\odot$ where for every $(a, b), (c, d) \in S$ we define $(a, b) \odot (c, d) = ac + bd$.

24. The set S of ordered pairs of positive integers (x, y) under $\odot$ where for every $(a, b), (c, d) \in S$ we define $(a, b) \odot (c, d) = (ac, b - d)$.

• • •

25. Give an example of a relation that is reflexive and symmetric but not transitive.

26. Give an example of a relation that is reflexive and transitive but not symmetric.

27. Give an example of a relation that is symmetric and transitive but not reflexive.

• 28. (a) A relation **R** is called **irreflexive** with respect to a set S if for every $a \in S$, $a \not{R} a$. Give an example of an irreflexive relation. (b) A relation **R** is called **nonreflexive** if for some but not all $a \in S$, $a \, \mathbf{R} \, a$. Give an example of a nonreflexive relation.

• 29. (a) A relation **R** is called **asymmetric** with respect to a set S if for every $a, b \in S$, if $a \, \mathbf{R} \, b$ then $b \not{R} a$. Give an example of an asymmetric relation. (b) A relation **R** is called **nonsymmetric** if it is sometimes but not always symmetric. Give an example of a nonsymmetric relation.

• 30. (a) A relation **R** is called **intransitive** with respect to a set S if for every $a, b, c \in S$, if $a \, \mathbf{R} \, b$ and $b \, \mathbf{R} \, c$, then $a \not{R} c$. Give an example of an intransitive relation. (b) A relation **R** is called **nontransitive** if it is sometimes but not always transitive. Give an example of a nontransitive relation.

• 31. Let S be the set of all integers. We define two integers a and b as congruent modulo m, denoted by $a \equiv b \pmod{m}$, if $a = b + km$ for some integer k. Prove that congruence, modulo m, is an equivalence relation.

§ 6-2 Groups

Consider the set Q of positive rational numbers (that is, numbers expressible as quotients $\frac{p}{q}$ of positive integers), the usual equivalence relation $=$, and the usual binary operation multiplication $\times$. Assuming that $=$ and $\times$ have their usual properties, we have a mathematical system as defined in § 6–1. This system has four important properties:

(i) *Closure:* If $a, b \in Q$, then $a \times b \in Q$.
(ii) *Associativity:* If $a, b, c \in Q$, then $a \times (b \times c) = (a \times b) \times c$.

SYSTEMS OF NUMBERS

(iii) *Identity element:* There exists an element μ (denoted by the Greek letter mu) where $\mu \in Q$ such that for every $a \in Q$, $a \times \mu = \mu \times a = a$. Note that $\mu = 1$ for the set Q under multiplication.

(iv) *Inverse elements:* For each $a \in Q$ there exists an element $a^* \in Q$ such that $a \times a^* = a^* \times a = \mu$. Note that $a^* = \dfrac{1}{a}$ for the set Q under multiplication.

The mathematical system involving Q is an example of a group, one of the simplest and most important abstract mathematical systems. A **group** is a mathematical system consisting of a set G of elements, an equivalence relation $=$, and a binary operation $\odot$ which is well-defined over the set G and such that the following axioms hold:

Closure: If $a, b \in G$, then $a \odot b \in G$.
Associativity: If $a, b, c \in G$, then $a \odot (b \odot c) = (a \odot b) \odot c$.
Identity element: There exists an element $\mu \in G$ such that for every $a \in G$, $a \odot \mu = \mu \odot a = a$.
Inverse elements: For each $a \in G$ there exists an element $a^* \in G$ such that $a \odot a^* = a^* \odot a = \mu$.

Example 1. Consider a set of elements $S = \{1, -1, i, -i\}$ where $i \times i = -1$. Determine whether or not S forms a group with $=$ as its equivalence relation and $\times$ as its well-defined binary operation.

		SECOND FACTOR			
	$\times$	1	-1	i	$-i$
FIRST FACTOR	1	1	-1	i	$-i$
	-1	-1	1	$-i$	i
	i	i	$-i$	-1	1
	$-i$	$-i$	i	1	-1

A multiplication table for the set S appears as shown. The set S is closed under multiplication since each entry in the body of the table is a member of S. The associative property holds. This can be shown by considering each of the 64 possible sets of three factors where the factors are elements of S. For example,

$$[(-1) \times i] \times (-i) = (-1) \times [i \times (-i)]$$
$$(-i) \times (-i) = (-1) \times 1$$
$$-1 = -1.$$

§ 6-2 GROUPS

The identity element for the set S under multiplication is 1. Examination of the given table shows that the inverse elements of $1, -1, i$, and $-i$ are $1, -1, -i$, and i respectively. That is,

$$1 \times 1 = 1 \times 1 = 1;$$
$$(-1) \times (-1) = (-1) \times (-1) = 1;$$
$$i \times (-i) = (-i) \times i = 1;$$
$$(-i) \times i = i \times (-i) = 1.$$

The set S with the equivalence relation = and the operation × satisfies the four properties of a group and forms a group under multiplication.

If a set G with the relation = and the operation $\odot$ forms a group and for every $a, b \in G$, $a \odot b = b \odot a$, then G forms a **commutative group**. For example, the set S in Example 1 forms a commutative group. Evidence of this commutativity may be found in the multiplication table where the entries are symmetric with respect to the entries along a diagonal from the upper left corner to the lower right corner.

If a group G contains only a finite number of elements, then G is a **finite group**. If G contains an infinite number of elements, G is an **infinite group**. The group S in Example 1 is a finite group; the group Q considered in the first paragraph of this section is an infinite group.

If in discussing groups we omit any mention of the type of equivalence relation under consideration, it is to be understood that ordinary equality is being used.

Example 2. Let S be the set of nonnegative integers, $\{0, 1, 2, 3, 4, \cdots\}$. Does S form a group under addition?

Since the sum of any two nonnegative integers is a nonnegative integer, the closure axiom is satisfied. It can be proved that the associative axiom is also satisfied. Since 0, the identity element for addition, is in S, the identity element axiom is satisfied. However, since 0 is the only element of S whose inverse under addition is in S, the inverse element axiom is not satisfied; therefore S does not form a group under addition.

Notice that the absence of the inverse for a single element, such as 3, is sufficient reason for asserting that the set does not form a group; that is, sufficient for answering the given question.

SYSTEMS OF NUMBERS

Example 3. Let S be the set of substitutions $\{A, B, C, D, E, F\}$ where

$$A = \begin{pmatrix} a & b & c \\ a & b & c \end{pmatrix}, \quad B = \begin{pmatrix} a & b & c \\ a & c & b \end{pmatrix}, \quad C = \begin{pmatrix} a & b & c \\ b & a & c \end{pmatrix},$$

$$D = \begin{pmatrix} a & b & c \\ b & c & a \end{pmatrix}, \quad E = \begin{pmatrix} a & b & c \\ c & a & b \end{pmatrix}, \quad F = \begin{pmatrix} a & b & c \\ c & b & a \end{pmatrix},$$

and each substitution such as $\begin{pmatrix} a & b & c \\ b & c & a \end{pmatrix}$ indicates the substitution for each letter on the first row of the array of the letter directly below it on the second row. For example, in D: a is replaced by b, b is replaced by c, and c is replaced by a; we may write this as

$$a \xrightarrow{D} b, \quad b \xrightarrow{D} c, \quad c \xrightarrow{D} a.$$

An operation $X \odot Y$ is defined for $X, Y \in S$ as the substitutions of X followed by the substitutions of Y. For example,

$$B \odot E = \begin{pmatrix} a & b & c \\ a & c & b \end{pmatrix} \odot \begin{pmatrix} a & b & c \\ c & a & b \end{pmatrix} = \begin{pmatrix} a & b & c \\ c & b & a \end{pmatrix} = F$$

since $\quad a \xrightarrow{B} a \xrightarrow{E} c; \quad b \xrightarrow{B} c \xrightarrow{E} b; \quad c \xrightarrow{B} b \xrightarrow{E} a.$

(a) Does the set S form a group under $\odot$? **(b)** Does the set S form a commutative group under $\odot$?

(a) We first complete a table for the set S under the operation $\odot$:

	SECOND ELEMENT					
$\odot$	A	B	C	D	E	F
A	A	B	C	D	E	F
B	B	A	D	C	F	E
C	C	E	A	F	B	D
D	D	F	B	E	A	C
E	E	C	F	A	D	B
F	F	D	E	B	C	A

(FIRST ELEMENT labels the rows.)

The closure axiom is satisfied since each entry in the completed table is an element of S.

We next prove that the associativity axiom is satisfied for any sequence of three substitutions. Basically, each substitution is a replacement of the elements a, b, c by the elements a, b, c not necessarily in the same order. Consider any three substitutions X, Y, and Z; and let x represent any one of the three elements a, b, c. Under the substitution X the element x is replaced by an element y which may or may not be the same as x. Under the substitution Y the element y is replaced by an element z. Under the substitution Z the element z is replaced by an element w. Note that x, y, z, and w may each represent any element of $\{a, b, c\}$. We may indicate this sequence of substitutions by

$$x \xrightarrow{X} y, \quad y \xrightarrow{Y} z, \quad z \xrightarrow{Z} w.$$

Then for $(X \odot Y) \odot Z$ we have

$$x \xrightarrow{X \odot Y} z \xrightarrow{Z} w$$

whence $x \longrightarrow w$; for $X \odot (Y \odot Z)$ we have

$$x \xrightarrow{X} y \xrightarrow{Y \odot Z} w$$

whence $x \longrightarrow w$. Thus $(X \odot Y) \odot Z = X \odot (Y \odot Z)$ since they have the same effect on each of the elements a, b, c. Since X, Y, and Z were any substitutions from the set $\{A, B, C, D, E, F\}$, the associativity axiom is satisfied for S under $\odot$.

Notice in the table that the elements on the first row of the table are just like the headings above them; in other words, $A \odot X = X$ for each $X \in S$. Similarly, the elements of the first column of the table are just like the elements in the caption column on their left; thus $X \odot A = X$ for each $X \in S$. Accordingly, A is the identity element for $\odot$; therefore the identity element axiom is satisfied for S under $\odot$.

In order to find the inverse under $\odot$ of an element $X \in S$, we look in the table for the identity element A on the row of X and note that the element at the head of the column in which we found A is the inverse of X. Thus the inverse of A is A since $A \odot A = A$. In a similar manner we find that the inverse of B is B since $B \odot B = A$, the inverse of C is C since $C \odot C = A$, the inverse of D is E since $D \odot E = A$, the inverse of E is D since $E \odot D = A$, and the inverse of F is F since $F \odot F = A$. Since each element of S has an inverse element in S, the inverse element axiom is satisfied.

The set S forms a group under $\odot$ since all four of the axioms of a group are satisfied. The group is finite since there are exactly six elements in S.

(b) The group is not commutative since $B \odot D = C$, $D \odot B = F$, and thus $B \odot D \neq D \odot B$.

269

SYSTEMS OF NUMBERS

In Example 3 notice how the table has been used to determine whether or not the set S is closed, has an identity element, and includes the inverse of each of its elements. If each entry in the table is an element of S, the set is closed. If there is an element X such that the row of X is just like the row of headings and the column of X is just like the column of headings, then X is the identity element μ. If the identity element occurs once and only once in each row and column in the body of the table, then each element has a unique inverse element.

The table may also be used to determine whether or not a group is commutative. To use a table for this purpose, we must set up the elements in the row of column headings in the same order (reading from left to right) that is used in the column of row headings (reading from top to bottom). Then the commutativity axiom holds if the elements in the table which are symmetrically placed with respect to the major diagonal (the diagonal of the table from the upper left corner to the lower right corner) are identical. For example, the set $S = \{0, 1, 2, 3, 4\}$ under the operation $\odot$ as defined in the given table is closed; has 1 as its identity element; and

$\odot$	0	1	2	3	4
0	0	0	0	0	0
1	0	1	2	3	4
2	0	2	4	1	3
3	0	3	1	4	2
4	0	4	3	2	1

does not have an inverse element for 0 under $\odot$ (thus the set does not form a group). The operation $\odot$ is commutative.

A number of theorems concerning abstract groups have elementary proofs. One such theorem is given with its proof in the next example.

Example 4. Prove: The identity element μ of a group under a given operation is unique.

> We shall use the indirect method of proof and assume that μ and μ' each represent an identity element for a group G. Then $\mu \odot \mu' = \mu$ by the identity axiom; and $\mu \odot \mu' = \mu'$ by the identity axiom. Under the symmetric and transitivity properties of the equivalence relation, $\mu = \mu'$. Thus μ' is merely another name for μ; therefore the identity element of a group is unique.

TEST YOURSELF

In Exercises 1 through 4 assume that the associativity axiom holds and determine whether or not the given set under the given operation forms a group:

1. The set of positive integers under addition.
2. The set of positive integers under multiplication.
3. The set of integers under addition.
4. The set $\{1, -1\}$ under multiplication.
5. Identify the groups in Exercises 1 through 4 which are (a) commutative; (b) finite.

EXERCISES

In Exercises 1 through 7 assume that the associativity axiom holds and determine whether or not the given set under the given operation forms a group:

1. The set of integers under multiplication.
2. The set of nonzero rational numbers under addition.
3. The set of rational numbers under addition.
4. The set of nonzero rational numbers under multiplication.
5. The set of odd integers under subtraction.
6. The set of even integers under addition.
7. The set of even integers under multiplication.
8. In Exercises 1 through 7 identify the groups which are commutative.

• • •

In Exercises 9 through 12 assume that the associativity axiom holds and determine whether or not the given set under the given operation forms a group:

9. The set S of substitutions of arrangements of the letters a, b under the operation used in Example 3.

10. The set of integers $\{0, 1, 2\}$ under the operation defined by the table on the right.

$\odot$	0	1	2
0	0	0	0
1	0	1	2
2	0	2	1

$\odot$	a	b
a	a	b
b	b	b

11. The set of elements $\{a, b\}$ under the operation defined by the table on the left.

SYSTEMS OF NUMBERS

12. The set of elements $\left\{r, \dfrac{1}{r}, 1-r, \dfrac{1}{1-r}, \dfrac{r-1}{r}, \dfrac{r}{r-1}\right\}$ under the operation of substitution of the second element for r in the first element. For example,

$$(1-r) \odot \left(\dfrac{1}{1-r}\right) = 1 - \dfrac{1}{1-r} = \dfrac{r}{r-1}.$$

13. Prove that in a group under $\odot$: (a) If $a \odot b = a \odot c$, then $b = c$. (b) If $b \odot a = c \odot a$, then $b = c$.

14. Prove that if a set G forms a group under $\odot$ and $a, b \in G$, then there exists an element $x \in G$ such that $a \odot x = b$.

• 15. Given a finite group G of n elements, then for each $a \in G$ there exists a positive integer $k \leq n$ such that $a^k = \mu$. By a^k we mean $a \odot a \odot \cdots \odot a$ where a is used in the operation k times. Verify this theorem for the elements of the group in Exercise 12.

§ 6–3 Integers

Your previous contacts with mathematics have given you an informal and intuitive understanding of systems of numbers such as the systems of natural numbers, integers, rational numbers, real numbers, and complex numbers. Each of these systems has many properties. Probably, as in § 1–3, you have assumed most of the properties of each system without proof. In this section we shall assume the properties of natural numbers, define integers as ordered pairs of natural numbers, and then prove some of the properties of integers. We shall prove some of the properties of rational numbers in § 6–4 and of complex numbers in § 6–7.

We assume that the set N of natural numbers $\{1, 2, 3, \cdots\}$ has an equivalence relation $=$, is closed under the binary operations of addition $+$ and multiplication $\times$, and satisfies the **commutative law for addition**

$$a + b = b + a;$$

the **commutative law for multiplication**

$$a \times b = b \times a;$$

the **associative law for addition**

$$a + (b + c) = (a + b) + c;$$

the **associative law for multiplication**

$$a \times (b \times c) = (a \times b) \times c;$$

§ 6-3 INTEGERS

and the **distributive law for multiplication with respect to addition**

$$a \times (b + c) = (a \times b) + (a \times c).$$

We also assume that:

(i) Addition and multiplication of natural numbers are well-defined operations.

(ii) For any natural numbers a, b, and k, if $a + k = b + k$, then $a = b$.

(iii) The **order relation** $a < b$ for natural numbers a, b holds if and only if there is a natural number c such that $a + c = b$.

(iv) For any two natural numbers a, b exactly one of these three statements must hold:

$$a < b, \quad a = b, \quad a > b.$$

The set of natural numbers is closed under addition and multiplication. The set of natural numbers is not closed under subtraction or under division; that is, differences and quotients of natural numbers may or may not represent natural numbers. In order to obtain a system which includes the set of natural numbers and is closed under subtraction, we need the set of integers.

The set N of natural numbers forms a mathematical system as defined in § 6-1. The positive integers correspond to the natural numbers. Any integer may be expressed as a difference of positive integers and thus as a difference of natural numbers. For example,

$$4 = 7 - 3; \quad -2 = 6 - 8; \quad 0 = 11 - 11.$$

Each difference may be represented by an ordered pair in which the second element is subtracted from the first:

$$\langle 7, 3 \rangle = 7 - 3; \quad \langle 6, 8 \rangle = 6 - 8; \quad \langle 11, 11 \rangle = 11 - 11.$$

Then any integer may be represented by an ordered pair of natural numbers. Notice that each integer may be expressed in many ways as a difference of natural numbers; for example,

$$3 = 7 - 4 = 5 - 2 = 25 - 22.$$

Let us pretend that we are familiar with natural numbers and their properties but that we know nothing about integers. We arbitrarily define the set I of **integers** to be the set of numbers expressible as ordered pairs $\langle a, b \rangle$ where $a, b \in N$. We define an equivalence relation for integers in terms of the equivalence relation for natural numbers:

$$\langle a, b \rangle = \langle c, d \rangle \text{ if and only if } a + d = b + c. \tag{1}$$

273

SYSTEMS OF NUMBERS

We define the binary operation addition for integers in terms of the addition of natural numbers:

$$\langle a, b \rangle + \langle c, d \rangle = \langle a + c, b + d \rangle. \tag{2}$$

Notice that, since the set of natural numbers is closed under addition, $(a + c)$ and $(b + d)$ both represent natural numbers. Accordingly, the sum of two ordered pairs of natural numbers is an ordered pair of natural numbers, that is, an integer. The set of integers is closed under addition.

Finally, we define the binary operation multiplication for integers in terms of the multiplication of natural numbers:

$$\langle a, b \rangle \times \langle c, d \rangle = \langle ac + bd, ad + bc \rangle. \tag{3}$$

Notice that since the set of natural numbers is closed under addition and multiplication, $ac, bd, (ac + bd) ad, bc,$ and $(ad + bc)$ represent natural numbers. Accordingly, the product of two ordered pairs of natural numbers is an ordered pair of natural numbers, that is, an integer. The set of integers is closed under multiplication.

The set I of ordered pairs of natural numbers with the definitions (1), (2), and (3) and the properties of the natural numbers forms a mathematical system. The correspondence of ordered pairs $\langle a, b \rangle$ to differences $a - b$ provides a basis for the definitions (1), (2), and (3) since

$$a - b = c - d \text{ if and only if } a + d = b + c;$$
$$(a - b) + (c - d) = (a + c) - (b + d);$$
$$(a - b) \times (c - d) = (ac + bd) - (ad + bc).$$

The properties of the set I can now be proved as theorems from the definitions and the properties of the set N of natural numbers.

Theorem 1. *For any natural numbers a, b, and k,*

$$\langle a + k, b + k \rangle = \langle a, b \rangle.$$

PROOF: Since $a, b, k \in N$, we may use the properties of natural numbers. By the definition (1)

$\langle a + k, b + k \rangle = \langle a, b \rangle$ if and only if $(a + k) + b = (b + k) + a$.

In order to prove this statement we use the transitive property of the equivalence of natural numbers and apply the commutative and associative properties of addition of natural numbers as follows:

$(a + k) + b = a + (k + b)$ Associativity
$ = (k + b) + a$ Commutativity
$ = (b + k) + a$ Commutativity.

274

§ 6-3 INTEGERS

Theorem 2. *The equality of integers is an equivalence relation.*

PROOF: We must prove that the equality of elements of I is reflexive, symmetric, and transitive. Consider any $\langle a, b \rangle, \langle c, d \rangle, \langle e, f \rangle \in I$ where $a, b, c, d, e, f \in N$.

Reflexive: We wish to prove that $\langle a, b \rangle = \langle a, b \rangle$. We know by the reflexive property of equality of natural numbers that $a + b = a + b$; also, by the commutative property for addition of natural numbers $a + b = b + a$. Thus by the definition (1) of equal integers, $\langle a, b \rangle = \langle a, b \rangle$.

Symmetric: We wish to prove that if $\langle a, b \rangle = \langle c, d \rangle$, then $\langle c, d \rangle = \langle a, b \rangle$. We know by the definition (1) for integers that $\langle a, b \rangle = \langle c, d \rangle$ if and only if $a + d = b + c$. Since by the commutative property of addition of natural numbers $d + a = c + b$, and by the symmetric property of equality of natural numbers $c + b = d + a$; then by the definition (1) for integers $\langle c, d \rangle = \langle a, b \rangle$.

Transitive: We wish to prove that if $\langle a, b \rangle = \langle c, d \rangle$ and $\langle c, d \rangle = \langle e, f \rangle$ then $\langle a, b \rangle = \langle e, f \rangle$. We know by the definition (1) for integers that $\langle a, b \rangle = \langle c, d \rangle$ if and only if $a + d = b + c$ and that $\langle c, d \rangle = \langle e, f \rangle$ if and only if $c + f = d + e$. Since addition of natural numbers is well-defined, $(a + d) + (c + f) = (b + c) + (d + e)$. We now apply the commutative and associative properties of addition of natural numbers as follows:

$$a + [d + (c + f)] = b + [c + (d + e)] \quad \text{Associativity}$$
$$a + [(d + c) + f] = b + [(c + d) + e] \quad \text{Associativity}$$
$$a + [f + (d + c)] = b + [e + (c + d)] \quad \text{Commutativity}$$
$$(a + f) + (d + c) = (b + e) + (c + d) \quad \text{Associativity}$$
$$(a + f) + (c + d) = (b + e) + (c + d) \quad \text{Commutativity.}$$

Then by the property (ii) of the equality of natural numbers $a + f = b + e$; and by the definition (1) for integers $\langle a, b \rangle = \langle e, f \rangle$.

Theorem 3. *The addition of integers is a well-defined binary operation.*

PROOF: If $\langle a, b \rangle = \langle c, d \rangle$ and $\langle e, f \rangle = \langle g, h \rangle$, then by the definition (1) for integers $a + d = b + c$ and $e + h = f + g$. Since addition is well-defined for natural numbers, $(a + d) + (e + h) = (b + c) + (f + g)$. By the commutative and associative properties of addition of natural numbers

$$(a + e) + (d + h) = (b + f) + (c + g),$$

and by the definition (1) for integers

$$\langle a + e, b + f \rangle = \langle c + g, d + h \rangle.$$

275

SYSTEMS OF NUMBERS

Since by the definition (2) for integers
$$\langle a, b \rangle + \langle e, f \rangle = \langle a + e, b + f \rangle$$
$$\langle c, d \rangle + \langle g, h \rangle = \langle c + g, d + h \rangle;$$
and since by Theorem 2 the equality of elements of I is symmetric and transitive, then
$$\langle a, b \rangle + \langle e, f \rangle = \langle c, d \rangle + \langle g, h \rangle$$
as was to be proved to show that addition of integers is well-defined.

The set of integers is closed under addition by the definition (2) and the closure of the set of natural numbers under addition. The commutative and associative properties of addition of integers can be proved (Exercises 19 and 25) but for our immediate use will be assumed. Then the next two theorems enable us to prove that the set of integers forms a commutative group under addition (§ 6–2).

Theorem 4. *The set of integers has an identity element $\langle z, z \rangle$ for addition.*

PROOF: For any $a, b, z \in N$ we have by the definition (2), Theorem 1, and the commutative property of addition of natural numbers,
$$\begin{aligned}\langle a, b \rangle + \langle z, z \rangle &= \langle a + z, b + z \rangle \\ &= \langle a, b \rangle \\ &= \langle z + a, z + b \rangle \\ &= \langle z, z \rangle + \langle a, b \rangle.\end{aligned}$$
For any $z, k \in N$ we have $\langle z, z \rangle = \langle k, k \rangle$ since $z + k = z + k$. Thus the set I of integers has a unique identity element for addition.

Theorem 5. *For any $a, b, c, d \in N$ the equation*
$$\langle a, b \rangle = \langle c, d \rangle + \langle x, y \rangle$$
has a unique solution $\langle x, y \rangle$ where
$$\langle x, y \rangle = \langle a + d, b + c \rangle.$$

PROOF: If $\langle a, b \rangle = \langle c, d \rangle + \langle x, y \rangle$, then
$$\begin{array}{ll}\langle a, b \rangle = \langle c + x, d + y \rangle & \text{Definition (2)} \\ a + (d + y) = b + (c + x) & \text{Definition (1)}.\end{array}$$
By the symmetric property of equality
$$b + (c + x) = a + (d + y).$$

276

By the associative and commutative properties of the addition of natural numbers

$$x + (b + c) = y + (a + d);$$

and by the definition (1)

$$\langle x, y \rangle = \langle a + d, b + c \rangle.$$

The solution is unique since the operations upon the natural numbers provide unique results. If any different appearing solution is given, it can be shown to be equal to $\langle a + d, b + c \rangle$ by the definition (1).

By Theorem 4 $\langle z, z \rangle$ is the additive identity element μ. By Theorem 5 the equation

$$\langle z, z \rangle = \langle a, b \rangle + \langle x, y \rangle$$

has a unique solution $\langle z + b, z + a \rangle$ which by the commutativity of addition of natural numbers and by Theorem 1 may be expressed as $\langle b, a \rangle$. For any integer $\langle a, b \rangle$ the integer $\langle b, a \rangle$ is its **negative**, that is, its **inverse under addition**. In general, the inverse under addition of any element is often called its **additive inverse**.

We have now seen that the set I of integers satisfies all of the properties of a group under addition. All of the properties of integers may be developed from appropriate definitions and the properties of natural numbers. For example, order relations ($<, >, \leq, \geq$) might be introduced and their properties developed. Multiplication is a well-defined binary operation, and the commutative and associative properties of multiplication hold for integers. Multiplication of integers is distributive with respect to addition. If $\langle a, b \rangle + \langle x, y \rangle = \langle c, d \rangle + \langle x, y \rangle$, then $\langle a, b \rangle = \langle c, d \rangle$. If $\langle a, b \rangle \times \langle x, y \rangle = \langle c, d \rangle \times \langle x, y \rangle$ and $x \neq y$, then $\langle a, b \rangle = \langle c, d \rangle$. The formal proofs for most of these properties are left for more advanced courses. Our purpose in mentioning them here is to assume them and to emphasize that the properties of integers may be proved from those of the natural numbers. For example, order relations among integers may be based upon Theorem 6.

Theorem 6. *Every integer $\langle x, y \rangle$ is of one of three types:*

$$\langle a + k, a \rangle, \quad \langle a, a \rangle, \quad \langle a, a + k \rangle.$$

PROOF: Given any two natural numbers x and y, then $x > y$, $x = y$, or $x < y$.

If $x > y$, then $x = y + k$ where k is some natural number; and $\langle x, y \rangle = \langle y + k, y \rangle$. By the definition (1) $\langle y + k, y \rangle = \langle a + k, a \rangle$; thus $\langle x, y \rangle = \langle a + k, a \rangle$.

SYSTEMS OF NUMBERS

If $x = y$, then $\langle x, y \rangle = \langle y, y \rangle$; and since $\langle y, y \rangle = \langle a, a \rangle$, we have $\langle x, y \rangle = \langle a, a \rangle$.

If $x < y$, then $x + k = y$ where k is some natural number; and $\langle x, y \rangle = \langle x, x + k \rangle$. By the definition (1) $\langle x, x + k \rangle = \langle a, a + k \rangle$, thus $\langle x, y \rangle = \langle a, a + k \rangle$.

We now define any integer expressible in the form $\langle a + k, a \rangle$ as a **positive integer**; the integer expressible in the form $\langle a, a \rangle$ as **zero**; and any integer expressible in the form $\langle a, a + k \rangle$ as a **negative integer**. By Theorem 4 zero is the identity element under addition. By Theorem 5 each positive integer $\langle a + k, a \rangle$ has a negative integer $\langle a, a + k \rangle$ as its inverse under addition. We observe that zero is its own inverse under addition, and that each negative integer $\langle a, a + k \rangle$ has a positive integer $\langle a + k, a \rangle$ as its inverse under addition. Each of the integers $\langle a + k, a \rangle$ and $\langle a, a + k \rangle$ is called the negative of the other.

Each natural number k corresponds to a positive integer $\langle a + k, a \rangle$ which we may also write as $+k$. We describe this situation by saying that the set of natural numbers is "embedded" in the set of integers. It can be shown that the properties of the natural numbers continue to hold when the numbers are considered as integers of the form $\langle a + k, a \rangle$; that is, as positive integers.

In ordinary arithmetic we mean by the difference $a - b$ the number x such that $a = b + x$. Thus in Theorem 5 we define the solution $\langle x, y \rangle$ of the equation

$$\langle a, b \rangle = \langle c, d \rangle + \langle x, y \rangle$$

as the **difference** $\langle a, b \rangle - \langle c, d \rangle$. Then

$$\langle a, b \rangle - \langle c, d \rangle = \langle a + d, b + c \rangle;$$

in other words

$$\langle a, b \rangle - \langle c, d \rangle = \langle a, b \rangle + \langle d, c \rangle.$$

Thus subtracting a number $\langle c, d \rangle$ may be thought of as adding the negative $\langle d, c \rangle$ of the number and the set of integers is closed under subtraction. We have started with the set of natural numbers which is not closed under subtraction (for example, consider $5 - 8$) and have defined the set I of integers which is closed under subtraction. Since the natural numbers are embedded in the integers, we have extended our system of numbers to obtain a new system in which most of the properties of the natural numbers are preserved and another operation (subtraction) can be performed. Additional insight into this procedure—and into the properties of integers—has been obtained by thinking of integers as ordered pairs of natural numbers.

§ 6-3 INTEGERS

Example 1. Express each integer as an ordered pair of natural numbers: (a) 7; (b) −3; (c) 0.

(a) $7 = \langle 8, 1 \rangle = \langle 9, 2 \rangle = \langle x + 7, x \rangle$ for any $x \in N$.
(b) $-3 = \langle 1, 4 \rangle = \langle 2, 5 \rangle = \langle x, x + 3 \rangle$ for any $x \in N$.
(c) $0 = \langle 1, 1 \rangle = \langle 2, 2 \rangle = \langle x, x \rangle$ for any $x \in N$.

Example 2. Find the product $(-2) \times (-3)$ in terms of ordered pairs of natural numbers.

The product $(-2) \times (-3)$ may be expressed as $\langle 3, 5 \rangle \times \langle 1, 4 \rangle$. By the definition (3) and the properties of natural numbers

$$\langle 3, 5 \rangle \times \langle 1, 4 \rangle = \langle (3)(1) + (5)(4), (3)(4) + (5)(1) \rangle$$
$$= \langle 23, 17 \rangle$$
$$= \langle a + 6, a \rangle.$$

Since $\langle a + 6, a \rangle$ corresponds to the positive integer 6, we have proved that $(-2) \times (-3) = 6$.

Example 3. Prove that the product of two negative integers is a positive integer.

Let $\langle a, a + m \rangle$ and $\langle b, b + n \rangle$ represent any two negative integers $-m$ and $-n$. By the definition (3) and the properties of natural numbers

$$\langle a, a + m \rangle \times \langle b, b + n \rangle = \langle ab + (a + m)(b + n),$$
$$a(b + n) + (a + m)b \rangle$$
$$= \langle 2ab + an + bm + mn, 2ab + an + bm \rangle$$
$$= \langle x + mn, x \rangle \text{ where } x = 2ab + an + bm.$$

Since $\langle x + mn, x \rangle$ corresponds to the positive integer mn, we have proved that $(-m) \times (-n)$ is a positive integer.

TEST YOURSELF

Express each integer as an ordered pair of natural numbers:

1. 3.   **2.** −1.   **3.** 4.   **4.** −5.

Determine whether or not the following integers are equal:

5. $\langle 2, 4 \rangle$ and $\langle 4, 2 \rangle$.   **7.** $\langle 6, 3 \rangle$ and $\langle 6, 2 \rangle$.
6. $\langle 5, 2 \rangle$ and $\langle 7, 4 \rangle$.   **8.** $\langle 7, 9 \rangle$ and $\langle 2, 4 \rangle$.

SYSTEMS OF NUMBERS

Determine which of the following represent positive integers:

9. $\langle 3, 6 \rangle$.
10. $\langle 4, 2 \rangle$.
11. $\langle 5, 5 \rangle$.
12. $\langle y + 1, y \rangle$ for $y \in N$.

Perform the indicated operations:

13. $\langle 2, 1 \rangle + \langle 5, 3 \rangle$.
14. $\langle 5, 2 \rangle \times \langle 7, 3 \rangle$.

EXERCISES

Express each integer as an ordered pair of natural numbers:

1. 5. 2. -2. 3. 15. 4. -3.

Determine whether or not the following integers are equal:

5. $\langle 3, 1 \rangle$ and $\langle 6, 2 \rangle$.
6. $\langle 7, 3 \rangle$ and $\langle 8, 4 \rangle$.
7. $\langle 9, 3 \rangle$ and $\langle 3, 9 \rangle$.
8. $\langle 0, 4 \rangle$ and $\langle 2, 6 \rangle$.

Determine which of the following represent positive integers:

9. $\langle 3, 3 \rangle$.
10. $\langle 2, 1 \rangle$.
11. $\langle k, 3 + k \rangle$ for $k \in N$.
12. $\langle x + y + z, x + z \rangle$ for $x, y, z \in N$.

Perform the indicated operations:

13. $\langle 8, 3 \rangle + \langle 4, 2 \rangle$.
14. $\langle 2, 4 \rangle + \langle 1, 1 \rangle$.
15. $\langle 9, 6 \rangle - \langle 6, 3 \rangle$.
16. $\langle 3, 3 \rangle \times \langle 2, 2 \rangle$.
17. $\langle 2, 5 \rangle \times \langle 3, 7 \rangle$.
18. $\langle 5, 1 \rangle \times \langle 1, 2 \rangle$.

• • •

Express each integer as a difference of natural numbers and prove:

19. Addition of integers is commutative.
20. If $b \in I$, then $0 + b = b + 0 = b$.
21. Multiplication of integers is commutative.
22. If $b \in I$, then $0 \times b = b \times 0 = 0$.
23. If $b \in I$, then $1 \times b = b \times 1 = b$.
24. The product of a negative integer and a positive integer is a negative integer.
25. Addition of integers is associative.
26. If $a, b, x \in I$ and $a + x = b + x$, then $a = b$.

280

§ 6-4 Rational numbers

You have used rational numbers and performed the usual operations upon them. Your understanding of the properties of rational numbers has probably been based upon intuitive rather than formal developments of these properties. We now use letters $a, b, c, \cdots$ to represent integers and define each rational number $\frac{a}{b}$ where $b \neq 0$ as an ordered pair $[a, b]$. We use square brackets to distinguish ordered pairs of integers $[a, b]$ from the ordered pairs of natural numbers $\langle a, b \rangle$. The distinction in notation is desirable since operations on the two sets of ordered pairs will be defined differently. Our formal development of rational numbers will not be exhaustive but should be sufficient to indicate the value of this approach when a rigorous development of the rational number system is desired.

We now define the set R of **rational numbers** to be the set of numbers expressible as ordered pairs $[a, b]$ where $a, b \in I$, $b \neq 0$. We define an equivalence relation for rational numbers in terms of the equivalence relation for integers.

$$[a, b] = [c, d] \text{ if and only if } ad = bc. \qquad (4)$$

We define the binary operation addition for rational numbers in terms of the addition of integers:

$$[a, b] + [c, d] = [ad + bc, bd]. \qquad (5)$$

Also we define the binary operation multiplication for rational numbers in terms of the multiplication of integers:

$$[a, b] \times [c, d] = [ac, bd]. \qquad (6)$$

Since the set of integers is closed under addition and multiplication, the set of rational numbers is closed under addition and multiplication.

The set R of ordered pairs of integers with the definitions (4), (5), and (6), and the properties of the integers (§ 6-3) forms a mathematical system. The properties of the set R of rational numbers can now be proved from the definitions and the properties of the set I of integers.

Theorem 7. *If $[a, b] \in R$ and m is a nonzero integer, then $[ma, mb] = [a, b]$.*

> PROOF: The reflexive property of the equivalence relation may be used for the integers a, b, and m and thus $(ma)b = (ma)b$; by the commutative and associative properties of the multiplication of integers $(ma)b = (mb)a$; by the definition (4) we have $[ma, mb] = [a, b]$. In other words, $[a, b]$ and $[ma, mb]$ are two expressions for the same rational number.

SYSTEMS OF NUMBERS

Theorem 8. *The equality of elements of R is an equivalence relation.*

PROOF: We must prove that the equality of elements of R is reflexive, symmetric, and transitive (§ 6–1).

Reflexive: We wish to prove that $[a, b] = [a, b]$. By the definition (4) this equality is reflexive since $ab = ba$ for any $a, b \in I$ where $b \neq 0$ and thus $[a, b] = [a, b]$.

Symmetric: We wish to prove that if $[a, b] = [c, d]$, then $[c, d] = [a, b]$. Since $[a, b] = [c, d]$, by the definition (4) $ad = bc$; by the symmetric property of the equality of integers $bc = ad$; by the commutative property for multiplication of integers $cb = da$; then by the definition (4) we have $[c, d] = [a, b]$.

Transitive: We wish to prove that if $[a, b] = [c, d]$ and $[c, d] = [e, f]$, then $[a, b] = [e, f]$. If $[a, b] = [c, d]$ and $[c, d] = [e, f]$, then by the definition (4) we have $ad = bc$ and $cf = de$; since multiplication is well-defined for integers,

$$(ad)(cf) = (bc)(de);$$

by the commutative and associative properties of multiplication of integers

$$(af)(cd) = (be)(cd);$$

then by one of the assumed properties of integers (§ 6–3) $af = be$; and by the definition (4) we have $[a, b] = [e, f]$.

Theorem 9. *The addition of rational numbers is a well-defined operation.*

PROOF: If $[a, b] = [c, d]$ and $[e, f] = [g, h]$, then by the definition (4) $ad = bc$ and $eh = fg$. Notice that by the definition (5)

$$[a, b] + [e, f] = [af + be, bf],$$
$$[c, d] + [g, h] = [ch + dg, dh].$$

In order to prove that addition of rational numbers is well-defined we need to prove that

$$[a, b] + [e, f] = [c, d] + [g, h];$$

that is,

$$[af + be, bf] = [ch + dg, dh].$$

The definition (4) shows us that we need to prove that

$$(af + be)(dh) = (bf)(ch + dg);$$

by the associative and commutative properties of addition and the distributive axiom for multiplication with respect to the addition of integers we need to prove that

$$(ad)(fh) + (bd)(eh) = (bc)(fh) + (bd)(fg).$$

Since $ad = bc$, we have $(ad)(fh) = (bc)(fh)$.

Since $eh = fg$, we have $(bd)(eh) = (bd)(fg)$.
Since the addition of integers is well-defined, we have

$$(ad)(fh) + (bd)(eh) = (bc)(fh) + (bd)(fg)$$

whence as we have observed

$$(af + be)(dh) = (bf)(ch + dg),$$
$$[af + be, bf] = [ch + dg, dh],$$
$$[a, b] + [e, f] = [c, d] + [g, h],$$

and our proof that the addition of rational numbers is well-defined is complete.

Theorem 10. *The addition of rational numbers is commutative.*

PROOF: By the definition (5) and the commutativity of addition and multiplication of integers

$$\begin{aligned}[a, b] + [c, d] &= [ad + bc, bd] \\ &= [bc + ad, bd] \\ &= [cb + da, db] \\ &= [c, d] + [a, b].\end{aligned}$$

The associative property of addition of rational numbers may be proved (Exercise 19). Also it may be proved that $[0, a]$ is the identity element for addition of rational numbers (Exercise 17); that for any $a, b \in I, b \neq 0$ the rational number $[-a, b]$ is the additive inverse of $[a, b]$ (Exercise 18); and that the set of rational numbers forms a commutative group under addition (Exercise 20). Subtraction may be defined in terms of adding the additive inverse (that is, the negative) of the number;

$$[a, b] - [c, d] = [a, b] + [-c, d].$$

The multiplication of rational numbers is a well-defined binary operation (Exercise 21) which is commutative (Exercise 22), associative (Exercise 23), and distributive with respect to addition (Exercise 24).

SYSTEMS OF NUMBERS

Theorem 11. *The set of rational numbers has an identity element $[a, a]$ for multiplication.*

> PROOF: For any $a \in I$, $a \neq 0$, we have by the definition (6), Theorem 7, and the commutative property of multiplication of integers
>
> $$[c, d] \times [a, a] = [ca, da] = [c, d] = [ac, ad] = [a, a] \times [c, d]$$
>
> for any $c, d \in I$ where $d \neq 0$. For any $a, b \in I$, $b \neq 0$, we have $[a, a] = [b, b]$ since $ab = ab$. Thus the set of rational numbers has a unique identity element for multiplication.

Theorem 12. *If $[c, d] \neq [0, a]$, then for any $a, b, c, d \in I$, $a \neq 0$, $b \neq 0$, $d \neq 0$, the equation $[a, b] = [c, d] \times [x, y]$ has a unique solution $[x, y]$ where $[x, y] = [ad, bc]$.*

> PROOF: If $[c, d] \neq [0, a]$ and $[a, b] = [c, d] \times [x, y]$, then by the definition (6) $[a, b] = [cx, dy]$; by the definition (4) $a(dy) = b(cx)$; by the symmetric property of the equality of integers $b(cx) = a(dy)$; by the associative and commutative properties of the multiplication of integers $x(bc) = y(ad)$; by the definition (4) $[x, y] = [ad, bc]$. The solution is unique since the operations upon the integers provide unique results. If any different appearing solution is given, it will be equal to $[ad, bc]$ by the definition (4).

In ordinary arithmetic we mean by the quotient $a \div b$ the number x such that $a = bx$. Thus when a solution exists, we define the solution $[x, y]$ in Theorem 12 for the equation

$$[a, b] = [c, d] \times [x, y]$$

to be the **quotient** $[a, b] \div [c, d]$. Then

$$[a, b] \div [c, d] = [ad, bc];$$

that is,

$$[a, b] \div [c, d] = [a, b] \times [d, c].$$

The **reciprocal**, that is, the **inverse under multiplication** (often called the **multiplicative inverse**), of any rational number not equal to $[0, a]$ may be obtained using Theorems 11 and 12. By Theorem 11 the identity element μ may be expressed as $[a, a]$; by Theorem 12 the equation $[a, a] = [c, d] \times [x, y]$ where $[c, d] \neq [0, a]$ has a solution $[ad, ac]$; and by

§ 6-4 RATIONAL NUMBERS

Theorem 7 $[ad, ac] = [d, c]$. Then by the commutativity of multiplication of integers

$$[c, d] \times [d, c] = [cd, cd] = [dc, dc] = [d, c] \times [c, d]$$

whence $[c, d]$ and $[d, c]$ are reciprocals; that is, each is the reciprocal of the other. Then, as in the definition of a quotient, division by any rational number different from $[0, a]$ may be performed by multiplying by its reciprocal. Accordingly, the set R of rational numbers is closed under the operation of dividing by a number different from $[0, a]$. The set of rational numbers different from $[0, a]$ forms a commutative group under multiplication (Exercise 25).

We now define a rational number expressible in the form $[a + k, a]$ as an **improper rational number**; the rational number expressible in the form $[a, a]$ as **unity** (the identity element under multiplication); and any rational number expressible in the form $[a, a + k]$ as a **proper rational number**. Note that each improper rational number has a proper rational number as its reciprocal, and conversely.

Each rational number $[a, b]$ may also be expressed in the usual form $\frac{a}{b}$. Each integer b corresponds to a rational number $[b, 1]$ which may also be expressed as $\frac{b}{1}$ or simply b. In particular, $[0, a]$ corresponds to zero. We describe this situation by saying that the set of integers is "embedded" in the set of rational numbers. It can be shown that the properties of integers continue to hold when they are considered as rational numbers. By Theorem 12 the set of rational numbers different from zero is closed under division. Thus the extension of the system of integers to obtain the rational number system provides a new system in which most of the properties of the integers are preserved and division, except for division by zero, can be performed. Additional insight into the properties of rational numbers can be obtained by thinking of them as ordered pairs of integers.

Example 1. Express each rational number as an ordered pair of integers:
(a) $\frac{3}{4}$;   (b) 2;   (c) -5.

> (a) We may express $\frac{3}{4}$ as $[3, 4]$, $[9, 12]$, and in general as $[3k, 4k]$ for any integer $k \neq 0$.
> (b) We may express 2 as $[2, 1]$, $[-6, -3]$, and in general as $[2k, k]$ for any integer $k \neq 0$.
> (c) We may express -5 as $[-5, 1]$, $[10, -2]$, and in general as $[-5k, k]$ for any integer $k \neq 0$.

SYSTEMS OF NUMBERS

Example 2. Verify that $\frac{1}{3}\left(\frac{2}{5} + \frac{1}{2}\right) = \frac{3}{10}$ by considering each rational number as an ordered pair of integers.

Let $\frac{1}{3}, \frac{2}{5}$, and $\frac{1}{2}$ be represented by the ordered pairs of integers [1, 3], [2, 5], and [1, 2] respectively. Then $\frac{1}{3}\left(\frac{2}{5} + \frac{1}{2}\right)$ is represented by

$$[1, 3] \times ([2, 5] + [1, 2]);$$

which by the definition (5) is equal to

$$[1, 3] \times [(2)(2) + (5)(1), (5)(2)];$$

which by the properties of integers is equal to

$$[1, 3] \times [9, 10];$$

which by the definition (6) is equal to

$$[9, 30];$$

which by Theorem 7 is equal to

$$[3, 10];$$

which may be expressed as $\frac{3}{10}$.

TEST YOURSELF

Express each rational number as an ordered pair of integers:

1. $\frac{5}{2}$.   **2.** -3.   **3.** 0.   **4.** $-\frac{1}{3}$.

Determine whether or not the following rational numbers are equal:

5. [3, 2] and [6, 4].   **7.** [−2, 5] and [4, −10].
6. [5, 2] and [10, 7].   **8.** [0, 2] and [0, 1].

Perform the indicated operations:

9. [1, 4] + [2, 3].   **10.** [1, 6] × [−3, 2].

286

§ 6-5   INTEGRAL DOMAINS AND FIELDS

EXERCISES

Express each rational number as an ordered pair of integers:

1. $\frac{2}{3}$. 2. -1. 3. 2. 4. $-\frac{17}{5}$.

Determine whether or not the following rational numbers are equal:

5. [3, 1] and [6, 2].
6. [−2, 3] and [4, −6].
7. [3, 3] and [4, 4].
8. [5, 2] and [2, 5].

Perform the indicated operations:

9. [3, 4] + [2, 3].
10. [7, 1] + [6, 2].
11. [−5, −3] × [6, −2].
12. [2, 5] × [5, 2].
13. [3, 7] − [6, 14].
14. [1, 2] − [1, 3].
15. [5, 1] + [2, 3].
16. [6, 2] + [3, 1].

● ● ●

Prove:

17. The rational numbers have an identity element [0, *a*] under addition.
18. For any $a, b \in I, b \neq 0$, the additive inverse of [*a*, *b*] is [−*a*, *b*].
19. The addition of rational numbers is associative.
20. The set of rational numbers forms a commutative group under addition.
21. The multiplication of rational numbers is a well-defined operation.
22. The multiplication of rational numbers is commutative.
23. The multiplication of rational numbers is associative.
● 24. The multiplication of rational numbers is distributive with respect to addition.
● 25. The set of rational numbers different from zero forms a commutative group under multiplication.

§ 6–5   Integral domains and fields

The system of integers (§ 6–3) is a model of an abstract mathematical system called an integral domain. The system of rational numbers (§ 6–4) is a model of a field. The algebraic structure known as an integral domain was suggested by the basic properties of the system of integers. The value of studying integral domains without reference to concrete or physical interpretations lies in the fact that many models of an integral domain exist. Each time a mathematician proves a general theorem for integral domains, he has proved many theorems; that is, one theorem for each model. In this sense the theorems of the abstract system furnish theorems for the models. Furthermore, by studying in the abstract those properties common to several concrete or physical models a better insight into the underlying principles of these models is gained.

An **integral domain** D is a mathematical system consisting of a set of elements $a, b, c, \cdots$ having an equivalence relation $=$ and two well-defined binary operations which we call addition ($+$) and multiplication ($\times$) such that the following axioms are satisfied:

Closure under addition: If $a, b \in D$, then $a + b \in D$.
Closure under multiplication: If $a, b \in D$, then $a \times b \in D$.
Commutative addition: If $a, b \in D$, then $a + b = b + a$.
Commutative multiplication: If $a, b \in D$, then $a \times b = b \times a$.
Associative addition: If $a, b, c \in D$, then $a + (b + c) = (a + b) + c$.
Associative multiplication: If $a, b, c \in D$, then $a \times (b \times c) = (a \times b) \times c$.
Additive identity element: There exists an element $z \in D$ such that for every $a \in D$, $a + z = z + a = a$.
Multiplicative identity element: There exists an element $\mu \in D$ such that for every $a \in D$, $a \times \mu = \mu \times a = a$.
Additive inverses: For each element $a \in D$ there exists an element $a^* \in D$ such that $a + a^* = a^* + a = z$.
Multiplication is distributive with respect to addition: For every $a, b, c \in D$, $a \times (b + c) = (a \times b) + (a \times c)$.
There are no "zero divisors": If $a, b \in D$ and $a \times b = z$, then $a = z$ or $b = z$.

If the product of two integers is 6, each of the two integers is a divisor of 6. Divisors different from 6 and 1 are of special interest. If the product of two numbers is zero and neither number is zero, then the numbers are divisors of zero; that is **zero divisors**. A situation of this kind cannot arise in ordinary arithmetic but can arise in some arithmetics modulo m. Thus the last property of an integral domain may also be stated: If the product of two elements of D is zero, then at least one of the two elements must be zero.

The additive identity element is called *zero;* however, it should be noted that in some models zero need not be the real number 0. The multiplicative identity element is called *unity*. Notice that in some models unity need not be the real number 1. The operations which we call "addition" and "multiplication" may be defined in some models as operations quite different from what we think of as ordinary addition and multiplication.

§ 6-5 INTEGRAL DOMAINS AND FIELDS

Example 1. Consider the set S of even integers,

$$S = \{\cdots, -4, -2, 0, 2, 4, \cdots\}.$$

Tell whether or not S forms an integral domain under ordinary addition and multiplication with equality as the equivalence relation.

> For any integers $a, b, c, \cdots$ and in particular for any even integers:
>
> $$a + b = b + a,$$
> $$a \times b = b \times a,$$
> $$(a + b) + c = a + (b + c),$$
> $$(a \times b) \times c = a \times (b \times c),$$
> $$a(b + c) = ab + ac,$$
>
> and $ab = 0$ implies that at least one of the numbers a, b is zero. Thus the fact that S is a subset of the set of integers implies that for arbitrary elements of S, the commutative and associative properties of addition and multiplication are satisfied; multiplication is distributive with respect to addition; and there are no zero divisors.
>
> The set S is closed under addition since the sum of two even integers is an even integer; S is closed under multiplication since the product of two even integers is an even integer.
>
> The additive identity element 0 is a member of S; the multiplicative identity element 1 is not a member of S.
>
> Since we have found an axiom which is not satisfied, we know that the set S does not form an integral domain. However, let us continue our check of all the axioms. The only remaining axiom is the one concerning additive inverses. This axiom is satisfied since the negative of any even integer is an even integer.

A detailed solution of Example 1 has been given to illustrate the procedure in general. A complete solution for Example 1 may also be given very briefly:

> The set S does not form an integral domain because the set does not contain a multiplicative identity element.

A mathematical system F is a **field** if it is an integral domain and if for each nonzero $a \in F$ there exists an element $a^{-1} \in F$ such that

$$a \times a^{-1} = a^{-1} \times a = \mu.$$

That is, a field is an integral domain with multiplicative inverses for all

289

SYSTEMS OF NUMBERS

elements except the additive identity element. Every theorem valid for an integral domain is valid for a field since every field is an integral domain. However, not every integral domain is a field. For example, the set of all integers forms an integral domain; but it does not form a field since at least one element (for instance, 3) of the set does not have a multiplicative inverse in the set.

The set of integers and the set of rational numbers are infinite sets. In order to obtain examples of finite integral domains and finite fields we define **congruence classes of integers;** that is, sets of integers which are congruent to each other. Two integers a and b are **congruent modulo m** where m is an integer if

$$a = b + km$$

for some integer k. We write

$$a \equiv b \pmod{m}.$$

For example,

$$7 = 1 + (2)(3), \qquad 7 \equiv 1 \pmod{3};$$
$$-2 = 3 + (-1)(5), \quad -2 \equiv 3 \pmod{5};$$
$$175 = 3 + (43)(4), \quad 175 \equiv 3 \pmod{4}.$$

If any integer N is divided by a given integer 2, then the remainder is 0 or 1 according as N is even or odd. Thus

$$N \equiv k \pmod{2}$$

where $k \in \{0, 1\}$. Similarly,

$$N \equiv t \pmod{3}$$

where $t \in \{0, 1, 2\}$ and in general

$$N \equiv r \pmod{m}$$

where $r \in \{0, 1, 2, 3, \cdots, m - 1\}$.

Any two integers which are congruent modulo m for a given integer m are in the same **congruence class modulo m.** For example, any two odd integers are in the same congruence class modulo 2. In a congruence system modulo m for a given integer m the usual operations of addition and multiplication are well-defined with congruence as the equivalence relation.

§ 6-5 INTEGRAL DOMAINS AND FIELDS

Example 2. Determine whether or not the set of integers modulo 5 forms a field.

Each integer N is congruent modulo 5 to an element of the set S where $S = \{0, 1, 2, 3, 4\}$. As in § 6-2, we construct a table for each of the operations:

+	0	1	2	3	4
0	0	1	2	3	4
1	1	2	3	4	0
2	2	3	4	0	1
3	3	4	0	1	2
4	4	0	1	2	3

×	0	1	2	3	4
0	0	0	0	0	0
1	0	1	2	3	4
2	0	2	4	1	3
3	0	3	1	4	2
4	0	4	3	2	1

The set S is closed under addition and multiplication since each entry of the table is an element of S. Addition is commutative since the addition table is symmetric with respect to its major diagonal (§ 6-2); multiplication is commutative since the multiplication table is symmetric with respect to its major diagonal. These commutative properties must also hold since the ordinary addition and multiplication of integers may be used. Similarly, the associative properties of addition and multiplication and the distributive property of multiplication with respect to addition follow from these properties of integers.

From the tables we observe that the additive identity element is 0; the multiplicative identity element is 1; each element has an additive inverse (since 0 occurs on each row and column of the addition table); each element except 0 has a multiplicative inverse (since 1 occurs on the row and column of each element except 0); there are no zero divisors (since 0 occurs in the multiplication table only on the row and the column of 0).

We have checked each of the axioms of a field and found that each is satisfied; therefore the set of integers modulo 5 forms a field.

Any integral domain has most of the properties of the set of integers since most of the axioms for integers hold. Similarly, any field has most of the properties of the set of rational numbers. Any set of numbers which forms a field is often called a **number system.** In this sense the set of integers is a mathematical system but not a number system; the set of rational numbers is a number system and we often speak of it as the rational number system.

SYSTEMS OF NUMBERS

TEST YOURSELF

Consider the operations as ordinary addition and multiplication unless otherwise stated. Then determine which of the sets of elements form: **(a)** *integral domains;* **(b)** *fields.*

1. The set of natural numbers.
2. The set of odd integers.
3. The set of integers modulo 3. Use congruence as the equivalence relation.
4. The set of integers modulo 4. Use congruence as the equivalence relation.

EXERCISES

Consider the operations as ordinary addition and multiplication unless otherwise stated. Then in Exercises 1 through 9 determine which of the sets of elements form: **(a)** *integral domains;* **(b)** *fields.*

1. The set of integral multiples of 3, $\{\cdots, -3, 0, 3, 6, \cdots\}$.
2. The set of nonnegative integers.
3. The set of integral multiples of 7.
4. The set of numbers expressible in the form $a + b\sqrt{3}$ where a and b represent integers.
5. The set of numbers expressible in the form $a + b\sqrt{2}$ where a and b represent rational numbers.
6. The set, $\{0\}$.
7. The set of integers modulo 2 with congruence as the equivalence relation.
8. The set of integers modulo 6 with congruence as the equivalence relation.
9. The set of integers modulo 7 with congruence as the equivalence relation.
10. Find: **(a)** $4 + 2 + 3 + 5 \pmod{7}$; **(b)** $3 \times 2 \times 6 \times 4 \pmod{7}$.

● ● ●

11. Prove that every integral domain is a commutative group under addition.
12. Prove that every field is a commutative group under addition and, after the additive identity element has been removed, the set of remaining elements is a commutative group under multiplication.
13. Is every group an integral domain? Is every group a field?
14. Prove that in any integral domain $(a^*)^* = a$.

15. Give a definition which may be used in any field for "division" by any element except the additive identity element.

16. Prove that in a field if $a \times c = b \times c$ and $c \neq 0$, then $a = b$.

• 17. Prove that in a field the assumption that there are no zero divisors may be proved as a theorem.

• 18. Solve for x: $2x \equiv 5 \pmod{6}$.

• 19. Solve for x: $2x \equiv 4 \pmod{6}$.

• 20. Make a conjecture as to the conditions required for a modulo system to form an integral domain.

• 21. Make a conjecture as to the conditions required for a modulo system to form a field.

§ 6-6 Real numbers

The extension of the rational number system to the real number system cannot be made in terms of ordered pairs. A new approach is needed which is based upon limits (Chapter 10). Thus instead of making a formal extension of the set of rational numbers to the set of real numbers, we shall consider only a few of the relationships between rational and real numbers.

We define a **real number** as a number which can be expressed in ordinary decimal notation as a **nonterminating (infinite) decimal**. The set of integers may be thought of as "embedded" in the set of real numbers. For example,
$$5 = 5.000\cdots,$$
$$-17 = -17.000\cdots.$$

The set of rational numbers may be thought of as "embedded" in the set of real numbers. For example,
$$\frac{1}{2} = 0.5\overline{0},$$
$$\frac{5}{3} = 1.\overline{6},$$
$$\frac{67}{7} = 9.\overline{571428}.$$

In each case the bar over a set of one or more digits indicates that the set of digits is repeated over and over without end. Any rational number may be expressed as a quotient of integers $\frac{p}{q}$ where $q > 0$ (§ 6-4). As in the case of $\frac{67}{7}$, the decimal expansion of $\frac{p}{q}$ is found by dividing p by q. The remainders at each step of the division are elements of the set $\{0, 1, 2, 3, \ldots, q-1\}$; thus, if $|p| < q$, the division continues for at most q steps

SYSTEMS OF NUMBERS

before a remainder is repeated and accordingly a set of n digits (where $1 \leq n \leq q - 1$) is repeated. Thus any rational number may be expressed as a **repeating infinite decimal.**

We assume that addition and multiplication of infinite decimals have the same properties as for rational numbers. For instance, we assume that any infinite decimal N in which a set of k digits is repeated may be multiplied by 10^k, and the difference $10^k N - N$ may be used as a first step to express the number as a quotient of integers. Consider $N = 3.\overline{12}$ where $k = 2$;

$$10^2 N = 312.\overline{12}$$
$$N = 3.\overline{12}$$
$$99N = 309.\overline{0}$$
$$N = \frac{309}{99} = \frac{103}{33}.$$

We might also express this rational number as the mixed number, $3\frac{4}{33}$. This procedure may be used to express any repeating infinite decimal as a quotient of integers, thus any such decimal represents a rational number.

We have now observed that any rational number may be represented by a repeating infinite decimal and any repeating infinite decimal represents a rational number. Infinite decimals which are not repeating infinite decimals are **nonrepeating infinite decimals.** Nonrepeating infinite decimals represent **irrational numbers.** Thus any real number is either an irrational number or is equivalent to a rational number. Here are a few examples of irrational numbers:

$$\sqrt{3} = 1.732 \cdots ;$$
$$\pi = 3.14159 \cdots ;$$
$$2\pi = 6.2831 \cdots .$$

Example 1. Show that $\frac{1}{7}$ can be written as a repeating infinite decimal.

```
         0.142857 ···
      7)1.000000 ···
         7
         ─
         30
         28
         ──
          20
          14
          ──
           60
           56
           ──
            40
            35
            ──
             50
             49
             ──
              10
```

§ 6-6 REAL NUMBERS

We now notice that the next digit is determined by dividing 10 by 7 which is the same as the first step of our division problem. Hence the digits 1, 4, 2, 8, 5, and 7 in that order will be repeated without end. Therefore, $\frac{1}{7} = 0.\overline{142857}$.

Example 2. Show that the repeating infinite decimal $1.3\overline{6}$ represents a rational number.

Let $N = 1.3\overline{6}$, thus $k = 2$. Then

$$100N = 136.\overline{36}$$
$$N = 1.\overline{36}$$
$$\overline{99N = 135.\overline{0}}$$
$$N = \frac{135}{99} = \frac{15}{11}.$$

Example 3. Show that the repeating infinite decimal $1.2\overline{3}$ represents a rational number.

Let $N = 1.2\overline{3}$, thus $k = 1$. Then

$$10N = 12.3\overline{3}$$
$$N = 1.2\overline{3}$$
$$\overline{9N = 11.1\overline{0}}$$
$$N = \frac{11.1}{9} = \frac{111}{90}.$$

Consider the repeating infinite decimal $N = 0.\overline{9}$; then

$$10N = 9.\overline{9}$$
$$N = 0.\overline{9}$$
$$\overline{9N = 9.\overline{0}}$$
$$N = \frac{9}{9} = 1.$$

The possibility of expressing 1 as $1.\overline{0}$ or as $0.\overline{9}$ implies that except for zero all integers and many other rational numbers may be expressed as infinite decimals in two different ways. For example,

$$2 = 2.\overline{0} = 1.\overline{9};$$
$$27 = 27.\overline{0} = 26.\overline{9};$$
$$\frac{1}{4} = 0.25\overline{0} = 0.24\overline{9};$$
$$\frac{8}{5} = 1.6\overline{0} = 1.5\overline{9}.$$

SYSTEMS OF NUMBERS

You learned years ago that $10 = 2 \times 5$ and thus $10^k = 2^k \times 5^k$. The identification of integers with certain infinite decimals in which zeros are repeated may be extended to the identification of rational numbers $\frac{p}{q}$ where $q = 10^k$ for any integer k with all infinite decimals in which only zeros are repeated. For example,

$$3.\bar{0} = \frac{3}{1} = \frac{3}{10^0} = \frac{3}{2^0 \times 5^0};$$

$$1.4\bar{0} = \frac{14}{10} = \frac{14}{2 \times 5};$$

$$25.13\bar{0} = \frac{2513}{10^2} = \frac{2513}{2^2 \times 5^2};$$

$$0.017\bar{0} = \frac{17}{10^3} = \frac{17}{2^3 \times 5^3}.$$

An infinite decimal with repeating zeros is often called a **terminating decimal** since the zeros may be omitted. Then

$$3.\bar{0} = 3 = \frac{3}{2^0 \times 5^0};$$

$$1.4\bar{0} = 1.4 = \frac{14}{2 \times 5};$$

$$25.13\bar{0} = 25.13 = \frac{2513}{2^2 \times 5^2};$$

$$0.017\bar{0} = 0.017 = \frac{17}{2^3 \times 5^3}.$$

These examples also illustrate another correspondence between rational numbers and decimals: <u>A rational number may be expressed as a terminating decimal if and only if it may be expressed as $\frac{p}{q}$ where p is an integer and $q = 2^k \times 5^n$ for some integers k and n.</u> For example,

$$\frac{1}{25} = \frac{1}{2^0 \times 5^2} = \frac{2^2}{2^2 \times 5^2} = \frac{4}{10^2} = 0.04;$$

$$\frac{3}{8} = \frac{3}{2^3 \times 5^0} = \frac{3 \times 5^3}{2^3 \times 5^3} = \frac{375}{10^3} = 0.375;$$

$$\frac{1}{80} = \frac{1}{2^4 \times 5^1} = \frac{5^3}{2^4 \times 5^4} = \frac{125}{10^4} = 0.0125.$$

§ 6-6 REAL NUMBERS

TEST YOURSELF

Tell whether or not each number may be expressed as a terminating decimal:

1. $\frac{13}{4}$.
2. $\frac{11}{16}$.
3. $\frac{7}{12}$.
4. $\frac{12}{7}$.

Express each number as a quotient of integers:

5. $0.1\overline{3}$.
6. $5.\overline{6}$.
7. $2.\overline{0}$.
8. $35.2\overline{9}$.

Express each number as an infinite repeating decimal:

9. $\frac{2}{5}$.
10. $\frac{11}{3}$.
11. $\frac{5}{6}$.
12. $\frac{3}{11}$.

EXERCISES

Tell whether or not each number may be expressed as a terminating decimal:

1. $\frac{7}{8}$.
2. $\frac{5}{30}$.
3. $\frac{6}{30}$.
4. $\frac{7}{40}$.
5. $\frac{16}{60}$.
6. 2π.
7. $\sqrt{5}$.
8. $\sqrt{121}$.

Express each number as a quotient of integers:

9. $0.125\overline{0}$.
10. $3.\overline{9}$.
11. $5.\overline{23}$.
12. $0.\overline{123}$.
13. $1.3\overline{5}$.
14. $0.00\overline{15}$.
15. $0.31\overline{24}$.
16. $1.0\overline{13}$.

Express each number as an infinite repeating decimal:

17. $\frac{1}{11}$.
18. $\frac{3}{8}$.
19. $\frac{5}{13}$.
20. $\frac{9}{7}$.

In Exercises 21 through 24 represent each number as an infinite decimal in two ways:

21. 2.562.
22. 1000.
23. $\frac{3}{16}$.
24. $\frac{623}{250}$.

• **25.** Explain how any terminating decimal except 0 may be expressed as an infinite decimal in two ways.

SYSTEMS OF NUMBERS

§ 6-7 Complex numbers

Complex numbers were originally considered in dealing with the problem of solving quadratic equations. The solution of a quadratic equation of the form $x^2 + c = 0$ where c is a positive real number made it necessary for mathematicians to consider the existence of a number whose square was a negative real number. Such a number could not belong to the real number system since any real number different from zero is positive or negative; the square of any positive number is positive; and the square of any negative number is positive. A new set of numbers was needed, so the complex number system was developed.

In 1748 the mathematician Euler proposed that the symbol i be defined such that $i^2 = -1$. We use this definition when we say that any number expressible in the form $a + bi$ where a and b represent real numbers is a **complex number**. The elements of the subset of the complex numbers for which $b = 0$ (that is, numbers $a + 0i$) correspond to real numbers a; and thus the set of real numbers is "embedded" in the set of complex numbers. The symbol i is the **imaginary unit**; the subset of complex numbers for which $a = 0$ and $b \neq 0$ is the set of **pure imaginary numbers**. Any complex number which is neither a real number nor a pure imaginary number is a **mixed imaginary number** as shown in the following array:

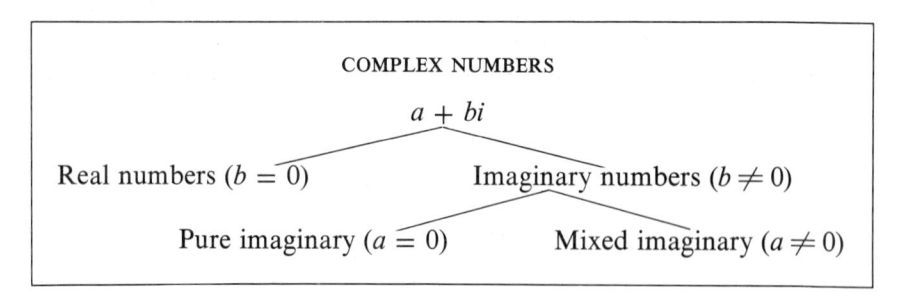

```
                    COMPLEX NUMBERS
                         a + bi
                    /            \
   Real numbers (b = 0)     Imaginary numbers (b ≠ 0)
                             /            \
                   Pure imaginary (a = 0)   Mixed imaginary (a ≠ 0)
```

For any two complex numbers $a + bi$ and $c + di$ we make use of these definitions:

$$a + bi = c + di \text{ if and only if } a = c \text{ and } b = d;$$
$$(a + bi) + (c + di) = (a + c) + (b + d)i;$$
$$(a + bi) \times (c + di) = (ac - bd) + (ad + bc)i.$$

Computations with expressions involving square roots of negative numbers are done after the expressions have been written in terms of i; that is, each complex number has been expressed in **rectangular form** as $a + bi$. When radicals are involved as in $(\sqrt{5})i$ and $(2\sqrt{3})i$, we write them as $i\sqrt{5}$ and $2i\sqrt{3}$.

Example 1. Find $(3 + 4i) + (2 - 3i)$.

$$(3 + 4i) + (2 - 3i) = (3 + 2) + (4 - 3)i = 5 + i.$$

Example 2. Find $(3 + \sqrt{-2}) \times (3 - \sqrt{-2})$.

$$(3 + \sqrt{-2}) \times (3 - \sqrt{-2}) = (3 + i\sqrt{2})(3 - i\sqrt{2})$$
$$= (9 + 2) + (3\sqrt{2} - 3\sqrt{2})i = 11 + 0i = 11.$$

Notice that, as in Example 2, the multiplication symbol may be omitted in expressing products of complex numbers in rectangular form.

Differences of complex numbers may be expressed as equivalent sums using the relation:

$$(a + bi) - (c + di) = (a + bi) + (-c - di).$$

Two complex numbers of the form $a + bi$ and $a - bi$ are **conjugate complex numbers**; each is the conjugate of the other. As in Example 2, the product of two conjugate numbers is a real number. This property is used in simplifying a quotient of two complex numbers: both numerator and denominator are multiplied by the conjugate of the denominator; notice that the original expression is multiplied by an expression which is equivalent to 1. A quotient is considered to be simplified when the denominator is an integer and no factors (except 1 and -1) are also factors of the numerator. All answers for exercises should be left in simplified form.

Example 3. Find $(3 + \sqrt{-4}) \div (2 - \sqrt{-1})$.

$$\frac{3 + \sqrt{-4}}{2 - \sqrt{-1}} = \frac{3 + 2i}{2 - i} \times \frac{2 + i}{2 + i} = \frac{(6 - 2) + (3 + 4)i}{(4 + 1) + (2 - 2)i}$$
$$= \frac{4 + 7i}{5} = \frac{4}{5} + \frac{7}{5}i.$$

These properties of complex numbers may be rigorously developed by defining a complex number to be a number which may be expressed as an ordered pair of real numbers (a, b) where

$$(a, b) = (c, d) \text{ if and only if } a = c \text{ and } b = d;$$
$$(a, b) + (c, d) = (a + c, b + d);$$
$$(a, b) \times (c, d) = (ac - bd, ad + bc).$$

We assume that the set of real numbers forms a field and then may prove that the set of complex numbers forms a field (B, Exercise 31).

SYSTEMS OF NUMBERS

Theorem 13. *The set of complex numbers is closed under addition.*

PROOF: Let (a, b) and (c, d) represent any two complex numbers. By definition $(a, b) + (c, d) = (a + c, b + d)$. Then $a + c$ and $b + d$ represent real numbers since the set of real numbers is closed under addition. Thus $(a + c, b + d)$ may be represented by an ordered pair of real numbers, and the set of complex numbers is closed under addition.

Theorem 14. *The addition of complex numbers is commutative.*

PROOF: Let (a, b) and (c, d) represent any two complex numbers. Then

$$(a, b) + (c, d) = (a + c, b + d)$$
$$= (c + a, d + b)$$
$$= (c, d) + (a, b)$$

where the reader should be able to provide the reason for each step.

We identify each complex number $(a, 0)$ with the real number a. Then the definitions imply that

$$(0, 1) \times (0, 1) = (0 - 1, 0 + 0) = (-1, 0) = -1$$

and thus $(0, 1)$ corresponds to i. In general, (a, b) corresponds to $a + bi$ where $i^2 = -1$ and we have a correspondence between the ordered pairs of the form (a, b) and the rectangular form $a + bi$ of complex numbers. Unless otherwise specified, answers to computations involving complex numbers should be left in rectangular form. In many cases the computations also can be performed most effectively after the given numbers have been expressed in rectangular form.

Example 4. Find $(2 + i)^6$.

By the binominal theorem (§ 2–4)
$$(2 + i)^6 = {}_6C_0(2)^6 + {}_6C_1(2)^5(i)^1 + {}_6C_2(2)^4(i)^2 + {}_6C_3(2)^3(i)^3$$
$$+ {}_6C_4(2)^2(i)^4 + {}_6C_5(2)^1(i)^5 + {}_6C_6(2)^0(i)^6$$
$$= 64 + 192i - 240 - 160i + 60 + 12i - 1$$
$$= (64 - 240 + 60 - 1) + (192 - 160 + 12)i$$
$$= -117 + 44i.$$

ALTERNATE METHOD: Since any positive integral power of a complex number is itself a complex number and thus a binominal, powers of complex numbers often may be obtained easily without using the binomial theorem. For example,

$$(2+i)^6 = [(2+i)^2]^3$$
$$= (4+4i-1)^3 = (3+4i)^3$$
$$= (3+4i)^2(3+4i)$$
$$= (9+24i-16)(3+4i) = (-7+24i)(3+4i)$$
$$= -117+44i.$$

TEST YOURSELF

Write (a) in rectangular form; (b) as an ordered pair of real numbers:

1. $\sqrt{-8}$. **2.** $2i$. **3.** -6. **4.** $3 + \sqrt{-2}$.

Find:

5. $(2-i) + (3+4i)$.
6. $(3+i) - (5-7i)$.
7. $\sqrt{-4} + \sqrt{-25}$.
8. $(3+2i) \times (7-i)$.
9. $(5+4i) \div (1+i)$.
10. $(3 - \sqrt{-2}) \times (2 + \sqrt{-8})$.
11. $(3 + \sqrt{-4})^5$.
12. $\dfrac{1}{i^3} - \dfrac{1}{i^5}$.

EXERCISES

A

Find the conjugate of each complex number:

1. $3+i$. **2.** i^7. **3.** 2. **4.** $7 - \sqrt{-2}$.

Find:

5. $(3+2i) + (5-2i)$.
6. $(6+7i) - (4-3i)$.
7. $(3 + 2\sqrt{-1}) + (1 - \sqrt{-4})$.
8. $(5 - \sqrt{-8}) - (3 - \sqrt{-18})$.
9. $(2b + t\sqrt{-4}) + (b - t\sqrt{-1})$.
10. $(\sqrt{-2} + \sqrt{-3}) + (\sqrt{-2} - \sqrt{-3})$.
11. $\sqrt{-3} + \sqrt{-12} + \sqrt{-8}$.
12. $(3+4i) \times (-2i)$.
13. $\sqrt{-a}(\sqrt{-a} + \sqrt{-b})$ where $a > 0$ and $b > 0$.
14. $\left(\dfrac{1}{i^2} - \dfrac{1}{i^3}\right)^2$.
15. $(\sqrt{-9} - \sqrt{-16}) \times (\sqrt{-4} + \sqrt{-1})$.
16. $(3+2i) \times (5+i)$.
17. $(2 - \sqrt{-3}) \times (2 + \sqrt{-3})$.

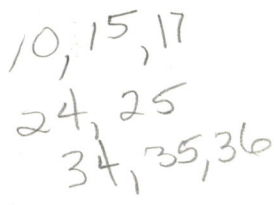

301

SYSTEMS OF NUMBERS

18. $(6 + \sqrt{-16}) \times (5 - \sqrt{-25})$.
19. $(1 - i)^2 \div 2$.
20. $(1 - i\sqrt{2}) \times (1 + i\sqrt{2})$.
21. $(i\sqrt{3} + \sqrt{2}) \times (i\sqrt{3} - \sqrt{2})$.
22. $(a + bi)^3$.
23. $(-2i)^7$.
24. i^{73}.
25. i^{-9}.
26. $(-\sqrt{-8})^3$.
27. $(2 + i) \times (3 - i) \times (1 + 4i)$.
28. $(2 - 3i) \div i$.
29. $(5 + i) \div (3 - 2i)$.
30. $(2 - \sqrt{-9}) \div (2 + \sqrt{-9})$.

• • •

31. $\dfrac{2}{i} - \dfrac{i}{2}$.

32. $2 \div (3 + i)$.

33. $\dfrac{1 + i}{1 - i} - \dfrac{1 - i}{1 + i}$.

In Exercises 34 through 36 prove:

34. The sum of a complex number and its conjugate is always a real number.

35. The product of a complex number and its conjugate is always a real number.

36. The difference of a complex number and its conjugate is zero or a pure imaginary number.

37. Is the conjugate of the sum of two complex numbers equal to the sum of the conjugates of the two complex numbers?

38. Is the conjugate of the product of two complex numbers equal to the product of the conjugates of the two complex numbers?

39. Is the conjugate of the difference of two complex numbers equal to the difference of the conjugates of the two complex numbers?

40. Is the conjugate of the quotient of two complex numbers equal to the quotient of the conjugates of the two complex numbers?

• **41.** Does the set of numbers of the form $\dfrac{a}{2} + \dfrac{b}{2}\sqrt{-3}$ where a and b are integers form an integral domain?

Find the real numbers x and y which satisfy the equation:

• **42.** $(x + yi)^2 = 3 - 4i$.
• **43.** $(x + i)^2 + 4i = (x - i)^2 + y$.

B

Write each complex number as an ordered pair of real numbers:

1. $2 - 3i$. **2.** $3 + \sqrt{-16}$. **3.** $x + iy$. **4.** $-3i$.

Determine whether or not the given complex numbers are equal:

5. $(2, 0)$ and $(3, 0)$.
6. $(2, \sqrt{2})$ and $(2, \sqrt{2})$.
7. $(\pi, 3)$ and $(2\pi, 6)$.
8. $(0, 0)$ and $(0, 3)$.

Determine which of the complex numbers are **(a)** *real numbers;* **(b)** *pure imaginary numbers:*

9. $(5, -\sqrt{2})$. **10.** $(0, \sqrt{2})$. **11.** $(3, 1)$. **12.** $(5, 0)$.

Perform the indicated operations on the complex numbers:

13. $(5, 2) + (3, 1)$.
14. $(-2, 0) + (3, \sqrt{6})$.
15. $(-3, 0) + (0, \sqrt{2})$.
16. $(5, \sqrt{2}) + (5, -\sqrt{2})$.
17. $(3, 0) \times (0, 4)$.
18. $(0, 1) \times (0, 2)$.
19. $(1, 1) \times (2, -3)$.
20. $(4, \sqrt{2}) \times (-2, \sqrt{3})$.

● ● ●

Consider complex numbers as ordered pairs of real numbers and prove:

21. The set of complex numbers is closed under multiplication.

22. The set of complex numbers has an additive identity element $(0, 0)$.

23. The set of complex numbers has a multiplicative identity element $(1, 0)$.

24. Each complex number (a, b) has an additive inverse $(-a, -b)$.

25. The multiplication of complex numbers is commutative.

26. Each complex number (a, b) different from $(0, 0)$ has a multiplicative inverse $\left(\dfrac{a}{a^2 + b^2}, \dfrac{-b}{a^2 + b^2}\right)$.

27. The addition of complex numbers is associative.

● **28.** The multiplication of complex numbers is associative.

● **29.** The multiplication of complex numbers is distributive with respect to addition.

● **30.** There are no zero divisors in the set of complex numbers.

● **31.** The set of complex numbers forms a field.

§ 6-8 Representations of complex numbers

As in § 6-7 any complex number may be represented as an ordered pair (a, b) of real numbers or in *rectangular form* as $a + bi$. We now consider three other ways of representing complex numbers. Each representation provides a basis for a model for the set of complex numbers.

SYSTEMS OF NUMBERS

Any points on an ordinary plane may be represented by an ordered pair of real numbers (x, y). Also any complex number may be represented by an ordered pair of real numbers. Accordingly, there is a one-to-one correspondence between the complex numbers (a, b) and the points (a, b) on an ordinary plane. Each point (a, b) corresponds to the complex number $a + bi$ and conversely. Since the graphs of complex numbers of the form $(a, 0)$ correspond to points on the x-axis, the x-axis is sometimes called the **axis of reals**. Since the graphs of complex numbers of the form $(0, b)$ correspond to points on the y-axis, the y-axis is sometimes called the **axis of imaginaries**. A plane used for graphing complex numbers is called a **complex plane** or an **Argand plane**. As in Figure 6–1, complex numbers such as $3 + i$ may be represented either by the point $P: (3, 1)$ or by the directed line segment OP (see § 11–1). When the negative $(-a, -b)$ of a complex number (a, b) is considered, the points are symmetric with respect to the origin; the directed line segments are of equal length and opposite in direction.

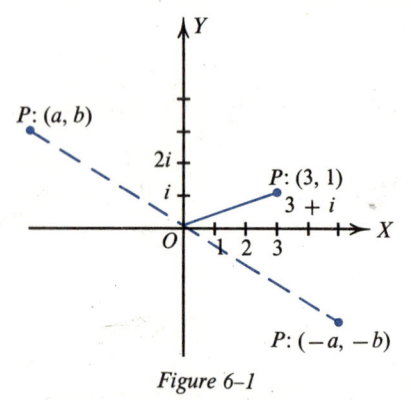

Figure 6–1

The operations of addition and subtraction may be illustrated, and indeed performed, graphically.

Example 1. Add the complex numbers $3 + 2i$ and $2 - i$ graphically.

Let the complex numbers $3 + 2i$ and $2 - i$ be represented by the points $P_1: (3, 2)$ and $P_2: (2, -1)$ as in Figure 6–2. The point $P_3: (5, 1)$ representing the sum $(3 + 2i) + (2 - i)$ may be obtained by starting at P_1 and moving two units in the positive direction parallel to the axis of reals and one unit in the negative direction parallel to the axis of imaginaries. The point $P_3: (5, 1)$ representing the sum $(2 - i) + (3 + 2i)$ may also be obtained by starting at P_2 and moving three units in the positive direction parallel to the axis of reals and two units in the positive direction parallel to the axis of imaginaries. Notice that in either case a parallelogram $OP_1P_3P_2$ is obtained where P_1 and P_2 represent the given addends, $\overline{OP_3}$ is a diagonal, and P_3 represents the sum.

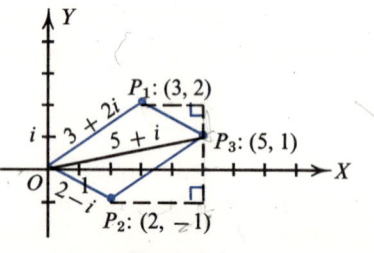

Figure 6–2

§ 6-8 REPRESENTATIONS OF COMPLEX NUMBERS

The procedure in Example 1 may be used to find the point representing the sum of any two given complex numbers. Let P_1: (a, b) and P_2: (c, d) represent any two complex numbers. Construct a parallelogram $OP_1P_3P_2$ on an Argand plane with origin O. Then P_3 corresponds to the sum $(a + c, b + d)$. This same procedure may be used for subtraction since any difference $(a, b) - (c, d)$ may be expressed as a sum $(a, b) + (-c, -d)$.

Example 2. Find the difference $(6 + i) - (2 + 3i)$ graphically.

Note that $(6+i)-(2+3i) = (6+i)+(-2-3i)$. Let P_1: $(6, 1)$ and P_2: $(-2, -3)$ represent the addends and construct a parallelogram $OP_1P_3P_2$ to obtain P_3: $(4, -2)$ where P_3 represents the desired difference $4 - 2i$ as in Figure 6–3.

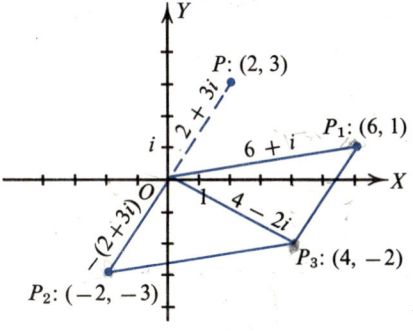

Figure 6–3

Multiplication and division of complex numbers may also be represented graphically. However, these representations are not as useful as those for addition and subtraction and thus will not be considered here.

Any complex number $a + bi$ in rectangular form corresponds to a point P: (a, b). The point P: (a, b) may also be identified by its polar coordinates r and θ. As in § 4–13, we take $r = \sqrt{a^2 + b^2}$ and θ as the angle XOP in standard position. Then, as in Figure 6–4, we have $a = r \cos \theta$ and $b = r \sin \theta$. Then $a + bi = r(\cos \theta + i \sin \theta)$. The expression $r(\cos \theta + i \sin \theta)$ is called the **trigonometric form** of the complex number. Note that $r(\cos \theta + i \sin \theta) = r[\cos (\theta + 2k\pi) + i \sin (\theta + 2k\pi)]$ for any integer k. The nonnegative number r is the **modulus** or **absolute value** of the complex number;

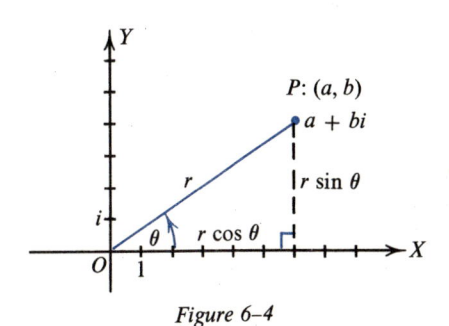

$$r = \sqrt{a^2 + b^2} = |a + bi|.$$

Figure 6–4

The angle θ is often called the **argument** or the **amplitude** of the complex number and may be expressed in degrees but is usually expressed in radian measure. The value of the argument is not unique for a given complex

305

SYSTEMS OF NUMBERS

number since two arguments for the same number may differ by integral multiples of 2π. Unless otherwise stated, we shall consider only θ where $0 \leq \theta < 2\pi$ and answers will be converted to that form when necessary.

Since the values of r and θ define completely a particular complex number in the trigonometric form, we recognize that a complex number may be written simply as an ordered pair of real numbers (r, θ). The ordered pair (r, θ) with reference to a polar coordinate system is called the **polar form** of a complex number.

Other notations which are often used to represent a complex number with modulus r and amplitude θ include $r \lfloor \theta$, r cis θ (an abbreviation for the trigonometric form), and $re^{i\theta}$. The last notation is based upon the identity

$$e^{i\theta} = \cos \theta + i \sin \theta$$

which may be proved in advanced courses but is assumed here. The irrational number e arises in many places including logarithms where it is the base for "natural logarithms" which are very convenient for theoretical purposes and are used extensively in calculus. The value of e is approximately 2.71828. The form $re^{i\theta}$ of a complex number is called its **exponential form**.

The most common representations for complex numbers, in addition to the graphical representation, are the rectangular form, the trigonometric form, the polar form, and the exponential form:

$$a + bi = r(\cos \theta + i \sin \theta) = (r, \theta) = re^{i\theta}.$$

We have seen that the rectangular form is easy to use when addition and subtraction are to be performed. In §§ 6–9 and 6–10 we shall see that the other forms are easy to use when multiplication and division are to be performed or powers and roots are to be obtained.

Example 3. Express $2 + 2i$ in trigonometric form, polar form, and exponential form.

The complex number $2 + 2i$ is represented by P: $(2, 2)$ on the Argand plane (Figure 6–5). Thus $\theta = 45°$; that is, $\frac{\pi}{4}$; $r = 2\sqrt{2}$; and

$$2 + 2i = 2\sqrt{2}\left(\cos \frac{\pi}{4} + i \sin \frac{\pi}{4}\right)$$

$$= \left(2\sqrt{2}, \frac{\pi}{4}\right)$$

$$= 2\sqrt{2} e^{\frac{\pi i}{4}}.$$

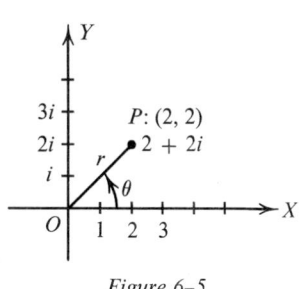

Figure 6–5

306

§ 6-8 REPRESENTATIONS OF COMPLEX NUMBERS

Example 4. Express the complex number which is represented in polar form by $\left(2, \frac{\pi}{3}\right)$ in rectangular form.

The complex number $\left(2, \frac{\pi}{3}\right)$ in polar form is equivalent to the complex number $2\left(\cos \frac{\pi}{3} + i \sin \frac{\pi}{3}\right)$ in trigonometric form;

$$2\left(\cos \frac{\pi}{3} + i \sin \frac{\pi}{3}\right) = 2\left(\frac{1}{2} + i\frac{\sqrt{3}}{2}\right) = 1 + i\sqrt{3}.$$

Hence the complex number represented by $\left(2, \frac{\pi}{3}\right)$ in polar form may be expressed as $1 + i\sqrt{3}$ in rectangular form.

TEST YOURSELF

1. Graph each complex number on an Argand plane:

(a) 3;   (b) i;   (c) $2 - i$;   (d) $-1 + i\sqrt{3}$.

Perform the indicated operations graphically:

2. $(4 - 2i) + (1 + 5i)$.   **3.** $(2 + 3i) - (2 - 3i)$.

Express each complex number in (a) trigonometric form; (b) polar form; (c) exponential form:

4. $1 + i$.   **5.** $-2 + 2i$.   **6.** -3.   **7.** $-\frac{1}{2} + \frac{i\sqrt{3}}{2}$.

Express in rectangular form each complex number given in polar form:

8. $\left(5, \frac{3\pi}{2}\right)$.   **9.** $(4, 45°)$.   **10.** $\left(1, -\frac{\pi}{6}\right)$.

EXERCISES

1. Graph each complex number on an Argand plane:

(a) 2;   (b) $-i$;   (c) $\sqrt{2} + i\sqrt{2}$;   (d) $-3 - i$.

Perform the indicated operations graphically:

2. $(2 + i) + (2 - i)$.   **5.** $(1 - i) - (-2 + 3i)$.
3. $(5 + 3i) + (1 - i)$.   **6.** $(3 - i) + (-2 + 2i)$.
4. $(-2 + 3i) - (1 - i)$.   **7.** $(2 - 3i) - (-2 + 3i)$.

SYSTEMS OF NUMBERS

In Exercises 8 and 9 graph the complex numbers given in polar form on an Argand plane:

8. (a) $\left(2, -\frac{\pi}{3}\right)$; (b) $(1, \pi)$; (c) $(3, 0)$.

9. (a) $(4, -135°)$; (b) $\left(2, \frac{\pi}{3}\right)$; (c) $\left(\sqrt{2}, \frac{5\pi}{2}\right)$.

10. State the modulus and the argument of each complex number given in Exercises 8 and 9.

Express each complex number in (a) trigonometric form; (b) polar form; (c) exponential form:

11. $2\sqrt{3} + 2i$.
12. $3i$.
13. -2.
14. $-5 - 5i$.
15. $\sqrt{3} + \sqrt{-1}$.
16. $3 - 3i\sqrt{3}$.

Express in rectangular form each complex number given in polar form:

17. $\left(3, \frac{5\pi}{6}\right)$.

18. $(1, 3\pi)$.

19. $\left(4, \frac{5\pi}{3}\right)$.

20. $\left(3, \frac{\pi}{2}\right)$.

21. $\left(\sqrt{2}, \frac{\pi}{4}\right)$.

22. $(3, 225°)$.

In Exercises 23 through 26 express in rectangular form the conjugate of each complex number given in polar form:

23. $\left(3, \frac{\pi}{3}\right)$.
24. $(2, \pi)$.
25. $\left(2, \frac{\pi}{2}\right)$.
26. $\left(1, \frac{\pi}{4}\right)$.

27. Prove that a complex number different from 0 has amplitude 0 if and only if it is a positive real number.

28. Find the modulus and the amplitude of the complex number
$$\frac{(1+i)(\sqrt{3}+i)^3}{(1-i\sqrt{3})^3}.$$

§ 6-9 Products and quotients

While the operations of addition and subtraction of complex numbers are easily performed upon complex numbers expressed in rectangular form, the operations of multiplication and division are sometimes more

§ 6-9 PRODUCTS AND QUOTIENTS

easily performed upon the complex numbers in trigonometric, polar, or exponential form. The operation of raising a complex number to a power (this includes the extraction of roots) is almost always more easily performed upon complex numbers in trigonometric, polar, or exponential form (§ 6–10).

Let (r_1, θ_1) and (r_2, θ_2) represent any two complex numbers in polar form. Then, as in § 6-8,

$$(r_1, \theta_1) = r_1(\cos \theta_1 + i \sin \theta_1) = r_1 e^{i\theta_1},$$
$$(r_2, \theta_2) = r_2(\cos \theta_2 + i \sin \theta_2) = r_2 e^{i\theta_2}.$$

For real numbers a, b, e, m, and n,

$$ae^m \times be^n = abe^{m+n}.$$

Thus we expect

$$r_1 e^{i\theta_1} \times r_2 e^{i\theta_2} = r_1 r_2 e^{i(\theta_1+\theta_2)};$$

that is,

$$(r_1, \theta_1) \times (r_2, \theta_2) = (r_1 r_2, \theta_1 + \theta_2).$$

We use the trigonometric forms of these numbers to verify this formula for the product of two complex numbers:

$$\begin{aligned}(r_1, \theta_1) \times (r_2, \theta_2) &= r_1(\cos \theta_1 + i \sin \theta_1) \times r_2(\cos \theta_2 + i \sin \theta_2) \\ &= r_1 r_2 [(\cos \theta_1 \cos \theta_2 - \sin \theta_1 \sin \theta_2) \\ &\quad + i(\sin \theta_1 \cos \theta_2 + \cos \theta_1 \sin \theta_2)] \\ &= r_1 r_2 [\cos (\theta_1 + \theta_2) + i \sin (\theta_1 + \theta_2)] \\ &= (r_1 r_2, \theta_1 + \theta_2).\end{aligned}$$

Example 1. Find $(\sqrt{3} + i) \times (2 + 2i\sqrt{3})$.

$$\sqrt{3} + i = \left(2, \frac{\pi}{6}\right)$$

$$2 + 2i\sqrt{3} = \left(4, \frac{\pi}{3}\right)$$

$$\left(2, \frac{\pi}{6}\right) \times \left(4, \frac{\pi}{3}\right) = \left(8, \frac{\pi}{2}\right)$$

$$= 8\left(\cos \frac{\pi}{2} + i \sin \frac{\pi}{2}\right)$$

$$= 8(0 + i)$$

$$= 8i;$$

$$(\sqrt{3} + i) \times (2 + 2i\sqrt{3}) = 8i.$$

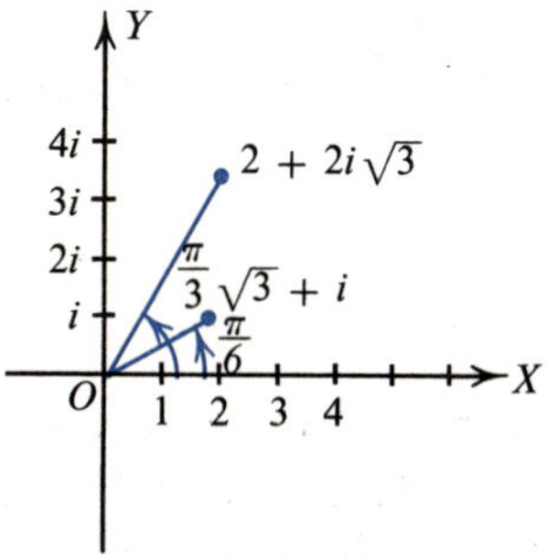

Figure 6–6

309

SYSTEMS OF NUMBERS

Note that this result can also be obtained as in § 6–7:
$$(\sqrt{3} + i)(2 + 2i\sqrt{3}) = (2\sqrt{3} - 2\sqrt{3}) + (6 + 2)i = 8i.$$
The purpose of the example is to show that the new formula may be used for products as well as providing a basis for finding quotients, powers, and roots.

Consider any quotient of complex numbers $\dfrac{(r_1, \theta_1)}{(r_2, \theta_2)}$ where $r_2 \neq 0$. Then

$$(r_1, \theta_1) = r_1(\cos \theta_1 + i \sin \theta_1) = r_1 e^{i\theta_1},$$
$$(r_2, \theta_2) = r_2(\cos \theta_2 + i \sin \theta_2) = r_2 e^{i\theta_2},$$

and we expect

$$r_1 e^{i\theta_1} \div r_2 e^{i\theta_2} = \frac{r_1}{r_2} e^{i(\theta_1 - \theta_2)};$$

that is,

$$\frac{(r_1, \theta_1)}{(r_2, \theta_2)} = \left(\frac{r_1}{r_2}, \theta_1 - \theta_2\right).$$

We note that

$$(r_2, \theta_2) \times \left(\frac{1}{r_2}, -\theta_2\right) = (1, 0) = 1$$

and we use multiplication to verify this formula for the quotient of two complex numbers:

$$\frac{(r_1, \theta_1)}{(r_2, \theta_2)} = \frac{(r_1, \theta_1)}{(r_2, \theta_2)} \times \frac{\left(\frac{1}{r_2}, -\theta_2\right)}{\left(\frac{1}{r_2}, -\theta_2\right)} = \frac{\left(\frac{r_1}{r_2}, \theta_1 - \theta_2\right)}{(1, 0)} = \left(\frac{r_1}{r_2}, \theta_1 - \theta_2\right).$$

Example 2. Find $\dfrac{2i}{1 + i}$.

$2i = \left(2, \dfrac{\pi}{2}\right)$ and $1 + i = \left(\sqrt{2}, \dfrac{\pi}{4}\right)$.

$$\frac{\left(2, \dfrac{\pi}{2}\right)}{\left(\sqrt{2}, \dfrac{\pi}{4}\right)} = \left(\frac{2}{\sqrt{2}}, \frac{\pi}{2} - \frac{\pi}{4}\right) = \left(\sqrt{2}, \frac{\pi}{4}\right)$$

$$= 1 + i;$$

$$\frac{2i}{1 + i} = 1 + i.$$

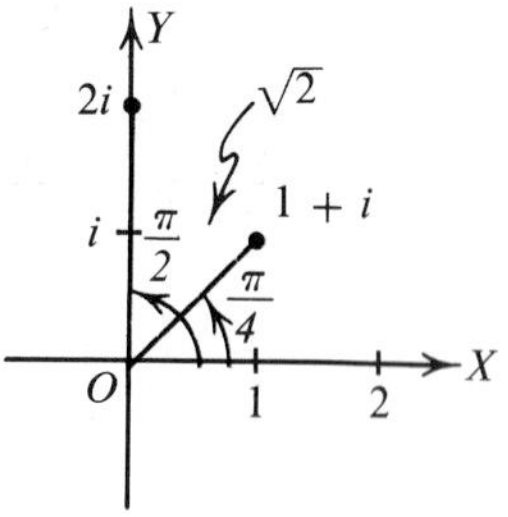

Figure 6–7

§ 6-9 PRODUCTS AND QUOTIENTS

Note that this result can also be obtained as in § 6-7:
$$\frac{2i}{1+i} = \frac{2i}{1+i} \times \frac{1-i}{1-i} = \frac{2i+2}{2} = 1+i.$$

Example 3. Find the reciprocal of the complex number (r, θ).

Since the complex number 1 may be written in polar form as $(1, 0)$, the reciprocal of (r, θ) is $\left(\frac{1}{r}, -\theta\right)$ and may be obtained from the formula for a quotient:
$$\frac{1}{(r, \theta)} = \frac{(1, 0)}{(r, \theta)} = \left(\frac{1}{r}, -\theta\right).$$

As noted in Examples 1 and 2, products and quotients may be found by the methods of § 6-7. The formulas introduced in this section may also be used and are important as an introduction to the discussion of powers and roots in § 6-10.

TEST YOURSELF

Use the formulas developed in this section and find:

1. $\left(2, \frac{\pi}{6}\right) \times \left(3, \frac{\pi}{2}\right).$
2. $(3, 30°) \times (2, -15°).$
3. $\left(5, \frac{\pi}{9}\right) \div \left(1, \frac{5\pi}{18}\right).$
4. $(x^2, 3\pi) \div (x, -3\pi).$

EXERCISES

Use the formulas developed in this section and find:

1. $(3, \pi) \times \left(2, \frac{\pi}{4}\right).$
2. $\left(5, \frac{\pi}{6}\right) \times \left(4, \frac{\pi}{3}\right).$
3. $\left(9, \frac{3\pi}{2}\right) \div \left(3, \frac{\pi}{4}\right).$
4. $(0, 90°) \div (1, 15°).$
5. $(2, 30°) \times \left(\frac{1}{2}, 45°\right) \times (1, -30°).$
6. $(x, \theta) \times \left(\frac{1}{x}, \theta\right).$
7. $\dfrac{\left(5, \frac{\pi}{6}\right) \times \left(2, -\frac{\pi}{3}\right)}{\left(2, \frac{\pi}{2}\right)}.$
8. $\dfrac{1}{(3, 30°)}.$

SYSTEMS OF NUMBERS

• • •

In Exercises 9 through 14 express the complex numbers in polar form, perform the indicated operations, and express the result in rectangular or trigonometric form:

9. $(\sqrt{2} - i\sqrt{2}) \times (1 + i\sqrt{3})$.

10. $(\sqrt{3} + i) \times (\sqrt{3} - i\sqrt{3})$.

11. $(1 + i)^4$.

12. $(2\sqrt{2} + 2i\sqrt{2}) \div 3i$.

13. $2i \div \left(-\dfrac{1}{2} + \dfrac{i\sqrt{3}}{2}\right)$.

14. $3 \div (2 - 2i)$.

• **15.** Find the set of complex numbers whose conjugates equal their reciprocals.

• **16.** Find the set of complex numbers which are equal to the squares of their conjugates.

• **17.** Express the statement $(1, \alpha) \times (1, \beta) = (1, \alpha + \beta)$ for complex numbers in polar form as a statement involving the trigonometric forms of the numbers and derive formulas for $\cos(\alpha + \beta)$ and $\sin(\alpha + \beta)$.

• **18.** Using a method similar to the one in Exercise 17, derive formulas for $\cos(\alpha - \beta)$ and $\sin(\alpha - \beta)$.

§ 6–10 De Moivre's theorem

Any complex number $a + bi$ may be expressed in trigonometric form, polar form, and exponential form (§ 6–8);

$$a + bi = r(\cos\theta + i\sin\theta) = (r, \theta) = re^{i\theta}$$

where $r = \sqrt{a^2 + b^2}$ and $\tan\theta = \dfrac{b}{a}$. Notice that for any integer k,

$$\cos\theta = \cos(\theta + 2\pi) = \cos(\theta + 4\pi) = \cos(\theta + 2k\pi);$$
$$\sin\theta = \sin(\theta + 2\pi) = \sin(\theta + 4\pi) = \sin(\theta + 2k\pi);$$
$$\cos\theta + i\sin\theta = \cos(\theta + 2k\pi) + i\sin(\theta + 2k\pi);$$
$$(r, \theta) = (r, \theta + 2k\pi);$$
$$re^{i\theta} = re^{i(\theta + 2k\pi)}.$$

In § 6–9 we multiplied and divided complex numbers in exponential form by treating them as products and powers in the same manner as real numbers;

$$r_1 e^{i\theta_1} \times r_2 e^{i\theta_2} = r_1 r_2 e^{i(\theta_1 + \theta_2)},$$

$$r_1 e^{i\theta_1} \div r_2 e^{i\theta_2} = \dfrac{r_1}{r_2} e^{i(\theta_1 - \theta_2)}.$$

§ 6–10 DE MOIVRE'S THEOREM

For any given positive integer n we could prove from the trigonometric form as in § 6–9 that

$$(r, \theta)^n = (re^{i\theta})^n = r^n e^{in\theta} = (r^n, n\theta).$$

We now assume without proof that a similar result holds for any real number n:

De Moivre's theorem. *For any complex number (r, θ) in polar form and any real number n,*

$$(r, \theta)^n = (r^n, n\theta).$$

Example 1. Find $(1 + i\sqrt{3})^6$.

$$\begin{aligned}
(1 + i\sqrt{3})^6 &= \left(2, \frac{\pi}{3}\right)^6 \\
&= \left(2^6, 6 \times \frac{\pi}{3}\right) \\
&= (2^6, 2\pi) \\
&= (64, 0) \\
&= 64(\cos 0 + i \sin 0) \\
&= 64(1 + 0i) \\
&= 64.
\end{aligned}$$

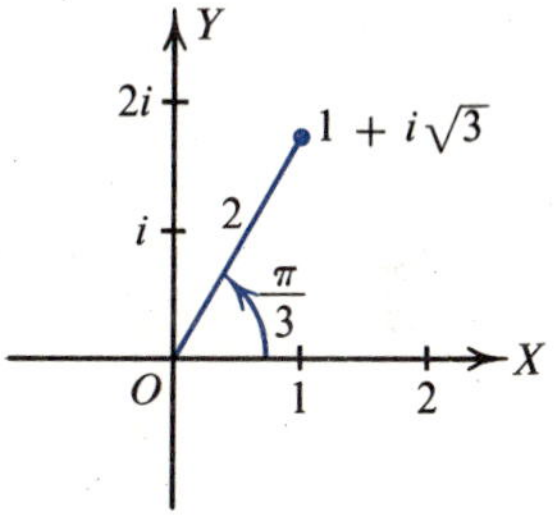

Figure 6–8

One of the most important applications of De Moivre's theorem is concerned with the finding of roots. In this case the argument θ should be considered in its general form $\theta + 2k\pi$ where k may represent any integer. For example, you already know that the four fourth roots of unity are $1, i, -1$, and $-i$ since these are the four solutions of the equation $x^4 = 1$. As we shall see in Chapter 8, any complex number has exactly n complex numbers as nth roots. Notice that in polar form and for any integer k

$$1 = (1, 0) = (1, 2\pi) = (1, 4\pi) = (1, 2k\pi);$$

$$i = \left(1, \frac{\pi}{2}\right) = \left(1, \frac{5}{2}\pi\right) = \left(1, \frac{9}{2}\pi\right) = \left(1, \left(2k + \frac{1}{2}\right)\pi\right);$$

$$-1 = (1, \pi) = (1, 3\pi) = (1, 5\pi) = (1, (2k + 1)\pi);$$

$$-i = \left(1, \frac{3}{2}\pi\right) = \left(1, \frac{7}{2}\pi\right) = \left(1, \frac{11}{2}\pi\right) = \left(1, \left(2k + \frac{3}{2}\right)\pi\right).$$

Then since the positive fourth root of the real number 1 is 1, by

313

SYSTEMS OF NUMBERS

De Moivre's theorem the four fourth roots of unity may be found as:

$$(1, 0)^{\frac{1}{4}} = \left(1^{\frac{1}{4}}, \frac{0}{4}\right) = (1, 0) = 1;$$

$$(1, 2\pi)^{\frac{1}{4}} = \left(1^{\frac{1}{4}}, \frac{2\pi}{4}\right) = \left(1, \frac{\pi}{2}\right) = i;$$

$$(1, 4\pi)^{\frac{1}{4}} = \left(1^{\frac{1}{4}}, \frac{4\pi}{4}\right) = (1, \pi) = -1;$$

$$(1, 6\pi)^{\frac{1}{4}} = \left(1^{\frac{1}{4}}, \frac{6\pi}{4}\right) = \left(1, \frac{3\pi}{2}\right) = -i.$$

If we continue this process, we again obtain:

$$(1, 8\pi)^{\frac{1}{4}} = (1^{\frac{1}{4}}, 2\pi) = 1;$$

$$(1, 10\pi)^{\frac{1}{4}} = \left(1^{\frac{1}{4}}, \frac{5\pi}{2}\right) = \left(1, \frac{\pi}{2}\right) = i;$$

and so forth. We may identify the four fourth roots of unity in polar form as

$$\left(1, \frac{2k\pi}{4}\right) \text{ where } k = 0, 1, 2, 3.$$

In general, the n nth roots of any complex number $(r, \theta) \neq (0, \theta)$ may be expressed as

$$\left(r^{\frac{1}{n}}, \frac{\theta + 2k\pi}{n}\right) \text{ where } k = 0, 1, 2, \cdots, n-1$$

using $r^{\frac{1}{n}}$ to denote the positive number which is the positive nth root of the positive number r. Notice that the nth roots of any real number (r, θ) may be obtained by multiplying the nth roots of unity by the positive nth root $r^{\frac{1}{n}}$ of r; the nth roots of any complex number (r, θ) may be obtained by multiplying the nth roots of unity by $\left(r^{\frac{1}{n}}, \frac{\theta}{n}\right)$.

Example 2. Find the three cube roots of $\sqrt{2} + i\sqrt{2}$.

$$\sqrt{2} + i\sqrt{2} = \left(2, \frac{\pi}{4} + 2k\pi\right) \text{ for any integer } k \text{ and has cube roots}$$

$$\left(2^{\frac{1}{3}}, \frac{\pi + 8k\pi}{12}\right) \text{ for } k = 0, 1, 2;$$

314

§ 6-10 DE MOIVRE'S THEOREM

that is,

$$\left(\sqrt[3]{2}, \frac{\pi}{12}\right), \left(\sqrt[3]{2}, \frac{3\pi}{4}\right), \left(\sqrt[3]{2}, \frac{17\pi}{12}\right).$$

Notice that the graphs of the three complex numbers are equally spaced around a circle of radius $\sqrt[3]{2}$ and center at the origin. The roots may also be obtained by multiplying $\left(\sqrt[3]{2}, \frac{\pi}{12}\right)$ by the three cube roots of unity: $(1, 0), \left(1, \frac{2\pi}{3}\right), \left(1, \frac{4\pi}{3}\right)$.

The graph of any complex number (r, θ) is on a circle of radius r and center at the origin. As in Example 2, the graphs of the three cube roots of any complex number $(r, \theta) \neq (0, \theta)$ divide the circle of radius $r^{\frac{1}{3}}$ and center at the origin into three equal arcs. In general, the graphs of the nth roots of any complex number $(r, \theta) \neq (0, \theta)$ divide the circle of radius $r^{\frac{1}{n}}$ and center at the origin into n equal arcs.

Example 3. Find the five fifth roots of -1.

$$-1 = (1, \pi + 2k\pi) \text{ for any integer } k \text{ and has fifth roots}$$

$$\left(1, \frac{\pi + 2k\pi}{5}\right) \text{ for } k = 0, 1, 2, 3, 4;$$

that is,

$$\left(1, \frac{\pi}{5}\right), \left(1, \frac{3\pi}{5}\right), (1, \pi), \left(1, \frac{7\pi}{5}\right), \left(1, \frac{9\pi}{5}\right).$$

The fifth roots of -1 obtained in Example 3 may be expressed in rectangular form if values are found from the table for $\sin \theta$ and for $\cos \theta$:

$$\left(1, \frac{\pi}{5}\right) = \cos 36° + i \sin 36° \approx 0.81 + 0.59i;$$

$$\left(1, \frac{3\pi}{5}\right) = \cos 108° + i \sin 108° \approx -0.31 + 0.95i;$$

$$(1, \pi) = \cos 180° + i \sin 180° = -1;$$

$$\left(1, \frac{7\pi}{5}\right) = \cos 252° + i \sin 252° \approx -0.31 - 0.95i;$$

$$\left(1, \frac{9\pi}{5}\right) = \cos 324° + i \sin 324° \approx 0.81 - 0.59i.$$

SYSTEMS OF NUMBERS

The graphs of these roots are five points on the unit circle. We could have determined geometrically the five fifth roots of -1 by considering a unit circle on the complex plane. Since -1 must be one of the desired fifth roots, we mark off five arcs having equal central angles of $\frac{2\pi}{5}$, that is, 72°, from the point $(-1, 0)$.

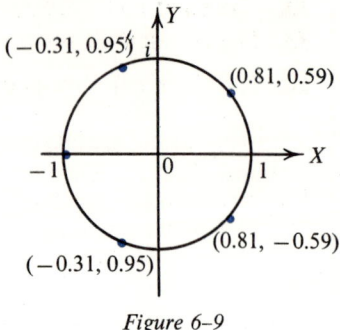

Figure 6-9

In general, we may locate geometrically the graphs of the n nth roots of a complex number $(r, \theta) \neq (0, \theta)$ by constructing a circle with center at the origin and radius equal to $r^{\frac{1}{n}}$ on the complex plane and inscribing an n-sided regular polygon with the point $\left(r^{\frac{1}{n}}, \frac{\theta}{n}\right)$ as one of the vertices. Each vertex will be the graph of a point whose polar coordinates are one of the n roots of the given complex number.

TEST YOURSELF

1. Find $(1 - i\sqrt{3})^5$.
2. Find $(\sqrt{2} + i\sqrt{2})^8$.
3. Find the three cube roots of unity.
4. Determine geometrically the graphs of the six sixth roots of 64.

EXERCISES

Find:

1. $\left(2, \frac{\pi}{6}\right)^3$.
2. $(3, 150°)^5$.
3. $\left(\frac{1}{2}, \frac{5\pi}{2}\right)^7$.
4. $(2\sqrt{3} + 2i)^{12}$.
5. $(4 + 4i)^3$.
6. $\left(\frac{1}{2} - \frac{\sqrt{3}}{2}i\right)^6$.
7. $2(\cos 300° + i \sin 300°)^4$.
8. $(\cos 120° + i \sin 120°)^3$.
9. The two square roots of $1 + i\sqrt{3}$.
10. The three cube roots of $8i$.
11. The four fourth roots of -16.

12. The eight eighth roots of unity.
13. The two square roots of i.
14. The three cube roots of $\left(8, \frac{3\pi}{2}\right)$.

Find in exponential form:

15. The six sixth roots of $32 + 32i\sqrt{3}$.
16. The eight eighth roots of $-128 - 128i$.

• • •

Determine geometrically:

17. The six sixth roots of unity.
18. The four fourth roots of $-i$.
19. The three cube roots of $\left(8, \frac{\pi}{6}\right)$.

In Exercises 20 through 24 prove:

20. The three cube roots of unity form a commutative group under multiplication.
21. The sum of the three cube roots of unity is zero.
22. The sum of the square roots of any complex number is zero.
• 23. Every rth root of unity is also an nth root of unity if n is an integral multiple of r.
• 24. The conjugates of the nth roots of $a + bi$ are the nth roots of the conjugate of $a + bi$.
• 25. Find expressions for $\cos 4\theta$ and $\sin 4\theta$ in terms of $\sin \theta$ and $\cos \theta$ by using De Moivre's theorem and the binomial theorem.

SUMMARY OF CHAPTER 6

1. In this chapter you have studied mathematical systems and in particular number systems. A mathematical system consists of a set of elements, relations among the elements, one or more well-defined operations on the elements, and a set of axioms which the elements, relations, and operations satisfy. (§ 6–1)

2. A set of elements with an equivalence relation forms a group under a well-defined binary operation if the set is closed under the operation, the associativity axiom holds for the operation, the set includes an identity element for the operation, and under the given operation each element of the set has an inverse element. (§ 6–2).

3. The integers may be treated as ordered pairs $\langle a, b \rangle$ of natural

SYSTEMS OF NUMBERS

numbers. Then the properties of integers may be proved using the definitions

$$\langle a, b \rangle = \langle c, d \rangle \text{ if and only if } a + d = b + c \tag{1}$$

$$\langle a, b \rangle + \langle c, d \rangle = \langle a + c, b + d \rangle \tag{2}$$

$$\langle a, b \rangle \times \langle c, d \rangle = \langle ac + bd, ad + bc \rangle \tag{3}$$

and the properties of the natural numbers. (§ 6-3)

4. The rational numbers may be treated as ordered pairs $[a, b]$ of integers. Then the properties of rational numbers may be proved using the definitions

$$[a, b] = [c, d] \text{ if and only if } ad = bc \tag{4}$$

$$[a, b] + [c, d] = [ad + bc, bd] \tag{5}$$

$$[a, b] \times [c, d] = [ac, bd] \tag{6}$$

and the properties of the integers. (§ 6-4)

5. The set of integers forms an integral domain; the set of rational numbers forms a field. (§ 6-5)

6. Any real number may be expressed as an infinite decimal. (§ 6-6)

7. The complex numbers may be treated as ordered pairs (a, b) of real numbers. Then the properties of complex numbers may be proved using the definitions

$$(a, b) = (c, d) \text{ if and only if } a = c \text{ and } b = d$$
$$(a, b) + (c, d) = (a + c, b + d)$$
$$(a, b) \times (c, d) = (ac - bd, ad + bc)$$

and the properties of the field of real numbers. (§ 6-7)

8. Any complex number may be graphed on a complex plane and expressed in rectangular form, trigonometric form, polar form, and exponential form:

$$a + bi = r(\cos \theta + i \sin \theta) = (r, \theta) = re^{i\theta}. \quad (\S \ 6\text{-}8)$$

9. Given any two complex numbers (r_1, θ_1) and (r_2, θ_2) in polar form

$$(r_1, \theta_1) \times (r_2, \theta_2) = (r_1 r_2, \theta_1 + \theta_2);$$

$$(r_1, \theta_1) \div (r_2, \theta_2) = \left(\frac{r_1}{r_2}, \theta_1 - \theta_2\right). \quad (\S \ 6\text{-}9)$$

10. We assumed De Moivre's theorem: For any complex number (r, θ) in polar form and any real number n,

$$(r, \theta)^n = (r^n, n\theta). \quad (\S \ 6\text{-}10).$$

11. The following words have been introduced or used extensively in this chapter:

SUMMARY OF CHAPTER 6

absolute value (§ 6–8)
additive inverse (§ 6–3)
amplitude (§ 6–8)
Argand plane (§ 6–8)
argument (§ 6–8)
associative property for addition (§ 6–3)
associative property for multiplication (§ 6–3)
axiom (§ 6–1)
axis of imaginaries (§ 6–8)
axis of reals (§ 6–8)
binary operation (§ 6–1)
closed (§ 6–1)
closure (§ 6–2)
commutative group (§ 6–2)
commutative property for addition (§ 6–3)
commutative property for multiplication (§ 6–3)
complex number (§ 6–7)
complex plane (§ 6–8)
congruence class (§ 6–5)
congruent modulo m (§ 6–5)
conjugate complex number (§ 6–7)
consistent (§ 6–1)
counter-example (§ 6–1)
De Moivre's theorem (§ 6–10)
difference (§ 6–3)
distributive property (§ 6–3)
equivalence relation (§ 6–1)
exponential form (§ 6–8)
field (§ 6–5)
finite group (§ 6–2)
group (§ 6–2)
identity element (§ 6–2)
imaginary unit (§ 6–7)
improper rational number (§ 6–4)
inconsistent (§ 6–1)
infinite decimal (§ 6–6)
infinite group (§ 6–2)

integer (§ 6–3)
integral domain (§ 6–5)
inverse element (§§ 6–2, 6–3, 6–4)
irrational number (§ 6–6)
mathematical system (§ 6–1)
mixed imaginary number (§ 6–7)
model (§ 6–1)
modulus (§ 6–8)
multiplicative inverse (§ 6–4)
n-ary operation (§ 6–1)
natural number (§ 6–3)
negative (§ 6–3)
negative integer (§ 6–3)
nonrepeating infinite decimal (§ 6–6)
nonterminating decimal (§ 6–6)
number system (§ 6–5)
order relation (§§ 6–1, 6–3)
polar form (§ 6–8)
positive integer (§ 6–3)
proper rational number (§ 6–4)
pure imaginary number (§ 6–7)
quotient (§ 6–4)
rational number (§ 6–4)
real number (§ 6–6)
reciprocal (§ 6–4)
rectangular form (§ 6–7)
reflexive (§ 6–1)
relation (§ 6–1)
repeating infinite decimal (§ 6–6)
symmetric (§ 6–1)
terminating decimal (§ 6–6)
ternary operation (§ 6–1)
transitive (§ 6–1)
trigonometric form (§ 6–8)
unary operation (§ 6–1)
unity (§ 6–4)
well-defined operation (§ 6–1)
zero (§ 6–3)
zero divisor (§ 6–5)

SYSTEMS OF NUMBERS

KEYED PRACTICE ON CHAPTER 6

1. Tell whether or not the relation "is north of" for the set of towns in the United States is **(a)** reflexive; **(b)** symmetric; **(c)** transitive. (§ 6–1)

2. Tell whether or not the set of integral multiples of 10 is closed under **(a)** addition; **(b)** multiplication. (§ 6–1)

3. Tell whether or not the set of integral multiples of 3 forms a commutative group under addition. (§ 6–2)

4. Express each integer as an ordered pair $\langle a, b \rangle$ of natural numbers: **(a)** 3; **(b)** -4; **(c)** 0. (§ 6–3)

5. Perform the indicated operations:
(a) $\langle 3, 7 \rangle + \langle 4, 1 \rangle$; **(b)** $\langle 5, 2 \rangle \times \langle 6, 5 \rangle$; **(c)** $\langle a, 3 \rangle - \langle 2, b \rangle$. (§ 6–3)

6. Express each rational number as an ordered pair $[a, b]$ of integers:
(a) $\frac{3}{7}$; **(b)** 11; **(c)** $-\frac{1}{4}$. (§ 6–4)

7. Perform the indicated operations:
(a) $[2, 5] + [3, 7]$; **(b)** $[2, 5] \times [3, 7]$; **(c)** $[2, 5] \div [3, 7]$. (§ 6–4)

8. Determine whether or not the set of integers modulo 8 under ordinary addition and multiplication forms an integral domain. (§ 6–5)

9. Express $5.23\overline{4}$ as a quotient of integers. (§ 6–6)

10. Find: **(a)** $(5 - \sqrt{-3}) \times (2 + \sqrt{-12})$; **(b)** $(2 + 3i) \div (1 + 2i)$. (§ 6–7)

11. Express $1 - i\sqrt{3}$ in trigonometric form, polar form, and exponential form. (§ 6–8)

12. Find for these complex numbers in polar form:
(a) $(6, 60°) \times (5, -15°)$; **(b)** $\left(6, \frac{\pi}{2}\right) \div \left(3, \frac{\pi}{3}\right)$. (§ 6–9)

13. Find the three cube roots of -8: **(a)** geometrically; **(b)** using De Moivre's theorem. (§ 6–10)

TESTS ON CHAPTER 6

A

1. Tell whether or not the set of integral multiples of 5 under addition **(a)** is associative; **(b)** forms a commutative group.

2. Perform the indicated operations where the ordered pairs of natural numbers represent integers:
(a) $\langle 1, 7 \rangle + \langle 5, 6 \rangle$; **(b)** $\langle 2, 11 \rangle \times \langle 8, 3 \rangle$.

3. Perform the indicated operations where the ordered pairs of integers represent rational numbers:
(a) $[1, 8] + [3, 5]$; **(b)** $[2, 3] \times [5, 7]$.

TESTS ON CHAPTER 6

4. Find: (a) $3 \times 4 + 5 \pmod{7}$; (b) $2 + 6 \times 5 - 3 \pmod{8}$.
5. Express: (a) $2.5\overline{1}$ as a quotient of integers; (b) $\frac{5}{12}$ as an infinite repeating decimal.
6. Find: (a) $(2\sqrt{-3})^4$; (b) $(3 - i) \div (2 + i)$.
7. Express $-2 + 2i$ in trigonometric form, polar form, and exponential form.
8. Perform the indicated operations for these complex numbers expressed as ordered pairs of real numbers:
(a) $(5, 2) + (-3, 1)$; (b) $(3, \sqrt{2}) \times (3, -\sqrt{2})$.
9. Find for these complex numbers in polar form and express in rectangular form: (a) $\left(2, \frac{\pi}{3}\right) \times \left(3, \frac{\pi}{6}\right)$; (b) $(10, \pi) \div \left(5, \frac{3\pi}{2}\right)$.
10. Find in polar form the five fifth roots of i.

B

1. Tell whether or not the set of even integers forms a group under subtraction. Explain your answer.
2. Consider integers as ordered pairs $\langle a, b \rangle$ of natural numbers and perform the indicated operations:
(a) $\langle r, s \rangle \times \langle r, s \rangle$; (b) $\langle r, s \rangle - \langle p, q \rangle$.
3. Consider rational numbers as ordered pairs $[a, b]$ of nonzero integers and perform the indicated operations:
(a) $[a, b] \div [a, b]$; (b) $[a, b] \div [r, s]$.
4. Determine whether or not the set of integral multiples of 5 under ordinary addition and multiplication forms an integral domain.
5. Express: (a) $78.5\overline{32}$ as a quotient of integers; (b) $\frac{5}{7}$ as an infinite decimal.
6. Find: (a) i^{27}; (b) $(i\sqrt{3} + 5) \times (i\sqrt{3} - 5)$.
7. Express the complex number which is represented in polar form by $\left(4, \frac{\pi}{6}\right)$ in (a) exponential form; (b) trigonometric form; (c) rectangular form.
8. Perform the indicated operations for these complex numbers expressed as ordered pairs of real numbers:
(a) $(-4, \sqrt{2}) + (-4, -\sqrt{2})$; (b) $(\sqrt{2}, 1) \times (2, 3)$.
9. Find for these complex numbers expressed in polar form and express in rectangular form:
(a) $\left(8, \frac{\pi}{4}\right) \times \left(3, \frac{7\pi}{2}\right)$; (b) $\left(12, \frac{5\pi}{6}\right) \div \left(4, \frac{\pi}{3}\right)$.
10. Find in polar form the five fifth roots of $-i$.

321

SYSTEMS OF NUMBERS

C

1. Tell whether or not the set of ordered pairs of real numbers (x, y) where $(x, y) = (s, t)$ if and only if $x + t = y + s$ and $(a, b) \odot (c, d) = (a + d, b + c)$ forms a group. Explain your answer.

2. Find: (a) for integers considered as ordered pairs of natural numbers, $\langle 5, 3 \rangle + (\langle 2, 5 \rangle \times \langle 7, 6 \rangle)$; (b) for rational numbers considered as ordered pairs of integers, $[5, 3] + ([2, 5] \times [7, 6])$; (c) for complex numbers considered as ordered pairs of real numbers, $(5, 3) + [(2, 5) \times (7, 6)]$.

3. Represent integers as ordered pairs of natural numbers and determine whether or not the set of integers is closed under subtraction.

4. Explain whether or not under division the set of rational numbers different from zero forms a (a) group; (b) commutative group.

5. Consider the numbers

$$\frac{3}{11}, \; 5.\overline{13}, \; \sqrt{484}, \; \frac{2}{\sqrt{5}}, \; \frac{5}{3}\sqrt{225},$$

and tell which of these numbers may be expressed as (a) terminating decimals; (b) infinite repeating decimals.

6. If $i^2 = -1$ and $i^k = i^t$, find a relationship between k and t.

7. Express $4 - 4i\sqrt{3}$ in (a) trigonometric form; (b) polar form; (c) exponential form. Then state its (d) amplitude; (e) modulus.

8. Find for these complex numbers in polar form and express in rectangular form:

(a) $\left(7, \dfrac{\pi}{6}\right) \times \left(3, \dfrac{5\pi}{3}\right)$; (b) $\left(3, \dfrac{7\pi}{6}\right) \div \left(2, \dfrac{3\pi}{2}\right)$.

9. Find the multiplicative inverse of each complex number: (a) $(2, t)$ expressed as an ordered pair of real numbers; (b) $(5, \theta)$ expressed in polar form; (c) $2e^{3\pi i}$.

10. Find in polar form the seven seventh roots of $(128, 210°)$.

ANSWERS TO TEST YOURSELF EXERCISES

§ 6-1. 1. (a) Yes; (b) yes; (c) yes; (d) yes.
2. (a) Yes; (b) no, 2 is a divisor of 4 but 4 is not a divisor of 2; (c) yes; (d) no, (b) fails.
3. (a) No, A is not east of A; (b) no, if A is east of B, B is not east of A; (c) yes; (d) no, (a) and (b) fail.
4. (a) Yes; (b) yes; (c) yes; (d) yes.
5. Not closed. 6. Closed. 7. Not closed. 8. Not closed.

ANSWERS TO TEST YOURSELF EXERCISES

§ 6-2. 1. No; the identity element (0) and the inverses (negatives) are not members of the set of positive integers.
2. No, the inverses (reciprocals) are not members of the set of positive integers.
3. Yes.
4. Yes.
5. (a) The set of integers under addition (Exercise 3) and the set $\{1, -1\}$ under multiplication (Exercise 4) form commutative groups; (b) the set in Exercise 4 forms a finite group.

§ 6-3. 1. $\langle 8, 5 \rangle$; in general, $\langle k + 3, k \rangle$ for any natural number k.
2. $\langle 5, 6 \rangle$; in general $\langle k, k + 1 \rangle$.
3. $\langle 6, 2 \rangle$; in general $\langle k + 4, k \rangle$.
4. $\langle 14, 19 \rangle$; in general $\langle k, k + 5 \rangle$.

5. No.
6. Yes.
7. No.
8. Yes.
9. Not positive.
10. Positive.
11. Not positive.
12. Positive.
13. $\langle 7, 4 \rangle$.
14. $\langle 41, 29 \rangle$.

§ 6-4. 1. [5, 2], in general [5k, 2k] for any integer $k \neq 0$.
2. [-3, 1], in general [$-3k$, k] for any integer $k \neq 0$.
3. [0, 1], in general [0, k] for any integer $k \neq 0$.
4. [-1, 3], in general [$-k$, 3k] for any integer $k \neq 0$.
5. Yes. **6.** No. **7.** Yes. **8.** Yes. **9.** [11, 12]. **10.** [-1, 4].

§ 6-5. 1. (a) No; the additive inverses and zero are not members of the set; (b) no.
2. (a) No; the set is not closed under addition ($3 + 5 = 8$) and zero is not a member of the set; (b) no.
3. Consider the tables:

+	0	1	2
0	0	1	2
1	1	2	0
2	2	0	1

×	0	1	2
0	0	0	0
1	0	1	2
2	0	2	1

(a) Yes; (b) yes.

SYSTEMS OF NUMBERS

4. Consider the tables:

+	0	1	2	3
0	0	1	2	3
1	1	2	3	0
2	2	3	0	1
3	3	0	1	2

×	0	1	2	3
0	0	0	0	0
1	0	1	2	3
2	0	2	0	2
3	0	3	2	1

(a) No, $2 \times 2 \equiv 0 \pmod{4}$ indicates that 2 is a zero divisor; (b) no.

§ 6-6. **1.** Terminating, $4 = 2^2 \times 5^0$.
2. Terminating, $16 = 2^4 \times 5^0$.
3. Nonterminating, $12 = 3^1 \times 2^2 \neq 2^k 5^n$.
4. Nonterminating, $7 \neq 2^k 5^n$.
5. $\frac{2}{15}$. **6.** $\frac{17}{3}$. **7.** $\frac{2}{1}$. **8.** $\frac{353}{10}$.
9. $0.4\overline{0}$. **10.** $3.\overline{6}$. **11.** $0.8\overline{3}$. **12.** $0.\overline{27}$.

§ 6-7. **1.** (a) $0 + 2i\sqrt{2}$; (b) $(0, 2\sqrt{2})$.
2. (a) $0 + 2i$; (b) $(0, 2)$.
3. (a) $-6 + 0i$; (b) $(-6, 0)$.
4. (a) $3 + i\sqrt{2}$; (b) $(3, \sqrt{2})$.
5. $5 + 3i$. **6.** $-2 + 8i$. **7.** $7i$.
8. $23 + 11i$. **9.** $\frac{9}{2} - \frac{1}{2}i$. **10.** $10 + 4i\sqrt{2}$.
11. $-597 + 122i$. **12.** $2i$.

§ 6-8. **1.** (a) through (d)

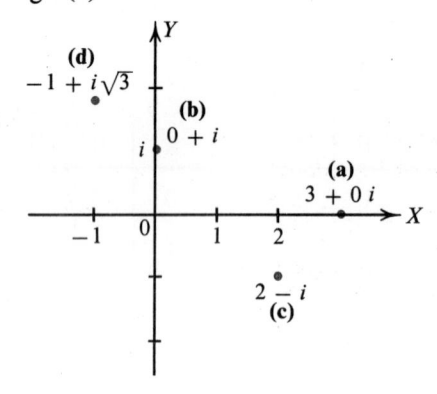

324

ANSWERS TO TEST YOURSELF EXERCISES

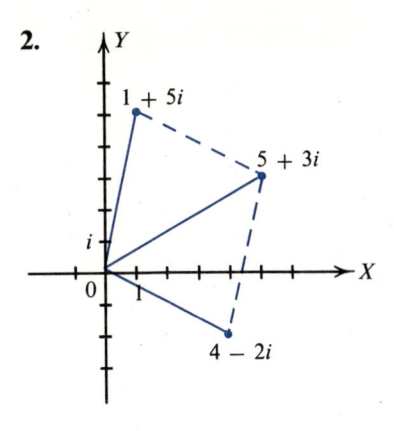

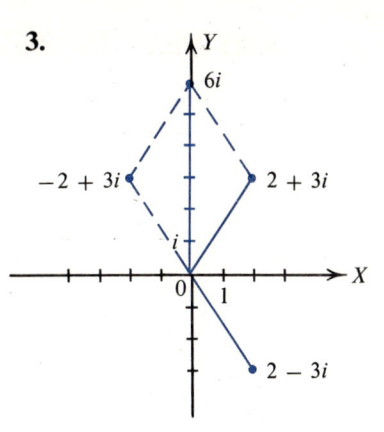

2. [graph showing points $1+5i$, $5+3i$, $4-2i$]

3. [graph showing points $6i$, $-2+3i$, $2+3i$, $2-3i$]

4. (a) $\sqrt{2}\left(\cos\frac{\pi}{4} + i\sin\frac{\pi}{4}\right)$; (b) $\left(\sqrt{2}, \frac{\pi}{4}\right)$; (c) $\sqrt{2}e^{\frac{\pi}{4}i}$.

5. (a) $2\sqrt{2}\left(\cos\frac{3\pi}{4} + i\sin\frac{3\pi}{4}\right)$; (b) $\left(\sqrt{2}, \frac{3\pi}{4}\right)$; (c) $2\sqrt{2}e^{\frac{3\pi}{4}i}$.

6. (a) $3(\cos\pi + i\sin\pi)$; (b) $(3, \pi)$; (c) $3e^{\pi i}$.

7. (a) $1\left(\cos\frac{2\pi}{3} + i\sin\frac{2\pi}{3}\right)$; (b) $\left(1, \frac{2\pi}{3}\right)$; (c) $e^{\frac{2\pi}{3}i}$.

8. $0 - 5i$.

9. $2\sqrt{2} + 2i\sqrt{2}$.

10. $\frac{\sqrt{3}}{2} - \frac{1}{2}i$.

§ 6–9. **1.** $\left(6, \frac{2\pi}{3}\right)$. **2.** $(6, 15°)$. **3.** $\left(5, -\frac{\pi}{6}\right)$. **4.** $(x, 0)$.

§ 6–10. **1.** $16 + 16i\sqrt{3}$. **2.** 256.

3. $1, -\frac{1}{2} + \frac{\sqrt{3}}{2}i, -\frac{1}{2} - \frac{\sqrt{3}}{2}i$.

4. The graphs of the six sixth roots of 64 include the graph of 2 and are equally spaced (vertices of a regular hexagon) around a circle with center at the origin and radius 2.

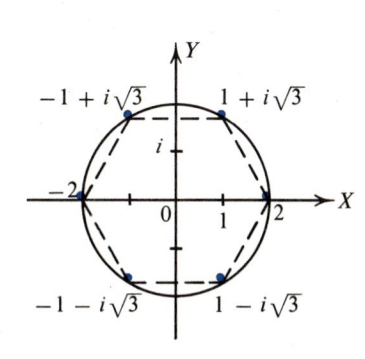

[graph showing sixth roots of 64: $-1+i\sqrt{3}$, $1+i\sqrt{3}$, -2, 2, $-1-i\sqrt{3}$, $1-i\sqrt{3}$]

325

SYSTEMS OF NUMBERS

ANSWERS TO KEYED PRACTICE EXERCISES

1. (a) No; (b) no; (c) yes.
2. (a) Yes; (b) yes.
3. Yes.
4. For any natural number a: (a) $\langle 3 + a, a \rangle$; (b) $\langle a, 4 + a \rangle$; (c) $\langle a, a \rangle$.
5. (a) $\langle 7, 8 \rangle$; (b) $\langle 40, 37 \rangle$; (c) $\langle a + b, 5 \rangle$.
6. For any integer $a \neq 0$, (a) $[3a, 7a]$; (b) $[11a, a]$; (c) $[-a, 4a]$.
7. (a) $[29, 35]$; (b) $[6, 35]$; (c) $[14, 15]$.
8. The set of integers modulo 8 includes zero divisors $(2 \times 4 \equiv 0 \pmod{8})$ and thus does not form an integral domain.
9. $\dfrac{4711}{900}$.
10. (a) $16 + 8i\sqrt{3}$; (b) $\dfrac{8}{5} - \dfrac{1}{5}i$.
11. $1 - i\sqrt{3} = 2\left(\cos\dfrac{5\pi}{3} + i \sin\dfrac{5\pi}{3}\right) = \left(2, \dfrac{5\pi}{3}\right) = 2e^{\frac{5\pi}{3}i}$.
12. (a) $(30, 45°)$; (b) $\left(2, \dfrac{\pi}{6}\right)$.
13. (a)   (b) $1 + i\sqrt{3}$; -2; $1 - i\sqrt{3}$.

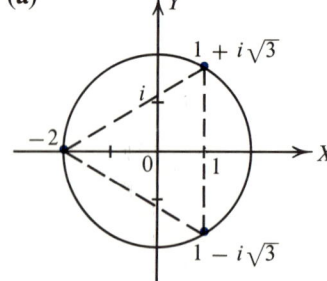

326

Chapter 7

Linear and Quadratic Expressions

§ 7-1 Equations of lines on a plane

Variables were introduced in § 1–5. We now use variables x and y and numbers (**constants**) to obtain equations for lines on a coordinate plane. The variables represent real numbers, and only real numbers are used as constants.

Equations of lines parallel to the axes of a coordinate plane involve one variable. Any line parallel to the y-axis has an equation of the form $x = k$. Any line parallel to the x-axis has an equation of the form $y = k$. Both equations are of the form

$$Ax + By + C = 0, \quad A^2 + B^2 \neq 0. \tag{1}$$

The numbers A and B are the **coefficients** of the equation; the condition $A^2 + B^2 \neq 0$ implies that the real numbers A and B are not both zero.

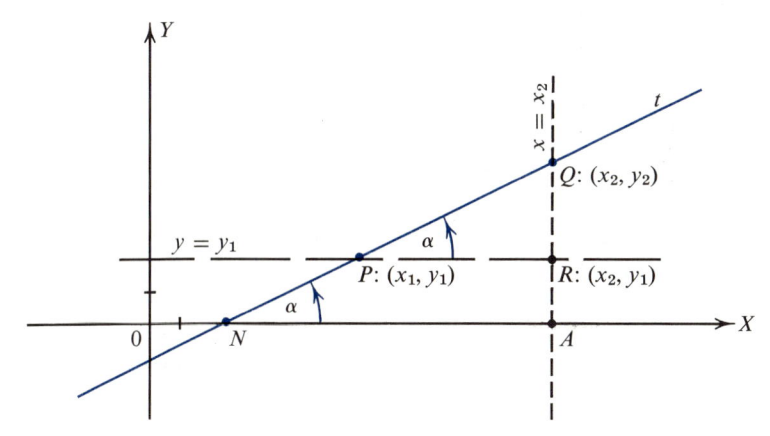

Figure 7-1

Consider a line such as t in Figure 7–1 where t is not parallel to either of the axes. Let $P: (x_1, y_1)$ and $Q: (x_2, y_2)$ be any two points on t. The line through P and parallel to the x-axis has equation $y = y_1$; the line through Q and parallel to the y-axis has equation $x = x_2$. These lines are perpendicular at the point $R: (x_2, y_1)$. We now use this figure as we consider some general properties of lines.

The **slope of a line** is defined as the quotient of the difference of the

327

LINEAR AND QUADRATIC EXPRESSIONS

ordinate values and the difference of the abscissa values of two points. That is, the slope of the line *PQ* in Figure 7–1 is the ratio $\frac{y_2 - y_1}{x_2 - x_1}$. This ratio is often denoted by *m*. Since division by zero is not allowed in our number system, the slope of a line is defined if and only if $x_2 \neq x_1$; that is, if and only if the line is not parallel to the *y*-axis. The slope *m* of the line *PQ* in Figure 7–1 might also have been obtained by finding the ratio $\frac{y_1 - y_2}{x_1 - x_2}$. Notice that in the first ratio the numerator and denominator were obtained by subtracting the ordinate and abscissa (§ 1–6) of *P* from the ordinate and abscissa of *Q* respectively; in the second ratio they were obtained by subtracting the ordinate and abscissa of *Q* from the ordinate and abscissa of *P*.

Any line *t* that is not parallel to the *x*-axis intersects the *x*-axis at a point *N*. Let *P* be a point of the line *t* such that *P* has a positive *y*-coordinate. Then the **angle of inclination** of the line *t* is angle *XNP* (Figure 7–1); that is, the angle formed by the positive *x*-axis and that part of the line *t* above the *x*-axis. The angle of inclination is measured counterclockwise. In Figure 7–1 the line *PR* is parallel to the *x*-axis and $\angle ANQ = \angle RPQ$. Then since triangle *PRQ* is a right triangle,

$$m = \frac{y_2 - y_1}{x_2 - x_1} = \tan \alpha \qquad (2)$$

where *m* is the slope of the line through (x_1, y_1) and (x_2, y_2), and α is the angle of inclination of the line. For all lines except those parallel to the *x*-axis, $0° < \alpha < 180°$. Any line parallel to the *x*-axis is said to have an angle of inclination of zero degrees.

For any given line *t*, the angle of inclination α is constant, $m = \tan \alpha$, and thus the slope *m* of *t* is constant. In other words, the slope of the line *t* does not depend upon the selection of the points (x_1, y_1) and (x_2, y_2) on the line.

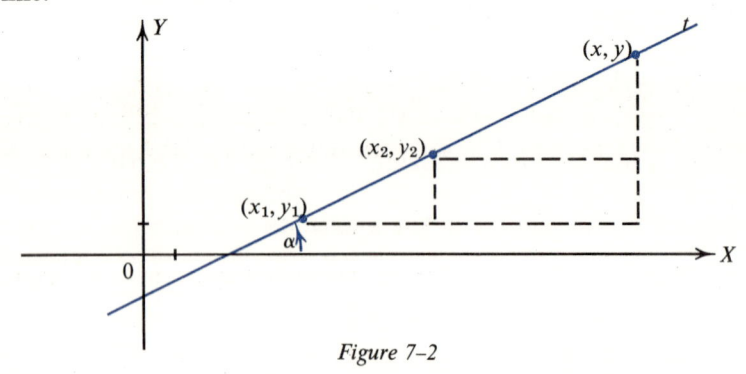

Figure 7–2

§ 7-1 EQUATIONS OF LINES ON A PLANE

Let (x_1, y_1) and (x_2, y_2) be two given (fixed) points on a line t, and let (x, y) be a variable point on that line; that is, consider x and y as variables so that (x, y) may represent any point on the line t. Then two expressions for the slope m may be used to obtain the **two-point form** of the equation of the line:

$$m = \frac{y - y_1}{x - x_1}, \qquad m = \frac{y_2 - y_1}{x_2 - x_1};$$

$$\frac{y - y_1}{x - x_1} = \frac{y_2 - y_1}{x_2 - x_1}. \tag{3}$$

When m is used for the right member of (3), that equation may be written in the **point-slope form** of the equation of the line:

$$y - y_1 = m(x - x_1). \tag{4}$$

Example 1. Find an equation in two-point form of a line determined by the points (1, 3) and (4, 5).

Let $(x_1, y_1) = (1, 3)$ and $(x_2, y_2) = (4, 5)$. Then the equation of the form (3) of the line is

$$\frac{y - 3}{x - 1} = \frac{5 - 3}{4 - 1};$$

$$\frac{y - 3}{x - 1} = \frac{2}{3}.$$

Example 2. Find an equation in point-slope form of the line passing through the point $(-2, 3)$ with slope equal to 4.

Let $m = 4$ and $(x_1, y_1) = (-2, 3)$ in the equation (4).

$$y - 3 = 4[x - (-2)];$$
$$y - 3 = 4(x + 2).$$

The **y-intercept** of a line is the y-coordinate of the point $(0, b)$ of intersection of the line with the y-axis. If the slope of a line is m and the y-intercept is b, then by (4) the point-slope form of the equation of the line is

$$y - b = m(x - 0).$$

This equation may be written in the **slope-intercept** form of the equation of the line:

$$y = mx + b. \tag{5}$$

LINEAR AND QUADRATIC EXPRESSIONS

Example 3. Find an equation in slope-intercept form of the line passing through the point (0, 2) and with slope equal to -3.

Let $m = -3$ and $b = 2$ in the equation (5). Then
$$y = -3x + 2.$$

The **x-intercept** of a line is the x-coordinate of the point $(a, 0)$ of intersection of the line with the x-axis. Consider a line with x-intercept a and y-intercept b. This line passes through the points $(a, 0)$ and $(0, b)$. By the two-point form of the equation of a line we have

$$\frac{y - 0}{x - a} = \frac{b - 0}{0 - a}$$

$$-ay = b(x - a)$$

$$bx + ay = ab$$

$$\frac{x}{a} + \frac{y}{b} = 1. \qquad (6)$$

This is the **intercept form** of the equation of a line.

Example 4. Find an equation in intercept form of the line which passes through the points (4, 0) and (0, 3).

The x- and y-intercepts are 4 and 3 respectively. Let $a = 4$ and $b = 3$ in the equation (6):

$$\frac{x}{4} + \frac{y}{3} = 1.$$

A line may be determined by any two of its points or by its slope and one point. If the two points have the same x-coordinate, that is, if the direction of the line is parallel to the y-axis, then the equation of the line is of the form $x = x_1$. In all other cases, if two points on a line are known, the equation of the line may be expressed in the two-point form or, if the points are on the axes, in the intercept form. If one point on a line and the slope of the line are known, the equation of the line may be expressed in the point-slope form or, if the point is on the y-axis, in the slope-intercept form. Thus if a line is determined on a coordinate plane, we can find an equation for the line.

Each form of the equation of a line may also be expressed in the form (1). For example, the equation (3) may be expressed in the form (1) as

$$(y_1 - y_2)x + (x_2 - x_1)y + (x_1 y_2 - x_2 y_1) = 0$$

where $A = y_1 - y_2$, $B = x_2 - x_1$, and $C = x_1 y_2 - x_2 y_1$; the equation (4)

§7-1 EQUATIONS OF LINES ON A PLANE

may be expressed in the form (1) as

$$-mx + y + (mx_1 - y_1) = 0$$

where $A = -m$, $B = 1$, and $C = mx_1 - y_1$. When an equation of a line is called for and the form is not specified, the form (1) should be used.

TEST YOURSELF

Find an equation of the line:

1. Through (0, 3) with slope 2.
2. Through (1, 2) with slope -3.
3. Through $(-2, -3)$ and $(1, -2)$.
4. Through (5, 0) and $(0, -3)$.

EXERCISES

Find the slope of the line whose equation is:

1. $y = -5x - 7$.
2. $3y - 2x + 5 = 0$.
3. $6x + 2y = 7$.
4. $\dfrac{3x - 7}{y + 2} = \dfrac{-2}{3}$.

Find an equation of the line:

5. Through (6, 7) and $(-3, 4)$.
6. Through (0, 4) and (4, 0).
7. Through (0, 0) and (1, 0).
8. Through (0, 2) and (0, 5).

Find and express in slope-intercept form an equation of the line:

9. Through (0, 5) with $m = -2$.
10. Through (2, 3) with slope 3.
11. Through (0, 2) and $(-5, 0)$.
12. Through $(2, -3)$ and $\left(-\dfrac{1}{3}, \dfrac{1}{2}\right)$.
13. Through (4, 0) with $\alpha = 30°$.
14. Through (3, 4) with $\alpha = 120°$.
15. Through (0, 0) with $\alpha = 90°$.
16. Through (3, 2) with $\alpha = \dfrac{\pi}{4}$.

LINEAR AND QUADRATIC EXPRESSIONS

• • •

If possible, write each equation in Exercises 17 through 24 in **(a)** *point-slope form;* **(b)** *slope-intercept form;* **(c)** *intercept form:*

17. $x = y$.
18. $3y - 2x = 6$.
19. $4y = -3x - 12$.
20. $5y + 6 = x$.
21. $6 - 5x = 0$.
22. $3x - 3y - 9 = 0$.
23. $2x + 3y - 1 = 0$.
24. $5y + 6x - 1 = 4y + 5x + 5$.

25. Find the x-coordinate of the point with y-coordinate 1 on the graph of each equation in Exercises 17 through 24.

26. Explain the fact that the slope of the graph of any equation of the form $x = k$ is not defined in the set of real numbers.

SUPPLEMENTARY EXERCISES

1. State in terms of the slopes m of the lines a general form for the equations of the lines through the origin.

2. State in terms of the y-intercepts b of the lines a general form for the equations of the lines with slope 3.

3. State in terms of the slopes m of the lines a general form for the equations of the lines through the point $(1, 2)$.

4. Use the angles of inclination of the lines and prove that parallel lines have the same slope.

5. Find an equation of the line parallel to the line $2x + 3y - 4 = 0$ and having y-intercept 2.

6. Find the value of k if the points $(k, -2)$, $(1, -1)$, and $(10, 2)$ are collinear.

7. Find the value of k if the equation $3x - 2ky + 7 = 0$ has slope $\frac{1}{6}$.

8. Find an equation for the line through $(3, 4)$ if the line has equal x- and y-intercepts.

9. Find the slopes of the medians of the triangle with vertices $A: (0, 1)$, $B: (3, 2)$, and $C: (1, -3)$.

• **10.** Prove that if two lines t_1 and t_2 have slopes m_1 and m_2 respectively, then the angle θ measured counterclockwise from t_1 to t_2 satisfies the equation

$$\tan \theta = \frac{m_2 - m_1}{1 + m_1 m_2}.$$

• **11.** Prove that two lines with slopes m_1 and m_2 are perpendicular if and only if $m_1 m_2 = -1$.

§ 7-2 Graphs of linear relations

We have seen in § 7-1 that any line on a coordinate plane has an equation of the form (1)

$$Ax + By + C = 0, A^2 + B^2 \neq 0.$$

Accordingly, any equation of the form (1) is called a **linear equation in x and y**. Similarly, an expression of the form $Ax + C$ where A is a constant different from zero and x is a variable is a **linear expression in x**. A linear expression in x is often called a **linear function of x** (in accord with the second usage of "function" mentioned in § 1–10). An expression of the form $Ax + By + C$ where A and B are not both zero is a **linear expression in x and y**. A linear expression in x and y is often called a **linear function of x and y**.

In this section we consider graphs of linear equations and inequalities. We first verify that the graph on a coordinate plane of any linear equation (1) is a line. The line is called the *graph of the equation;* the equation is called an *equation of the graph.* Each point of the graph represents an ordered pair of values (x, y) which satisfy the equation and illustrate the *ordered pair* interpretation of the linear relation. We shall often speak of the line in terms of the equation. For example, we may speak of the line $x - y = 2$ and mean thereby the line which is the graph of the equation $x - y = 2$.

If $A = B = 0$, the equation (1) is not a linear equation. In this case the equation is an identity if $C = 0$; an impossible equation if $C \neq 0$.

Suppose that A and B are not both zero. Then if $B = 0$ and $A \neq 0$, the equation (1) may be expressed as

$$x = -\frac{C}{A};$$

that is, as the equation of a line parallel to, or coinciding with, the y-axis. If $A = 0$ and $B \neq 0$, the equation (1) may be expressed as

$$y = -\frac{C}{B};$$

that is, as the equation of a line parallel to, or coinciding with, the x-axis. If $A \neq 0$ and $B \neq 0$, the equation (1) may be expressed as

$$y = -\frac{A}{B}x - \frac{C}{B};$$

that is, as the equation in slope-intercept form of a line through $\left(0, -\frac{C}{B}\right)$ and with slope $-\frac{A}{B}$.

LINEAR AND QUADRATIC EXPRESSIONS

Example 1. Prove that any linear equation $Ax + By + C = 0$ with real numbers as coefficients is satisfied by infinitely many ordered pairs of real numbers.

The equation $Ax + By + C = 0$ is linear if and only if A and B are not both zero. As we have just seen, the equation may be expressed in the form $x = -\frac{C}{A}$ if $B = 0$; the equation may be expressed in the form $y = -\frac{C}{B}$ if $A = 0$; the equation may be expressed in the form $y = -\frac{A}{B}x - \frac{C}{B}$ if $A \neq 0$ and $B \neq 0$.

If the equation may be expressed in the form $x = -\frac{C}{A}$, then for each value of the real variable y the ordered pair $\left(-\frac{C}{A}, y\right)$ satisfies the equation since there is no restriction upon y; $A\left(-\frac{C}{A}\right) + 0(y) + C = 0$.

In a similar manner the equation $y = -\frac{C}{B}$ is satisfied by the ordered pair $\left(x, -\frac{C}{B}\right)$ for each value of the real variable x since there is no restriction upon x; $0(x) + B\left(-\frac{C}{B}\right) + C = 0$.

If the equation may be expressed in the form $y = -\frac{A}{B}x - \frac{C}{B}$, then for each value of the real variable x the ordered pair of the form $\left(x, -\frac{A}{B}x - \frac{C}{B}\right)$ satisfies the equation.

Example 2. Express each equation as a set of ordered pairs of real numbers in the form $\{(x, f(x))\}$ and also in the form $\{(g(y), y)\}$:
(a) $x - 2y + 3 = 0$; (b) $3x - y = 5$.

(a) $x - 2y + 3 = 0$ $x = 2y - 3$
     $2y = x + 3$ $\{(2y - 3, y)\}$.
     $\left\{\left(x, \frac{x+3}{2}\right)\right\}$;

(b) $3x - y = 5$ $3x = y + 5$
     $y = 3x - 5$ $x = \frac{y+5}{3}$
     $\{(x, 3x - 5)\}$; $\left\{\left(\frac{y+5}{3}, y\right)\right\}$.

§ 7-2 GRAPHS OF LINEAR RELATIONS

Example 3. Graph: $6x - 3y - 1 = 0$.

The equation may be expressed in the form

$$y = 2x - \frac{1}{3}$$

which is the equation of a line with slope 2 and y-intercept $-\frac{1}{3}$.

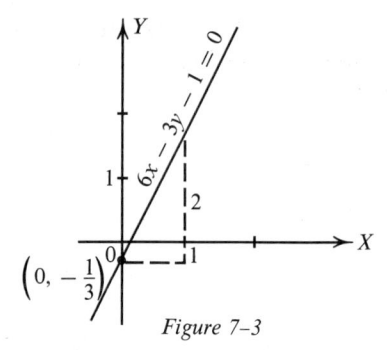

Figure 7-3

Each point of the line with equation $6x - 3y - 1 = 0$ may be represented as in Example 2 by an ordered pair $\left(x, 2x - \frac{1}{3}\right)$ since $y = 2x - \frac{1}{3}$. The coordinates of points on a plane are real numbers. Any real numbers a and b satisfy exactly one of the relations

$$a < b, \qquad a = b, \qquad a > b.$$

Thus when points (x, y) on the coordinate plane are considered relative to the line of points $\left(x, 2x - \frac{1}{3}\right)$, exactly one of the relations

$$y < 2x - \frac{1}{3}, \qquad y = 2x - \frac{1}{3}, \qquad y > 2x - \frac{1}{3}$$

must be satisfied. If $y < 2x - \frac{1}{3}$, then $6x - 3y - 1 > 0$; and the point (x, y) is in the region below the line $y = 2x - \frac{1}{3}$ (Figure 7-4). If $y = 2x - \frac{1}{3}$, the point is on the line. If $y > 2x - \frac{1}{3}$, then $6x - 3y - 1 < 0$; and the point is above the line. The regions below and above the line are both called half-planes. Any line divides a plane into two **half-planes** for which the line is the common edge. Notice that the line $6x - 3y - 1 = 0$ is shown as a dashed line in the figure since the points of the line do not belong to the graph of either half-plane.

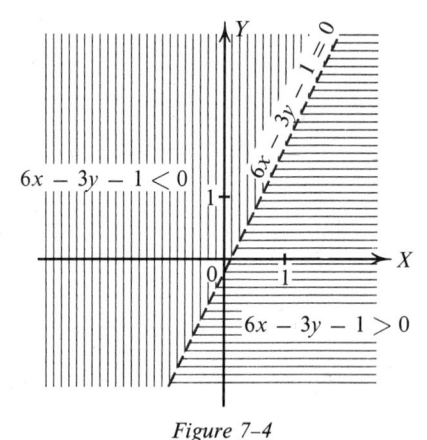

Figure 7-4

335

LINEAR AND QUADRATIC EXPRESSIONS

In general, any line $Ax + By + C = 0$ divides the plane into two half-planes on each of which the expression $Ax + By + C$ has constant sign; that is, $Ax + By + C < 0$ for all (x, y) in one half-plane and $Ax + By + C > 0$ for all (x, y) in the other half-plane. To identify the particular half-plane on which a given inequality is satisfied, simply test one of the points from one of the half-planes by substituting the coordinates of the point in the expression under consideration. For example, in Figure 7–4 the expression $6x - 3y - 1$ is positive in one half-plane and negative in the other. Since $6(0) - 3(0) - 1$ is negative, $6x - 3y - 1$ is negative in the half-plane which includes the origin.

Any inequality of one of the forms

$$Ax + By + C < 0, \qquad Ax + By + C > 0 \qquad (7)$$

where A and B are not both zero is a **linear inequality in x and y**. The graph of any linear inequality is a half-plane. As in Example 4, linear inequalities may be used to graph other types of statements.

Example 4. Graph: $|x| + |y| < 1$.

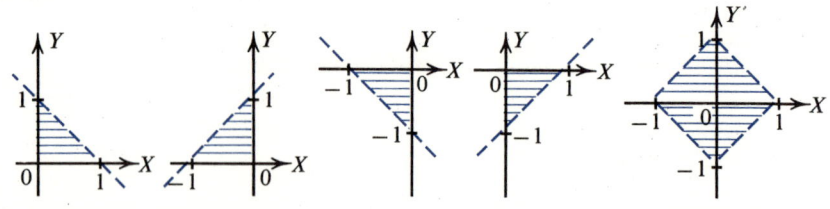

Figure 7–5   *Figure 7–6*   *Figure 7–7*   *Figure 7–8*   *Figure 7–9*

As in § 1–4, $|x| = x$ if $0 \leq x$ and $|x| = -x$ if $0 > x$; $|y| = y$ if $0 \leq y$ and $|y| = -y$ if $0 > y$. Then in the first quadrant the inequality $|x| + |y| < 1$ may be expressed as $x + y < 1$ and has as its graph that portion of the half-plane below the line $x + y = 1$. (See Figure 7–5.)

In the second quadrant the given inequality has the form $-x + y < 1$ and has as its graph that portion of the half-plane below the line $-x + y = 1$. (See Figure 7–6.)

In the third quadrant the given inequality has the form $-x - y < 1$, that is, $x + y > -1$; and has as its graph that portion of the half-plane above the line $x + y = -1$. (See Figure 7–7.)

In the fourth quadrant the given inequality has the form $x - y < 1$ and has as its graph that portion of the half-plane above the line $x - y = 1$. (See Figure 7–8.)

The union of the graphs in the four quadrants is the desired graph. (See Figure 7–9.)

§ 7-2 GRAPHS OF LINEAR RELATIONS

Example 5. Graph: $|x| \leq 2$.

If $x \geq 0$, then the relation $|x| \leq 2$ may be expressed in the form $x \leq 2$ with points on the left of or on the line $x = 2$ as points of its graph. If $x < 0$, then the given relation becomes $-x \leq 2$; that is, $x \geq -2$; with points on the right of or on the line $x = -2$ as points of its graph (Figure 7-10). Note that the lines $x = 2$ and $x = -2$ are shown as solid lines in the figure since the points of those lines are part of the desired graph.

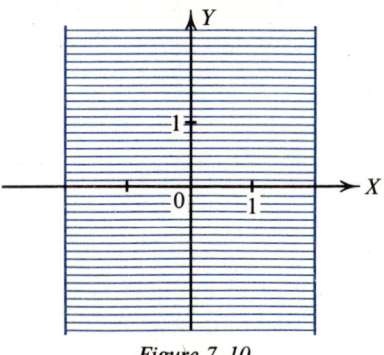

Figure 7-10

TEST YOURSELF

1. Express the equation $2x - y + 1 = 0$ as a set of ordered pairs of real numbers in the form $\{(x, f(x))\}$ and also in the form $\{(g(y), y)\}$.

Graph:

2. $2x - y + 1 = 0$.
3. $x - y < 0$.
4. $8x + 2y - 5 > 0$.
5. $1 - 2x < y - 5$.

EXERCISES

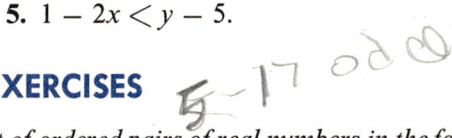

Express each equation as a set of ordered pairs of real numbers in the form $\{(x, f(x))\}$ and also in the form $\{(g(y), y)\}$:

1. $x + 2y = 4$.
2. $2x + 3y = 6$.
3. $3x - 5y = 15$.
4. $4x - 3y = 12$.

In Exercises 5 through 18 graph:

5. $x > 0$.
6. $y - x \geq 0$.
7. $2x - 3y > x - y + 1$.
8. $x - 5y + 3 \geq 0$.
9. $|x| \leq 1$.
10. $|y| \geq 2$.

• • •

11. $|2x - y| > 0$.
12. $|2x - y| = 1$.
13. $|x - y| = 2$.
14. $|3x - 2y| = 6$.
15. $\sqrt{x - y + 5} \geq 0$.
16. $\sqrt{2x - y + 4} \geq 0$.
17. $\sqrt{2x - 3y + 6} \leq 0$.
• 18. $|x + y| \leq |x| + |y|$.

337

LINEAR AND QUADRATIC EXPRESSIONS

• **19.** Prove that the slope of any linear function $Ax + By + C = 0$, $AB \neq 0$, is the reciprocal of the slope of the inverse of the function (§ 1-9).

• **20.** Prove that the distance from the point (x_1, y_1) to the line $By + C = 0$ and to the line $Ax + C = 0$ may be expressed in the form

$$\left| \frac{Ax_1 + By_1 + C}{\sqrt{A^2 + B^2}} \right|.$$

Assume that the distance from (x_1, y_1) to the line $Ax + By + C = 0$ may be expressed in this same form and find the distance from:

(a) $(0, 0)$ to $5x - 12y + 13 = 0$; (b) $(1, 2)$ to $4x - 3y + 8 = 0$;
(c) $(2, 3)$ to $x + 2y - 3 = 0$; (d) $(2, 1)$ to $2x + y - 5 = 0$.

§ 7-3 Systems of linear relations

Any linear equation in one variable with real numbers as coefficients is satisfied by one and only one real number; if $ax + b = 0$ and $a \neq 0$, then $x = -\frac{b}{a}$. In other words, the *solution set* of the equation consists of a single number; the equation has one real number as a **root**.

Any linear equation in two variables with real numbers as coefficients has a line as its graph and is satisfied by infinitely many ordered pairs of real numbers. If $Ax + By + C = 0$ and A and B are not both zero, then either $B \neq 0$ or $B = 0$ and $A \neq 0$. If $B \neq 0$, then $y = -\frac{A}{B}x - \frac{C}{B}$; and the equation is satisfied by all ordered pairs of real numbers of the form $\left(x, -\frac{A}{B}x - \frac{C}{B}\right)$. If $B = 0$, then $A \neq 0$, $x = -\frac{C}{A}$, and the equation is satisfied by all ordered pairs of the form $\left(-\frac{C}{A}, y\right)$.

Two linear equations in two variables are each satisfied by infinitely many ordered pairs of real numbers and often both may be satisfied by an ordered pair of real numbers. For example, $x + y = 5$ is satisfied by $\{(x, 5 - x)\}$; $x - y = 1$ is satisfied by $\{(x, x - 1)\}$. When $5 - x = x - 1$; that is, when $x = 3$, the ordered pair $(3, 2)$ belongs to both solution sets. Thus $(3, 2)$ satisfies both equations. When solutions are sought which satisfy two or more equations at the same time, the equations are called a **system of equations** (or, a **system of simultaneous equations**). It is customary to use a single large brace to show that the equations are to be considered together as a system. For example,

$$\begin{cases} x + y = 5 \\ x - y = 1 \end{cases}$$

§ 7-3 SYSTEMS OF LINEAR RELATIONS

others. If the equations of a system are not linearly dependent, they are **linearly independent**. The equations of the system (9) are linearly independent; the equations of the system (11) also are linearly independent. The equations of the following system are linearly dependent:

$$\begin{cases} x + y = 5 \\ 2x + 2y = 10 \end{cases} \qquad \begin{pmatrix} 1 & 1 & 5 \\ 2 & 2 & 10 \end{pmatrix}. \qquad (12)$$

If we try to solve the system, we obtain

$$\begin{cases} x + y = 5 \\ 0 = 0 \end{cases} \qquad \begin{pmatrix} 1 & 1 & 5 \\ 0 & 0 & 0 \end{pmatrix}$$

which indicates that the second equation is superfluous in that it does not contain any information that is not given by the first equation. Notice that both the equations in (12) have the same line as their graph. In general, linearly dependent equations in a system of two linear equations in two variables have coincident lines as their graphs.

Consider the system

$$\begin{cases} 2x - y = 5 \\ x + 2y = 5 \\ 3x + y = 10 \end{cases} \qquad \begin{pmatrix} 2 & -1 & 5 \\ 1 & 2 & 5 \\ 3 & 1 & 10 \end{pmatrix}. \qquad (13)$$

If we try to solve the system, we may obtain by subtracting the sum of the first two equations from the third

$$\begin{cases} 2x - y = 5 \\ x + 2y = 5 \\ 0 = 0 \end{cases} \qquad \begin{pmatrix} 2 & -1 & 5 \\ 1 & 2 & 5 \\ 0 & 0 & 0 \end{pmatrix}.$$

This system (or matrix) indicates that the third equation is superfluous and that the three equations are linearly dependent. Notice that the third equation is equal to the sum of the other two. Notice also that the graph of the third equation contains the point of intersection of the graphs of the other two equations. On a plane, the equation of any line through the intersection of two given lines is linearly dependent upon the equations of the given lines. We use this property of the lines through a point when we solve a given system of equations in two variables by finding the equations of the lines which are through the point and parallel to the coordinate axes.

A system such as (13) which has three linearly dependent linear equations in two variables may be solved if and only if it includes two consistent linearly independent equations. To solve such a system drop one of the equations such that the remaining two equations are linearly independent and solve the system of two equations. The system (13) may be

LINEAR AND QUADRATIC EXPRESSIONS

solved by dropping any one of the given equations and solving the system which contains the remaining two equations. Since the graphs of the three original equations intersect in one and only one point, that point will be the graph of the solution obtained regardless of which two equations are used to find the solution.

Consistent and inconsistent systems, linearly dependent and linearly independent sets of equations, and the solution of a system of two linear equations in two variables may be summarized in terms of a general system:

$$\begin{cases} a_1x + b_1y = c_1 \\ a_2x + b_2y = c_2 \end{cases} \qquad \begin{pmatrix} a_1 & b_1 & c_1 \\ a_2 & b_2 & c_2 \end{pmatrix}. \qquad (14)$$

If we try to solve the system, we obtain

$$\begin{cases} a_1b_2x + b_1b_2y = b_2c_1 \\ a_2b_1x + b_1b_2y = b_1c_2 \end{cases} \qquad \begin{pmatrix} a_1b_2 & b_1b_2 & b_2c_1 \\ a_2b_1 & b_1b_2 & b_1c_2 \end{pmatrix}$$

$$\begin{cases} (a_1b_2 - a_2b_1)x \qquad\qquad = b_2c_1 - b_1c_2 \\ a_2b_1x + b_1b_2y = b_1c_2 \end{cases} \qquad \begin{pmatrix} a_1b_2 - a_2b_1 & 0 & b_2c_1 - b_1c_2 \\ a_2b_1 & b_1b_2 & b_1c_2 \end{pmatrix}.$$

If $a_1b_2 - a_2b_1 = 0$ and $b_2c_1 - b_1c_2 = 0$ as in the system (12), then either one of the equations may be considered superfluous since the equations of the system are linearly dependent. In this case the system is composed of consistent, linearly dependent equations.

If $a_1b_2 - a_2b_1 = 0$ and $b_2c_1 - b_1c_2 \neq 0$ as in the system (11), then the system is composed of inconsistent, linearly independent equations.

To solve for x we need to divide by $(a_1b_2 - a_2b_1)$. This is possible if and only if $a_1b_2 - a_2b_1 \neq 0$. The system (14) is composed of consistent, linearly independent equations if and only if $a_1b_2 - a_2b_1 \neq 0$. If the system is composed of linearly independent equations and is consistent, then we have

$$x = \frac{b_2c_1 - b_1c_2}{a_1b_2 - a_2b_1}.$$

The value for y may be obtained in a similar manner,

$$y = \frac{a_1c_2 - a_2c_1}{a_1b_2 - a_2b_1}.$$

These values for x and y in the solution of the system (14) may be obtained directly from the matrix of the system by means of determinants. Any square matrix (that is, any matrix with the same number of rows and

§ 7-3 SYSTEMS OF LINEAR RELATIONS

columns) has an associated polynomial or number called its **determinant**. In particular, the determinant of any matrix of two rows and two columns $\begin{pmatrix} p & q \\ s & t \end{pmatrix}$ is written as $\begin{vmatrix} p & q \\ s & t \end{vmatrix}$ and has value $pt - qs$. Notice that the value of a **second order determinant** is equal to the product of the elements in the upper left and lower right corners minus the product of the elements in the upper right and lower left corners:

$$\begin{vmatrix} p & q \\ s & t \end{vmatrix} = pt - qs.$$

Example 2. Evaluate: $\begin{vmatrix} 3 & -5 \\ 1 & 2 \end{vmatrix}$.

$$\begin{vmatrix} 3 & -5 \\ 1 & 2 \end{vmatrix} = (3)(2) - (-5)(1) = 6 + 5 = 11.$$

The coefficients of the variables (that is, the first two columns of the matrix) of the system (14) may be used to form a determinant:

$$\begin{vmatrix} a_1 & b_1 \\ a_2 & b_2 \end{vmatrix}. \qquad (15)$$

This determinant has the value $a_1b_2 - a_2b_1$ and is called the **determinant of the coefficients**. As we have noted, this determinant of the system is different from zero if and only if the system (14) is composed of consistent, linearly independent equations. Notice that the determinants of the coefficients for (11) and (12) are both

$$\begin{vmatrix} 1 & 1 \\ 2 & 2 \end{vmatrix}$$

and have the value zero. The equations of these systems do not have the two properties of consistency and linear independence; the equations of the system (11) are not consistent and the equations of the system (12) are not linearly independent.

The determinant (15) is the denominator of the fractions which are obtained as the values for x and y in the solution of the system (14). The numerators for these fractions for x and y are respectively

$$b_2c_1 - b_1c_2 \qquad \text{and} \qquad a_1c_2 - a_2c_1$$

and may be expressed as the determinants

$$\begin{vmatrix} c_1 & b_1 \\ c_2 & b_2 \end{vmatrix} \qquad \text{and} \qquad \begin{vmatrix} a_1 & c_1 \\ a_2 & c_2 \end{vmatrix}.$$

LINEAR AND QUADRATIC EXPRESSIONS

In each case the column of coefficients of the particular variable under consideration has been replaced by the column of constant terms from the matrix (14). In general, any system of equations (14) with determinant of the coefficients different from zero has the solution

$$x = \frac{\begin{vmatrix} c_1 & b_1 \\ c_2 & b_2 \end{vmatrix}}{\begin{vmatrix} a_1 & b_1 \\ a_2 & b_2 \end{vmatrix}}, \quad y = \frac{\begin{vmatrix} a_1 & c_1 \\ a_2 & c_2 \end{vmatrix}}{\begin{vmatrix} a_1 & b_1 \\ a_2 & b_2 \end{vmatrix}}. \tag{16}$$

The rows and columns of the matrix (14)

$$\begin{pmatrix} a_1 & b_1 & c_1 \\ a_2 & b_2 & c_2 \end{pmatrix}$$

may be selected to form three *second order determinants* (that is, three determinants of matrices of two rows and two columns):

$$\begin{vmatrix} a_1 & b_1 \\ a_2 & b_2 \end{vmatrix}, \quad \begin{vmatrix} b_1 & c_1 \\ b_2 & c_2 \end{vmatrix}, \quad \begin{vmatrix} a_1 & c_1 \\ a_2 & c_2 \end{vmatrix}.$$

If at least one of these determinants has a value different from zero, the matrix (14) has **rank 2**; if all three of these determinants equal zero and at least one of the elements of the matrix is different from zero, the matrix has **rank 1**. For example, the matrix (11) has rank 1.

Any system of two linear equations in two variables

$$\begin{cases} a_1x + b_1y = c_1 \\ a_2x + b_2y = c_2 \end{cases}$$

has a matrix (14) sometimes called the *augmented matrix* and a *matrix of the coefficients* $\begin{pmatrix} a_1 & b_1 \\ a_2 & b_2 \end{pmatrix}$. If these two matrices have the same rank, the system is consistent. There are infinitely many elements of the solution set (the lines coincide, the equations are linearly dependent) if both matrices have rank 1. There is a unique solution (the equations are linearly independent) as in (16) if both matrices have rank 2. If the two matrices have different ranks, the system is inconsistent as in the case of (11).

TEST YOURSELF

Evaluate:

1. $\begin{vmatrix} 2 & 4 \\ 3 & 9 \end{vmatrix}.$
2. $\begin{vmatrix} 2 & 0 \\ 3 & 0 \end{vmatrix}.$

§7-3 SYSTEMS OF LINEAR RELATIONS

Tell whether or not each system is **(a)** *consistent;* **(b)** *composed of linearly independent equations.* **(c)** *Solve the consistent systems of linearly independent equations by matrices.*

3. $\begin{cases} x + 3y = 10 \\ 3x - y = 0. \end{cases}$ 4. $\begin{cases} x + y = 5 \\ x + y = 3. \end{cases}$

EXERCISES

Evaluate:

1. $\begin{vmatrix} 3 & 5 \\ 4 & 6 \end{vmatrix}.$ 3. $\begin{vmatrix} -8 & -6 \\ 5 & 3 \end{vmatrix}.$ 5. $\begin{vmatrix} 0.5 & 6 \\ 0.1 & 2 \end{vmatrix}.$

2. $\begin{vmatrix} 6 & 8 \\ 7 & 10 \end{vmatrix}.$ 4. $\begin{vmatrix} \frac{1}{2} & 4 \\ \frac{1}{4} & 6 \end{vmatrix}.$ 6. $\begin{vmatrix} 6.3 & 0.7 \\ 0.6 & 1.4 \end{vmatrix}.$

Tell whether or not each system is **(a)** *consistent;* **(b)** *composed of linearly independent equations.* **(c)** *Solve the consistent systems of linearly independent equations by matrices.*

7. $\begin{cases} x + y = 9 \\ x - y = 1. \end{cases}$ 11. $\begin{cases} 4x + 3y = 11 \\ x - 5y = 3. \end{cases}$

8. $\begin{cases} x - 3y = 7 \\ 2x - 6y = 14. \end{cases}$ 12. $\begin{cases} 4x + 5y = 11 \\ 2x - y = 7. \end{cases}$

9. $\begin{cases} 3x - 2y = 5 \\ -x + \frac{2}{3}y = 0. \end{cases}$ 13. $\begin{cases} 2x + 4y = 6 \\ 3x + 6y = 9. \end{cases}$

10. $\begin{cases} 3x + 2y = 20 \\ x - 3y = 14. \end{cases}$ 14. $\begin{cases} 3x - 4y = 6 \\ 5x + 2y = 15. \end{cases}$

• • •

Find the value of k for which the system is inconsistent:

15. $\begin{cases} 2x - y = 5 \\ x + ky = 6. \end{cases}$ 17. $\begin{cases} 2x + 3y = 5 \\ x - ky = 2. \end{cases}$

16. $\begin{cases} x + 2y = 13 \\ kx + y = 5. \end{cases}$ 18. $\begin{cases} x + y = 7 \\ kx + ky = 5. \end{cases}$

Solve graphically:

19. $\begin{cases} x + y < 4 \\ x > 0 \\ y > 0. \end{cases}$ 20. $\begin{cases} x - y < 0 \\ x + 3 > 0 \\ y - 2 < 0. \end{cases}$

347

LINEAR AND QUADRATIC EXPRESSIONS

- 21. $\begin{cases} x + 2y \leq 4 \\ 2y \not< 1 \\ 2x \neq 6. \end{cases}$
- 22. $\begin{cases} |x| > 2 \\ |x| \not> 3 \\ |y| \not> 1. \end{cases}$

§ 7-4 Linear equations in several variables

Any equation of the form
$$Ax = B, A \neq 0$$
is linear in one variable and has a unique solution $\frac{B}{A}$. Any equation of the form
$$Ax + By = C, A^2 + B^2 \neq 0$$
is linear in two variables and has infinitely many elements in its solution set. A system of two linear equations in two variables may have a unique solution. Any equation of the form
$$Ax + By + Cz = D, \text{ where } A^2 + B^2 + C^2 \neq 0$$
is linear in three variables, and a system of three such equations may have a unique solution. In general, for any positive integer n an equation of the form
$$A_1x_1 + A_2x_2 + \cdots + A_nx_n = B$$
where at least one of the coefficients $A_j \neq 0$ is linear in n variables, and a system of n such equations may have a unique solution.

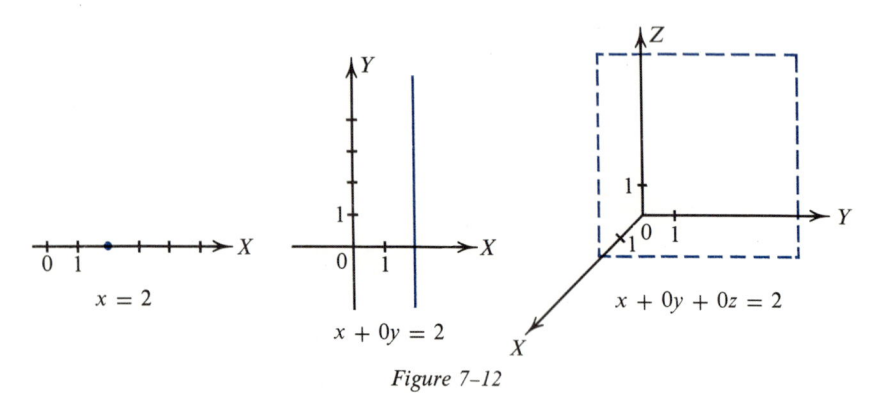

Figure 7-12

An equation such as $x = 2$ may be considered as being in any one of the forms
$$x = 2, \quad x + 0y = 2, \quad x + 0y + 0z = 2,$$

§ 7-4 LINEAR EQUATIONS IN SEVERAL VARIABLES

and in general
$$x + 0x_2 + 0x_3 + \cdots + 0x_n = 2.$$

The graph of the equation (Figure 7-12) and thus the solution set which the graph represents depends upon the form in which the equation is considered.

The methods introduced in § 7-3 may be extended to obtain methods for solving systems of linear equations in several variables. For example, the matrix solution of a system of equations in several variables follows the same steps as for two variables.

Example 1. Solve by matrices: $\begin{cases} 2x - y + z = 2 \\ x + y - 2z = 7 \\ 2x + 3y + z = -2. \end{cases}$

Note that the variables are in the same order in each equation and the constant terms are on the right. The matrix of the system is

$$\begin{pmatrix} 2 & -1 & 1 & 2 \\ 1 & 1 & -2 & 7 \\ 2 & 3 & 1 & -2 \end{pmatrix}$$

We seek a matrix such that in the first three columns there is only one element different from zero in each row and each column. Many sequences of matrices may be used including the following:

$$\begin{pmatrix} 0 & -4 & 0 & 4 \\ 1 & 1 & -2 & 7 \\ 0 & 1 & 5 & -16 \end{pmatrix}$$ We subtracted the third row from the first; then subtracted twice the second row from the third.

$$\begin{pmatrix} 0 & 1 & 0 & -1 \\ 1 & 0 & -2 & 8 \\ 0 & 0 & 5 & -15 \end{pmatrix}$$ We divided the first row by -4; then subtracted the new first row from the second row and also from the third.

$$\begin{pmatrix} 0 & 1 & 0 & -1 \\ 1 & 0 & 0 & 2 \\ 0 & 0 & 1 & -3 \end{pmatrix}$$ We divided the third row by 5; then added twice the new third row to the second.

The rows of this matrix represent the solution:
$$y = -1, x = 2, z = -3; \text{ that is, } (x, y, z) = (2, -1, -3).$$

In § 7-3 we observed that solving a system of consistent, linearly independent equations in two variables involves finding the equations of the two lines ($x = k$ and $y = n$) which are parallel to the coordinate axes and

349

LINEAR AND QUADRATIC EXPRESSIONS

pass through the common point of the graphs of the given equations. Any linear equation in three variables has a plane as its graph, and any plane in three-space has a linear equation in three variables as its equation (§ 11–10). Notice that the solution of the system of three equations in Example 1 involved finding the equations (§ 1–7) of the three planes ($x = 2, y = -1$, and $z = -3$) which are parallel to the coordinate planes and pass through the common point of the graphs of the given equations.

The solution of any system of three equations in three variables whose graphs determine a unique point (k, n, t) may be visualized as finding the equations of planes ($x = k, y = n$, and $z = t$) which are parallel to the coordinate planes and pass through the common point of the graphs of the given equations. We shall not extend this interpretation for equations in more than three variables. However, the method of matrix solution may be used for any finite number of variables. Also any system which has the coordinates of one and only one point as its solution must include at least as many linearly independent equations as variables.

Example 2. Solve by matrices:
$$\begin{cases} 3x - y + z + 2w + t = 19 \\ x - 2y - z + w + t = 3 \\ 2x + z - t = 9 \\ x + y - w = -1 \\ y + z - t = 4. \end{cases}$$

The following sequence of matrices may be used:

$$\begin{pmatrix} 3 & -1 & 1 & 2 & 1 & 19 \\ 1 & -2 & -1 & 1 & 1 & 3 \\ 2 & 0 & 1 & 0 & -1 & 9 \\ 1 & 1 & 0 & -1 & 0 & -1 \\ 0 & 1 & 1 & 0 & -1 & 4 \end{pmatrix}$$ Be sure that the variables correspond to columns and the equations to rows.

$$\begin{pmatrix} 0 & -4 & 1 & 5 & 1 & 22 \\ 0 & -3 & -1 & 2 & 1 & 4 \\ 0 & -2 & 1 & 2 & -1 & 11 \\ 1 & 1 & 0 & -1 & 0 & -1 \\ 0 & 1 & 1 & 0 & -1 & 4 \end{pmatrix}$$ We subtracted three times the fourth row from the first; the fourth row from the second; and twice the fourth row from the third.

$$\begin{pmatrix} 0 & 0 & -1 & 1 & 3 & 0 \\ 0 & 0 & 2 & 2 & -2 & 16 \\ 0 & 0 & 3 & 2 & -3 & 19 \\ 1 & 0 & -1 & -1 & 1 & -5 \\ 0 & 1 & 1 & 0 & -1 & 4 \end{pmatrix}$$ We subtracted twice the third row from the first; added three times the fifth row to the second; added twice the fifth row to the third; and subtracted the fifth row from the fourth.

350

§ 7-4   LINEAR EQUATIONS IN SEVERAL VARIABLES

$$\begin{pmatrix} 0 & 0 & -1 & 1 & 3 & 0 \\ 0 & 0 & 0 & 4 & 4 & 16 \\ 0 & 0 & 0 & 5 & 6 & 19 \\ 1 & 0 & 0 & -2 & -2 & -5 \\ 0 & 1 & 0 & 1 & 2 & 4 \end{pmatrix}$$ We added twice the first row to the second; added three times the first row to the third; subtracted the first row from the fourth; and added the first row to the fifth.

$$\begin{pmatrix} 0 & 0 & -1 & 0 & 2 & -4 \\ 0 & 0 & 0 & 1 & 1 & 4 \\ 0 & 0 & 0 & 0 & 1 & -1 \\ 1 & 0 & 0 & 0 & 0 & 3 \\ 0 & 1 & 0 & 0 & 1 & 0 \end{pmatrix}$$ We divided the second row by four; subtracted the new second row from the first and fifth; subtracted five times the new second row from the third; and added twice the new second row to the fourth.

$$\begin{pmatrix} 0 & 0 & 1 & 0 & 0 & 2 \\ 0 & 0 & 0 & 1 & 0 & 5 \\ 0 & 0 & 0 & 0 & 1 & -1 \\ 1 & 0 & 0 & 0 & 0 & 3 \\ 0 & 1 & 0 & 0 & 0 & 1 \end{pmatrix}$$ We multiplied the first row by negative one; added twice the third row to the new first row; subtracted the third row from the second; and subtracted the third row from the fifth.

rows of this matrix represent the solution: $z = 2, w = 5, t = -1$, 3, $y = 1$; that is,

$$(x, y, z, w, t) = (3, 1, 2, 5, -1).$$

The method of determinants may also be extended for systems of equations in several variables. However in this section we shall consider this method only for systems of three equations in three variables. For these we shall need to find the value of determinants of three rows and three columns; that is, **third order determinants.**

Any determinant of the third order has the form

$$\begin{vmatrix} a_1 & b_1 & c_1 \\ a_2 & b_2 & c_2 \\ a_3 & b_3 & c_3 \end{vmatrix}. \tag{17}$$

The value of this determinant is defined as

$$a_1 b_2 c_3 + a_3 b_1 c_2 + a_2 b_3 c_1 - a_3 b_2 c_1 - a_1 b_3 c_2 - a_2 b_1 c_3.$$

The value of a third order determinant may be remembered by a particular

LINEAR AND QUADRATIC EXPRESSIONS

pattern. Copy the first two columns on the right of the determinant, and form the products of the elements along each arrow. Consider the positive value of the products along the arrows extending downward to the right and the negative value of the products along the arrows extending upward to the right. The sum of the six terms is the value of the determinant.

$$-a_3b_2c_1 \quad -a_1b_3c_2 \quad -a_2b_1c_3$$

$$\begin{vmatrix} a_1 & b_1 & c_1 \\ a_2 & b_2 & c_2 \\ a_3 & b_3 & c_3 \end{vmatrix} \begin{matrix} a_1 & b_1 \\ a_2 & b_2 \\ a_3 & b_3 \end{matrix}$$

$$+a_1b_2c_3 \quad +a_3b_1c_2 \quad +a_2b_3c_1$$

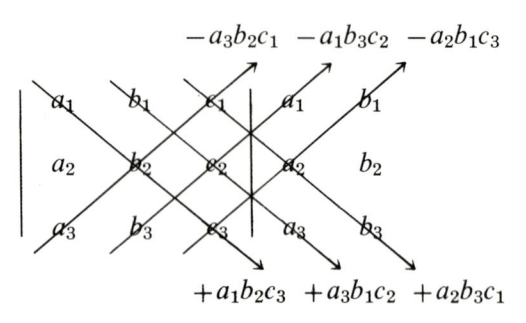

Example 3. Evaluate the determinant: $\begin{vmatrix} 2 & 1 & 3 \\ 4 & -2 & 1 \\ -2 & 3 & 2 \end{vmatrix}$

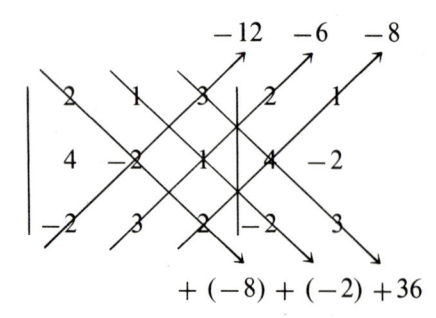

$$-12 \quad -6 \quad -8$$

$$+(-8) + (-2) + 36$$

Hence the value of the determinant is

$$(-8) + (-2) + 36 - 12 - 6 - 8 = 0.$$

The expansion of a general second order determinant has 2! (that is, 2) terms and may be identified in terms of diagonals of the square array (§ 7–3). The expansion of a general third order determinant has 3! (that is, 6) terms and may be identified in terms of diagonals as represented by the arrows in Example 3. The expansion of a general determinant of order four has 4! (that is, 24) terms and *cannot* be identified in terms of

§ 7-4 LINEAR EQUATIONS IN SEVERAL VARIABLES

ordinary diagonals. The method involving diagonals does not hold for determinants of order greater than three. The expansion of determinants of order greater than three is considered in § 12–5.

Any system of three linear equations in three variables may be expressed in the form

$$\begin{cases} a_1x + b_1y + c_1z = d_1 \\ a_2x + b_2y + c_2z = d_2 \\ a_3x + b_3y + c_3z = d_3. \end{cases} \qquad (18)$$

The matrix of the system (18) is

$$\begin{pmatrix} a_1 & b_1 & c_1 & d_1 \\ a_2 & b_2 & c_2 & d_2 \\ a_3 & b_3 & c_3 & d_3 \end{pmatrix} \qquad (19)$$

The matrix of the coefficients of the system (18) is

$$\begin{pmatrix} a_1 & b_1 & c_1 \\ a_2 & b_2 & c_2 \\ a_3 & b_3 & c_3 \end{pmatrix}$$

and has the determinant (17) as the determinant of the coefficients. We assume the following properties for the system (18). Notice that these properties are precisely analogous to some of those considered in § 7–3 for systems of two equations in two variables.

The system (18) is composed of consistent linearly independent equations if and only if the determinant of the coefficients is different from zero.

Whenever the determinant of the coefficients is different from zero, each variable may be expressed as a quotient of determinants with determinant of the coefficients as denominator and the determinant in the numerator obtained from the determinant of the coefficients by replacing the column of coefficients of the particular variable under consideration by the column of constant terms (fourth column) of the matrix (19). This method of solution by determinants is sometimes called **Cramer's Rule.**

Example 4. Solve by determinants: $\begin{cases} x + 2y - z = 4 \\ 2x - y + 3z = 3 \\ 7x - 2y + 4z = 7. \end{cases}$

The determinant of the coefficients may be evaluated:

$$\begin{vmatrix} 1 & 2 & -1 \\ 2 & -1 & 3 \\ 7 & -2 & 4 \end{vmatrix} = -4 + 42 + 4 - 7 - (-6) - 16 = 25.$$

353

LINEAR AND QUADRATIC EXPRESSIONS

Then solving for the particular variables:

$$x = \frac{\begin{vmatrix} 4 & 2 & -1 \\ 3 & -1 & 3 \\ 7 & -2 & 4 \end{vmatrix}}{25} = \frac{(-16) + 42 + 6 - 7 - (-24) - 24}{25}$$

$$= \frac{25}{25} = 1;$$

$$y = \frac{\begin{vmatrix} 1 & 4 & -1 \\ 2 & 3 & 3 \\ 7 & 7 & 4 \end{vmatrix}}{25} = \frac{12 + 84 + (-14) - (-21) - 21 - 32}{25}$$

$$= \frac{50}{25} = 2;$$

$$z = \frac{\begin{vmatrix} 1 & 2 & 4 \\ 2 & -1 & 3 \\ 7 & -2 & 7 \end{vmatrix}}{25} = \frac{(-7) + 42 + (-16) - (-28) - (-6) - 28}{25}$$

$$= \frac{25}{25} = 1.$$

Thus $(x, y, z) = (1, 2, 1)$.

TEST YOURSELF

1. Solve by matrices: $\begin{cases} x + y + z = 4 \\ 2x - 3y - z = 1 \\ x + 2y + 2z = 5. \end{cases}$

2. Solve the system in Exercise 1 by determinants.

EXERCISES

Solve by matrices:

1. $\begin{cases} x + 2y + z = 6 \\ 3x + 4y - z = 5 \\ 9x - 2y - z = 14. \end{cases}$

2. $\begin{cases} 12y - z = -15 \\ 3x - y = 7 \\ 4x - 3z = -1. \end{cases}$

3. $\begin{cases} x + 2y = 14 - 3z \\ 2x + y + 3z = 4 \\ 3(x + y) + 7 = -z. \end{cases}$

4. $\begin{cases} ax + by + az = 2a \\ bx + by = b \\ ax + by + z = a + 1. \end{cases}$

NOTE: Assume that the determinant of the coefficients of the system in Ex. 4 is different from zero.

§ 7-5 QUADRATIC FUNCTIONS OF ONE VARIABLE

5 through 8. Solve the systems in Exercises 1 through 4 by determinants.

● ● ●

9. The sum of the digits of a three-digit integer is 19; if the digits are reversed, the new number formed is 594 greater than the original number; 100 times the hundreds' digit plus the tens' digit is equal to 10 times the units' digit plus 217. Find the number.

10. An integer consists of three digits whose sum is 6. The middle digit is one-half the sum of the other two digits. The number is increased by 198 if the digits are reversed. Find the number.

11. When weighed in water, gold appears to lose $\frac{4}{77}$ of its weight in air. When weighed in water, silver appears to lose $\frac{2}{21}$ of its weight in air. An alloy of gold and silver that weighs 18 ounces in air appears to weigh only $16\frac{16}{21}$ ounces in water. How much gold and how much silver are in the alloy?

12. Hieron, King of Syracuse, had a crown that weighed 20 pounds. The workman who made it claimed that it was of pure gold, but King Hieron suspected that it was an alloy of gold and silver. His friend Archimedes, the greatest mathematician of antiquity, weighed it in water and found that it appeared to weigh only $18\frac{3}{4}$ pounds. Assume that the king's suspicions were correct, and determine how much silver the crown contained. (Use the data in Exercise 11.)

§ 7-5 Quadratic functions of one variable

An expression of the form

$$ax^2 + bx + c, \, a \neq 0 \quad (20)$$

is a **quadratic function** of x. If the constants a, b, and c are restricted to the set of real numbers, then the function is a **real quadratic function,** and unless otherwise specified we shall assume that x is a real variable (that is, that x represents a real number).

The graph of the equation

$$y = ax^2 + bx + c$$

is often called the graph of the quadratic function (20) and is defined to

LINEAR AND QUADRATIC EXPRESSIONS

be a *parabola* (§ 7–7). Notice that by *completing the square*

$$ax^2 + bx + c = a\left(x^2 + \frac{b}{a}x + \frac{b^2}{4a^2}\right) + c - \frac{b^2}{4a}$$

$$= a\left(x + \frac{b}{2a}\right)^2 + \frac{4ac - b^2}{4a}$$

Thus if $a > 0$, $y = \frac{4ac - b^2}{4a}$ when $x = -\frac{b}{2a}$ and $y > \frac{4ac - b^2}{4a}$ for all other values of x. That is, the function takes on its minimum value $\frac{4ac - b^2}{4a}$ when $x = -\frac{b}{2a}$; the point $\left(-\frac{b}{2a}, \frac{4ac - b^2}{4a}\right)$ is the **minimum point** of the graph of the function (Figure 7–13).

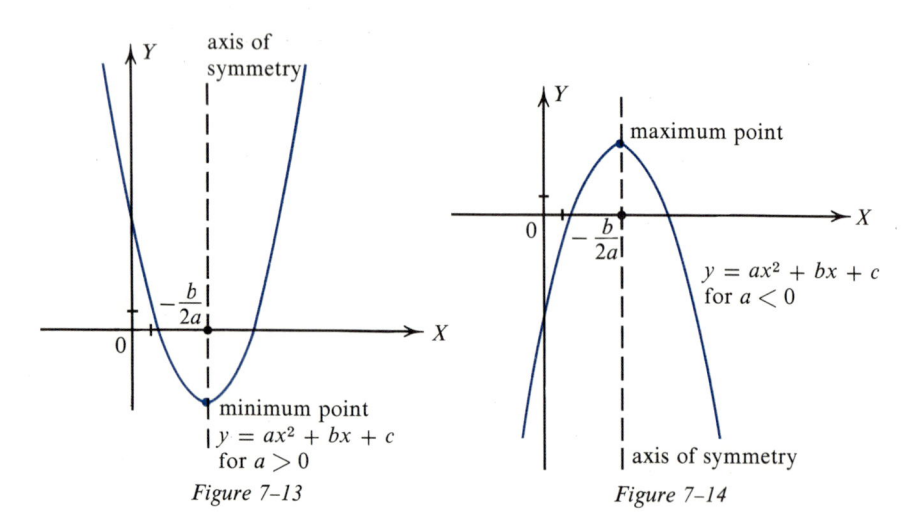

Figure 7–13

Figure 7–14

If $a < 0$, $y = \frac{4ac - b^2}{4a}$ when $x = -\frac{b}{2a}$ and $y < \frac{4ac - b^2}{4a}$ for all other values of x. That is, the function takes on its maximum value $\frac{4ac - b^2}{4a}$ when $x = -\frac{b}{2a}$; the point $\left(-\frac{b}{2a}, \frac{4ac - b^2}{4a}\right)$ is the **maximum point** of the graph of the function (Figure 7–14).

In both Figure 7–13 and Figure 7–14 the graph has the line $x = -\frac{b}{2a}$ as an axis of symmetry (§ 1–9). The y-coordinate of the point at which the curve crosses the y-axis is called the **y-intercept**. The x-coordinates of the point or points, if they exist, at which the curve crosses the x-axis are called the **x-intercepts** or the **zeros of the function**.

§ 7-5 QUADRATIC FUNCTIONS OF ONE VARIABLE

The zeros of the quadratic function (20) are the real **roots** of the quadratic equation
$$ax^2 + bx + c = 0, \; a \neq 0. \tag{21}$$
When all complex values for x are considered, the equation (21) has two linear factors and may be expressed as
$$a(x - r_1)(x - r_2) = 0$$
where by the quadratic formula
$$x = \frac{-b \pm \sqrt{b^2 - 4ac}}{2a}$$
the roots r_1 and r_2 may be expressed as
$$r_1 = \frac{-b + \sqrt{b^2 - 4ac}}{2a}, \quad r_2 = \frac{-b - \sqrt{b^2 - 4ac}}{2a}.$$

The expression $b^2 - 4ac$ is the **discriminant** of the function (20) and also of the equation (21). When the constants a, b, and c represent real numbers, the roots are:

real and equal if $b^2 - 4ac = 0$;
real and unequal if $b^2 - 4ac > 0$;
conjugate imaginary if $b^2 - 4ac < 0$.

Thus the graph of the function has at least one x-intercept if and only if $b^2 - 4ac \geq 0$.

Notice that the sum $r_1 + r_2$ of the roots of any quadratic equation (21) is $-\frac{b}{a}$; the product $r_1 r_2$ of the roots is $\frac{c}{a}$. To find the sum and product of the roots of any quadratic equation (21), write the equation in the form
$$x^2 + \frac{b}{a} x + \frac{c}{a} = 0.$$

In this form the sum of the roots is equal to the negative of the coefficient of x; the product of the roots is equal to the constant term.

Example 1. Find the sum and product of the roots of the equation:
$$3x^2 - 17x + 15 = 0.$$
The equation $3x^2 - 17x + 15 = 0$ may be written in the form:
$$x^2 - \frac{17}{3} x + 5 = 0.$$
Then, $r_1 + r_2 = \frac{17}{3}$; $r_1 r_2 = 5.$

357

LINEAR AND QUADRATIC EXPRESSIONS

Suppose that the zeros of a quadratic function (20) are -2 and 3. Then for the equation (21) $r_1 + r_2 = 1$ and $r_1 r_2 = -6$. Thus

$$y = a\left(x^2 + \frac{b}{a}x + \frac{c}{a}\right);$$

$$y = a(x^2 - x - 6).$$

The function is not determined since a may have any value different from zero. The graphs for this function when $a = 1, 2, 3, -1, -2$, and -3 are shown in Figure 7–15. Notice that for each positive value of a the point $\left(\frac{1}{2}, -\frac{25}{4}a\right)$ is the minimum point of the curve; for each negative value of a the point $\left(\frac{1}{2}, -\frac{25}{4}a\right)$ is the maximum point of the curve. The set of graphs obtained by considering different values for a is called a **family of graphs**. In Figure 7–15 the y-scale has been chosen different from the x-scale to make the graphing more convenient.

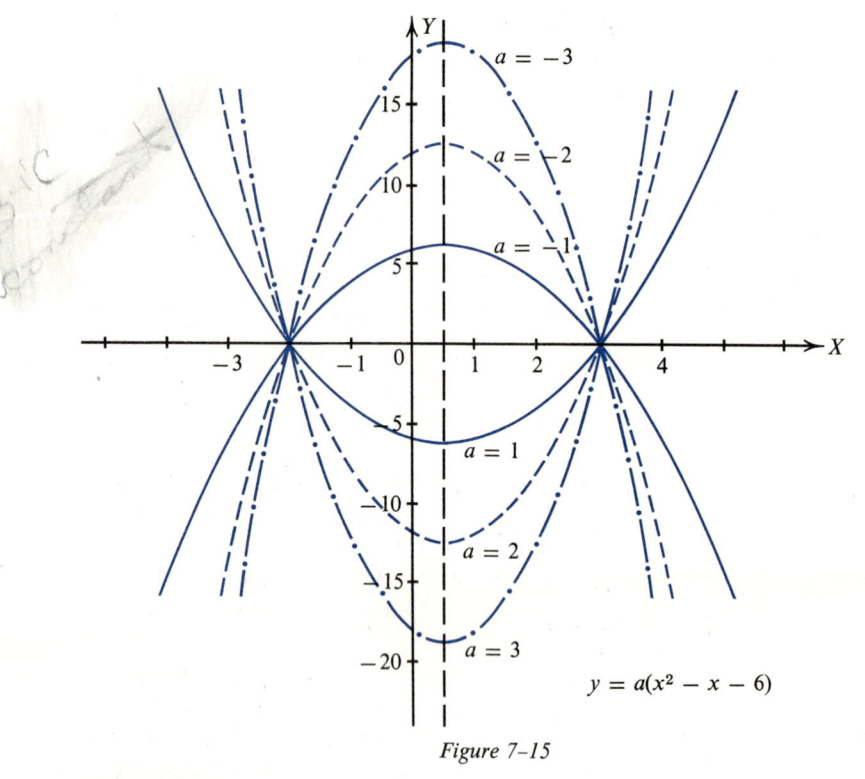

Figure 7–15

A particular graph could be selected from the family of graphs in Figure 7–15 by finding the graph which contains a specified point (x_1, y_1) where

358

§ 7-5 QUADRATIC FUNCTIONS OF ONE VARIABLE

$y_1 \neq 0$. For example, the graph through the point (5, 28) will be the graph of the quadratic equation

$$y = a(x^2 - x - 6)$$

such that $y = 28$ when $x = 5$;

$$28 = a(25 - 5 - 6) = 14a; \quad a = 2.$$

The graph containing the point (5, 28) is the graph of the equation

$$y = 2x^2 - 2x - 12.$$

We next consider the influence of the values of the constants a, b, and c on the graphs of quadratic functions (20). As in Figure 7–15, the sign of a determines whether the graph has a minimum or a maximum point. The smaller the absolute value of a, the "broader" the parabola; the larger the absolute value of a, the "narrower" the parabola. If a sequence of values of a such as 1, $\frac{1}{2}$, $\frac{1}{4}$, $\frac{1}{8}$, and so forth are taken which approach zero; then the parabolas approach the x-axis. The influence of the value of a may be observed in Figure 7–16 for the equation

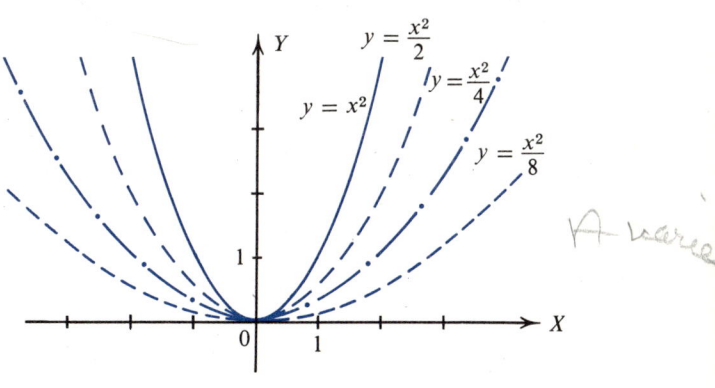

$$y = ax^2, \quad a \neq 0.$$

Figure 7–16

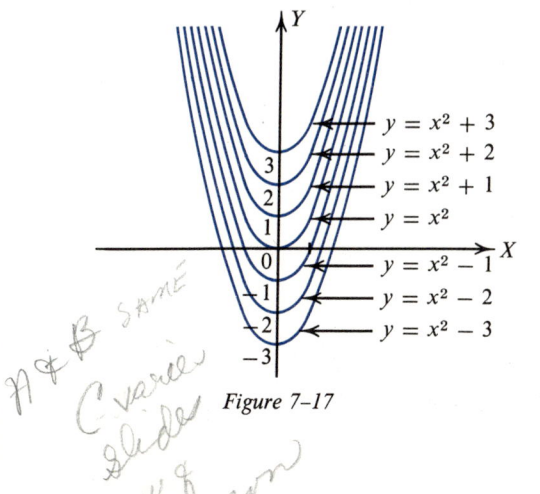

The influence of the value of c upon the graph of a quadratic function (20) may be observed by considering the graphs of the family of parabolas

$$y = x^2 + c$$

for $c = -3, -2, -1, 0, 1, 2, 3$ (Figure 7–17). Notice that c is the y-intercept of the graph and thus the graph is "raised" or "lowered" as c increases or de-

Figure 7–17

359

LINEAR AND QUADRATIC EXPRESSIONS

creases. For any quadratic function (20) a change in the value of c represents a translation (sliding) of the graph along the y-axis.

The influence of the value of b upon the graph of a quadratic function (20) is more complicated. For given values of a and c, the axis of symmetry $x = -\dfrac{b}{2a}$ depends upon the value of b and the minimum or maximum value $\dfrac{4ac - b^2}{4a}$ of the function depends upon b. The graphs for $b = -2, -1, 0, 1, 2$ of the family of parabolas

$$y = x^2 + bx$$

are shown in Figure 7-18. Notice that the y-intercept is not affected by the value of b; the minimum value of the function decreases as $|b|$ increases; for this particular family of parabolas the x-intercepts are 0 and $-b$.

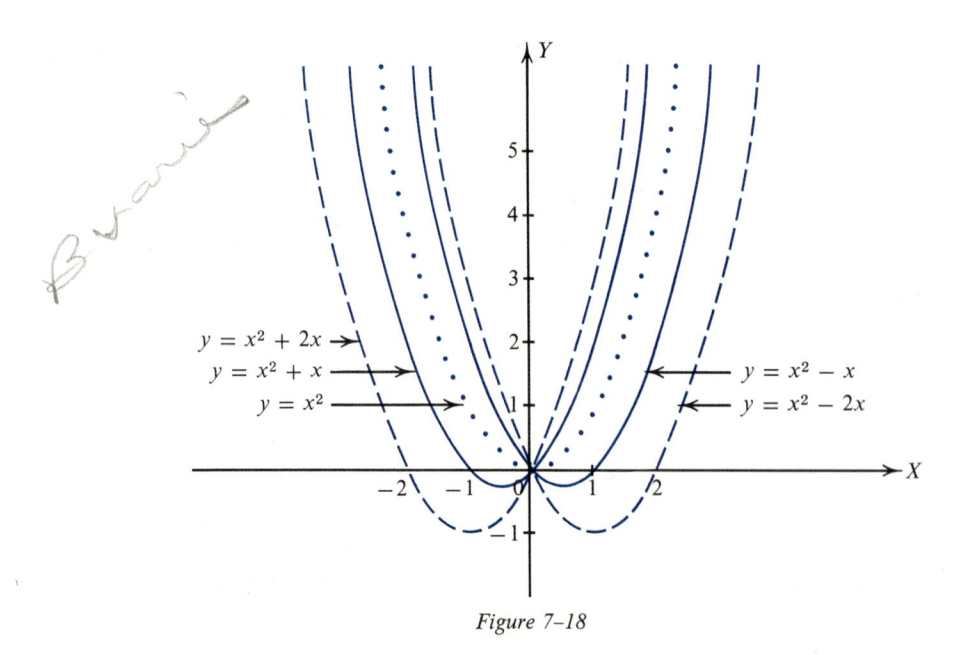

Figure 7-18

The axis of symmetry, minimum or maximum point, x-intercepts, and influences of the constants may be used in graphing any quadratic function of one variable. Usually we graph the axis of symmetry, the maximum or minimum point, and at least two pairs of points which are symmetric with respect to the axis of symmetry before sketching the curve through these points.

§ 7-5 QUADRATIC FUNCTIONS OF ONE VARIABLE

Example 2. Graph: $y = x^2 + 2x - 8$.

The axis of symmetry $x = -1$ may be found either by setting the squared term equal to zero after completing the square

$$y = (x + 1)^2 - 9$$

or by taking $a = 1$, $b = 2$, and $c = -8$ and using the formula $x = -\dfrac{b}{2a}$. The coordinates of the minimum point $(-1, -9)$ may also be obtained either from substitution in the equation or from the general form. The y-intercept is -8; the point symmetric to $(0, -8)$ with respect to the line $x = -1$ is $(-2, -8)$. The x-intercepts -4 and 2 may be obtained by setting $y = 0$ and solving the equation

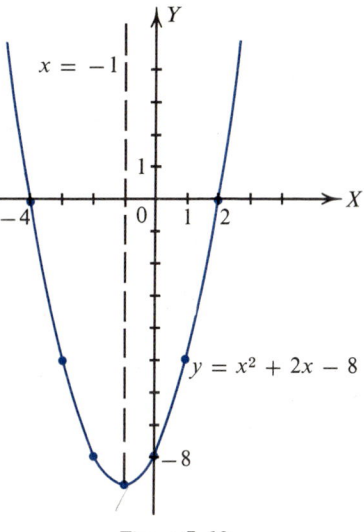

Figure 7-19

$0 = x^2 + 2x - 8$ by factoring: $(x + 4)(x - 2) = 0$; $x = -4, 2$.

Additional points may be found by substituting values for x in the given equation. For example, if $x = 3$, $y = 9 + 6 - 8 = 7$ whence $(3, 7)$ is a point of the graph. In the same manner, if $x = 1$, $y = 1 + 2 - 8 = -5$ whence $(1, -5)$ is a point of the graph. Symmetric to $(1, -5)$ with respect to the line $x = -1$ is the point $(-3, -5)$ which is also a point of the graph.

Consider the domain and the range of the function in Example 2. The domain of the function is the set of all possible values of x; that is, the set of real numbers. The range of the function is the set of all possible values for y. Since $y = (x + 1)^2 - 9$ and $(x + 1)^2 \geq 0$, we know that $y \geq -9$; that is, the range of the function is the set of real numbers greater than or equal to -9.

Example 3. State the domain and range, then graph:

$$y = 2x^2 - 4x + 3.$$

The domain is the set of real numbers. Since

$$y = 2(x^2 - 2x + 1) + 1 = 2(x - 1)^2 + 1,$$

$y \geq 1$ and the range is the set of real numbers greater than or equal to 1.

361

LINEAR AND QUADRATIC EXPRESSIONS

The axis of symmetry is $x = 1$; the minimum point is $(1, 1)$; the y-intercept is 3. The graph contains the point $(0, 3)$ and this point is symmetric to the point $(2, 3)$ with respect to the axis $x = 1$. If $x = -1$, $y = 2 + 4 + 3 = 9$. Thus $(-1, 9)$ and $(3, 9)$ are points of the graph. Note that the graph (Figure 7–20) does not have any x-intercepts.

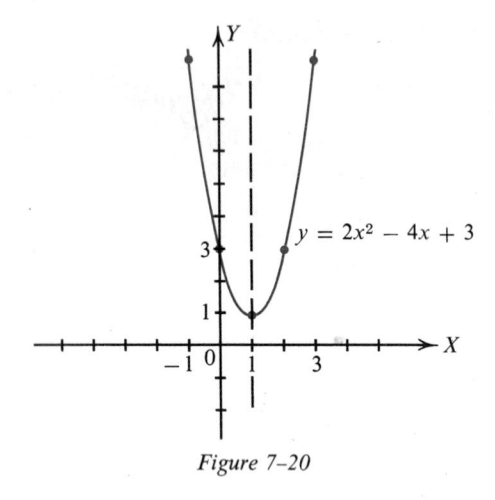

Figure 7–20

In Example 3, the graph of the equation $y - (2x^2 - 4x + 3) = 0$ divides the plane into two regions. All points such as A: $(2, 6)$ in Figure 7–21 which lie in a region above the parabola have a y-coordinate greater than the y-coordinate of a point such as P: $(2, 3)$ on the parabola where P has the same x-coordinate as A. The set of points

$$\{(x, y) \mid y - (2x^2 - 4x + 3) = 0\}$$

lies on the parabola. (See Figure 7–20 and the broken line in Figure 7–21.) The set of points

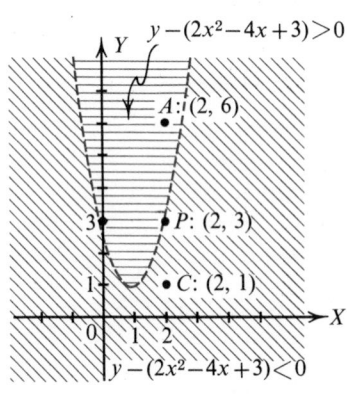

$$\{(x, y) \mid y - (2x^2 - 4x + 3) > 0\}$$

Figure 7–21

is represented graphically by the shaded region which contains the point A; these are the **interior points of the parabola**. The set of points

$$\{(x, y) \mid y - (2x^2 - 4x + 3) < 0\}$$

is represented graphically by the shaded region which contains the point C: $(2, 1)$; these are the **exterior points of the parabola**. In general, the graph of any quadratic function (20) divides the plane into two regions on each of which the expression $y - (ax^2 + bx + c)$ has constant sign. The regions may be identified by testing any point from one of the regions in the expression.

§ 7-5 QUADRATIC FUNCTIONS OF ONE VARIABLE

TEST YOURSELF

Consider the equation: $y = 3x^2 - 6x + 1$.

1. Find the y-intercept of the graph of the given equation.
2. Tell whether the curve has a maximum or a minimum point.
3. Find the equation of the axis of symmetry.
4. Find the coordinates of the maximum or minimum point.
5. Find the sum and the product of the roots of the equation obtained when $y = 0$.
6. Find the x-intercepts of the graph of the given equation.
7. Graph the equation.

EXERCISES

Find (a) the sum and (b) the product of the roots of each equation:

1. $x^2 - 3x + 5 = 0$.
2. $x^2 + 4x - 6 = 0$.
3. $2x^2 - x - 7 = 0$.
4. $5x^2 + 7x - 11 = 0$.
5. $3x^2 - 5x + 7 = 0$.
6. $2x^2 + x = 0$.

In Exercises 7 through 14 find the (a) y-intercept; (b) equation of the axis of symmetry; (c) coordinates of the maximum or minimum point; (d) x-intercepts:

7. $y = 2x^2 + 4x - 5$.
8. $y = -3x^2 + 12x - 8$.
9. $y = -4x^2 - 8x - 12$.
10. $y = 2x^2 + 3x + 1$.
11. $y = 5x^2 - 13x - 12$.
12. $y = -2x^2 + x$.
13. $y = 3x^2 + 8$.
14. $y = -3x^2 + 13x$.

15. State the range of each function in Exercises 7 through 14.

Graph the equation given in:

16. Exercise 7.
17. Exercise 8.
18. Exercise 10.
19. Exercise 13.

• • •

Graph:

20. $y < 2x^2 - 3x + 2$.
21. $y > -3x^2 + 5x - 2$.

Find the quadratic function whose graph:

22. Contains the origin and has x-intercept 5.
23. Contains (2, 5) and has x-intercepts -5 and -6.
24. Has y-intercept 5 and x-intercepts -2 and 3.

363

LINEAR AND QUADRATIC EXPRESSIONS

In Exercises 25 through 29 find the set of values of k such that:

25. One root of $x^2 + kx - 72 = 0$ is 14 more than the negative of the other.

26. One root of $x^2 + bx + k = 0$ is one-half of the other.

27. The graph of $y = x^2 + kx - 25$ is symmetric about the y-axis.

28. The graph of $y = x^2 + kx + 3$ is symmetric about the line $x = 2$.

29. The graph of $y = x^2 + 3x - k$ has two distinct x-intercepts.

30. After t seconds the height s of a ball thrown upward with an initial velocity of 3200 feet per second is given by $s = 3200t - 16t^2$. Find (a) the time needed for the ball to reach its maximum height; (b) the maximum height; (c) the amount of time the ball is in the air.

31. A rectangular garden beside a river is to be separated from a pasture by a fence. No fence is needed along the river, and 1000 feet of fencing is available. Find the dimensions of the largest garden that can be fenced off with the fencing available.

32. Mr. Johnson has a field of wheat which he wishes to cut. If the field is 80 rods wide and 160 rods long, how wide a strip must he cut around the field in order to have cut one-half of it? Give your answer correct to the nearest tenth of a rod.

33. Steve cut a rectangular piece of metal by removing 3-inch squares from each corner. He then turned up the edges to form an open box with a volume of 810 cubic inches. If the rectangular piece of metal was twice as long as it was wide, what were its original dimensions? Give your answers correct to the nearest tenth of an inch.

• **34.** Identify the set of values for k such that the graph of $y = x^2 + 2kx + k$ does not intersect the x-axis.

§ 7-6 Circles and spheres

The formula for the distance between any two points (x_1, y_1) and (x_2, y_2) on a coordinate plane was introduced in § 1-7 and extended to provide a formula for the distance between any two points (x_1, y_1, z_1) and (x_2, y_2, z_2) in a coordinate space. These formulas were used to obtain equations for circles and spheres.

On a coordinate plane the locus of points at a given distance r from a given point (h, k) is a circle with center (h, k) and radius r;

$$(x - h)^2 + (y - k)^2 = r^2. \qquad (22)$$

If the center is at the origin, then the equation of the circle has the form

$$x^2 + y^2 = r^2. \tag{23}$$

In a coordinate space the locus of points at a given distance r from a given point (h, k, n) is a sphere with center (h, k, n) and radius r;

$$(x - h)^2 + (y - k)^2 + (z - n)^2 = r^2. \tag{24}$$

If the center is at the origin, then the equation of the sphere has the form

$$x^2 + y^2 + z^2 = r^2. \tag{25}$$

Each of the equations (22) and (23) is a **standard form** of the equation of a circle. The equation (22) of any circle may be written in the standard form (23) for a circle with its center at the origin by a **transformation** (change) in the coordinate system. We take the lines $x = h$ and $y = k$ as the new coordinate axes and (h, k) as the origin of the new system. Then the coordinates $(x'\ y')$ of any point with reference to the new system may be expressed in terms of the coordinates of the original system as

$$\begin{cases} x' = x - h \\ y' = y - k. \end{cases} \tag{26}$$

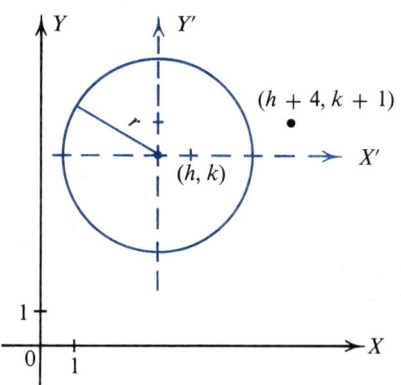

Figure 7-22

It is often convenient to express the transformation (26) by the equation $(x', y') = (x - h, y - k)$. As an example of the effect of the transformation, notice in Figure 7-22 that the point with coordinates $(h + 4, k + 1)$ with reference to the original coordinate axes has coordinates $(4, 1)$ with reference to the new coordinate axes. The equation (23) has the form

$$x'^2 + y'^2 = r^2$$

and thus is in standard form for a circle with center at the origin with reference to the new coordinate system. Any transformation of coordinate systems of the form (26) is called a **translation** of the axes. A translation may be visualized either as transforming the points with reference to a fixed set of axes or as transforming the axes and considering the points of the coordinate plane as fixed. The second interpretation is more useful for our present purposes.

LINEAR AND QUADRATIC EXPRESSIONS

Example 1. Find the equation of the circle
$$x^2 - 4x + y^2 - 6y = 3$$
with reference to the new axes obtained using the translation (a) which may be used to express the equation of the circle in standard form with the center at the origin; (b) $(x', y') = (x - 2, y - 1)$.

(a) We first complete the square in x, complete the square in y, and express the given equation as
$$(x^2 - 4x + 4) + (y^2 - 6y + 9) = 3 + 4 + 9$$
$$(x - 2)^2 + (y - 3)^2 = 16.$$

The translation $(x', y') = (x - 2, y - 3)$ obtained by taking $h = 2$ and $k = 3$ in (26) may be used to obtain the equation
$$x'^2 + y'^2 = 16$$
for the given circle.

(b) We need to substitute in the given equation for x and y. Thus we need to solve the equations
$$\begin{cases} x' = x - 2 \\ y' = y - 1 \end{cases}$$
of the given translation for x and y;
$$\begin{cases} x = x' + 2 \\ y = y' + 1. \end{cases}$$
Then
$$(x' + 2)^2 - 4(x' + 2) + (y' + 1)^2 - 6(y' + 1) = 3$$
$$x'^2 + 4x' + 4 - 4x' - 8 + y'^2 + 2y' + 1 - 6y' - 6 = 3$$
$$x'^2 + y'^2 - 4y' = 12$$
$$x'^2 + (y' - 2)^2 = 16.$$

Any circle with equation $x^2 + y^2 = r^2$ is **symmetric with respect to the x-axis** since for each point $P: (x, \sqrt{r^2 - y^2})$ of the circle there is a point $P': (x, -\sqrt{r^2 - y^2})$ such that the x-axis is the perpendicular bisector of $\overline{PP'}$. The circle is **symmetric with respect to the y-axis** since for each point $Q: (\sqrt{r^2 - x^2}, y)$ of the circle there is a point $Q': (-\sqrt{r^2 - x^2}, y)$ of the circle such that the y-axis is the perpendicular bisector of $\overline{QQ'}$. The circle is **symmetric with respect to the origin** since for each point $P: (x, \sqrt{r^2 - y^2})$ of the circle there is a point $P'': (-x, -\sqrt{r^2 - y^2})$ of the circle such that the origin is the mid-point of $\overline{PP''}$. In general, a curve is **symmetric with respect to a line** m if for each point P of the curve there is a point P' of the

366

§ 7-6 CIRCLES AND SPHERES

curve such that the line m is the perpendicular bisector of $\overline{PP'}$; the line m is called the **axis of symmetry**. A curve is **symmetric with respect to a point** M if for each point P of the curve there is a point P'' of the curve such that M is the mid-point of $\overline{PP''}$; the point M is called the **center of symmetry**. Any circle is symmetric with respect to its center and to any line through its center. In particular, any circle (22) is symmetric with respect to the point (h, k) and the lines $x = h$ and $y = k$ (Exercise 31).

Each of the equations (24) and (25) is sometimes called the **standard form** of the equation of a sphere. The equation (24) of any sphere may be written in the standard form (25) for a sphere with its center at the origin

$$x'^2 + y'^2 + z'^2 = r^2$$

by a translation of the coordinate planes;

$$\begin{cases} x' = x - h \\ y' = y - k \\ z' = z - n. \end{cases}$$

Notice that for $-r < z_0 < r$ the plane $z = z_0$ intersects the sphere (24) in a circle

$$x^2 + y^2 = r^2 - z_0^2;$$

for $|z_0| = r$, the intersection is a point $(0, 0, z_0)$ satisfying

$$x^2 + y^2 = 0;$$

and for $|z_0| > r$, $z_0^2 > r^2$, $r^2 - z_0^2 < 0$ and the intersection is the empty set.

The equation of any circle with center (h, k) and radius r is of the form

$$x^2 - 2hx + h^2 + y^2 - 2ky + k^2 = r^2$$

and thus of the form

$$x^2 + y^2 + Dx + Ey + F = 0 \qquad (27)$$

where $D = -2h$, $E = -2k$, and $F = h^2 + k^2 - r^2$. Conversely, if on a coordinate plane the graph of an equation of the form (27) has at least one point, then the graph is either a circle or a single point. To prove this statement, we first complete the square in x and in y:

$$\left(x^2 + Dx + \frac{D^2}{4}\right) + \left(y^2 + Ey + \frac{E^2}{4}\right) = -F + \frac{D^2}{4} + \frac{E^2}{4};$$

$$\left(x + \frac{D}{2}\right)^2 + \left(y + \frac{E}{2}\right)^2 = \frac{D^2}{4} + \frac{E^2}{4} - F;$$

$$\left(x - \frac{-D}{2}\right)^2 + \left(y - \frac{-E}{2}\right)^2 = \frac{D^2}{4} + \frac{E^2}{4} - F.$$

LINEAR AND QUADRATIC EXPRESSIONS

If $\frac{D^2}{4} + \frac{E^2}{4} - F$ is negative, the equation states that the sum of the squares of the two numbers is negative and there are no real numbers for which this is true; that is, the graph of the equation under these conditions is the empty set. If $\frac{D^2}{4} + \frac{E^2}{4} - F = 0$, the graph consists of the single point $\left(-\frac{D}{2}, -\frac{E}{2}\right)$. If $\frac{D^2}{4} + \frac{E^2}{4} - F$ is positive, then there is a real number r such that this expression equals r^2 and the graph is a circle with center $\left(-\frac{D}{2}, -\frac{E}{2}\right)$ and radius r. Thus the graph of the equation (27) is the empty set, a point, or a circle according as $\frac{D^2}{4} + \frac{E^2}{4} - F$ is negative, zero, or positive. If the graph is a circle, its equation may be placed in standard form with its center at the origin by a translation of the axes

$$(x', y') = \left(x + \frac{D}{2}, y + \frac{E}{2}\right).$$

We shall need one other type of transformation of coordinate systems in our discussion of quadratic expressions of two variables. We shall obtain new coordinate axes by a rotation of the original axes about the origin and through an angle α in standard position (Figure 7–23). Any point $P: (x, y)$ has coordinates $(r \cos \theta, r \sin \theta)$ with reference to the original axes and coordinates

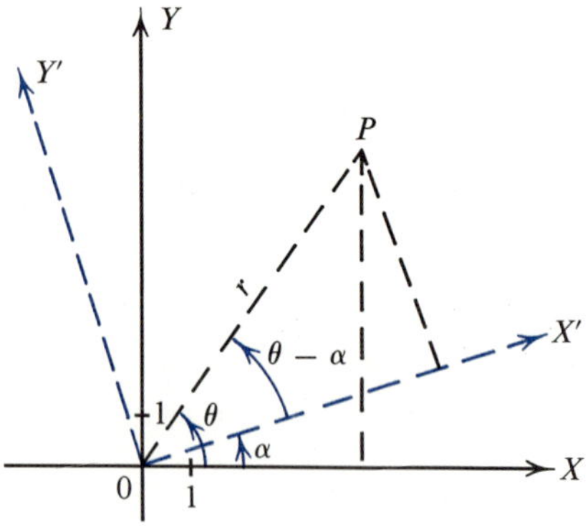

$$[r \cos (\theta - \alpha), r \sin (\theta - \alpha)]$$

with reference to the new axes. Thus

$$\begin{aligned} x' = r \cos (\theta - \alpha) &= r (\cos \theta \cos \alpha + \sin \theta \sin \alpha) \\ &= (r \cos \theta) \cos \alpha + (r \sin \theta) \sin \alpha \\ &= x \cos \alpha + y \sin \alpha; \end{aligned}$$

$$\begin{aligned} y' = r \sin (\theta - \alpha) &= r (\sin \theta \cos \alpha - \cos \theta \sin \alpha) \\ &= (r \sin \theta) \cos \alpha - (r \cos \theta) \sin \alpha \\ &= y \cos \alpha - x \sin \alpha. \end{aligned}$$

Figure 7–23

The **rotation** of the coordinate axes about the origin through an angle α in standard position assigns new coordinates (x', y') to each point (x, y) such that

§ 7-6   CIRCLES AND SPHERES

$$\begin{cases} x' = x \cos \alpha + y \sin \alpha \\ y' = -x \sin \alpha + y \cos \alpha. \end{cases} \qquad (28)$$

As in the case of translations, rotations are sometimes visualized as transforming the axes while the points of the coordinate plane remain fixed. The equations (28) are used for rotating the axes. Equations for rotating the points of the plane may be obtained by replacing α by $-\alpha$.

When the equation of a curve is given and the new equation of the curve with reference to axes obtained by a rotation (28) is desired, we need to substitute for x and y in the given equation of the curve. Thus we need to solve the system (28) for x and y in terms of x' and y'. This may be done as in § 7–3; it may also be done using the fact that the old axes may be obtained by rotating the new axes through the angle $-\alpha$. In either case we obtain

$$\begin{cases} x = x' \cos \alpha - y' \sin \alpha \\ y = x' \sin \alpha + y' \cos \alpha. \end{cases} \qquad (29)$$

Example 2. Express in standard form the equation of the circle

$$x^2 - 6x + y^2 - 6y = 3$$

with reference to the new axes obtained by a rotation of 45°.

We use the equations (29) for $\alpha = 45°$ where

$$(x, y) = \left(\frac{x'}{\sqrt{2}} - \frac{y'}{\sqrt{2}}, \frac{x'}{\sqrt{2}} + \frac{y'}{\sqrt{2}} \right)$$

and substitute in the given equation:

$$\left(\frac{x'}{\sqrt{2}} - \frac{y'}{\sqrt{2}} \right)^2 - 6 \left(\frac{x'}{\sqrt{2}} - \frac{y'}{\sqrt{2}} \right) + \left(\frac{x'}{\sqrt{2}} + \frac{y'}{\sqrt{2}} \right)^2$$

$$- 6 \left(\frac{x'}{\sqrt{2}} + \frac{y'}{\sqrt{2}} \right) = 3$$

$$\frac{x'^2}{2} - x'y' + \frac{y'^2}{2} - \frac{6x'}{\sqrt{2}} + \frac{6y'}{\sqrt{2}} + \frac{x'^2}{2} + x'y'$$

$$+ \frac{y'^2}{2} - \frac{6x'}{\sqrt{2}} - \frac{6y'}{\sqrt{2}} = 3$$

$$x'^2 + y'^2 - 6\sqrt{2}\, x' = 3$$
$$(x' - 3\sqrt{2})^2 + y'^2 = 21.$$

(If you cannot visualize immediately why the new equation is the correct one, graph the given equation, draw the new coordinate system, and solve the example again from your graph.)

369

LINEAR AND QUADRATIC EXPRESSIONS

Any circle (24) divides the plane into two regions on each of which the expression $(x - h)^2 + (y - k)^2 - r^2$ has constant sign. For each point (x, y) on the plane this expression is positive, zero, or negative. With respect to the circle the point (x, y) is an **exterior point** if the expression is positive, a point of the circle if the expression is zero, an **interior point** if the expression is negative.

TEST YOURSELF

1. Find the center and radius of each circle: (a) $x^2 + y^2 - 9 = 0$; (b) $x^2 + y^2 - 4x + 2y = 1$.
2. Express in standard form the equation for the circle in Exercise 1 (b) with reference to the new axes obtained by the translation $(x', y') = (x - 2, y + 1)$.
3. Express in standard form the equation for the circle in Exercise 1 (a) with reference to the new axes obtained by a rotation through an angle of 30°.

EXERCISES

Find the center and radius of each circle:

1. $x^2 + y^2 = 4$.
2. $(x - 2)^2 + (y + 3)^2 = 20$.
3. $x^2 + (y - 2)^2 = 4$.
4. $x^2 + 4x = -12 + 6y - y^2$.
5. $x^2 + y^2 - 2x - 4y - 20 = 0$.
6. $2x^2 + 2y^2 - 7x + 4y - 6 = 0$.
7. $(2x - 3)^2 + (2y - 5)^2 = 36$.
8. $(3x - 1)^2 + (3y + 2)^2 = 45$.

Find the center and radius of each sphere:

9. $x^2 + y^2 + z^2 = 9$.
10. $(x - 1)^2 + y^2 + z^2 + 2z = 3$.
11. $x^2 + y^2 + z^2 + 2x - 6y = 3$.
12. $x^2 + y^2 + z^2 - 6x + 5y + 3z = -1.5$.

Graph:

13. $x^2 + y^2 - 4 < 0$.
14. $x^2 - 2x + y^2 < 0$.
15. $x^2 + y^2 - 6y > 0$.
16. $x^2 - 2x + y^2 < 2y$.

17 through 23. Find the translations that may be used to express the circles in Exercises 2 through 8 in standard form with center at the origin.

• • •

In Exercises 24 through 29 express in standard form the equation of each circle with reference to the new axes obtained by the given transformation:

24. $x^2 + y^2 - 2x = 0$; $(x', y') = (x - 1, y + 1)$.
25. $x^2 + y^2 + 2x + 3y = 0$; $(x', y') = (x + 2, y - 2)$.
26. $x^2 + y^2 - 2x = 0$; a rotation of 90° about the origin.
27. $x^2 + 3x + y^2 - 3y = 0$; a rotation of 45° about the origin.
28. $x^2 - 2x + y^2 = 5$; a rotation of 30° about the origin.
29. $x^2 + 3x + y^2 - 7y = 1$; a rotation of 60° about the origin.
30. Use the methods of § 7–3 to solve for x and y:

$$\begin{cases} x' = x \cos \alpha + y \sin \alpha \\ y' = -x \sin \alpha + y \cos \alpha. \end{cases}$$

31. Prove that any circle $(x - h)^2 + (y - k)^2 = r^2$ is symmetric with respect to (a) $x = h$; (b) $y = k$; (c) (h, k).

32. Prove that the coefficients of the equation of any circle with center at the origin are not changed by a rotation of the axes about the origin.

33. Use the distance formula and find an equation of the circle through $(4, -1)$, $(-1, 4)$, and $(2, 3)$.

34. Use the distance formula and find an equation of the circle through $(0, 1)$, $(3, 0)$, and $(1, -1)$.

35. Solve Exercises 33 and 34 by substituting the coordinates of each point for x and y in $x^2 + y^2 + Dx + Ey + F = 0$ and solving the system of equations for D, E, and F.

• **36.** Prove that the set of translations (26) where h and k may represent any real numbers forms a group (§ 6–2) under the operation of applying one translation after another.

• **37.** Prove that the set of all rotations about the origin (28) forms a group under the operation of applying one rotation after another.

§ 7–7 Parabolas

On a plane the locus of points which are equidistant from a given point and from a given line not containing the point is a **parabola**. The given point is the **focus of the parabola;** the given line is the **directrix of the**

LINEAR AND QUADRATIC EXPRESSIONS

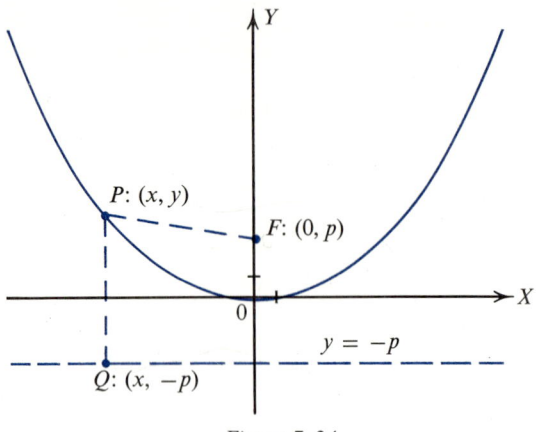

Figure 7-24

parabola. In Figure 7-24 the focus is $F: (0, p)$; the directrix is the line $y = -p$. The distance of any point $P: (x, y)$ from the directrix is the length of $\overline{PQ}$ where $Q: (x, -p)$ is on the directrix and $\overrightarrow{PQ}$ is perpendicular to the directrix. For any point P of the parabola, $\overline{PF} = \overline{PQ}$;

$$\sqrt{(x - 0)^2 + (y - p)^2} = \sqrt{(x - x)^2 + (y + p)^2}$$
$$x^2 + y^2 - 2py + p^2 = y^2 + 2py + p^2$$
$$x^2 = 4py. \tag{30}$$

The equation (30) would have been considered in the form $y = \dfrac{1}{4p}x^2$ in § 7-5. As in § 7-5 the line through the focus and perpendicular to the directrix is the axis of symmetry of the curve; that is, the **axis of the parabola.** The point at which the axis intersects the parabola is the **vertex of the parabola.** This point corresponds to the minimum or maximum point discussed in § 7-5. The equation (30) is the standard form for a parabola with the origin as its vertex and the y-axis as its axis.

Any parabola with equation

$$y = ax^2 + bx + c, \, a \neq 0$$

may be expressed in the forms

$$y = a\left(x + \frac{b}{2a}\right)^2 + \frac{4ac - b^2}{4a}$$

$$\left(x + \frac{b}{2a}\right)^2 = \frac{1}{a}\left(y - \frac{4ac - b^2}{4a}\right)$$

and thus in the form

$$(x - h)^2 = 4p(y - k) \tag{31}$$

372

§ 7-7 PARABOLAS

where $h = -\dfrac{b}{2a}$, $p = \dfrac{1}{4a}$, and $k = \dfrac{4ac - b^2}{4a^2}$. The equation (31) is the **standard form** of the equation of any parabola with its axis parallel to or coincident with the *y*-axis. Notice that the equation (30) is a special case of this more general form. Any equation in this general form may be expressed in the form (30) by the translation of the coordinate axes; $(x', y') = (x - h, y - k)$. Therefore the graph of the general form (Figure 7–25) may be obtained using the properties of the graph in Figure 7–24. Notice that these graphs represent parabolas with $p > 0$; parabolas with $p < 0$ have graphs as in Figure 7–14 of § 7–5.

Whenever the equation of a parabola is obtained from other data, it should be expressed in standard form (31). Whenever an equation of a parabola is to be graphed, the equation should first be expressed in standard form. For any parabola (31) the equation of the axis is $x - h = 0$; the vertex is at (h, k); the equation of the directrix is $y = k - p$; the focus is at $(h, k + p)$. The points of the parabola that are on the line $y = k + p$ through the focus and perpendicular to the axis of the parabola are particularly useful in graphing since their coordinates can be stated in terms of h, k, and p. If $k + p$ is substituted for y in the equation (31), then $(x - h)^2 = 4p(p)$; $x - h = \pm 2p$, and $x = h \pm 2p$. Thus the points $(h - 2p, k + p)$ and $(h + 2p, k + p)$ are points of the parabola. The line segment having these two points as end points is the **latus rectum of the parabola**. The length $|4p|$ of the latus rectum is the **focal width** of the parabola; that is, the width of the parabola at its focus.

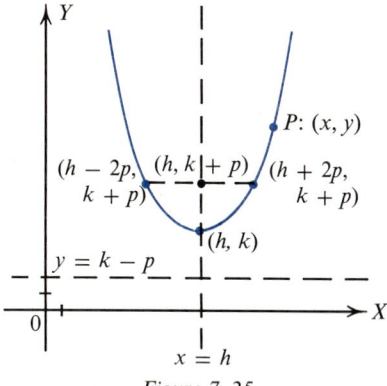

Figure 7–25

Example 1. Write the equation of the parabola $y = 6x - x^2 + 7$ in standard form and identify the (**a**) axis; (**b**) vertex; (**c**) directrix; (**d**) focus; (**e**) focal width; (**f**) end points of the latus rectum.

$$y = -1(x^2 - 6x + 9) + 9 + 7$$
$$(x - 3)^2 = (-1)(y - 16);\ h = 3,\ k = 16,\ p = -\tfrac{1}{4}.$$

(**a**) $x - 3 = 0$, $x = 3$; (**b**) $(3, 16)$; (**c**) $y = 16\tfrac{1}{4}$; (**d**) $(3, 15\tfrac{3}{4})$; (**e**) 1; (**f**) $(2\tfrac{1}{2}, 15\tfrac{3}{4})$, $(3\tfrac{1}{2}, 15\tfrac{3}{4})$.

LINEAR AND QUADRATIC EXPRESSIONS

Any parabola with its axis parallel to or coincident with the x-axis becomes a parabola with its axis parallel to or coincident with the new y-axis with an equation of the form (31) after the coordinate axes have been rotated 90°. The equations for this transformation of the coordinate axes are

$$\begin{cases} x' = x \cos 90° + y \sin 90° = y \\ y' = -x \sin 90° + y \cos 90° = -x. \end{cases}$$

Since an equation of the form (31) is obtained by this transformation, the original equation must have been of the form

$$(y - k)^2 = 4p(x - h),$$

the **standard form** of the equation of any parabola with its axis parallel to or coincident with the x-axis. Parabolas with axes which are not parallel to or coincident with either coordinate axis will be considered in § 7–10.

Example 2. Find the equation of the parabola with focus at (7, 3) and directrix $x = 1$.

We use the definition of a parabola as a locus. The distance from (x, y) to the point (7, 3) is represented by

$$\sqrt{(x - 7)^2 + (y - 3)^2}.$$

The distance from (x, y) to the line $x = 1$ is represented by

$$\sqrt{(x - 1)^2 + (y - y)^2}; \text{ that is, } \sqrt{(x - 1)^2}.$$

Since these distances must be equal,

$$\sqrt{(x - 7)^2 + (y - 3)^2} = \sqrt{(x - 1)^2}$$
$$x^2 - 14x + 49 + y^2 - 6y + 9 = x^2 - 2x + 1$$
$$y^2 - 6y + 9 = 12x - 48$$
$$(y - 3)^2 = 12(x - 4).$$

ALTERNATE METHOD: The axis is the line $y = 3$ since it is perpendicular to the directrix and passes through the focus. The vertex is the point (4, 3) since it is on the axis and halfway from the focus to the directrix. Then $p = 3$ since the focus is on the positive side of the vertex and 3 units from it. The desired equation is

$$(y - 3)^2 = 12(x - 4).$$

§ 7-7   PARABOLAS

Example 3. Identify the axis, directrix, focal width, and equation of the parabola with vertex at $(-2, 5)$ and focus at $(-2, 3)$.

The axis is the line $x = -2$; since $p = -2$, the directrix is the line $y = 7$; the focal width is 8; and the equation is

$$(x + 2)^2 = -8(y - 5).$$

TEST YOURSELF

1. Consider the parabola $y = x^2 + 6x - 3$ and identify the (a) axis; (b) vertex; (c) directrix; (d) focus; (e) focal width.
2. Find (a) the focal width and (b) the equation of the parabola with vertex $(3, -2)$ and focus $(0, -2)$.

EXERCISES

A

For each parabola identify the (a) axis; (b) vertex; (c) directrix; (d) focus; (e) focal width:

1. $y^2 = 16x$.
2. $x^2 = -8y$.
3. $y^2 + 2x = y - 6$.
4. $y^2 + 2x = 2y - 5$.
5. $4x^2 + 8y - 12x = 4$.
6. $2y^2 + 2y - x - 2 = 0$.
7. $x + 2 = y^2 - 4y$.
8. $y^2 - 4y = 9x + 2y$.

In Exercises 9 through 16 find the equation of the parabola with vertex V and focus F:

9. $V: (0, 0)$; $F: (0, 4)$.
10. $V: (4, 6)$; $F: (4, 8)$.
11. $V: (-2, -5)$; $F: (0, -5)$.
12. $V: (0, 2)$; directrix $y = 0$.
13. $V: (4, 0)$; directrix $x = 0$.
14. $F: (0, 3)$; directrix $y = -3$.
15. $V: (4, -2)$; directrix $y = -6$.
16. $F: (4, -2)$; directrix $y = -6$.

• • •

17. Find the points of intersection of the parabola $y^2 = 4x$ and the line $y = x - a$. Show that the mid-point of the line segment intercepted by the parabola has a constant ordinate.

LINEAR AND QUADRATIC EXPRESSIONS

18. A roadbed 60 feet wide is crowned so that a cross-section is parabolic in shape. The center of the road surface is 12 inches higher than the edges. Take the origin of your coordinate system at the vertex of the parabola and **(a)** find the equation of the graph shown by the cross-section; and **(b)** find at the center, ten feet from the center, twenty feet from the center, and thirty feet from the center, the heights of the road surface above the edges.

19. A ball was thrown obliquely into the air. The ball reached a maximum height of 20 feet and landed 100 feet away. Assume that the path of the ball was a parabola and find its equation.

20. Repeat Exercise 19 for a ball that reaches a maximum height of 25 feet and lands 60 feet away.

21. If resistance of the air is disregarded, the height s in feet of a ball thrown up with an initial upward velocity of v_0 feet per second would be given approximately by the formula $s = v_0 t - 16t^2$ where t is the time in seconds after the ball is thrown. **(a)** Graph this formula for $v_0 = 48$. **(b)** Find the maximum height which the ball would reach and the time at which it reaches this height.

22. Repeat Exercise 21 for $v_0 = 80$.

B

Use the definition of a parabola as a locus and derive the equation of the parabola with:

1. Focus at (3, 2) and directrix $y = -2$.
2. Focus at (5, 1) and directrix $y = 7$.
3. Focus at (3, 7) and directrix $x = -3$.
4. Focus at (5, -2) and directrix $x = 11$.

Find the set of possible values for h, k, and p for equations in standard form for parabolas with:

5. Vertex at the origin.
6. Axis $x = 5$.
7. Axis $y = 7$.
8. Vertex at (3, -2).
9. Directrix $y = 1$ and focal width 12.
10. Directrix $x = -3$ and focal width 8.
11. Axis $x = 2$ and directrix $y = 3$.
12. Axis $y = 3$ and directrix $x = 5$.

• • •

Find, specifying sets of values for h, k, and p where necessary, equations for all possible parabolas with axes parallel to or coincident with coordinate axes:

13. Focal width 12 and vertex at (0, 0).
14. Focal width 8 and vertex at (3, 4).
15. Focal width 3 and vertex at (-2, 5).

16. Focal width 12 and focus at (0, 3).
17. Focal width 8 and focus at (5, 0).
18. Focal width 20 and focus at (3, 2).

§ 7-8 Ellipses

An **ellipse** is the locus on a plane of points P such that the sum of the distances of P from two given points is a constant. The given points are called the **foci of the ellipse.** The path of an earth satellite is an ellipse; the path of the earth around the sun is an ellipse.

Consider the set of points $P: (x, y)$ such that the sum of the distances from the foci $F: (c, 0)$ and $F': (-c, 0)$ is $2a$. Then $2a > 2c$; $\overline{PF} + \overline{PF'} = 2a$;

$$\sqrt{(x-c)^2 + y^2} + \sqrt{(x+c)^2 + y^2} = 2a$$
$$\sqrt{(x-c)^2 + y^2} = 2a - \sqrt{(x+c)^2 + y^2}$$
$$x^2 - 2cx + c^2 + y^2 = 4a^2 - 4a\sqrt{(x+c)^2 + y^2} + x^2 + 2cx + c^2 + y^2$$
$$4a\sqrt{(x+c)^2 + y^2} = 4a^2 + 4cx$$
$$a\sqrt{(x+c)^2 + y^2} = a^2 + cx$$
$$a^2(x+c)^2 + a^2y^2 = a^4 + 2a^2cx + c^2x^2$$
$$a^2x^2 + 2a^2cx + a^2c^2 + a^2y^2 = a^4 + 2a^2cx + c^2x^2$$
$$(a^2 - c^2)x^2 + a^2y^2 = a^2(a^2 - c^2).$$

Since $2a > 2c$, $a^2 - c^2 > 0$ and we may let $a^2 - c^2 = b^2$ and obtain

$$b^2x^2 + a^2y^2 = a^2b^2$$

$$\frac{x^2}{a^2} + \frac{y^2}{b^2} = 1. \tag{32}$$

The equation (32) is graphed in Figure 7-26. Notice that the origin is the mid-point of the line segment whose end points are the foci; that is, the origin is the **center of the ellipse.** The equation (32) is the standard form for the equation of an ellipse with the origin as its center and its foci on the x-axis. The x-axis contains the center, the foci, and two points $A: (a, 0)$ and $A': (-a, 0)$ of the ellipse. The points A and A' are the **vertices**

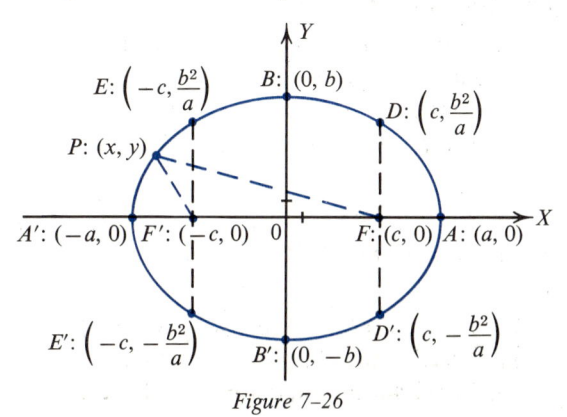

Figure 7-26

377

of the ellipse; the line segment AA' is the **major axis of the ellipse** and has length $2a$. The y-axis contains the center of the ellipse, is perpendicular to the major axis of the ellipse, and contains the points $B: (0, b)$ and $B': (0, -b)$ of the ellipse. The line segment BB' is the **minor axis of the ellipse** and has length $2b$; that is, $2\sqrt{a^2 - c^2}$.

The points of the ellipse that are on one of the lines $x = c$ and $x = -c$ through a focus and perpendicular to the major axis are particularly useful in graphing since their coordinates can be stated in terms of a, b, and c. If $x = c$ or $x = -c$ in the equation (32), then

$$\frac{c^2}{a^2} + \frac{y^2}{b^2} = 1; \quad \frac{y^2}{b^2} = 1 - \frac{c^2}{a^2} = \frac{a^2 - c^2}{a^2} = \frac{b^2}{a^2}; \quad y = \pm\frac{b^2}{a}.$$

Thus the points $D: \left(c, \frac{b^2}{a}\right)$, $D': \left(c, -\frac{b^2}{a}\right)$, $E: \left(-c, \frac{b^2}{a}\right)$, and $E': \left(-c, -\frac{b^2}{a}\right)$ are points of the ellipse. The line segments DD' and EE' are the **latera recta** (plural of latus rectum) **of the ellipse.** The length $\frac{2b^2}{a}$ of each latus rectum is the **focal width of the ellipse.**

Any ellipse with an equation of the form (32) may be graphed by plotting the vertices, the end points of the minor axis, the end points of the latera recta, and sketching the curve through these eight points. The graph of the equation (32) is symmetric with respect to the x-axis, the y-axis, and the origin (Exercise 21). The graph is bounded since $x^2 = \frac{a^2}{b^2}(b^2 - y^2)$, $x^2 \le a^2$, $-a \le x \le a$; and similarly $y^2 = \frac{b^2}{a^2}(a^2 - x^2)$, $y^2 \le b^2$, $-b \le y \le b$. The set of possible values of x is the *domain* of the relation (32); the set of possible values of y is the *range* of the relation.

The standard form of the equation of an ellipse with its center at the origin and foci on the y-axis may be obtained by a 90° rotation of the coordinate axes; $(x', y') = (y, -x)$ as in § 7–7.

$$\frac{x^2}{b^2} + \frac{y^2}{a^2} = 1. \tag{33}$$

An equation of the general form of (32) and (33) is of the form (32) if the denominator of x^2 is greater than the denominator of y^2; of the form (33) if the denominator of y^2 is the greater.

The equation of any ellipse with center (h, k) and major axis parallel to or coincident with a coordinate axis may be expressed in the form (32) or (33) by a translation of the coordinate axes and thus has one of the forms

$$\frac{(x-h)^2}{a^2} + \frac{(y-k)^2}{b^2} = 1; \quad \frac{(x-h)^2}{b^2} + \frac{(y-k)^2}{a^2} = 1.$$

These equations are the **standard forms** for the equations of ellipses with their axes parallel to or coincident with the coordinate axes. Notice that the equations (32) and (33) are special cases of these more general forms. If an equation of an ellipse is obtained from other data, it should be presented in one of these forms. Ellipses with axes which are not parallel to coordinate axes are considered in § 7–10.

If an equation of an ellipse is to be graphed, it should first be expressed in standard form. The influences of the constants on the graph are shown in Figure 7–27.

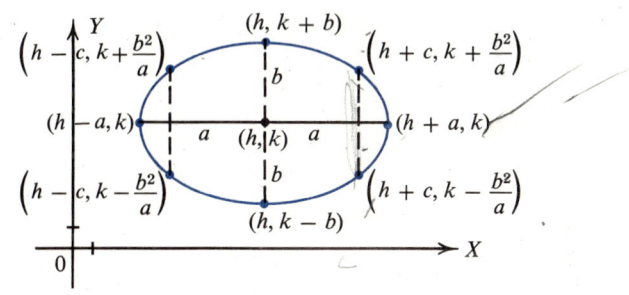

Figure 7–27

Circles (§ 7–6) with centers at the origin and ellipses with centers at the origin and axes coincident with coordinate axes have equations of the form

$$Ax^2 + Cy^2 = H$$

where A, C, and H are all positive. If $A = C$, the graph is a circle; if $A \neq C$, the equation may be expressed in the form (32) or the form (33) and the graph is an ellipse. In a sense a circle is a special case of an ellipse in which the major and minor axes are equal ($a = b$) and the foci coincide ($c = 0$). The relationship between a circle and an ellipse may also be considered in terms of the ratio $\frac{c}{a}$ which is called the **eccentricity** of the ellipse. If $c = 0$, the eccentricity is zero and the ellipse is a circle. As c increases the ellipse appears to become flatter. As c approaches the value of a the ellipse approaches the line segment AA'.

Any ellipse or circle with equation $Ax^2 + Cy^2 = H$ where A, C, and H are all positive divides the plane into regions on which the expression $Ax^2 + Cy^2 - H$ has constant sign. The points (x, y) at which $Ax^2 + Cy^2 - H > 0$ are the **exterior points of the ellipse**; the points

LINEAR AND QUADRATIC EXPRESSIONS

(x, y) at which $Ax^2 + Cy^2 - H = 0$ (that is, has no sign) are the points of the ellipse; the points (x, y) at which $Ax^2 + Cy^2 - H < 0$ are the **interior points of the ellipse.**

Example 1. Graph: $4x^2 + 9y^2 \leq 36$.

The corresponding equation may be expressed in the form

$$\frac{x^2}{9} + \frac{y^2}{4} = 1.$$

The graph of the equation is an ellipse ($a = 3$, $b = 2$, $c = \sqrt{a^2 - b^2} = \sqrt{5}$) with its major axis on the x-axis; its center at the origin; vertices at $(3, 0)$ and $(-3, 0)$; foci at $(\sqrt{5}, 0)$ and $(-\sqrt{5}, 0)$; end points of its minor axis at $(0, 2)$ and $(0, -2)$; and since $\frac{b^2}{a} = \frac{4}{3}$, end points of latera recta at $\left(\sqrt{5}, \frac{4}{3}\right), \left(\sqrt{5}, -\frac{4}{3}\right), \left(-\sqrt{5}, \frac{4}{3}\right), \left(-\sqrt{5}, -\frac{4}{3}\right)$. The ellipse may now be sketched. The inequality is satisfied by the origin which is inside the ellipse and thus by all points inside the ellipse (Figure 7–28).

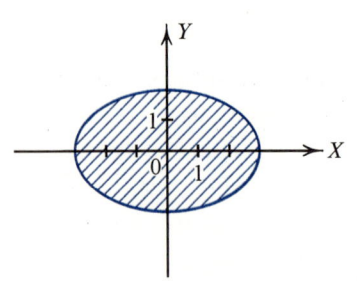

Figure 7–28

Example 2. Find the equation of the ellipse with center at $(1, 3)$, a focus at $(13, 3)$, and major axis of length 26.

The graph is similar to the one in Figure 7–27; $h = 1$, $k = 3$, $c = 12$, $a = 13$, $b^2 = a^2 - c^2 = 25$, $b = 5$, and the equation is

$$\frac{(x - 1)^2}{169} + \frac{(y - 3)^2}{25} = 1.$$

Example 3. Identify the center, vertices, end points of the minor axis, foci, and focal width of the ellipse

$$16(x - 3)^2 + 9(y + 2)^2 = 144.$$

The equation may be expressed as

$$\frac{(x-3)^2}{9} + \frac{(y+2)^2}{16} = 1.$$

The center is at $(3, -2)$; the major axis has length 8 and is on the line $x = 3$; the vertices $(3, 2)$ and $(3, -6)$ are the end points of the major axis; $a^2 - b^2 = 16 - 9 = 7 = c^2$, hence the foci are at $(3, -2 + \sqrt{7})$ and $(3, -2 - \sqrt{7})$; the minor axis has length 6 and is on the line $y = -2$; the end points of the minor axis are at $(0, -2)$ and $(6, -2)$; the focal width $\frac{2b^2}{a}$ is 4.5 units.

TEST YOURSELF

1. Graph: $x^2 + 4y^2 = 4$.

2. Find the equation of the ellipse with a focus at $(3, 2)$ and vertices at $(-5, 2)$ and $(5, 2)$.

3. Identify the center, vertices, end points of the minor axis, foci, and focal width of the ellipse

$$\frac{x^2}{100} + \frac{y^2}{64} = 1.$$

EXERCISES

Find the equation of the ellipse with:

1. Center at $(0, 0)$, a vertex at $(6, 0)$, $b = 4$.
2. Center at $(0, 0)$, a vertex at $(0, 10)$, $b = 5$.
3. Center at $(0, 0)$, a focus at $(0, 3)$, $a = 5$.
4. Center at $(0, 0)$ a vertex at $(8, 0)$, focal width $\frac{25}{4}$.
5. Center at $(0, 0)$, a focus at $(0, 8)$, length of minor axis 12.
6. Vertices at $(6, 0)$ and $(-6, 0)$, foci at $(3, 0)$ and $(-3, 0)$.

LINEAR AND QUADRATIC EXPRESSIONS

In Exercises 7 through 18 identify the (a) center; (b) vertices; (c) end points of the minor axis; (d) foci; and (e) focal width of each related ellipse. Graph the relations in Exercises 7, 8, 9, 12, and 15.

7. $\dfrac{x^2}{16} + \dfrac{y^2}{9} = 1$.

8. $9x^2 + 36y^2 < 144$.

9. $36x^2 + 25y^2 = 900$.

10. $\dfrac{x^2}{225} + \dfrac{y^2}{289} = 1$.

11. $100x^2 + 25y^2 = 400$.

12. $\dfrac{9x^2}{4} + \dfrac{16y^2}{9} > 1$.

13. $25(x - 2)^2 + 36(y + 1)^2 = 900$.
14. $9(x + 1)^2 + 4(y + 3)^2 - 36 = 0$.
15. $49x^2 + 16(y - 4)^2 \geq 784$.
16. $25x^2 + 9y^2 - 50x - 200 = 0$.
17. $5x^2 + 2y^2 - 30x + 8y + 43 = 0$.
18. $3x^2 + y^2 - 3x + y - 11 = 0$.
19. State the domain for each quadratic relation in Exercises 7 through 18.
20. State the range for each quadratic relation in Exercises 7 through 18.
21. Prove that any ellipse $b^2x^2 + a^2y^2 = a^2b^2$ is symmetric with respect to the (a) x-axis; (b) y-axis; (c) origin.
22. Prove that any ellipse $b^2(x - h)^2 + a^2(y - k)^2 = a^2b^2$ is symmetric with respect to (a) $x = h$; (b) $y = k$; (c) (h, k).
23. The roadbed over a certain bridge is supported by an arch in the shape of the part of an ellipse on one side of its major axis. The roadbed is parallel to the base and 5 feet above the center of the arch. The arch is 100 feet wide at its base and is 30 feet high. Find equations for the arch and the roadbed using coordinates with the x-axis parallel to the base of the arch and the origin (a) at the center of the base; (b) at an end of the base; (c) at the top of the arch.
- 24. If $AC > 0$, prove that the equation

$$Ax^2 + Cy^2 + Dx + Ey + F = 0$$

has a point, a circle, or an ellipse as its graph.

§ 7-9 Hyperbolas

A **hyperbola** is the locus on a plane of points P such that a difference of the distances of P from two given points is a constant. The given points are the **foci of the hyperbola**. Let $F: (c, 0)$ and $F': (-c, 0)$ be the

§ 7-9   HYPERBOLAS

foci of a hyperbola, and consider the set of points $P: (x, y)$ such that $|\overline{PF} - \overline{PF'}| = 2a$. Then $2a < 2c$;

$$\sqrt{(x-c)^2 + y^2} - \sqrt{(x+c)^2 + y^2} = \pm 2a$$
$$\sqrt{(x-c)^2 + y^2} = \sqrt{(x+c)^2 + y^2} \pm 2a$$
$$x^2 - 2cx + c^2 + y^2 = x^2 + 2cx + c^2 + y^2 \pm 4a\sqrt{(x+c)^2 + y^2} + 4a^2$$
$$cx + a^2 = \pm a\sqrt{(x+c)^2 + y^2}$$
$$c^2x^2 + 2a^2cx + a^4 = a^2(x+c)^2 + a^2y^2$$
$$c^2x^2 + 2a^2cx + a^4 = a^2x^2 + 2a^2cx + a^2c^2 + a^2y^2$$
$$c^2x^2 - a^2x^2 - a^2y^2 = a^2c^2 - a^4$$
$$(c^2 - a^2)x^2 - a^2y^2 = a^2(c^2 - a^2).$$

Since $2c > 2a$, $c^2 > a^2$; and we may let $c^2 - a^2 = b^2$ and obtain

$$b^2x^2 - a^2y^2 = a^2b^2$$

$$\frac{x^2}{a^2} - \frac{y^2}{b^2} = 1. \tag{34}$$

Example 1. Find the equation of the hyperbola such that the difference of the distances of each point from $(5, 0)$ and $(-5, 0)$ is 8. **(a)** Use the distance formula. **(b)** Use the equation (34).

(a) $\sqrt{(x+5)^2 + y^2} - \sqrt{(x-5)^2 + y^2} = \pm 8$
$$x^2 + 10x + 25 + y^2 = x^2 - 10x + 25 + y^2$$
$$\pm 16\sqrt{(x-5)^2 + y^2} + 64$$
$$20x - 64 = \pm 16\sqrt{(x-5)^2 + y^2}$$
$$5x - 16 = \pm 4\sqrt{(x-5)^2 + y^2}$$
$$25x^2 - 160x + 256 = 16x^2 - 160x + 400 + 16y^2$$
$$9x^2 - 16y^2 = 144$$
$$\frac{x^2}{16} - \frac{y^2}{9} = 1.$$

(b) Since the foci are at $(5, 0)$ and $(-5, 0)$, $c = 5$. Since $2a = 8$, $a = 4$. Since $b^2 = c^2 - a^2$, $b^2 = 25 - 16 = 9$; thus $b = 3$. Therefore the equation (34) has the form

$$\frac{x^2}{16} - \frac{y^2}{9} = 1.$$

The equation (34) is graphed in Figure 7–29. Notice that the origin is the mid-point of the line segment whose end points are the foci; that is, the origin is the **center of the hyperbola**. The equation (34) is the stand-

LINEAR AND QUADRATIC EXPRESSIONS

Figure 7-29

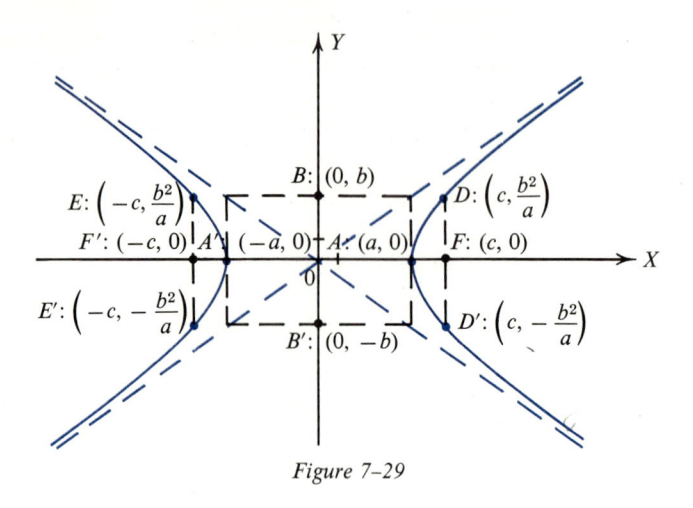

ard form for the equation of a hyperbola with the origin as center and its foci on the x-axis. The x-axis contains the center, the foci, and two points $A: (a, 0)$ and $A': (-a, 0)$ of the hyperbola. The points A and A' are the **vertices of the hyperbola;** the line segment AA' is the **tranverse axis of the hyperbola** and has length $2a$. The y-axis contains the center of the hyperbola, is perpendicular to the transverse axis, and does *not* intersect the hyperbola. The points $B: (0, b)$ and $B': (0, -b)$ are not on the hyperbola but are useful in graphing the hyperbola. The line segment BB' is the **conjugate axis of the hyperbola** and has length $2b$; that is, $2\sqrt{c^2 - a^2}$.

The points of the hyperbola that are on one of the lines $x = c$ and $x = -c$ through a focus and perpendicular to the transverse axis are particularly useful in graphing since their coordinates can be stated in terms of a, b, and c. If $x = c$ or $x = -c$ in the equation (34), then

$$\frac{c^2}{a^2} - \frac{y^2}{b^2} = 1;\ \frac{y^2}{b^2} = \frac{c^2}{a^2} - 1 = \frac{c^2 - a^2}{a^2} = \frac{b^2}{a^2};\ y = \pm \frac{b^2}{a}.$$

Thus the points $D: \left(c, \frac{b^2}{a}\right)$, $D': \left(c, -\frac{b^2}{a}\right)$, $E: \left(-c, \frac{b^2}{a}\right)$, and $E': \left(-c, -\frac{b^2}{a}\right)$ are points of the hyperbola. The line segments DD' and EE' are the **latera recta of the hyperbola.** The length $\frac{2b^2}{a}$ of each latus rectum is the **focal width of the hyperbola.**

The values of x for points of the graph of the hyperbola (34) may increase without bound since $y = \pm \frac{b}{a}\sqrt{x^2 - a^2}$. If $|x| > a$, then

$x \neq 0$ and $y = \pm \dfrac{bx}{a} \sqrt{1 - \dfrac{a^2}{x^2}}$. Since a has a fixed numerical value for any given hyperbola, $\dfrac{a^2}{x^2}$ approaches zero as $|x|$ increases without bound, $\sqrt{1 - \dfrac{a^2}{x^2}}$ approaches 1, and y approaches $\pm \dfrac{bx}{a}$. Thus as $|x|$ increases without bound the hyperbola gets closer and closer to the lines $y = \dfrac{b}{a}x$ and $y = -\dfrac{b}{a}x$ as in Figure 7-29. We describe this situation by calling the lines **asymptotes** of the hyperbola.

Any hyperbola with an equation of the form (34) may be graphed by plotting the vertices A: $(a, 0)$ and A': $(-a, 0)$; the end points B: $(0, b)$ and B': $(0, -b)$ of the conjugate axis; sketching the rectangle with sides parallel to the coordinate axes and passing through A, B, A', and B' and extending the diagonals of the rectangle to obtain the asymptotes; plotting the end points of the latera recta; and sketching the curve through these points and the vertices and approaching the asymptotes.

The graph of the hyperbola (34) does not intersect the y-axis since, if $x = 0, y^2 = -b^2$ and there are no real values for y which satisfy this equation. If we write the equation (34) as $x^2 = \dfrac{a^2}{b^2}(b^2 + y^2)$, we may observe that $b^2 + y^2 \geq b^2$ for all real values of y and thus $x^2 \geq a^2$; that is, either $x \leq -a$ or $a \leq x$. Accordingly there are no points of the graph of (34) when $-a < x < a$. The set of possible values of x is the *domain* of the relation (34); the set of possible values of y is the *range* of the relation. Notice that any hyperbola (34) is symmetric with respect to the x-axis, the y-axis, and the origin (Exercise 18).

The standard form of the equation of a hyperbola with its center at the origin and foci on the y-axis may be obtained by a 90° rotation of the coordinate axes; $(x', y') = (y, -x)$:

$$\frac{y^2}{a^2} - \frac{x^2}{b^2} = 1. \tag{35}$$

The asymptotes for the hyperbola (35) are $y = \pm \dfrac{a}{b}x$. Notice that the graph of (34) intersects the x-axis but not the y-axis; the graph of (35) intersects the y-axis but not the x-axis.

The equation of any hyperbola with center (h, k) and transverse axis parallel to or coincident with a coordinate axis may be expressed in the form (34) or (35) by a translation of the coordinate axes and thus has one

LINEAR AND QUADRATIC EXPRESSIONS

of the forms

$$\frac{(x-h)^2}{a^2} - \frac{(y-k)^2}{b^2} = 1; \quad \frac{(y-k)^2}{a^2} - \frac{(x-h)^2}{b^2} = 1.$$

These equations are the **standard forms** for the equations of hyperbolas with their axes parallel to or coincident with coordinate axes. Notice that the equations (34) and (35) are special cases of these more general forms. If an equation of a hyperbola is obtained from other data, it should be presented in one of these forms. If an equation of a hyperbola is to be graphed, it should first be expressed in one of these forms. Hyperbolas with axes which are not parallel to or coincident with the coordinate axes are considered in § 7–10.

Any hyperbola (34) divides the plane into regions on which the expression $b^2x^2 - a^2y^2 - a^2b^2$ has constant sign. The points (x, y) at which $b^2x^2 - a^2y^2 - a^2b^2 > 0$ are the **interior points** (Figure 7–30) of the hyperbola (the points through which it is not possible to draw lines tangent to the hyperbola); the points (x, y) at which $b^2x^2 - a^2y^2 - a^2b^2 = 0$ (that is, has no sign) are points on the hyperbola; the points (x, y) at which $b^2x^2 - a^2y^2 - a^2b^2 < 0$ are the **exterior points** (Figure 7–31) of the hyperbola (the points from which tangents may be drawn to the hyperbola). Notice that the foci of ellipses and hyperbolas are always interior points.

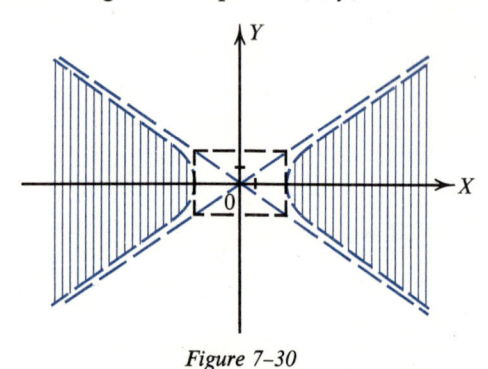

Figure 7–30

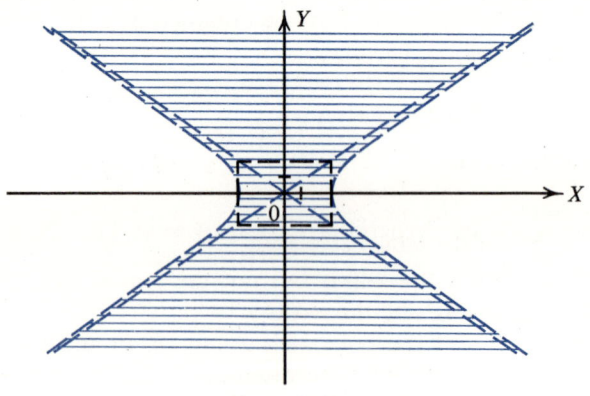

Figure 7–31

§ 7-9 HYPERBOLAS

Example 2. Graph: $4(x - 1)^2 - 9(y + 1)^2 \leq 36$.

We first graph the hyperbola

$$\frac{(x - 1)^2}{9} - \frac{(y + 1)^2}{4} = 1.$$

The center is at $(1, -1)$ and the transverse axis is parallel to the x-axis Then since $a = 3$, the vertices are at $(-2, -1)$ and $(4, -1)$; since $b = 2$, the end points of the conjugate axis are at $(1, 1)$ and $(1, -3)$. As in Figure 7–32 we now draw the rectangle through these points and with sides parallel to the coordinate axes; then we draw the asymptotes along the diagonals of the rectangle. Since $\frac{b}{a} = \frac{2}{3}$, the asymptotes are the lines through $(1, -1)$ with slopes $\frac{2}{3}$ and $-\frac{2}{3}$; that is, the lines with equations $2x - 3y - 5 = 0$ and $2x + 3y + 1 = 0$. Since $c^2 = a^2 + b^2$, $c^2 = 9 + 4 = 13$, $c = \sqrt{13}$, and the foci are at $(1 + \sqrt{13}, -1)$ and $(1 - \sqrt{13}, -1)$; that is, approximately $(4.6, -1)$ and $(-2.6, -1)$. Since $\frac{b^2}{a} = \frac{4}{3}$, we approximate the end points of each latus rectum as $(4.6, 0.3)$, $(4.6, -2.3)$, $(-2.6, 0.3)$, and $(-2.6, -2.3)$. We sketch the curve and shade the region which is the graph of the inequality. This region includes the origin.

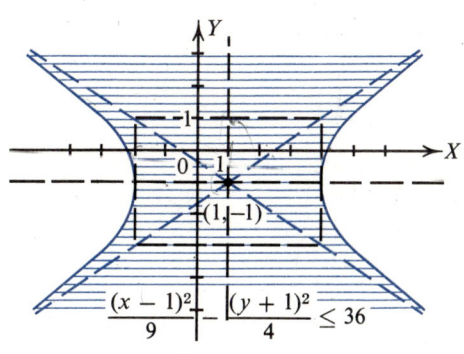

Figure 7–32

TEST YOURSELF

Consider the equation $\frac{x^2}{9} - \frac{(y - 1)^2}{16} = 1$ and identify:

1. The center.
2. The length of the transverse axis.
3. The vertices.
4. The end points of the conjugate axis.
5. The foci.
6. The end points of each latus rectum.
7. The equations of the asymptotes.

LINEAR AND QUADRATIC EXPRESSIONS

Find the equation of the hyperbola with:

8. Center at (0, 0); a vertex at (4, 0); a focus at (5, 0).
9. A vertex at (0, −3); foci at (0, 5) and (0, −5).
10. Vertices at (5, 7) and (−3, 7); a focus at (6, 7).

EXERCISES

Find the equation of the hyperbola with:

1. Center at (0, 0); a vertex at (5, 0); a focus at (13, 0).
2. Center at (0, 0); a vertex at (0, 5); a focus at (0, −6).
3. Center at (−2, 3); a vertex at (0, 3); a focus at (1, 3).
4. Center at (5, −4); a vertex at (5, 0); a focus at (5, −9).
5. Center at (0, 0); a vertex at (0, 2); focal width 16.
6. Center at (1, 3); a vertex at (−3, 3); focal width 18.

Graph:

7. $x^2 - y^2 = 8$.
8. $x^2 - y^2 = -1$.
9. $\dfrac{x^2}{5} - \dfrac{y^2}{4} = 1$.
10. $x^2 - y^2 < 1$.
11. $4x^2 - 9y^2 > 36$.
12. $9x^2 - 16y^2 < 144$.
13. $(y - 3)^2 - (x - 2)^2 > 4$.
14. $25y^2 - 9(x - 1)^2 < 225$.

• • •

In Exercises 15 through 17 identify for each graph in Exercises 7 through 14:

15. The domain.
16. The range.
17. The equations of the asymptotes of the related hyperbola.
18. Prove that any hyperbola $b^2x^2 - a^2y^2 = a^2b^2$ is symmetric with respect to the (a) x-axis; (b) y-axis; (c) origin.
19. Prove that any hyperbola $b^2(y - k)^2 - a^2(x - h)^2 = a^2b^2$ is symmetric with respect to (a) $x = h$; (b) $y = k$; (c) (h, k).
20. Use the definition of a hyperbola as a locus to derive the equation of a hyperbola with foci at (5, 3) and (5, 13) where the difference of the distances is 8.
21. Repeat Exercise 20 with foci at (−1, −3) and (−1, 5) where the difference of the distances is 7.

§ 7-10 Quadratic expressions in two variables

In this section we shall observe that any circle, parabola, ellipse, or hyperbola has an equation of the form

$$Ax^2 + Bxy + Cy^2 + Dx + Ey + F = 0, \quad A^2 + B^2 + C^2 \neq 0. \quad (36)$$

Conversely, if the equation (36) has at least two points on its graph and cannot be expressed as a product of two linear expressions equal to zero, then its graph is a circle, parabola, ellipse, or hyperbola. We shall find conditions upon A, B, and C in (36) which determine the nature of the graph. These conditions therefore make it possible for us to identify the type of graph directly from the equation. Any equation of the form (36) which satisfies the conditions that we have just stated can be replaced by an equation in the standard forms for a circle, parabola, ellipse, or hyperbola by a rotation of the coordinates axes.

Consider the effect upon the equation (36) of a rotation of the coordinate axes about the origin through an angle θ. As in § 7-6 we substitute $x' \cos \theta - y' \sin \theta$ for x and $x' \sin \theta + y' \cos \theta$ for y in the equation (36). We obtain an equation

$$A'x'^2 + B'x'y' + C'y'^2 + D'x' + E'y' + F' = 0$$

where, as may be checked by performing the substitution,

$$A' = A \cos^2 \theta + B \sin \theta \cos \theta + C \sin^2 \theta,$$
$$B' = B(\cos^2 \theta - \sin^2 \theta) - 2(A - C) \sin \theta \cos \theta,$$
$$C' = A \sin^2 \theta - B \sin \theta \cos \theta + C \cos^2 \theta,$$
$$D' = D \cos \theta + E \sin \theta,$$
$$E' = -D \sin \theta + E \cos \theta,$$
$$F' = F.$$

Notice that the last equation indicates in particular that if the origin is a point of the graph of (36) then it is a point of the graph of the new equation.

If a value for θ is selected such that

$$B(\cos^2 \theta - \sin^2 \theta) - 2(A - C) \sin \theta \cos \theta = 0,$$

then the $x'y'$ term has coefficient zero. Notice that this condition upon θ can be expressed as

$$B \cos 2\theta = (A - C) \sin 2\theta,$$

$$\tan 2\theta = \frac{B}{A - C}.$$

Such a value for θ can always be found since the range of $\tan 2\theta$ is the set of all real numbers. Thus if the coordinate axes are rotated about the

389

LINEAR AND QUADRATIC EXPRESSIONS

origin through an angle θ where $\tan 2\theta = \dfrac{B}{A - C}$, any equation (36) can be replaced by an equation of the form

$$Ax^2 + Cy^2 + Dx + Ey + F = 0 \tag{37}$$

where the primes have been dropped since only the form of the equation is being specified.

We next consider the effect upon the equation (36) of a translation of the coordinate axes $(x', y') = (x - h, y - k)$. As in § 7–6 we substitute $x' + h$ for x and $y' + k$ for y in the equation. We obtain an equation

$$A'x'^2 + B'x'y' + C'y'^2 + D'x' + E'y' + F' = 0$$

where, as may be checked by performing the substitution,

$$\begin{aligned}
&A' = A, \quad B' = B, \quad C' = C, \\
&D' = 2Ah + Bk + D, \\
&E' = Bh + 2Ck + E, \\
&F' = Ah^2 + Bhk + Ck^2 + Dh + Ek + F.
\end{aligned}$$

Notice that the last equation indicates in particular that if (h, k) is a point of the graph of (36), then the constant term of the new equation is zero as might have been expected.

If values for h and k are selected such that

$$\begin{cases} 2Ah + Bk = -D \\ Bh + 2Ck = -E, \end{cases}$$

then $D' = 0$, $E' = 0$, and the new equation has the form

$$Ax^2 + Bxy + Cy^2 = H \tag{38}$$

where the primes have been dropped since only the form of the equation is being specified. As in § 7–3 values for h and k can be found to satisfy this system of equations if the determinant of the coefficients is different from zero. Thus if $B^2 - 4AC \neq 0$, a translation of the coordinate axes may be used to express the equation (36) in the form (38).

If $B^2 - 4AC = 0$, we first obtain the form (37) of the equation and then apply the translation to the new form. Note that now since $B^2 - 4AC = 0$ and $B = 0$, we have $AC = 0$. For any quadratic relation (36) at least one of the coefficients A, B, C must be different from zero. Thus if $A = 0$, $C \neq 0$, then the equation has the form $Cy^2 + Dx + Ey + F = 0$ and may be expressed in the form $y^2 + \dfrac{E}{C}y = -\dfrac{D}{C}x - \dfrac{F}{C}$ which has a parabola as its graph when $D \neq 0$; if $D = 0$, the equation is factorable into linear factors or has no points on its graph. Similarly, if $C = 0$,

§ 7-10 QUADRATIC EXPRESSIONS IN TWO VARIABLES

$A \neq 0$, then the equation has a parabola as its graph, factors into linear factors, or has no points on its graph.

We know that under a translation A, B, and C and thus $B^2 - 4AC$ are unchanged. We may prove that under a rotation $B^2 - 4AC = B'^2 - 4A'C'$. The proof may be accomplished by substituting the values established early in this section for A', B', and C' under a rotation in the expression $B'^2 - 4A'C'$. Since the manipulations necessary to complete the proof are cumbersome (although not beyond your abilities if you care to try it), we shall assume that the value of $B^2 - 4AC$ is not affected by rotations of the axes. Thus if $B^2 - 4AC = 0$ for the equation (36), then $AC = 0$ for (37) and $B^2 - 4AC = 0$ for (38). Then any quadratic equation (36) which has at least one point on its graph and does not factor into linear factors has a parabola as its graph if $B^2 - 4AC = 0$. Conversely, any parabola has an equation of the form (36) with $B^2 - 4AC = 0$ since the equation of any parabola can be obtained from $y^2 = 4px$ by a translation and a rotation of the coordinate axes.

Any equation (36) with $B^2 - 4AC \neq 0$ may be expressed in the form (37) and in the form (38) and thus in the form

$$A'x^2 + C'y^2 = H$$

with $A'C' \neq 0$ since $A'C' = B^2 - 4AC$. If $H = 0$, then the equation can either be expressed as a product of linear factors or has only one point (0, 0) on its graph. If $H \neq 0$, the equation can be expressed in the form

$$A''x^2 + C''y^2 = 1$$

where $A'' = \dfrac{A'}{H}$ and $C'' = \dfrac{C'}{H}$. If A'' and C'' are both negative, there are no points on the graph; if A'' and C'' are both positive, the graph is a circle if $A'' = C''$, an ellipse if $A'' \neq C''$; if A'' and C'' are of opposite signs, the graph is a hyperbola. Since $A''C'' > 0$ implies $B^2 - 4AC > 0$ and $A''C'' < 0$ implies $B^2 - 4AC < 0$, the graph of any equation (36) which has at least two points on its graph and cannot be expressed as a product of linear factors is a

parabola	if $B^2 - 4AC = 0$,
circle	if $B^2 - 4AC < 0$ and $A'' = C''$,
ellipse	if $B^2 - 4AC < 0$ and $A'' \neq C''$,
hyperbola	if $B^2 - 4AC > 0$.

As we mentioned in § 7-8, a circle is often considered as a special case of an ellipse. Whenever an equation of the form (36) is to be graphed, an effort should be made to express the equation in one of the standard

LINEAR AND QUADRATIC EXPRESSIONS

forms that we have studied. To do this you should always first express the equation in the form (37); this is always possible. If the left member of the new equation can be factored, graph the factors. If the left member cannot be factored, it can be expressed in one of the standard forms and then graphed.

The cases in which (36) has other graphs may also be summarized. The absence of any points on the graph arises when the equation may be expressed in the form $a^2x^2 + b^2y^2 = -1$; a single point as the graph arises when $a^2x^2 + b^2y^2 = 0$; intersecting lines arise when $a^2x^2 - b^2y^2 = 0$; parallel lines arise when $x^2 + bx = 0$ and $b \neq 0$ or $y^2 + cy = 0$ and $c \neq 0$; coincident lines arise when $(ax + by)^2 = 0$.

The circle, ellipse, parabola, and hyperbola are often called **conic sections** since they may be obtained as plane sections of a conical surface (Figure 7-33). If the axis of a right circular conical surface is taken as the z-axis with the origin at the vertex of the conical surface, then each plane $z = n \neq 0$ intersects the conical surface in a circle. The equation of the conical surface may be taken as

$$x^2 + y^2 = z^2.$$

The plane $z = my + 1$ intersects the conical surface in a curve such that

$$x^2 = (m^2 - 1)y^2 + 2my + 1.$$

If $m = 0$, we have $x^2 + y^2 = 1$ and the plane section is a circle. If $|m| < 1$, we have $x^2 + (1 - m^2)y^2 - 2my = 1$ and the plane section is an ellipse. If $|m| = 1$, we have $x^2 = 2y + 1$ or $x^2 = -2y + 1$ and the plane section is a parabola. If $|m| > 1$, we have $x^2 - (m^2 - 1)y^2 - 2my = 1$ and the plane section is a hyperbola. By an appropriate selection of the conical surface (§ 3-6) and the plane, any circle, ellipse, parabola, or hyperbola can arise as a plane section of a conical surface.

Circle   Ellipse   Parabola   Hyperbola

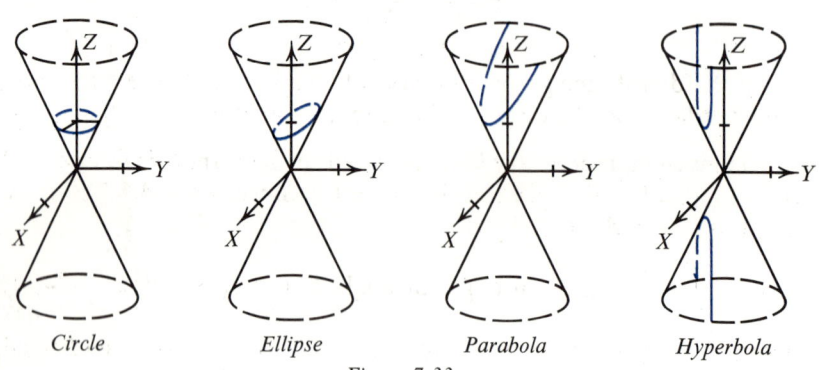

Figure 7-33

§ 7-10 QUADRATIC EXPRESSIONS IN TWO VARIABLES

The conical surface in Figure 7-33 is intersected by the *xy*-plane in a point (the origin), by the plane $y = z$ in a line, and by the *yz*-plane in a pair of intersecting lines ($y = z, y = -z$). A point, a line, and a pair of lines (intersecting or parallel) are often called **degenerate conic sections.** The parallel lines arise from a plane section of a cylindrical surface instead of a conical surface. Notice that the degenerate conic sections arise from the equation (36) if and only if that equation can be expressed as a product of linear factors or has exactly one point on its graph.

Example 1. Find the value of $B^2 - 4AC$, identify the type of conic section represented by the graph of the equation $16x^2 - 9y^2 + 160x + 18y + 247 = 0$, and obtain a new equation for the conic section with respect to new axes such that the center of the conic section is at the origin of the new coordinate system.

$$A = 16, \quad B = 0, \quad C = -9;$$
$$B^2 - 4AC = 0 - 4(16)(-9) = 0 + 576 = 576.$$

Since $576 > 0$, the graph of the equation is a hyperbola. The equation may be written in the form

$$16(x^2 + 10x) - 9(y^2 - 2y) = -247$$
$$16(x^2 + 10x + 25) - 9(y^2 - 2y + 1) = -247 + 400 - 9$$
$$16(x + 5)^2 - 9(y - 1)^2 = 144$$
$$\frac{(x + 5)^2}{9} - \frac{(y - 1)^2}{16} = 1.$$

The translation $(x', y') = (x + 5, y - 1)$ provides a new set of coordinate axes with origin at the center of the hyperbola. The new equation is

$$\frac{x'^2}{9} - \frac{y'^2}{16} = 1.$$

Example 2. Identify the graph of the equation $xy = 1$. Express the equation in standard form and sketch the graph.

The given equation may be considered in the form (36) with $A = 0$, $B = 1$, $C = 0$; $B^2 - 4AC = 1 - 0 = 1$. Since $B^2 - 4AC > 0$, the graph is a hyperbola.

We rotate the axes through an angle θ where $\tan 2\theta = \dfrac{B}{A - C}$ to obtain an equation in standard form. Since $\dfrac{B}{A - C}$ is undefined,

393

LINEAR AND QUADRATIC EXPRESSIONS

tan 2θ is undefined; thus $2\theta = 90°$, and $\theta = 45°$. Since $\sin 45° = \frac{\sqrt{2}}{2} = \cos 45°$, we use the equations

$$x = x'\frac{\sqrt{2}}{2} - y'\frac{\sqrt{2}}{2}, \quad y = x'\frac{\sqrt{2}}{2} + y'\frac{\sqrt{2}}{2}$$

and substitute in the given equation. We obtain

$$\frac{x'^2}{2} - \frac{y'^2}{2} = 1.$$

This is the new equation in standard form.

Then the hyperbola intersects the x'-axis at $(\sqrt{2}, 0)$ and $(-\sqrt{2}, 0)$; $a = \sqrt{2}$, $b = \sqrt{2}$, and $c = 2$ with reference to the new axes; also the asymptotes are $x' = y'$ and $x' = -y'$ with reference to the new axes; that is, the asymptotes are the original coordinate axes.

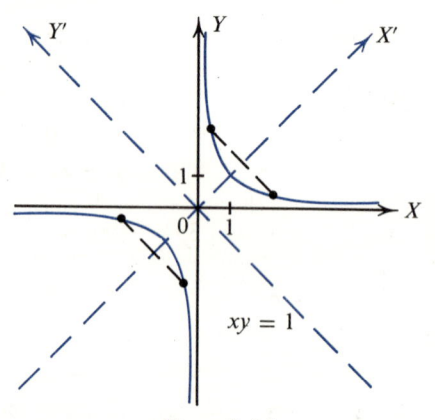

Figure 7-34

Any equation $xy = c$ where $c \neq 0$ has a hyperbola as its graph as in Example 2. The coordinate axes are the asymptotes, and the vertices are at $(\sqrt{c}, \sqrt{c})$ and $(-\sqrt{c}, -\sqrt{c})$. The given equation can be expressed in standard form as

$$\frac{x'^2}{2c} - \frac{y'^2}{2c} = 1.$$

Hyperbolas with perpendicular asymptotes are often called **rectangular hyperbolas** or **equilateral hyperbolas**. Any hyperbola with an equation of the form $xy = c$ or whose equation in standard form has $a = b$ is rectangular.

TEST YOURSELF

Identify the type of conic section represented by the graph of each equation:

1. $x^2 + 2y^2 = 5$.
2. $x^2 - 2y^2 = 0$.
3. $x^2 + 2y^2 = 0$.
4. $xy = 4$.
5. $x^2 - xy + y^2 + x - y = 5$.
6. $x^2 + 4xy + 4y^2 - 2x = 0$.

EXERCISES

Identify the type of conic section represented by the graph of each equation:

1. $4y^2 - x^2 + 16y = 0$.
2. $y^2 + 3y - 5x = 0$.
3. $4x^2 = y^2$.
4. $2x^2 + 3y^2 = 0$.
5. $x^2 + y^2 = 2x - 3$.
6. $4x^2 + 24x = 4y - y^2 - 32$.
7. $4xy = 31$.
8. $4x^2 + 9y^2 + 46 = 4x + 54y$.
9. $3y - 13 = x^2 + 8x$.
10. $x^2 + x + 2y^2 + y = 0$.
11. $x^2 - 2xy + y^2 + 10x + 10y - 25 = 0$.
12. $x^2 + 2y^2 - 4x + 12y + 25 = 0$.
13. $y^2 + 6y + 6x^2 - 3 = 0$.
14. $3x^2 + 8xy + 3y^2 - 28y - 28x + 49 = 0$.
15. $91x^2 - 24xy + 84y^2 - 7500 = 0$.
16. $3x^2 + 6x + y^2 - 2y = -4$.

• • •

In Exercises 17 through 23 use a change of coordinate axes to express the equation in the specified exercise in standard form:

17. Exercise 2.
18. Exercise 6.
19. Exercise 7.
20. Exercise 9.
21. Exercise 10.
22. Exercise 11.
23. Exercise 14.

24. Find the equation of a rectangular hyperbola with vertices at $(3, 3)$ and $(-3, -3)$.

25. Find the equation of a rectangular hyperbola with vertices at $(-2, -1)$ and $(4, 5)$.

• 26. Use a change in coordinates axes to express the equation in Exercise 15 in standard form.

§ 7–11 Systems of relations

The solution set of a system of equations or inequalities in x and y is the set of ordered pairs of real numbers which satisfy each of the statements of the system. The graph of the solution set of the system is the intersection of the graphs of the statements of the system.

LINEAR AND QUADRATIC EXPRESSIONS

The solution set of any system involving a linear equation and a quadratic equation may be obtained by substituting one variable from the linear equation into the quadratic equation, solving the resulting quadratic equation in one variable, and substituting in the *linear* (not the quadratic) equation to find the corresponding values of the second variable.

Example 1. Solve: $\begin{cases} x^2 - 3y^2 = 1 \\ 2x + 3y = 7 \end{cases}$

From the linear equation, $x = \dfrac{7 - 3y}{2}$. We substitute this value for x in the quadratic equation and solve:

$$\frac{49 - 42y + 9y^2}{4} - 3y^2 = 1$$

$$49 - 42y + 9y^2 - 12y^2 = 4$$

$$45 - 42y - 3y^2 = 0$$

$$-3(y^2 + 14y - 15) = 0$$

$$(y + 15)(y - 1) = 0$$

$$y = -15, \; y = 1.$$

If $y = -15$, $x = \dfrac{7 - 3(-15)}{2} = \dfrac{7 + 45}{2} = 26.$

If $y = 1$, $x = \dfrac{7 - 3(1)}{2} = \dfrac{7 - 3}{2} = 2.$

The solution set is $\{(26, -15), (2, 1)\}$.

In Example 1 the line $2x + 3y = 7$ intersects the hyperbola $x^2 - 3y^2 = 1$ in the two points with coordinates $(26, -15)$ and $(2, 1)$. In general, consider any linear equation and any quadratic equation which is not satisfied by all of the elements of the solution set of the linear equation. The quadratic equation obtained by substituting for one of the variables from the linear into the quadratic equation has two distinct real roots, two equal real roots, or two imaginary roots. The solution set of any system composed of such a linear and a quadratic equation consists of two, one, or no ordered pairs of real numbers. In terms of the graphs, the line intersects the graph of the quadratic equation in two distinct points, is tangent to that graph, or does not intersect it. In this chapter we consider only real variables and equations with real coefficients.

§ 7-11 SYSTEMS OF RELATIONS

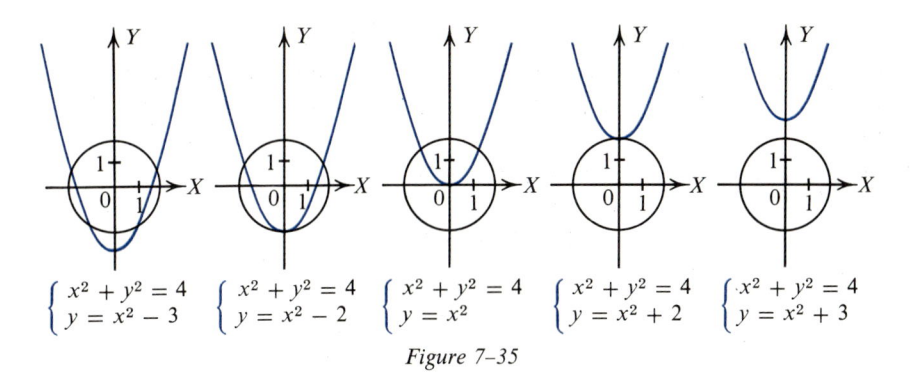

$\begin{cases} x^2 + y^2 = 4 \\ y = x^2 - 3 \end{cases}$ $\begin{cases} x^2 + y^2 = 4 \\ y = x^2 - 2 \end{cases}$ $\begin{cases} x^2 + y^2 = 4 \\ y = x^2 \end{cases}$ $\begin{cases} x^2 + y^2 = 4 \\ y = x^2 + 2 \end{cases}$ $\begin{cases} x^2 + y^2 = 4 \\ y = x^2 + 3 \end{cases}$

Figure 7-35

The graph of the solution set of a system of two quadratic equations may involve four, three, two, one, or no points (Figure 7-35) unless the graphs of the equations coincide or include a common line. Solutions obtained graphically, that is, geometric solutions, usually involve estimates of the coordinates from the graph; algebraic solutions should be exact, possibly involving radicals.

Example 2. Solve: $\begin{cases} x^2 + y^2 = 1 \\ y = x^2. \end{cases}$

Since $x^2 = y$, $y + y^2 = 1$

$$y^2 + y - 1 = 0$$

$$y = \frac{-1 \pm \sqrt{1 - 4(1)(-1)}}{2} = \frac{-1 \pm \sqrt{5}}{2}.$$

If $y = \frac{-1 + \sqrt{5}}{2}$, then $x = \pm \frac{1}{2}\sqrt{-2 + 2\sqrt{5}}$.

If $y = \frac{-1 - \sqrt{5}}{2}$, then x stands for an imaginary number. For real variables the solution set is

$$\left\{ \left(\frac{1}{2}\sqrt{-2 + 2\sqrt{5}}, -\frac{1}{2} + \frac{1}{2}\sqrt{5}\right), \right.$$
$$\left. \left(-\frac{1}{2}\sqrt{-2 + 2\sqrt{5}}, -\frac{1}{2} + \frac{1}{2}\sqrt{5}\right) \right\}.$$

For many purposes a graphical solution is sufficiently accurate. The solution set may be estimated from a carefully drawn graph as $\{(0.8, 0.6), (-0.8, 0.6)\}$.

LINEAR AND QUADRATIC EXPRESSIONS

Example 3. Solve: $\begin{cases} 9x^2 + 25y^2 = 225 \\ x + y = 10. \end{cases}$

$$\begin{cases} \dfrac{x^2}{25} + \dfrac{y^2}{9} = 1 \\ x + y = 10 \end{cases}$$

The solution set is the empty set since $|x| \leq 5$; $|y| \leq 3$; and $5 + 3 < 10$. This answer may also be obtained by substituting $10 - x$ for y in the quadratic equation and obtaining a quadratic equation which has only imaginary roots.

Some systems of quadratic equations may be solved by addition and subtraction in much the same manner as systems of linear equations. Notice that in Example 4 if x^2 and y^2 are considered as new variables, then the equations are linear in these new variables. Consider the equation $s + t = 34$ in s and t where $s = x^2$ and $t = y^2$. This equation is linear in the new variables s and t and thus is linear in x^2 and y^2 whether they remain as stated or be designated by s and t. Therefore the equation $x^2 + y^2 = 34$ is a *quadratic* equation in x and y but is a *linear* equation in x^2 and y^2.

Example 4. Solve: $\begin{cases} x^2 + y^2 = 34 \\ 2x^2 - 3y^2 = 23. \end{cases}$

Let $x^2 = s$ and $y^2 = t$, then $\begin{cases} s + t = 34 \\ 2s - 3t = 23. \end{cases}$

$$\begin{cases} 3s + 3t = 102 \\ 2s - 3t = 23 \end{cases}$$

$5s = 125, \qquad s = 25, \qquad t = 9.$

Since $s = x^2$, $x^2 = 25$, $x = 5$, $x = -5$; since $t = y^2$, $y^2 = 9$, $y = 3$, $y = -3$. If $x = 5$, $y = 3$ or $y = -3$ in both equations. If $x = -5$, $y = 3$ or -3 in both equations. The solution set is $\{(5, 3), (5, -3), (-5, 3), (-5, -3)\}$.

ALTERNATE METHOD:

$$\begin{cases} 3x^2 + 3y^2 = 102 \\ 2x^2 - 3y^2 = 23 \end{cases}$$

$5x^2 = 125$, $x^2 = 25$, $x = 5$, $x = -5$. The solution set follows as in the first method of solution.

The solution set of the system of equations $\begin{cases} y + 2x = 3xy \\ y - 2x = -xy \end{cases}$ includes

398

§ 7-11 SYSTEMS OF RELATIONS

(0, 0). All other elements of the solution set satisfy the system
$\begin{cases} \frac{1}{x} + \frac{2}{y} = 3 \\ \frac{1}{x} - \frac{2}{y} = -1 \end{cases}$ which is linear in $\frac{1}{x}$ and $\frac{1}{y}$ and may be solved as in
§ 7-3; $\frac{2}{x} = 2$ whence $x = 1$; $\frac{4}{y} = 4$ whence $y = 1$. The solution set of the given system is $\{(0, 0), (1, 1)\}$. Whenever the equations of a system are linear in expressions such as x^2 and y^2 in Example 4 or as $\frac{1}{x}$ and $\frac{1}{y}$ in the system we have just considered, it is usually easier to solve them for one or more of these expressions using the methods of § 7-3.

Systems of inequalities are usually solved graphically. All of the inequalities of the system are graphed on the same coordinate plane. The intersection of their graphs is the graph of the solution set of the system.

Example 5. Solve graphically: $\begin{cases} x^2 + y^2 < 9 \\ 2x - 3y > 6 \end{cases}$

The graph of $x^2 + y^2 < 9$ is the interior of the circle with center at the origin and radius 3. The graph of $2x - 3y > 6$ is the half-plane below the line $2x - 3y = 6$. The graph of the solution set of the system is the cross-hatched region inside the circle.

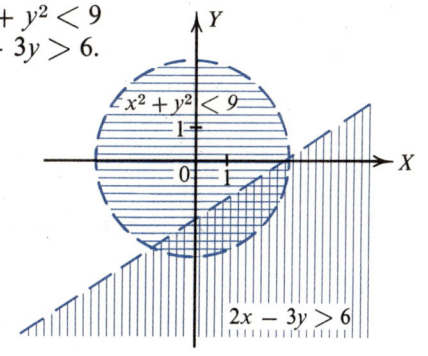

Figure 7-36

TEST YOURSELF

Solve:

1. $\begin{cases} x^2 + y^2 + 2x + 6y - 10 = 0 \\ x + y = 2 \end{cases}$

2. $\begin{cases} 2x^2 + y^2 = 16 \\ 4y^2 - x^2 = 24 \end{cases}$

3. $\begin{cases} x^2 + y^2 > 9 \\ y > x^2 \end{cases}$

399

LINEAR AND QUADRATIC EXPRESSIONS

EXERCISES

A

In Exercises 1 through 21 solve:

1. $\begin{cases} x^2 + y^2 = 25 \\ 7x + y = 25. \end{cases}$

2. $\begin{cases} 9x^2 - 4y^2 = 36 \\ 3x + 2y = 6. \end{cases}$

3. $\begin{cases} x^2 + y^2 = 6y \\ x^2 = 3y. \end{cases}$

4. $\begin{cases} x^2 + y^2 = 16 \\ x^2 + y^2 - 4y = 0. \end{cases}$

5. $\begin{cases} x^2 - y^2 = 7 \\ x^2 + y^2 = 25. \end{cases}$

6. $\begin{cases} 5x^2 + 2y^2 = 22 \\ 3y - 2x = 7. \end{cases}$

7. $\begin{cases} x^2 + 9y^2 = 9 \\ x^2 - y - 1 = 0. \end{cases}$

8. $\begin{cases} x^2 + y^2 = 25 \\ 25x^2 + 16y^2 = 400. \end{cases}$

9. $\begin{cases} 9x^2 + 16y^2 = 144 \\ 4x^2 + 4y^2 = 43. \end{cases}$

10. $\begin{cases} x^2 + y^2 = 16 \\ 17x^2 + y^2 = 25. \end{cases}$

11. $\begin{cases} x^2 + 2y^2 < 32 \\ 4x^2 + y^2 > 36. \end{cases}$

12. $\begin{cases} x^2 + y^2 > 0 \\ 4x^2 + y^2 < 4. \end{cases}$

• • •

13. $\begin{cases} x^2 + y^2 - 2x + 4y - 48 = 0 \\ x^2 + y^2 - 18x - 12y + 80 = 0. \end{cases}$

14. $\begin{cases} x^2 + y^2 - 4x + 6y - 19 = 0 \\ x^2 + y^2 + 6x - 2y + 9 = 0. \end{cases}$

15. $\begin{cases} \dfrac{7}{x} = 6 + \dfrac{3}{y} \\ \dfrac{9}{x} - \dfrac{5}{y} = 2. \end{cases}$

16. $\begin{cases} \dfrac{1}{x} + \dfrac{1}{y} = 8 \\ \dfrac{1}{x} - \dfrac{1}{z} = 1 \\ \dfrac{2}{x} - \dfrac{1}{y} + \dfrac{1}{z} = 2. \end{cases}$

17. $\begin{cases} \dfrac{1}{x} + \dfrac{1}{y} + \dfrac{1}{z} = 6 \\ \dfrac{2}{x} + \dfrac{3}{y} + \dfrac{5}{z} = 10 \\ \dfrac{3}{x} - \dfrac{2}{y} - \dfrac{3}{z} = 19. \end{cases}$

18. $\begin{cases} \sqrt{x} - \sqrt{y} = 1 \\ \sqrt{x} + \sqrt{y} = 3. \end{cases}$

19. $\begin{cases} \sqrt{x} + 2\sqrt{y} = 11 \\ 2\sqrt{x} - \sqrt{y} = 7. \end{cases}$

20. $\begin{cases} \sqrt{x} + \sqrt{y} = 7 \\ x - y = 7. \end{cases}$

21. $\begin{cases} \sqrt{x} - 2\sqrt{y} = -1 \\ x - 3y = 6. \end{cases}$

22. Express the solution set of the system $\begin{cases} x^2 + y^2 < 25 \\ 3y = 4x \end{cases}$ as a set of ordered pairs $\{(x, f(x))\}$ for a specified set of values for x.

23. Find two positive integers such that the sum of their squares is 346 and the difference of their squares is 104.

§ 7-11 SYSTEMS OF RELATIONS

24. Find the lengths of the edges of two cubes if the surface of one is 1.43 square centimeters less than three times the surface of the other, and the edge of one is 1.2 centimeters less than twice the edge of the other.

25. A monument 7 feet high consists of two cubical blocks with the smaller placed upon the larger. The total exposed surface is 141 square feet. Find the lengths of the edges of the blocks.

B

Solve algebraically for x and y and check:

1. $\begin{cases} ax^2 + by^2 = 4a \\ bx^2 - ay^2 = 4b. \end{cases}$

2. $\begin{cases} x^2 + y^2 = 4a^2 + 1 \\ x^2 + a^2y^2 = 5a^2. \end{cases}$

3. $\begin{cases} x^2 + xy + y^2 = 19 \\ x - y = 1. \end{cases}$

4. $\begin{cases} \dfrac{a}{x} + \dfrac{2a}{y} = 23 \\ \dfrac{5a}{x} - \dfrac{3a}{y} = 24. \end{cases}$

Graph each equation, identify each graph, and estimate the solution set for each system:

5. $\begin{cases} xy = 6 \\ x^2 + y^2 = 25. \end{cases}$

6. $\begin{cases} x^2 - y^2 = 0 \\ x^2 + y^2 = 4x. \end{cases}$

7. $\begin{cases} (x - 1)^2 + (y - 2)^2 = 5 \\ xy = 6. \end{cases}$

8. $\begin{cases} x^2 - 4y^2 = 0 \\ x^2 + y^2 = 2x + 15. \end{cases}$

In Exercises 9 through 14 solve graphically:

9. $\begin{cases} x = y \\ x^2 + y^2 < 4. \end{cases}$

10. $\begin{cases} x + y < 0 \\ xy > 0. \end{cases}$

11. $\begin{cases} x^2 + 4y^2 > 4 \\ y < x^2. \end{cases}$

12. $\begin{cases} x + 2y = 1 \\ y > 2x^2 + 3x + 1. \end{cases}$

13. $\begin{cases} x^2 + y^2 = 25 \\ x + y < 7. \end{cases}$

14. $\begin{cases} x^2 + y^2 \geq 25 \\ x^2 + y^2 - 2x - 6y + 1 = 0. \end{cases}$

• • •

15. Find two numbers such that their difference is equal to their product, and the sum of their reciprocals is 5.

16. Find two numbers such that the square of the first is 23 more than the square of the second, and the square of the second is 5 more than four times the first.

17. The total area of two circular regions is 74π square feet, and the sum of their perimeters is 24π feet. Find the lengths of the radii.

LINEAR AND QUADRATIC EXPRESSIONS

18. Express the length b and the width w of a rectangle in terms of its area A and the length d of one of its diagonals.

19. Express the radius r and the height h of a right circular cylinder in terms of its lateral area S and its total area T.

20. Express the radius r and the height h of a right circular cone in terms of its slant height s and lateral area S.

21. Express the edge s of the base and the height h of a regular square pyramid in terms of its lateral area S and the length e of an edge which is not an edge of the base.

22. Consider the system $\begin{cases} 2x^2 - xy = 12 \\ xy + y^2 = 6 \end{cases}$ with the points of intersection of two hyperbolas as its solution set. Add the given equations to find an ellipse through the points of intersection of the hyperbolas. Subtract twice the second equation from the first and factor the new left member to find two lines which intersect the ellipse at the points of intersection of the hyperbolas. Solve the given system by finding the points of intersection of the ellipse and the lines.

23. Use the method described in Exercise 22 to solve:

$$\begin{cases} x^2 + y^2 = 5 \\ 3xy - y^2 = 5. \end{cases}$$

Solve:

● **24.** $\begin{cases} 3x^2 + 4xy + 5y^2 = 36 \\ x^2 + xy + y^2 = 9. \end{cases}$ ● **25.** $\begin{cases} 4x^2 + 9y^2 = 10 \\ 2x^2 - 3xy = 2. \end{cases}$

● **26.** $\begin{cases} 2x^2 - xy - 28 = 0 \\ 4x^2 - 9xy - 28y^2 = 0. \end{cases}$

§ 7–12 Variation

The quotient $\frac{a}{b}$ is often called the **ratio** of a to b; this ratio may also be written in the form $a:b$. A statement of the equality of two ratios is a **proportion**. If values of two variables such as x and y correspond such that the ratio of y to x is constant, then y **varies directly as** x. Notice that if y varies directly as x then

$$\frac{y}{x} = k \quad \text{and} \quad y = kx$$

where k is a constant. Consider the perimeter p and the side s of any square. For all squares the perimeter varies directly as the side. Whenever one variable varies directly as another, we have an example of **direct variation**. In direct variation the ratio of the variables is constant and the constant k is the **constant of proportionality** (sometimes called the constant of variation).

Example 1. Use the proper value of the constant of proportionality and write the equation stating that the area A of an equilateral triangle varies directly as the square of a side s.

$$A = \frac{\sqrt{3}}{4} s^2.$$

If the values of two variables x and y are so related that their product is a constant, then y **varies inversely as** x (also x varies inversely as y); $xy = k$ where k is the constant of proportionality. Notice that if y varies inversely as x, then y varies directly as the reciprocal (multiplicative inverse) of x; $y = k\left(\frac{1}{x}\right)$. Whenever one variable varies inversely as another, we have an example of **inverse variation**. For instance, consider the lengths b and widths w of rectangles of area 20 square feet. The values of b and w are paired so that $bw = 20$; that is, b varies inversely as w and the constant of proportionality is 20.

If the values of three variables x, y, and z correspond such that z varies directly as the product of x and y, then z **varies jointly as** x and y; $z = kxy$ where k is the constant of proportionality. Whenever one variable varies jointly as two others, we have an example of **joint variation**. For instance, consider the familiar relation $D = rt$ which is used in distance, rate, and time problems; the distance varies jointly as the rate and the time. The units may be selected so that the constant of proportionality is 1; for instance, the constant of proportionality is 1 when the units are miles, miles per hour, and hours. If the distance is constant, the rate varies inversely as the time. If the rate is constant, the distance varies directly as the time.

Direct, inverse, and joint variations may be combined. For example, if z varies directly as x and inversely as y^2, then $z = \frac{kx}{y^2}$; if z varies jointly as x^2 and y and inversely as t, then $z = \frac{kx^2y}{t}$.

Most problems involving variation may be solved by
(i) stating the variation as an equation with a constant of proportionality;
(ii) using a known set of values for the variables to find the value of the constant of proportionality;
(iii) using the equation and the value of the constant to find additional values of a variable.

LINEAR AND QUADRATIC EXPRESSIONS

Example 2. The intensity I of the illumination from a given source of light varies inversely as the square of the distance d from the source. A certain light provides 160 foot-candles of illumination at a distance of 3 feet. Find the illumination at **(a)** 4 feet; **(b)** 6 feet; **(c)** 18 inches. (One foot-candle is 1 lumen of illumination per square foot.)

$$Id^2 = k; \quad 160 \times 9 = k; \quad Id^2 = 1440.$$

(a) $I(16) = 1440; I = 90$ foot-candles.
(b) $I(36) = 1440; I = 40$ foot-candles.
(c) $I\left(\frac{3}{2}\right)^2 = I\left(\frac{9}{4}\right); I\left(\frac{9}{4}\right) = 1440; I = 640$ foot-candles.

TEST YOURSELF

In Exercises 1 through 3 **(a)** *identify the value of the constant of proportionality; then* **(b)** *write the equation stating that:*

1. The surface S of a cube varies directly as the square of an edge e.
2. The volume V of a right circular cylinder varies jointly as the square of the radius r and the height h.
3. The height h of a right cylindrical gallon can (1 gallon = 231 cubic inches) varies inversely as the square of the radius r.
4. In an electric circuit with a constant electromotive force the current I (in amperes) varies inversely as the resistance R (in ohms). In a certain circuit $I = 20$ when $R = 2$. Find **(a)** I when $R = 1$; **(b)** I when $R = 0.5$; **(c)** R when $I = 5$.
5. State in the language of variation: for a circle $A = \pi r^2$.

EXERCISES

Use k as the constant of proportionality if necessary, and write the equation stating that:

1. The perimeter P of a regular hexagon varies directly as its side s.
2. The volume V of a cone varies jointly as the square of the radius r of its base and its altitude h.
3. The square of the time t for a satellite to complete one orbital trip about the earth varies directly as the cube of its average distance d from the center of the earth.
4. The force of attraction F between two objects of masses m_1 and m_2 varies directly as the product of their masses and inversely as the square of the distance d between them.

5. The force F needed to keep a car from skidding as it makes a turn varies inversely as the radius r of the turn and jointly as the mass m of the car and the square of its speed s.

• • •

In Exercises 6 through 8 state in the language of variation:

6. For a sphere: (a) $S = 4\pi r^2$; (b) $V = \dfrac{4}{3}\pi r^3$.
7. For a right circular cylinder: (a) $S = 2\pi rh$; (b) $V = \pi r^2 h$.
8. For a cube: (a) $V = e^3$; (b) $V = \dfrac{1}{36}\sqrt{6S^3}$.
9. If y varies directly as the square of x and $y = 80$ when $x = 2$, then find (a) y when $x = 0.5$; (b) x when $y = 0.2$.
10. The distance traveled by a freely falling body varies directly as the square of its time of fall t. If such a body falls 64 feet during the first 2 seconds, find the time required to fall (a) 144 feet; (b) 400 feet.
11. The volume V of an "ideal" gas varies directly as its temperature T and inversely as its pressure P. If 40 cubic feet of gas at a pressure of 15 pounds per square inch is kept at constant temperature and subjected to a pressure of 25 pounds per square inch, what is its new volume?
12. The maximum safe load L for a horizontal beam supported at both ends varies jointly as the breadth b of the beam and the square of its thickness t and inversely as the distance d between the supports. If a 2-by-8 floor timber of a certain length will hold 1600 pounds when placed with the 2-inch side down, how much will it hold when placed with the 8-inch side down? (Assume the actual dimensions of the beam to be 2 inches by 8 inches.)

SUMMARY OF CHAPTER 7

1. In this chapter you have studied linear and quadratic expressions in one and two variables. The equation of a line may be expressed in two-point form

$$\frac{y - y_1}{x - x_1} = \frac{y_2 - y_1}{x_2 - x_1};$$

point-slope form

$$y - y_1 = m(x - x_1);$$

slope-intercept form

$$y = mx + b;$$

LINEAR AND QUADRATIC EXPRESSIONS

intercept form

$$\frac{x}{a} + \frac{y}{b} = 1. \quad (\S\ 7\text{-}1)$$

2. Any linear equation in two variables has a line as its graph. The two half-planes into which the graph of any line $Ax + By + C = 0$ divides the plane are the graphs of the inequalities $Ax + By + C < 0$ and $Ax + By + C > 0$. (§ 7-2)

3. Matrices may be used to solve systems of consistent, linearly independent, linear equations. Determinants may be used to solve such systems for two linear equations in two variables or for three linear equations in three variables. (§§ 7-3 and 7-4)

4. The graph of $y = ax^2 + bx + c$ where $a \neq 0$ is a parabola with the line $x = -\frac{b}{2a}$ as an axis of symmetry, a minimum point at $\left(-\frac{b}{2a}, \frac{4ac - b^2}{4a}\right)$ if $a > 0$ or a maximum point at $\left(-\frac{b}{2a}, \frac{4ac - b^2}{4a}\right)$ if $a < 0$. The quadratic equation $ax^2 + bx + c = 0$ where $a \neq 0$ and a, b, and c are real numbers has roots $\frac{-b + \sqrt{b^2 - 4ac}}{2a}$ and $\frac{-b - \sqrt{b^2 - 4ac}}{2a}$ which are real and equal if $b^2 - 4ac = 0$, real and unequal if $b^2 - 4ac > 0$, conjugate imaginary if $b^2 - 4ac < 0$. (§ 7-5)

5. On the xy-plane the circle with center at (h, k) and radius r has the equation

$$(x - h)^2 + (y - k)^2 = r^2;$$

in coordinate three-space the sphere with center at (h, k, n) and radius r has the equation

$$(x - h)^2 + (y - k)^2 + (z - n)^2 = r^2.$$

The translation

$$\begin{cases} x' = x - h \\ y' = y - k \end{cases}$$

may be used to transform the coordinate system to obtain new axes parallel to the original axes and with the new origin at (h, k) relative to the original system. The rotation

$$\begin{cases} x' = x \cos \theta + y \sin \theta \\ y' = -x \sin \theta + y \cos \theta \end{cases}$$

may be used to rotate the coordinate axes about the origin through an angle θ. (§ 7-6)

SUMMARY OF CHAPTER 7

6. The equation of any parabola with its axis parallel to or coincident with a coordinate axis may be expressed in one of the standard forms

$$(x - h)^2 = 4p(y - k); \ (y - k)^2 = 4p(x - h). \quad (\S\ 7\text{--}7)$$

7. The equation of any ellipse with its axes parallel to or coincident with coordinate axes may be expressed in one of the standard forms

$$\frac{(x - h)^2}{a^2} + \frac{(y - k)^2}{b^2} = 1; \ \frac{(x - h)^2}{b^2} + \frac{(y - k)^2}{a^2} = 1. \quad (\S\ 7\text{--}8)$$

8. The equation of any hyperbola with its axes parallel to or coincident with coordinate axes may be expressed in one of the standard forms

$$\frac{(x - h)^2}{a^2} - \frac{(y - k)^2}{b^2} = 1; \ \frac{(y - k)^2}{a^2} - \frac{(x - h)^2}{b^2} = 1. \quad (\S\ 7\text{--}9)$$

9. The equation of any circle, parabola, ellipse, or hyperbola has the general form

$$Ax^2 + Bxy + Cy^2 + Dx + Ey + F = 0,\ A^2 + B^2 + C^2 \neq 0;$$

conversely, any equation of this form where the equation has at least two points on its graph and cannot be expressed as a product of two linear expressions equal to zero has as its graph a circle or an ellipse if $B^2 - 4AC < 0$, a parabola if $B^2 - 4AC = 0$, a hyperbola if $B^2 - 4AC > 0$. (§ 7–10)

10. Systems of quadratic or of linear and quadratic relations may be solved algebraically or graphically. (§ 7–11)

11. A variable y varies directly as x if $y = kx$ for some constant of proportionality k; y varies inversely as x if $xy = k$; z varies jointly as x and y if $z = kxy$. (§ 7–12)

12. The following words have been introduced or used extensively in this chapter:

angle of inclination (§ 7–1)
asymptote (§ 7–9)
axis of symmetry (§ 7–5)
center (§§ 7–6, 7–8, 7–9)
circle (§ 7–6)
coefficient (§ 7–1)
conic section (§ 7–10)
conjugate axis (§ 7–9)
consistent system (§ 7–3)
constant (§ 7–1)
constant of proportionality (§ 7–12)

Cramer's rule (§ 7–4)
degenerate conic section (§ 7–10)
determinant (§ 7–3)
direct variation (§ 7–12)
directrix (§ 7–7)
discriminant (§ 7–5)
eccentricity (§ 7–8)
ellipse (§ 7–8)
equilateral hyperbola (§ 7–10)
exterior point (§§ 7–5, 7–6, 7–8, 7–9)
family of graphs (§ 7–5)

407

LINEAR AND QUADRATIC EXPRESSIONS

focal width (§§ 7-7, 7-8, 7-9)
focus (§§ 7-7, 7-8, 7-9)
graph (§ 7-2)
half-plane (§ 7-2)
hyperbola (§ 7-9)
inconsistent system (§ 7-3)
interior point (§§ 7-5, 7-6, 7-8, 7-9)
inverse variation (§ 7-12)
joint variation (§ 7-12)
latus rectum (§§ 7-7, 7-8, 7-9)
linear equation (§§ 7-1, 7-2)
linear expression (§§ 7-2, 7-10)
linear function (§§ 7-2, 7-11)
linear inequality (§ 7-2)
linearly dependent (§ 7-3)
linearly independent (§ 7-3)
major axis (§ 7-8)
matrix (§ 7-3)
maximum point (§ 7-5)
minimum point (§ 7-5)
minor axis (§ 7-8)
parabola (§§ 7-5, 7-7)
proportion (§ 7-12)
quadratic function (§§ 7-5, 7-10)

rank (§ 7-3)
ratio (§ 7-12)
rectangular hyperbola (§ 7-10)
root (§§ 7-3, 7-5)
rotation (§ 7-6)
simultaneous equations (§§ 7-3, 7-11)
slope (§ 7-1)
sphere (§ 7-6)
standard form (§§ 7-6, 7-7, 7-8, 7-9)
symmetric (§§ 7-5, 7-6)
system of equations (§§ 7-3, 7-11)
transformation (§ 7-6)
translation (§ 7-6)
transverse axis (§ 7-9)
variation (§ 7-12)
varies directly (§ 7-12)
varies inversely (§ 7-12)
varies jointly (§ 7-12)
vertices (§§ 7-7, 7-8, 7-9)
x-intercept (§§ 7-1, 7-5)
y-intercept (§§ 7-1, 7-5)
zeros of a function (§ 7-5)

KEYED PRACTICE ON CHAPTER 7

1. Write the equation $2x - 3y = 6$ in (a) point-slope form; (b) slope-intercept form; (c) intercept form. (§ 7-1)

2. Graph: $|x - y| = 1$. (§ 7-2)

3. Given $\begin{cases} x - 2y = 1 \\ 2x + ky = 11 \end{cases}$ (a) find the value of k for which the system is inconsistent; (b) solve the system when $k = -1$. (§ 7-3)

4. Solve by matrices and check the value of x by determinants:
$$\begin{cases} x - y + 2z = 1 \\ 2x + y - 2z = 2 \\ x + y - z = 0. \end{cases}$$
(§ 7-4)

5. Find (a) the sum and (b) the product of the roots of $x^2 + 5x - 7 = 0$. (§ 7-5)

6. Consider the equation $y = 2x^2 + 6x - 3.5$ and find the **(a)** y-intercept; **(b)** equation of the axis of symmetry; **(c)** coordinates of the maximum or minimum point; **(d)** x-intercepts. (§ 7–5)

7. Find the center and the length of the radius of
(a) $x^2 - 2x + y^2 = 0$; **(b)** $x^2 + y^2 + 4y + z^2 - 6z = 3$. (§ 7–6)

8. Consider the parabola $y = x^2 - 6x + 5$ and identify the **(a)** axis; **(b)** vertex; **(c)** directrix; **(d)** focus; **(e)** focal width. (§ 7–7)

9. Consider the ellipse $4x^2 + 169y^2 = 676$ and identify the **(a)** center; **(b)** vertices; **(c)** end points of the minor axis; **(d)** foci; **(e)** focal width. (§ 7–8)

10. Find the equation of the hyperbola with center at $(2, -3)$, a vertex at $(6, -3)$, and focal width 18. (§ 7–9)

11. Identify by name the graph on a plane of
(a) $x^2 + 2xy + y^2 - 10x + 10y - 25 = 0$;
(b) $3x^2 - 6x + y^2 - 2y + 4 = 0$. (§ 7–10)

12. Solve: $\begin{cases} 3x^2 - y^2 = 3 \\ x + y = 5. \end{cases}$ (§ 7–11)

13. If y varies directly as the square of x and $y = 1$ when $x = 0.5$; find **(a)** y when $x = 3$; **(b)** x when $y = 100$. (§ 7–12)

TESTS ON CHAPTER 7

A

1. Find an equation of the line through $(5, 2)$ and $(-3, 6)$.

2. Graph: $2x - 3y > 6$.

3. Given $\begin{cases} 2x - 3y = -2 \\ x + ky = -8 \end{cases}$ **(a)** find the value of k for which the system is inconsistent; **(b)** solve the system when $k = 2$.

4. Solve by matrices: $\begin{cases} x + 3y + 2z = 1 \\ -x + y + 7z = 0 \\ 2x + 5y + 3z = 3. \end{cases}$

5. Find **(a)** the sum and **(b)** the product of the roots of the equation $x^2 + 7x - 15 = 0$.

6. Find the center and the length of the radius of the circle with equation $x^2 - 6x + y^2 + 8y = 0$.

7. Consider the ellipse $25x^2 + 64y^2 = 1600$ and identify the **(a)** center; **(b)** vertices; **(c)** end points of the minor axis; **(d)** foci; **(e)** focal width.

8. Find the equation of the hyperbola with center at $(-3, 2)$, a vertex at $(-3, 0)$, and focal width 16.

LINEAR AND QUADRATIC EXPRESSIONS

9. Solve graphically: $\begin{cases} x^2 + y^2 \geq 36 \\ x - y = 10 \end{cases}$

10. If z varies jointly as x and the square of y and $z = 60$ when $x = 3$ and $y = 2$, find **(a)** z when $x = 1$ and $y = -2$; **(b)** x when $z = 90$ and $y = 3$.

B

1. Write the equation $5x = 3y + 30$ in **(a)** point-slope form; **(b)** slope-intercept form; **(c)** intercept form.

2. Graph: $|x + y| = 2$.

3. Solve by matrices: $\begin{cases} x - y + z = 6 \\ 2x + y + 3z = 5 \\ -x + 2y + 2z = -3 \end{cases}$

4. Consider the equation $y = 4x^2 + 8x - 12$ and find the **(a)** y-intercept; **(b)** equation of the axis of symmetry; **(c)** coordinates of the maximum or minimum point; **(d)** x-intercepts.

5. Find the center and the length of the radius of the sphere with equation $x^2 + y^2 + z^2 + 2x - 6y + 4z = 2$.

6. Find the equation of the ellipse with center at $(3, 5)$, a focus at $(3, 8)$, and a vertex at $(3, 10)$.

7. Graph: $4x^2 - 9(y - 1)^2 < 36$.

8. Consider the equation $25y^2 - 9(x - 2)^2 = 25$ and identify the **(a)** center; **(b)** end points of the transverse axis; **(c)** end points of the conjugate axis; **(d)** foci; **(e)** equations of the asymptotes.

9. Solve: $\begin{cases} x^2 - 2y^2 = 2 \\ 2x^2 + 3y = 5 \end{cases}$

10. Identify by name the graph on a plane of each equation:

    (a) $2x^2 - 2x = y^2$;
    (b) $x^2 + y^2 + 4x + 4 = 0$;
    (c) $(x + y)^2 = 2xy + 2y^2$;
    (d) $3x^2 + 7x - 5y = 4$;
    (e) $2x^2 + 2xy + y^2 - x = 25$.

C

1. Graph: $|x - 2y| = 1$.   **2.** Solve graphically: $\begin{cases} x - 2y > 0 \\ x + y < 6 \\ y + 1 > 0 \end{cases}$

3. Find the set of possible values of k such that the graph of $y = x^2 + 2x + k$ has two distinct x-intercepts.

ANSWERS TO TEST YOURSELF EXERCISES

4. Find (a) the focal width; and (b) the equation of the parabola with vertex at $(3, -2)$ and directrix $y = 2$.

5. Consider the equation $9x^2 + 4y^2 - 18x + 24y + 9 = 0$ and identify the (a) center; (b) vertices; (c) end points of the minor axis; (d) foci; (e) focal width.

6. Find the equation of the hyperbola with foci at $(2, -4)$ and $(2, 6)$ and focal width 4.5.

7. Identify by name the graph on a plane of each equation:

(a) $x^2 + 2y^2 - 5x + 7y = 157$;
(b) $x^2 + 2x + 5 = (x + 2y)^2$;
(c) $3x^2 + (x - y)^2 + 4xy = (x + y)^2 + 12$;
(d) $2x^2 + 6x + y^2 - 10y + 50 = 0$;
(e) $(x - 2y)^2 + 4(x - 2y) + 4 = 0$.

8. Solve: $\begin{cases} x^2 + y^2 - 2x - 4y = 5 \\ 2x + 3y = 11 \end{cases}$

9. Use the definition of an ellipse as a locus and find the equation of the ellipse with foci at $(d, \sqrt{a^2 - b^2})$ and $(d, -\sqrt{a^2 - b^2})$ if the sum of the distances of each point from the foci is $2a$.

10. The volume V of an "ideal" gas varies directly as its temperature T and inversely as its pressure P. If 40 cubic feet of gas at 60° and 15 pounds pressure is subjected to 20 pounds pressure and then has temperature 50°, what is its new volume?

ANSWERS TO TEST YOURSELF EXERCISES

§ 7-1. 1. $2x - y + 3 = 0$.   3. $x - 3y - 7 = 0$.
2. $3x + y - 5 = 0$.   4. $3x - 5y - 15 = 0$.

§ 7-2. 1. $\{(x, 2x + 1)\}$; $\left\{\left(\dfrac{y - 1}{2}, y\right)\right\}$.

2.

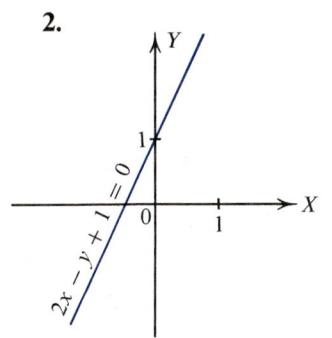

3.

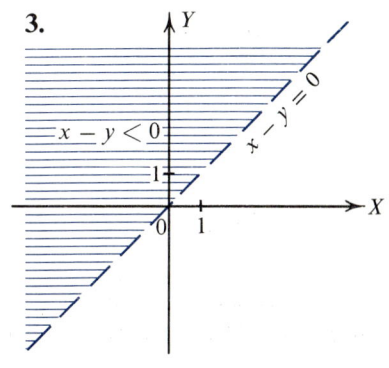

411

LINEAR AND QUADRATIC EXPRESSIONS

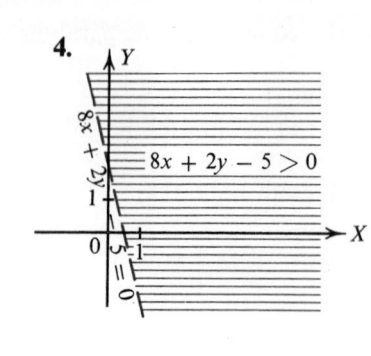

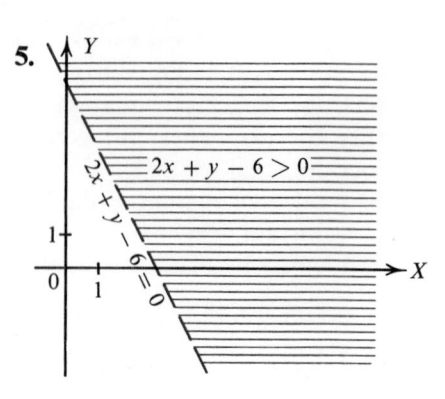

4., **5.** [graphs showing $8x + 2y - 5 > 0$ and $2x + y - 6 > 0$]

§ 7-3. 1. 6.   **2.** 0.

3. (a) Consistent;   **(b)** linearly independent;   **(c)** (1, 3).

4. (a) Inconsistent;   **(b)** linearly independent.

§ 7-4. 1. $\begin{pmatrix} 1 & 1 & 1 & 4 \\ 2 & -3 & -1 & 1 \\ 1 & 2 & 2 & 5 \end{pmatrix}, \begin{pmatrix} 1 & 1 & 1 & 4 \\ 0 & -5 & -3 & -7 \\ 0 & 1 & 1 & 1 \end{pmatrix},$

$\begin{pmatrix} 1 & 0 & 0 & 3 \\ 0 & 0 & 2 & -2 \\ 0 & 1 & 1 & 1 \end{pmatrix}, \begin{pmatrix} 1 & 0 & 0 & 3 \\ 0 & 0 & 1 & -1 \\ 0 & 1 & 0 & 2 \end{pmatrix}$; these matrices represent one possible sequence leading to the solution; $(3, 2, -1)$.

2. $(3, 2, -1)$.

§ 7-5. 1. 1.

2. Minimum point.

3. $x = 1$.

4. $(1, -2)$.

5. Sum, 2; product, $\frac{1}{3}$.

6. $1 + \frac{1}{3}\sqrt{6}, 1 - \frac{1}{3}\sqrt{6}$.

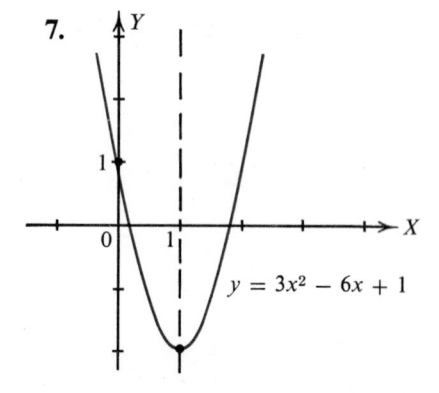

7. [graph of $y = 3x^2 - 6x + 1$]

§ 7-6. 1. (a) Center $(0, 0)$; radius 3;   **(b)** center $(2, -1)$; radius $\sqrt{6}$.
2. $x'^2 + y'^2 = 6$.   **3.** $x'^2 + y'^2 = 9$.

§ 7-7. 1. (a) $x + 3 = 0$;   **(b)** $(-3, -12)$;   **(c)** $y + 12.25 = 0$;
(d) $(-3, -11.75)$;   **(e)** 1.
2. (a) 12;   **(b)** $(y + 2)^2 = -12(x - 3)$.

ANSWERS TO TEST YOURSELF EXERCISES

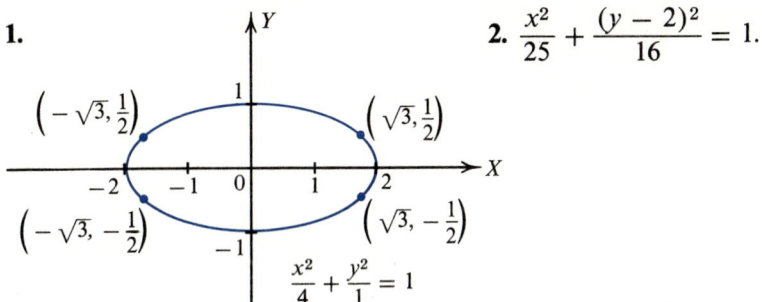

§ 7-8. **1.**

$$\frac{x^2}{4} + \frac{y^2}{1} = 1$$

Points: $\left(-\sqrt{3}, \frac{1}{2}\right)$, $\left(\sqrt{3}, \frac{1}{2}\right)$, $\left(-\sqrt{3}, -\frac{1}{2}\right)$, $\left(\sqrt{3}, -\frac{1}{2}\right)$

2. $\dfrac{x^2}{25} + \dfrac{(y-2)^2}{16} = 1$.

3. Center $(0, 0)$; vertices $(10, 0)$ and $(-10, 0)$; end points of minor axis $(0, 8)$ and $(0, -8)$; foci $(-6, 0)$ and $(6, 0)$; focal width 12.8.

§ 7-9. **1.** $(0, 1)$. **2.** 6. **3.** $(3, 1), (-3, 1)$.
4. $(0, 5), (0, -3)$. **5.** $(5, 1), (-5, 1)$.
6. $(5, 6\frac{1}{3}), (5, -4\frac{1}{3}); (-5, 6\frac{1}{3}), (-5, -4\frac{1}{3})$.
7. $4x - 3y + 3 = 0;\ 4x + 3y - 3 = 0$.
8. $\dfrac{x^2}{16} - \dfrac{y^2}{9} = 1$. **9.** $\dfrac{y^2}{9} - \dfrac{x^2}{16} = 1$.
10. $\dfrac{(x-1)^2}{16} - \dfrac{(y-7)^2}{9} = 1$.

§ 7-10. **1.** Ellipse. **2.** Two intersecting lines. **3.** One point, the origin.
4. Equilateral hyperbola. **5.** Ellipse. **6.** Parabola.

§ 7-11. **1.** $\{(1, 1), (3, -1)\}$.
2. $\left\{\left(\dfrac{2\sqrt{10}}{3}, \dfrac{8}{3}\right), \left(\dfrac{2\sqrt{10}}{3}, -\dfrac{8}{3}\right), \left(-\dfrac{2\sqrt{10}}{3}, \dfrac{8}{3}\right), \left(-\dfrac{2\sqrt{10}}{3}, -\dfrac{8}{3}\right)\right\}$.

3. The graph of the solution set consists of points in the cross-hatched region.

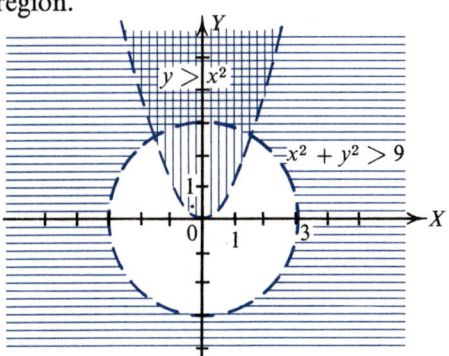

$y > x^2$

$x^2 + y^2 > 9$

LINEAR AND QUADRATIC EXPRESSIONS

§ 7-12. 1. (a) 6; (b) $S = 6e^2$.
2. (a) π; (b) $V = \pi r^2 h$.
3. (a) $\dfrac{231}{\pi}$; (b) $r^2 h = \dfrac{231}{\pi}$.
4. (a) 40 amperes; (b) 80 amperes; (c) 8 ohms.
5. The area of a circle varies directly as the square of its radius.

ANSWERS TO KEYED PRACTICE EXERCISES

1. (a) $y + 2 = \dfrac{2}{3}(x - 0)$; (b) $y = \dfrac{2}{3}x - 2$; (c) $\dfrac{x}{3} + \dfrac{y}{-2} = 1$.

2.

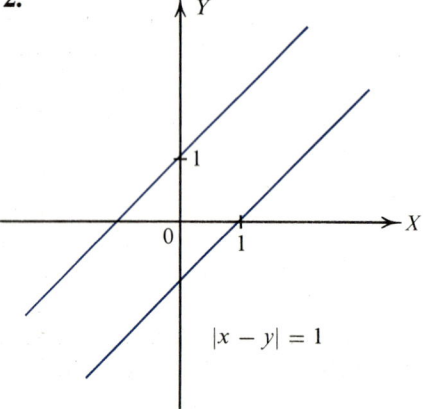

(graph showing two parallel lines, $|x - y| = 1$)

3. (a) -4; (b) $\{(7, 3)\}$.
4. $\{(1, -2, -1)\}$.
5. (a) -5; (b) -7.
6. (a) -3.5; (b) $x = -\dfrac{3}{2}$; (c) $\left(-\dfrac{3}{2}, -8\right)$, minimum;
(d) $\dfrac{1}{2}, -3\tfrac{1}{2}$.
7. (a) Center (1, 0), radius 1; (b) center (0, -2, 3), radius 4.
8. (a) $x = 3$; (b) (3, -4); (c) $y = -4.25$; (d) (3, -3.75); (e) 1.
9. (a) (0, 0); (b) (13, 0), (-13, 0); (c) (0, 2), (0, -2);
(d) ($\sqrt{165}$, 0), ($-\sqrt{165}$, 0); (e) $\dfrac{8}{13}$.
10. $\dfrac{(x - 2)^2}{16} - \dfrac{(y + 3)^2}{36} = 1$.
11. (a) Parabola; (b) a point, (1, 1).
12. $\{(2, 3), (-7, 12)\}$.
13. (a) 36; (b) 5, -5.

Chapter 8

Polynomials

§ 8-1 Polynomial expressions

Linear and quadratic expressions in one and two variables have been discussed in Chapter 7. These expressions are a part of a much larger class of expressions which are called rational integral expressions or, more commonly, *polynomials*. It is our object now to examine this larger class of expressions to determine the fundamental characteristics and properties of its members. The interest expressed in polynomials is due to the fact that many physical problems when translated into mathematical language result in statements involving polynomials. The solution of these problems requires a knowledge of the properties of polynomial equations and methods of solution of such equations.

The following definitions should be familiar to you from your previous study of mathematics: A **term** may be a constant, a product or quotient of constants, a literal number symbol, a product or quotient of literal number symbols, or a product or quotient of constants and literal number symbols. The term xy^2 may be expressed as $1xy^2$; it has **numerical coefficient** 1 and **literal part** xy^2. The term 2π has numerical **coefficient** 2π and does not have a literal part. In the term $\pi r^2 h$ the coefficient of r^2 is πh. If the literal parts of two terms are alike, the terms are **similar terms** (or like terms). The distributive law for multiplication with respect to addition may be used to add or subtract similar terms, that is, to combine similar terms. An expression which consists of a single term is a **monomial;** an expression with two terms is a **binomial;** an expression with three terms is a **trinomial.**

The constant zero, 0, is a term but does not have any degree; any constant b different from zero has degree zero, since $b = bx^0$; any term of positive integral degree in x may be expressed in the form ax^k and has **degree** k in x where the coefficient a stands for a constant different from zero, x is a variable, and k stands for a positive integer. The constant 0, any constant different from zero, and any finite sum of terms of positive integral degree in x, are often called **polynomials in** x.

The constant zero is a polynomial which does not have any degree. Any other polynomial (that is, each polynomial except the polynomial 0) has at least one term that is not 0 and thus at least one term which has a degree. The similar terms of any polynomial may be combined. Then the polynomial will consist of a sum of terms of different degrees which may be

415

POLYNOMIALS

arranged in the order of their degrees (highest to lowest) as in the expression

$$a_0x^n + a_1x^{n-1} + a_2x^{n-2} + \cdots + a_{n-1}x + a_n$$

where the coefficients $a_0, a_1, \cdots, a_n$ are constants and either $a_0 \neq 0$ or the polynomial consists of the single term 0. The terms of the expression $a_0x^n + a_1x^{n-1} + \cdots + a_n$ are said to be arranged in order of the **descending powers of x**. If $a_0 \neq 0$, the polynomial has degree n. If $a_0 \neq 0$ and $n = 0$, the polynomial is a constant different from zero. If $a_0 \neq 0$ and $n \neq 0$, the **degree of the polynominal** is the positive integer n.

If $n = 1$ and $a_0 \neq 0$, the polynomial is a linear expression,

$$a_0x + a_1.$$

As in § 7-2 the graph of any linear function $\{(x, a_0x + a_1)\}$ is a straight line.

If $n = 2$ and $a_0 \neq 0$, the polynomial is a quadratic expression,

$$a_0x^2 + a_1x + a_2.$$

As in § 7-5 the graph of the quadratic function $\{(x, a_0x^2 + a_1x + a^2)\}$ is a parabola.

If $a_0 \neq 0$, the polynomial is called a **cubic polynomial** when $n = 3$, a **quartic polynomial** when $n = 4$, and a **polynomial of higher degree** when $n > 4$.

It should be noted here that the coefficients $a_0, a_1, \cdots a_n$ may be real numbers, complex numbers, or members of any other specified set of numbers. Usually it is sufficient to state merely that the coefficients are complex numbers since all real numbers belong to the set of complex numbers; the polynomial is then called a **complex polynomial**. When the coefficients are restricted to the set of real numbers, the polynomial is called a **real polynomial**. If the coefficients are restricted to the set of rational numbers, the polynomial is called a **rational polynomial**. The polynomial

$$3x^5 - \frac{7}{2}x + 2$$

has degree five, is a real polynomial, and is also a rational polynomial. The polynomial

$$3x^3 + \sqrt{2}x^2 + x + 3$$

is a real cubic polynomial. The polynomial

$$x^2 - (2 + i)x + i$$

is a complex polynomial of degree two.

§ 8-1 POLYNOMIAL EXPRESSIONS

The **domain** of a polynomial in x is the set of possible values (domain) of the variable x. However, whenever we graph a real polynomial, we shall assume that the domain is the set of real numbers. The graph of any real polynomial function $\{(x, p(x))\}$ is "continuous"; that is, the curve may be traced by a point moving in a continuous motion from left to right. It is therefore a single, unbroken curve. Furthermore, the graph of a real polynomial function possesses "smoothness," having no corners or angles.

The graphs of many polynomial functions $\{(x, p(x))\}$ have axes of symmetry and centers of symmetry (§ 7-6). Consider the equation $y = x^{2k}$ for any positive integer k. Each point $P: (a, a^{2k})$ of the graph of $y = x^{2k}$ has a corresponding point $P': (-a, a^{2k})$ which is also a point of the graph of $y = x^{2k}$ since $a^{2k} = (-a)^{2k}$. Then since the y-axis is the perpendicular bisector of the line segment PP', the y-axis is an axis of symmetry for the graph of $y = x^{2k}$.

In general, if for any function $\{(x, f(x))\}$ the equation $f(x) = f(-x)$ holds for all values of x, then the y-axis is an axis of symmetry for the graph of the function and the function is called an **even function.** For example, any polynomial such as $x^6 - 5x^4 + 10$, with all of its terms of even degree in x defines an even function of x. Symmetry with respect to the y-axis may also be described as follows: <u>The set of points (x, y) of a graph is symmetric with respect to the y-axis if for each point (x, y) of the graph, the point $(-x, y)$ is also a point of the graph.</u> <u>Similarly, the set of points (x, y) of a graph is symmetric with respect to the x-axis if for each point (x, y) of the graph, the point $(x, -y)$ is also a point of the graph.</u>

Example 1. Find the equation of the axis of symmetry for the points $P: (2, 3)$ and $P': (6, 9)$.

The axis of symmetry s must pass through the mid-point of $\overline{PP'}$. This mid-point has coordinates $\left(\dfrac{2+6}{2}, \dfrac{3+9}{2}\right)$, that is, $(4, 6)$. Since s is perpendicular to the line PP', the slope of s is the negative reciprocal of the slope of $\overleftrightarrow{PP'}$. The slope of $\overleftrightarrow{PP'} = \dfrac{9-3}{6-2}$, that is, $\dfrac{3}{2}$. Therefore, the slope of s is $-\dfrac{2}{3}$. The equation of s may now be written in point-slope form as $y - 6 = -\dfrac{2}{3}(x - 4)$. Simplifying, we have

$$2x + 3y - 26 = 0$$

as the equation of the desired axis of symmetry.

POLYNOMIALS

As in § 7–8 the ellipse $9x^2 + 16y^2 = 144$ is symmetric with respect to both the x-axis and the y-axis. Note that the symmetry of this graph makes it possible to use a table of values for the points in the first quadrant, then obtain the points in the second quadrant using symmetry with respect to the y-axis, and then obtain the points in the third and fourth quadrants using symmetry with respect to the x-axis.

Consider the equation $y = x^{2k+1}$ for any nonnegative integer k. Each point P: (a, a^{2k+1}) of the graph of $y = x^{2k+1}$ has a corresponding point P': $(-a, -a^{2k+1})$ which is a point of the graph of $y = x^{2k+1}$ since $(-a)^{2k+1} = -a^{2k+1}$. Then since the origin $(0, 0)$ is the midpoint of the line segment PP', the origin is a **center of symmetry** for the graph of $y = x^{2k+1}$. In general, the set of points (x, y) of a graph is symmetric with respect to the origin if for each point (x, y) of the graph, the point $(-x, -y)$ is also a point of the graph. The graph of any function $\{(x, f(x))\}$ such that $f(x) = -f(-x)$ for all values of x is symmetric with respect to the origin; and any such function is called an **odd function**. For example, any polynomial, such as $x^5 - 7x^3 + 4x$, with all of its terms of odd degree in x defines an odd function of x.

Terms and polynomials may involve more than one variable as in Chapter 7. Also, as in § 7–11, a polynomial equation such as $x^2 + y^2 = 34$ in x and y may be considered as a polynomial equation in x^2 and y^2.

Example 2. State the coefficient and degree when the term $5x^6y^2$ is considered as a term in **(a)** x; **(b)** y; **(c)** x and y; **(d)** x^2; **(e)** x^3; **(f)** y^2; **(g)** z.

(a) $5x^6y^2$ has coefficient $5y^2$ and degree 6 in x.
(b) $5x^6y^2$ has coefficient $5x^6$ and degree 2 in y.
(c) $5x^6y^2$ has coefficient 5 and degree 8 in x and y.
(d) $5(x^2)^3y^2$ has coefficient $5y^2$ and degree 3 in x^2.
(e) $5(x^3)^2y^2$ has coefficient $5y^2$ and degree 2 in x^3.
(f) $5x^6y^2$ has coefficient $5x^6$ and degree 1 in y^2.
(g) $5x^6y^2z^0$ has coefficient $5x^6y^2$ and degree 0 in z.

TEST YOURSELF

1. State the coefficient and degree when the term $\pi r^2 h$ is considered as a term in **(a)** r; **(b)** r and h; **(c)** r^2.

2. Prove that the graph of $y^2 = x^2 - 5$ is symmetric with respect to **(a)** the x-axis; **(b)** the origin.

3. Find the equation of the axis of symmetry for the points P: $(2, -3)$ and P': $(8, 3)$.

§ 8–1 POLYNOMIAL EXPRESSIONS

EXERCISES

A

In Exercises 1 through 12 identify the expressions which are, or may be expressed as, polynomials in x:

1. $2x^6 + 5$.
2. $5x^{\frac{1}{2}} - 2$.
3. $3 - \frac{1}{x^2}$.
4. $(x - 1)(x - 2)(x - 3)$.
5. $8\sqrt[3]{x + 2}$.
6. $4ix^2 - (2 + i)x + 3$.
7. $x^2 + x^{\frac{3}{2}}$.
8. $x + \sqrt{2}$.
9. $\sqrt{x} + 2$.
10. $\sqrt{x + 2}$.
11. $\frac{1}{2}x^4 - 3x^2 + \frac{7}{2}$.
12. $\sqrt{2}x^2 + 3x - x^0$.

13. Identify the expressions in Exercises 1 through 12 which are (a) real polynomials in x; (b) rational polynomials in x.

• • •

14. State the coefficient and degree when the term $2x^3y^8$ is considered as a term in (a) x^3; (b) x and y; (c) y^2; (d) y^4; (e) y and t.
15. Prove that the sum of any two polynomials is a polynomial.
• 16. Prove that the product of any two polynomials is a polynomial.

B

Find the equation of the axis of symmetry for the given points:

1. $(3, 5)$ and $(-2, 1)$.
2. $(-5, 6)$ and $(2, -1)$.

In Exercises 3 through 15 prove that the graph of each statement is symmetric with respect to the indicated line or point:

3. $y = x^2 + 5$, y-axis.
4. $y^2 = x$, x-axis.
5. $y = x^5 - 3x^3 + 2x$, origin.
6. $y = x^4$, y-axis.

• • •

7. $x^2 + 2y^2 = 2$, x-axis, y-axis, and origin.
8. $y = \cos x$, y-axis.

POLYNOMIALS

9. $y = \sin x$, origin.
10. $|y| < 3$, x-axis.
11. $y \geq x^2$, y-axis.
12. $y^2 = x^3$, x-axis.
13. $xy = 1$, origin.
● **14.** $|x| + |y| = 1$, x-axis, y-axis, and origin.
● **15.** $y = 1$ if $x \geq 0$ and $y = -1$ if $x \leq 0$, origin.
● **16.** Find the value of p if the equation of the axis of symmetry of $y = 2x^2 + px + q$ is $x = 3$.
● **17.** Prove that the graph of $Ax^2 + Cy^2 + Dx + Ey + F = 0$ where $AC \neq 0$ has at least two axes of symmetry whenever there is a graph.

C

Copy the given figures (a), (b), and (c) and add to each of them whatever is necessary so that the new figure will be symmetric with respect to the specified line:

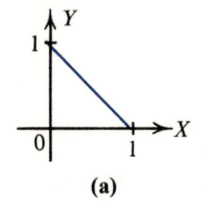

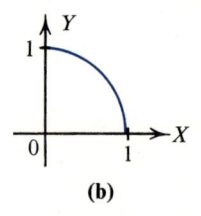

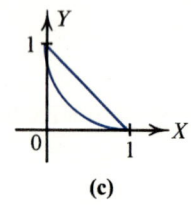

1. $x = 0$. **2.** $y = 1$. **3.** $x = 2$. **4.** $x = -1$.

In Exercises 5 through 13 state whether each expression $f(x)$ defines an odd function of x, an even function of x, or neither:

5. $x^5 - 3x$.   **8.** 5.   **11.** $x \sin x$.
6. $x^3 + 5$.   **9.** 2^x.   **12.** $|x|$.
7. $x^2 + 4$.   **10.** $\sin x$.   **13.** $|x - 1|$.

● ● ●

14. State the coefficient and degree when the term $7r^4s^6$ is considered as a term in (a) r and s; (b) r^2; (c) s^2; (d) r^2 and s^2; (e) s^2 and t.

15. State the coefficient and degree when the term $3x^{10}y^2z^3$ is considered as a term in (a) x^2; (b) y^2; (c) x and z; (d) x^2 and z; (e) y and z.

16. Prove that any polynomial that is an even function of x is a polynomial in x^2.

● **17.** Prove that the product of any two even functions of x is an even function of x.

§ 8-2 Remainder and factor theorems

The Remainder Theorem states that when a polynomial $p(x)$ is divided by a linear polynomial of the form $(x - c)$, the remainder R is numerically equal to the value of the polynomial when the variable takes on the value c. Theorem 1 is called the **Remainder Theorem:**

Theorem 1. *The remainder when any polynomial $p(x)$ is divided by $(x - c)$ is $p(c)$.*

> PROOF: When any polynomial $p(x)$ is divided by an expression $(x - c)$, we obtain a quotient $q(x)$ and a remainder R;
>
> $$p(x) = q(x) \times (x - c) + R$$
>
> where $q(x)$ stands for a polynomial of degree one less than the degree of $p(x)$ and R is the remainder, a constant. Then when $x = c$,
>
> $$p(c) = q(c) \times 0 + R$$
>
> and
>
> $$p(c) = R.$$

Example 1. Prove that when $p(x) = x^4 - 3x^3 + 4x^2 - x - 2$ and $p(x)$ is divided by $(x - 2)$, the remainder is equal to $p(2)$.

> Dividing $p(x)$ by $(x - 2)$, we have
>
> $$\begin{array}{r} x^3 - x^2 + 2x + 3 \\ x - 2 \overline{\smash{)}x^4 - 3x^3 + 4x^2 - x - 2} \\ \underline{x^4 - 2x^3} \\ -x^3 + 4x^2 \\ \underline{-x^3 + 2x^2} \\ 2x^2 - x \\ \underline{2x^2 - 4x} \\ 3x - 2 \\ \underline{3x - 6} \\ 4 \end{array}$$
>
> $$x^4 - 3x^3 + 4x^2 - x - 2 = (x^3 - x^2 + 2x + 3)(x - 2) + 4.$$
>
> Therefore, the remainder equals 4 when $p(x)$ is divided by $(x - 2)$. Now, $p(2) = (2)^4 - 3(2)^3 + 4(2)^2 - (2) - 2$
> $= 16 - 24 + 16 - 2 - 2$
> $= 4.$
>
> Hence, $p(2)$ equals the remainder, 4, which may be found without doing the long division.

POLYNOMIALS

Example 2. Find the remainder when $(x^6 - 2x^5 + 3)$ is divided by $(x + 1)$.

By the Remainder Theorem, if $p(x)$ is divided by $(x - c)$, the remainder is $p(c)$. Now, $p(x) = x^6 - 2x^5 + 3$, and $x - c = x + 1$ or $c = -1$. Hence, the remainder we desire is $p(-1)$ where

$$p(-1) = (-1)^6 - 2(-1)^5 + 3 = 1 + 2 + 3 = 6.$$

Theorem 2 is an important consequence of the Remainder Theorem and is called the **Factor Theorem:**

Theorem 2. *If a polynomial $p(x) = 0$ when $x = c$, then $(x - c)$ is a factor of $p(x)$.*

PROOF: If $p(x) = 0$ when $x = c$, then $p(c) = 0$; by the Remainder Theorem, $R = 0$ in the identity

$$p(x) = q(x) \times (x - c) + R;$$
$$p(x) = q(x) \times (x - c).$$

In other words, $(x - c)$ is a factor of $p(x)$ since $p(x)$ may be expressed as the product of two polynomial factors, one of which is $(x - c)$.

The converse of Theorem 2 is also true and we state it as a theorem:

Theorem 3. *If $(x - c)$ is a factor of $p(x)$, then $p(x) = 0$ when $x = c$.*

PROOF: If $(x - c)$ is a factor of $p(x)$, then

$$p(x) = q(x) \times (x - c);$$
$$p(x) = q(x) \times (x - c) + 0;$$

the remainder R is 0; and by the Remainder Theorem, $R = p(c) = 0$; that is, $p(x) = 0$ when $x = c$.

Example 3. Use the Factor Theorem and prove that $(x - 2)$ is a factor of $p(x)$ when $p(x) = x^3 - x^2 - x - 2$.

$$p(2) = 2^3 - 2^2 - 2 - 2 = 8 - 4 - 2 - 2 = 0$$

Since $p(x) = 0$ when $x = 2$, the expression $(x - 2)$ is a factor of $p(x)$.

Example 4. Prove that $(x - 1)$ is a factor of $(x^n - 1)$ for any positive integer n.

Let $p(x) = x^n - 1$. Then $p(1) = 0$ for any positive integer n, and by the Factor Theorem $(x - 1)$ is a factor of $(x^n - 1)$ for any positive integer n.

§ 8-2 REMAINDER AND FACTOR THEOREMS

Example 5. For what value of k is $(x - 1)$ a factor of $p(x)$ where $p(x) = 3x^{15} + kx^9 - 5$?

By Theorem 3, if $(x - 1)$ is a factor of $p(x)$, then $p(1) = 0$. Now, $p(1) = 3(1)^{15} + k(1)^9 - 5 = 3 + k - 5 = k - 2$. Since $p(1) = 0$ if and only if $k = 2$, we know that $(x - 1)$ is a factor of $p(x)$ if and only if $k = 2$.

A statement that a polynomial is equal to zero is a **polynomial equation.** Any polynomial equation, $p(x) = 0$, may be expressed in the form

$$a_0 x^n + a_1 x^{n-1} + a_2 x^{n-2} + \cdots + a_{n-1} x + a_n = 0.$$

The values of x for which the equation is a true statement (that is, the values which *satisfy* the equation) are called **solutions** or **roots** of the equation. By Theorems 2 and 3 we know that if an equation $p(x) = 0$ has a root $x = c$, then $(x - c)$ is a factor of $p(x)$, and conversely.

Example 6. Prove that 2 is a root of the equation

$$x^4 - 3x^3 + 4x^2 - x - 6 = 0.$$

By definition 2 is a root if and only if 2 satisfies the equation. Thus the statement

$$2^4 - 3(2)^3 + 4(2)^2 - 2 - 6 = 16 - 24 + 16 - 2 - 6 = 0$$

proves that 2 is a root of the given equation.

If the equation in Example 6 is represented by the equation $p(x) = 0$, then $p(2) = 0$ and $(x - 2)$ is a factor of $p(x)$. Indeed

$$p(x) = (x - 2)(x^3 - x^2 + 2x + 3)$$

as may be checked by multiplying the two factors. The equation in Example 6 may be expressed in the form

$$(x - 2)(x^3 - x^2 + 2x + 3) = 0.$$

The root 2 satisfies the equation

$$x - 2 = 0$$

obtained by setting the first factor equal to zero. The remaining roots satisfy the equation

$$x^3 - x^2 + 2x + 3 = 0$$

which is called the **depressed equation** relative to the root 2 and is obtained by setting the second factor equal to zero.

POLYNOMIALS

TEST YOURSELF

1. Find the remainder when $(2x^3 - 4x - 3)$ is divided by $(x - 2)$.
2. Show that $(x - 1)$ is a factor of $(x^2 - 5x + 4)$.
3. Find the value of k if $(x + 1)$ is a factor of $(2x^{19} + kx^{13} + 5)$.

EXERCISES

In Exercises 1 through 6 find the remainder when:

1. $x^4 - 5x^3$ is divided by $(x - 2)$.
2. $x^4 + 2x^3 - x + 8$ is divided by $(x + 3)$.
3. $x^{16} + 5$ is divided by $(x + 1)$.
4. $2x^8 + 6x^4 + 7$ is divided by $(x - 1)$.
5. $x^3 + 3x^2 + 3x + 2$ is divided by $(x - k)$.
6. $x^5 - 3x^3 + x - 3$ is divided by $(x + 2k)$.

7. When $p(x)$ is divided by $(x + 2)$, the quotient is $(x^3 - x + 1)$ and the remainder is 4. Find $p(x)$.
8. Find the value of k if $(x - 1)$ is a factor of $(2x^{17} + kx^9 - 4)$.
9. Find the value of k if $(x + 1)$ is a factor of $(x^{23} - kx^7 + 3)$.
10. If $p(x) = (x - 5) \times q(x) + 3$, find $p(5)$.

• • •

11. Find a factor of $(x^5 - 32)$.
12. Find a factor of $(x^3 + 216)$.
13. Find c if $(x^3 - 4cx^2 + cx + 6)$ is exactly divisible by $(x - 2)$.
14. When $(x^3 + 2x^2 + cx - 9)$ is divided by $(x - 2)$, the remainder is 3. Find the value of c.
15. One root of the equation $2x^3 + 7x^2 + 6x = 5$ is $\frac{1}{2}$. Write a quadratic equation which can be used to find the other two roots.
16. Prove that $(x^{2n+1} + 1)$ has $(x + 1)$ as a factor for any positive integer n.
• 17. If n is a positive integer, under what conditions is $(x^n + a^n)$ divisible by $(x + a)$? By $(x - a)$?
• 18. If n is a positive integer, under what condtions is $(x^n - a^n)$ divisible by $(x + a)$? By $(x - a)$?
• 19. Prove that $(10 - 1)$ is a factor of $(10^n - 1)$ for any positive integer n.
• 20. Any four-digit integer N can be written in the form $(10^3a + 10^2b + 10c + d)$ where a, b, c, and d are elements of the set $\{0, 1, 2, \cdots, 9\}$ and

$a \neq 0$. Then $N = [(10^3 - 1)a + (10^2 - 1)b + (10 - 1)c] + (a + b + c + d)$. Use the result obtained in Exercise 19 to prove that any four-digit integer is divisible by 9 if the sum of its digits is divisible by 9.
- 21. Give and explain a test for the divisibility of any integer by 9.

§ 8-3 Synthetic division

Dividing a given polynomial $p(x)$ by a linear polynomial of the form $(x - c)$ by the method of long division is rather laborious. There is a simpler procedure called synthetic division which makes use of only c and the coefficients of $p(x)$. To illustrate the method consider the polynomial $(x^4 + 2x^2 - 6x + 13)$ which we shall divide by $(x - 3)$. We first use long division:

$$
\begin{array}{r}
x^3 + 3x^2 + 11x + 27 \\
x - 3 \overline{\smash{\big)}\, x^4 + 2x^2 - 6x + 13} \\
\underline{x^4 - 3x^3} \\
3x^3 + 2x^2 \\
\underline{3x^3 - 9x^2} \\
11x^2 - 6x \\
\underline{11x^2 - 33x} \\
27x + 13 \\
\underline{27x - 81} \\
94
\end{array}
$$

Notice that we first arranged both polynomials in the order of the descending powers of x and that a space was left for the missing power, $0x^3$; that is, we treated the polynomials as though there were a term $0x^3$. Then the coefficients of the dividend may be represented as

$$1 \quad 0 \quad 2 \quad -6 \quad 13.$$

The pattern of coefficients in the long division was

$$
\begin{array}{r}
1 \quad 3 \quad 11 \quad 27 \\
1 - 3 \overline{\smash{\big)}\, 1 0 2 -6 13} \\
\underline{1 -3} \\
3 2 \\
\underline{3 -9} \\
11 -6 \\
\underline{11 -33} \\
27 13 \\
\underline{27 -81} \\
94
\end{array}
$$

425

POLYNOMIALS

This array may be simplified by leaving out the numbers in dark type, that is, the numbers which are just the same as the ones above them. Then we have the array

$$\begin{array}{r|rrrrr} & & 1 & 3 & 11 & 27 \\ 1-3 & 1 & 0 & 2 & -6 & 13 \\ & & -3 & -9 & -33 & -81 \\ \hline & 1 & 3 & 11 & 27 & 94 \end{array}$$

where the **1** has been inserted so that the first four elements on the bottom row will be just like the elements on the top row. This makes the top row superfluous. Finally, we have used only "-3" from the coefficients "$1-3$" and we subtracted "-3." We may replace any subtraction problem with an addition problem by changing the sign of the subtrahend and adding. Accordingly, we now use "$+3$" so that we may add instead of subtract the elements on the second row:

$$\begin{array}{r|rrrrr} 3 & 1 & 0 & 2 & -6 & 13 \\ & & 3 & 9 & 33 & 81 \\ \hline & 1 & 3 & 11 & 27 & 94 \end{array}$$

The following properties hold whenever we divide by $(x-c)$:

1. The first row is formed by the coefficients of the dividend with the powers in descending order. (Be sure to include a zero coefficient for any missing powers.)

2. The first number on the first row is also used as the first number on the third row; the second row is left blank in this first column.

3. In each column after the first: the number on the second row is obtained by multiplying the number in the preceding column on the third row by c; each number on the third row is obtained by adding the numbers above it.

4. The last number on the third row is the remainder; the others are the coefficients of the polynomial part of the answer.

The fourth property indicates that we may use the array to obtain the result

$$x^4 + 2x^2 - 6x + 13 = (x-3)(x^3 + 3x^2 + 11x + 27) + 94.$$

Notice that when the factor is $(x-3)$ we used 3. Similarly, for $(x-2)$ we would use 2; for $(x+1)$ we would use -1 since $x+1 = x-(-1)$.

The use of an array of three lines, such as the array we have just considered, instead of long division is called **synthetic division**. We now prove

§ 8-3 SYNTHETIC DIVISION

that the process of synthetic division is valid for finding the quotient and remainder when any polynomial $p(x)$ is divided by $(x - h)$. Consider any polynomial $p(x)$ given in the form

$$a_0 x^n + a_1 x^{n-1} + a_2 x^{n-2} + \cdots + a_{n-1} x + a_n, \text{ where } a_0 \neq 0.$$

We know that $p(x)$ also may be expressed in the form

$$p(x) = (x - h) \times q(x) + R$$

where $q(x)$ is a polynomial of degree $(n - 1)$ and R is a constant. Let

$$q(x) = c_0 x^{n-1} + c_1 x^{n-2} + c_2 x^{n-3} + \cdots + c_{n-2} x + c_{n-1},$$

where the coefficients $c_0, c_1, c_2, \cdots, c_{n-2}, c_{n-1}$ are to be determined. When we expand the expression $(x - h) \times q(x) + R$, we obtain

$$c_0 x^n + (c_1 - c_0 h) x^{n-1} + (c_2 - c_1 h) x^{n-2} + \cdots \\ + (c_{n-1} - c_{n-2} h) x + (R - c_{n-1} h).$$

This expression must be another way of writing the given polynomial $p(x)$. Accordingly, the coefficients of the powers of x in this expression must equal the corresponding coefficients of the terms of $p(x)$. Therefore we have

$$a_0 = c_0$$
$$a_1 = c_1 - c_0 h$$
$$a_2 = c_2 - c_1 h$$
$$\vdots$$
$$a_{n-1} = c_{n-1} - c_{n-2} h$$
$$a_n = R - c_{n-1} h.$$

These relations may be expressed in the following forms which make it easier for us to calculate the c_i's and R:

$$c_0 = a_0$$
$$c_1 = a_1 + c_0 h$$
$$c_2 = a_2 + c_1 h$$
$$\vdots$$
$$c_{n-1} = a_{n-1} + c_{n-2} h$$
$$R = a_n + c_{n-1} h.$$

If we employ the method of synthetic division for $p(x)$ divided by

POLYNOMIALS

$(x - h)$, it will become evident that the elements of the third row are the c_i's and R:

$$
\begin{array}{c|ccccccc}
h & a_0 & a_1 & a_2 & \cdots & a_{n-1} & a_n \\
 & & c_0 h & c_1 h & \cdots & c_{n-2} h & c_{n-1} h \\
\hline
 & a_0 & a_1 + c_0 h & a_2 + c_1 h & \cdots & a_{n-1} + c_{n-2} h & \boxed{a_n + c_{n-1} h}
\end{array}
$$

that is,

$$
\begin{array}{cccccc}
c_0 & c_1 & c_2 & \cdots & c_{n-1} & R.
\end{array}
$$

Example 1. Use synthetic division to divide

$$(2x^4 + x^3 + 4x - 12) \text{ by } (x + 2).$$

Note that the x^2 term is missing. Remember that its zero coefficient must be considered in synthetic division. The divisor $(x - c)$ is $(x + 2)$ which we think of as $x - (-2)$ and use -2.

$$
\begin{array}{c|ccccc}
-2 & 2 & 1 & 0 & 4 & -12 \\
 & & -4 & 6 & -12 & 16 \\
\hline
 & 2 & -3 & 6 & -8 & \boxed{4}
\end{array}
$$

The polynomial part of the quotient is $(2x^3 - 3x^2 + 6x - 8)$, and the remainder is 4.

CHECK: The dividend must be obtained when the remainder is added to the product of the divisor and the quotient.

$$p(x) = (x + 2)(2x^3 - 3x^2 + 6x - 8) + 4 = 2x^4 + x^3 + 4x - 12.$$

Example 2. Given that the polynomial equation $x^3 - 8x^2 + 17x - 10 = 0$ has 5 as a root, find two other roots.

Since 5 is a root of the given equation we know that $(x - 5)$ is one factor of the polynomial. The other factor is the quotient obtained when the given polynomial is divided by $(x - 5)$. The coefficients of this factor may be obtained by synthetic division:

$$
\begin{array}{c|cccc}
5 & 1 & -8 & 17 & -10 \\
 & & 5 & -15 & 10 \\
\hline
 & 1 & -3 & 2 & \boxed{0}
\end{array}
$$

Hence,

$$x^3 - 8x^2 + 17x - 10 = (x - 5)(x^2 - 3x + 2) = 0.$$

The other roots of the given equation may be obtained by solving the

depressed equation
$$x^2 - 3x + 2 = 0.$$
Factoring we have
$$(x - 1)(x - 2) = 0.$$
Therefore the other roots are 1 and 2.

Synthetic division may also be used to divide by a product of linear factors. Divide by each of the factors in order. The order used is unimportant since multiplication is commutative.

TEST YOURSELF

1. Use synthetic division to find the quotient and remainder when $(x^4 - 3x^2 + 5x - 7)$ is divided by $(x + 2)$.

2. Use synthetic division to find $f(2)$ if $f(x) = x^4 - 3x^2 + 5x - 7$.

EXERCISES

A

Use synthetic division to find the quotient and remainder when:

1. $(x^3 + 4x^2 - 15x + 12)$ is divided by $(x - 2)$.
2. $(2x^4 - 6x^3 - 3x^2 + x - 16)$ is divided by $(x - 4)$.
3. $(x^5 + x^4 - x^3 + x^2 + x - 1)$ is divided by $(x + 1)$.

• • •

4. $(x^4 + kx^3 - k^2x^2 + k^3x + 2)$ is divided by $(x - k)$.
5. $(64x^3 - 1)$ is divided by $\left(x + \frac{1}{4}\right)$.
6. $(x^3 - 2x^2 - 4x)$ is divided by $(x + 1)$.
7. $(x^3 - 3x^2 + 4)$ is divided by $(x - 2)^2$.
8. $(x^4 - 4x^3 - 15x^2 + 58x - 25)$ is divided by $(x - 5)(x + 4)$.

B (Supplementary)

Use synthetic division to find:

1. $f(3)$ if $f(x) = 2x^4 - 5x^3 + 3x - 15$.
2. $f(-2)$ if $f(x) = x^5 - 4x^3 + 3x + 7$.
3. $f(k)$ if $f(w) = w^3 - 2w^2 + w - 3$.
4. $f(3k)$ if $f(x) = x^5 - 5k^2x^3 - 10k^3x^2 - k^4x - 10k$.

POLYNOMIALS

• • •

Find the depressed equations and solve for the additional roots of each of the equations in Exercises 5 through 7:

5. $x^4 - 5x^3 + 5x^2 + 5x - 6 = 0$ with roots 3 and 1.
6. $2v^3 + 5v^2 + v - 2 = 0$ with root $\frac{1}{2}$.
7. $x^3 - 2x^2 + x - 2 = 0$ with root 2.

• 8. Notice that $p(x) = ax^4 + bx^3 + cx^2 + dx + e$ may be written in the **nested form**

$$p(x) = \{[(ax + b)x + c]x + d\}x + e.$$

Evaluate $p(2)$ by evaluating $p(x)$ in its nested form. Show that when one starts with the innermost parentheses and works outward step by step, this is equivalent to evaluating $p(2)$ by synthetic division.

Computer Method

The procedure for evaluating a polynomial expression $p(x)$ for some value of x using an electronic computer is customarily based upon the nested form of the polynomial expression as considered in Exercise 8.

---

§ 8–4 Number of roots of a polynomial equation

Any polynomial equation of the first degree in x with real numbers as coefficients may be expressed in the form

$$ax + b = 0, \, a \neq 0$$

and has exactly one real number as its root. Any polynomial equation of the second degree in x with real numbers as coefficients may be expressed in the form

$$ax^2 + bx + c = 0, \, a \neq 0$$

and has exactly two complex numbers as roots. These roots are real and equal if $b^2 - 4ac = 0$; real and unequal (that is, distinct) if $b^2 - 4ac > 0$; conjugate imaginary if $b^2 - 4ac < 0$. (See § 7–5.) The polynomial equation

$$x^2 - 6x + 9 = 0$$

has roots 3 and 3. The two equal roots are associated with two equal

430

§ 8-4 NUMBER OF ROOTS OF A POLYNOMIAL EQUATION

linear factors and each linear equation has a root. For example, if $x^2 - 6x + 9 = 0$, then $(x - 3)(x - 3) = 0$ and at least one of the factors must equal zero. If the first factor $(x - 3)$ equals zero, then $x = 3$; if the second factor $(x - 3)$ equals zero, then $x = 3$. Therefore we recognize two equal roots 3 and 3, one from each factor.

Systematic procedures exist for the solution of third degree and fourth degree polynomial equations. These procedures are involved and difficult beyond the scope of our work. Furthermore, it has been proved that no systematic procedure exists for the solution of general fifth or higher degree polynomial equations. It is our purpose to examine some fundamental concepts which may be useful in the solution of particular polynomial equations.

Mathematical problems arise in many ways and we have no guarantee that a solution exists whenever a mathematical problem may be stated. However, when presented with the problem of solving an nth degree complex polynomial equation, we can be assured that not only does a solution exist, but there are exactly n solutions. In order to prove that exactly n solutions exist we need to make use of a theorem which is known as the **Fundamental Theorem of Algebra:**

Theorem 4. *Every complex polynomial equation of degree n has at least one complex number as a root.*

Many proofs of this theorem are known but each is too difficult for us to discuss here. Accordingly we shall accept the Fundamental Theorem of Algebra without proof; that is, we shall postulate it. This enables us to prove the following theorem:

Theorem 5. *Every complex polynomial equation of degree n has exactly n complex numbers, not necessarily distinct, as roots.*

> PROOF: Consider any equation $p(x) = 0$, where $p(x)$ is a complex polynomial of degree n. From the Fundamental Theorem of Algebra we know that the equation $p(x) = 0$ has at least one complex number as a root; call this root r_1. Then, using the Factor Theorem, we may write
>
> $$p(x) = (x - r_1) \times p_1(x) = 0$$
>
> where $p_1(x)$ is a polynomial in x of degree $(n - 1)$.
> We apply the same argument to the depressed equation $p_1(x) = 0$.

431

POLYNOMIALS

This equation must have a root r_2. Then
$$p_1(x) = (x - r_2) \times p_2(x) = 0$$
where $p_2(x)$ is of degree $(n - 2)$. Substituting $(x - r_2) \times p_2(x)$ for $p_1(x)$ in our previous equation we have
$$p(x) = (x - r_1)(x - r_2)p_2(x) = 0.$$
Proceeding in this manner we finally obtain
$$p(x) = (x - r_1)(x - r_2)(x - r_3)\cdots(x - r_{n-1}) \times p_{n-1}(x) = 0$$
where $p_{n-1}(x)$ is a polynomial of the first degree with leading coefficient a_0. Therefore
$$p_{n-1}(x) = a_0(x - r_n);$$
$$p(x) = a_0(x - r_1)(x - r_2)(x - r_3)\cdots(x - r_{n-1})(x - r_n) = 0.$$

We have proved that $p(x)$ can be expressed as the product of the constant a_0 and n linear factors. The equation $p(x) = 0$ is satisfied whenever one of the linear factors is equal to zero. By Theorem 3 the n linear factors give rise to n complex numbers, not necessarily distinct, which are roots of the equation $p(x) = 0$.

We have now proved that if $p(x)$ is any complex polynomial in x of degree n, then the polynomial equation $p(x) = 0$ has at least n complex numbers as roots.

In order to complete the proof of this theorem we need to show that there cannot exist another value, say r_{n+1}, distinct from $r_1, r_2, \cdots, r_n$, which satisfies the equation
$$p(x) = a_0(x - r_1)(x - r_2)(x - r_3)\cdots(x - r_{n-1})(x - r_n) = 0.$$
Suppose r_{n+1} is different from $r_1, r_2, \cdots, r_n$ and is a root of $p(x) = 0$, then
$$p(r_{n+1}) = a_0(r_{n+1} - r_1)(r_{n+1} - r_2)(r_{n+1} - r_3)\cdots(r_{n+1} - r_{n-1})$$
$$\times (r_{n+1} - r_n).$$
But since $a_0 \neq 0$, and every factor $(r_{n+1} - r_i) \neq 0$, it follows that $p(r_{n+1}) \neq 0$ and r_{n+1} cannot be a root. If r_{n+1} is equal to a root r_j, we exclude this $(n + 1)$st root because there does not exist a linear factor associated with it. In other words, we count a root according to the number of linear factors which it satisfies.

Consider the following polynomial equation
$$a_0(x - r_1)^2(x - r_2)^3(x - r_3) = 0.$$

432

§ 8-4 NUMBER OF ROOTS OF A POLYNOMIAL EQUATION

The polynomial has degree six; there are six roots: $r_1, r_1, r_2, r_2, r_2, r_3$. Since the linear factor $(x - r_1)$ appears twice yielding the two identical roots r_1 and r_1, we speak of r_1 as being a **double root** or being a root of **multiplicity** two. Similarly, r_2 is a **triple root** or a root of multiplicity three and r_3 is a **simple root** or a root of multiplicity one. If a number is a root and is not a simple root, it is called a **multiple root**.

In order for Theorem 5 to be valid in cases in which multiple roots occur, each root is to be counted according to its multiplicity.

Example. Find a polynomial whose equation has the following roots: 2, -1, $(2 + i)$, and $(2 - i)$.

A polynomial of the fourth degree with the given numbers as roots may be written as:

$$(x - 2)(x + 1)[x - (2 + i)][x - (2 - i)] = 0;$$
$$(x^2 - x - 2)(x^2 - 4x + 5) = 0;$$
$$x^4 - 5x^3 + 7x^2 + 3x - 10 = 0.$$

Notice that if $p(x) = x^4 - 5x^3 + 7x^2 + 3x - 10$, then any polynomial equation of the form

$$a_0 \times p(x) = 0, \ a_0 \neq 0$$

also has the numbers given in the example as roots. Furthermore, any polynomial equation of the form

$$q(x) \times p(x) = 0$$

where $q(x)$ is a polynomial of positive degree, has the given numbers as roots along with others. In solving problems such as the one stated in the example, we usually select the answer $p(x) = 0$ where $p(x)$ is the polynomial of lowest possible degree and the coefficient of the term of highest degree is either 1 or the smallest possible positive integer such that the other coefficients are integers.

TEST YOURSELF

1. State the number of complex roots of the equation $x^3 - 2x + x^5 + 17 = 0$.
2. Find a polynomial equation with roots -2, 1, and 3.
3. State the multiplicity of each root of the equation $5(x + 3)^3(x - 1)^2(x^2 - 4)^5 = 0$.

POLYNOMIALS

EXERCISES

State the number of complex roots of each polynomial equation:

1. $x^5 - 3x^2 + 7 = 0.$
2. $5x^3 + 4x^2 + 3x + 2 = 0.$
3. $x^2 - x^4 + 2 = 0.$
4. $x - x^3 + x^5 + 7 = 0.$

State the multiplicity of each root of:

5. $3(x - 1)(x + 2)^3(x - 4)^2 = 0.$
6. $2(x^2 + 1)(x - 2)^3(x^2 - 9)^2 = 0.$

Find complex polynomial equations which have the following roots:

7. 1, 2, 3.
8. $-4, 5.$
9. $2, -2, 1, -1.$
10. $1, \sqrt{2}, -\sqrt{2}.$

• • •

11. $0, 1, i, -i.$
12. $2 + \sqrt{3}, 2 - \sqrt{3}, -2.$
13. $\frac{1}{2} + \frac{\sqrt{3}}{2}i, \frac{1}{2} - \frac{\sqrt{3}}{2}i, 1.$
14. $0, 1, i.$

Find the roots of the equations in Exercises 15 through 18.

15. $x^3 - 8 = 0.$
16. $x^4 - 1 = 0.$
17. $x^3 + 1 = 0.$
• **18.** $x^6 - 1 = 0.$

• **19.** If one root of the equation $x^2 + ax + b = 0$ is twice the other root, find b in terms of a.

§ 8–5 Descartes' Rule of Signs

We note that any real number is a positive number, a negative number, or zero. Conversely, since the complex numbers cannot be ordered on a line and thus cannot be classified as positive or negative, any positive number is a real number and any negative number is a real number.

In § 8–4 we were able to determine the number of complex roots of a polynomial equation. However, we could not determine how many of the complex roots were real roots. Furthermore we could not determine the nature of the real roots, that is, whether the real roots were integral, rational, or irrational. In this section we consider ways of determining the number of real roots; in the next section, ways of finding the rational roots.

We now consider the determination of the number of possible real positive and negative roots for a real polynomial equation, $p(x) = 0$, of

§ 8-5 DESCARTES' RULE OF SIGNS

the form
$$a_0x^n + a_1x^{n-1} + a_2x^{n-2} + \cdots + a_{n-1}x + a_n = 0, \ a_0 \neq 0.$$
Note that the terms are arranged in the order of the descending powers of x. Some of the coefficients
$$a_0, a_1, a_2, \cdots, a_{n-1}, a_n$$
may be zero. We exclude the zero coefficients, since zero is neither positive nor negative, and consider the remaining terms in the order in which they appear:
$$a_0, a_i, a_j, \cdots, a_k.$$
Each term of this sequence represents either a positive or a negative number. Whenever two *consecutive* terms of this sequence represent numbers of opposite sign (that is, one positive and one negative), we have a **variation in signs.** The total number of variations in sign for the sequence depends upon the coefficients of the given polynomial and is denoted by $V(a_0, a_1, a_2, \cdots, a_{n-1}, a_n)$. For example, the polynomial
$$3x^5 - 2x^4 + x^2 + 5x - 2$$
has associated with it the ordered sequence of coefficients
$$3, -2, 1, 5, -2$$
when the zero coefficient for x^3 is omitted. There exists a variation in signs for each of these pairs of consecutive terms: 3 and -2, -2, and 1, and 5 and -2. The total number of variations is three. Hence, we write
$$V(3, -2, 1, 5, -2) = 3.$$
Careful note should be made that V depends upon the ordered array of the coefficients of the given polynomial after its terms have been arranged in the order of the descending powers of x.

We now assume (postulate) the following theorem which is often called **Descartes' Rule of Signs:**

Theorem 6. *The number of positive roots of any real polynomial equation*
$$a_0x^n + a_1x^{n-1} + a_2x^{n-2} + \cdots + a_{n-1}x + a_n = 0$$
is $V(a_0, a_1, a_2, \cdots, a_{n-1}, a_n) - 2k$, *where k is some nonnegative integer.*

The integer k must be selected so that $V - 2k \geq 0$. For example, if $V = 5$, then there may be 5, 3, or 1 positive roots; if $V = 4$, there may be 4, 2, or 0 positive roots; if $V = 1$, there must be exactly 1 positive root.

POLYNOMIALS

Example 1. Determine the number of positive roots of the equation
$$2x^3 - 7x^2 + x - 5 = 0.$$

The sequence of coefficients is 2, -7, 1, -5 and has 3 variations in signs. By Descartes' Rule of Signs there are either 3 or 1 positive roots.

We next try to determine the number of real roots (positive, negative, or zero) of the equation given in Example 1. The equation has three or one positive roots. Consider the equation in the form $p(x) = 0$; there are no zero roots since $p(0) = -5 \neq 0$. Consider the equation in the form $a_0(x - r)(x - s)(x - t) = 0$ with roots r, s, and t. If we replace this equation by $a_0(-x - r)(-x - s)(-x - t) = 0$, we obtain the equation $(-1)a_0(x + r)(x + s)(x + t) = 0$ with roots $-r$, $-s$, and $-t$. The positive roots of $p(-x) = 0$ will be the negatives of the negative roots of $p(x) = 0$; in other words, if we replace x by $-x$ throughout the given equation, each root r of the given equation will correspond to a root $-r$ of the new equation. Note that for the equation given in Example 1

$$p(-x) = -2x^3 - 7x^2 - x - 5;$$

the sequence of coefficients is -2, -7, -1, -5 and has no variation in signs. By Descartes' Rule of Signs the equation of $p(-x) = 0$ has no positive roots and therefore the equation $p(x) = 0$ has no negative roots.

In order to determine the number of negative roots of any real polynomial equation $p(x) = 0$, we may apply Descartes' Rule of Signs to the equation $p(-x) = 0$. The positive roots of the equation $p(-x) = 0$ are the negatives of the negative roots of $p(x) = 0$ since each value of x has been transformed or changed to $-x$. As in Example 2 we must be careful to replace the variable x by $-x$ and not merely change the sign of each term of $p(x)$.

Any complex polynomial equation of degree n has exactly n complex numbers, not necessarily distinct, as roots (Theorem 5). Any complex number is real (positive, negative, or zero) or imaginary. For any given real polynomial equation we may determine the number of zero roots by observation, the numbers of possible positive roots and the numbers of possible negative roots by Descartes' Rule of Signs, and the numbers of possible imaginary roots by subtracting the numbers of possible real roots from the total number of roots.

Example 2. Determine the number of possible positive, zero, negative, and imaginary roots of the equation $p(x) = 0$ where
$$p(x) = 2x^4 + 7x^2 - x - 5.$$

§ 8-5 DESCARTES' RULE OF SIGNS

The ordered sequence of coefficients associated with $p(x)$ is $2, 7, -1, -5$ and $V(2, 7, -1, -5) = 1$. Hence, $p(x) = 0$ has exactly one positive real root.

The negative roots of $p(x) = 0$ are the negatives of the positive roots of $p(-x) = 0$ where

$$p(-x) = 2(-x)^4 + 7(-x)^2 - (-x) - 5$$
$$= 2x^4 + 7x^2 + x - 5.$$

Note that the sequence of coefficients of $p(-x)$ is $2, 7, 1, -5$, and has one variation in signs. Thus the equation $p(x) = 0$ has exactly one negative root.

The given equation has no zero root since $p(0) = -5 \neq 0$. The given equation has one positive and one negative root. Since the equation has degree 4, it must have 4 complex numbers as roots. Only two real numbers (one negative and one positive) can be roots. Thus there must be two imaginary numbers as roots.

We next prove that, as in Example 2, the imaginary roots of any real polynomial equation must occur in pairs $a + bi$, $a - bi$; that is, in **conjugate pairs**. The fact that there must be an even number of imaginary roots provides a basis for the number $V - 2k$ of positive roots.

Theorem 7. *If a real polynomial equation has a root $(a + bi)$ where a and b are real numbers and $b \neq 0$, then $(a - bi)$ is also a root of the equation.*

PROOF: Let $p(x) = 0$ represent any real polynomial equation where $p(a + bi) = 0$, a and b are real numbers, and $b \neq 0$. By the Factor Theorem $(x - a - bi)$ is a factor of $p(x)$. Consider the product $(x - a - bi)(x - a + bi)$; that is, $(x^2 - 2ax + a^2 + b^2)$. For any given real polynomial $p(x)$ we may find by long division a real polynomial $q(x)$ and real numbers s and t such that

$$p(x) = (x^2 - 2ax + a^2 + b^2) \times q(x) + sx + t.$$

Note that since we divided by a quadratic polynomial, the remainder may be a linear polynomial. When $x = a + bi$, we have

$$0 = 0 \times q(a + bi) + s \times (a + bi) + t$$
$$0 = sa + sbi + t$$
$$0 = (sa + t) + sbi$$
$$\begin{cases} sa + t = 0 \\ sb = 0. \end{cases}$$

Since $b \neq 0$, the equation $sb = 0$ implies that $s = 0$. Then the equation $sa + t = 0$ implies $t = 0$ and we have

$$p(x) = (x^2 - 2ax + a^2 + b^2) \times q(x)$$
$$p(x) = (x - a - bi)(x - a + bi) \times q(x).$$

We have proved that $(x - a + bi)$ is a factor of $p(x)$ and thus by Theorem 3, the converse of the Factor Theorem, $(a - bi)$ is a root of the equation $p(x) = 0$.

Example 3. Describe the nature of the roots of the equation $p(x) = 0$ where

$$p(x) = x^9 - 4x^3 - x^2.$$

Since the constant term of $p(x)$ is missing, at least one root must be zero. In this case the root zero is of multiplicity two since x^2 is a factor of every term of $p(x)$ and thus of the polynomial $p(x)$. That is, $p(x) = x^2(x^7 - 4x - 1) = 0$, and we need only to consider further the roots of the depressed equation $q(x) = 0$ where

$$q(x) = x^7 - 4x - 1.$$

Since $V(1, -4, -1) = 1$, the depressed equation must have one positive real root. We next form $q(-x)$:

$$q(-x) = -x^7 + 4x - 1.$$

Since $V(-1, 4, -1) = 2$, the depressed equation has two negative real roots or none.

As in § 8–4 the depressed equation must have seven complex roots. It has one positive root and no zero root. Accordingly, it must have either two negative and four imaginary roots or no negative and six imaginary roots.

Therefore the original equation $p(x) = 0$ has two zero roots, one positive root and either two negative roots and four imaginary roots or no negative roots and six imaginary roots. Remember, that the imaginary roots occur in conjugate pairs since $p(x)$ is a real polynomial.

TEST YOURSELF

Determine the number of possible positive, negative, zero, and imaginary roots of each of the following equations:

1. $x^4 + x^3 - 2x = 0$.
2. $x^5 - x^3 + 2x^2 = 0$.

EXERCISES

Determine the number of possible positive, negative, zero, and imaginary roots of each of the equations stated in Exercises 1 through 10:

1. $x^3 + 2x^2 + 3 = 0$.
2. $w^3 - 4w - 2 = 0$.
3. $v^6 - 2v^3 + 3v - 4 = 0$.
4. $x^3 + 3x - 4 = 0$.
5. $w^4 + w^3 + w^2 + w + 3 = 0$.
6. $x^5 + x^3 + 1 = 0$.
7. $x^6 + x^4 + x^2 - 1 = 0$.
8. $y^4 - 3y^3 + 2y^2 - y - 4 = 0$.

• • •

9. $x^n - a = 0$, where n is even.
10. $x^n - a = 0$, where n is odd.
- 11. Prove that a real polynomial equation $p(x) = 0$ has no real roots if all the terms of $p(x)$ are of even degree, all the coefficients have like signs, and the constant term is not zero.
- 12. Prove that a real polynomial equation $p(x) = 0$ has no negative roots if the coefficients have alternating signs and no coefficient is zero.
- 13. Prove that every real third degree polynomial equation has at least one real root.
- 14. If $(2 + i\sqrt{3})$ is a root of $x^4 - 4x^3 + 8x^2 - 4x + 7 = 0$, find the other roots.
- 15. If $(1 - i\sqrt{2})$ is a root of $4x^4 - 8x^3 + 3x^2 + 18x - 27 = 0$, find the other roots.
- 16. Prove that the polynomial equation $x^n - 1 = 0$ has no multiple real roots.

§ 8–6 Rational roots

We now seek a relationship between the roots $r_1, r_2, \ldots, r_n$ of a polynomial equation

$$a_0 x^n + a_1 x^{n-1} + \cdots + a_{n-1} x + a_n = 0$$

and the coefficients a_0 and a_n. As in § 8–4 the equation may be expressed in the form

$$a_0(x - r_1)(x - r_2) \cdots (x - r_n) = 0$$

where the constant term is $(-1)^n a_0 r_1 r_2 \cdots r_n$. When we compare the two forms of the equation we have

$$a_n = (-1)^n a_0 r_1 r_2 \cdots r_n.$$

Thus when the coefficients and roots of a polynomial equation are integers, each root must be a factor of the constant term, a_n.

439

POLYNOMIALS

Example 1. Find the integral roots of the equation
$$x^4 - 6x^3 + x^2 + 24x - 20 = 0.$$

The integral roots must be factors of 20. Thus the only possible integral roots are $\pm 1, \pm 2, \pm 4, \pm 5, \pm 10, \pm 20$. Before testing each of these numbers by synthetic division or substitution we apply Descartes' Rule of Signs. Since $V(1, -6, 1, 24, -20) = 3$, there are either 3 or 1 positive roots. The corresponding $p(-x)$ is
$$x^4 + 6x^3 + x^2 - 24x - 20$$
which has exactly one positive root and thus the original equation has exactly one negative root.

We use synthetic division for $x = 1$:

$$\underline{1|} \quad \begin{array}{rrrrr} 1 & -6 & 1 & 24 & -20 \\ & 1 & -5 & -4 & 20 \\ \hline 1 & -5 & -4 & 20 & \underline{|0} \end{array}$$

Thus 1 is a root and the remaining roots must satisfy the depressed equation
$$x^3 - 5x^2 - 4x + 20 = 0.$$

We next use synthetic division for $x = 1$:

$$\underline{1|} \quad \begin{array}{rrrr} 1 & -5 & -4 & 20 \\ & 1 & -4 & -8 \\ \hline 1 & -4 & -8 & \underline{|-12} \end{array}$$

Thus 1 is not a root of the depressed equation and therefore not a multiple root of the given equation. We use synthetic division for $x = 5$:

$$\underline{5|} \quad \begin{array}{rrrr} 1 & -5 & -4 & 20 \\ & 5 & 0 & -20 \\ \hline 1 & 0 & -4 & \underline{|0} \end{array}$$

Thus 5 is a root and the other two roots must satisfy $x^2 - 4 = 0$. These roots are 2 and -2.

We have found that the integral roots of the given equation are 1, 5, 2, and -2. If we had found the root -2 at an early stage we would have known by Descartes' Rule of Signs that, since there was exactly one negative root, there were no other negative roots. If we had tried $-1, -4, -5, -10, -20, 4, 10,$ or 20, we would have obtained a remainder different from zero and then tried another number.

If a real polynomial equation has rational coefficients, we may obtain a polynomial equation with integral coefficients and having the same roots as the given equation. For example, the equations

$$x^2 - \frac{5}{6}x + \frac{1}{6} = 0 \quad \text{and} \quad 6x^2 - 5x + 1 = 0$$

each have roots $\frac{1}{2}$ and $\frac{1}{3}$. In general, if M is the lowest common multiple of the denominators of the coefficients of any rational polynomial $p(x)$, then the equation $M \times p(x) = 0$ has integral coefficients and has the same roots as the equation $p(x) = 0$. Thus <u>any rational polynomial equation may be replaced by an equivalent polynomial equation with integral coefficients</u>. Hence, the following theorem may be made applicable to any rational polynomial equations. In the statement of the theorem the condition that p and q are **relatively prime integers** implies that p and q have no common integral factors greater than one and thus that the rational number $\frac{p}{q}$ is expressed in **reduced form,** that is, in its **lowest terms.**

Theorem 8. *If a polynomial equation*

$$a_0x^n + a_1x^{n-1} + a_2x^{n-2} + \cdots + a_{n-1}x + a_n = 0,$$

where $a_0, a_1, a_2, \cdots, a_{n-1}, a_n$ are integers, has a rational root $\frac{p}{q}$ (where p and q are relatively prime integers), then p is a factor of a_n and q is a factor of a_0.

PROOF: Since $\frac{p}{q}$ is a root of the given equation, we have

$$a_0\left(\frac{p}{q}\right)^n + a_1\left(\frac{p}{q}\right)^{n-1} + a_2\left(\frac{p}{q}\right)^{n-2} + \cdots + a_{n-1}\left(\frac{p}{q}\right) + a_n = 0.$$

After multiplying both sides of the equation by q^n, we have

$$a_0p^n + a_1p^{n-1}q + a_2p^{n-2}q^2 + \cdots + a_{n-1}pq^{n-1} + a_nq^n = 0$$

whence

$$a_0p^n = -a_1p^{n-1}q - a_2p^{n-2}q^2 - \cdots - a_{n-1}pq^{n-1} - a_nq^n$$

and

$$a_0p^n = q(-a_1p^{n-1} - a_2p^{n-2}q - \cdots - a_{n-1}pq^{n-2} - a_nq^{n-1}).$$

Now since $a_0, a_1, a_2, \cdots, a_{n-1}, a_n, p,$ and q are integers, both members of this equation are integers. Since q is a factor of the right

POLYNOMIALS

member of the equation, it must be a factor of $a_0 p^n$. However, p and q are relatively prime. Hence, q must be a factor of a_0.

In a similar manner, we may write the second equation in the forms

$$a_n q^n = -a_0 p^n - a_1 p^{n-1} q - a_2 p^{n-2} q^2 - \cdots - a_{n-1} p q^{n-1}$$
$$a_n q^n = p(-a_0 p^{n-1} - a_1 p^{n-2} q - a_2 p^{n-3} q^2 - \cdots - a_{n-1} q^{n-1})$$

from which we see that p must be a factor of a_n.

It is possible that a polynomial equation with integral coefficients may not have any rational roots. However, if there are any rational roots, Theorem 8 specifies the form that the possible rational roots must take and thus enables us to identify the possible rational roots of any given polynomial equation with integral coefficients. Once the possible rational roots have been identified, the process of synthetic division can be employed to determine which, if any, are roots.

Example 2. Determine the rational roots, if any exist, of

$$2x^4 - 11x^3 + 21x^2 - 20x + 6 = 0.$$

The integral factors of the constant term 6 are $\pm 1, \pm 2, \pm 3, \pm 6$ while the integral factors of the leading coefficient 2 are $\pm 1, \pm 2$. Letting $p = \pm 1, \pm 2, \pm 3, \pm 6$ and $q = \pm 1, \pm 2$; the possible rational roots $\frac{p}{q}$ are $\pm 1, \pm \frac{1}{2}, \pm 2, \pm 3, \pm \frac{3}{2}, \pm 6$. Using synthetic division we find by trial that neither 1 nor -1 is a root:

```
1 |  2   -11    21   -20    6
          2    -9    12   -8
      2   -9    12    -8 | -2

-1 |  2   -11    21   -20    6
         -2    13   -34   54
      2  -13    34   -54 | 60
```

Since $p(0) = 6$ and $p(1) = -2$, we expect from the change in sign that there will be at least one real root between 0 and 1. (This will be considered in detail in § 8-7.) We next try $\frac{1}{2}$ and find that it is a root:

```
1/2 |  2   -11    21   -20    6
            1    -5     8   -6
        2  -10    16   -12 |  0
```

§ 8-6   RATIONAL ROOTS

The depressed equation then becomes

$$2x^3 - 10x^2 + 16x - 12 = 0;$$
$$x^3 - 5x^2 + 8x - 6 = 0.$$

The possible rational roots of the depressed equation are ± 1, ± 2, ± 3, ± 6. However, we know by Descartes' Rule of Signs that the depressed equation has no negative real roots. Furthermore since 1 was not a root of the original equation, it cannot be a root for the depressed equation. The remaining possibilities are 2, 3, and 6. Now 2 is not a root:

$$\underline{2|}\ \ 1\ \ -5\ \ \ \ 8\ \ -6$$
$$\phantom{\underline{2|}\ \ 1\ \ }\ \ \ \ \ \ \ 2\ \ -6\ \ \ \ 4$$
$$\phantom{\underline{2|}\ \ }\ \ 1\ \ -3\ \ \ \ 2\ \underline{|-2}$$

but 3 is a root:

$$\underline{3|}\ \ 1\ \ -5\ \ \ \ 8\ \ -6$$
$$\phantom{\underline{3|}\ \ 1\ \ }\ \ \ \ \ \ \ 3\ \ -6\ \ \ \ 6$$
$$\phantom{\underline{3|}\ \ }\ \ 1\ \ -2\ \ \ \ 2\ \underline{|\ \ 0}$$

The new depressed equation is the quadratic equation $x^2 - 2x + 2 = 0$, which can be solved by means of the quadratic formula for the roots $(1 + i)$ and $(1 - i)$. Hence, the roots of the given equation are $\frac{1}{2}$, 3, $(1 + i)$, $(1 - i)$.

Example 3. Prove that $\sqrt{2}$ is irrational.

Let $x = \sqrt{2}$. After squaring both sides we have $x^2 = 2$; that is, $x^2 - 2 = 0$. Since this is a polynomial equation with integral coefficients, the only possible rational roots are ± 1 and ± 2. None of these values satisfy the equation and thus no rational roots exist. Since $\sqrt{2}$ is a root of the equation, it follows that $\sqrt{2}$ is not rational; that is, $\sqrt{2}$ is irrational.

TEST YOURSELF

Determine the rational roots, if any exist, of each equation:

1. $2x^3 + x^2 - 4x + 2 = 0$.
2. $x^4 - 6x^2 - 4x = 0$.

443

POLYNOMIALS

EXERCISES

Determine the rational roots, if any exist, of each equation:

1. $2x^3 - x^2 - 4x - 2 = 0$.
2. $3x^3 - 2x^2 + 6x - 4 = 0$.
3. $x^4 - 6x^2 + 4x = 0$.
4. $x^4 + 2x^2 + 1 = 0$.
5. $24x^3 - 2x^2 - 5x + 1 = 0$.
6. $x^4 - 4x^3 + 5x^2 - 4x + 4 = 0$.

• • •

7. $x^5 - 12x^4 + 55x^3 - 120x^2 + 124x - 48 = 0$.
8. $x^5 + x^4 + 5x^2 - 3x + 2 = 0$.
9. $2x^3 + x^2 + 3x - 7 = 0$.
10. $6x^3 - 2x^2 + 3x + 4 = 0$.

In Exercises 11 through 16 solve each equation completely:

11. $2x^4 - 9x^3 + 11x^2 - 4x - 6 = 0$.
12. $3w^3 + 4w^2 + 13w + 4 = 0$.
13. $2x^4 - 5x^3 + 4x^2 - 5x + 2 = 0$.
14. $5x^3 + 6x^2 + 6x + 1 = 0$.
15. $y^4 - 3y^3 + y^2 - y - 6 = 0$.
16. $2x^4 + x^3 - 3x^2 + 5x - 2 = 0$.
17. Prove that $\sqrt{3}$ is irrational.
18. Prove that $\sqrt{5}$ is irrational.
19. It can be shown that if one root of a rational polynomial equation is $(a + \sqrt{b})$ where a and b are rational and $\sqrt{b}$ is irrational, then $(a - \sqrt{b})$ is a root of the equation. Given that $(2 + \sqrt{3})$ is a root of $x^4 - 4x^3 - 4x^2 + 20x - 5 = 0$, find the other roots.
20. If two roots of a rational polynomial equation are $3i$ and $(2 - \sqrt{7})$, what is the lowest possible degree of the equation?
• 21. Prove that $(\sqrt{2} + \sqrt{3})$ is irrational.
• 22. Prove that if a rational polynomial equation has a root $(a + \sqrt{b})$ where $\sqrt{b}$ is irrational, then the equation also has $(a - \sqrt{b})$ as a root.

§ 8–7 Location principle

Descartes' Rule of Signs (§ 8–5) and Theorem 8 (§ 8–6) have provided information which may be useful in attempting to solve real polynomial equations. The graph of a real polynomial equation $p(x) = 0$ provides another useful aid since it enables us to estimate the x-coordinates (abscissas) of the points where the graph intersects the x-axis. However it should be emphasized that values of x which are not integral values may be needed to avoid the possibility of sketching the graph so poorly that it is misleading.

§ 8-7 LOCATION PRINCIPLE

Consider the problem of sketching the graph of $p(x) = 0$ where $p(x) = 9x^4 - 18x^3 - 7x^2 + 16x - 4$. The following table of values of $p(x)$ for successive integral values of x may be obtained by synthetic division:

x	-1	0	1	2
$p(x)$	0	-4	-4	0

Figure 8-1

After plotting these points $(x, p(x))$ one might be inclined to sketch the curve as in Figure 8–1.

From Figure 8–1 it appears that the curve is shaped like a parabola and that only two real roots of the equation $p(x) = 0$ exist. However, a table of values with the one additional pair of values $\left(\frac{1}{2}, \frac{9}{16}\right)$ indicates that the sketch of the graph of $p(x) = 0$ in Figure 8–1 is in serious error and should appear as in Figure 8–2. A sketch of a curve connecting the points whose coordinates are $(x, p(x))$ now indicates the existence of two additional real roots. The use of Descartes' Rule of Signs would have informed us of this possibility.

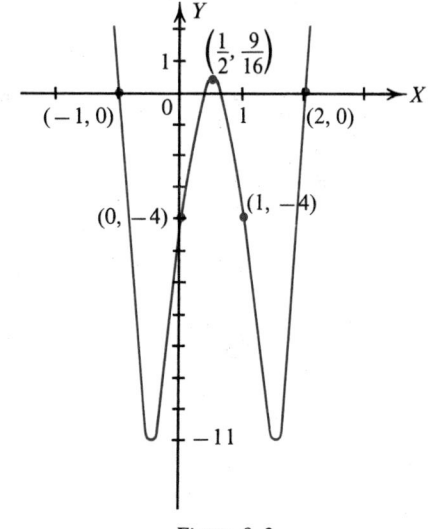

Figure 8-2

It must be remembered that the passing of a smooth curve through the plotted points, regardless of how many we choose, involves the assumptions of continuity of the curve and smoothness of the curve. Both assumptions are shown in advanced mathematics to be valid for graphs of polynomial equations.

An especially important aspect of the graphical approach to the solution of a real polynomial equation is the determination of two real numbers, a and b, which isolate a root. A real root r is said to be **isolated** between a and b if $a < r < b$. Also all real roots of a real polynomial equation in x are said to be separated when each one is isolated in a separate interval of values of x which does not overlap with the other intervals.

POLYNOMIALS

Let $p(x)$ be any given real polynomial and let a and b be real numbers such that $p(a)$ and $p(b)$ have opposite signs; for example, suppose $p(a) < 0$ and $p(b) > 0$. Then from the graphs in Figure 8–3 it is intuitively evident that the assumption of a continuous curve implies that the graph of $p(x) = 0$ must intersect the x-axis in at least one point of the interval from a to b. The x-coordinate of each such point satisfies the equation of $p(x) = 0$.

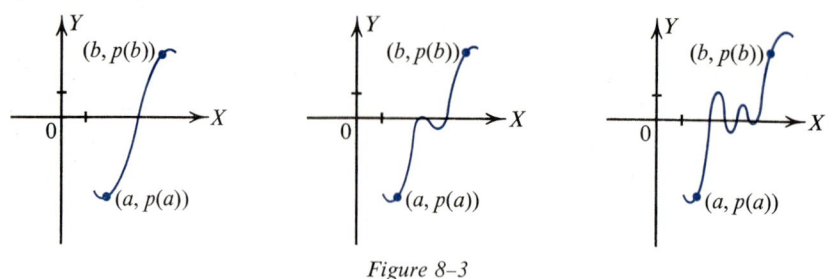

Figure 8–3

We assume (postulate) the correctness of the appearance of these graphs by assuming Theorem 9. This theorem is sometimes referred to as the **location principle.**

Theorem 9. *If any real polynomial p(x) and real numbers a and b are given such that p(a) and p(b) have opposite signs, then there exists at least one real root of the equation p(x) = 0 between a and b.*

We must be careful in interpreting Theorem 9. If $p(a)$ and $p(b)$ differ in signs, the theorem guarantees the existence of an odd number of roots in the interval between a and b. However, if $p(a)$ and $p(b)$ are alike in signs we must not assume that no root exists in the interval. Rather we must conclude that either no root exists between a and b or there are an even number of roots in that interval (Figure 8–4). Whether $p(a)$ and $p(b)$ have the same or different signs, multiplicities must be considered in counting the number of roots on the interval.

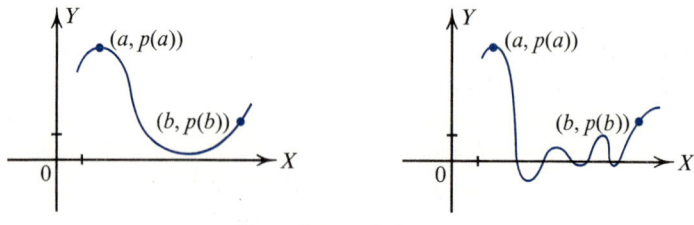

Figure 8–4

The location principle and synthetic division make it possible to approximate a real root of any given real polynomial as accurately as desired.

§ 8-7 LOCATION PRINCIPLE

If the polynomial has rational coefficients, any rational root may be found exactly as in § 8-6. If the polynomial has irrational coefficients or an irrational root is involved, the root may be approximated to the nearest integral unit by finding successive integers a and $(a + 1)$ such that $a \leq r < a + 1$. Then the root may be approximated to the nearest tenth, to the nearest hundredth, and so forth.

Consider the real polynomial equation

$$x^3 - 2x - 6 = 0$$

and think of it as $p(x) = 0$. We know by Descartes' Rule of Signs that there is one real positive root. The possible rational roots may be determined as in § 8-6 and checked to show that no rational root exists. We may use synthetic division to show that the positive root is between 2 and 3.

$$\begin{array}{r|rrrr} 2 & 1 & 0 & -2 & -6 \\ & & 2 & 4 & 4 \\ \hline & 1 & 2 & 2 & \underline{|-2} \end{array}$$

$$\begin{array}{r|rrrr} 3 & 1 & 0 & -2 & -6 \\ & & 3 & 9 & 21 \\ \hline & 1 & 3 & 7 & \underline{|\,15} \end{array}$$

Since $p(2) = -2$ and $p(3) = 15$, the root appears to be closer to 2 than 3. By synthetic division, we find $p(2.1) = -0.939$ and $p(2.2) = 0.248$.

$$\begin{array}{r|rrrr} 2.1 & 1 & 0 & -2 & -6 \\ & & 2.1 & 4.41 & 5.061 \\ \hline & 1 & 2.1 & 2.41 & \underline{|-0.939} \end{array}$$

$$\begin{array}{r|rrrr} 2.2 & 1 & 0 & -2 & -6 \\ & & 2.2 & 4.84 & 6.248 \\ \hline & 1 & 2.2 & 2.84 & \underline{|\,0.248} \end{array}$$

Since $p(2.1)$ is negative and $p(2.2)$ is positive, $2.1 < r < 2.2$. Furthermore, $p(2.15)$ is negative since

$$\begin{array}{r|rrrr} 2.15 & 1 & 0 & -2 & -6 \\ & & 2.15 & 4.6225 & 5.638375 \\ \hline & 1 & 2.15 & 2.6225 & \underline{|-0.361625} \end{array}$$

Thus $2.15 < r < 2.20$. Hence, the positive real root equals 2.2 to the nearest tenth of a unit.

POLYNOMIALS

Synthetic division may also be used to find "bounds" for the real roots. For example, the work just done using synthetic division by 3 enables us to write

$$p(x) = (x - 3)(x^2 + 3x + 7) + 15$$

Note that all of the numbers on the third row of the array for synthetic division are nonnegative. The remainder 15 is positive; each term of $(x^2 + 3x + 7)$ is positive where $x \geq 3$ and therefore the entire expression is positive. Furthermore when $x > 3$, the factor $(x - 3)$ is positive. The product of two positive terms is positive. Thus, whenever $x \geq 3$ the polynomial $p(x)$ is equal to a sum of two nonnegative terms, at least one of which is positive. In other words, for all values of x greater than or equal to 3 the polynomial $p(x)$ is positive. This means that $p(x)$ has no real roots $r \geq 3$ and thus that 3 is an upper bound of the roots of the equation $p(x) = 0$.

Any number which is greater than or equal to the largest root of $p(x) = 0$ is called an **upper bound** of the roots. Similarly any number which is less than or equal to the smallest root is called a **lower bound** of the roots. There are infinitely many sets of upper and lower bounds. However, the determination of a reasonably small upper bound and a reasonably large lower bound is helpful in isolating and evaluating the roots.

The next theorem may be used to find bounds for the roots of any real polynomial equation $p(x) = 0$. The proof of the theorem is similar to the explanation that has just been given for $x = 3$; thus, the proof is left as an exercise for the reader. (See Exercise 7.)

Theorem 10. *Let any real polynomial equation $p(x) = 0$ be given where $p(x) = a_0 x^n + a_1 x^{n-1} + a_2 x^{n-2} + \cdots + a_{n-1} x + a_n$ and $a_0 > 0$. If $L \geq 0$ and synthetic division of $p(x)$ by $(x - L)$ yields a third row of numbers such that all numbers that are different from zero have the same sign, then L is an upper bound of the roots of $p(x) = 0$.*

Often a good estimate for an upper bound of the roots of

$$a_0 x^n + a_1 x^{n-1} + a_2 x^{n-2} + \cdots + a_{n-1} x + a_n = 0$$

may be found by solving the equation $a_0 x + a_1 = 0$ for x. This estimate may be a poor one if the coefficients $a_2, a_3, \cdots$ are much larger than a_0 and a_1. Lower bounds may be found by following a similar procedure for $p(-x) = 0$ and changing the signs of the numbers so obtained. In other words, the negative of an upper bound of the real roots of $p(-x) = 0$ is a lower bound of the roots of $p(x) = 0$. (See Exercise 8.)

Example. Find a lower bound of the roots of
$$x^4 + x^3 + 5x^2 + 6x + 7 = 0.$$

Let $p(x) = x^4 + x^3 + 5x^2 + 6x + 7$, then
$p(-x) = x^4 - x^3 + 5x^2 - 6x + 7;$

$$\underline{1|}\;\; \begin{array}{rrrrr} 1 & -1 & 5 & -6 & 7 \\ & 1 & 0 & 5 & -1 \\ \hline 1 & 0 & 5 & -1 & \underline{|6} \end{array}$$

Since 1 does not appear to be an upper bound of the roots of $p(-x) = 0$, we try 2.

$$\underline{2|}\;\; \begin{array}{rrrrr} 1 & -1 & 5 & -6 & 7 \\ & 2 & 2 & 14 & 16 \\ \hline 1 & 1 & 7 & 8 & \underline{|23} \end{array}$$

Thus 2 is an upper bound of the roots of $p(-x) = 0$ and -2 is a lower bound of the roots of $p(x) = 0$.

TEST YOURSELF

1. Prove that 4 is an upper bound of the roots of
$$2x^3 - 7x^2 - 3x + 6 = 0.$$

2. Prove that -2 is a lower bound of the roots of
$$2x^3 - 7x^2 - 3x + 6 = 0.$$

EXERCISES

1. Prove that 3 is an upper bound of the roots of the equation $2x^3 - 3x^2 - 3x - 5 = 0$.

2. Prove that -1 is a lower bound of the roots of the equation $2x^3 - 6x^2 - x + 5 = 0$.

3. Between what two consecutive integers does the positive root of $x^3 - 10x - 8 = 0$ lie?

• • •

4. Find to the nearest tenth the real root of $2x^3 + x^2 + 2x - 8 = 0$.
5. Find to the nearest tenth the real root of $2x^3 - 5x^2 - 2 = 0$.

POLYNOMIALS

6. Find to the nearest tenth of an inch the amount by which each edge of a box 3" by 2" by 6" must be increased to double its volume.

7. Prove Theorem 10.

• 8. Prove that for any real polynomial $p(x)$ the negative of an upper bound of the roots of $p(-x) = 0$ is a lower bound of the roots of the polynomial equation $p(x) = 0$.

§ 8-8 Roots and coefficients

We now extend the discussion in § 8-6 and consider several relations that exist between the roots $r_1, r_2, \cdots, r_n$ of a polynomial equation and its coefficients. Any polynomial equation $p(x) = 0$ may be expressed in each of these forms:

$$a_0 x^n + a_1 x^{n-1} + a_2 x^{n-2} + \cdots + a_{n-1} x + a_n = 0, \quad a_0 \neq 0;$$

$$x^n + \frac{a_1}{a_0} x^{n-1} + \frac{a_2}{a_0} x^{n-2} + \cdots + \frac{a_{n-1}}{a_0} x + \frac{a_n}{a_0} = 0; \qquad (1)$$

$$(x - r_1)(x - r_2)(x - r_3) \cdots (x - r_{n-1})(x - r_n) = 0.$$

Note that the constant term of the product of the n linear factors is equal to the product of the n constant terms, one from each linear factor and each term taken with its appropriate sign. In general, each term of the product is itself a product of n terms, one from each linear factor. Components of the linear term of the product arise when the x term is selected from exactly one of the linear factors and the constant terms are selected from the other $n - 1$ linear factors. The x can be selected from any one of n factors and thus can be selected in $_nC_1$ ways to obtain the n linear terms which are combined as similar terms to obtain the linear term of the product. Components of the term of degree k of the product arise when the x term is selected from exactly k of the linear factors and the constant terms are selected from the other $n - k$ linear factors. For each value of k, $0 \leq k \leq n$, the k linear factors from which the x terms are used may be selected in $_nC_k$ ways. For each value of k the sum of such expressions with the associated factor $(-1)^{n-k}$ is the term of degree k of the product. In other words, $p(x) = 0$ may be expressed in the form

$$x^n - (r_1 + r_2 + r_3 + \cdots + r_n)x^{n-1} + (r_1 r_2 + r_1 r_3 + \cdots + r_1 r_n + \cdots + r_{n-1} r_n)x^{n-2} - (r_1 r_2 r_3 + r_1 r_2 r_4 + \cdots + r_1 r_2 r_n + \cdots + r_{n-2} r_{n-1} r_n)x^{n-3} + \cdots + (-1)^n (r_1 r_2 r_3 \cdots r_n) = 0.$$

Since this is another way of writing the polynomial in equation (1), the

§ 8-8 ROOTS AND COEFFICIENTS

coefficients of the powers of x in this equation must equal the corresponding coefficients in equation (1):

$$\frac{a_1}{a_0} = -(r_1 + r_2 + r_3 + \cdots + r_n);$$

$$\frac{a_2}{a_0} = (r_1r_2 + r_1r_3 + \cdots + r_1r_n + \cdots + r_{n-1}r_n);$$

$$\frac{a_3}{a_0} = -(r_1r_2r_3 + r_1r_2r_4 + \cdots + r_1r_2r_n + \cdots + r_{n-2}r_{n-1}r_n);$$

.
.
.

$$\frac{a_n}{a_0} = (-1)^n (r_1 r_2 r_3 \cdots r_n).$$

The relations expressed by these equations may be stated conveniently as a theorem.

Theorem 11. *If $r_1, r_2, r_3, \cdots, r_n$ are the roots of a polynomial equation $p(x) = 0$ of the form*

$$a_0 x^n + a_1 x^{n-1} + a_2 x^{n-2} + \cdots + a_{n-1} x + a_n = 0, \ a_0 \neq 0,$$

then the sum of all the possible products of the r_i's taken k at a time for any value of $k = 1, 2, 3, \cdots, n$ is equal to $(-1)^k \dfrac{a_k}{a_0}$.

Example 1. Find the sum and the product of the roots of $p(x) = 0$ where

$$p(x) = 4x^3 + 8x^2 + 7x - 64.$$

Consider $p(x)$ in the form $a_0 x^3 + a_1 x^2 + a_2 x + a_3$. Then $a_0 = 4$, $a_1 = 8$, $a_2 = 7$, and $a_3 = -64$. Furthermore, let the roots of $p(x) = 0$ be r_1, r_2, and r_3. Then according to Theorem 11,

$$r_1 + r_2 + r_3 = (-1)\frac{a_1}{a_0} = -2, \text{ and } r_1 r_2 r_3 = (-1)^3 \frac{a_3}{a_0} = 16.$$

Example 2. Find a polynomial equation $p(x) = 0$ whose roots are 2, 3, and -1.

Let $r_1 = 2$, $r_2 = 3$, and $r_3 = -1$. Then $r_1 + r_2 + r_3 = 2 + 3 - 1 = 4$, $r_1 r_2 + r_1 r_3 + r_2 r_3 = 6 - 2 - 3 = 1$, and $r_1 r_2 r_3 = -6$. Finally,

POLYNOMIALS

as in Theorem 11,

$$p(x) = x^3 - (r_1 + r_2 + r_3)x^2 + (r_1r_2 + r_1r_3 + r_2r_3)x - r_1r_2r_3$$

and the equation is $x^3 - 4x^2 + x + 6 = 0$.

Note that this example could also have been solved by expanding the left member of the equation

$$(x - 2)(x - 3)(x + 1) = 0.$$

Example 3. Find a polynomial equation whose roots are equal to the roots of $y^3 + 12y^2 - 20y - 7 = 0$, each multiplied by 2.

Let the roots of the given equation be r_1, r_2, and r_3. Then

$$r_1 + r_2 + r_3 = -12,$$
$$r_1r_2 + r_1r_3 + r_2r_3 = -20, \text{ and}$$
$$r_1r_2r_3 = 7.$$

Therefore, $2r_1 + 2r_2 + 2r_3 = -24$
$(2r_1)(2r_2) + (2r_1)(2r_3) + (2r_2)(2r_3) = -80$, and
$(2r_1)(2r_2)(2r_3) = 56.$

Hence, the desired polynomial equation is

$$x^3 + 24x^2 - 80x - 56 = 0.$$

In Examples 2 and 3 note that, as in § 8–4, we select for our answers a polynomial of the lowest possible degree and with coefficients which do not have any integral common divisors greater than 1; that is, with relatively prime integral coefficients.

TEST YOURSELF

Find the sum and the product of the roots of each polynomial equation:

1. $x^4 + 2x^3 - 5x^2 + 7 = 0.$
2. $2x^3 - 5x^2 + 12 = 0.$
3. $3x^4 - 6x^2 - 5 = 0.$

Find a polynomial equation whose roots are:

4. $-2, -3, 1.$
5. $2, -2, 0.$

§ 8-8 ROOTS AND COEFFICIENTS

EXERCISES

A

Find the sum and the product of the roots of each polynomial equation:

1. $x^4 - 3x^3 + 5x^2 - 12x + 8 = 0$.
2. $3x^3 + 6x^2 - 5x + 12 = 0$.
3. $x^3 - 5x + 2 = 0$.
4. $x^5 - x^3 + 1 = 0$.
5. $2x^6 + 4x^5 - x = 0$.
6. $5x^5 - 3x^3 + x = 0$.

In Exercises 7 through 14 find a polynomial equation whose roots are:

7. $2, -1, 5$.

8. $\frac{1}{3}, \frac{1}{2}, -\frac{1}{2}$.

9. $-\frac{3}{2}, -4, 6$.

10. $0, 1, 2, -3$.

• • •

11. $2 - i, 2 + i, 1, 3$.
12. $1 + i, 1 - i, 2 - 3i, 2 + 3i$.
13. $3 + \sqrt{5}, 3 - \sqrt{5}, 1, 2$.
14. $3 + \sqrt{2}, 3 - \sqrt{2}, 2 + i, 2 - i$.

15. Find the roots of the general quadratic equation $ax^2 + bx + c = 0$ and show that Theorem 11 is satisfied.

16. The equation $ax^5 + bx^4 + cx^3 + dx^2 + ex + f = 0$ with roots r_1, r_2, r_3, r_4, r_5 is given. Write the relations between the coefficients and the roots.

• 17. Prove that for any integer $n \geq 2$ the sum of the n nth roots of any real number M is zero.

• 18. Determine the relationship between a and b if the equation $x^3 + ax + b = 0$ has a multiple root.

B (Supplementary)

In Exercises 1 through 6 solve each equation and determine the values of the coefficients represented by a, b, and c when the roots satisfy the given conditions:

1. $2x^3 + 6x^2 + ax + b = 0$; $r_1 = 0, r_2 = 1$.
2. $2x^2 - 20x + 40 + a = 0$; $r_1 = r_2$.
3. $x^3 - ax^2 + bx + c = 0$; $r_1 = 2, r_2 = 1 - i$.

453

POLYNOMIALS

4. $x^3 + ax + 4b = 0$; $r_1 = 3$, $r_2 = -1$.
5. $x^4 + 8x^3 + ax^2 + bx + c = 0$; $r_1 = r_2 = r_3 = r_4$.
6. $5x^3 - 15x^2 + 16x - 4a = 0$; $r_1 = -r_2$.

• • •

7. Find a polynomial equation $p(x) = 0$ whose roots are twice the roots of the equation $y^3 - 5y^2 + 3y + 2 = 0$.

8. Find a polynomial equation $p(x) = 0$ whose roots are -3 times the roots of the equation $y^3 + 3y^2 - 2y + 1 = 0$.

9. Find a polynomial equation $p(x) = 0$ whose roots are one-half those of the equation $y^3 - y^2 - 14y + 24 = 0$. Then solve both equations and verify that the roots satisfy the proper relationship.

10. Find the general form of a quartic equation if its roots are r_1, $-r_1$, r_2, and $-r_2$.

11. Prove that if one root of $x^3 + ax^2 + bx + c = 0$ is the negative of the other, then $ab = c$.

• 12. Prove that if r_1, r_2, and r_3 are the roots of the equation $x^3 + ax + b = 0$, then $r_1^2 + r_2^2 + r_3^2 = -2a$.

§ 8-9   Polynomial inequalities

Consider the problem of graphing $y = p(x)$ where $p(x) = x^3 - 5x^2 + 2x + 8$. Once the real roots of the polynomial equation $p(x) = 0$ have been found to be -1, 2, and 4, the polynomial function may be written in factored form:

$$p(x) = (x + 1)(x - 2)(x - 4).$$

Now, we know that the graph of $p(x)$ intersects the x-axis at -1, 2, and 4. The problem remains to determine how the graph behaves for other values of x. If $-1 < x < 2$, the factor $(x + 1)$ is positive while the factors $(x - 2)$ and $(x - 4)$ are negative. Since two of the factors are negative, the product of the three factors is positive. Therefore, $p(x) > 0$ for $-1 < x < 2$ and the graph is above the x-axis throughout this interval. If $2 < x < 4$, the factors $(x + 1)$ and $(x - 2)$ are positive while the factor $(x - 4)$ is negative. Since only one of the factors is negative, the product of the three factors is negative. Hence, $p(x) < 0$ for $2 < x < 4$ and the graph is below the x-axis throughout this interval. By reasoning in a similar manner for $x < -1$ it follows that $p(x) < 0$, and for $x > 4$ we have $p(x) > 0$. In addition, we could have reasoned that as x becomes larger positively (or negatively) the term x^3 in $p(x)$ becomes the dominant term in determining the value of $p(x)$. Then for large positive values of x, $p(x) > 0$ since x^3 is positive, while for large negative values of x, $p(x) < 0$

§ 8-9 POLYNOMIAL INEQUALITIES

since x^3 is negative. The graph of $y = p(x)$ appears in Figure 8-5.

As we have noted previously, the graph of any curve $y = p(x)$ where $p(x)$ is a real polynomial in x is a continuous curve. The polynomial $p(x)$ is equal to zero if and only if one of its factors is equal to zero; the polynomial changes sign if and only if one of its factors changes sign. As shown in Figure 8-5, the polynomial $(x + 1)(x - 2)(x - 4)$ is positive for $x > 4$ since its term of highest degree is positive for large values of x and the largest real root of $p(x) = 0$ is 4. The polynomial changes sign at $x = 4$, since the equation $p(x) = 0$ has a simple root at $x = 4$. The next root as x decreases is the simple root 2. Thus, $p(x) < 0$ for $2 < x < 4$ and $p(x)$ changes sign at $x = 2$. The remaining root is the simple root -1. Thus $p(x) > 0$ for $-1 < x < 2$, $p(x)$ changes sign at $x = -1$, and $p(x) < 0$ for $x < -1$. The phraseology "changes sign at $x = r$" means that "as the values of x increase continuously through the value r there is a change in the sign of $p(x)$." In other words, for any arbitrarily small positive number k, the expressions $p(r - k)$ and $p(r + k)$ have different signs. We may summarize these statements on a number line as in Figure 8-6. Note that $p(x) = 0$ and thus is neither positive nor negative at $x = -1, 2,$ and 4.

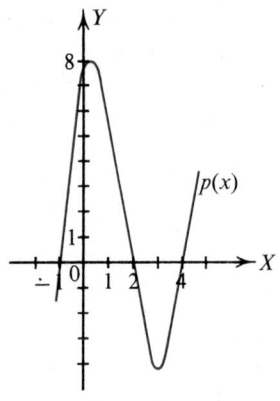

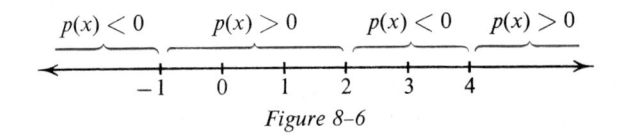

Figure 8-5

Figure 8-6

We shall use this type of analysis of the graphs of polynomial equations to solve polynomial inequalities. From the previous discussion we assert that the polynomial inequality $p(x) > 0$, that is,

$$x^3 - 5x^2 + 2x + 8 > 0,$$

has the solution set $-1 < x < 2$ and $x > 4$. The polynomial inequality $p(x) < 0$, that is,

$$x^3 - 5x^2 + 2x + 8 < 0,$$

has the solution set $x < -1$ and $2 < x < 4$. The same methods of solution apply when there are multiple roots. In this case the number of changes in sign at $x = r$ is the same as the multiplicity of the root r. Thus

POLYNOMIALS

the net effect is a change in the sign of $p(x)$ at a root of odd multiplicity and no change in sign at a root of even multiplicity.

Example 1. Solve: $5(x + 1)(x - 5)^2(x - 7) < 0$.

Let $p(x) = 5(x + 1)(x - 5)^2(x - 7)$. Note that the factor $5 \neq 0$ and is positive; $x + 1 = 0$ when $x = -1$; $x - 5 = 0$ when $x = 5$; and $x - 7 = 0$ when $x = 7$. Also note that the factor $(x - 5)^2$ is positive whenever $x \neq 5$. Without graphing $p(x)$, we may visualize the sign of $p(x)$ for any real value of x as indicated in Figure 8-7.

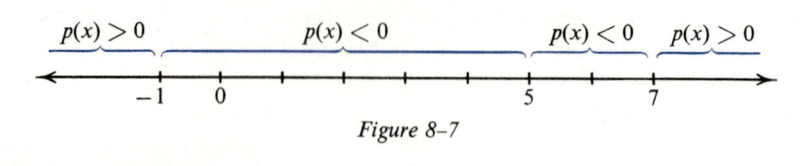

Figure 8-7

Hence, the solution set for $5(x + 1)(x - 5)^2(x - 7) < 0$ is $-1 < x < 5$ and $5 < x < 7$.

We solve systems of inequalities in a similar manner.

Example 2. Solve the system $\begin{cases} p(x) > 0 \\ q(x) > 0 \end{cases}$ where $p(x) = (x + 2)(x - 1)$ and $q(x) = x(x - 2)$.

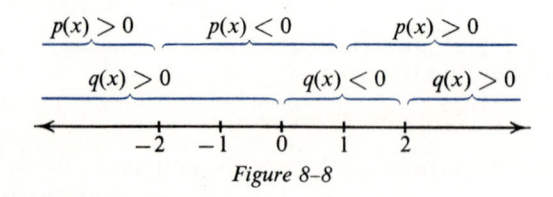

Figure 8-8

As in Figure 8-8, $p(x) > 0$ and $q(x) > 0$ when $x < -2$ or $x > 2$.

TEST YOURSELF

1. Solve: $(x - 1)(x + 1) > 0$.
2. Solve: $x(x + 1)(x + 2) > 0$.
3. Solve the system: $\begin{cases} (x - 1)(x + 1) > 0 \\ x(x + 1)(x + 2) > 0. \end{cases}$

456

EXERCISES

Solve:

1. $(x - 1)(x + 3) > 0$.
2. $(x + 2)(x + 1) > 0$.
3. $3(x - 1)(x + 4) < 0$.
4. $2(x - 2)(x - 3) > 0$.
5. $(x - 1)(x - 2)(x - 3) > 0$.
6. $(x + 1)(x + 3)(x - 5) < 0$.

• • •

7. $-2(x - 2)(x - 3) > 0$.
8. $-3(x + 2)(x - 3)(x - 5) > 0$.
9. $x^2 - x - 12 > 0$.
10. $x^2 + 9 < 0$.
11. $x^2 - 12 < 4x$.
12. $(x^2 - 1)(x^2 - 4) > 0$.
13. $2(x^2 - 4)(x^2 - 9) > 0$.
14. $3(x - 1)(x + 2)^2(x - 3) > 0$.
15. $(x + 2)(x + 1)(x - 1)(x - 2) < 0$.
16. $6x^3 + 9x^2 + 2x + 5 < 2x^2 + 2x + 6$.

Solve each system:

• 17. $\begin{cases} (x - 1)(x + 2) < 0 \\ x(x + 1) < 0. \end{cases}$

• 18. $\begin{cases} x^3 - 2x^2 - x + 2 > 0 \\ 2x^2 - 3x > 0. \end{cases}$

Find:

• 19. The set of values of x for which $x(x^2 - 1)$ may represent the area of the surface of a sphere.

• 20. The set of values of x for which the logarithm of the product $(x - 2)(x - 3)(x + 4)$ may be expressed as a real number.

§ 8-10 Rational functions

Any number expressible as a quotient of integers $\frac{a}{b}$, $b \neq 0$ is a *rational* number. Any function $\{(x, f(x))\}$ where $f(x)$ is expressible as a quotient $\frac{g(x)}{h(x)}$ of polynomials is a **rational function** of x. The rational function is said to be **defined** whenever $h(x) \neq 0$ and to be **undefined** when $h(x) = 0$. If r is a value of x such that $g(r) = 0$ and $h(r) \neq 0$, then r is a **root** of the equation that is obtained when the rational function is set equal to zero. If

457

POLYNOMIALS

b is a value of x such that $g(b) \neq 0$ and $h(b) = 0$, then the rational function is undefined at $x = b$ and the line $x = b$ is a **vertical asymptote** of the graph of the rational function. The **multiplicity of the root** (§ 8–4) is the same as its multiplicity as a root of the polynomial equation $g(x) = 0$; the **multiplicity of the asymptote** is the same as its multiplicity as a root of the polynomial equation $h(x) = 0$. The influence of the multiplicities upon the graphs may be observed in Figure 8–9.

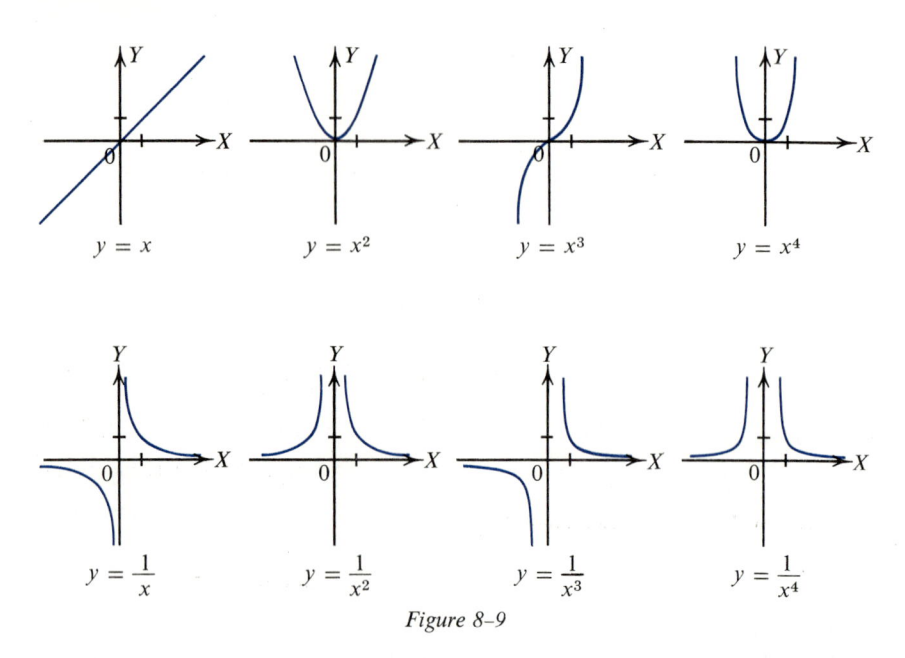

Figure 8–9

For any integer n the graphs of $y = x^{2n}$ and $y = \dfrac{1}{x^{2n}}$ do not change sign as x increases from negative to positive values; the graphs of $y = x^{2n+1}$ and $y = \dfrac{1}{x^{2n+1}}$ always change sign as x increases from negative to positive values. In other words, the sign of y does not change as x increases through a root or asymptote of even multiplicity; the sign of y always changes as x increases through a root or asymptote of odd multiplicity. Since the graph of any real polynomial equation $y = p(x)$ is a continuous curve, whenever the roots of $p(x) = 0$ are known we may use the multiplicity of the roots to obtain a sketch of the graph of any polynomial equation showing the sign but not the magnitude of y. Such a sketch may be used to solve polynomial inequalities (§ 8–9) and has other uses in advanced mathematics.

§ 8–10 RATIONAL FUNCTIONS

Example 1. Solve graphically: $x^3(x + 2)^2(x - 3)^4 > 0$.

Let $p(x) = x^3(x + 2)^2(x - 3)^4$. The equation $p(x) = 0$ has a root 0 of multiplicity three, a root -2 of multiplicity two, and a root 3 of multiplicity four. Since $p(x) > 0$ for large (greater than 3) values of x, the curve may be sketched as in Figure 8–10 and the inequality has as its solution set $\{x \mid 0 < x < 3\} \cup \{x \mid 3 < x\}$.

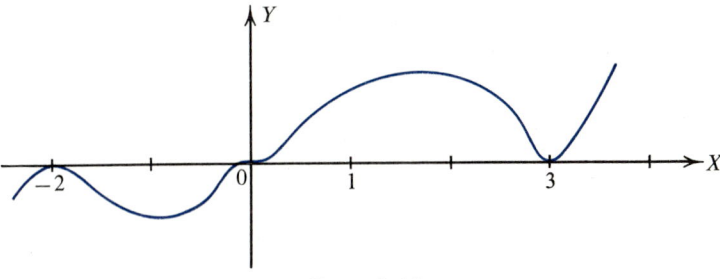

Figure 8–10

For any polynomial $p(x)$ the expressions $p(x)$ and $\dfrac{1}{p(x)}$ have the same sign whenever $p(x) \neq 0$. Accordingly, the shape of the graph of $y = \dfrac{1}{x^3(x + 2)^2(x - 3)^4}$ may be observed from Figure 8–10 to be as in Figure 8–11.

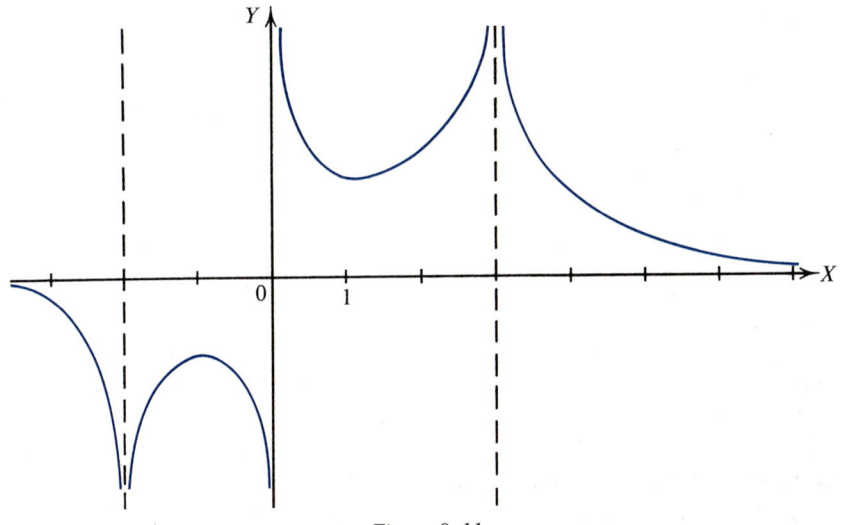

Figure 8–11

459

POLYNOMIALS

The behavior of the graph of any polynomial equation $y = p(x)$ for numerically large values of x can be observed from the term of highest degree. If that term is ax^n, then

y has the same sign as a when $x > 0$;
if n is even, y has the same sign as a when $x < 0$;
if n is odd, the sign of y is different from that of a when $x < 0$.

In all cases y is numerically large when x is numerically large.

The behavior of the graph for numerically large values of x when y is equal to a rational function of x such as

$$y = \frac{a_0 x^n + a_1 x^{n-1} + a_2 x^{n-2} + \cdots + a_n}{b_0 x^m + b_1 x^{m-1} + b_2 x^{m-2} + \cdots + b_m}, \quad a_0 b_0 \neq 0 \qquad (2)$$

can also be observed in terms of the coefficients. We consider three cases:

$$n = m, \quad n < m, \quad n > m.$$

If $n = m$, the equation (2) may be expressed as

$$y = \frac{a_0 + \dfrac{a_1}{x} + \dfrac{a_2}{x^2} + \cdots + \dfrac{a_n}{x^n}}{b_0 + \dfrac{b_1}{x} + \dfrac{b_2}{x^2} + \cdots + \dfrac{b_m}{x^n}}.$$

As $|x|$ increases without bound, $\dfrac{1}{x}$ approaches zero, and y approaches $\dfrac{a_0}{b_0}$.

If $n < m$, the equation may be expressed as

$$y = \frac{a_0 + \dfrac{a_1}{x} + \dfrac{a_2}{x^2} + \cdots + \dfrac{a_n}{x^n}}{b_0 x^{m-n} + b_1 x^{m-n-1} + \cdots + \dfrac{b_m}{x^n}}$$

and as $|x|$ increases, y approaches zero. (See Figure 8–11.) If $n > m$, then

$$y = \frac{a_0 x^{n-m} + a_1 x^{n-m-1} + \cdots + \dfrac{a_n}{x^m}}{b_0 + \dfrac{b_1}{x} + \cdots + \dfrac{b_m}{x^m}}$$

and y behaves like $\dfrac{a_0}{b_0} x^{n-m}$ as $|x|$ increases without bound. We may summarize these results as follows: In the equation (2) y behaves like $\dfrac{a_0 x^n}{b_0 x^m}$ for

§ 8–10 RATIONAL FUNCTIONS

numerically large values of x. As $|x|$ increases without bound,

y approaches $\dfrac{a_0}{b_0}$ if $n = m$;

y approaches 0 if $n < m$;

y behaves like $\dfrac{a_0}{b_0} x^{n-m}$ if $n > m$.

Whenever y approaches a constant k as $|x|$ increases without bound, the line $y = k$ is a **horizontal asymptote** of the graph. In Figure 8–11 the line $y = 0$ is a horizontal asymptote.

Example 2. Sketch the graph of $y = \dfrac{(x^2 - 1)(x^2 - 9)^2}{x^4(x^2 - 4)}$.

$$y = \frac{1(x - 1)(x + 1)(x - 3)^2(x + 3)^2}{1(x^4)(x - 2)(x + 2)}$$

The polynomials in the numerator and the denominator each have degree six; thus $y = 1$ is a horizontal asymptote. The roots are $1, -1$, 3 with multiplicity two, and -3 with multiplicity two. The vertical asymptotes are $x = 2$, $x = -2$, and $x = 0$ with multiplicity four. These facts enable us to sketch the curve by considering, in the algebraic order of the values of x, the effect upon y of the roots and the asymptotes with their multiplicities. Notice that the graph is symmetric with respect to the y-axis as could have been expected (§ 8–1).

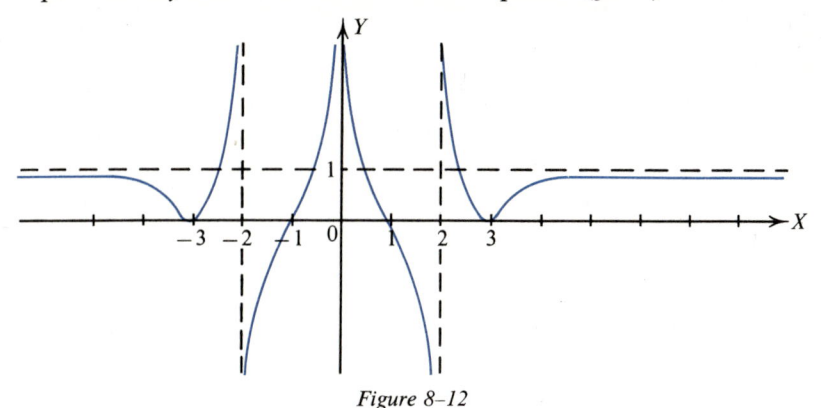

Figure 8–12

TEST YOURSELF

Sketch the graph of each equation:

1. $y = x(x + 1)^2(x - 2)^3$.
2. $y = \dfrac{2x(x^2 - 4)}{(x^2 - 1)^2}$.

461

POLYNOMIALS

EXERCISES

Sketch the graph of each equation:

1. $y = (x - 1)^2$.
2. $y = (x - 2)^3$.
3. $y = x(x^2 - 1)$.
4. $y = x(x - 1)^2$.
5. $y = x^2(x^2 - 4)$.
6. $y = (x^2 - 4)(x^2 - 1)^2$.
7. $y = x(x - 1)(x - 2)(x - 3)$.
8. $y = (x + 1)^2(x - 1)(x - 2)^3$.

• • •

9. $y = \dfrac{1}{(x - 1)^2}$.

10. $y = \dfrac{1}{x(x - 3)}$.

11. $y = \dfrac{1}{x^2(x^2 - 1)}$.

12. $y = \dfrac{1}{(x^2 - 4)^2(x^2 - 9)}$.

13. $y = \dfrac{x^3(x^2 - 1)}{x^2 - 4}$.

14. $y = \dfrac{x^2(x^2 - 4)}{(x^2 - 1)^2}$.

• 15. $y = \dfrac{(x^2 - 1)(x + 3)}{(x^2 - 9)(x + 2)}$.

• 16. $y = \dfrac{x^2(x^2 - 4)}{(x^2 - 3x + 2)(x^2 + 9)}$.

§ 8-11 Formula for $\sqrt[r]{N}$ (Supplementary)

We now illustrate for $\sqrt{N}$ a procedure which may be used to estimate as closely as we like $\sqrt[r]{N}$ for any positive integer r and any positive real number N. The procedure is important as an example of an **iteration process,** a process which may be used again and again to obtain a sequence of values $x_1, x_2, x_3, \cdots$ in which each x_{i+1} will be a better approximation than the preceding x_i to the desired result. Such processes are used extensively with electronic computers.

We obtain $\sqrt{N}$ by taking $r = 2$. We first estimate $\sqrt{N}$ as a positive number x_1 and compare x_1 with $\dfrac{N}{x_1}$. If $x_1 = \dfrac{N}{x_1}$, then $x_1^2 = N$ and $\sqrt{N} = x_1$. If $x_1 \neq \dfrac{N}{x_1}$, then either $x_1 < \dfrac{N}{x_1}$ or $\dfrac{N}{x_1} < x_1$. In either case $\sqrt{N}$ is between x_1 and $\dfrac{N}{x_1}$ and we take the mid-point of this interval as our next estimate; that is,

$$x_2 = \frac{1}{2}\left[\frac{N}{x_1} + x_1\right].$$

If $x_2^2 \neq N$, we take

$$x_3 = \frac{1}{2}\left[\frac{N}{x_2} + x_2\right].$$

§ 8–11 FORMULA FOR $\sqrt[r]{N}$

If $x_3^2 \neq N$, we take

$$x_4 = \frac{1}{2}\left[\frac{N}{x_3} + x_3\right].$$

In general, for any positive integer j, we take

$$x_{j+1} = \frac{1}{2}\left[\frac{N}{x_j} + x_j\right].$$

Consider $\sqrt{11}$ where $r = 2$ and $N = 11$. The symbol $\sqrt{11}$ means the nonnegative square root and thus the positive root of the equation $x^2 - 11 = 0$. According to Descartes' Rule of Signs this equation has exactly one positive root, namely, $\sqrt{11}$. If we estimate $\sqrt{11}$ as 3, then $x_1 = 3$ and we take as our next estimate

$$\frac{1}{2}\left[\frac{11}{3} + 3\right], \text{ that is, } x_2 = 3\tfrac{1}{3}.$$

Our next approximation is

$$\frac{1}{2}\left[\frac{11}{3\tfrac{1}{3}} + 3\tfrac{1}{3}\right], \text{ that is, } x_3 = 3\tfrac{19}{60}.$$

We may repeat this process for as many steps as we like. Usually we approximate the values of $x_1, x_2, \cdots$ by decimals. For $\sqrt{11}$ we would then have

$$x_1 = 3,$$

$$x_2 = \frac{1}{2}\left[\frac{11}{3} + 3\right] \approx 3.3,$$

$$x_3 = \frac{1}{2}\left[\frac{11}{3.3} + 3.3\right] \approx 3.32,$$

$$x_4 = \frac{1}{2}\left[\frac{11}{3.32} + 3.32\right] \approx 3.318,$$

and so forth until the approximation is as close as desired.

Example 1. Find $\sqrt{18}$ to the nearest hundredth of a unit.

We choose $x_1 = 4$, then

$$x_2 = \frac{1}{2}\left[\frac{18}{4} + 4\right] = 4.25,$$

$$x_3 = \frac{1}{2}\left[\frac{18}{4.25} + 4.25\right] \approx 4.24,$$

and

$$x_4 = \frac{1}{2}\left[\frac{18}{4.24} + 4.24\right] \approx 4.24.$$

Hence, $\sqrt{18} \approx 4.24$ is correct to the nearest hundredth of a unit.

POLYNOMIALS

This method for estimating $\sqrt{N}$ can be extended for $\sqrt[r]{N}$ for any positive integer r. In the general case, we seek the one positive root of $x^r - N = 0$. It can be shown by means of the calculus that if we choose an approximation to the rth root of N, say x_1, then the expression

$$\frac{1}{r}\left[\frac{N}{x_1^{r-1}} + (r-1)x_1\right]$$

yields a closer approximation, x_2. Using x_2 in place of x_1 in the above expression a closer approximation x_3 can be obtained. Continuing in this manner a sequence of values $x_1, x_2, \cdots$ will be obtained in which each x_{i+1} will be a better approximation than the preceding term x_i. The process may be terminated when two successive approximations agree to the nearest desired unit. The general *iterative* formula is

$$x_{i+1} = \frac{1}{r}\left[\frac{N}{x_i^{r-1}} + (r-1)x_i\right].$$

Example 2. Find $\sqrt[3]{100}$ to the nearest thousandth of a unit.

We are seeking an approximation for the one positive root of the polynomial equation $x^3 - 100 = 0$. We choose 4 as our first approximation. Then according to our iterative formula

$$x_1 = 4,$$

$$x_2 = \frac{1}{3}\left[\frac{100}{4^2} + (2)(4)\right] = 4.75,$$

$$x_3 = \frac{1}{3}\left[\frac{100}{(4.75)^2} + (2)(4.75)\right] \approx 4.644,$$

$$x_4 = \frac{1}{3}\left[\frac{100}{(4.644)^2} + (2)(4.644)\right] \approx 4.642,$$

$$x_5 = \frac{1}{3}\left[\frac{100}{(4.642)^2} + (2)(4.642)\right] \approx 4.641,$$

$$x_6 = \frac{1}{3}\left[\frac{100}{(4.641)^2} + (2)(4.641)\right] \approx 4.641.$$

The iteration may be terminated here since two successive approximations agree to the nearest thousandth of a unit; $\sqrt[3]{100} \approx 4.641$.

Note that $\sqrt[3]{-100} = -\sqrt[3]{100}$. Accordingly, if we need to find $\sqrt[3]{-N}$ or $\sqrt[r]{-N}$ for any positive odd integer r and any negative number $-N$, we may find $\sqrt[3]{N}$ or $\sqrt[r]{N}$ and take its negative.

TEST YOURSELF

Find to the nearest hundredth of a unit:

1. $\sqrt{23}$. 2. $\sqrt[3]{0.025}$.

EXERCISES

Find to the nearest hundredth of a unit:

1. $\sqrt{65}$. 2. $\sqrt[3]{9}$. 3. $\sqrt[3]{120}$. 4. $\sqrt[5]{39}$. 5. $\sqrt[3]{-150}$.

SUMMARY OF CHAPTER 8

1. In this chapter you have studied polynomials in one variable and related topics. Any polynomial is a sum of terms. Any polynomial except 0 has the degree of its term of highest degree. (§ 8-1)

2. Factors of polynomials and roots of polynomial equations are closely related.

Remainder Theorem: The remainder when any polynomial $p(x)$ is divided by $(x - c)$ is $p(c)$.

Factor Theorem: If a polynomial $p(x) = 0$ when $x = c$, then $(x - c)$ is a factor of $p(x)$.

The converse of the Factor Theorem is also true. (§ 8-2)

3. Synthetic division may be used to find the quotient and remainder when any polynomial $p(x)$ is divided by an expression of the form $(x - h)$. (§ 8-3)

4. Every complex polynomial equation of degree n has exactly n complex numbers, not necessarily distinct, as roots. (§ 8-4)

5. By Descartes' Rule of Signs, the number of positive roots of any real polynomial equation

$$a_0 x^n + a_1 x^{n-1} + a_2 x^{n-2} + \cdots + a_{n-1} x + a_n = 0$$

is $V(a_0, a_1, a_2, \cdots, a_{n-1}, a_n) - 2k$ where k is some nonnegative integer. In order to determine the number of negative roots of any real polynomial equation $p(x) = 0$, we apply Descartes' Rule of Signs to the equation $p(-x) = 0$. The positive roots of the equation $p(-x) = 0$ are the negatives of the negative roots of $p(x) = 0$. (§ 8-5)

6. The integral and rational roots of any given polynomial equation with integral coefficients may be found by trial and error. If a rational number $\frac{p}{q}$ is a root of a polynomial equation $a_0 x^n + a_1 x^{n-1} + \cdots + a_n = 0$ where $a_0 \neq 0$ and the a_j are integers, then p is a factor of a_n and q is a factor of a_0. (§ 8-6)

POLYNOMIALS

7. The real roots of a real polynomial equation often may be isolated by means of the location principle:

If any real polynomial $p(x)$ and real numbers a and b are given such that $p(a)$ and $p(b)$ have opposite signs, then there exists at least one real root of the equation $p(x) = 0$ between a and b.

Synthetic division and Descartes' Rule of Signs may be used to find upper and lower bounds of the roots of any given polynomial equation. (§ 8–7)

8. The sum and the product of the roots of any polynomial equation may be expressed in terms of the coefficients. (§ 8–8)

9. The solution set of any polynomial inequality consists of a set of intervals of values of the variable. These intervals may be of the form $x < b_1$, $b_2 < x < b_3$, $b_4 < x$ where $p(b_j) = 0$ and $p(x)$ has constant sign on any given interval. (§ 8–9)

10. Rational functions may be graphed (as rough sketches) from information conveyed by the multiplicity of their roots and their asymptotes. (§ 8–10)

11. For any positive integer r and any positive real number N we may approximate $\sqrt[r]{N}$ to any desired number of significant digits. (§ 8–11)

12. The following words have been introduced or used extensively in this chapter:

axis of symmetry (§ 8–1)
binomial (§ 8–1)
center of symmetry (§ 8–1)
coefficient (§ 8–1)
complex polynomial (§ 8–1)
conjugate pairs (§ 8–5)
degree (§ 8–1)
depressed equation (§ 8–2)
Descartes' Rule of Signs (§ 8–5)
even function (§ 8–1)
Factor Theorem (§ 8–2)
horizontal asymptote (§ 8–10)
isolated root (§ 8–7)
iteration process (§ 8–11)
literal part (§ 8–1)
location principle (§ 8–7)
lower bound (§ 8–7)
monomial (§ 8–1)

multiple root (§ 8–4)
numerical coefficient (§ 8–1)
odd function (§ 8–1)
polynomial (§ 8–1)
polynomial equation (§ 8–2)
rational function (§ 8–10)
rational polynomial (§ 8–1)
real polynomial (§ 8–1)
relatively prime (§ 8–6)
Remainder Theorem (§ 8–2)
similar terms (§ 8–1)
simple root (§ 8–4)
synthetic division (§ 8–3)
term (§ 8–1)
trinomial (§ 8–1)
upper bound (§ 8–7)
variation in signs (§ 8–5)
vertical asymptote (§ 8–10)

KEYED PRACTICE ON CHAPTER 8

1. State the coefficient and degree when the term $3x^3y^8$ is considered as a term in (**a**) x; (**b**) y; (**c**) x and y; (**d**) y^2; (**e**) x^3. (§ 8–1)

2. Prove that the graph of $y = \tan x$ is symmetric with respect to the origin. (§ 8–1)

3. Find the remainder when $(x^5 - 2x^4 + 3x^2 - 9)$ is divided by $(x - 2)$. (§ 8–2)

4. Find the value of k if $(x + 2)$ is a factor of $(x^3 + kx^2 - 8)$. (§ 8–2)

5. Use synthetic division to find the quotient and remainder when $(x^5 - 2x^4 + x^3 + 7)$ is divided by $(x - 2)$. (§ 8–3)

6. Find a polynomial equation with roots 3, −3, 1, −1. (§ 8–4)

7. Determine the number of possible positive, negative, zero, and imaginary roots of the equation $x^4 - 2x^3 + x^2 - x + 5 = 0$. (§ 8–5)

8. Solve completely: $2x^4 - x^3 - 3x^2 - 5x - 2 = 0$. (§ 8–6)

9. Prove that -2 is a lower bound of the roots of the equation
$$x^4 - 2x^3 + x^2 + 5x - 7 = 0. \quad (\S\ 8\text{–}7)$$

10. Between what two consecutive integers does the positive root of the equation $x^3 - 7x - 2 = 0$ lie? (§ 8–7)

11. Find the sum and the product of the roots of the equation
$$3x^5 - 2x^4 + x^2 - 2x + 6 = 0. \quad (\S\ 8\text{–}8)$$

12. Solve: $x(x^2 + x - 6) < 0$. (§ 8–9)

13. Sketch the graph of the equation $y = \dfrac{x^2(x^2 - 4)}{(x^2 - 1)^2}$. (§ 8–10)

• **14.** Find $\sqrt{43}$ to the nearest hundredth of a unit. (§ 8–11)

TESTS ON CHAPTER 8

A

1. State the coefficient and degree when the term $5x^4y^{12}$ is considered as a term in (**a**) x; (**b**) y; (**c**) x and y; (**d**) x^2; (**e**) y^3.

2. Find the quotient and remainder when $(x^5 - 3x^3 + 2x^2 - 4)$ is divided by $(x - 1)$.

POLYNOMIALS

3. Find a polynomial equation with roots 1, 2, and -3.

4. Determine the number of possible positive, negative, zero, and imaginary roots of the equation $2x^5 - x^3 + 3x^2 + 5x - 7 = 0$.

5. Solve completely: $3x^3 - 4x^2 + 13x - 4 = 0$.

6. Prove that 1 is an upper bound of the roots of the equation
$$3x^3 - x^2 + 2x - 3 = 0.$$

7. Find the sum and the product of the roots of the equation
$$2x^4 + 5x^3 - 2x - 7 = 0.$$

8. Solve: $x(x^2 - 2x - 8) < 0$.

9. Sketch the graph of the equation $y = \dfrac{x(x^2 - 9)}{(x^2 - 4)(x - 5)}$.

10. Find to the nearest tenth the real root of $x^3 - 5x^2 - 7 = 0$.

B

1. Identify the expressions which are, or may be expressed as, polynomials in x: (a) $2x^2 + 3\sqrt{x}$; (b) $1 + x^2 - 3x$; (c) $2x^0$; (d) $(\sqrt{x})^3 + 2(\sqrt{x})^2 - 4$; (e) $(x^2)^5 - 4(x^2)^3 + 3x^2 - 7$.

2. Find the quotient and remainder when $(x^5 - 2x^3 + x^2 - 3x + 5)$ is divided by $(x + 1)$.

3. Find a polynomial equation with roots 0, 2, $1 + i$, and $1 - i$.

4. Determine the number of possible positive, negative, zero, and imaginary roots of the equation $7x^5 + 4x^3 - x^2 + 11 = 0$.

5. Solve completely: $2x^4 + 5x^3 + 4x^2 + 5x + 2 = 0$.

6. Prove that -3 is a lower bound of the roots of the equation
$$x^4 + 3x^3 + x^2 + 2x - 1 = 0.$$

7. Find the sum of the cube roots of -5.

8. Solve: $(x^2 - 1)^2(x - 3) < 0$.

9. Sketch the graph of the equation $y = \dfrac{(x^2 - 1)(x^2 - 16)}{x^2(x^2 - 9)}$.

10. Find to the nearest tenth the real root of $x^3 - 4x^2 - 2 = 0$.

C

1. State whether each expression $f(x)$ defines an odd function of x, an even function of x, or neither: (a) $x^2 - 3$; (b) $x^3 + 2x$; (c) $|x| + 5$; (d) $x \tan x$; (e) 7.
2. Find the quotient and remainder when $(x^7 + x^5 + x^3 + 3)$ is divided by $(x + 1)$.
3. Find a polynomial equation with roots $1 + \sqrt{2}, 1 - \sqrt{2}, i$, and $-i$.
4. Prove that the polynomial equation $x^{13} - 1 = 0$ has no multiple real roots.
5. Prove that $(3 + \sqrt{2})$ is irrational.
6. Find to the nearest tenth the real root of $2x^3 - 6x^2 - 3 = 0$.
7. Find a polynomial equation $p(x) = 0$ whose roots are twice the roots of the equation $y^3 + 3y^2 - 2y + 5 = 0$.
8. Solve: $2(x^2 - 1)(x^2 - 4)^2 < 0$.
9. Sketch the graph of the equation

$$y = \frac{(x^2 - x - 6)(x^2 - 16)}{(x^2 - 9)(x^2 - 4)}.$$

10. Find $\sqrt[3]{35}$ to the nearest hundredth of a unit.

ANSWERS TO TEST YOURSELF EXERCISES

§ 8–1. 1. (a) Coefficient πh, degree two; (b) coefficient π, degree three; (c) coefficient πh, degree one.
2. (a) If $y^2 = x^2 - 5$, then $(-y)^2 = x^2 - 5$.
(b) If $y^2 = x^2 - 5$, then $(-y)^2 = (-x)^2 - 5$.
3. $x + y - 5 = 0$.

§ 8–2. 1. 5. 2. If $p(x) = x^2 - 5x + 4$, then $p(1) = 1 - 5 + 4 = 0$ and $(x - 1)$ is a factor of $p(x)$ by the Factor Theorem. 3. 3.

§ 8–3. 1. Quotient $x^3 - 2x^2 + x + 3$, remainder -13. 2. 7.

§ 8–4. 1. 5. 2. $x^3 - 2x^2 - 5x + 6 = 0$. 3. The root -3 has multiplicity three, 1 has multiplicity two, -2 has multiplicity five, and 2 has multiplicity five.

§ 8–5. 1. One positive root, one zero root, and either two negative roots or no negative roots and two conjugate imaginary roots.
2. One negative root, two zero roots, and either two positive roots or no positive roots and two conjugate imaginary roots.

469

POLYNOMIALS

§ 8-6. 1. None. 2. 0, −2.

§ 8-7. 1. 4 | 2 −7 −3   6
              8   4   4
           ──────────────────
           2   1   1 | 10

Since all elements of the third row are positive, 4 is an upper bound of the roots of the given polynomial equation.

2. Consider $p(-x) = -2x^3 - 7x^2 + 3x + 6 = 0$ which has the same roots as $2x^3 + 7x^2 - 3x - 6 = 0$.

2 | 2   7   −3   −6
        4   22   38
    ──────────────────
    2   11   19 | 32

Thus 2 is an upper bound of the roots of $p(-x) = 0$ and -2 is a lower bound of the roots of $p(x) = 0$.

§ 8-8. 1. Sum −2, product 7.

2. Sum $\frac{5}{2}$, product −6.

3. Sum 0, product $-\frac{5}{3}$.

4. $x^3 - 4x^2 + x + 6 = 0$.

5. $x^3 - 4x = 0$.

§ 8-9. 1. $x < -1, x > 1$.

2. $-2 < x < -1, x > 0$.

3. $-2 < x < -1, x > 1$.

§ 8-10. 1.

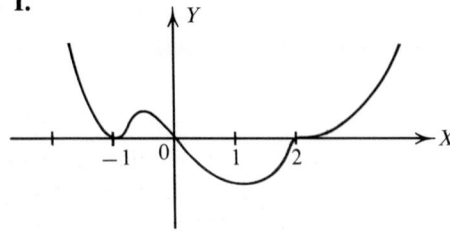

470

2.

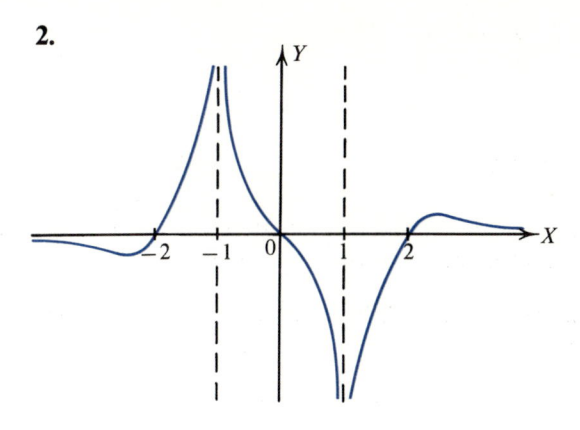

[Graph showing y = tan x with vertical asymptotes]

§ 8–11. 1. 4.80.

2. 0.29.

ANSWERS TO KEYED PRACTICE EXERCISES

1. (a) Coefficient $3y^8$, degree three; (b) coefficient $3x^3$, degree eight; (c) coefficient 3, degree eleven; (d) coefficient $3x^3$, degree four; (e) coefficient $3y^8$, degree one.

2. If (x, y) is a point of the graph of $y = \tan x$, then $(-x, -y)$ is also a point of the graph since $-y = \tan(-x)$; that is, $-y = -\tan x$; therefore the graph of $y = \tan x$ is symmetric with respect to the origin.

3. $f(2) = 3$.

4. $\underline{-2\,|}$ 1 k 0 -8
                  -2 $-2k + 4$ $4k - 8$
         1    $k - 2$ $-2k + 4$ $\boxed{4k - 16}$; $4k - 16 = 0$; $k = 4$.

5. $\underline{2\,|}$ 1 -2 1   0   0   7
                 2   0   2   4   8
      1   0   1   2   4 $\boxed{15}$

Quotient $x^4 + x^2 + 2x + 4$; remainder 15.

6. $x^4 - 10x^2 + 9 = 0$.

7. The equation has no negative roots; no zero roots; either four positive roots, or two positive and two conjugate imaginary roots, or no positive and two pairs of conjugate imaginary roots.

8. Roots are 2, $-\dfrac{1}{2}$, $\dfrac{-1 + i\sqrt{3}}{2}$, $\dfrac{-1 - i\sqrt{3}}{2}$.

9. Let $p(x) = x^4 - 2x^3 + x^2 + 5x - 7$; then

$p(-x) = x^4 + 2x^3 + x^2 - 5x - 7.$

2	1	2	1	−5	−7
		2	8	18	26
	1	4	9	13	19

Since all the elements of the third row have the same sign, 2 is an upper bound of the roots of $p(-x) = 0$ and -2 is a lower bound of the roots of $p(x) = 0$.

10. The positive root lies between 2 and 3.

11. Sum $\dfrac{2}{3}$, product -2.

12. $x < -3$, $0 < x < 2$.

13.

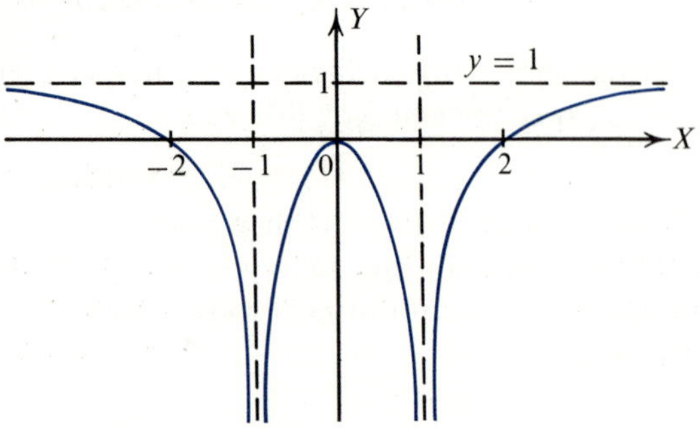

14. 6.56.

Chapter 9

Special Functions

§ 9-1 Power functions

Any real polynomial in x is expressible as the sum of a finite number of terms of the form ax^n where a is a real number, x is a variable, and n is a nonnegative integer (§ 8-1). For any negative integral values of n, $ax^n = \dfrac{a}{x^{|n|}}$ and the term is a rational function of x (§ 8-10). In this section we consider terms ax^n where n may represent any real number.

Any term ax^n where a is a real number, x is a real variable, and n is a real number is a real **power function** of x of **degree** n. Thus any power function of x of an integral degree n is a polynomial in x if $n \geq 0$, a rational function of x if $n < 0$.

Let us take $a = 1$ and consider power functions of the form x^n. As in § 8-10, the term $x^n > 0$ when $x > 0$ for all integral values (positive, negative, and zero) of n. The term 0^0 is not uniquely defined therefore if $x = 0$, then x^n is defined if and only if $n > 0$. If n is an even integer, $x^n > 0$ when $x < 0$; if n is an odd integer, $x^n < 0$ when $x < 0$. These properties of the power function x^n for integral values of n have been considered in § 8-10 and are illustrated by the graphs in Figure 9-1 for $n = 1, 2,$ and 3 in (a); for $n = 0$ and -1 in (b); and for $n = -2$ in (c).

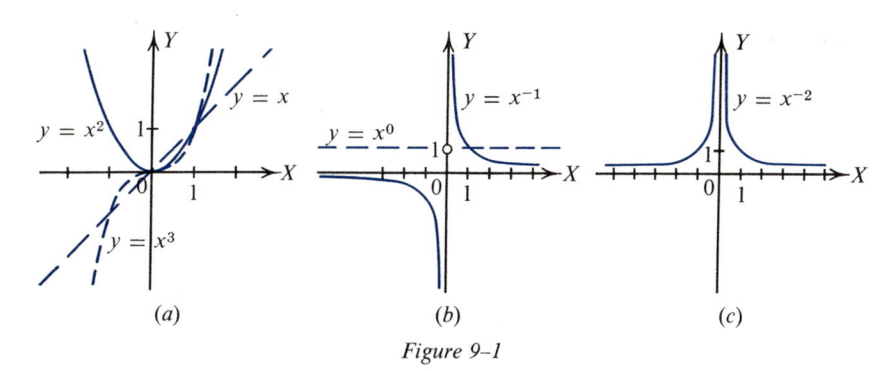

Figure 9-1

The properties of the power functions graphed in Figure 9-1 may also be considered in terms of a table of values. The values in the table are

473

SPECIAL FUNCTIONS

correct to the nearest hundredth of a unit.

x	x^2	x^3	x^0	x^{-1}	x^{-2}
-2.00	4.00	-8.00	1.00	-0.50	0.25
-1.75	3.06	-5.36	1.00	-0.57	0.33
-1.50	2.25	-3.38	1.00	-0.67	0.44
-1.25	1.56	-1.95	1.00	-0.80	0.64
-1.00	1.00	-1.00	1.00	-1.00	1.00
-0.75	0.56	-0.42	1.00	-1.33	1.78
-0.50	0.25	-0.12	1.00	-2.00	4.00
-0.25	0.06	-0.02	1.00	-4.00	16.00
0.00	0.00	0.00	—	—	—
0.25	0.06	0.02	1.00	4.00	16.00
0.50	0.25	0.12	1.00	2.00	4.00
0.75	0.56	0.42	1.00	1.33	1.78
1.00	1.00	1.00	1.00	1.00	1.00
1.25	1.56	1.95	1.00	0.80	0.64
1.50	2.25	3.38	1.00	0.67	0.44
1.75	3.06	5.36	1.00	0.57	0.33
2.00	4.00	8.00	1.00	0.50	0.25

Let us next consider the properties of power functions x^n for any real number n. The term x^n is defined at $x = 0$ if and only if $n > 0$. When $x > 0$, we assume that there exists a unique positive real value of x^n for any real number n. For example, if $n = 0.5$, there are two real square roots of any positive number x and the symbol $x^{0.5}$ stands for the positive square root; if $n = -0.5$, then $x^{-0.5}$ may be found as the reciprocal of $x^{0.5}$. If $n = 0.25$, there are four fourth roots (one positive, one negative, and two imaginary) of any positive number x and the symbol $x^{0.25}$ stands for the positive fourth root; for example, $16^{0.25} = 2$. Such definitions of the symbol x^n may be extended to define any power function ax^n as a unique real number for any real number a, any positive value of x, and any real number n. Only rational values $\frac{p}{q}$ in reduced form will be considered for n when $x < 0$. Then $x^{\frac{p}{q}}$ is undefined if q is an even integer and defined if q is an odd integer.

The definition of x^n as a unique real number for negative values of x is not always possible since square roots and, in general, "even" roots of negative numbers are imaginary numbers. We shall not attempt a complete formal definition of x^n for negative values of x. We can accept intuitively the statement that x^n may be defined for negative values of x if and

§ 9–1 POWER FUNCTIONS

only if x^n does not involve an "even" root. For example, as shown in the table of values correct to the nearest hundredth of a unit and in Figure 9–2, $x^{\frac{1}{2}}$ is undefined if $x < 0$; $x^{\frac{2}{3}}$ is defined for all real values of x; $x^{-\frac{1}{2}}$ is undefined if $x \leq 0$.

Rational powers $x^{\frac{p}{q}}$ of negative numbers may be defined as real numbers if and only if q is an odd integer. Irrational powers of negative numbers are not defined since irrational numbers may be represented as decimals, and the decimal approximations may be represented by rational numbers with an even integer as the denominator. For example, $\sqrt{3} = 1.732 \cdots$; $\sqrt{3} \approx \frac{1732}{1000}$.

x	$x^{\frac{1}{2}}$	$x^{\frac{2}{3}}$	$x^{-\frac{1}{2}}$
−2.00	—	1.59	—
−1.75	—	1.45	—
−1.50	—	1.31	—
−1.25	—	1.16	—
−1.00	—	1.00	—
−0.75	—	0.82	—
−0.50	—	0.62	—
−0.25	—	0.40	—
0.00	0.00	0.00	—
0.25	0.50	0.40	2.00
0.50	0.71	0.62	1.41
0.75	0.87	0.82	1.15
1.00	1.00	1.00	1.00
1.25	1.12	1.16	0.89
1.50	1.22	1.31	0.82
1.75	1.32	1.45	0.75
2.00	1.41	1.59	0.71

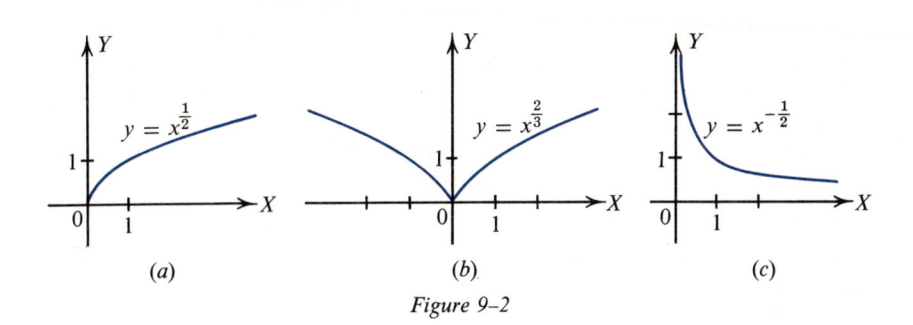

(a) $y = x^{\frac{1}{2}}$

(b) $y = x^{\frac{2}{3}}$

(c) $y = x^{-\frac{1}{2}}$

Figure 9–2

We have assumed that the power function x^n is *defined* as a unique real number

(i) for all real numbers n when $x > 0$;
(ii) for all positive numbers n when $x = 0$;
(iii) for rational values $\frac{p}{q}$ of n where p and q are relatively prime integers and q is an odd integer when $x < 0$.

475

SPECIAL FUNCTIONS

The following properties of power functions may be established: The *domain* of the power function x^n is

(i) the set of all real numbers when $n = \frac{p}{q} > 0$ and q is an odd integer [see Figures 9–1 (*a*) and 9–2 (*b*)];

(ii) the set of nonzero real numbers when $n = \frac{p}{q} \leq 0$ and q is an odd integer [see Figure 9–1 (*b*)];

(iii) the set of nonnegative real numbers when n is a positive irrational number or a positive rational number $\frac{p}{q}$ where q is an even integer;

(iv) the set of positive real numbers when n is a negative irrational number or a negative rational number $\frac{p}{q}$ where q is an even integer.

The *range* of the power function x^n is

(i) the set of all real numbers when $n = \frac{p}{q} > 0$, q is an odd integer, and p is an odd integer (see Figure 9–1 (*a*) for $n = 1$ or 3);

(ii) the set of nonnegative real numbers when n is positive and equal to

  (a) $\frac{p}{q}$ where q is an odd integer and p is an even integer;

  (b) $\frac{p}{q}$ where q is an even integer [see Figure 9–2 (*a*)];

  (c) an irrational number;

(iii) the set of nonzero real numbers when $n = \frac{p}{q} < 0$ where q is an odd integer and p is an odd integer (see Figure 9–1 (*b*) for $n = -1$);

(iv) the single number 1 when $n = 0$ (see Figure 9–1 (*b*) for $n = 0$).

The *graph* of $y = x^n$

(i) always includes the point (1, 1);

(ii) includes (0, 0) if $n > 0$;

(iii) has the coordinate axes as asymptotes if $n < 0$ [see Figure 9–1 (*b*) and (*c*) and Figure 9–2 (*c*)];

(iv) is symmetric with respect to the origin if $n = \frac{p}{q}$ where p and q are odd integers (see Figure 9–1 (*a*) for $n = 3$ and Figure 9–1 (*b*) for $n = -1$);

(v) is symmetric with respect to the *y*-axis if $n = \frac{p}{q}$ where q is an odd integer and p is an even integer [see Figure 9–1 (*a*) and (*c*) and Figure 9–2 (*b*)].

§ 9-2 EXPONENTIAL AND LOGARITHMIC FUNCTIONS

TEST YOURSELF

State the domain and range of each power function and sketch its graph:

1. $2x^3$. 2. $x^{\frac{1}{3}}$. 3. $x^{-\frac{1}{3}}$. 4. $x^{\frac{1}{4}}$.

EXERCISES

State the domain and range of each power function and sketch its graph:

1. $-2x$.
2. $-x^2$.
3. $-x^3$.
4. $2x^{\frac{1}{2}}$.
5. $-x^{-\frac{1}{2}}$.
6. $-x^{\frac{2}{3}}$.
7. $x^{-\frac{2}{3}}$.
8. $x^{\frac{3}{2}}$.
9. $x^{-\frac{3}{2}}$.

• • •

Arrange the power functions x^3, $x^{\frac{5}{3}}$, $x^{-\frac{5}{3}}$, $x^{\frac{2}{3}}$, $x^{-\frac{2}{3}}$ in the order of their (a) *algebraic values;* (b) *numerical values;* if

10. $x > 1$.
11. $x < -1$.
12. $0 < x < 1$.
13. $-1 < x < 0$.

§ 9-2 Exponential and logarithmic functions

Any term b^n is a power function of the real variable b for any given real number n (§ 9–1). In this section we think of b as the given real number and n as the variable.

For any positive number b the term b^x is defined for all real numbers x (§ 9–1) and is an **exponential function** of x. If $b = 1$, then $b^x = 1$ for all values of x. If $b \neq 1$, the *domain* of the exponential function is the set of real numbers; the *range* is the set of positive numbers.

Consider the exponential function 2^x. Values of 2^x for integral values of x may be obtained from the usual laws of exponents; values of 2^x for $x = \frac{1}{2}, \frac{1}{3}, \frac{2}{3}, \frac{1}{4}, \frac{3}{4}, \frac{1}{5}$, and in general, any rational number may also be obtained. Values of terms such as $2^{\sqrt{3}}$ and 2^π may be found by considering what is meant by $\sqrt{3}$ and by π. We use a sequence of decimals 1, 1.7, 1.73, 1.732 and so forth to approximate the value of $\sqrt{3}$ as closely as we wish; we also use the sequence 2^1, $2^{1.7}$, $2^{1.73}$, $2^{1.732}$, and so forth to approximate $2^{\sqrt{3}}$ as closely as we wish. We approximate π using 3, 3.1, 3.14, 3.142, 3.1416, and so forth; we approximate 2^π using 2^3, $2^{3.1}$, $2^{3.14}$, $2^{3.142}$, $2^{3.1416}$, and so forth. Any real number may be expressed as a

477

SPECIAL FUNCTIONS

decimal (§ 6–6) thus a value of 2^x may be defined for any real number x. For any x, 2^x may be obtained as the number whose common logarithm is $x \log 2$. The graph of 2^x (Figure 9–3) is continuous and may be sketched from a table of values.

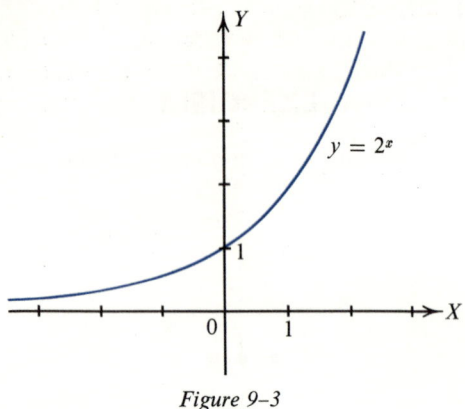

Figure 9–3

The graphs of all exponential functions include the point (0, 1) since $b^0 = 1$. If $b > 1$, the graph of $y = b^x$ has the negative x-axis as a horizontal asymptote and b^x increases without bound as x increases without bound. (See Figure 9–3.) We consider $y = \left(\frac{1}{2}\right)^x$; that is $y = \frac{1}{2^x}$; as an example of b^x for $b < 1$. Notice that the graph of $y = \left(\frac{1}{2}\right)^x$ may be obtained by reflecting the graph of $y = 2^x$ in the y-axis. If $0 < b < 1$, the graph of $y = b^x$ has the positive x-axis as a horizontal asymptote and b^x increases without bound as x decreases without bound. (See Figure 9–4.)

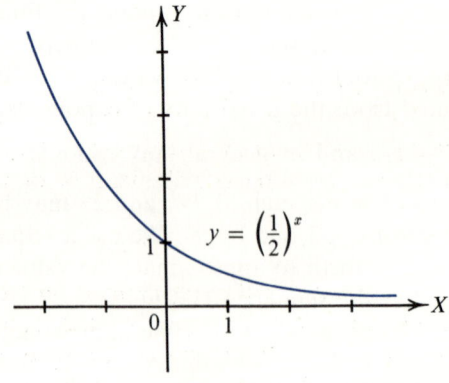

Figure 9–4

§ 9-2 EXPONENTIAL AND LOGARITHMIC FUNCTIONS

Compare the graphs in Figures 9-3 and 9-4. For $x > 0$, $2^x > \left(\frac{1}{2}\right)^x$; for $x < 0$, $2^x < \left(\frac{1}{2}\right)^x$. In general, if a and b are two positive numbers such that $a > b$, then $a^x > b^x$ for $x > 0$; and $a^x < b^x$ for $x < 0$. In Figure 9-5 the graphs of the exponential functions b^x where $b = 2, e, 3$, and 10 may be compared. The number e is an irrational number whose definition we shall discuss in Chapter 10; 2.71828 is an approximation for e to five decimal places.

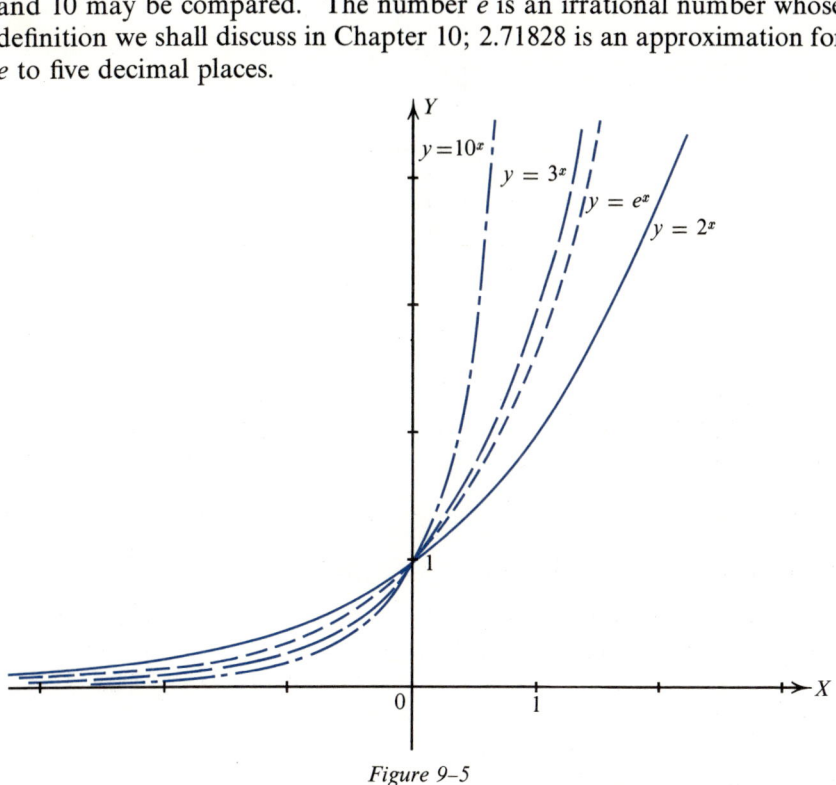

Figure 9-5

The inverse relation (§ 1-9) of any exponential function $\{(x, b^x)\}$ is a function $\{(b^y, y)\}$. We write $x = b^y$, assume that two numbers are equal if and only if their logarithms to any given base b, $0 < b \neq 1$, are equal, define the new function to be a **logarithmic function** of x, and express the function

$$x = b^y \quad \text{as} \quad y = \log_b x.$$

The real number b is the **base** of the logarithmic function. The *domain* of any logarithmic function is the set of positive numbers; the *range* is the set of real numbers. As in § 1-9, the graph of any logarithmic function is symmetric to the graph of the corresponding exponential function with

SPECIAL FUNCTIONS

respect to the line $y = x$ (Figure 9-6). A comparison of the graphs of the logarithmic functions with bases 2, e, 3, and 10 is shown in Figure 9-7.

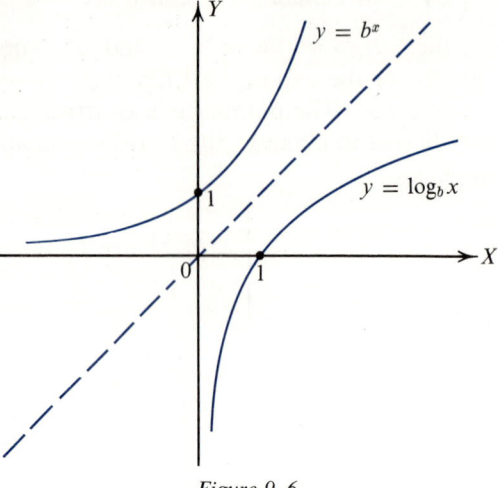

Figure 9-6

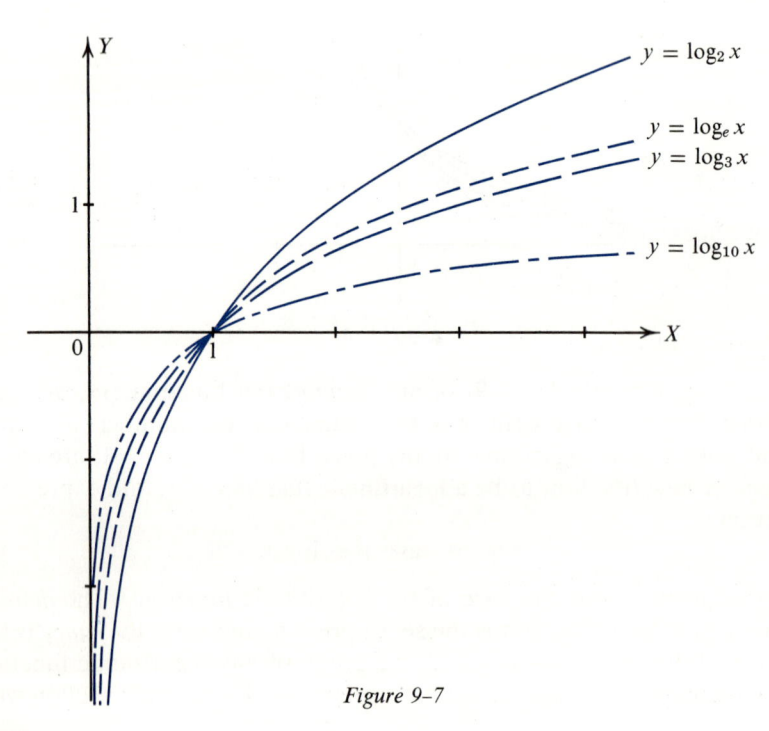

Figure 9-7

480

§ 9-2 EXPONENTIAL AND LOGARITHMIC FUNCTIONS

The logarithmic function $\log_{10} x$ which has base 10 is the **common logarithmic function** of x. You have used tables of values for common logarithms for computations in previous courses. The logarithmic function $\log_e x$ which has base e is the **natural logarithmic function** of x and is usually denoted by the symbol $\ln x$. The natural logarithmic function has special properties which are very important in calculus and advanced mathematics. Tables of values for natural logarithms are often available but are harder to use for computation than tables of values for common logarithms.

The evaluation of y where $y = \log_b x$ is equivalent to the evaluation of y where $x = b^y$. This is the basis for the following definition of a logarithm: The **logarithm** of a number is the power to which the base must be raised to obtain the number. We have assumed that if $b^y = b^k$ for any real numbers y, k and $0 < b \neq 1$, then $y = k$.

Example. Evaluate each expression: (a) $\log_2 16$; (b) $\log_{\frac{1}{2}} 8$; (c) $\log_3 \frac{1}{27}$; (d) $\ln e^{a^2+2}$; (e) $e^{\ln 7}$.

(a) $y = \log_2 16$; $16 = 2^y$; $2^4 = 2^y$; $y = 4$.
(b) $y = \log_{\frac{1}{2}} 8$; $8 = \left(\frac{1}{2}\right)^y$; $\left(\frac{1}{2}\right)^{-3} = \left(\frac{1}{2}\right)^y$; $y = -3$.
(c) $y = \log_3 \frac{1}{27}$; $\frac{1}{27} = 3^y$; $3^{-3} = 3^y$; $y = -3$.
(d) $y = \log_e e^{a^2+2}$; $e^{a^2+2} = e^y$; $y = a^2 + 2$.
(e) $x = e^{\ln 7}$; $\ln 7 = \log_e x$; $x = 7$. In other words, when e is raised to the power to which e is raised to obtain 7, the result is 7.

TEST YOURSELF

Evaluate each expression:

1. $\log_5 125$. 2. $\log_{10} 0.001$. 3. $\ln e^{2a^2-1}$. 4. $e^{\ln x^{-2}}$.

EXERCISES

A

Evaluate each expression:

1. $\log_2 \frac{1}{8}$.
2. $\log_{10} 0.0001$.
3. $\log_5 625$.
4. $\log_{\frac{3}{2}} \frac{2}{3}$.
5. $\log_3 27$.
6. $3^{\log_4 2}$.

481

SPECIAL FUNCTIONS

7. $5^{\log_5 25}$.
8. $\ln e^3$.
9. $\ln e^x$.
10. $\ln e^{x^2-2x+1}$.

11. $10^{\log 17}$.
12. $e^{\ln x}$.
13. $10^{5(\log 2)}$.
14. $e^{3(\ln x)}$.

• • •

15. $10^{\log 8 - \log 2}$.
16. $10^{-\log 5}$.
17. $10^{-\log x}$.

18. $10^{-3(\log x)}$.
19. $e^{\ln x - 2(\ln x)}$.
20. $e^{-\ln \frac{1}{x}}$.

B (Supplementary)

Sketch each set of functions on the same coordinate axes:

1. 3^x, 7^x, e^x, 1^x.
2. e^x, e^{-x}, 5^x, 5^{-x}.
3. $\log_2 x$, $\log_3 x$, $\log_4 x$.
4. $\log_{\frac{1}{2}} x$, $\log_2 x$.
5. $\log_3 x$, 3^x.

In Exercises 6 through 16 sketch the graph:

6. $y = \log_{0.25} x$.
7. $y = 3^{x-2}$. Use a translation of the coordinate axes (§ 7–6) and the graph of $y = 3^x$ (Exercise 5).
8. $y = e^{x+1}$. Use a translation of the coordinate axes and the graph of $y = e^x$.

• • •

9. $y = \ln(2x+1)$.
10. $y > \log_2 x$.
11. $y - 3^x \geq 0$.
12. $y = \log_2 |x|$.

13. $y = e^{-x^2}$.
14. $y = \dfrac{3^x}{x!}$ for $x = 0, 1, 2, \cdots, 10$.
15. $y = \dfrac{e^x + e^{-x}}{2}$.
16. $y = \dfrac{e^x - e^{-x}}{2}$.

NOTE: The function in Exercise 15 is the **hyperbolic cosine function**; the function in Exercise 16 is the **hyperbolic sine function.**

• 17. Sketch $y = \log_1 x$ and tell why it is not a function.

§ 9-3 Exponential and logarithmic equations

Equations which involve an exponential function of a variable are called **exponential equations;** equations which involve a logarithmic function of a variable are called **logarithmic equations.** As in the evaluation of exponential and logarithmic functions for given values of the variables, the solution of elementary exponential and logarithmic equations depends upon the assumption that:

Two numbers are equal if and only if their logarithms to any given base b, $0 < b \neq 1$, are equal (§ 9–2).

The solutions of some exponential equations are obvious, but the solutions of most equations of this type involve the use of logarithms and their properties. The definition and properties of logarithms are used also in solving logarithmic equations. The methods of solution are easily observed by considering some illustrative examples.

Example 1. Solve: $2^{3x+1} = 1024$.

Since $1024 = 2^{10}$, we have

$$2^{3x+1} = 2^{10}.$$

Since two numbers 2^{3x+1} and 2^{10} are equal if and only if their logarithms $(3x + 1)$ and 10 to the base 2 are equal, we have

$$3x + 1 = 10$$
$$3x = 9$$
$$x = 3.$$

Example 2. Solve: $\log_3 (x + 1) + \log_3 (x + 3) = 1$.

Since the sum of two logarithms may be expressed as the logarithm of a product, we may write

$$\log_3 (x + 1)(x + 3) = 1$$

which may be expressed in exponential form as

$$(x + 1)(x + 3) = 3^1$$
$$x^2 + 4x + 3 = 3$$
$$x^2 + 4x = 0$$
$$x(x + 4) = 0$$
$$x = 0 \quad \text{or} \quad x = -4.$$

When $x = -4$, the given equation involves logarithms of negative

SPECIAL FUNCTIONS

numbers. Such logarithms cannot be defined as real numbers, therefore the value -4 is an extraneous solution (sometimes called an *extraneous root*). When $x = 0$, the given equation becomes

$$\log_3 1 + \log_3 3 = 1$$
$$0 + 1 = 1;$$

therefore 0 is the only element in the solution set of the given equation.

As in Example 2, roots are **extraneous** if they involve logarithms of negative numbers in the *given* statement of the equation. If the equation in Example 2 had been given in the form

$$\log_3 (x + 1)(x + 3) = 1,$$

then -4 would not have been extraneous since

$$(-4 + 1)(-4 + 3) = 3, \text{ and } \log_3 3 = 1.$$

Consider the exponential equation

$$2^x = 3^{x+1} \tag{1}$$

where the equal expressions are powers expressed with different bases. We can solve the equation (1) by the method used in Example 1 if we can find a common base. The common base 10 can be used since within the accuracy of the four place table of common logarithms:

$$\log 2 = 0.3010 \qquad\qquad \log 3 = 0.4771$$
$$2 = 10^{0.3010} \qquad\qquad 3 = 10^{0.4771}$$
$$2^x = (10^{0.3010})^x \qquad 3^{x+1} = (10^{0.4771})^{x+1}$$
$$2^x = 10^{0.3010x} \qquad 3^{x+1} = 10^{0.4771x+0.4771}.$$

Then the equation (1) may be expressed as

$$10^{0.3010x} = 10^{0.4771x+0.4771}.$$

Since the numbers are equal if and only if their logarithms to the base 10 are equal, this equation may be expressed as:

$$0.3010x = 0.4771x + 0.4771$$
$$-0.1761x = 0.4771$$
$$x = -\frac{0.4771}{0.1761}$$
$$x \approx -2.709.$$

The equation (1) may also be solved by applying immediately the principle that two numbers are equal if and only if their logarithms to the

484

§ 9-3 EXPONENTIAL AND LOGARITHMIC EQUATIONS

same base are equal. If we use base 2, the equation (1) becomes

$$\log_2 2^x = \log_2 3^{x+1}$$
$$x \log_2 2 = (x + 1)\log_2 3$$
$$x \log_2 2 = x \log_2 3 + \log_2 3$$
$$x = \frac{\log_2 3}{1 - \log_2 3}. \tag{2}$$

We shall return to the computation of $\log_2 3$ after considering equation (1) using base 3 and base 10. If we use base 3, the equation (1) becomes

$$\log_3 2^x = \log_3 3^{x+1}$$
$$x \log_3 2 = (x + 1)\log_3 3$$
$$x \log_3 2 = x + 1$$
$$x = \frac{1}{\log_3 2 - 1}. \tag{3}$$

If we use base 10, the equation (1) becomes

$$\log 2^x = \log 3^{x+1}$$
$$x \log 2 = (x + 1)\log 3$$
$$x \log 2 = x \log 3 + \log 3$$
$$x = \frac{\log 3}{\log 2 - \log 3}$$
$$x = \frac{0.4771}{0.3010 - 0.4771}$$
$$x = \frac{0.4771}{-0.1761}$$
$$x \approx -2.709.$$

Notice that, as before, the use of base 10 enables us to solve the equation using the table of common logarithms. Indeed the arithmetic computations are exactly the same as they were when powers of 10 were used.

Common logarithms may also be used to solve the equation (1) when it is expressed in the forms (2) and (3). In general, common logarithms may be used to find $\log_b N$ for any positive number N and any positive number $b \neq 1$. Let $y = \log_b N$, then

$$N = b^y$$
$$\log N = \log b^y$$
$$\log N = y \log b.$$

485

SPECIAL FUNCTIONS

Then since $y = \log_b N$,
$$\log N = (\log_b N) \log b$$
$$\log_b N = \frac{\log N}{\log b}.$$

The equation (2) may be solved using
$$\log_2 3 = \frac{\log 3}{\log 2} = \frac{0.4771}{0.3010} \approx 1.585;$$
$$x \approx \frac{1.585}{1 - 1.585} = \frac{1.585}{-0.585} \approx -2.709.$$

The equation (3) may be solved using
$$\log_3 2 = \frac{\log 2}{\log 3} = \frac{0.3010}{0.4771} \approx 0.6309;$$
$$x \approx \frac{1}{0.6309 - 1} = \frac{1}{-0.3691} \approx -2.709.$$

The general procedures that we have considered for the equation (1) may be used for any exponential equation. Either powers of the same base or a direct application of logarithms may be used. When logarithms are used, the base 10 is particularly convenient because of the availability of the table of common logarithms. However, other bases may be used and a table of common logarithms may be used to find logarithms to other bases.

Example 3. Solve: $\log_5 x = -0.7$.

The corresponding exponential equation is
$$x = 5^{-0.7} = \frac{1}{5^{0.7}}.$$

Logarithms are needed to evaluate the numerical term of the equation, and it is just as easy to use the logarithms immediately:
$$\log_5 x = \frac{\log x}{\log 5} = -0.7;$$
$$\log x = -0.7 \log 5 = (-0.7)(0.6990) = -0.4893 = 0.5107 - 1;$$
$$x \approx 0.3241.$$

TEST YOURSELF

Solve:

1. $5^x = 25$.
2. $2^x = 33$.
3. $\log_3 (2x + 1) = 4$.
4. $\log (2x + 3) + \log (4x - 1) = 2 \log 3$.
5. $x = \log_2 5$.
6. $\log_3 x = -1.52$.

EXERCISES

Solve:

1. $4^x = 256$.
2. $2^{-x} = 8$.
3. $2^{x^2-1} = 64$.
4. $5^{2x} - 12^{x+1} = 0$.
5. $5^{6+x} = 7^{5+x}$.
6. $\log (2x + 13) = 4$.
7. $2^{3x} = 25$ using (a) base 10; (b) base 2.
8. $2^{x+3} = 3^{x-1}$ using (a) base 10; (b) base 3.
9. $\log_2 32 - \log_2 x + \log_4 8 = 0$.
10. $\log_6 (x - 1) + \log_6 x = 1$.

• • •

11. $\log x(x - 3) = 1$.
12. $\dfrac{\log (x + 6)}{\log x} = 2$.
13. $\log_2 x(3x - 5) = 1$.
14. $\dfrac{\log (7x - 12)}{\log x} = 2$.
15. $\log_7 x = -2$ using (a) the corresponding exponential equation; (b) logarithms.
16. $\sqrt[3]{3^{x+7}} = 2^x$.
17. $\log_{11} x = -0.8$.
18. $\log_5 x^2 = -1.2$.
• 19. $x^{\log x} = 0.1x^2$.
• 20. $x^{\log x} = 10{,}000x^3$.

§ 9-4 Parametric equations

In some cases it may not be possible or desirable to describe directly a relation between two variables x and y to determine a set of ordered pairs (x, y). However, it may be possible or desirable to determine one relation between x and a third variable t and another relation between y and that same variable t. For example, consider the set of equations $x = 2t$ and $y = t^2 + 1$. Here we have a relation between x and y expressed indirectly in terms of a third variable t. In this case it is possible, if we wish, to eliminate the variable t from consideration and express the relation

SPECIAL FUNCTIONS

between x and y by means of a single equation. Since $t = \frac{x}{2}$, substituting for t in $y = t^2 + 1$, we have the **Cartesian equation** $y = \frac{x^2}{4} + 1$.

A set of equations of the form $\begin{cases} x = f(t) \\ y = g(t) \end{cases}$ is called **parametric equations** for x and y. The variable t is called the **parameter**. We can graph a relation expressed by a set of parametric equations by setting up a table of values obtained by assigning values to the parameter. For example, here is a table of values for the parametric equations $\begin{cases} x = 2t \\ y = t^2 + 1 \end{cases}$.

t	-3	-2	-1	0	1	2	3
x	-6	-4	-2	0	2	4	6
y	10	5	2	1	2	5	10

The graph of this relation is shown in Figure 9–8 and is a parabola as would be expected from its Cartesian equation.

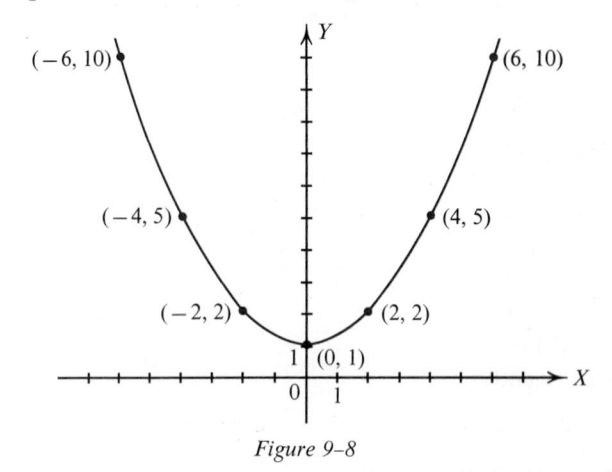

Figure 9–8

Example 1. Eliminate the parameter and describe the graph of
$$\begin{cases} x = r \cos \theta \\ y = r \sin \theta. \end{cases}$$

Note that $\sin \theta = \frac{y}{r}$, $\cos \theta = \frac{x}{r}$, and since $\sin^2 \theta + \cos^2 \theta = 1$ for each value of the parameter θ, $x^2 + y^2 = r^2$. The graph is a circle of radius r with center at the origin.

§ 9-4 PARAMETRIC EQUATIONS

Example 2. Eliminate the parameter t and describe the graph of

$$\begin{cases} x = \dfrac{p}{t^2} \\ y = \dfrac{2p}{t}. \end{cases}$$

Note that $t = \dfrac{2p}{y}$; $t^2 x = p$; $\left(\dfrac{2p}{y}\right)^2 x = p$; $4p^2 x = py^2$; $y^2 = 4px$.

The graph is a parabola with the x-axis as axis of symmetry, the origin as vertex, and focus at $(p, 0)$.

Frequently parametric equations have a portion of a familiar graph as their graph. Consider the line with equation $x + y = 1$. The parametric equations

$$\begin{cases} x = \sin^2 \theta \\ y = \cos^2 \theta \end{cases}$$

have as their graph the portion of the line in the first quadrant and on the coordinate axes since $x \geq 0$ and $y \geq 0$. The part of the line not in the second quadrant is the graph of the parametric equations

$$\begin{cases} x = t^2 \\ y = 1 - t^2. \end{cases}$$

TEST YOURSELF

Eliminate the parameter and describe the graph:

1. $\begin{cases} x = t^2 \\ y = t. \end{cases}$

2. $\begin{cases} x = 3t + 2 \\ y = 25 - t. \end{cases}$

EXERCISES

Eliminate the parameter and describe the graph:

1. $\begin{cases} x = 3t \\ y = 2t^2. \end{cases}$

2. $\begin{cases} x = 3t - 1 \\ y = 2t + 1. \end{cases}$

3. $\begin{cases} x = 3 \cos \theta \\ y = 3 \sin \theta. \end{cases}$

4. $\begin{cases} x = 2 \cos \theta \\ y = 2 \sin \theta. \end{cases}$

5. $\begin{cases} x = \dfrac{4}{t^2} \\ y = \dfrac{8}{t}. \end{cases}$

6. $\begin{cases} x = \dfrac{1}{t^2} \\ y = \dfrac{1}{t}. \end{cases}$

7. $\begin{cases} x = \cos \theta + 2 \\ y = \sin \theta - 3. \end{cases}$

8. $\begin{cases} x = 2 \cos \theta - 1 \\ y = 3 \sin \theta + 5. \end{cases}$

SPECIAL FUNCTIONS

● ● ●

9. $\begin{cases} x = \sin \theta \\ y = \sin^2 \theta. \end{cases}$

10. $\begin{cases} \sqrt{x} = t \\ y = t^2 - 1. \end{cases}$

11. $\begin{cases} \sqrt{-x} = t \\ y = 1 + t^2. \end{cases}$

12. $\begin{cases} x = \sec \theta \\ y = \tan \theta. \end{cases}$

13. $\begin{cases} x = t^2 - 1 \\ y = t^2 + 1. \end{cases}$

14. $\begin{cases} x = t + 2 \\ y = t^2 + 4. \end{cases}$

15. $\begin{cases} x = t(t + 1) \\ y = t(t - 1). \end{cases}$

16. $\begin{cases} x = 4t \\ y = t^2 + 3t. \end{cases}$

§ 9-5 Absolute value and other functions

The absolute value of a real number x, represented by the symbol $|x|$, was defined in § 1-4 as:

$$|x| = x \text{ if } x \geq 0,$$
$$|x| = -x \text{ if } x < 0.$$

The function $\{(x, |x|)\}$ is the **basic absolute value function.** The domain of the function y where $y = |x|$ is the set of real numbers, and the range of the function y is the set of nonnegative real numbers. Figure 9-9 shows the graph of the basic absolute value function. The graph of the function is continuous (unbroken), but it is not a smooth curve since it has a "corner" at the origin.

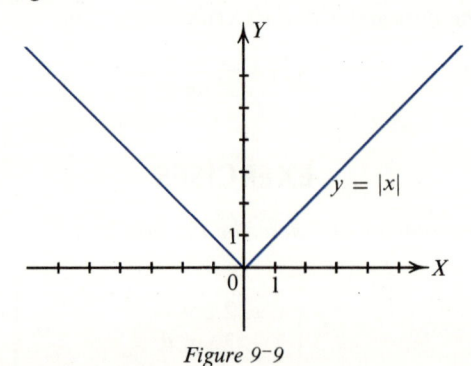

Figure 9-9

The **absolute value of a function** of x is a generalization of the absolute value function and is defined by

$$|f(x)| = f(x) \text{ if } f(x) \geq 0,$$
$$|f(x)| = -f(x) \text{ if } f(x) < 0.$$

§ 9-5 ABSOLUTE VALUE AND OTHER FUNCTIONS

Note that this is a case where we have a function of a function. For example, consider $f(x) = 2x + 1$, then

$$|f(x)| = |2x + 1| = 2x + 1 \text{ if } 2x + 1 \geq 0,$$
$$|f(x)| = |2x + 1| = -(2x + 1) \text{ if } 2x + 1 < 0.$$

Since $2x + 1 \geq 0$ when $x \geq -\frac{1}{2}$ and $2x + 1 < 0$ when $x < -\frac{1}{2}$, then

$$|2x + 1| = 2x + 1 \text{ if } x \geq -\frac{1}{2},$$

$$|2x + 1| = -2x - 1 \text{ if } x < -\frac{1}{2}.$$

Notice that these conditions depend upon the sign of the expression $2x + 1$ rather than the sign of x. The graph of y where $y = |2x + 1|$ is shown in Figure 9–10.

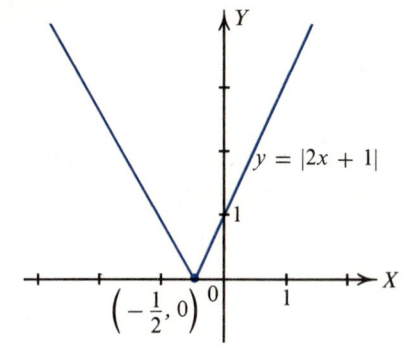

Figure 9–10

The **greatest integer function** denoted by $\{(x, [\![x]\!])\}$ is another type of special function and is defined as the greatest integer less than or equal to x. The domain of the greatest integer function is the set of real numbers, and the range of the function is the set of integers. For example,

$[\![2.3]\!] = 2;$

$[\![\pi]\!] = 3;$

$[\![1]\!] = 1;$

$[\![-3.1]\!] = -4.$

The graph of $y = [\![x]\!]$ shown in Figure 9–11 appears as a series of "steps."

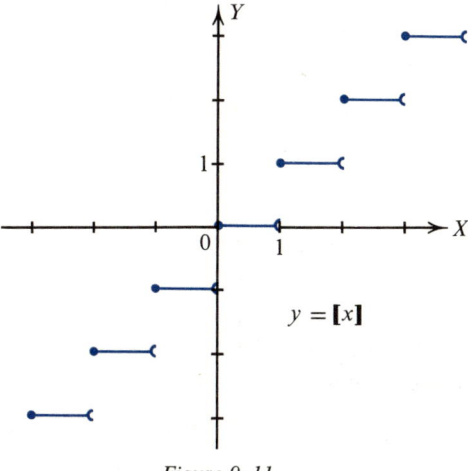

Figure 9–11

SPECIAL FUNCTIONS

TEST YOURSELF

1. Find $|3x|$ for $x = -1, 0, 1, 2$.
2. Graph $y = |2x - 3|$.
3. Find: (a) $[\![3.7]\!]$; (b) $[\![e]\!]$; (c) $[\![0]\!]$; (d) $[\![-2.1]\!]$.
4. Graph $y = [\![2x]\!]$ for $-3 < x < 3$.

EXERCISES

Find for $x = -2, -1, 0, 1, 2$:

1. $|3x - 1|$. 2. $\left|\dfrac{1}{3}x - \dfrac{1}{2}\right|$. 3. $[\![x + 1]\!]$. 4. $[\![x - 2]\!]$.

In Exercises 5 through 23 graph for $-4 \leq x \leq 4$:

5. $y = |3x - 1|$.
6. $y = |-x + 1|$.
7. $y = \left|\dfrac{1}{2}x + 2\right|$.
8. $y = \left|\dfrac{1}{3}x - \dfrac{1}{2}\right|$.

9. $y = [\![x - 1]\!]$.
10. $y = [\![x + 1]\!]$.
11. $y = [\![x - 2]\!]$.
12. $y = [\![x + 2]\!]$.

• • •

13. $y = |x^3|$.
14. $y = x - |x|$.
15. $y = x - [\![x]\!]$.
16. $y - 1 = [\![x]\!]$.
17. $y = |x| - [\![x]\!]$.

18. $|y| = x$.
19. $|y| \leq x$.
20. $|y| = [\![x]\!]$.
21. $|y| \leq [\![x]\!]$.
22. $x = [\![y]\!]$.

23. $[\![x]\!] + |y| = 1$.
24. If $f(x) = [\![x]\!]$, find $f(f(x))$.

§ 9-6 Probability density functions

Mathematical probability was defined in § 2-5 where the probability of an event could have been considered a function of that event. In this section we approach the definition of a probability function, more precisely called a probability density function, from a different point of view. This new definition for a probability density function will allow us to avoid the necessity of considering for an experiment only those sample spaces (§ 2-6) which can be characterized by a set of "equally likely" points. In

§ 9-6 PROBABILITY DENSITY FUNCTIONS

order to define a probability density function we shall first consider the concept of a random variable.

Quite often in probability problems we are not as interested in the probabilities associated with individual events of an experiment as we are interested in the probabilities associated with sets of events. Whenever a set of mutually exclusive events which exhaust a sample space can be placed in one-to-one correspondence with an appropriate set of real numbers, we can change the domain of the associated probability function from a nonnumerical domain (sets of events) to a numerical one (a set of real numbers). A variable x which represents any one of the numerical values corresponding to a member of a set of mutually exclusive and exhaustive events for an experiment is called a **random variable.**

Example 1. Specify one possible domain of a random variable for the experiment concerned with the sum of the face values which may be obtained in a single throw of a pair of dice.

> In Example 2 of § 2–6 we considered for this experiment a sample space S for the set of ordered pairs (r, w) where $r \in \{1, 2, 3, 4, 5, 6\} = A$ and represents the face value of one die, $w \in \{1, 2, 3, 4, 5, 6\} = B$ and represents the face value of the other die, and $(r, w) \in A \times B$. However, the present experiment is concerned with the set $T = \{2, 3, 4, 5, 6, 7, 8, 9, 10, 11, 12\}$ of possible sums of the face values of the two dice. Associated with each sum is a set of events corresponding to a subset of the sample space S. These events are mutually exclusive and exhaustive (include all possibilities); therefore we may use the set T as a domain for the random variable for the experiment.
>
> We could also use other domains such as $\{0, 1, 2, 3, 4, 5, 6, 7, 8, 9, 10\}$, $\{0, 0.1, 0.2, 0.3, 0.4, 0.5, 0.6, 0.7, 0.8, 0.9, 1.0\}$, $\{0, 10, 20, 30, 40, 50, 60, 70, 80, 90, 100\}$, or any set W of real numbers such that $n(W) = 11$. In each case the elements of W must be such that they can be placed in a one-to-one correspondence with the elements of T. Ordinarily we would use the domain T.

Let x be a random variable whose values $x_1, x_2, x_3, \cdots, x_n$ correspond to n mutually exclusive and exhaustive events $A_1, A_2, A_3, \cdots, A_n$, respectively, of a sample space. A **probability density function,** denoted by $f(x)$, is a function of x such that

$$f(x_i) = P(A_i)$$

where $P(A_i)$ is the probability of A_i, $i = 1, 2, 3, \cdots, n$. That is, <u>the value of a probability density function for each value of the random variable is equal to the probability of the event which corresponds to that value</u>

SPECIAL FUNCTIONS

of the random variable. The abbreviation "p. d. f." is frequently used for "probability density function." The probability density function provides a **probability measure** defined over the subsets of the sample space with the properties

(i) $f(x) \geq 0$ for $x = x_1, x_2, \cdots,$ or x_n;
(ii) $f(x_1) + f(x_2) + \cdots + f(x_n) = 1$;
(iii) if A and B are events corresponding to the distinct values x_i and x_j respectively of x then

$$P(A \cup B) = f(x_i) + f(x_j).$$

We note that x_i may be a value of the random variable x corresponding to several sample points which make up an individual event. For example, $x_i = 4$ for the dice experiment of Example 1 corresponds to the set of points $\{(1, 3), (2, 2), (3, 1)\}$; while $x_i = 5$ in the same experiment corresponds to the set of points $\{(1, 4), (2, 3), (3, 2), (4, 1)\}$. Hence $f(4) = \frac{3}{36} = \frac{1}{12}$ and $f(5) = \frac{4}{36} = \frac{1}{9}$.

Notice that the definition of a probability density function allows us to consider the set of values of a random variable as our sample space. Since the points of such a sample space may not be equally likely, we no longer need to consider only sample spaces of equally likely events. However, in many elementary probability problems we still will need to consider initially a set of equally likely outcomes in order to make an acceptable assignment of values for the probability density function for values of some random variable.

Example 2. Describe a probability density function (p. d. f.) for the experiment of tossing two coins.

> A sample space for this experiment is
>
> $$S = \{(h, h), (h, t), (t, h), (t, t)\}.$$
>
> Let x be a random variable whose value is equal to the number of heads obtained when two coins are tossed. Then we may consider a new sample space S' where
>
> $$S' = \{x \mid x = 0, 1, 2\}.$$
>
> If $f(x)$ is a p. d. f. for this experiment, then $f(0) = \frac{1}{4}$, $f(1) = \frac{1}{2}$, and $f(2) = \frac{1}{4}$. Notice that we made use of the information obtained from our sample space S to determine the value for each $f(x_i)$. Notice also that we may check one property of our p. d. f. by observing that the sum of the $f(x_i)$ is 1.

§ 9-6 PROBABILITY DENSITY FUNCTIONS

Descriptive techniques such as charts and tables may be used to represent a probability density function.

Example 3. Describe by means of a table of values a probability density function for the experiment in Example 1.

x	2	3	4	5	6	7	8	9	10	11	12
$f(x)$	$\frac{1}{36}$	$\frac{1}{18}$	$\frac{1}{12}$	$\frac{1}{9}$	$\frac{5}{36}$	$\frac{1}{6}$	$\frac{5}{36}$	$\frac{1}{9}$	$\frac{1}{12}$	$\frac{1}{18}$	$\frac{1}{36}$

Notice that $f(x)$ is a possible p. d. f. since $f(x) \geq 0$ for $x = 2, 3, \cdots, 12$ and $f(2) + f(3) + \cdots + f(12) = 1$.

Example 4. Describe by means of a graph the probability density function for Example 3.

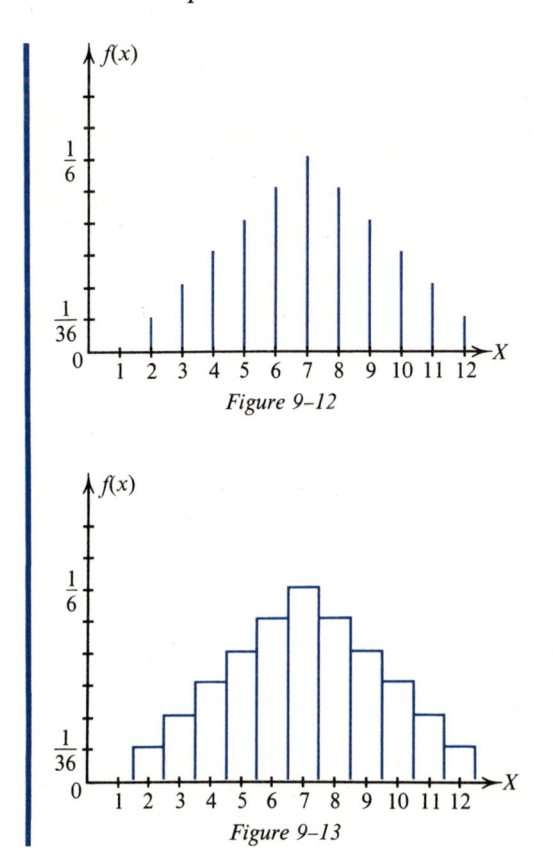

Figure 9-12

The graph in Figure 9-12 is called a **probability bar chart.**

We also may represent a p. d. f. graphically by means of a **probability histogram** (Figure 9-13). Rectangles whose heights are equal to $f(x_i)$ are constructed on intervals of one unit centered about x_i. Notice that each rectangle of the histogram constructed on the interval about x_i has an area numerically equal to $f(x_i)$ and that the numerical value of the total area of the histogram is equal to 1.

Figure 9-13

495

SPECIAL FUNCTIONS

TEST YOURSELF

1. Describe a domain for a random variable for the number of heads obtained when three coins are tossed.

In Exercises 2 and 3 determine whether or not each function $f(x)$ defined by the given tables of values is a possible probability density function.

2.

x	1	2	3
$f(x)$	1	0	1

3.

x	0	2	5
$f(x)$	$\frac{1}{3}$	$\frac{1}{4}$	$\frac{5}{12}$

4. Determine the values of a p. d. f. for x where x is the number of red beads obtained when in a single drawing two beads are selected from a container which has two red beads and one blue bead.

EXERCISES

1. Find a domain for a random variable for the outcomes of an experiment concerned with the sum of the face values when **(a)** three dice are tossed; **(b)** four dice are tossed; **(c)** n dice are tossed.

2. Find a domain for a random variable for the experiment of tossing **(a)** five pennies; **(b)** seven pennies; **(c)** n pennies.

In Exercises 3 through 10 determine which of the given functions may not be considered probability density functions for the specified domains of x:

3. $f(x) = \frac{x}{12}$, for $x = 3, 4, 5$.

4.

x	-2	0	1
$f(x)$	$\frac{1}{2}$	$\frac{1}{6}$	$\frac{1}{3}$

5.

x	1	2	3	4	5
$f(x)$	0.15	0.20	0.40	0.15	0

6.

x	0	1	2	3
$f(x)$	1	0	1	0

7. $f(x) = \dfrac{1}{3}$, for $x = 0, 1, 2, 3$.

8. $f(x) = \dfrac{3!}{x!\,(3-x)!}\left(\dfrac{1}{5}\right)^x\left(\dfrac{4}{5}\right)^{3-x}$, for $x = 0, 1, 2, 3$.

9. $f(x) = \dfrac{{}_3C_x \times {}_3C_{3-x}}{{}_6C_3}$, for $x = 0, 1, 2, 3$.

10. $f(x) = \dfrac{{}_4C_x \times {}_4C_x}{{}_8C_4}$, for $x = 0, 1, 2, 3, 4$.

11. (a) Find the constant C such that $f(x)$ may be considered a p. d. f. for $x = 1, 2, 3, 4, 5, 6$ if $f(x) = \dfrac{x}{C}$. (b) Construct a probability bar chart for $f(x)$.

12. Let a coin be tossed three times. (a) Construct a table of values of a p. d. f. for the number of heads obtained. (b) Construct a histogram of the p. d. f.

• • •

13. A die is weighted so that the probability of a particular face value appearing is proportional to that number. Determine a table of values for a p. d. f. for the face values of the die.

14. If the die described in Exercise 13 is thrown with an unbiased die, determine the probability that the sum of the face values is (a) 2; (b) 3; (c) 4; (d) 5.

15. Repeat Exercise 14 for (a) 6; (b) 7; (c) 8; (d) 9.

16. Repeat Exercise 14 in parts (*a*) through (*c*) for (a) 10; (b) 11; (c) 12; (d) Use the results obtained in Exercises 14 and 15 and in this exercise and state a table of values for a p. d. f. for the face values. (e) Check that the table of values is a possible p. d. f.

• 17. A box contains three blue beads and two white beads. Find a p. d. f. for the following random variables: (a) The number of selections without replacement needed to obtain at least one blue bead. (b) The number of blue beads obtained if two beads are selected in a single draw.

§ 9-7 Mean, variance, standard deviation

The **mathematical expectation of a random variable** x, denoted by $E(x)$, is defined as

$$E(x) = x_1 f(x_1) + x_2 f(x_2) + \cdots + x_n f(x_n).$$

We usually call the mathematical expectation of a random variable x the **mean of x**. The mean is denoted by the symbol μ (the Greek letter, mu); that is,

$$\mu = E(x).$$

SPECIAL FUNCTIONS

Example 1. Find the mean number of heads for the experiment of tossing two coins.

Let x be the random variable representing the possible number of heads when two coins are tossed. In Example 2 of § 9-6 we found $f(0) = \frac{1}{4}, f(1) = \frac{1}{2}$, and $f(2) = \frac{1}{4}$. Hence,

$$\mu = E(x) = (0)\left(\frac{1}{4}\right) + (1)\left(\frac{1}{2}\right) + (2)\left(\frac{1}{4}\right)$$

$$\mu = 0 + \frac{1}{2} + \frac{1}{2}$$

$$\mu = 1.$$

We should note that a p. d. f. may be considered a theoretical model for a physical situation. For example, if we toss two coins a large number of times, we cannot expect a head and a tail to occur exactly twice as many times as two heads or twice as many times as two tails. However, if the coins are not biased, we would expect a head and a tail to occur approximately twice as many times as two heads or twice as many times as two tails. The probability density function for the number of heads when two coins are tossed may be considered as the proportion of the times 0, 1, and 2 heads will occur *in the long run;* that is, as the number of times the experiment is performed increases. In this sense the mean of a random variable x represents the value we can expect x to have on the average for a large number of repetitions of an experiment.

Example 2. Consider a bag containing five red balls and three white balls. If three balls simultaneously are selected at random, find the expected number of white balls.

When three balls are selected at random, 0, 1, 2, or 3 white balls may be included in the selection. Let x represent the number of white balls selected, and let $f(x)$ be a p. d. f. Then

$$f(0) = \frac{_5C_3}{_8C_3} = \frac{5}{28},$$

$$f(1) = \frac{_3C_1 \times _5C_2}{_8C_3} = \frac{15}{28},$$

$$f(2) = \frac{_3C_2 \times _5C_1}{_8C_3} = \frac{15}{56},$$

$$f(3) = \frac{_3C_3}{_8C_3} = \frac{1}{56}.$$

§ 9-7 MEAN, VARIANCE, STANDARD DEVIATION

In general, $f(x)$ for this random variable x may be expressed by the equation

$$f(x) = \frac{{}_3C_x \times {}_5C_{n-x}}{{}_8C_3}.$$

The expected number of white balls, the mean of x, is

$$\mu = E(x) = (0)\left(\frac{5}{28}\right) + (1)\left(\frac{15}{28}\right) + (2)\left(\frac{15}{56}\right) + (3)\left(\frac{1}{56}\right)$$

$$\mu = 0 + \frac{15}{28} + \frac{15}{28} + \frac{3}{56} = \frac{9}{8}.$$

If the physical experiment in this example is performed n times and the total number of white balls selected in the n experiments is divided by n we would expect the quotient to be $\frac{9}{8}$.

While the mean of a random variable tells us something about the average value of the random variable for an experiment, it does not convey any information about the variability of the values of the random variable. For example, consider a die whose six faces each are marked with three dots, and a second die whose six faces are marked with 1, 2, 2, 4, 4, and 5 dots respectively. The p. d. f.'s for the two dice are

x	1	2	3	4	5	6
$f(x)$	0	0	1	0	0	0

and

x	1	2	3	4	5	6
$f(x)$	$\frac{1}{6}$	$\frac{1}{3}$	0	$\frac{1}{3}$	$\frac{1}{6}$	0

respectively. In both cases the mathematical expectation is 3. However, in the case of the first die there will be no variation in the face value on successive tosses; while in the case of the second die there may theoretically be considerable variation in the face value of the die on successive tosses.

One measure of variability which mathematicians use for a random variable is called the variance. The **variance** of a random variable x whose p. d. f. is $f(x)$ is denoted by σ^2 (the Greek letter, sigma) and is defined as

$$\sigma^2 = (x_1 - \mu)^2 f(x_1) + (x_2 - \mu)^2 f(x_2) + \cdots + (x_n - \mu)^2 f(x_n);$$

that is

$$\sigma^2 = E(x - \mu)^2.$$

SPECIAL FUNCTIONS

The variance is the expected value of the squares of the deviation of the random variable from the mean. Notice that since $(x_i - \mu)^2$ and $f(x_i)$ are both nonnegative quantities, $\sigma^2 \geq 0$. The variance of the random variable for the experiment with the die whose six faces each bear three dots is zero. In the case of the second die,

$$\sigma^2 = (1-3)^2\left(\frac{1}{6}\right) + (2-3)^2\left(\frac{1}{3}\right) + (4-3)^2\left(\frac{1}{3}\right) + (5-3)^2\left(\frac{1}{6}\right)$$

$$\sigma^2 = \frac{2}{3} + \frac{1}{3} + \frac{1}{3} + \frac{2}{3} = 2.$$

We would expect the variance for the random variable for this second experiment to be greater than zero since the random variable for this experiment assumes more than one value.

While the mean of a random variable is measured in the same units as the random variable x, the variance is measured in terms of the square of the units. In order to have a measure of variation in the same units as x we shall define another measure of variation called the **standard deviation** σ as the square root of the variance.

Example 3. Find (a) the mean and the standard deviation for the face values obtained when a single die is thrown; (b) the probability that the face value differs from the mean by less than one standard deviation; (c) the probability that the face value differs from the mean by less than two standard deviations.

(a) The p. d. f. may be taken as

x	1	2	3	4	5	6
$f(x)$	$\frac{1}{6}$	$\frac{1}{6}$	$\frac{1}{6}$	$\frac{1}{6}$	$\frac{1}{6}$	$\frac{1}{6}$

Then $\mu = 1\left(\frac{1}{6}\right) + 2\left(\frac{1}{6}\right) + 3\left(\frac{1}{6}\right) + 4\left(\frac{1}{6}\right) + 5\left(\frac{1}{6}\right) + 6\left(\frac{1}{6}\right)$

$\mu = \frac{21}{6} = 3\frac{1}{2}.$

$\sigma^2 = \frac{1}{6}(1 - 3\frac{1}{2})^2 + \frac{1}{6}(2 - 3\frac{1}{2})^2 + \frac{1}{6}(3 - 3\frac{1}{2})^2 + \frac{1}{6}(4 - 3\frac{1}{2})^2$

$\quad + \frac{1}{6}(5 - 3\frac{1}{2})^2 + \frac{1}{6}(6 - 3\frac{1}{2})^2$

§ 9-7 MEAN, VARIANCE, STANDARD DEVIATION

$$\sigma^2 = \frac{1}{6}\left[\left(\frac{5}{2}\right)^2 + \left(\frac{3}{2}\right)^2 + \left(\frac{1}{2}\right)^2 + \left(\frac{1}{2}\right)^2 + \left(\frac{3}{2}\right)^2 + \left(\frac{5}{2}\right)^2\right]$$

$$\sigma^2 = \frac{1}{24}(25 + 9 + 1 + 1 + 9 + 25) = \frac{70}{24} = \frac{35}{12} = \frac{105}{36}$$

$$\sigma \approx \frac{1}{6}(10.2) = 1.7.$$

(b) The interval $\mu - \sigma < x < \mu + \sigma$ is $1.8 < x < 5.2$; the probability that x is on this interval is the sum of the probabilities that x is 2, 3, 4, or 5; that is, $\frac{2}{3}$.

(c) The interval $\mu - 2\sigma < x < \mu + 2\sigma$ is $0.1 < x < 6.9$; the probability that x is on this interval is 1.

The values of any random variable may be visualized as lying on some interval $a \leq x \leq b$. The mean μ is necessarily on that interval but is not necessarily the mid-point. The standard deviation σ may be taken as a unit of measure on this interval with μ as the origin of this new scale. Thus we may consider the values of x on the intervals $\mu - \sigma < x < \mu + \sigma$, or the interval $\mu - 2\sigma < x < \mu + 2\sigma$, and, in general, the values of x on an interval $\mu - k\sigma < x < \mu + k\sigma$; that is, within k standard deviations of μ. The probability that x assumes a value on such an interval is given in a famous theorem called Chebyshev's Theorem. We shall accept this theorem without proof.

Chebyshev's Theorem: *If a random variable x has a mean μ and a standard deviation σ, then the probability that x assumes a value within k standard deviations of μ is greater than or equal to $1 - \frac{1}{k^2}$.*

According to Chebyshev's Theorem the probability that a random variable differs from the mean by less than two standard deviations in either direction is at least $1 - \frac{1}{2^2}$, that is, $\frac{3}{4}$; the probability that a random variable is within three standard deviations is at least $1 - \frac{1}{3^2}$, that is, $\frac{8}{9}$.

SPECIAL FUNCTIONS

Example 4. Verify that Chebyshev's Theorem holds for two standard deviations with the p. d. f. for the random variable associated with the face values when a pair of ordinary dice are thrown.

The p. d. f. for this experiment appears in Example 3 of § 9–6. From Example 2 of § 2–9 we know that $\mu = 7$. Then

$$\sigma^2 = (2-7)^2\left(\frac{1}{36}\right) + (3-7)^2\left(\frac{2}{36}\right) + (4-7)^2\left(\frac{3}{36}\right) + (5-7)^2\left(\frac{4}{36}\right)$$
$$+ (6-7)^2\left(\frac{5}{36}\right) + (7-7)^2\left(\frac{6}{36}\right) + (8-7)^2\left(\frac{5}{36}\right) + (9-7)^2\left(\frac{4}{36}\right)$$
$$+ (10-7)^2\left(\frac{3}{36}\right) + (11-7)^2\left(\frac{2}{36}\right) + (12-7)^2\left(\frac{1}{36}\right)$$

$$\sigma^2 = \frac{25}{36} + \frac{32}{36} + \frac{27}{36} + \frac{16}{36} + \frac{5}{36} + \frac{5}{36} + \frac{16}{36} + \frac{27}{36} + \frac{32}{36} + \frac{25}{36} = \frac{210}{36}.$$

Hence $\sigma = \dfrac{\sqrt{210}}{6} \approx 2.41$.

According to Chebyshev's Theorem the probability that
$$7 - 2(2.41) < x < 7 + 2(2.41);$$
that is, $\qquad 2.18 < x < 11.82;$

is greater than or equal to $\dfrac{3}{4}$. For $2.18 < x < 11.82$,

$x = 3, 4, 5, 6, 7, 8, 9, 10,$ and $11.$ Then

$$f(3) + f(4) + f(5) + f(6) + f(7) + f(8) + f(9) + f(10) + f(11)$$
$$= 1 - \{f(2) + f(12)\}$$
$$= 1 - \left(\frac{1}{36} + \frac{1}{36}\right) = \frac{17}{18}.$$

Since $\dfrac{17}{18} \geq \dfrac{3}{4}$, the theorem is verified for this p. d. f. for two standard deviations.

Chebyshev's Theorem is a very general theorem applicable to any p. d. f., therefore we should not expect it to yield precise results with every p. d. f. Its usefulness lies in its universality.

§9-7 MEAN, VARIANCE, STANDARD DEVIATION

TEST YOURSELF

Find the mean and the variance of the random variable with each probability density function:

1.

x	1	2	3	4
$f(x)$	$\frac{1}{4}$	$\frac{1}{8}$	$\frac{1}{2}$	$\frac{1}{8}$

2. $f(x) = \frac{1}{3}$, for $x = 0, 1, 2$.

EXERCISES

In Exercises 1 through 7 find the mean and the variance of the random variable with each probability density function:

1.

x	0	1	2	3
$f(x)$	$\frac{1}{6}$	0	$\frac{1}{2}$	$\frac{1}{3}$

2.

x	1	2	3	4	5	6
$f(x)$	$\frac{1}{3}$	$\frac{1}{6}$	0	$\frac{1}{6}$	$\frac{1}{3}$	0

3.

x	-3	0	1	4
$f(x)$	$\frac{3}{10}$	$\frac{1}{4}$	$\frac{1}{4}$	$\frac{1}{5}$

4. $f(x) = \frac{1}{4}$, for $x = 0, 1, 2, 3$.

5. $f(x) = \frac{x}{10}$, for $x = 1, 2, 3, 4$.

6. $f(x) = {}_3C_x \left(\frac{1}{3}\right)^x \left(\frac{2}{3}\right)^{3-x}$, for $x = 0, 1, 2, 3$.

7. $f(x) = \frac{{}_4C_x \times {}_3C_{2-x}}{{}_7C_2}$.

503

SPECIAL FUNCTIONS

8 through **14.** Verify Chebyshev's Theorem for the case of two standard deviations for the p. d. f.'s in Exercises 1 through 7 respectively.

• • •

15. Find the mean and the variance of the number of heads obtained in the tossing of **(a)** three coins; **(b)** four coins; **(c)** five coins.

16. Show that Chebyshev's Theorem does not yield any useful information for k standard deviations where $0 < k < 1$.

17. If a random variable x has a value such that it maximizes the p. d. f. $f(x)$, then that value of x is called the **mode** of the random variable. Find the mode, if it exists, of the random variable with each of these probability density functions:

(a) $f(x) = {}_4C_x \left(\frac{1}{3}\right)^x \left(\frac{2}{3}\right)^{4-x}$, for $x = 0, 1, 2, 3, 4$;

(b) $f(x) = \dfrac{{}_4C_x \times {}_3C_{2-x}}{{}_7C_2}$.

18. A value of x_i of a random variable x such that $P(x < x_i) \leq \frac{1}{2}$ and $P(x \leq x_i) \geq \frac{1}{2}$ is called the **median** of the random variable. Find the medians of the random variables in Exercise 17.

19. Show that $\sigma^2 = E(x^2) - \mu^2$.

20. Show that $E(x^2) \geq [E(x)]^2$.

21. Show that $E[x - E(x)] = 0$ for any random variable x.

22. If x is a random variable, show that $E(ax + b) = aE(x) + b$.

• **23.** Show that the variance of the function ax of the random variable x is equal to the product of a^2 and the variance of x.

• **24.** Show that the variance of the linear function $ax + b$ of the random variable x is equal to the product of a^2 and the variance of x.

§ 9-8 Probability distribution functions

In many applications of Chebyshev's Theorem (§ 9–7) the probability that $x \leq x_i$ for some x_i is very useful information. For any random variable x let $F(x_i) = P(x \leq x_i)$. The function $F(x)$ is called a **probability distribution function** for the random variable x. Notice that $0 \leq F(x) \leq 1$, and $F(x)$ is a nondecreasing function; that is, if $x_i \leq x_j$, then $F(x_i) \leq F(x_j)$. A table of values for any probability distribution function $F(x)$ of a random variable x may be easily constructed from a table of values of the probability density function of x.

§ 9-8 PROBABILITY DISTRIBUTION FUNCTIONS

Example 1. Determine the respective probabilities that the sum of the face values of a pair of dice is at least 2, 3, 4, 5, 6, 7, 8, 9, 10, 11, or 12.

Let x be a random variable for the set 2, 3, 4, 5, 6, 7, 8, 9, 10, 11, 12 with $f(x)$ as its p. d. f. Then from Example 3 of § 9-6

x	2	3	4	5	6	7	8	9	10	11	12
$f(x)$	$\frac{1}{36}$	$\frac{2}{36}$	$\frac{3}{36}$	$\frac{4}{36}$	$\frac{5}{36}$	$\frac{6}{36}$	$\frac{5}{36}$	$\frac{4}{36}$	$\frac{3}{36}$	$\frac{2}{36}$	$\frac{1}{36}$
$F(x)$	$\frac{1}{36}$	$\frac{1}{12}$	$\frac{1}{6}$	$\frac{5}{18}$	$\frac{5}{12}$	$\frac{7}{12}$	$\frac{13}{18}$	$\frac{5}{6}$	$\frac{11}{12}$	$\frac{35}{36}$	1

where the third row of the table has been included to show the probability distribution function $F(x_i) = P(x \leq x_i)$.

Example 2. Describe the probability distribution function for Example 1 by means of **(a)** a graph; **(b)** a histogram.

(a) A graph of the probability distribution function $F(x)$ for Example 1 is shown in Figure 9-14.

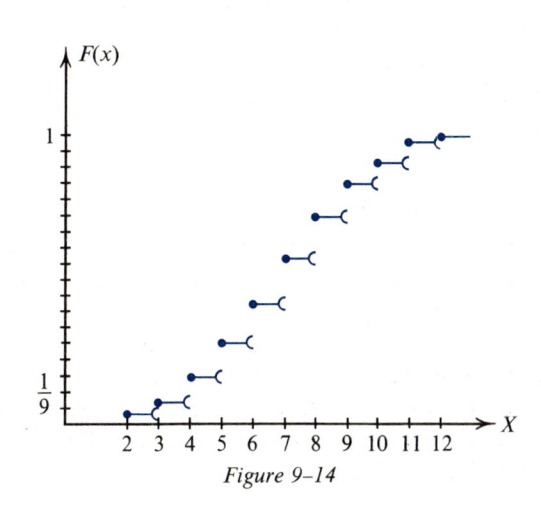

Figure 9-14

SPECIAL FUNCTIONS

(b) A histogram for the probability distribution function $F(x)$ for Example 1 is shown in Figure 9–15.

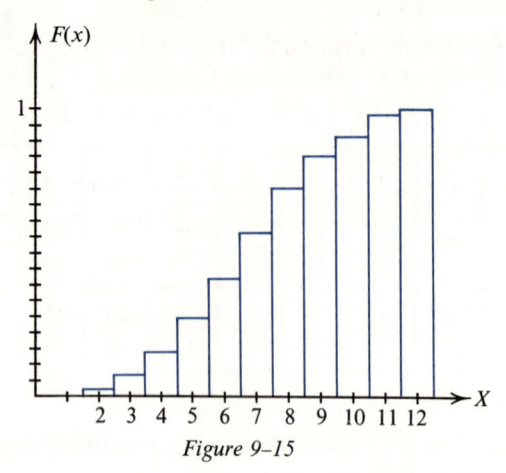

Figure 9–15

TEST YOURSELF

Determine the probability distribution function for the random variable x having the given probability density function:

1.

x	0	1	2	3	4	5	6
$f(x)$	0.05	0.10	0.05	0.25	0.15	0.30	0.10

2. $f(x) = \frac{1}{5}$, for $x = 1, 2, 3, 4, 5$.

3. $f(x) = \frac{x}{6}$, for $x = 1, 2, 3$.

4. $f(x) = \frac{{}_3C_x \times {}_2C_{2-x}}{{}_5C_2}$.

EXERCISES

1 through 7. Determine the probability distribution function $F(x)$ for the probability density functions of Exercises 1 through 7 in § 9–7.

8 through 13. For Exercises 1, 2, and 4 through 7 construct histograms for **(a)** the probability density function; **(b)** the probability distribution function.

• • •

§ 9-9 BINOMIAL DENSITY FUNCTIONS

14. From the table of values of $F(x)$ in Example 1 find the probability in tossing a pair of dice of obtaining a face value of:
  (a) not more than five;
  (b) more than four but less than eight;
  (c) at least six.

15. If $f(x) = {}_2C_x(p)^x(1-p)^{2-x}$ for $x = 0, 1, 2$ and $F(1) = \frac{5}{9}$, find the value of p.

16. Let x be the number of heads obtained when four coins are tossed.
  (a) Construct a table of values for the probability distribution function $F(x)$.
  (b) Find the probability of obtaining not more than two heads.
  (c) Find the probability of obtaining at least one head but not more than three heads.

§ 9-9 Binomial density functions

One of the probability density functions which is most useful in describing experiments is the binomial density function. In order to discuss this function we shall first consider a very simple p. d. f. related to the binomial density function.

Consider an experiment whose outcomes all belong to one of two mutually exclusive events which we usually refer to as success and failure. Let us call event A success and event $\bar{A}$ failure. If $P(A) = p$, then $P(\bar{A}) = 1 - p$; that is, the probability of success and the probability of failure are p and $1 - p$ respectively. A random variable for such an experiment may have only two values, and it is convenient to select the value 1 corresponding to A and the value 0 corresponding to $\bar{A}$. Then

$$f(1) = p,$$
$$f(0) = 1 - p;$$

and the p. d. f. $f(x)$ may be expressed as

$$f(x) = p^x(1-p)^{1-x}$$

for $x = 1$ or 0, the values of the random variable x corresponding to success and failure respectively. Also, the mean (§ 9-7)

$$\mu = 1[f(1)] + 0[f(0)] = 1(p) + 0(1-p) = p;$$

the variance (§ 9-7)

$$\sigma^2 = (x_1 - \mu)^2 f(x_1) + (x_2 - \mu)^2 f(x_2)$$
$$\sigma^2 = (1 - p)^2 p + (0 - p)^2 (1 - p)$$
$$\sigma^2 = p(1-p)^2 + p^2(1-p)$$
$$\sigma^2 = p(1-p)(1 - p + p)$$
$$\sigma^2 = p(1-p).$$

SPECIAL FUNCTIONS

A random variable x with exactly the two values 0 and 1 is called a **Bernoulli random variable;** its probability density function is called a **Bernoulli density function** and has the form $f(x) = p^x(1-p)^{1-x}$ for $x = 0, 1$ where 0 and 1 are the values of the random variable x corresponding respectively to the failure and the success of an event whose probability of success is p. An experiment with a Bernoulli random variable is called a **Bernoulli experiment.**

Example 1. A die has four faces colored red and two faces colored blue. Determine and graph a probability density function and a probability distribution function for the outcomes of a single throw of the die.

Let A be the event that a blue face appears; then $\overline{A}$ is the event that a blue face does not appear (that is, a red face appears). We associate the value 1 of the random variable x with A and the value 0 with $\overline{A}$. Then $p = \frac{2}{6} = \frac{1}{3}$; $f(1) = \frac{1}{3}$; $f(0) = \frac{2}{3}$. The probability density function is a Bernoulli density function

$$f(x) = \left(\frac{1}{3}\right)^x \left(\frac{2}{3}\right)^{1-x}$$

for $x = 0, 1$. Graphs of this Bernoulli density function $f(x)$ and the associated Bernoulli distribution function $F(x)$ are shown in Figure 9–16.

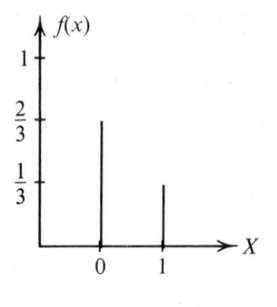

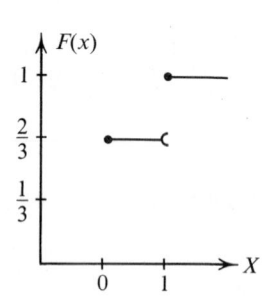

Figure 9–16

If we consider an experiment which consists of a sequence of trials of a Bernoulli experiment such as the tossing of a coin n times or the throwing of a die n times the random variable for this experiment is called a **binomial random variable.** The possible values of a binomial random variable are $0, 1, 2, \cdots, n$ and represent the number of successes in the n independent Bernoulli trials. A probability density function for such a random variable is called a **binomial density function.** To obtain a general expression

§ 9-9 BINOMIAL DENSITY FUNCTIONS

for a binomial density function consider n trials of a Bernoulli experiment with success on each trial equal to p. The probability of x successes followed by $n - x$ failures is given by $p^x(1 - p)^{n-x}$. We recognize that a total of x successes may be achieved by several different sequences of successes and failures. That is, the x successes could occur on any x of the n trials. Since there are $_nC_x$ such sequences of successes and failures which total x successes and since these sequences are mutually exclusive events, the probability of exactly x successes is given by $_nC_x p^x(1 - p)^{n-x}$. Hence, the general form of a binomial density function is

$$f(x) = {}_nC_x p^x(1 - p)^{n-x} \text{ for } x = 0, 1, 2, \cdots, n.$$

The name, binomial density function, arises from the fact that each value of $f(x)$ may be interpreted as a term of the binomial expansion of $(a + b)^n$ where $a = p$ and $b = 1 - p$. Since p and $1 - p$ are each greater than or equal to zero, each value of $f(x) \geq 0$. Hence $f(x)$ satisfies the first of the necessary properties of a p. d. f. (§ 9-6). Since $[p + (1 - p)]^n = 1$, $f(x)$ satisfies the second necessary property of a p. d. f.; the third property is also satisfied.

Example 2. Consider the experiment concerned with the number of heads obtained when five coins are tossed. Describe and graph a p. d. f. for the experiment.

Let p denote the probability of obtaining a head on a single toss, and let x denote the number of heads which appear when five coins are tossed. Since for each toss either a head appears or a head does not appear, the probability of exactly x heads in five tosses is given by

$$f(x) = {}_5C_x p^x(1 - p)^{5-x}.$$

Since $p = \frac{1}{2}$, the p. d. f. for the number of heads when five coins are tossed is the binomial density function

$$f(x) = {}_5C_x \left(\frac{1}{2}\right)^x \left(\frac{1}{2}\right)^{5-x}$$

$$f(x) = {}_5C_x \left(\frac{1}{2}\right)^5.$$

x	0	1	2	3	4	5
$f(x)$	$\frac{1}{32}$	$\frac{5}{32}$	$\frac{10}{32}$	$\frac{10}{32}$	$\frac{5}{32}$	$\frac{1}{32}$

SPECIAL FUNCTIONS

The values of this binomial density function are shown in the table and in Figure 9–17.

Figure 9–17

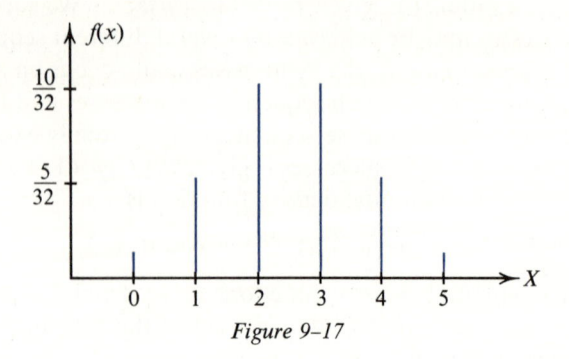

Tables of values for many binomial density functions have been computed and are used whenever extensive work with such functions is to be undertaken. The mean and the variance of a binomial random variable may be computed from the corresponding Bernoulli trial where $\mu = E(x) = p$ and $\sigma^2 = p(1 - p)$. Consider two trials of a Bernoulli experiment which has expectation $E(x)$. We assume that the expectation for the two trials is $E(x) + E(x)$; that is, $p + p$; thus for $n = 2$ the **mean of a binomial random variable** is $2p$. Similarly, for $n = 3$, the mean is $3p$; for each positive integer n, the mean is np. Consider now the variance for a Bernoulli trial

$$\sigma_1^2 = (x_1 - \mu)^2 f(x_1) + (x_2 - \mu)^2 f(x_2) = p(1 - p);$$

the variance for two Bernoulli trials of this experiment is

$$\sigma_2^2 = \sigma_1^2 + \sigma_1^2 = 2\sigma_1^2 = 2p(1 - p).$$

In general, the variance for n Bernoulli trials of the same experiment, that is, the **variance of a binomial random variable,** is

$$\sigma_n^2 = n\sigma_1^2 = np(1 - p).$$

Example 3. A box contains two black beads, one red bead, and four blue beads. Three selections of single beads are made at random with replacements between selections. **(a)** Determine a p. d. f. for the number of black beads selected. **(b)** Determine the expected number of black beads selected.

(a) Let p be the probability of selecting a black bead. Since two of the seven beads are black and each bead is equally likely to be selected,

$p = \frac{2}{7}$. Each selection represents a Bernoulli trial since either a black bead is selected or a black bead is not selected. If we let x be a random variable representing the number of black beads selected in a sequence of three Bernoulli trials, then the p. d. f. for x is a binomial density function given by

$$f(x) = {}_3C_x \left(\frac{2}{7}\right)^x \left(\frac{5}{7}\right)^{3-x}.$$

The table gives the values for $f(x)$.

x	0	1	2	3
$f(x)$	$\frac{125}{343}$	$\frac{150}{343}$	$\frac{60}{343}$	$\frac{8}{343}$

(b) The expected number of black beads selected is the mean μ of the binomial random variable. Hence

$$\mu = 3p = 3\left(\frac{2}{7}\right) = \frac{6}{7}.$$

TEST YOURSELF

In Exercises 1 and 2 construct a table of values for (a) the binomial density function; (b) the probability distribution function when:

1. $n = 3, p = \frac{1}{2}$. 2. $n = 3, p = \frac{1}{3}$.

3. Find the p. d. f. for the number of threes in four throws of a single die.

4. Find the means of the random variables in Test Yourself Exercises 1 through 3.

EXERCISES

In Exercises 1 through 3 construct a table of values for (a) the binomial density function; (b) the probability distribution function when:

1. $n = 4, p = \frac{1}{2}$. 2. $n = 4, p = \frac{4}{5}$. 3. $n = 4, p = \frac{1}{4}$.

SPECIAL FUNCTIONS

4. Construct a histogram for the binomial density function in Exercise 1.

5. Find the mean of the random variable in Exercise 3.

• • •

6. If five dice are thrown, find the probability of getting **(a)** exactly two sixes; **(b)** more than two sixes.

7. If ten coins are tossed, what is the probability that exactly four heads appear?

8. A die is thrown four times. Find the probability that **(a)** no two appears; **(b)** exactly one two appears; **(c)** at least one two appears.

9. A die is thrown ten times. What is the probability that there will be at least twice as many fives and sixes as there are other values?

10. A submarine captain has the option of firing two, three, or four torpedoes at an enemy ship during a one minute interval. If he fires only two, each torpedo has a probability of 0.5 of hitting the enemy ship. The probability of each torpedo hitting the enemy ship is reduced to 0.4 if he fires three or 0.3 if he fires four torpedoes in the same time interval. If two hits are necessary to sink the enemy ship, how many torpedoes should the captain fire?

11. A random selection of a single card is repeated three times with replacement after each selection from an ordinary deck of cards. Find a p. d. f. for the number of hearts selected. Actually perform this experiment 64 times and compare your results with what theory suggested would happen.

12. A machine manufactures 100 items per minute; on the average, three of these items will be defective. If a sample of five items is selected at random, what is the probability that no more than one is defective?

13. If 60 percent of the people of a town favor candidate A for mayor, find the probability that a random sample of voters favor him if the sample size is **(a)** three; **(b)** five; **(c)** seven.

14. If x corresponds to the number of heads appearing when five coins are tossed, find **(a)** $E(x^2)$; **(b)** $E(x - \mu)^2$; **(c)** the variance of the random variable.

• **15.** Show that $f(x + 1)$ and $f(x)$ for a binomial density function are related by the formula

$$f(x + 1) = \left(\frac{n - x}{x + 1}\right)\left(\frac{p}{1 - p}\right)f(x).$$

Such a formula is called a **recursion formula** and allows values of $f(x + 1)$ to be found from values of $f(x)$.

• **16.** Use the recursion formula of Exercise 15 and find the values of the binomial density function for x heads in seven tosses of a coin.

§ 9-10 Other density functions (Supplementary)

The Bernoulli and binomial density functions (§ 9-9) were special cases of probability density functions (§ 9-6). In this section we consider some other types of probability density functions. If a p. d. f. is constant for all values of the random variable x, then $f(x)$ may be expressed in the form

$$f(x) = \frac{1}{n} \text{ for } x = 1, 2, 3, \cdots, n$$

and is a **uniform density function.**

Example 1. Determine the p. d. f. for x where x is the face value obtained on a single throw of an unbiased die.

x	1	2	3	4	5	6
$f(x)$	$\frac{1}{6}$	$\frac{1}{6}$	$\frac{1}{6}$	$\frac{1}{6}$	$\frac{1}{6}$	$\frac{1}{6}$

Consider an experiment in which there are r mutually exclusive and exhaustive outcomes $A_1, A_2, \cdots, A_r$ with probabilities of occurrence $p_1, p_2, \cdots, p_r$ respectively. Suppose we are interested in determining the probability that $A_1, A_2, \cdots, A_r$ occur respectively exactly $n_1, n_2, \cdots, n_r$ times in n trials where $n = n_1 + n_2 + \cdots + n_r$. A specific favorable sequence of events would be

$$\underbrace{A_1, A_1, \cdots, A_1}_{n_1}; \underbrace{A_2, A_2, \cdots, A_2}_{n_2}; \cdots; \underbrace{A_r, A_r, \cdots, A_r}_{n_r}.$$

However, other mutually exclusive sequences of events are possible such that the sequence shall have n_1 A_1's, n_2 A_2's, $\cdots$, and $n_r A_r$'s. The number of such sequences is equal to the number of ways in which n elements may be arranged where $n_1, n_2, \cdots$, and n_r of the elements are alike; that is, as in (§ 2-3)

$$\frac{n!}{n_1! \, n_2! \, \cdots \, n_r!}.$$

Hence, the probability that in n trials A_1 occurs n_1 times, A_2 occurs n_2 times, $\cdots$, A_r occurs n_r times is

$$\frac{n!}{n_1! \, n_2! \, \cdots \, n_r!} (p_1)^{n_1} (p_2)^{n_2} \cdots (p_r)^{n_r}$$

where $n_1 + n_2 + \cdots + n_r = n$ and each n_i is an integer greater than or

SPECIAL FUNCTIONS

equal to zero for $i = 1, 2, \cdots, r$. The function $f(n_1, n_2, \cdots, n_r) = \dfrac{n!}{n_1! \, n_2! \, \cdots \, n_r!} (p_1)^{n_1} (p_2)^{n_2} \cdots (p_r)^{n_r}$ of r random variables $n_1, n_2, \cdots, n_r$ is called a **multinomial density function.** The reason this p. d. f. is called multinomial lies in the fact that each term of the p. d. f. is a term in the expansion of the multinomial

$$(p_1 + p_2 + \cdots + p_r)^n.$$

If $r = 2$, the multinomial density function becomes a binomial density function.

Example 2. Find a multinomial density function for the number of black beads, red beads, and blue beads in the experiment in Example 3 of § 9–9.

The probability of the selection of a black bead is $\dfrac{2}{7}$; of a red bead, $\dfrac{1}{7}$; of a blue bead, $\dfrac{4}{7}$. Let n_1, n_2, and n_3 represent the number of black beads, red beads, and blue beads selected, respectively, when three selections of single beads are made with replacement between selections. Then $n_1 + n_2 + n_3 = 3$. The p. d. f. for the number of black beads, red beads, and blue beads selected is the multinomial density function

$$f(n_1, n_2, n_3) = \dfrac{3!}{n_1! \, n_2! \, n_3!} \left(\dfrac{2}{7}\right)^{n_1} \left(\dfrac{1}{7}\right)^{n_2} \left(\dfrac{4}{7}\right)^{n_3}$$

for $n_1, n_2, n_3 = 0, 1, 2, 3$ where $n_1 + n_2 + n_3 = 3$.

A list of the ten possible values of $f(n_1, n_2, n_3)$ is given in the array.

$f(3, 0, 0) = \dfrac{8}{343}$ $f(1, 0, 2) = \dfrac{96}{343}$

$f(2, 1, 0) = \dfrac{12}{343}$ $f(0, 3, 0) = \dfrac{1}{343}$

$f(2, 0, 1) = \dfrac{48}{343}$ $f(0, 2, 1) = \dfrac{12}{343}$

$f(1, 2, 0) = \dfrac{6}{343}$ $f(0, 1, 2) = \dfrac{48}{343}$

$f(1, 1, 1) = \dfrac{48}{343}$ $f(0, 0, 3) = \dfrac{64}{343}$

Each of these values may be verified using the formula. Notice that their sum equals 1.

§ 9-10 OTHER DENSITY FUNCTIONS

We observe that in the p. d. f. for Example 2 the selection may include three black beads in exactly one way, and $f(3, 0, 0) = \frac{8}{343}$; the selection may include exactly two black beads in two ways, and $f(2, 1, 0) + f(2, 0, 1) = \frac{60}{343}$; the selection may include exactly one black bead in three ways, and $f(1, 2, 0) + f(1, 1, 1) + f(1, 0, 2) = \frac{150}{343}$; the selection may include no black beads in four ways, and $f(0, 3, 0) + f(0, 2, 1) + f(0, 1, 2) + f(0, 0, 3) = \frac{125}{343}$. Thus the expected number of black beads is given by the equation

$$3\left(\frac{8}{343}\right) + 2\left(\frac{6}{343}\right) + 1\left(\frac{150}{343}\right) + 0\left(\frac{125}{343}\right) = \frac{6}{7}.$$

The binomial density function arose from an attempt to determine the number of successes in performing a sequence of trials in which the probability of success remained constant after each trial. Experiments in which random variables have binomial density functions can also be thought of as corresponding to the problem of selecting beads of two types from a box with replacement after each selection. Consider now the problem of selecting k beads from a box containing n_1 beads of one kind and n_2 beads of a second kind without replacement and without regard to order of selection. Let x be a random variable representing the number of beads selected of the first kind. We can select x beads of this kind in $_{n_1}C_x$ ways and the remaining $k - x$ beads, those of the second kind, in $_{n_2}C_{k-x}$ ways. Since we can make both selections in $_{n_1}C_x \times {_{n_2}C_{k-x}}$ ways, the probability density function $f(x)$ for selecting exactly x beads of the first kind is given by

$$f(x) = \frac{{_{n_1}C_x} \times {_{n_2}C_{k-x}}}{_nC_k} \quad \text{for } x = 0, 1, 2, \cdots, k$$

where $k \leq n_1$, $k \leq n_2$, and $n_1 + n_2 = n$. The p. d. f. in this case is called a **hypergeometric density function.**

Example 3. Find a p. d. f. for the number of spades in a hand of five cards selected at random from a deck of bridge cards.

Let x represent the number of spades possible in a hand of five cards selected at random. Since there are thirteen spades in a bridge deck of fifty-two cards, we can select x spades in $_{13}C_x$ ways and the remaining $5 - x$ cards in $_{39}C_{5-x}$ ways. Since we can select any five cards from

SPECIAL FUNCTIONS

the entire deck in $_{52}C_5$ ways, the p. d. f. for x is the hypergeometric density function

$$f(x) = \frac{_{13}C_x \times {_{39}C_{5-x}}}{_{52}C_5} \text{ for } x = 0, 1, 2, 3, 4, 5.$$

Notice that $5 \leq 13$ and $5 \leq 39$ which is a necessary condition that a hypergeometric density function be the possible p. d. f.

Example 4. Find a p. d. f. for the number of blue beads selected in Example 3 of § 9–9 if the selections are made without replacement and without regard to order. Find the probability of selecting at least one blue bead.

Let x represent the number of blue beads selected when three beads are selected. We can select x blue beads from the four blue beads in $_4C_x$ ways and the remaining $3 - x$ beads from the three beads which are not blue in $_3C_{3-x}$ ways. We can make both selections in $_4C_x \times {_3C_{3-x}}$ ways. Since we can select three beads from the total of seven beads in $_7C_3$ ways, the p. d. f. for x is the hypergeometric density function

$$f(x) = \frac{_4C_x \times {_3C_{3-x}}}{_7C_3} \text{ for } x = 0, 1, 2, 3.$$

This function may be used to verify the entries in the table of values for $f(x)$ and $F(x)$.
The probability of selecting at least one blue bead is

$$1 - F(0) = 1 - \frac{1}{35} = \frac{34}{35}.$$

x	0	1	2	3
$f(x)$	$\frac{1}{35}$	$\frac{12}{35}$	$\frac{18}{35}$	$\frac{4}{35}$
$F(x)$	$\frac{1}{35}$	$\frac{13}{35}$	$\frac{31}{35}$	1

TEST YOURSELF

1. A box contains three white beads, two green beads, and two yellow beads. Find a multinomial density function for the number of white beads, green beads, and yellow beads when three beads are selected at random with replacement.

2. After the double blank (zero) domino has been removed, a set of four dominoes is selected at random from the remaining dominoes of a standard set consisting of double zero through double six. Find a p. d. f. for the number of dominoes bearing blanks in the selected set.

§ 9-10 OTHER DENSITY FUNCTIONS

EXERCISES

1. If $x = 1, 2, 3, \cdots, 10$, **(a)** construct a table of values for the uniform distribution function $F(x)$; **(b)** construct a bar chart for $F(x)$.

2. For the random variable with the uniform density function used in Exercise 1 find **(a)** the mean; **(b)** the variance.

3. Show that for the given value of n the multinomial density function $f(n_1, n_2, n_3)$ of Example 2 is really a function of only two of the three random variables n_1, n_2, and n_3.

4. Find the expected number of red beads in the experiment described in Example 2.

5. Find the expected number of blue beads in the experiment described in Example 2.

6. An urn contains three red and five white balls. If two balls are selected at random without replacement, find the mean and the variance of the number of red balls selected.

7. Determine the expected number of blue beads in the experiment described in Example 4.

8. Six people are selected for a team game from a group of eight men, six women, and ten children. Find the probability that equal numbers of men, women, and children were selected.

• • •

9. Find the probability that five men were selected in the experiment described in Exercise 8.

10. Let x be a random variable representing the number of aces in a bridge hand of thirteen cards. Find an expression for the p. d. f. of x.

11. Fifty manufactured items have among them six defective items. If six items were selected at random from the set of fifty, find the probability that at least two defective items are included in the selection.

12. A p. d. f. for a random variable x given by

$$f(x) = \frac{m^x e^{-m}}{x!}, \text{ for } x = 0, 1, 2, \cdots$$

is called a **Poisson density function**. Given that a random variable x has a Poisson density function such that $f(1) = f(2)$, find $f(x)$.

13. Construct a table of values for the Poisson density function

$$f(x) = \frac{3^x e^{-3}}{x!} \text{ for } x = 0, 1, 2, 3.$$

Note that this is only a partial representation of the p. d. f. (See Exercise 12.)

517

SPECIAL FUNCTIONS

§ 9-11 Probability for continuous variables (Supplementary)

The definitions and principles of mathematical probability which we have studied thus far are applicable to experiments where the number of possible outcomes or events is a finite number. The events of any finite set of events may be considered individually and are said to form a *discrete* set of events. A random variable for an experiment involving a discrete set of events is often called a **discrete variable.**

Many experiments involve outcomes for each value of a rational or real variable on an interval such as $a < x < b$. There are infinitely many values of the variable on any such interval, and it is not possible to consider each one individually. As examples of types of experiments which might involve such an interval of values, consider the representations of events involving distances, areas, or time. A random variable for such an experiment is called a **continuous variable.** While no new principle of probability is involved, the methods of application of the basic principle vary. A geometric approach is especially useful.

The simplest geometric examples involve the position of points on a line or on a plane, or the position of points, lines, and planes in space. The probability density function of a continuous random variable may then be expressed in terms of the ratios of two lengths, two areas, or two volumes. The following examples illustrate the use of a geometric technique in the calculation of such probabilities.

Example 1. If every point on a twelve-inch ruler is equally likely to be chosen, what is the probability that a point between the 2- and the 5-inch marks is chosen?

> Let A represent the event that a point between the 2- and the 5-inch marks is chosen. Since the ruler is 12 inches long and the interval favorable to the event A is $5 - 2$, that is, 3, inches long, the probability of event A is $\frac{3}{12}$, that is, $\frac{1}{4}$.

Example 2. Consider a line segment of length k. If two interior points of the segment are chosen at random, what is the probability that the three segments thus determined will have lengths suitable for the sides of a triangle?

> In order to answer this question we shall consider two random variables x and y as representing the distances of the two interior points from the two extremities of the line segment of length k as shown in

§ 9-11 PROBABILITY FOR CONTINUOUS VARIABLES

Figure 9–18.

Figure 9–18

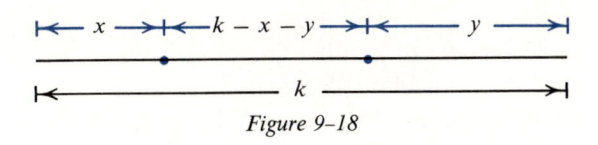

Assume $0 < x < k$, $0 < y < k$, and $x + y < k$. Consider x and y as the coordinates of a point on a Cartesian plane. The points representing the possible values of x and y are interior points of the triangular region bounded by the x-axis, the y-axis, and the line with equation $x + y = k$ (Figure 9–19).

If the segments x, y, and $k - x - y$ are to be appropriate sides of the triangle, then the sum of any two segments must be greater than the third. Hence

$$x + y > k - x - y$$
$$2(x + y) > k$$
$$x + y > \tfrac{1}{2}k$$

which eliminates points of the region marked I in Figure 9–19. Also,

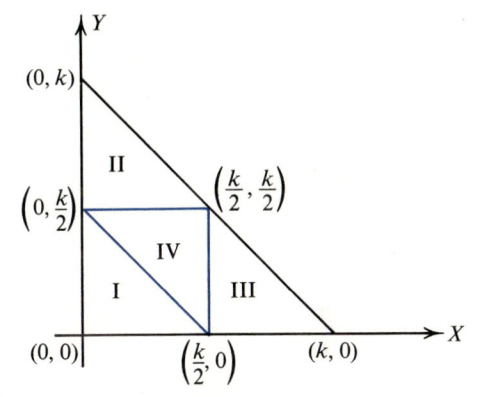

Figure 9–19

$$x + (k - x - y) > y$$
$$k - y > y$$
$$k > 2y$$
$$\tfrac{1}{2}k > y$$

which eliminates points of the region marked II. Finally

$$y + (k - x - y) > x$$
$$\tfrac{1}{2}k > x$$

which eliminates points of the region marked III. The favorable points are contained in the region marked IV. Since the regions I, II, III, and IV are determined by congruent triangles, the areas of the regions are equal and the desired probability is $\tfrac{1}{4}$; that is, the ratio of the area of the region IV to the sum of the areas of the regions I, II, III, and IV.

519

SPECIAL FUNCTIONS

Example 3. A plane is covered by a set of parallel lines a units apart and a second set of parallel lines b units apart such that the two sets of lines are perpendicular. A coin of diameter d where $d < a$ and $d < b$ is dropped at random upon the plane. What is the probability that the coin will intersect at least one of the given lines?

The center of the coin must rest in or on one of the rectangles, and the center of the coin is as likely to occupy one point in that rectangle as another. The coin will not intersect one of the lines if its center is at a distance greater than $\frac{d}{2}$ from the sides of the rectangle. As in Figure 9-20, the coin will not intersect any of the given lines if the center falls within a rectangle with sides $a - d$ and $b - d$. The probability that the coin does not intersect one of the given lines is $\frac{(a-d)(b-d)}{ab}$; therefore the required probability that the coin will intersect at least one of the given lines is $1 - \frac{(a-d)(b-d)}{ab}$, that is, $\frac{d}{a} + \frac{d}{b} - \frac{d^2}{ab}$.

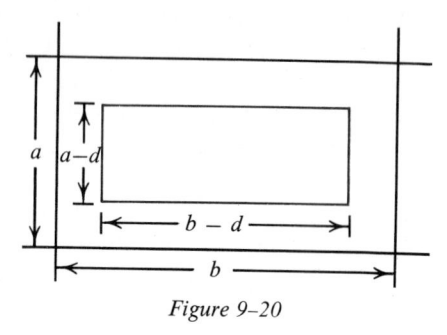

Figure 9-20

TEST YOURSELF

A line segment of length 10 *inches is divided into two line segments by a point chosen at random. Find the probability that:*

1. The shorter segment is not greater than 2 inches long.
2. The shorter segment is at least 4 inches long.
3. The longer segment is at least 8 inches long.
4. The longer segment is at least twice as long as the shorter segment.
5. The segments are equal.

EXERCISES

1. If a number is chosen at random between 1 and 3, what is probability that it is between 1 and 2?

2. If a watch stops at random, what is the probability that the hour hand is between 5 and 7 or between 9 and 11?

§ 9–11   PROBABILITY FOR CONTINUOUS VARIABLES

3. If every point on a twelve-inch ruler is equally likely to be chosen, what is the probability that a point is chosen between 2 and 5 inches from an extremity?

4. A spinning pointer is pivoted at the center of a circle whose radius is five inches. Find the probability that the pointer will stop within a particular two-inch arc of the circle.

5. Find the probability that the roots of the equation $4x^2 + 4kx + k + 2 = 0$ will be real if k is chosen at random in the interval $0 \leq k \leq 4$.

6. Find the probability that none of the three parts of a line segment determined by two points of the segment selected at random is greater than one-half of the original line segment.

7. Two points are selected at random on opposite sides of the midpoint of a line segment of length k. Determine the probability that the distance between the two points is greater than $\frac{k}{3}$.

8. If two points are selected at random on adjacent sides of a square, find a geometric representation for the probability that a triangle formed by the sides of the square and the line segment connecting the two points is greater than one-fourth the area of the square.

9. Two sides x and y of a rectangle are selected at random such that $0 < x < 1$ and $0 < y < 1$. Find the probability that the diagonal of the rectangle is less than 1.

● ● ●

10. Consider the problem of Example 3 using only one set of parallel lines a units apart and a coin of diameter $d < a$. Find the probability that the coin will come to rest so that it intersects one of the parallel lines.

11. Steven agrees to meet Betty between 3 and 4 P.M. outside the high school auditorium. Each agrees not to wait more than fifteen minutes for the other. Find the probability that they meet if they arrive at times selected at random.

12. Find the probability that three points selected at random on a circle lie on the same semicircle.

● **13.** The most famous and oldest (1733) geometrical probability problem is known as Buffon's Needle problem. Consider a plane ruled with a set of parallel lines d units apart. If a fine needle of length k units where $k \leq d$ is thrown down at random upon the plane, the probability that the needle will intersect one of the lines can be shown by use of calculus to be $\frac{2k}{\pi d}$. Calculate an approximation for the value of π by performing the experiment 100 times. (In 1901 a mathematician named Lazzerini performed 3048 such trials and calculated $\pi = 3.1415929$, an error of 3×10^{-7}.)

SPECIAL FUNCTIONS

SUMMARY OF CHAPTER 9

1. In this chapter you have studied several special functions which are used frequently in mathematics. The power function x^n is defined as a unique real number
   (i) for all real numbers n when $x > 0$;
   (ii) for all positive numbers n when $x = 0$;
   (iii) for rational values $\frac{p}{q}$ of n where p and q are relatively prime integers and q is an odd integer k when $x < 0$. (§ 9–1)

2. For any positive number b the exponential function b^x is defined for all real numbers x. If $x = b^y$, then $y = \log_b x$. For any positive number $b \neq 1$ the logarithmic function $\log_b x$ is defined for all positive numbers x. (§ 9–2)

3. Elementary exponential and logarithmic equations may be solved since two numbers are equal if and only if their logarithms to any given base b, $0 < b \neq 1$, are equal. (§ 9–3)

4. Relations in x and y are often expressed in terms of a parameter such as t. (§ 9–4)

5. The absolute value function $\{(x, |x|)\}$ and the greatest integer function $\{(x, [\![x]\!])\}$ may be defined for all real numbers x. (§ 9–5)

6. The probability density function (p. d. f.) makes it possible to consider probabilities of events which are not based upon sample spaces of equally likely events. (§ 9–6)

7. If a random variable x has a mean μ and a standard deviation σ, then the probability that x assumes a value within k standard deviations of μ is greater than or equal to $1 - \frac{1}{k^2}$ (Chebyshev's Theorem). (§ 9–7)

8. The probability distribution function is the cumulative probability density function; $F(x_i) = P(x \leq x_i)$. (§ 9–8)

9. Each binomial density function is based upon n trials of a Bernoulli experiment. The binomial random variable has mean np and variance $np(1 - p)$. (§ 9–9)

10. Other types of probability density functions include uniform density functions, multinomial density functions, and hypergeometric density functions. (§ 9–10)

11. Probabilities for continuous variables may be represented geometrically. (§ 9–11)

12. The following words have been introduced or used extensively in this chapter:

KEYED PRACTICE ON CHAPTER 9

absolute value function (§ 9–5)
base (§ 9–2)
basic absolute value function (§ 9–5)
Bernoulli density function (§ 9–9)
Bernoulli experiment (§ 9–9)
Bernoulli random variable (§ 9–9)
binomial density function (§ 9–9)
binomial random variable (§ 9–9)
Cartesian equation (§ 9–4)
Chebyshev's Theorem (§ 9–7)
common logarithmic function (§ 9–2)
continuous variable (§ 9–11)
discrete variable (§ 9–11)
domain (§ 9–1)
exponential equation (§ 9–3)
exponential function (§ 9–2)
extraneous root (§ 9–3)
greatest integer function (§ 9–5)
hypergeometric density function (§ 9–10)
logarithmic equation (§ 9–3)

logarithmic function (§ 9–2)
mathematical expectation (§ 9–7)
mean (§ 9–7)
multinomial density function (§ 9–10)
natural logarithmic function (§ 9–2)
parameter (§ 9–4)
parametric equation (§ 9–4)
power function (§ 9–1)
probability bar chart (§ 9–6)
probability density function (§ 9–6)
probability distribution function (§ 9–8)
probability histogram (§ 9–6)
probability measure (§ 9–6)
random variable (§ 9–6)
range (§ 9–1)
standard deviation (§ 9–7)
uniform density function (§ 9–10)
variance (§ 9–7)

KEYED PRACTICE ON CHAPTER 9

1. State the domain and range of the power function $x^{\frac{4}{3}}$, and sketch its graph. (§ 9–1)

2. Evaluate: **(a)** $e^{\ln 2x}$; **(b)** $\log_{\frac{1}{2}} 16$. (§ 9–2)

3. Solve: **(a)** $2^{(x^2)} = 16$; **(b)** $\log_5 x^3 = -3$. (§ 9–3)

4. Eliminate the parameter and describe the graph of

$$\begin{cases} x = 2 + 3 \cos \theta \\ y = 5 + \sin \theta. \end{cases} \quad (\S\ 9\text{–}4)$$

5. Graph for $-4 \leq x \leq 4$: **(a)** $y = |x + 2|$; **(b)** $y = [\![x + 3]\!]$. (§ 9–5)

6. Let a coin be tossed five times. **(a)** Determine a table of values of a p. d. f. for the number of heads obtained. **(b)** Construct a histogram of the p. d. f. (§ 9–6)

7. Find the mean and the variance of the random variable x in the given table. (§ 9–7)

x	0	1	2	3	4
$f(x)$	0.2	0.4	0	0.3	0.1

SPECIAL FUNCTIONS

8. Determine the probability distribution function for the random variable x having the p. d. f. given in Exercise 7. (§ 9-8)

9. Construct a table of values for the binomial density function and the probability distribution function when $n = 5$ and $p = \frac{1}{3}$. (§ 9-9)

• 10. If $x = 1, 2, 3, 4, 5, 6, 7, 8$, construct a table of values for the uniform distribution function $F(x)$. (§ 9-10)

• 11. A string 12 inches long is cut at random into two pieces. Find the probability that one of the pieces is at least twice as long as the other. (§ 9-11)

TESTS ON CHAPTER 9

A

1. State the domain and range of the power function $x^{\frac{3}{4}}$, and sketch its graph.

2. Evaluate: (a) $10^{\log 7}$; (b) $\log_{\frac{1}{3}} 81$.

3. Solve: (a) $3^{-x} = 27$; (b) $\log (x + 79) = 2$.

4. Eliminate the parameter and describe the graph of
$$\begin{cases} x = 2t + 3 \\ y = 5 - t. \end{cases}$$

5. Graph $y = |2x - 1|$.

6. Use numerals 0, 1, 2, ⋯ as needed and find a domain for a random variable for the experiment of tossing ten pennies.

7. Find the mean and the variance of the random variable x in the table on the right.

x	−1	0	1	2	3
f(x)	0.2	0.1	0.4	0	0.3

8. Determine the probability distribution function for the random variable x having the p. d. f. given in Exercise 7.

9. Construct a table of values for the binomial density function and for the probability distribution function when $n = 5$ and $p = \frac{2}{3}$.

10. If six coins are tossed, what is the probability that at least four heads will appear?

B

1. State the domain and range of the power function $x^{-\frac{4}{3}}$, and sketch its graph.

2. Evaluate: (a) $\log_{\frac{1}{2}} 32$; (b) $e^{3(\ln 2)}$.

3. Solve: (a) $\log_3 x^2 = -2$; (b) $\log (3x - 5) = -1$.

4. Eliminate the parameter and describe the graph of
$$\begin{cases} x = 5 + 2\cos\theta \\ y = \sin\theta - 1. \end{cases}$$
5. Graph $y = [\![x - 3]\!]$ for $-4 \leq x \leq 4$.
6. Let a coin be tossed four times. Construct a table of values of a p. d. f. for the number of heads obtained.
7. Find the mean and the variance of the random variable x:

x	-2	-1	0	1	2	3
$f(x)$	$\frac{1}{4}$	$\frac{1}{6}$	$\frac{1}{6}$	0	$\frac{1}{3}$	$\frac{1}{12}$

8. Construct a histogram for the probability distribution function for the random variable x having the p. d. f. given in Exercise 7.
9. If twelve coins are tossed, what is the probability that exactly four heads appear?
10. In the experiment described in Exercise 9, what is the probability that at least four heads appear?

C

1. Evaluate: (a) $\log_{0.2} 25$; (b) $e^{\ln 2x - 2(\ln x)}$.
2. Solve: (a) $x = 5^{\log_2 0.25}$; (b) $\log_3(x - 2) = -1$.
3. Eliminate the parameter and describe the graph of
$$\begin{cases} x = \sqrt{t} - 1 \\ y = t + 2. \end{cases}$$
4. Graph $y > [\![x]\!]$ for $-4 \leq x \leq 4$.
5. Find a constant k such that $f(x)$ may be considered a p. d. f. for $x = 1, 2, 3, 4, 5$ if $f(x) = \frac{x^2}{k}$.

6. Find the mean and the variance of the random variable x in the table on the right.

x	-2	1	2	3	5
$f(x)$	$\frac{1}{3}$	$\frac{1}{6}$	$\frac{1}{4}$	$\frac{1}{6}$	$\frac{1}{12}$

7. Construct a histogram for the probability distribution function for the random variable $x = -2, 0, 2, 4, 6$ if $f(-2) = 0.2$, $f(0) = 0.2$, $f(2) = 0$, $f(4) = 0.5$, and $f(6) = 0.1$.
8. A die is thrown five times. What is the probability that there will be at least twice as many ones and sixes as there are other values?

SPECIAL FUNCTIONS

9. An urn contains two red and five white balls. If two balls are selected at random without replacement, find the mean and the variance of the number of red balls selected.

10. A string eleven inches long is cut at random into two pieces. Find the probability that both pieces are at least three inches long.

ANSWERS TO TEST YOURSELF EXERCISES

§ 9-1. **1.** Domain: all real values of x.
Range: all real values of y.

3. Domain: all real $x \neq 0$.
Range: all real $y \neq 0$.

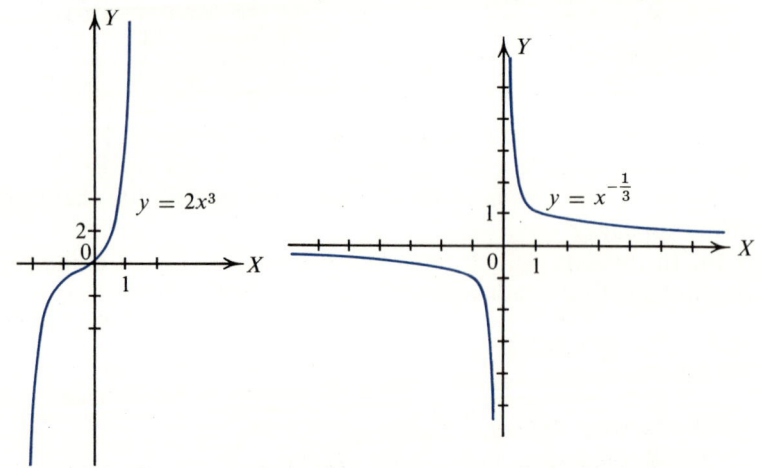

2. Domain: all real values of x.
Range: all real values of y.

4. Domain: all nonnegative real x.
Range: all non-negative real y.

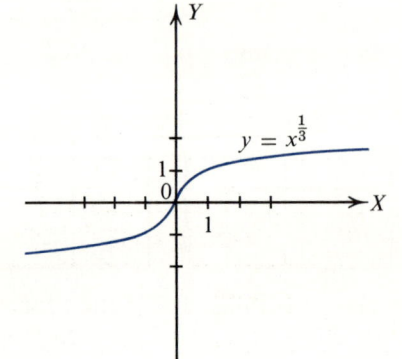

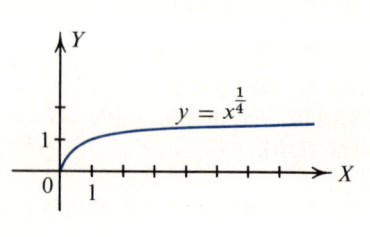

§ 9-2. **1.** 3. **2.** -3. **3.** $2a^2 - 1$. **4.** $\dfrac{1}{x^2}$.

526

ANSWERS TO TEST YOURSELF EXERCISES

§ 9-3. **1.** $x = 2$. **2.** $x \approx 5.0449$. **3.** $x = 40$. **4.** $x = \frac{3}{4}$. (Notice that -2 is extraneous.) **5.** $x \approx 2.322$. **6.** $x \approx 0.1883$.

§ 9-4. **1.** $x = y^2$; parabola, vertex at $(0, 0)$, focus at $\left(\frac{1}{4}, 0\right)$.

2. $x + 3y = 77$; line through $\left(0, \frac{77}{3}\right)$ and $(77, 0)$.

§ 9-5. **1.** $f(-1) = 3, f(0) = 0,$
$f(1) = 3, f(2) = 6.$

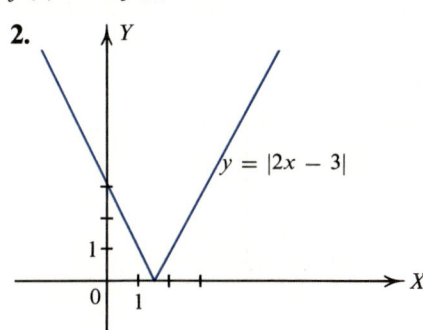

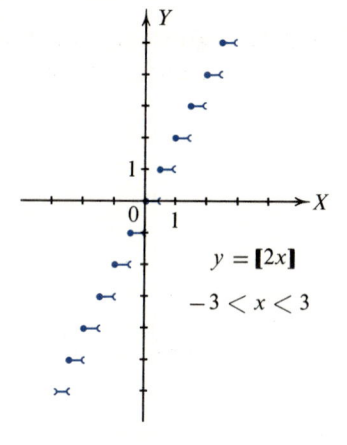

2. [graph of $y = |2x - 3|$]

4. [graph of $y = [2x]$, $-3 < x < 3$]

3. (a) 3; (b) 2; (c) 0; (d) -3.

§ 9-6. **1.** $\{x \mid x = 0, 1, 2, 3\}$.

2. This cannot be a p. d. f. since the sum of the probabilities of a p. d. f. may not be greater than 1.
3. This satisfies the requirements for a p. d. f.

4.

x	1	2
$f(x)$	$\frac{2}{3}$	$\frac{1}{3}$

§ 9-7. **1.** $\mu = \frac{5}{2}$; $\sigma^2 = 1$. **2.** $\mu = 1$; $\sigma^2 = \frac{2}{3}$.

§ 9-8. **1.**

x	0	1	2	3	4	5	6
$F(x)$	0.05	0.15	0.20	0.45	0.60	0.90	1.00

2.

x	1	2	3	4	5
$F(x)$	$\frac{1}{5}$	$\frac{2}{5}$	$\frac{3}{5}$	$\frac{4}{5}$	1

SPECIAL FUNCTIONS

3.
x	1	2	3
$F(x)$	$\frac{1}{6}$	$\frac{1}{2}$	1

4.
x	0	1	2
$F(x)$	$\frac{1}{10}$	$\frac{7}{10}$	1

§ 9-9. 1.

(a)
x	0	1	2	3
$f(x)$	$\frac{1}{8}$	$\frac{3}{8}$	$\frac{3}{8}$	$\frac{1}{8}$

(b)
x	0	1	2	3
$F(x)$	$\frac{1}{8}$	$\frac{1}{2}$	$\frac{7}{8}$	1

2.

(a)
x	0	1	2	3
$f(x)$	$\frac{8}{27}$	$\frac{4}{9}$	$\frac{2}{9}$	$\frac{1}{27}$

(b)
x	0	1	2	3
$F(x)$	$\frac{8}{27}$	$\frac{20}{27}$	$\frac{26}{27}$	1

3.
x	0	1	2	3	4
$f(x)$	$\frac{625}{1296}$	$\frac{125}{324}$	$\frac{25}{216}$	$\frac{5}{324}$	$\frac{1}{1296}$

4. *(1)* $\mu = \frac{3}{2}$. *(2)* $\mu = 1$. *(3)* $\mu = \frac{2}{3}$.

§ 9-10. 1. In $f(w, g, y)$ let w represent the number of white beads, g represent the number of green beads, and y represent the number of yellow beads; also $w, g, y = 0, 1, 2, 3$.

$f(3, 0, 0) = \frac{27}{343}$ $f(1, 1, 1) = \frac{72}{343}$

$f(2, 1, 0) = \frac{54}{343}$ $f(0, 2, 1) = \frac{24}{343}$

$f(2, 0, 1) = \frac{54}{343}$ $f(0, 1, 2) = \frac{24}{343}$

$f(1, 2, 0) = \frac{36}{343}$ $f(0, 3, 0) = \frac{8}{343}$

$f(1, 0, 2) = \frac{36}{343}$ $f(0, 0, 3) = \frac{8}{343}$.

ANSWERS TO KEYED PRACTICE EXERCISES

2. After the double blank has been removed, twenty-seven dominoes remain in the set; of these, six bear blanks. Therefore a p. d. f. may be expressed as

$$f(x) = \frac{_6C_x \times {_{21}C_{4-x}}}{_{27}C_4} \text{ for } x = 0, 1, 2, 3, 4; \text{ where } f(0) = \frac{133}{390},$$

$f(1) = \frac{266}{585}$, $f(2) = \frac{7}{39}$, $f(3) = \frac{14}{585}$, and $f(4) = \frac{1}{1170}$.

§ 9–11. **1.** $\frac{2}{5}$. **2.** $\frac{1}{5}$. **3.** $\frac{2}{5}$. **4.** $\frac{2}{3}$. **5.** 0.

ANSWERS TO KEYED PRACTICE EXERCISES

1. Domain: all real values of x. Range: all non-negative real values of y.

2. (a) $2x$; (b) -4.

3. (a) $x = 2, x = -2$;

(b) $x = \frac{1}{5}$.

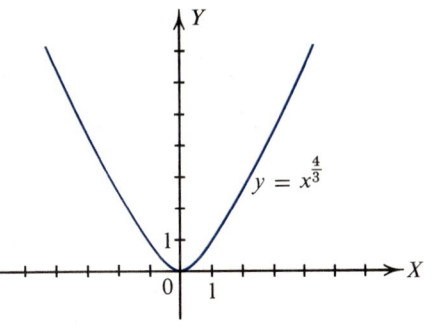

$y = x^{\frac{4}{3}}$

4. $\dfrac{(x-2)^2}{9} + \dfrac{(y-5)^2}{1} = 1$; graph is an ellipse with center at (2, 5); end points of major axis at (−1, 5) and (5, 5); end points of minor axis at (2, 4) and (2, 6).

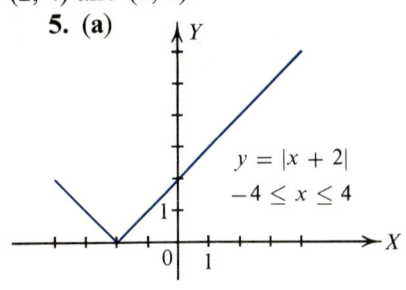

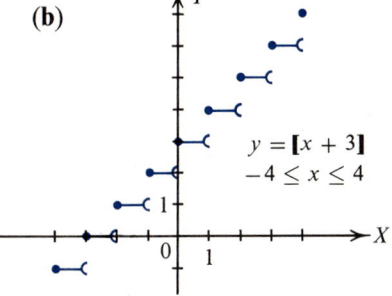

5. (a) $y = |x + 2|$, $-4 \leq x \leq 4$

(b) $y = [x + 3]$, $-4 \leq x \leq 4$

6. (a)

x	0	1	2	3	4	5
$f(x)$	$\frac{1}{32}$	$\frac{5}{32}$	$\frac{10}{32}$	$\frac{10}{32}$	$\frac{5}{32}$	$\frac{1}{32}$

SPECIAL FUNCTIONS

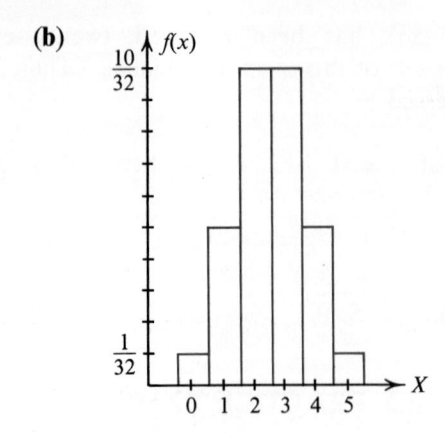

(b)

[Histogram with f(x) axis showing values 1/32 and 10/32, bars over x = 0,1,2,3,4,5]

7. $\mu = 1.7$; $\sigma^2 = 1.810$.

8.
x	0	1	2	3	4
$F(x)$	0.2	0.6	0.6	0.9	1.0

9.
x	0	1	2	3	4	5
$f(x)$	$\frac{32}{243}$	$\frac{80}{243}$	$\frac{80}{243}$	$\frac{40}{243}$	$\frac{10}{243}$	$\frac{1}{243}$
$F(x)$	$\frac{32}{243}$	$\frac{112}{243}$	$\frac{64}{81}$	$\frac{232}{243}$	$\frac{242}{243}$	1

10.
x	1	2	3	4	5	6	7	8
$F(x)$	$\frac{1}{8}$	$\frac{1}{4}$	$\frac{3}{8}$	$\frac{1}{2}$	$\frac{5}{8}$	$\frac{3}{4}$	$\frac{7}{8}$	1

11. Let A represent the event that one piece of string is at least twice as long as the other. Since the only place where the string might be cut so that A fails to occur is on the middle third of the original piece, $P(A) = 1 - \frac{1}{3} = \frac{2}{3}$.

Chapter 10

Sequences, Series, and Limits

§ 10-1 Limits

The concept of limit is the fundamental concept upon which the theory of calculus is built. The principles of calculus were discovered independently by two famous mathematicians, Newton (1642–1727) and Leibniz (1646–1716). However, the concept of limit had its origin long before the time of these mathematicians. Archimedes, in the third century B.C., almost discovered the concept of limit in his "method of exhaustion." In this section we shall examine this method to obtain an intuitive idea of what we mean by the word limit.

Consider the problem of determining the area A of the plane region bounded by the graph of $y = x^2$, the line $x = 1$, and the segment of the x-axis from $(0, 0)$ to $(1, 0)$ as in Figure 10–1. We should recognize that Archimedes did not have a clear definition of what was meant by the "area" of such a region; that is, a region bounded in part or entirely by a curved line. A precise definition of such an area will be given in § 10–10.

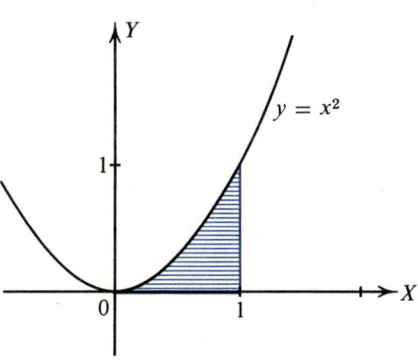

Figure 10-1

An approximation A_1 to the area A may be obtained by the following method. Divide the line segment with the end points $(0, 0)$ and $(1, 0)$ into two equal subintervals. Then the point of division has coordinates $\left(\frac{1}{2}, 0\right)$. At this point construct the **ordinate** to the curve; that is, construct the line segment whose length may be measured to find the y-coordinate of the point $\left(\frac{1}{2}, y\right)$ of the curve. Then construct the **inner rectangles** with the subintervals as bases; that is, construct the largest possible rectangles with the given bases such that the rectangular regions are subsets of the region A. In Figure 10–2 the rectangle on the subinterval from $(0, 0)$ to $\left(\frac{1}{2}, 0\right)$ has height zero and thus is disregarded; the rectangle on the subinterval

SEQUENCES, SERIES, AND LIMITS

from $\left(\frac{1}{2}, 0\right)$ to $(1, 0)$ has height $\frac{1}{4}$ and is shown. The area A_1 of this rectangle is numerically equal to $\frac{1}{8}$, is a first approximation to A, and satisfies the inequality $A_1 \leq A$.

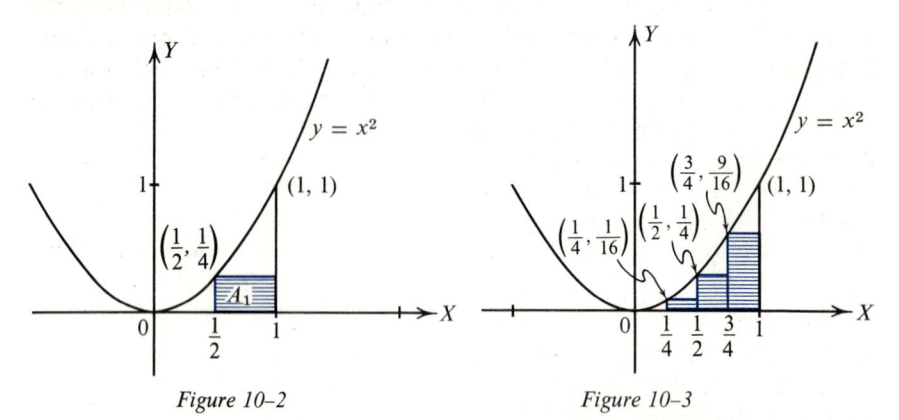

Figure 10–2   *Figure 10–3*

A second approximation A_2 may be obtained by dividing the line segment from $(0, 0)$ to $(1, 0)$ into four equal subintervals, constructing ordinates at the points of division, and forming the three inner rectangles as in Figure 10–3. Let A_2 be the sum of the areas of the three rectangles. Then $A_1 \leq A_2 \leq A$ since

$$A_2 = \frac{1}{4}\left(\frac{1}{4}\right)^2 + \frac{1}{4}\left(\frac{2}{4}\right)^2 + \frac{1}{4}\left(\frac{3}{4}\right)^2 = \left(\frac{1}{4}\right)^3(1^2 + 2^2 + 3^2) = \frac{7}{32}.$$

We may continue in this manner and divide the line segment into 8, 16, 32, $\cdots$ equal subintervals. In each case the sum of the areas A_3, A_4, A_5, $\cdots$ of the inner rectangles can be obtained. These areas are $\frac{35}{128}, \frac{155}{512}, \frac{651}{2048}, \cdots$ respectively. Notice that $A_1 \leq A_2 \leq A_3 \leq A_4 \leq A_5 \leq \cdots \leq A$. Archimedes argued that as the number of rectangles increased the sums of the areas of the inner rectangles $A_1, A_2, A_3, \cdots, A_n, \cdots$ would yield closer and closer approximations to the true area A. In other words, as the number of rectangles is increased, the difference between A and A_n is "exhausted" and vanishes.

In general, the difference $A - A_n$ can never be made equal to zero by the method of exhaustion. However, by choosing a large enough number of inner rectangles with equal bases we can make $A - A_n$ arbitrarily small in absolute value; that is, less than any preassigned positive number

§ 10-1 LIMITS

regardless of how small it may be. In other words, the nth member A_n of the set of ordered numbers $A_1, A_2, A_3, \cdots, A_n, \cdots$ approaches A as n becomes larger and larger without bound. We call A the **limit** of the set of ordered numbers. Remember that we are *not* saying that the nth member of the set of ordered numbers $A_1, A_2, A_3, \cdots$ is equal to A.

The area A in Figure 10–1 may also be approached by a sequence of the sums of the areas of **outer rectangles;** that is, the smallest possible rectangles with given subintervals as bases and such that the region under consideration is a subset of the union of the rectangular regions. One set of outer rectangles is shown in Figure 10–4. This method of approximating the area A is developed in Exercises 6 through 10. For each division of the line segment from $(0, 0)$ to $(1, 0)$ into equal subintervals the sum A_n of the areas of the inner rectangles is less than or equal to A; the sum B_n of the areas of the outer rectangles is greater than or equal to A; $A_n \leq A \leq B_n$; and thus A_n and B_n are bounds for the area A.

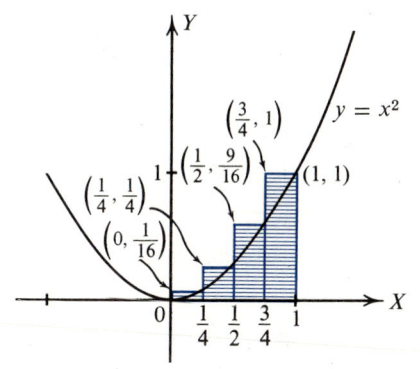

Figure 10–4

TEST YOURSELF

In Exercises 1 through 4 use inner rectangles as in the method of exhaustion to approximate the area of the triangle bounded by the x-axis, the line $y = 2x$, and the line $x = 1$ when the number of equal subintervals into which the line segment from $(0, 0)$ to $(1, 0)$ is divided is:

1. Two.   **2.** Four.   **3.** Eight.   **4.** Ten.

5. Subtract the approximation from the actual area of the triangle and thus find the error of the approximation in **(a)** Exercise 1; **(b)** Exercise 2; **(c)** Exercise 3; **(d)** Exercise 4.

EXERCISES

In Exercises 1 through 4 use inner rectangles as in the method of exhaustion to approximate the area of the triangle bounded by the coordinate axes and the line $3x + y = 3$ when the number of equal subintervals into which the line segment from $(0, 0)$ to $(1, 0)$ is divided is:

1. Two.   **2.** Four.   **3.** Eight.   **4.** Ten.

SEQUENCES, SERIES, AND LIMITS

5. Subtract the approximation from the actual area of the triangle and thus find the error of the approximation in **(a)** Exercise 1; **(b)** Exercise 2; **(c)** Exercise 3; **(d)** Exercise 4.

As in the Figure 10–4 use outer rectangles in Exercises 6 through 10 to approximate the area of the region bounded by the x-axis, the line $x = 1$, and the curve $y = x^2$ when the number of equal subintervals into which the line segment from (0, 0) to (1, 0) is divided is:

6. Two. **7.** Four. **8.** Eight. **9.** Sixteen.

10. Compare the answers obtained in Exercises 6, 7, 8, and 9 with the results A_1, A_2, A_3, and A_4 respectively obtained in this section; state bounds upon A for each comparison; and use the average of each set of bounds to obtain an estimate of the value of A.

• • •

11. Repeat Exercises 1 through 4 using outer rectangles instead of inner rectangles.

12. Repeat Exercises 6 through 9 for the regions bounded by the graphs of $x = 1$, $y = x^3$, and the x-axis.

13. Repeat Exercise 12 using inner rectangles instead of outer rectangles.

14. Compare the answers obtained in Exercises 12 and 13 and state bounds on the area of the region when the number of equal subintervals into which the line segment from (0, 0) to (1, 0) is divided is **(a)** two; **(b)** four; **(c)** eight; **(d)** sixteen.

• **15.** Divide the line segment from (0, 0) to (1, 0) into eight equal subintervals and use both inner and outer rectangles to find bounds for the area of the region in the first quadrant bounded by the coordinate axes and the circle $x^2 + y^2 = 1$. Estimate the area as the average of its bounds and state the corresponding approximation for π.

§ 10–2 Sequences of numbers

We now consider sets of ordered numbers in more detail so that we may discuss limits more precisely. We have noted that a function may be considered a rule whereby to each number n which belongs to the domain of the function is associated a number $f(n)$ which belongs to the range of the function (§§ 1–8 and 1–10). If we restrict the domain of a function to the set of positive integers $n = 1, 2, 3, \cdots$, then the set of ordered values of the function $f(1), f(2), f(3), \cdots$ is called a **sequence.** Each value of the function is called an **element,** or **term,** of the sequence. The functional expression $f(n)$ is sometimes called the **generator,** or **nth term,** of the

§ 10-2 SEQUENCES OF NUMBERS

sequence. If the generator of a sequence is known, we may denote the sequence by $\{f(n)\}$.

Here are a few examples of sequences:

$$1, 2, 3, 4;$$

$$1, \frac{1}{2}, \frac{1}{3}, \frac{1}{4}, \cdots, \frac{1}{100};$$

$$0, 2, 4, 8, \cdots, 2^n, \cdots;$$

$$0, 2, 0, 2, \cdots, 1 + (-1)^n, \cdots;$$

$$\frac{2}{1}, \frac{3}{2}, \frac{4}{3}, \frac{5}{4}, \cdots, \frac{n+1}{n}, \cdots.$$

The first two sequences are examples of **finite sequences** since each contains only a finite number of terms. The first sequence has four terms; the second sequence has one hundred terms. The remaining three sequences are examples of **infinite sequences**. We shall be concerned primarily with infinite sequences and, unless otherwise stated, we shall mean by "sequence" an infinite sequence.

It is often desirable or necessary to determine succeeding terms of a sequence when we have been given the first several terms. Succeeding terms of a sequence can be written only if the generator is known or some assumption is made which allows us to determine a generator. If an assumption is necessary, we shall choose what appears to be the simplest generator indicated by the pattern of the terms of the sequence.

Example 1. Find the first five terms of the sequence $\{n^2 + 1\}$.

We let n equal 1, 2, 3, 4, and 5 to obtain 2, 5, 10, 17, and 26 respectively as the first five terms of the sequence whose generator is $n^2 + 1$.

Example 2. Find the next four terms of the sequence 3, 6, 9, 12, $\cdots$.

Since the generator is not given for the sequence we must make some assumption concerning the generator. From the pattern of the first four terms of the sequence we choose to make the assumption that the generator is $3n$. Hence we assume that the next four terms of the sequence are 15, 18, 21, and 24.

Note that we can never be certain what the succeeding terms of a sequence will be unless the generator is known. For example, in Example 2 the generator of the sequence 3, 6, 9, 12, $\cdots$ might be $3n + k(n-1)(n-2)(n-3)(n-4)$ for any number k. In this case the next four terms would be $15 + 4!k$, $18 + 5!k$, $21 + \frac{6!}{2!}k$, $24 + \frac{7!}{3!}k$.

535

SEQUENCES, SERIES, AND LIMITS

We next consider the differences between the successive given terms in Example 2:

Given terms   3 6 9 12
First differences   3 3 3

These differences are called first differences because we may repeat the process calling the differences of the first differences second differences, and so forth. The fact that the first differences are the same (constant) implies that we may assume that the generator is a linear polynomial; the fact that the constant is 3 implies that the polynomial has the form $3n + b$ for some constant b. In general, it can be shown that if the nth differences of the given terms of a sequence are constant, then a polynomial of degree at most n may be used to generate a sequence with the given terms as terms of the sequence. Since for four given terms there are three first differences, two second differences, and one third difference, at most third differences need to be considered to obtain constant differences. Thus for any given four terms a polynomial of degree at most three may be used to generate a sequence with those four terms. In general, at most $(k - 1)$st differences are needed for any k given terms and a polynomial of degree at most $k - 1$ may be used to generate a sequence which includes the given terms.

Throughout our study of sequences instructions such as "Find the next four terms of the sequence $\cdots$" in Example 2 are used to mean "Find the next four terms of a sequence having the terms of the given finite sequence as its first few terms." Differences may be used directly in solving such problems; that is, in determining a pattern by which successive terms may be found for a sequence having the given terms as its first few terms. The **method of differences** is illustrated in Example 3.

Example 3. Find the next three terms of the sequence 2, 7, 15, 26, 40, $\cdots$.

Given terms and others	2	7	15	26	40	57	77	100	$\cdots$
First differences		5	8	11	14	17	20	23	$\cdots$
Second differences			3	3	3	3	3	3	$\cdots$

The five given terms are listed on the first row of an array. Their four first differences are calculated and listed on the second row. Then the three second differences are calculated and listed on the third row. Since these second differences are constant, we *assume* that second differences are constant for all terms of the desired sequence. Then the third row may be continued as $\cdots, 3, 3, 3, \cdots$; these second differences

§ 10–2 SEQUENCES OF NUMBERS

may be used to continue the second row $\cdots$, $14 + 3 = 17, 17 + 3 = 20$, $20 + 3 = 23, \cdots$; and these first differences may be used to continue the listing of terms of the desired sequence on the first row $\cdots$, $40 + 17 = 57, 57 + 20 = 77, 77 + 23 = 100, \cdots$.

TEST YOURSELF

Find the first five terms of each sequence:

1. $\{3^n\}$. 2. $\{n^3 - n\}$. 3. $\{n!\}$. 4. $\{(-1)^n\}$.

Find the next four terms of each sequence:

5. 2, 4, 6, 8, $\cdots$.
6. 1, 4, 9, 16, $\cdots$.
7. $a^2, a, 1, a^{-1}, \cdots$.
8. 11, 15, 19, 23, $\cdots$.
9. 4, 7, 12, 19, $\cdots$.
10. 1, 4, 16, $\cdots$.

EXERCISES

Find the first five terms of each sequence:

1. $\{n + 3\}$.
2. $\{(-1)^n \, 2^n\}$.
3. $\left\{\dfrac{3n - 5}{n + 1}\right\}$.
4. $\{n^3\}$.
5. $\{2n(2n - 1)\}$.
6. $\{\log n\}$.
7. $\left\{\dfrac{1}{(n - 1)!}\right\}$.
8. $\left\{(-1)^{n+1} \dfrac{x^{2n-1}}{(2n - 1)!}\right\}$.

Find the next four terms of each sequence:

9. $\dfrac{1}{2}, \dfrac{1}{3}, \dfrac{1}{4}, \dfrac{1}{5}, \cdots$.
10. $\sqrt{3}, 3, 3\sqrt{3}, 9, \cdots$.
11. $2, -4, 8, -16, \cdots$.
12. $a, -a, a, -a, \cdots$.
13. $2, 5, 8, 11, \cdots$.
14. $\dfrac{x}{2^2}, \dfrac{x^2}{3^2}, \dfrac{x^3}{4^2}, \dfrac{x^4}{5^2}, \cdots$.
15. 3, 6, 11, 18, 27, $\cdots$.
16. 2, 9, 28, 65, 126, $\cdots$.
17. 2, 3, 5, 7, 11, 13, $\cdots$.
18. 1, 1, 2, 3, 5, 8, $\cdots$.

HINT: In Exercise 18 try to find each term from the preceding terms. Do not use the method of differences.

• • •

In Exercises 19 through 22 find a generator for each sequence:

19. $\dfrac{1}{1 \times 2}, \dfrac{1}{3 \times 4}, \dfrac{1}{5 \times 6}, \dfrac{1}{7 \times 8}, \cdots$.

20. 2, 6, 18, 54, $\cdots$.

21. $\dfrac{5}{2!}, \dfrac{7}{4!}, \dfrac{9}{6!}, \dfrac{11}{8!}, \cdots$.

22. $1, x, \dfrac{x^2}{2}, \dfrac{x^3}{6}, \cdots$.

537

SEQUENCES, SERIES, AND LIMITS

23. Consider the sequence 1, 3, ···· . Consider also the sequences **(a)** $\{2n - 1\}$; **(b)** $\{n^2 - n + 1\}$; **(c)** $\{2n - 1 + 5(n - 1)(n - 2)\}$; **(d)** for any integer x, $\{2n - 1 + x(n - 1)(n - 2)\}$ and show that there are many sequences 1, 3, ···· . Find five terms of each sequence (a) through (d).

• **24.** Find **(a)** the first four terms of the sequence $\{f(n)\}$ where $f(n)$ is the number of terms of the multinomial $(a + b + c)^n$; **(b)** the next three terms of the sequence.

§ 10-3 Null sequences

Consider these sequences and try to find their common property or properties:

$$\left\{\frac{1}{n}\right\}: \quad 1, \frac{1}{2}, \frac{1}{3}, \frac{1}{4}, \cdots;$$

$$\left\{\frac{1}{2n}\right\}: \quad \frac{1}{2}, \frac{1}{4}, \frac{1}{6}, \frac{1}{8}, \cdots;$$

$$\left\{\frac{1}{n+2}\right\}: \quad \frac{1}{3}, \frac{1}{4}, \frac{1}{5}, \frac{1}{6}, \cdots;$$

$$\left\{\frac{1}{2n-5}\right\}: \quad -\frac{1}{3}, -1, 1, \frac{1}{3}, \frac{1}{5}, \cdots;$$

$$\left\{\frac{1}{2^n}\right\}: \quad \frac{1}{2}, \frac{1}{4}, \frac{1}{8}, \frac{1}{16}, \cdots;$$

$$\left\{\frac{(-1)^n}{n}\right\}: \quad -1, \frac{1}{2}, -\frac{1}{3}, \frac{1}{4}, \cdots.$$

Each sequence $\{a_n\}$ is an infinite sequence. The absolute values of the terms of each sequence approach zero as n increases. That is, for any given positive number p it is possible to find a value N_p of n such that for all $n > N_p$ we have $|a_n| < p$. For example, if $p = 0.1$ and the sequence $\left\{\frac{1}{n}\right\}$ is under discussion, the value $N_{0.1}$ may be taken as 10 or as any integer greater than 10 since if $n > 10$, then $\left|\frac{1}{n}\right| < 0.1$. We use the subscript p in the symbol N_p to emphasize that N_p depends upon (is a function of) p.

The determination of N_p often involves inequalities. Remember that $a < b$ if and only if $0 < b - a$; also

if $a < b$ and $0 < c$, then $ac < bc$;
if $a < b$ and $c < 0$; then $ac > bc$.

These properties of inequalities are used primarily in cases such as the following:

if $0 < n$, $0 < p$, and $\frac{1}{n} < p$, then $\frac{1}{p} < n$;

if $n > 5$, $0 < p$, and $\frac{1}{5-n} < p$, then $\frac{1}{p} > 5 - n$ and $n > 5 - \frac{1}{p}$.

Example 1. Use $p = 0.02$ and find a value N_p of n such that for all $n > N_p$, $|a_n| < p$ in the sequence

(a) $\left\{\frac{(-1)^n}{n}\right\}$; (b) $\left\{\frac{1}{3n}\right\}$; (c) $\left\{\frac{1}{2n-5}\right\}$; (d) $\left\{\frac{2n}{n^2+1}\right\}$.

> (a) $a_n = \frac{(-1)^n}{n}$; $|a_n| = \frac{1}{n}$; $|a_n| < 0.02$ if and only if $\frac{1}{n} < 0.02$; that is, if and only if $n > 50$. Any integer such as 51 which is greater than or equal to 50 may be taken as N_p instead of 50. Usually N_p is selected as small as possible or as the smallest acceptable value of n. In this exercise we take N_p as 50.
>
> (b) $|a_n| = \frac{1}{3n}$ since $n > 0$; $|a_n| < 0.02$ if and only if $\frac{1}{3n} < 0.02$; that is, if and only if $3n > 50$. We may take $N_p = 16$.
>
> (c) $|a_n| = \frac{1}{2n-5}$ when $2n - 5 > 0$, that is, $n \geq 3$; $\frac{1}{2n-5} < 0.02$ when $\frac{1}{2n-5} < \frac{1}{50}$, that is, $2n - 5 > 50$; $2n > 55$, $n \geq 28$. We may take $N_p = 27$.
>
> (d) $|a_n| = \frac{2n}{n^2+1}$ since $n > 0$; $\frac{2n}{n^2+1} < 0.02$ when $\frac{2n}{n^2+1} < \frac{1}{50}$; $100n < n^2 + 1$; $0 < n^2 - 100n + 1$ which is certainly satisfied if $n \geq 100$. We may take $N_p = 100$ since $n^2 - 100n + 1$ is obviously positive for $n > 100$.

As in Example 1 we often can choose N_p from an inspection of the equation without solving for the roots of the equation. Thus the value of N_p that is selected is often a matter of convenience subject only to the restriction that it is sufficiently large. In mathematical exposition it is customary to use the Greek letter epsilon ϵ instead of p to represent any positive number. If a sequence $\{a_n\}$ has the property that for each given positive number ϵ there exists a number N_ϵ such that $|a_n| < \epsilon$ whenever $n > N_\epsilon$, the sequence is called a **null sequence.** Notice that the sequences in Example 1 have not been proved to be null sequences since a special value of ϵ has been used. However, the method used in Example 1 illustrates the general procedure.

539

SEQUENCES, SERIES, AND LIMITS

Example 2. Determine whether or not each sequence is a null sequence:

(a) $\left\{\dfrac{10^6}{n^2+1}\right\}$; (b) $\left\{\dfrac{n}{10^6}\right\}$; (c) $\{5^{-n}\}$; (d) $\left\{\dfrac{1}{\log n}\right\}$.

In each case we assume that a positive number ϵ is given and consider the inequality $|a_n| < \epsilon$ to determine whether or not N_ϵ can be found with the desired property and whether the possibility of determining N_ϵ is independent of the value of ϵ.

(a) $\left|\dfrac{10^6}{n^2+1}\right| < \epsilon$ if and only if $\dfrac{10^6}{\epsilon} < n^2 + 1$. This inequality is satisfied whenever $\dfrac{10^6}{\epsilon} < n^2$ and thus whenever $n > \dfrac{10^3}{\sqrt{\epsilon}}$. We may use the greatest integer function and take $N_\epsilon = \left[\dfrac{10^3}{\sqrt{\epsilon}}\right]$ for any given ϵ. Thus the sequence is a null sequence.

(b) $\left|\dfrac{n}{10^6}\right| < \epsilon$ if and only if $n < 10^6\epsilon$. Thus it is not possible to find an N_ϵ and the sequence is not a null sequence.

(c) $|5^{-n}| < \epsilon$ if and only if $\dfrac{1}{\epsilon} < 5^n$; that is, $\log_5 \dfrac{1}{\epsilon} < n$. For any given $\epsilon > 0$ we may take $N_\epsilon = \left[\log_5 \dfrac{1}{\epsilon}\right]$ and thus the sequence is a null sequence.

(d) $\left|\dfrac{1}{\log n}\right| < \epsilon$ if and only if $\dfrac{1}{\epsilon} < \log n$; that is, $10^{1/\epsilon} < n$. For any given $\epsilon > 0$ we may take $N_\epsilon = [\,10^{1/\epsilon}\,]$ and thus the sequence is a null sequence.

TEST YOURSELF

1. Use $\epsilon = 0.01$ and find an N_ϵ such that $|a_n| < \epsilon$ for all $n > N_\epsilon$:
(a) $\left\{\dfrac{1}{2n}\right\}$; (b) $\left\{\dfrac{1}{3n}\right\}$.

2. Determine whether or not each sequence is a null sequence:
(a) $\{n^2 - 10^8\}$; (b) $\{10^{2-n}\}$.

EXERCISES

Use $\epsilon = 0.01$ and find an N_ϵ such that $|a_n| < \epsilon$ for all $n > N_\epsilon$:

1. $\left\{\dfrac{1}{5n}\right\}$.
2. $\left\{\dfrac{1}{n+100}\right\}$.
3. $\left\{\dfrac{1}{100-n}\right\}$.
4. $\left\{\dfrac{1}{2n+80}\right\}$.
5. $\left\{\dfrac{1}{2n-20}\right\}$.
6. $\left\{\dfrac{25}{n^2}\right\}$.
7. $\left\{\dfrac{10}{n^3}\right\}$.
8. $\left\{\dfrac{1}{3^n}\right\}$.

Determine whether or not each sequence is a null sequence:

9. $\left\{\dfrac{n^2}{2n}\right\}$.

10. $\{10^{-n^2}\}$.

11. $\left\{\dfrac{5^n}{10^n}\right\}$.

12. $\left\{\dfrac{10^n}{2n}\right\}$.

13. $\{\log 10^{-n}\}$.

14. $\{\log 10^{1/n}\}$.

• • •

15. $\left\{\dfrac{\sin n}{n}\right\}$.

16. $\left\{\dfrac{\cos n}{n}\right\}$.

17. $\left\{\dfrac{1}{n \csc n}\right\}$.

• 18. $\left\{\dfrac{1}{\csc^2 n}\right\}$.

• 19. $\left\{\dfrac{1}{\log 2n}\right\}$.

• 20. $\left\{\dfrac{3}{5 \log n}\right\}$.

§ 10–4 Limit of a sequence of numbers

Any infinite sequence $\{a_n\}$ of real numbers

$$a_1, a_2, a_3, \ldots$$

has a **limit** a if the sequence $\{a_n - a\}$ is a null sequence. Thus a sequence $\{a_n\}$ has a limit a if and only if for any positive number ϵ there exists an integer N_ϵ such that $|a_n - a| < \epsilon$ for all $n > N_\epsilon$. If $\{a_n\}$ has a limit a we write

$$\lim \{a_n\} = a.$$

Any null sequence has limit 0 since $|a_n| = |a_n - 0|$ and thus the inequality $|a_n| < \epsilon$ can be written as $|a_n - 0| < \epsilon$. In other words the absolute value of the difference between a_n and 0 can be made smaller than any given positive number by selecting n sufficiently large.

Example 1. Prove that $\lim \left\{1 + \dfrac{n-1}{n}\right\} = 2$.

Consider the difference $a_n - a$;

$$a_n - a = \left(1 + \frac{n-1}{n}\right) - 2 = 1 + 1 - \frac{1}{n} - 2 = -\frac{1}{n}.$$

Then $\{a_n - a\} = \left\{-\dfrac{1}{n}\right\}$; for any given positive number ϵ, $|a_n - a| = \left|-\dfrac{1}{n}\right| = \dfrac{1}{n} < \epsilon$ if and only if $n > \dfrac{1}{\epsilon}$ and we may take $N_\epsilon = \left[\dfrac{1}{\epsilon}\right]$.

541

SEQUENCES, SERIES, AND LIMITS

Example 2. Prove that $\lim \left\{ 3 + \dfrac{(-1)^n}{n} \right\} = 3$ and illustrate geometrically the meaning for this sequence of the inequality $|a_n - a| < \epsilon$ with $\epsilon = 0.1$.

$a_n - a = \left[3 + \dfrac{(-1)^n}{n} \right] - 3 = \dfrac{(-1)^n}{n}$. For any given positive number ϵ, $|a_n - a| = \dfrac{1}{n} < \epsilon$ whenever $n > \dfrac{1}{\epsilon}$ and we may take $N_\epsilon = \left[\dfrac{1}{\epsilon} \right]$.

Thus for $\epsilon = 0.1$, $N_\epsilon = 10$.

The inequality $|a_n - a| < \epsilon$ may also be expressed in each of these forms:

$$-\epsilon < a_n - a < \epsilon;$$
$$a - \epsilon < a_n < a + \epsilon.$$

The second form expresses the statement that for sufficiently large values of n each term of the sequence a_n differs from the limit a by at most ϵ. For the given sequence we have $a = 3$, $\epsilon = 0.1$, $N_\epsilon = 10$, and $2.9 < 3 + \dfrac{(-1)^n}{n} < 3.1$ for $n > 10$. We may illustrate this fact geometrically by plotting a few points of the sequence $\{(n, a_n)\}$; that is, $\left\{ \left(n, 3 + \dfrac{(-1)^n}{n} \right) \right\}$. Then we may observe that for $n > 10$ the points are between the lines $y = 2.9$ and $y = 3.1$. The points may be approximated as: (1, 2), (2, 3.5), (3, 2.67), (4, 3.25), (5, 2.80), (6, 3.17), (7, 2.86), (8, 3.12), (9, 2.89), (10, 3.10), (11, 2.91), (12, 3.08), (13, 2.92), (14, 3.07), and so forth. For $n = 6, 7, 8, \cdots, 14$ the points are shown in Figure 10–5 where the omitted portions of the scales are indicated by the broken line. The definition of a limit implies that for $n > N_\epsilon$ the terms a_n are within ϵ of the limit.

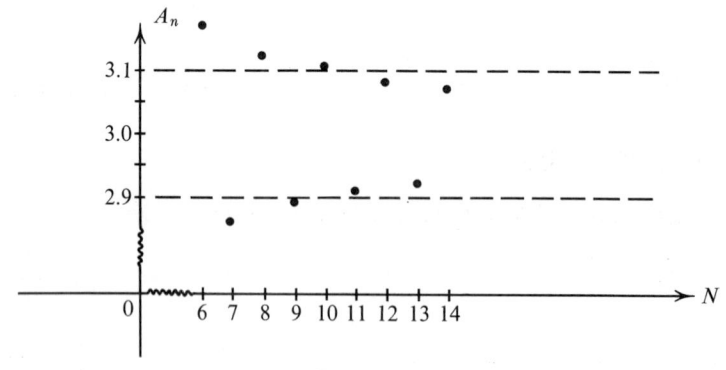

Figure 10–5

§ 10-4 LIMIT OF A SEQUENCE OF NUMBERS

Example 3. Prove that the sequence $\{(-1)^n\}$ does not have a limit.

Suppose that the sequence $\{(-1)^n\}$ had a limit a for some real number a. For $\epsilon = 1.5$ we could try $a = 0$ and find that $|(-1)^n - 0| < 1.5$ for all n. However, the sequence has a limit a if and only if $|a_n - a| < \epsilon$ for *any* given $\epsilon > 0$ and $n > N_\epsilon$. For $\epsilon = 0.5$ there cannot exist an N_ϵ for $a = 0$ or any other real number a since for any integer n we have $|(-1)^n - (-1)^{n+1}| = 2$; any two successive terms of the sequence differ by 2 and thus cannot both differ from any real number a by less than ϵ.

Example 4. Prove that the sequence $\{n\}$ does not have a limit; that is, does not have a real number a as a limit.

For any real number a the sequence $\{n - a\}$ cannot be a null sequence since a is a fixed real number and n increases without bound. Thus $|n - a|$ increases without bound and $\{n\}$ does not have a limit.

The illustrative examples show the method of proving that a sequence has or does not have a particular limit. However, these examples do not show how to find the limit. The student must study the values of successive terms of the sequence and use his ingenuity in determining the limit. The ultimate test as to whether or not the limit is correct is the determination of N_ϵ as a function of ϵ. We shall introduce some theorems on limits in the next section which will assist the student in determining limits.

Example 5. Find the limit, if there is one, for each sequence:

(a) $\left\{\dfrac{n-1}{n}\right\}$; (b) 2, 2, 2, $\cdots$.

(a) $\left\{\dfrac{n-1}{n}\right\} = \left\{1 - \dfrac{1}{n}\right\}$. Since $\left\{\dfrac{1}{n}\right\}$ is a null sequence and $\left|\left(1 - \dfrac{1}{n}\right) - 1\right| = \dfrac{1}{n}$, $\lim \left\{\dfrac{n-1}{n}\right\} = 1$.

(b) $\lim \{2\} = 2$ since $|2 - 2| = 0 < \epsilon$ for any positive number ϵ.

TEST YOURSELF

State the limit, if there is one, for each sequence:

1. $\left\{\dfrac{2n-1}{n}\right\}$.

2. $\left\{\dfrac{n^2+1}{n}\right\}$.

3. $\left\{\dfrac{2n+(-1)^n}{n}\right\}$.

4. 3, 3, 3, 3, $\cdots$.

5. $1, \dfrac{1}{2}, 1, \dfrac{1}{3}, 1, \dfrac{1}{4}, \cdots$.

6. $\dfrac{1}{2}, -\dfrac{1}{4}, \dfrac{1}{6}, -\dfrac{1}{8}, \cdots$.

SEQUENCES, SERIES, AND LIMITS

EXERCISES

State the limit, if there is one, for each sequence:

1. $\left\{\dfrac{1}{2n}\right\}$.

2. $\left\{\dfrac{n+1}{n}\right\}$.

3. $\left\{3 - \dfrac{1}{n^2}\right\}$.

4. $\{1 + (-1)^n\}$.

5. $\{\log n\}$.

6. $\left\{\dfrac{n+3}{2n}\right\}$.

7. $1, \dfrac{1}{2}, 1, \dfrac{2}{3}, 1, \dfrac{3}{4}, \cdots$.

8. $\dfrac{1}{4}, \dfrac{2}{5}, \dfrac{3}{6}, \dfrac{4}{7}, \cdots$.

• • •

9. $0.2, 0.22, 0.222, 0.2222, \cdots$.
10. $1, -1, 1, -1, \cdots$.
11. $\dfrac{4}{3}, \dfrac{2}{3}, \dfrac{1}{3}, \dfrac{1}{6}, \cdots$.
12. $\dfrac{5}{2}, \dfrac{3}{2}, \dfrac{7}{3}, \dfrac{5}{3}, \dfrac{9}{4}, \dfrac{7}{4}, \cdots$.

In Exercises 13 through 16 estimate the limit of each sequence if $\lim \{a_n\} = a$:

13. $2a_1, 2a_2, 2a_3, \cdots$.
14. $a_1 + 3, a_2 + 3, a_3 + 3, \cdots$.
15. $a - a_1, a - a_2, a - a_3, \cdots$.
16. $a_1, a_3, a_5, \cdots$.

17. Prove that the limit of the sequence $\left\{2 - \dfrac{n+1}{n}\right\}$ is 1.

18. Find N_ϵ such that when $n > N_\epsilon$ the nth and subsequent terms of the sequence $\left\{\dfrac{1}{n+1}\right\}$ will differ from 0 by less than **(a)** 10^{-3}; **(b)** ϵ.

19. Find N_ϵ such that when $n > N_\epsilon$ the nth and subsequent terms of the sequence $\left\{\dfrac{n}{n+1}\right\}$ will differ from 1 by less than 10^{-3}.

20. Find N_ϵ such that when $n > N_\epsilon$ the nth and subsequent terms of the sequence $\left\{\dfrac{2n-3}{n+1}\right\}$ will differ from 2 by less than 10^{-4}.

§ 10–5 Theorems on limits

In this section we prove some theorems on limits and use the theorems to identify the limits of sequences whose general terms are rational expressions in n in terms of the limits of known sequences. We first prove that if each term of a sequence $\{a_n\}$ is multiplied by a constant k, then the limit of the new sequence $\{ka_n\}$ is k times the limit of the given sequence.

Theorem 1. *If* $\lim \{a_n\} = a$, *then* $\lim \{ka_n\} = ka$.

PROOF: The sequence $\{ka_n\}$ has a limit ka if $|ka_n - ka| < \epsilon$ for n sufficiently large. We know that
$$|ka_n - ka| = |k(a_n - a)| = |k||a_n - a| < \epsilon$$
if $|a_n - a| < \dfrac{\epsilon}{|k|}$, where $\dfrac{\epsilon}{|k|}$ is a positive number. However, $|a_n - a|$ can be made smaller than any positive number, and thus smaller than $\dfrac{\epsilon}{|k|}$, by choosing n sufficiently large, since by hypothesis $\lim \{a_n\} = a$. Hence, $\lim \{ka_n\} = ka = k \lim \{a_n\}$.

Theorem 2. *If* $\lim \{a_n\} = a$ *and* $\lim \{b_n\} = b$, *then* $\lim \{a_n + b_n\} = a + b$ *and* $\lim \{a_n - b_n\} = a - b$.

PROOF: Since $\lim \{a_n\} = a$ and $\lim \{b_n\} = b$, there exist integers N_1 and N_2 such that for any positive number $\dfrac{\epsilon}{2}$
$$|a_n - a| < \frac{\epsilon}{2} \text{ for } n > N_1;$$
$$|b_n - b| < \frac{\epsilon}{2} \text{ for } n > N_2.$$
Then $a - \dfrac{\epsilon}{2} < a_n < a + \dfrac{\epsilon}{2}$ for $n > N_1$;
$$b - \frac{\epsilon}{2} < b_n < b + \frac{\epsilon}{2} \text{ for } n > N_2.$$
If we add these inequalities, we have for $n > N$ where N is the larger of N_1 and N_2
$$a + b - \epsilon < a_n + b_n < a + b + \epsilon;$$
$$|(a_n + b_n) - (a + b)| < \epsilon;$$
$$\lim \{a_n + b_n\} = a + b = \lim \{a_n\} + \lim \{b_n\}.$$
Then by Theorem 1 and the result which we have just proved:
$$\begin{aligned}\lim \{a_n - b_n\} &= \lim \{a_n + (-1)b_n\} \\ &= \lim \{a_n\} + \lim \{(-1)b_n\} \\ &= \lim \{a_n\} + (-1) \lim \{b_n\} \\ &= \lim \{a_n\} - \lim \{b_n\} = a - b.\end{aligned}$$

SEQUENCES, SERIES, AND LIMITS

Example 1. If $\lim \{a_n\} = 3$ and $\lim \{b_n\} = 5$, find the limit of the sequence

$$2a_1 + b_1, \quad 2a_2 + b_2, \quad 2a_3 + b_3, \quad \cdots.$$

The general term of the given sequence is $2a_n + b_n$;

$$\begin{aligned} \lim \{2a_n + b_n\} &= \lim \{2a_n\} + \lim \{b_n\}, \text{ by Theorem 2;} \\ &= 2 \lim \{a_n\} + \lim \{b_n\}, \text{ by Theorem 1;} \\ &= 2(3) + 5 = 11. \end{aligned}$$

We shall assume the following theorem. The proof may be completed using extensions of the methods used for Theorems 1 and 2; however, the details are numerous and more suitable for a future course.

Theorem 3. *If* $\lim \{a_n\} = a$ *and* $\lim \{b_n\} = b$, *then* $\lim \{a_n b_n\} = ab$ *and, if* $b \neq 0$, $\lim \left\{ \dfrac{a_n}{b_n} \right\} = \dfrac{a}{b}$.

Theorems 1, 2, and 3 enable us to find the limit of any sequence $\{a_n\}$ which has a limit if a_n is a rational function of n with constant coefficients. For example,

$$\lim \left\{ \frac{1}{n} \right\} = 0, \text{ as in § 10–3;}$$

$$\lim \left\{ \frac{1}{n^2} \right\} = 0, \text{ by Theorem 3;}$$

$$\lim \left\{ \frac{k}{n^2} \right\} = k \times 0 = 0, \text{ by Theorems 1 and 3;}$$

$$\lim \left\{ \frac{(n-1)(n+2)}{n^2} \right\} = \lim \left\{ 1 + \frac{1}{n} - \frac{2}{n^2} \right\} = 1 + 0 - 0 = 1$$

by Theorems 1 and 3; and, as developed informally in § 8–10, if $b_0 \neq 0$,

$$\lim \left\{ \frac{a_0 n^k + a_1 n^{k-1} + \cdots + a_k}{b_0 n^k + b_1 n^{k-1} + \cdots + b_k} \right\}$$

$$= \lim \left\{ \frac{a_0 + a_1 \dfrac{1}{n} + a_2 \dfrac{1}{n^2} + \cdots + a_k \dfrac{1}{n^k}}{b_0 + b_1 \dfrac{1}{n} + b_2 \dfrac{1}{n^2} + \cdots + b_k \dfrac{1}{n^k}} \right\} = \frac{a_0}{b_0};$$

$$\lim \left\{ \frac{a_0 n^k + a_1 n^{k-1} + \cdots + a_k}{b_0 n^{k+t} + b_1 n^{k+t-1} + \cdots + b_{k+t}} \right\} = 0$$

for any positive integers k and t.

§ 10-5 THEOREMS ON LIMITS

In § 10-1 we considered sequences of sums of areas of inner rectangles $A_1, A_2, A_3, \cdots$ which approached the area A of a region. We also considered sequences of sums of areas of outer rectangles which approached that same area A. We observed that $A_n \leq A \leq B_n$ for all values of n. In § 10-10 we shall use the formal definition of a limit and the following theorem to define the area A.

Theorem 4. *If $\{a_n\}$ has a limit, $\{b_n\}$ has a limit, $\lim \{b_n - a_n\} = 0$, and k is a constant such that $a_n \leq k$ and $b_n \geq k$ for all values of n, then $\lim \{a_n\} = \lim \{b_n\} = k$.*

> PROOF: Given any positive number ϵ there exists an N_ϵ such that $|b_n - a_n| < \epsilon$ for $n > N_\epsilon$ since $\lim \{b_n - a_n\} = 0$. Since $a_n \leq k$ and $b_n \geq k$, $k - a_n \geq 0$, $b_n - k \geq 0$, and the inequality $|b_n - a_n| < \epsilon$ for $n > N_\epsilon$ implies
> $$|(b_n - k) + (k - a_n)| < \epsilon,$$
> $$|b_n - k| + |k - a_n| < \epsilon,$$
> $$|b_n - k| < \epsilon \text{ whence } \lim \{b_n\} = k,$$
> $$|a_n - k| < \epsilon \text{ whence } \lim \{a_n\} = k.$$

Theorem 4 is closely related to the **domination principle** which we state as Theorem 5 and assume leaving the proof for a future course.

Theorem 5. *If $\lim \{a_n\} = k$, $\lim \{c_n\} = k$, and for all n greater than some integer N the terms of $\{b_n\}$ satisfy the inequalities $a_n \leq b_n \leq c_n$, then $\lim \{b_n\} = k$.*

Example 2. Find $\lim \left\{ \dfrac{\sin n}{n} \right\}$ if it exists.

> Notice that $-1 \leq \sin n \leq 1$ and thus $-\dfrac{1}{n} \leq \dfrac{\sin n}{n} \leq \dfrac{1}{n}$. Apply the domination principle (Theorem 5) with $\{a_n\} = \left\{-\dfrac{1}{n}\right\}$, $\{c_n\} = \left\{\dfrac{1}{n}\right\}$, and $\{b_n\} = \left\{\dfrac{\sin n}{n}\right\}$. Since $\lim \{a_n\} = 0$ and $\lim \{c_n\} = 0$, $\lim \left\{\dfrac{\sin n}{n}\right\} = 0$.

TEST YOURSELF

Find each limit if it exists:

1. $\lim \left\{ 3 - \dfrac{1}{n} + \dfrac{2}{n^2} \right\}$.

2. $\lim \left\{ \dfrac{2n - 1}{3n + 2} \right\}$.

SEQUENCES, SERIES, AND LIMITS

3. $\lim \left\{ \dfrac{n}{n^2 + 1} \right\}$.

4. $\lim \left\{ \dfrac{n^3 + 1}{n^2 + 2} \right\}$.

Find the limit, if it exists, of each sequence when $\lim \{a_n\} = a$ and $\lim \{b_n\} = b$:

5. $a_1 - 3b_1,\ a_2 - 3b_2,\ a_3 - 3b_3,\ \cdots$.

6. $\dfrac{a_1}{b_2},\ \dfrac{a_3}{b_4},\ \dfrac{a_5}{b_6},\ \cdots$.

EXERCISES

Find each limit if it exists:

1. $\lim \left\{ \dfrac{1}{2} + \dfrac{2}{n} + \dfrac{3}{n^2} \right\}$.

2. $\lim \left\{ 2 + \dfrac{3n}{n+1} \right\}$.

3. $\lim \left\{ \dfrac{3n^2}{3 + n^2} \right\}$.

4. $\lim \left\{ \left(\dfrac{n}{3n+1} \right)^2 \right\}$.

5. $\lim \left\{ \dfrac{3n^2 + 2n - 5}{n^2 + 5n + 3} \right\}$.

6. $\lim \left\{ \dfrac{(n+1)(n+2)(n+3)}{n^3} \right\}$.

7. $\lim \left\{ 2 + \dfrac{n^2 + 1}{n} \right\}$.

8. $\lim \left\{ (-1)^n \dfrac{n+1}{n} \right\}$.

• • •

9. $\lim \left\{ \dfrac{n!}{(n+1)!} \right\}$.

10. $\lim \{\sqrt{n+1} - \sqrt{n}\}$.

11. $\lim \{\tan n\}$.

12. $\lim \left\{ \dfrac{\cos n}{2n} \right\}$.

In Exercises 13 through 16 find the limit, if it exists, of each sequence when $\lim \{a_n\} = a$ and $\lim \{b_n\} = b$:

13. $a_1 + 2,\ a_2 + 2,\ a_3 + 2,\ \cdots$.
14. $b_5,\ b_{10},\ b_{15},\ \cdots$.
15. $a_1 + a_2,\ a_3 + a_4,\ a_5 + a_6,\ \cdots$.
16. $a_1^2 b_1,\ a_2^2 b_2,\ a_3^2 b_3,\ \cdots$.

17. State the limit, if it exists, of each sequence: (a) $\left\{ (-1)^n \dfrac{2}{n} \right\}$; (b) $\{(-1)^n\, 2^{-n}\}$; (c) $\{(-1)^n\, k\}$ where $k \neq 0$.

18. State the limit of the sequence $\{(-1)^n a_n\}$ if $\lim \{a_n\} = k$ where (a) $k = 0$; (b) $k \neq 0$.

19. If $\lim \{r^n\} = 0$, note that the constant $r \neq 1$ and find $\lim \left\{ \dfrac{1 - r^n}{1 - r} \right\}$.

548

20. Use the domination principle and prove that $\lim\left\{\dfrac{1}{n^p}\right\} = 0$ for any positive integer p.
- **21.** If $a_n > 0$ for all n and $\lim\{a_n\} = L$, prove that $0 \leq L$.
- **22.** State the limit if it exists: $\lim\{2^{1/n}\}$.

§ 10-6 Finite series

Arithmetic and geometric progressions are reviewed in this section to provide a basis for our study of other sequences and series. The indicated sum of the terms of a finite sequence $\{a_n\}$ is called a **finite series.** In other words, the sequence

$$a_1, a_2, a_3, \cdots, a_n$$

has associated with it the finite series

$$a_1 + a_2 + a_3 + \cdots + a_n.$$

The value S_n obtained as a result of the addition of the n terms is called the **sum of the finite series.**

Certain finite sequences and their associated series occur frequently in mathematics and hence are of special importance. One such sequence is the arithmetic sequence. An **arithmetic sequence** is a sequence in which the difference of any two consecutive terms taken in the same order is a constant. Hence an arithmetic sequence of n terms is a finite sequence of the form

$$a, a + d, a + 2d, \cdots, a + (n-1)d.$$

An arithmetic sequence is sometimes called an **arithmetic progression.** Each term a_j may be expressed by the formula

$$a_j = a + (j-1)d \qquad (1)$$

where $a = a_1$ and d is the constant difference of any two consecutive terms taken in order; $d = a_{j+1} - a_j$ for any positive integer j. This difference is often called the **common difference.** The formula (1) holds for infinite as well as finite arithmetic sequences.

Example 1. Find the twenty-third term of the arithmetic sequence 3, 7, 11, 15, $\cdots$.

$a = 3;\ a_2 = 7 = a + d = 3 + d;\ d = 4.$
$a_{23} = a + 22d = 3 + 22(4) = 91.$

SEQUENCES, SERIES, AND LIMITS

Example 2. The sixth term of an arithmetic sequence is 7; the thirty-ninth term is 73. Find a and d; then write the first four terms of the sequence.

$a_6 = a + 5d = 7$; $a_{39} = a + 38d = 73$.

Then $33d = 66$, $d = 2$, and $a = -3$. The first four terms of the sequence are $-3, -1, 1, 3$.

In Example 2 the sixth and thirty-ninth terms of an arithmetic sequence were used to determine a and d. In general, since each term a_j may be expressed in terms of a and d as in the formula (1), any desired term or terms of an arithmetic sequence are completely determined by two given terms. Thus relative to the sequences considered in § 10–2 the assumption or hypothesis that a sequence is an arithmetic sequence implies that the sequence may be continued in one and only one way.

The terms between any two given terms a_k and a_{k+t} of an arithmetic sequence are called **arithmetic means.** When $t = 2$, the single term a_{k+1} between a_k and a_{k+2} is **the arithmetic mean** (or the **average**) of the terms a_k and a_{k+2}.

Example 3. Find (a) two arithmetic means between 11 and 20; (b) the arithmetic mean of 0.5 and 5.5; (c) the arithmetic mean of p and q.

(a) Consider a_1, a_2, a_3, a_4 where $a_1 = 11$ and $a_4 = a_1 + 3d = 20$. Then $d = 3$, $a_2 = 14$, and $a_3 = 17$. The desired arithmetic means are 14 and 17.

(b) Consider a_1, a_2, a_3 where $a_1 = 0.5$ and $a_3 = a_1 + 2d = 5.5$. Then $d = 2.5$ and $a_2 = 3$.

(c) Consider a_1, a_2, a_3 where $a_1 = p$ and $a_3 = a_1 + 2d = q$. Then $2d = q - p$, and $a_2 = p + \dfrac{q-p}{2} = \dfrac{p+q}{2}$.

The finite series

$$a + (a + d) + (a + 2d) + \cdots + [a + (n - 1)d]$$

is called a **finite arithmetic series.** The sum S_n of a finite arithmetic series may be written in either one of two forms:

$$S_n = a + (a + d) + (a + 2d) + \cdots + (l - d) + l,$$
$$S_n = l + (l - d) + (l - 2d) + \cdots + (a + d) + a$$

where l denotes the nth or last term. We add the terms of these two equations and obtain

$$2S_n = (a + l) + (a + l) + (a + l) + \cdots + (a + l) = n(a + l).$$

Hence the formula for the sum S_n of a finite arithmetic series of n terms with first term a and last term l is

$$S_n = \frac{n}{2}(a + l). \qquad (2)$$

Since $l = a + (n - 1)d$, we may also write

$$S_n = \frac{n}{2}[2a + (n - 1)d]. \qquad (3)$$

If any three of the numbers a, d, n, l, and S_n for a finite arithmetic series are known, we can find the other two.

Example 4. Find the sum of the first 100 positive odd integers.

Since $a = 1$, $d = 2$, $n = 100$, we may use the formula (3):
$$S_{100} = \frac{100}{2}[2(1) + (100 - 1)(2)] = 50(2 + 198) = 10{,}000.$$

A second type of finite sequence which occurs frequently in mathematics and its applications is the geometric sequence. A **geometric sequence** is a sequence in which the quotient of any two consecutive terms taken in the same order is a constant. Hence, a geometric sequence of n terms is a finite sequence of the form

$$a, ar, ar^2, \cdots, ar^{n-1}.$$

A geometric sequence is sometimes called a **geometric progression**. Each term a_j may be expressed by the formula

$$a_j = ar^{j-1} \qquad (4)$$

where $a = a_1$ and r is the constant ratio of any two consecutive terms taken in order. This ratio is often called the **common ratio** since $\frac{a_{j+1}}{a_j} = r$ for any positive integer j. The formula (4) holds for infinite as well as finite geometric sequences.

Example 5. Find the tenth term of the geometric sequence

$$3, 6, 12, \cdots.$$

$a = 3$, $a_2 = 6 = ar = 3r$; $r = 2$.
$a_{10} = ar^9 = 3 \times 2^9 = 1536.$

The terms between any two given terms a_k and a_{k+t} of a geometric sequence are called **geometric means**. When $t = 2$ the single term a_{k+1} between a_k and a_{k+2} is **a geometric mean** (or **mean proportional**) of the two terms a_k and a_{k+2}.

SEQUENCES, SERIES, AND LIMITS

Example 6. Find **(a)** two real geometric means between 5 and 135; **(b)** a geometric mean of p and q.

(a) Consider a_1, a_2, a_3, a_4 where $a_1 = 5$ and $a_4 = ar^3 = 135$. Then $r^3 = 27$, $r = 3$, $a_2 = 15$ and $a_3 = 45$. The desired geometric means are 15 and 45.

(b) Consider a_1, a_2, a_3 where $a_1 = p$ and $a_3 = ar^2 = q$. Then $r^2 = \frac{q}{p}$, r equals either $\sqrt{\frac{q}{p}}$ or $-\sqrt{\frac{q}{p}}$, and a_2 equals either $\sqrt{pq}$ or $-\sqrt{pq}$. Each of these two possible values of a_2 is a geometric mean of p and q.

The finite series

$$a + ar + ar^2 + ar^3 + \cdots + ar^{n-1}$$

is called a **finite geometric series**. If $r \neq 1$, the sum S_n of a geometric series of n terms may be derived as follows:

$$\begin{aligned} S_n &= a + ar + ar^2 + ar^3 + \cdots + ar^{n-1} \\ rS_n &= \quad\quad ar + ar^2 + ar^3 + ar^4 + \cdots + ar^n \\ S_n - rS_n &= a - ar^n \\ (1-r)S_n &= a(1 - r^n) \end{aligned}$$

$$S_n = \frac{a(1 - r^n)}{1 - r}, \quad r \neq 1. \tag{5}$$

When $r > 1$, the formula (5) is written in the form $S_n = \frac{a(r^n - 1)}{r - 1}$. If we define the last term l, then $l = ar^{n-1}$ and we may write

$$S_n = \frac{a - rl}{1 - r}, \quad r \neq 1. \tag{6}$$

When $r = 1$, $S_n = na$. If any three of the numbers a, r, n, l, and S_n for a finite geometric series are known, we can find the other two.

Example 7. The first two terms of a sequence of eight terms are 2 and 6 respectively. **(a)** Assume that the sequence is an arithmetic sequence and find the last term and the sum of the associated series. **(b)** Assume that the sequence is a geometric sequence and find the last term and the sum of the associated series.

(a) For an arithmetic sequence, $a = 2$ and $d = 4$. Since $n = 8$, the last term is $l = 2 + (8 - 1)(4) = 30$; from the formula (2) we have

$$S_8 = \frac{8}{2}(2 + 30) = 128.$$

(b) For a geometric sequence, $a = 2$ and $r = 3$. Since $n = 8$, the last term is $l = 2(3)^{8-1} = 4374$; from the formula (6) we have

$$S_8 = \frac{2 - (3)(4374)}{1 - 3} = 6560.$$

Example 8. Find the sum of the first twelve terms of the geometric series $2 + 1 + \frac{1}{2} + \cdots$.

Since $a = 2$, $r = \frac{1}{2}$, and $n = 12$, we may use the formula (5):

$$S_{12} = \frac{2\left[1 - \left(\frac{1}{2}\right)^{12}\right]}{1 - \frac{1}{2}} = 4\left(1 - \frac{1}{4096}\right) = \frac{4095}{1024}.$$

TEST YOURSELF

1. Find the common difference and the next four terms of the arithmetic sequence 2, 5, 8, 11, $\cdots$.

2. Find the fortieth term of the sequence in Exercise 1.

3. What term of the arithmetic sequence $-4, -1, 2, \cdots$ is 89?

4. Find the sum of the arithmetic series $4 + 8 + 12 + \cdots + 276$.

5. Find the common ratio and the next four terms of the sequence $\sqrt{a}, a, a\sqrt{a}, \cdots$.

6. Find the thirteenth term of the sequence in Exercise 5.

7. Find the sum of the first seven terms of the series

$$4 - 12 + 36 - \cdots.$$

8. Find the sum of the geometric series $6 + 2 + \frac{2}{3} + \cdots + \frac{2}{243}$.

EXERCISES

A

Determine whether the given sequence is arithmetic or geometric, and find the stated term:

1. Fourteenth term of 1, 6, 11, 16, $\cdots$.

2. Sixth term of 81, 27, 9, $\cdots$.

SEQUENCES, SERIES, AND LIMITS

3. Seventh term of $\frac{1}{2}, 1, 2, 4, \cdots$.

4. Twenty-fifth term of $b, c, 2c - b, 3c - 2b, \cdots$.

Find the sum of the first ten terms of the series associated with the sequence in:

5. Exercise 1.   6. Exercise 2.

Find:

7. Five arithmetic means between 10 and 28.
8. Eight arithmetic means between $\frac{1}{2}$ and $18\frac{1}{2}$.
9. The arithmetic mean of $(a^2 + 2ab + b^2)$ and $(a^2 - b^2)$.
10. Two real geometric means between 8 and 64.
11. Three real geometric means between 2 and 162.
12. A geometric mean of $\sqrt{2}$ and $\sqrt{18}$.

In Exercises 13 through 15 find the sum of each finite arithmetic series:

13. $3 + \cdots + 6; n = 8$.
14. $a = 1, d = \frac{1}{2}, n = 12$.
15. $7 + 13 + 19 + \cdots + 91$.

● ● ●

16. The seventh term of an arithmetic sequence is 21; the twenty-ninth term is 87. Find a and d; then write the first four terms of the sequence.

17. In the sequence $10, 5, 0, -5, \cdots$ which term is -75?

18. The seventh term of a geometric sequence is 64; the eleventh term is 1024. Find a and r; then write the first four terms of the sequence.

19. In the sequence $16, 8, 4, 2, \cdots$ which term is $\frac{1}{256}$?

20. The common ratio of a geometric sequence is $\sqrt{3}$; the ninth term is 243. Find the first term.

21. Find the sum of the integers which are divisible by 6 and lie between 1 and 500.

22. Find three numbers in arithmetic progression such that their sum is 18 and the product of the first and the third is 14 greater than the second.

23. For an arithmetic sequence with $a_1 = a$ and $a_2 = d$ find a_{n+2} and a_{2n}.

24. Find the term a_{n-3} for the sequence $2, 7, 12, 17, \cdots$.

25. If $\{a_n\}$ is an arithmetic sequence, prove that $a_1, a_3, a_5, \cdots$ is an arithmetic sequence.

§ 10-6 FINITE SERIES

26. A bottle containing antifreeze is emptied of one-half its contents and then filled with water. Half of this mixture is then drawn off and the bottle refilled with water. This is done six times. What part of the contents of the bottle is then water?

27. It is shown in geometry that the altitude to the hypotenuse of a right triangle is the geometric mean between the segments of the hypotenuse. In triangle ABC, angle C is a right angle and $\overline{CD}$ is the altitude to $\overline{AB}$. (a) If $\overline{AD} = 10$ and $\overline{BD} = 40$, find $\overline{CD}$. (b) In the right triangle $\overline{AC}$ is the geometric mean of $\overline{AD}$ and $\overline{AB}$. Find $\overline{AC}$ if $\overline{AD} = 5$ and $\overline{AB} = 11$.

B

Determine whether the given sequence is arithmetic or geometric and find the stated term:

1. Tenth term of $4, -3, -10, -17, \cdots$.
2. Tenth term of $3, -6, 12, \cdots$.
3. Eighth term of $0.8, 1.1, 1.4, 1.7, \cdots$.
4. Ninth term of $\frac{2}{3}, x, \frac{3}{2}x^2, \cdots$.

Find the sum of the first ten terms of the series associated with the sequence in:

5. Exercise 1.   6. Exercise 2.

Find:

7. Three arithmetic means between $\frac{2}{b}$ and $\frac{4}{b}$.
8. The arithmetic mean of 8 and 20.
9. Four real geometric means between 9 and $\frac{1}{27}$.
10. The positive geometric mean of $\frac{1}{2}$ and 512.
11. A geometric mean of a and ab^2.

In Exercises 12 through 14 find the sum of each finite geometric series:

12. $a = 2, r = -3, n = 5$.
13. $a = 1, r = \frac{1}{2}, l = \frac{1}{1024}$.
14. $81 + \cdots + \frac{1}{27}; n = 8$.

555

SEQUENCES, SERIES, AND LIMITS

• • •

15. The common difference of an arithmetic sequence is 2; the twenty-fifth term is 55. Find the first term.

16. Find the common difference of an arithmetic sequence if the first term is -4 and the sixteenth term is 71. Find the fortieth term.

17. Find the sum of the first 100 positive even integers.

18. How many terms of the arithmetic series $6 + 4 + 2 + \cdots$ must be taken to have a sum of -60?

19. Find the common ratio of a geometric sequence if the first term is 4 and the sixth term is $-\frac{1}{8}$.

20. How many terms of the geometric series $1 + 2 + 4 + \cdots$ must be taken to have a sum of 63?

21. The sum of three numbers in arithmetic progression is 21, and the sum of their squares is 179. Find the numbers.

22. Prove that the sum of the first n positive odd integers is n^2.

23. An object falling freely in a vacuum falls approximately 16 feet the first second, 48 feet the next second, 80 feet the next, and so on. How far will it fall in 10 seconds? In 20 seconds? In 30 seconds?

24. If $\overrightarrow{PA}$ is tangent to a circle at A and $\overrightarrow{PB}$ cuts the circle at B and C, then $\overline{PA}$ is the geometric mean of $\overline{PB}$ and $\overline{PC}$. **(a)** Find $\overline{PA}$ if $\overline{PB} = 7$ and $\overline{PC} = 12$. **(b)** Find $\overline{PB}$ if $\overline{PA} = 8$ and $\overline{PC} = 16$.

• **25.** Prove that the positive geometric mean of two positive numbers is less than or equal to their arithmetic mean.

§ 10-7 Infinite series

The indicated sum of the terms of an infinite sequence $\{a_n\}$ is called an **infinite series.** In other words, the sequence

$$a_1, a_2, a_3, \ldots, a_n, \ldots$$

has associated with it the infinite series

$$a_1 + a_2 + a_3 + \cdots + a_n + \cdots.$$

The sum S_n of the first n terms of the infinite series is called its **nth partial sum.** Thus

$$S_1 = a_1,$$
$$S_2 = a_1 + a_2,$$
$$S_3 = a_1 + a_2 + a_3,$$
$$\cdots \qquad \cdots$$
$$S_n = a_1 + a_2 + a_3 + \cdots + a_n,$$
$$\cdots \qquad \cdots$$

§ 10-7 INFINITE SERIES

The **sum S of an infinite series** is defined as the limit of the sequence of partial sums, if the limit exists. Thus S, where $S = a_1 + a_2 + a_3 + \cdots + a_n + \cdots$, is defined by $S = \lim \{S_n\}$, if the limit exists. If $\lim \{S_n\}$ does not exist, then S is not defined for the infinite series. When a sum is defined for an infinite series, we sometimes say that the series is **convergent**; when the sum is not defined for an infinite series, we sometimes say that the series is **divergent**.

Example 1. Find the sum, if it exists, of the infinite series

$$\frac{1}{6} + \frac{1}{12} + \frac{1}{20} + \frac{1}{30} + \cdots + \frac{1}{(n+1)(n+2)} + \cdots.$$

The sequence of partial sums may be computed directly. The following approach illustrates a special procedure which simplifies the calculations.

The given series may be written in the form

$$\left(\frac{1}{2} - \frac{1}{3}\right) + \left(\frac{1}{3} - \frac{1}{4}\right) + \left(\frac{1}{4} - \frac{1}{5}\right) + \left(\frac{1}{5} - \frac{1}{6}\right) + \cdots$$
$$+ \left(\frac{1}{n+1} - \frac{1}{n+2}\right) + \cdots.$$

The partial sums are

$$S_1 = \frac{1}{2} - \frac{1}{3},$$

$$S_2 = \left(\frac{1}{2} - \frac{1}{3}\right) + \left(\frac{1}{3} - \frac{1}{4}\right) = \frac{1}{2} - \frac{1}{4},$$

$$S_3 = \left(\frac{1}{2} - \frac{1}{4}\right) + \left(\frac{1}{4} - \frac{1}{5}\right) = \frac{1}{2} - \frac{1}{5},$$

$$S_4 = \left(\frac{1}{2} - \frac{1}{5}\right) + \left(\frac{1}{5} - \frac{1}{6}\right) = \frac{1}{2} - \frac{1}{6},$$

$\cdots \qquad \cdots$

$$S_n = \left(\frac{1}{2} - \frac{1}{n+1}\right) + \left(\frac{1}{n+1} - \frac{1}{n+2}\right) = \frac{1}{2} - \frac{1}{n+2},$$

$\cdots \qquad \cdots.$

Thus $\lim \{S_n\} = \lim \left\{\frac{1}{2} - \frac{1}{n+2}\right\} = \lim \left\{\frac{1}{2}\right\} - \lim \left\{\frac{1}{n+2}\right\} = \frac{1}{2}$;

hence the series is convergent with sum S equal to $\frac{1}{2}$.

The procedure used in Example 1 to express each fraction of the form

SEQUENCES, SERIES, AND LIMITS

$\dfrac{1}{(n+1)(n+2)}$ as an algebraic sum $\dfrac{1}{n+1} - \dfrac{1}{n+2}$ is a special case of a general procedure for expressing *proper* fractions as algebraic sums of fractions, called **partial fractions,** with denominators of lower degree than the given fraction. The partial fractions used in Example 1 illustrate the fact that any given fraction

$$\frac{ax+b}{(x-r)(x-s)}$$

where the coefficients are real numbers, $r \neq s$, and $r \neq -\dfrac{b}{a} \neq s$ if $a \neq 0$, may be expressed in the form

$$\frac{A}{x-r} + \frac{B}{x-s}$$

where A and B are real numbers. The general procedure for doing this may be illustrated by considering the fractions used in Example 1.

$$\frac{1}{(n+1)(n+2)} = \frac{A}{n+1} + \frac{B}{n+2}$$
$$1 = A(n+2) + B(n+1)$$
$$1 = (A+B)n + (2A+B)$$

This equation must hold for all values of n for which the expression $\dfrac{1}{(n+1)(n+2)}$ is defined. If $n = 0$, then $1 = 2A + B$; and under this condition on A and B, if $n \neq 0$, then the given equation becomes $0 = A + B$. Note that this system of equations in A and B may also be obtained by equating the constant terms of the two members of the given equation and equating the coefficients of n in the two members. The system

$$\begin{cases} 2A + B = 1 \\ A + B = 0 \end{cases}$$

may be solved to obtain $A = 1$, $B = -1$. Therefore as in Example 1

$$\frac{1}{(n+1)(n+2)} = \frac{1}{n+1} + \frac{-1}{n+2}.$$

The sequence of partial sums for any arithmetic series

$$a + (a+d) + (a+2d) + (a+3d) + \cdots$$

is

$$a, \quad 2a+d, \quad 3a+3d, \quad 4a+6d, \quad \cdots, \quad na + \frac{n(n-1)}{2}d, \quad \cdots.$$

Thus except in the trivial case in which all terms are zero (that is, $a = d = 0$) the arithmetic series cannot converge.

§ 10-7 INFINITE SERIES

One of the most useful infinite series is the infinite geometric series

$$a + ar + ar^2 + ar^3 + \cdots + ar^{n-1} + \cdots.$$

The nth partial sum of the infinite geometric series is

$$S_n = a + ar + ar^2 + ar^3 + \cdots + ar^{n-1};$$

by formula (5) we have

$$S_n = \frac{a(1-r^n)}{1-r}, \text{ if } r \neq 1.$$

The sum S of the infinite geometric series is given by the definition:

$$S = \lim \{S_n\} = \lim \left\{ \frac{a(1-r^n)}{1-r} \right\}.$$

By Theorem 3 of § 10–5 we have

$$S = \lim \left\{ \frac{a}{1-r} \right\} \times \lim \{1-r^n\} = \frac{a}{1-r} \times \lim \{1-r^n\}.$$

If $|r| > 1$, then $\lim \{1 - r^n\}$ does not exist since the absolute values of successive terms increase without bound; then since $\lim \{S_n\}$ does not exist, S does not exist. If $|r| < 1$, then $\lim \{1 - r^n\} = 1$; $\lim \{S_n\} = S = 1 \times \frac{a}{1-r} = \frac{a}{1-r}$.

If $r = 1$, the infinite geometric series is of the form

$$a + a + a + a + \cdots;$$

the sequence $\{S_n\}$ of partial sums equals $\{na\}$; and $\lim \{na\}$ does not exist for $a \neq 0$ since the absolute values of successive terms increase without bound. If $r = -1$, the infinite geometric series is of the form

$$a - a + a - a + a - \cdots;$$

the sequence of partial sums is $a, 0, a, 0, a, \cdots$; for $a \neq 0$ the sequence $\{S_n\}$ does not have a limit and thus S does not exist.

We have proved that the sum S of an infinite geometric series with $a \neq 0$ is defined if and only if $|r| < 1$ and is given by the formula

$$S_n = \frac{a}{1-r}. \tag{7}$$

Observe that the limit of $\{S_n\}$ for an infinite geometric series which converges is never obtained as the sum of a finite number of terms of the sequence.

SEQUENCES, SERIES, AND LIMITS

Example 2. Find the sum of the infinite geometric series

$$3 + 1 + \frac{1}{3} + \frac{1}{9} + \cdots.$$

Since $a = 3$, $r = \frac{1}{3}$, and $|r| < 1$; the series is convergent and by the formula (7) we have $S = \dfrac{3}{1 - \frac{1}{3}} = \dfrac{9}{2}.$

Example 3. Find the rational number represented by the repeating infinite decimal $0.\overline{72}$.

We may write $0.\overline{72}$ as the infinite geometric series

$$0.72 + 0.0072 + 0.000072 + \cdots.$$

For this series $r = 10^{-2}$, and the series is convergent. Since $a = 0.72$, we have from the formula (7)

$$S = \frac{0.72}{1 - 10^{-2}} = \frac{0.72}{0.99} = \frac{8}{11}.$$

One of the most important types of infinite series is the power series. A **power series** is an infinite series of the form

$$a_0 + a_1 x + a_2 x^2 + \cdots + a_n x^n + \cdots$$

where the a_i's are constants. Such series are studied in calculus and for given values of the a_i's may be shown to be convergent for specified sets of values of x. The importance of power series lies in the fact that certain basic functions such as the trigonometric, exponential, and logarithmic functions, as well as others, may be represented by them. Then the power series may be used to evaluate these functions for given values of x for which the series is convergent. We shall state without deriving them the power series representations of some familiar functions and indicate for what values of x the series converge:

$$e^x = 1 + x + \frac{x^2}{2!} + \frac{x^3}{3!} + \cdots \text{ for all complex values of } x; \tag{8}$$

$$\sin x = x - \frac{x^3}{3!} + \frac{x^5}{5!} - \frac{x^7}{7!} + \cdots \text{ for all real values of } x; \tag{9}$$

$$\cos x = 1 - \frac{x^2}{2!} + \frac{x^4}{4!} - \frac{x^6}{6!} + \cdots \text{ for all real values of } x; \tag{10}$$

§ 10-7 INFINITE SERIES

$$\ln \frac{1+x}{1-x} = 2\left(x + \frac{x^3}{3} + \frac{x^5}{5} + \frac{x^7}{7} + \cdots\right) \text{ for } |x| < 1; \tag{11}$$

$$\arctan x = x - \frac{x^3}{3} + \frac{x^5}{5} - \frac{x^7}{7} + \cdots \text{ for } |x| \leq 1. \tag{12}$$

Example 4. Find an approximation for the irrational number e by using the first seven terms of the power series (8) which represents e^x.

Since the power series (8) converges for all complex values of x, we may let $x = 1$. Then

$$e \approx 1 + 1 + \frac{1}{2!} + \frac{1}{3!} + \frac{1}{4!} + \frac{1}{5!} + \frac{1}{6!}$$

$$\approx 1 + 1 + 0.5 + 0.167 + 0.042 + 0.008 + 0.001 \approx 2.718.$$

Example 5. Prove: $e^{i\theta} = \cos \theta + i \sin \theta$.

We substitute $i\theta$ for x in the formula (8) and obtain

$$e^{i\theta} = 1 + i\theta + \frac{i^2\theta^2}{2!} + \frac{i^3\theta^3}{3!} + \frac{i^4\theta^4}{4!} + \cdots.$$

Since $i^2 = -1$, $i^3 = -i$, and $i^4 = 1$, we may write

$$e^{i\theta} = 1 + i\theta - \frac{\theta^2}{2!} - i\frac{\theta^3}{3!} + \frac{\theta^4}{4!} + i\frac{\theta^5}{5!} - \cdots$$

$$= \left(1 - \frac{\theta^2}{2!} + \frac{\theta^4}{4!} - \cdots\right) + i\left(\theta - \frac{\theta^3}{3!} + \frac{\theta^5}{5!} - \cdots\right)$$

$$= \cos \theta + i \sin \theta, \text{ by formulas (9) and (10).}$$

TEST YOURSELF

Find the sum, if it exists, of each infinite geometric series:

1. $4 + 3 + 2\frac{1}{4} + \cdots$.
2. $5^3 + 5^3(0.1) + 5^3(0.1)^2 + \cdots$.

In Exercises 3 and 4 find the rational number represented by each repeating infinite decimal:

3. $0.\overline{12}$.
4. $2.\overline{3}$.

5. Find the first four partial sums of the series

$$1 + \frac{1}{2} + \frac{1}{3} + \frac{1}{4} + \cdots.$$

6. Find a series whose partial sums are 1, 9, 36, 100, $\cdots$.

7. Find the sum, if it exists, of the infinite series
$$\left(1 - \frac{1}{3}\right) + \left(\frac{1}{3} - \frac{1}{5}\right) + \left(\frac{1}{5} - \frac{1}{7}\right) + \cdots.$$

8. Approximate $\sqrt{e}$ by using four terms of the formula (8).

EXERCISES

Find the sum, if it exists, of each infinite geometric series:

1. $\dfrac{1}{3} + \dfrac{1}{2} + \dfrac{3}{4} + \cdots.$

2. $100 + 50 + 25 + \cdots.$

3. $\dfrac{1}{8} + \dfrac{1}{4} + \dfrac{1}{2} + \cdots.$

4. $12 + 4 + \dfrac{4}{3} + \cdots.$

5. $3 - 1 + \dfrac{1}{3} - \dfrac{1}{9} + \cdots.$

6. $1 + 1 + 1 + \cdots.$

In Exercises 7 through 12 find the rational number represented by each repeating infinite decimal:

7. $0.\overline{6}.$

8. $0.\overline{45}.$

9. $0.\overline{142857}.$

10. $0.04\overline{16}.$

11. $1.3\overline{8}.$

12. $0.03\overline{27}.$

13. Find the sequence of partial sums of the series
$$1 + 3 + 5 + 7 + \cdots.$$

14. Find the first four terms of a series whose partial sums are 3, 11, 25, 49,....

• • •

15. In a certain infinite geometric series the common ratio is $\dfrac{1}{5}$. Find the first term if the sum is 35.

16. Approximate $\dfrac{1}{e}$ by using eight terms of the formula (8).

17. Approximate ln 3 by using four terms of the formula (11) with $x = \dfrac{1}{2}$.

18. State the first four terms for the formula (9) for sin 20°. Do not evaluate.

19. Describe how π may be approximated using the formula (12). Do not evaluate since the power series (12) is a rather slowly convergent series; that is, many terms are needed to obtain even a few significant digits for π.

20. Use the formulas (9) and (10) to prove that **(a)** $\sin(-x) = -\sin x$; **(b)** $\cos(-x) = \cos x$.

21. Assume that formulas (9) and (10) hold for all complex values of x and prove that **(a)** $\sin i\theta = i\dfrac{e^\theta - e^{-\theta}}{2}$; **(b)** $\cos i\theta = \dfrac{e^\theta + e^{-\theta}}{2}$.

22. Find the first four terms of an infinite geometric series if the third term is 8 and the sum is 54.

23. A ball having a coefficient of elasticity of 0.7, when dropped upon a smooth surface, theoretically will rebound to a height which is seven-tenths of the height from which it was dropped. (Note that the ball is to be dropped, not thrown.) Consider such a ball dropped from a height of 10 feet. How far does the ball theoretically travel before coming to rest?

24. The circles $A, B, C, \cdots$ are tangent internally at P. The diameter of B is $\dfrac{1}{2}$ that of A; the diameter of C is $\dfrac{1}{2}$ that of B, and so on. If the diameter of A is 8 inches and the number of circles is infinite, find the sum of the circumferences of all the circles.

25. Find the sum of the areas of the circles described in Exercise 24 if the diameter of A is 6 inches.

§ 10-8 The binomial series

In § 2-4 we derived the binomial theorem which enabled us to express $(a + b)^n$ for any positive integer n as a sum of $(n + 1)$ terms. In this section we extend the binomial theorem to obtain an infinite series representing $(a + b)^n$ for real numbers n.

Consider the last three terms of $(a + b)^n$ where n is a positive integer:

$$_nC_{n-2}a^2b^{n-2} = \frac{n(n-1)(n-2)\cdots 3}{1(2)(3)\cdots(n-2)} a^2 b^{n-2};$$

$$_nC_{n-1}a\,b^{n-1} = \frac{n(n-1)(n-2)\cdots 2}{1(2)(3)\cdots(n-1)} a\,b^{n-1};$$

$$_nC_n b^n = \frac{n(n-1)(n-2)\cdots 1}{1(2)(3)\cdots(n)} a^0 b^n.$$

If we continued the pattern, we would have

$$\frac{n(n-1)(n-2)\cdots(1)(0)}{1(2)(3)\cdots(n)(n+1)} a^{-1} b^{n+1}.$$

Similarly the numerator of each later term has a factor 0. Thus each additional term would be 0. However, if n is not a positive integer the factor 0 does not arise in the numerator of the $(n + 2)$th term and later

SEQUENCES, SERIES, AND LIMITS

terms; the pattern may be continued indefinitely; and we get an infinite series. For all real values of n, where n is not a positive integer, the pattern of the binomial theorem applied to $(a + b)^n$ yields an infinite series called the **binomial series**. The usefulness of the binomial series depends upon whether or not it is convergent. In advanced studies of infinite series it can be shown that the binomial series for $(a + b)^n$ can be written as $a^n \left(1 + \dfrac{b}{a}\right)^n$ and is convergent if $|a| > |b|$. If $a = 1$ and $b = x$, the binomial series is a power series (§ 10–7).

Example 1. Find the first four terms in the expansion of $(1 + x)^{0.5}$.

$$(1 + x)^{0.5} = 1^{0.5} + (0.5)(1)^{-0.5}x + \frac{(0.5)(-0.5)}{(1)(2)}(1)^{-1.5}x^2$$

$$+ \frac{(0.5)(-0.5)(-1.5)}{(1)(2)(3)}(1)^{-2.5}x^3 + \cdots$$

$$= 1 + 0.5x - 0.125x^2 + 0.0625x^3 - \cdots$$

$$= 1 + \frac{x}{2} - \frac{x^2}{8} + \frac{x^3}{16} - \cdots.$$

Example 2. Find the first five terms of $(3 + x)^{-2}$.

$$(3 + x)^{-2} = 3^{-2} + (-2)3^{-3}x + \frac{(-2)(-3)}{(1)(2)}3^{-4}x^2$$

$$+ \frac{(-2)(-3)(-4)}{(1)(2)(3)}3^{-5}x^3 + \frac{(-2)(-3)(-4)(-5)}{(1)(2)(3)(4)}3^{-6}x^4 + \cdots$$

$$= \frac{1}{9} - \frac{2x}{27} + \frac{x^2}{27} - \frac{4x^3}{243} + \frac{5x^4}{729} - \cdots.$$

Example 3. Find $\sqrt[5]{29}$ to two decimal places.

$$\sqrt[5]{29} = \sqrt[5]{32 - 3} = \sqrt[5]{32\left(1 - \frac{3}{32}\right)} = 2\left(1 - \frac{3}{32}\right)^{\frac{1}{5}}.$$

$$2\left(1 - \frac{3}{32}\right)^{\frac{1}{5}} = 2\left[1^{\frac{1}{5}} + \frac{1}{5} \times 1^{-\frac{4}{5}}\left(-\frac{3}{32}\right) + \right.$$

$$\left. \frac{\frac{1}{5}\left(-\frac{4}{5}\right)}{(1)(2)}1^{-\frac{9}{5}}\left(-\frac{3}{32}\right)^2 + \cdots\right]$$

$$= 2\left[1 - \frac{3}{160} - \frac{72}{100 \times (32)^2} - \cdots\right]$$

§ 10-8 THE BINOMIAL SERIES

$$= 2(1 - 0.01875 - 0.000703125 - \cdots)$$
$$\approx 2(1 - 0.019) = 2(0.981) = 1.962$$
$$\approx 1.96.$$

To estimate a root such as $\sqrt[n]{b}$ using the binomial series: write $\sqrt[n]{b}$ in the form $\sqrt[n]{s^n + k}$ where s^n is approximately equal to b, factor as in Example 3, and expand.

Consider the sequence $\left\{\left(1 + \dfrac{1}{n}\right)^n\right\}$. The binomial expansion of the general term of this sequence may be expressed in the form

$$1 + n\left(\frac{1}{n}\right) + \frac{n(n-1)}{2!}\left(\frac{1}{n}\right)^2 + \frac{n(n-1)(n-2)}{3!}\left(\frac{1}{n}\right)^3 + \cdots.$$

If we simplify each term, we obtain

$$\left(1 + \frac{1}{n}\right)^n = 1 + 1 + \frac{1}{2!}\left(1 - \frac{1}{n}\right) + \frac{1}{3!}\left(1 - \frac{1}{n}\right)\left(1 - \frac{2}{n}\right) + \cdots.$$

Then by the theorems on limits of sequences:

$$\lim\left\{\left(1 + \frac{1}{n}\right)^n\right\} = 1 + 1 + \frac{1}{2!} + \frac{1}{3!} + \cdots.$$

By the formula (8) of § 10–7 this infinite series represents the irrational number e. Thus we may define e as $\lim\left\{\left(1 + \dfrac{1}{n}\right)^n\right\}$.

TEST YOURSELF

1. Find the first four terms of $(1 - x)^{\frac{3}{2}}$.
2. Find the first four terms of $(2 + x)^{-3}$.
3. Find $\sqrt[3]{127}$ correct to two decimal places.

EXERCISES

A

In Exercises 1 through 15 find the first four terms of the binomial series for each expression:

1. $(1 + x)^{-1}$.
2. $(1 - x)^{-1}$.
3. $(1 + x)^{-2}$.
4. $(1 - x)^{-2}$.
5. $(1 - x^3)^{-1}$.
6. $(1 - t)^{-3}$.
7. $(1 - x)^{\frac{1}{2}}$.
8. $(1 - x)^{\frac{1}{3}}$.
9. $(1 + x)^{\frac{1}{4}}$.
10. $(x + 2)^{\frac{1}{2}}$.

SEQUENCES, SERIES, AND LIMITS

• • •

11. $(1 - 2x)^{\frac{1}{2}}$.
12. $(b + a)^{\frac{1}{3}}$.
13. $(1 + x^2)^{-\frac{1}{2}}$.
14. $(1 - 9y^3)^{-\frac{1}{3}}$.
15. $(m^{-\frac{1}{2}} - n^{-\frac{1}{2}})^{-\frac{1}{2}}$.
• 16. Find $\lim \left\{ \left(1 - \dfrac{1}{n^2}\right)^n \right\}$.

B

Use a binomial series to find each root correct to two decimal places:

1. $\sqrt{10}$.
2. $\sqrt[3]{9}$.
3. $\sqrt[3]{65}$.
4. $\sqrt[3]{26}$.
5. $\sqrt[4]{15}$.
6. $\sqrt[4]{79}$.

• • •

7. $\sqrt[5]{34}$.
8. $\sqrt[5]{2}$.
9. $\sqrt[5]{245}$.
10. $\sqrt[7]{3}$.
11. $\sqrt{1\frac{1}{5}}$.
12. $\sqrt{4\frac{1}{6}}$.
13. $\sqrt{25.1}$.
14. $\sqrt[3]{1.75}$.
15. $\sqrt[3]{0.123}$.

§ 10-9 Mathematical induction

In this section we shall examine a method of proof called mathematical induction. In the physical sciences if an experimenter makes a large number of observations of some physical phenomena he may make inferences about the phenomena. In such a case he is using inductive reasoning, that is, he is making an educated guess and his "proofs" are inductive in nature. However, the term mathematical induction does not involve inductive reasoning at all. In fact this method of proof is a deductive method of proof which is based upon the following postulate.

Postulate of Finite Induction: *If a set S of natural numbers (i) contains the natural number 1 and (ii) contains the natural number $(k + 1)$ whenever it contains the natural number k, then S is the set of all natural numbers.*

The proof by the method of mathematical induction that a proposition (statement, expression, $\cdots$), say $P(n)$, is true for all natural numbers n involves two steps. We must show that
  (i) $P(1)$ is true;
  (ii) if $P(k)$ is true, then $P(k + 1)$ is true, where k is any natural number.
Then by the Postulate of Finite Induction $P(n)$ is true for all natural numbers; that is, the set S of natural numbers for which $P(n)$ is true is the set of all natural numbers.

Example 1. Prove that
$$1^2 + 2^2 + 3^2 + \cdots + n^2 = \frac{n(n + 1)(2n + 1)}{6}.$$

§ 10-9 MATHEMATICAL INDUCTION

In order to prove this formula for the sum of the squares of the first n natural numbers, we must show that
(i) the formula is true when $n = 1$;
$$1^2 = \frac{1(1 + 1)(2 + 1)}{6} = \frac{(1)(2)(3)}{6} = 1;$$
(ii) if the formula is true for $n = k$, that is, if
$$1^2 + 2^2 + 3^2 + \cdots + k^2 = \frac{k(k + 1)(2k + 1)}{6},$$
then the formula is true for $n = k + 1$. Consider the addition of $(k + 1)^2$ to each member of the formula for $n = k$:
$$1^2 + 2^2 + 3^2 + \cdots + k^2 + (k + 1)^2$$
$$= \frac{k(k + 1)(2k + 1)}{6} + (k + 1)^2$$
$$= \frac{k(k + 1)(2k + 1) + 6(k + 1)^2}{6}$$
$$= \frac{(k + 1)(2k^2 + k + 6k + 6)}{6}$$
$$= \frac{(k + 1)(2k^2 + 7k + 6)}{6}$$
$$= \frac{(k + 1)(k + 2)(2k + 3)}{6}$$
$$= \frac{(k + 1)[(k + 1) + 1][2(k + 1) + 1]}{6}$$
which is of the desired form. Hence by the method of mathematical induction the formula is true for all natural numbers n.

Example 2. Prove that $(n^3 + 2n)$ is a multiple of 3 for all natural numbers n.
(i) When $n = 1$, $1^3 + 2(1) = 3$, a multiple of 3.
(ii) If for $n = k$ we have $k^3 + 2k = 3r$ for some integer r, then for $n = k + 1$ we have
$$(k + 1)^3 + 2(k + 1) = k^3 + 3k^2 + 3k + 1 + 2k + 2$$
$$= (k^3 + 2k) + (3k^2 + 3k + 3)$$
$$= 3r + 3(k^2 + k + 1)$$
$$= 3[r + (k^2 + k + 1)]$$
which is a multiple of 3 since r and k are integers. Hence, $(n^3 + 2n)$ is a multiple of 3 for all natural numbers n by the method of mathematical induction.

567

SEQUENCES, SERIES, AND LIMITS

TEST YOURSELF

Prove by mathematical induction for all natural numbers n:

1. $1 + 2 + 3 + \cdots + n = \dfrac{n(n + 1)}{2}.$

2. $1(2) + 2(3) + 3(4) + \cdots n(n + 1) = \dfrac{n(n + 1)(n + 2)}{3}.$

3. $\dfrac{1}{1(2)} + \dfrac{1}{2(3)} + \dfrac{1}{3(4)} + \cdots + \dfrac{1}{n(n + 1)} = \dfrac{n}{n + 1}.$

EXERCISES

1. What is the error in the following "proof" that
$$1 + 3 + 5 + \cdots + (2n - 1) = n^2 + 4?$$
Assume $1 + 3 + 5 + \cdots + (2k - 1) = k^2 + 4$;
then $1 + 3 + 5 + \cdots + (2k - 1) + (2k + 1) = k^2 + 4 + (2k + 1)$
$$= (k^2 + 2k + 1) + 4$$
$$= (k + 1)^2 + 4.$$

2. Verify the results of Test Yourself Exercise 1 for $n = 10$.
3. Verify the results of Example 1 of this section for $n = 5$.

Prove by mathematical induction or identify as not true for all natural numbers n:

4. $1 + 3 + 5 + \cdots + (2n - 1) = n^2.$
5. $2 + 4 + 6 + \cdots + 2n = n^2 + n + 2.$
6. $1^3 + 2^3 + 3^3 + \cdots + n^3 = \dfrac{n^2(n + 1)^2}{4}.$
7. $4 + 8 + 12 + \cdots + 4n = 3n^2 - n + 2.$
8. $a + (a + d) + (a + 2d) + \cdots + [a + (n - 1)d]$
$$= \dfrac{n}{2}[2a + (n - 1)d].$$
9. $a + ar + ar^2 + \cdots + ar^{n-1} = \dfrac{a(1 - r^n)}{1 - r},$ if $r \neq 1.$
10. $\dfrac{1}{1(3)} + \dfrac{1}{3(5)} + \dfrac{1}{5(7)} + \cdots + \dfrac{1}{(2n - 1)(2n + 1)} = \dfrac{n}{2n + 1}.$

• • •

11. $1^2 + 3^2 + 5^2 + \cdots + (2n - 1)^2 = \dfrac{n(4n^2 - 1)}{3}.$

12. $\left(1 - \frac{1}{2}\right)\left(1 - \frac{1}{3}\right) \cdots \left(1 - \frac{1}{n+1}\right) = \frac{1}{n+1}$.
13. $5^{2n} - 1$ is a multiple of 24.
14. $1(1!) + 2(2!) + 3(3!) + \cdots + n(n!) = (n+1)! - 1$.
- 15. $(x^n - y^n)$ is divisible by $(x - y)$.
- 16. $2^n > n$.
- 17. $1^3 + 2^3 + 3^3 + \cdots + n^3 = (1 + 2 + 3 + \cdots + n)^2$.

§ 10-10 Area

In § 10-1 areas were approximated by sums of inner rectangles (as in Figure 10-3) and also by sums of outer rectangles (as in Figure 10-4). We now introduce the Greek capital letter sigma, Σ, as a **summation symbol** to indicate "the sum of" terms of a given form. Then we use this notation in a formal approach to the concept of area.

The summation symbol is used with an **index** which is an integral variable with an indicated domain as in the following illustrations:

$$\sum_{n=1}^{5} n^2 = 1^2 + 2^2 + 3^2 + 4^2 + 5^2;$$

$$\sum_{n=1}^{6} \frac{1}{n} = 1 + \frac{1}{2} + \frac{1}{3} + \frac{1}{4} + \frac{1}{5} + \frac{1}{6};$$

$$\sum_{j=0}^{n} a_j x^j = a_0 x^0 + a_1 x + a_2 x^2 + a_3 x^3 + \cdots + a_n x^n;$$

$$\sum_{j=1}^{4} (3x^j + j) = (3x + 1) + (3x^2 + 2) + (3x^3 + 3) + (3x^4 + 4).$$

Notice that the sum S_k of the first k terms of any sequence $\{a_n\}$ may be expressed as $\sum_{j=1}^{k} a_j$. In all cases the general term of the summation is written immediately after the summation symbol. The index varies in increments of one unit with the value given below the summation symbol as its first value and the value given above the summation symbol as its last value. The index j of any summation $\sum_{j=1}^{k} a_j$ is a "dummy index" in that it does not appear in the expanded sum and any appropriate letter may be used.

Example 1. Use the summation symbol to express the sum of the first 100 positive odd integers.

The general term of the sum $1 + 3 + 5 + 7 + \cdots + 199$ may be taken as $(2j - 1)$ with $j = 1, 2, \cdots, 100$. Thus the sum may be

SEQUENCES, SERIES, AND LIMITS

expressed as $\sum_{j=1}^{100} (2j - 1)$. Notice that this sum could also be expressed as $\sum_{n=0}^{99} (2n + 1)$, as $\sum_{k=5}^{104} (2k - 9)$, and in many other ways.

Now, let us return to the problem of finding the area A under the graph of $y = x^2$ over the interval $0 \le x \le 1$ which we considered in § 10–1; that is, the area bounded by the graph of $y = x^2$, the x-axis, and the line $x = 1$. Let the interval from $(0, 0)$ to $(1, 0)$ on the x-axis be divided into n equal subintervals of length $\frac{1}{n}$. Consider the set of inner rectangles constructed on these subintervals. For this particular region the height of each inner rectangle is equal to the ordinate value at the left-hand end point of its subinterval as in Figure 10–3. We denote the sum of the areas of the inner rectangles by s_n;

$$s_n = \frac{1}{n}(0)^2 + \frac{1}{n}\left(\frac{1}{n}\right)^2 + \frac{1}{n}\left(\frac{2}{n}\right)^2 + \frac{1}{n}\left(\frac{3}{n}\right)^2 + \cdots + \frac{1}{n}\left(\frac{n-1}{n}\right)^2$$

$$= \frac{1}{n^3} \sum_{j=1}^{n-1} j^2.$$

By Example 1 of § 10–9 we know that $\sum_{j=1}^{n-1} j^2 = 1^2 + 2^2 + 3^2 + \cdots +$
$(n-1)^2 = \frac{(n-1)[(n-1)+1][2(n-1)+1]}{6} = \frac{(n-1)(n)(2n-1)}{6}$.

Thus

$$s_n = \frac{1}{n^3} \times \frac{(n-1)(n)(2n-1)}{6} = \frac{2n^2 - 3n + 1}{6n^2} = \frac{1}{3} - \frac{1}{2n} + \frac{1}{6n^2};$$

$$\lim \{s_n\} = \lim \left\{ \frac{1}{3} - \frac{1}{2n} + \frac{1}{6n^2} \right\} = \frac{1}{3}.$$

Consider also the set of outer rectangles constructed on these n equal subintervals. For this particular region the height of each outer rectangle is equal to the ordinate value at the right-hand end point of its subinterval as in Figure 10–4. We denote the sum of the areas of the outer rectangles by S_n;

$$S_n = \frac{1}{n}\left(\frac{1}{n}\right)^2 + \frac{1}{n}\left(\frac{2}{n}\right)^2 + \frac{1}{n}\left(\frac{3}{n}\right)^2 + \frac{1}{n}\left(\frac{4}{n}\right)^2 + \cdots + \frac{1}{n}\left(\frac{n}{n}\right)^2$$

$$= \frac{1}{n^3} \sum_{j=1}^{n} j^2.$$

By Example 1 of § 10–9, as before,

$$S_n = \frac{1}{n^3} \times \frac{n(n+1)(2n+1)}{6} = \frac{2n^2 + 3n + 1}{6n^2} = \frac{1}{3} + \frac{1}{2n} + \frac{1}{6n^2};$$

$$\lim \{S_n\} = \lim \left\{ \frac{1}{3} + \frac{1}{2n} + \frac{1}{6n^2} \right\} = \frac{1}{3}.$$

The area A of the region bounded by the x-axis, the line $x = 1$, and the curve $y = x^2$ is a constant; $s_n \leq A \leq S_n$ for all positive integral values of n as in § 10–1; $\lim \{s_n\} = \frac{1}{3}$; $\lim \{S_n\} = \frac{1}{3}$. Thus the conditions of Theorem 4, § 10–5 are satisfied and $\lim \{A\} = \frac{1}{3}$; that is, $A = \frac{1}{3}$.

We are now in a position to generalize the process that we have just illustrated and to define the area under a graph over an interval. Consider a "continuous," nonnegative function $f(x)$ over the interval $a \leq x \leq b$ as indicated in Figure 10–6. We shall speak of the area A under the graph from a to b as the area bounded by the graph of $y = f(x)$, the x-axis, and the lines $x = a$ and $x = b$. This area is shaded in Figure 10–6.

Let the interval from $(a, 0)$ to $(b, 0)$ be divided into n equal subintervals. Then each subinterval has length $\frac{b-a}{n}$ and we use the

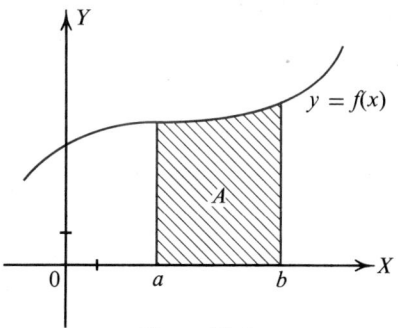

Figure 10–6

symbol Δx (read as, delta x) for this common unit of length. We assume that $a < b$ as in Figure 10–6 and think of the subintervals in order as:

$$\{x \mid a \leq x \leq a + \Delta x\},$$

$$\{x \mid a + \Delta x \leq x \leq a + 2\Delta x\},$$

$$\{x \mid a + 2\Delta x \leq x \leq a + 3\Delta x\},$$

and so forth where in general, for $j = 1, 2, 3, \cdots, n$ the jth subinterval is

$$\{x \mid a + (j-1)\Delta x \leq x \leq a + j\Delta x\}.$$

For each subinterval we consider the set of values of $f(x)$ and define

SEQUENCES, SERIES, AND LIMITS

min $f(x_j)$ as the (or one of the) smallest value of $f(x)$ when x is on the jth subinterval; max $f(x_j)$ as the (or one of the) largest value of $f(x)$ when x is on the jth subinterval. Since we have assumed that $f(x)$ is "continuous" for $a \leq x \leq b$, there will exist values for min $f(x_j)$ and max $f(x_j)$ for each subinterval; min $f(x_j)$ is the height of the inner rectangle with the jth subinterval as its base; max $f(x_j)$ is the height of the outer rectangle with the jth subinterval as its base. Since each of the subintervals has length Δx, we may let

$$s_n = \Delta x \sum_{j=1}^{n} \min f(x_j); \quad S_n = \Delta x \sum_{j=1}^{n} \max f(x_j).$$

Also, since for each subinterval min $f(x_j) \leq$ max $f(x_j)$, we know that $s_n \leq S_n$. Then from our previous consideration of the problem we know that $s_n \leq A \leq S_n$ for all positive integral values of n. By Theorem 5, if lim $\{s_n\}$ = lim $\{S_n\}$, then A = lim $\{s_n\}$ = lim $\{S_n\}$. It can be shown in advanced courses that if either lim $\{s_n\}$ or lim $\{S_n\}$ exists, then the other limit exists and they are equal.

Consider any value x_j of x on the jth equal subinterval of the interval from $(a, 0)$ to $(b, 0)$. From the definition of min $f(x_j)$ and max $f(x_j)$ we know that

$$\min f(x_j) \leq f(x_j) \leq \max f(x_j);$$

$$\sum_{j=1}^{n} \min f(x_j) \leq \sum_{j=1}^{n} f(x_j) \leq \sum_{j=1}^{n} \max f(x_j);$$

$$s_n \leq \Delta x \sum_{j=1}^{n} f(x_j) \leq S_n.$$

If either lim $\{s_n\}$ or lim $\{S_n\}$ exists, then

$$\lim \{s_n\} = \lim \Delta x \sum_{j=1}^{n} f(x_j) = \lim \{S_n\}$$

and any one of these may be taken as the area A. Thus the **area** under a graph over an interval may be defined as the limit, if the limit exists, of a sequence of sums of areas of rectangles on equal subintervals and with any value x_j of x on each subinterval as the height of the rectangle on that subinterval.

There are intervals on which curves such as the graph of $y = \dfrac{1}{x}$ are not "continuous." In such cases lim $\{s_n\}$ and lim $\{S_n\}$ may not exist. If these limits do not exist, then the area under the graph being considered and over the interval being considered is not defined.

The method for finding the area under the graph of a given equation and over a given interval is shown in Example 2. Note the extensive use of finite series from § 10–9.

Example 2. Find the area under the graph of $y = x^3$ over the interval $2 \leq x \leq 4$.

Each of the equal subintervals has length $\frac{2}{n}$; $\Delta x = \frac{2}{n}$. The values of x on the jth subinterval are

$$2 + (j-1)\left(\frac{2}{n}\right) \leq x \leq 2 + j\left(\frac{2}{n}\right)$$

and we may select $x_j = 2 + j\left(\frac{2}{n}\right)$. Then the desired area A is given by:

$$A = \lim \Delta x \sum_{j=1}^{n} f(x_j)$$

$$= \lim \frac{2}{n} \sum_{j=1}^{n} \left(2 + \frac{2j}{n}\right)^3$$

$$= \lim \frac{2}{n} \sum_{j=1}^{n} \frac{2^3}{n^3}(n+j)^3$$

$$= \lim \frac{2^4}{n^4} \sum_{j=1}^{n} (n^3 + 3n^2 j + 3nj^2 + j^3)$$

$$= \lim \frac{2^4}{n^4} \left[n^3 \sum_{j=1}^{n} 1 + 3n^2 \sum_{j=1}^{n} j + 3n \sum_{j=1}^{n} j^2 + \sum_{j=1}^{n} j^3 \right]$$

$$= \lim 2^4 \left[\frac{1}{n} \sum_{j=1}^{n} 1 + \frac{3}{n^2} \sum_{j=1}^{n} j + \frac{3}{n^3} \sum_{j=1}^{n} j^2 + \frac{1}{n^4} \sum_{j=1}^{n} j^3 \right].$$

As in § 10–9 we have

$$\frac{1}{n} \sum_{j=1}^{n} 1 = \frac{1}{n} \sum_{j=1}^{n} 1 j^0 = \frac{1}{n} \times n = 1;$$

$$\frac{3}{n^2} \sum_{j=1}^{n} j = \frac{3}{n^2} \times \frac{n(n+1)}{2} = \frac{3n^2 + 3n}{2n^2} = \frac{3}{2} + \frac{3}{2n};$$

$$\frac{3}{n^3} \sum_{j=1}^{n} j^2 = \frac{3}{n^3} \times \frac{n(n+1)(2n+1)}{6} = \frac{2n^2 + 3n + 1}{2n^2}$$

$$= 1 + \frac{3}{2n} + \frac{1}{2n^2};$$

$$\frac{1}{n^4} \sum_{j=1}^{n} j^3 = \frac{1}{n^4} \times \frac{n^2(n+1)^2}{4} = \frac{n^2 + 2n + 1}{4n^2} = \frac{1}{4} + \frac{1}{2n} + \frac{1}{4n^2}.$$

SEQUENCES, SERIES, AND LIMITS

Then

$$A = \lim 2^4 \left[1 + \left(\frac{3}{2} + \frac{3}{2n}\right) + \left(1 + \frac{3}{2n} + \frac{1}{2n^2}\right) + \left(\frac{1}{4} + \frac{1}{2n} + \frac{1}{4n^2}\right) \right]$$

$$= 2^4\left(1 + \frac{3}{2} + 1 + \frac{1}{4}\right) = 16 + 24 + 16 + 4 = 60.$$

The importance of calculating the area under a graph often lies in the use of the area as a measure of a physical quantity. For example, if x represents time and y represents velocity, then the area under the curve over an interval of values of x represents the distance traversed by an object over that time interval when traveling with a varying velocity $f(x)$. Several such examples are shown in the array.

INDEPENDENT VARIABLE	DEPENDENT VARIABLE	AREA
Time	Acceleration	Velocity
Time	Velocity	Distance
Time	Force	Momentum
Distance	Force	Work

Example 3. If an object falling from rest has a velocity of v feet per second after t seconds where $v = 32t$, find the distance that the object falls in the first three seconds.

A graph of the function $v = 32t$ appears in Figure 10–7. The distance the object falls during the interval $0 \leq t \leq 3$ is measured by the area under the graph over this interval. This area is shaded in Figure 10–7 and may be found by applying the formula for the area of a triangle. Since the base represents time measured in seconds and the altitude represents velocity measured in feet per second, the product and area represent distance measured in feet. Hence the distance the object falls in the first three seconds is given by $\frac{1}{2}(3)(96) = 144$; that is, 144 feet.

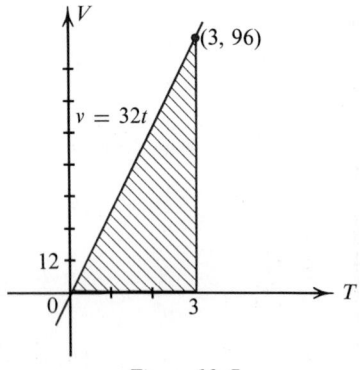

Figure 10–7

In Example 3 we could have evaluated the area under the graph by means of our definition of area as a limit of a sequence of sums. However, since the function was a linear function, it was easier to use the formula for the area of a triangle. In cases where the graph is not a straight line it is often necessary to determine the area as a limit of a sequence of sums.

In this section we have presented the definition of area as a limit of a sequence of sums. The calculations of areas by the definition are often difficult. In calculus, theorems and a convenient notation are developed from this definition which make the finding of the area under a graph a much simpler process.

TEST YOURSELF

Write each series without using the summation symbol:

1. $\sum_{j=1}^{5} j^3.$
2. $\sum_{j=2}^{10} (-1)^j (j + 3).$
3. $\sum_{j=0}^{n-1} ar^j.$

In Exercises 4 through 6 write each series using the summation symbol:

4. $1 + 2 + 3 + \cdots + 100.$
5. $3^2 + 4^2 + 5^2 + \cdots + 17^2.$
6. $2x_1 - 4x_2 + 8x_3 - \cdots + 128x_7.$
7. Find the area under the graph of $y = x$ over the interval $0 \leq x \leq 4$ using the definition of area as a limit of a sum.
8. Find the area under the graph of $y = x^2$ over the interval $1 \leq x \leq 2$.

EXERCISES

Write each series without using the summation symbol:

1. $\sum_{j=1}^{n} j^2.$
2. $\sum_{j=1}^{n} (j + j^2).$
3. $\sum_{j=1}^{n} 2x^j.$
4. $\sum_{j=5}^{9} (2j + 3).$
5. $\sum_{j=0}^{3} (-1)^j \times {}_3C_j.$
6. $\sum_{j=1}^{n} \frac{1}{j^2}.$

Write each expression using the summation symbol:

7. $a + (a + d) + (a + 2d) + \cdots + [a + (n - 1)d].$
8. $3 + 3 + 3 + 3 + 3 + 3.$
9. $f(x_1) + f(x_2) + f(x_3) + f(x_4) + \cdots + f(x_n).$

575

SEQUENCES, SERIES, AND LIMITS

10. $x + 3x^2 + 5x^3 + 7x^4 + \cdots + 21x^{11}$.

11. $\dfrac{x_1^2 y_1 + x_2^2 y_2 + x_3^2 y_3 + \cdots + x_6^2 y_6}{y_1 + y_2 + y_3 + \cdots + y_6}$.

Determine whether each statement is true or false. If a statement is false, find a new right member such that the new statement is true:

12. $\sum_{j=0}^{n}(j+1) = \sum_{j=1}^{n+1} j$.

13. $\sum_{j=1}^{n}(5+j) = 5 + \sum_{j=1}^{n} j$.

14. $\sum_{j=1}^{n} 2j = 2 \sum_{j=1}^{n} j$.

15. $\sum_{j=1}^{100}(3j+j^2) = \sum_{j=1}^{100} 3j + \sum_{j=1}^{100} j^2$.

16. $\sum_{j=0}^{n} j = \sum_{j=1}^{n} j$.

17. $\sum_{j=1}^{n} k = k$.

18. $\sum_{j=1}^{100} j^3 = 3 + \sum_{j=3}^{100} j^3$.

19. $\sum_{j=1}^{n} j^3 = \sum_{j=1}^{n} j \times \sum_{j=1}^{n} j^2$.

In Exercises 20 through 24 find the area under the graph of each equation and over the interval indicated:

20. $y = x^2$; $0 \le x \le 2$.
21. $y = x^2 + 3$; $0 \le x \le 1$.
22. $y = 3x^2$; $0 \le x \le 1$.
23. $y = x^2 + x$; $0 \le x \le 2$.
24. $y = x^3$; $0 \le x \le 1$.

• • •

25. If an object falling from rest has a velocity of v feet per second after t seconds where $v = 32t$, find the distance the object falls during the interval $3 \le t \le 6$.

26. If a force of f pounds is required to compress a spring x inches where $f = 30x$, find the work done in compressing the spring 4 inches.

• 27. Find a formula for the area under the graph of $y = x^2$ over the interval $0 \le x \le a$.

• 28. Find a formula for the area under the graph of $y = x^2$ over the interval $a \le x \le b$.

§ 10–11 Limits of functions

We have considered limits of sequences of numbers and applied these limits to determine when the sum of an infinite series is defined and when the area under a curve over a given interval is defined. In this section we define another type of limit, the limit of a function at a given value of the independent variable. In a sense the limit of a sequence with a function

§ 10-11 LIMITS OF FUNCTIONS

as its general term is a special case of a limit of a function. However, the limit of a sequence is defined only when the independent variable takes on integral values and increases without bound. We now consider as values of the independent variable a sequence of real numbers which has a real number as a limit.

Consider any function $f(x)$ and any sequence $\{a_n\}$ of real numbers. If the numbers a_n are taken as values of x, then a sequence $\{f(a_n)\}$ of values of the function is obtained. For example, if

$$f(x) = \frac{x^2 - 4}{x - 2},$$

then $f(x) = x + 2$ for all values of $x \neq 2$ and $f(x)$ is undefined when $x = 2$. If the sequence of values $\left\{\frac{1}{n}\right\}$ is used for x, then $f(x)$ assumes the sequence of values

$$\left\{f\left(\frac{1}{n}\right)\right\} = \left\{\frac{\frac{1}{n^2} - 4}{\frac{1}{n} - 2}\right\} = \left\{\frac{1}{n} + 2\right\}.$$

If the sequence of values $\left\{\frac{2n}{n+1}\right\}$ is used for x, then $f(x)$ assumes the sequence of values

$$\left\{f\left(\frac{2n}{n+1}\right)\right\} = \left\{\frac{\left(\frac{2n}{n+1}\right)^2 - 4}{\frac{2n}{n+1} - 2}\right\} = \left\{\frac{4n+2}{n+1}\right\}.$$

Each of these sequences may be considered in terms of n and thus we may consider the limits of the sequences:

$$\lim \left\{\frac{1}{n}\right\} = 0; \ \lim \left\{\frac{1}{n} + 2\right\} = 2; \ \lim \left\{\frac{2n}{n+1}\right\} = 2; \ \lim \left\{\frac{4n+2}{n+1}\right\} = 4.$$

As in these examples it is possible to consider the limit of the sequence of values assumed by a function when a sequence of values is used for the independent variable.

We have seen that if $f(x) = \frac{x^2 - 4}{x - 2}$ and the null sequence of values $\left\{\frac{1}{n}\right\}$ is used for x, then the sequence of values of $f(x)$ has 2 as a limit. There are many other null sequences such as $\left\{-\frac{1}{n}\right\}$, $\left\{\frac{1}{n^2}\right\}$, and $\left\{\frac{1}{2^n}\right\}$ consisting of values which could be used for x. If for *every* sequence of values of x with limit 0, the sequence of values of $f(x)$ has limit 2, then we

577

SEQUENCES, SERIES, AND LIMITS

say that the limit of $f(x)$ is 2 as x approaches 0 and we write

$$\lim_{x \to 0} f(x) = 2.$$

The fact that $f(0) = 2$ where 2 is the limit of $f(x)$ as x approaches 0 implies that the curve $y = f(x)$ is "continuous" at $x = 0$. Notice that when the new limit symbol is compared with the old one as in $\lim \{a_n\}$, the absence of any notation below "lim" implies that an integral variable is increasing without bound.

If for every sequence of values of x with limit 2, the sequence of values of $f(x)$ has limit 4, then

$$\lim_{x \to 2} f(x) = 4.$$

The fact that the function $f(x) = \dfrac{x^2 - 4}{x - 2}$ is not defined at $x = 2$ implies that the given function is not "continuous" at $x = 2$. In this particular case we may *define* $f(2) = 4$ and thereby obtain the continuous function

$$f(x) = \frac{x^2 - 4}{x - 2}, \text{ if } x \neq 2$$

$$f(x) = 4, \text{ if } x = 2,$$

where $\lim_{x \to 2} f(x) = f(2)$. The function

$$g(x) = \frac{x^2 - 4}{x - 2}, x \neq 2$$

$$g(x) = 1, \text{ if } x = 2$$

is defined such that $\lim_{x \to 2} g(x) \neq g(2)$ and the function $g(x)$ is not continuous at $x = 2$. In general, a function $f(x)$ is **continuous** at $x = a$ if $\lim_{x \to a} f(x)$ exists and is equal to $f(a)$. This is a formal statement of the property of continuity which we have previously described and visualized intuitively. A real function $f(x)$ is continuous over an interval if it is continuous for all real values of x on that interval.

Consider the greatest integer function $h(x) = [\![x]\!]$. If the sequence of values $\left\{\dfrac{1}{n}\right\}$ is used for x, then for $n > 1$ the sequence of values of $h(x)$ is $\{0\}$ which approaches 0 as a limit. If the sequence of values $\left\{-\dfrac{1}{n}\right\}$ is used for x, then the sequence of values of $h(x)$ is $\{-1\}$ which approaches -1 as a limit. Since the limit of the sequence of values of $h(x)$ depends upon the selection of the sequence of values for x with limit 0, the function $h(x)$ does not have a limit as x approaches 0 and the function is not continuous at $x = 0$.

The requirement that the sequences of values of a function $f(x)$ have the same limit for all possible sequences of values of x with a given limit a cannot be verified by checking each of the possible sequences of values of x. Thus some other approach is needed. The function has a limit L if and only if $|f(x) - L|$ can be made less than any given positive number ϵ for each possible sequence of values. The sequence of values of x has a limit a if and only if $|x - a|$ can be made less than any given positive number δ, where the Greek small letter delta, δ, is used to avoid confusion with ϵ. The condition $|x - a| < \delta$ is satisfied by taking n sufficiently large in the sequence of values $\{a_n\}$ used for x; the condition $|f(x) - L| < \epsilon$ is satisfied by taking n sufficiently large in the sequence of values $\{f(a_n)\}$. Notice that this second condition can, in a sense, be imposed by the selection of δ. Accordingly, the function $f(x)$ has a limit L as x approaches a (that is, $\lim_{x \to a} f(x) = L$) if and only if for any given positive number ϵ there exists a positive number δ_ϵ such that $|f(x) - L| < \epsilon$ for all values of x such that $|x - a| < \delta_\epsilon$. The subscript ϵ in the symbol δ_ϵ is used to emphasize the dependence of δ_ϵ upon ϵ.

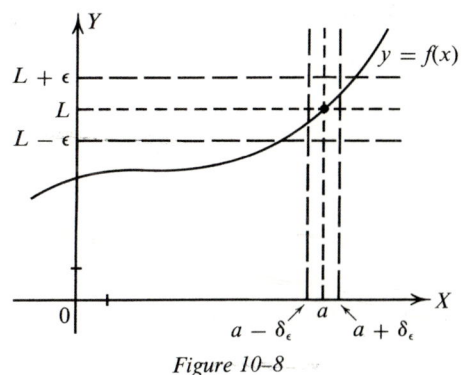

Figure 10-8

We recognize intuitively that $\lim_{x \to a} f(x) = L$ if for any $\epsilon > 0$, $|f(x) - L| < \epsilon$ for x sufficiently close to a. This is shown in Figure 10-8 where for any given ϵ there exists a δ_ϵ such that if $a - \delta_\epsilon < x < a + \delta_\epsilon$, then $L - \epsilon < f(x) < L + \epsilon$; that is, if x is within δ_ϵ of a, then $f(x)$ is within ϵ of L.

Example 1. Prove that $\lim_{x \to 1} (2x + 3) = 5$.

> Let $\epsilon > 0$ be given. The condition $|f(x) - L| < \epsilon$ may be expressed in each of these forms:
> $$|(2x + 3) - 5| < \epsilon$$
> $$|2x - 2| < \epsilon$$
> $$|x - 1| < \frac{\epsilon}{2}.$$
> Thus if we choose $\delta_\epsilon = \frac{\epsilon}{2}$, the condition $|f(x) - L| < \epsilon$ is satisfied. This is possible since for any $\epsilon > 0$, we have $\frac{\epsilon}{2} > 0$.

579

SEQUENCES, SERIES, AND LIMITS

Each of the theorems considered in § 10–5 may be restated for limits of functions. We shall assume these theorems even though some of the proofs are quite simple.

Theorem 6. *If* $\lim_{x \to a} f(x) = L$, *then* $\lim_{x \to a} k \times f(x) = kL$.

Theorem 7. *If* $\lim_{x \to a} f(x) = L$ *and* $\lim_{x \to a} g(x) = K$, *then*

$$\lim_{x \to a} [f(x) + g(x)] = L + K \text{ and } \lim_{x \to a} [f(x) - g(x)] = L - K.$$

Theorem 8. *If* $\lim_{x \to a} f(x) = L$ *and* $\lim_{x \to a} g(x) = K$, *then*

$$\lim_{x \to a} [f(x) \times g(x)] = L \times K \text{ and, if } K \neq 0, \lim_{x \to a} \frac{f(x)}{g(x)} = \frac{L}{K}.$$

Theorem 9. *If* $\lim_{x \to a} f(x)$ *exists,* $\lim_{x \to a} g(x)$ *exists,* $\lim_{x \to a} [f(x) - g(x)] = 0$, *and k is a constant such that* $f(x) \leq k \leq g(x)$ *for all x such that* $|x - a| < \delta$ *for some* $\delta > 0$, *then* $\lim_{x \to a} f(x) = \lim_{x \to a} g(x) = k$.

Theorem 10. (Domination principle) *If* $\lim_{x \to a} f(x) = k$, $\lim_{x \to a} h(x) = k$, *and for some* $\delta > 0$, $f(x) \leq g(x) \leq h(x)$ *for all x such that* $|x - a| < \delta$, *then* $\lim_{x \to a} g(x) = k$.

The following statements are also useful. Their proofs are given as Exercises 11, 12, and 13. For the present we shall assume them:

$$\lim_{x \to a} k = k; \quad \lim_{x \to a} x = a; \quad \lim_{x \to a} \frac{x - a}{x - a} = 1.$$

Example 2. Find each limit if it exists:

(a) $\lim_{x \to 2} 3x^2$; (b) $\lim_{x \to 3} \frac{x^2 - 9}{x - 3}$; (c) $\lim_{x \to 0} \sin x$.

(a) $\lim_{x \to 2} 3x^2 = \lim_{x \to 2} 3 \times \lim_{x \to 2} x \times \lim_{x \to 2} x = 3 \times 2 \times 2 = 12.$

(b) $\lim_{x \to 3} \frac{x^2 - 9}{x - 3} = \lim_{x \to 3} \frac{x - 3}{x - 3} \times \lim_{x \to 3} (x + 3)$

$$= \lim_{x \to 3} \frac{x - 3}{x - 3} \times [\lim_{x \to 3} x + \lim_{x \to 3} 3]$$

$$= 1 \times (3 + 3) = 6.$$

(c) Since $\sin x = x - \dfrac{x^3}{3!} + \dfrac{x^5}{5!} - \cdots = x - \left(\dfrac{x^3}{3!} - \dfrac{x^5}{5!} + \cdots\right)$, $|\sin x| < |x|$ when $|x| < 1$; $-|x| \leq \sin x \leq |x|$. Then by Theorem 10 since $\lim_{x \to 0} |x| = 0$, $\lim_{x \to 0} \sin x = 0$.

TEST YOURSELF

In Exercises 1 through 3 find each limit if it exists:

1. $\lim_{x \to 1} (x^2 + 2x + 3)$.

2. $\lim_{x \to 2} \dfrac{x^3 - 8}{x - 2}$.

3. $\lim_{x \to 2} \dfrac{x^2 - 7x + 10}{x + 1}$.

4. Prove that $\lim_{x \to 1} (x + 1) = 2$ using the definition of a limit of a function.

EXERCISES

Find each limit if it exists:

1. $\lim_{x \to 1} (3x^2 + x + 4)$.

2. $\lim_{x \to 2} \dfrac{x^4 - 16}{x^2 - 4}$.

3. $\lim_{x \to 0} \sin^2 x$.

4. $\lim_{x \to 0} \dfrac{(2 + x)^2 - 4}{x}$.

5. $\lim_{x \to 1} \dfrac{x + 2}{x - 1}$.

6. $\lim_{x \to 0} \dfrac{4 + x^2 - 2}{x}$.

• • •

7. $\lim_{x \to 0} (x + \sin x)$.

8. $\lim_{x \to 0} \cos x$.

9. $\lim_{x \to 0} \dfrac{|x|}{x}$.

10. $\lim_{x \to 0} \cos^2 x$.

In Exercises 11 through 15 use the definition of the limit of a function to prove each limit:

11. $\lim_{x \to a} x = a$.

12. $\lim_{x \to a} k = k$.

13. $\lim_{x \to a} \dfrac{x - a}{x - a} = 1$.

14. $\lim_{x \to 0} x^2 = 0$.

SEQUENCES, SERIES, AND LIMITS

15. $\lim_{x \to 3}(2x + 3) = 9$.

16. Prove by mathematical induction that $\lim_{x \to a} x^n = a^n$, where n is any positive integer.

§ 10-12 Rates of change

We now consider the problem of determining the rate at which a function $f(x)$ changes as x changes. Our approach to the problem is the same as that used to find average velocity in a time, rate, distance problem. If the mileage on a car speedometer is 27,512 at 1:30 P.M. and at 1:40 P.M. of the same day the mileage is 27,520, then the change Δt in time is 10 minutes (that is, $\frac{1}{6}$ of an hour) and the change Δd in distance is $27,520 - 27,512$ (that is, 8 miles). The average velocity $\frac{\Delta d}{\Delta t}$ is $8 \div \frac{1}{6}$; that is, 48 miles per hour over the interval of time from 1:30 until 1:40 P.M. Notice that the ratio $\frac{\Delta d}{\Delta t}$ is the average rate of change of distance with respect to time over the interval Δt.

In general, consider a function $f(x)$. If $x = x_0$, then $f(x) = f(x_0)$. If x changes from x_0 to $x_0 + \Delta x$, then $f(x)$ changes from $f(x_0)$ to $f(x_0 + \Delta x)$. The difference $(x_0 + \Delta x) - x_0$ is the change Δx in x; the difference $f(x_0 + \Delta x) - f(x_0)$ is the change in the function and is denoted by $\Delta f(x)$. The ratio $\frac{\Delta f(x)}{\Delta x}$ is defined as the **average rate of change** of $f(x)$ with respect to x over the interval Δx.

Example 1. If an object falling from rest falls d feet in t seconds where $d = 16t^2$, find the average rate of change of d with respect to t over the interval (a) $1 \leq t \leq 3$; (b) $1 \leq t \leq 2$.

(a) When $t = 1$, $d = 16$; when $t = 3$, $d = 144$. As t changes from 1 to 3, d changes from 16 to 144; that is, $\Delta t = 3 - 1 = 2$ and $\Delta d = 144 - 16 = 128$ over the interval $1 \leq t \leq 3$. Then $\frac{\Delta d}{\Delta t} = \frac{128}{2} = 64$. Hence the average rate of change of the distance with respect to the change in time is 64 feet per second over the two second interval $1 \leq t \leq 3$. Since the rate of change of a directed distance with respect to time is velocity, we may interpret our answer to mean that although the object falls with varying velocity it traverses the same distance in the time interval $1 \leq t \leq 3$ as it would traverse if it fell with a constant velocity of 64 feet per second, its average velocity during this time interval.

582

§ 10–12 RATES OF CHANGE

(b) When $t = 1$, $d = 16$; when $t = 2$, $d = 64$. As t changes from 1 to 2, d changes from 16 to 64; that is, $\Delta t = 1$ and $\Delta d = 48$ over the interval $1 \leq t \leq 2$. Therefore, $\frac{\Delta d}{\Delta t} = 48$. Hence the average rate of change of the distance with respect to the change in time (average velocity) is 48 feet per second over the one second interval $1 \leq t \leq 2$.

The average rate of change of a function $f(x)$ with respect to x over an interval Δx may be interpreted geometrically as a measure of the slope of the secant through the points $(x, f(x))$ and $(x + \Delta x, f(x + \Delta x))$. For example, in Figure 10–9 $\frac{\Delta f(x)}{\Delta x}$ is a measure of the slope of the secant AB.

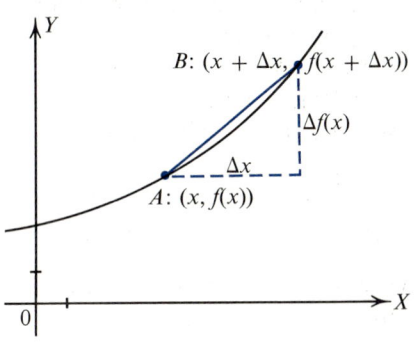

Figure 10–9

Consider the problem of determining the velocity of the falling object in Example 1 at the instant $t = 1$. We assume that at $t = 1$ the distance d is a continuous function of the time t and calculate a sequence of average velocities over smaller and smaller intervals of time after $t = 1$. That is, we determine a sequence $\left\{\frac{\Delta d}{\Delta t}\right\}$ where Δt is a measure of the change in time from $t = 1$ to $t = 1 + \Delta t$ and Δt approaches zero. The necessary calculations for one such sequence of values of Δt are shown in the following table.

t	$t + \Delta t$	Δt	d	$d + \Delta d$	Δd	$\frac{\Delta d}{\Delta t}$
1	3	2	16	144	128	64
1	2	1	16	64	48	48
1	1.5	0.5	16	36	20	40
1	1.1	0.1	16	19.36	3.36	33.6
1	1.01	0.01	16	16.3216	0.3216	32.16
1	1.001	0.001	16	16.032016	0.032016	32.016
1	1.0001	0.0001	16	16.00320016	0.00320016	32.0016
...	...	...	...	...	...	...

It appears from the table that the sequence of values $\left\{\frac{\Delta d}{\Delta t}\right\}$ has a limit equal to 32; that is, that the instantaneous velocity of the falling object is 32 feet per second at $t = 1$.

Now let us consider this problem in another manner using the fact that

583

SEQUENCES, SERIES, AND LIMITS

$\dfrac{\Delta d}{\Delta t}$ is a function of Δt for any fixed value t. Since $d = 16t^2$, $d + \Delta d = 16(t + \Delta t)^2$, $\Delta d = 16(t + \Delta t)^2 - 16t^2$, and $\dfrac{\Delta d}{\Delta t} = \dfrac{16(t + \Delta t)^2 - 16t^2}{\Delta t} = 32t + 16\Delta t$ for all values of $\Delta t \neq 0$. Then for any fixed value of t

$$\lim_{\Delta t \to 0} \dfrac{\Delta d}{\Delta t} = \lim_{\Delta t \to 0} (32t + 16\Delta t) = 32t.$$

We call $\lim\limits_{\Delta t \to 0} \dfrac{\Delta d}{\Delta t}$ the instantaneous rate of change of d with respect to t. For $t = 1$, $\lim\limits_{\Delta t \to 0} \dfrac{\Delta d}{\Delta t} = 32$. That is, instantaneous velocity of the falling object at $t = 1$ is 32 feet per second.

The **instantaneous rate of change** of a function $f(x)$ with respect to x for any given value of x is the limit, if it exists, of the average rate of change of $f(x)$ over the interval from x to $(x + \Delta x)$ as Δx approaches zero; that is, $\lim\limits_{\Delta x \to 0} \dfrac{\Delta f(x)}{\Delta x}$. When this limit exists, it is called the **derivative** of $f(x)$ and is sometimes denoted by $f'(x)$. Then

$$f'(x) = \lim_{\Delta x \to 0} \dfrac{\Delta f(x)}{\Delta x} = \lim_{\Delta x \to 0} \dfrac{f(x + \Delta x) - f(x)}{\Delta x}.$$

Example 2. Find the derivative of $(3x^2 + 1)$ for any value of x. Evaluate the derivative at $x = 2$.

$$\begin{aligned}
f(x) &= 3x^2 + 1 \text{ for any value of } x;\\
f(x + \Delta x) &= 3(x + \Delta x)^2 + 1\\
&= 3x^2 + 6x(\Delta x) + 3(\Delta x)^2 + 1;\\
\Delta f(x) &= f(x + \Delta x) - f(x)\\
&= 3x^2 + 6x(\Delta x) + 3(\Delta x)^2 + 1 - (3x^2 + 1)\\
&= 6x(\Delta x) + 3(\Delta x)^2;\\
\dfrac{\Delta f(x)}{\Delta x} &= 6x + 3(\Delta x);\\
f'(x) &= \lim_{\Delta x \to 0} \dfrac{\Delta f(x)}{\Delta x} = \lim_{\Delta x \to 0} [6x + 3(\Delta x)] = 6x.
\end{aligned}$$

At $x = 2$ the value of the derivative is $f'(2)$ and equals 6×2; that is, 12.

The average rate of change of a continuous function $f(x)$ may be interpreted as in Figure 10–10 as the slope of a secant passing through two points $(x, f(x))$ and $(x + \Delta x, f(x + \Delta x))$ on the curve $y = f(x)$. A sequence of secants AB, AB_1, AB_2, AB_3, $\cdots$ is shown in Figure 10–10. As Δx

approaches zero, the points B_i approach A since the function is continuous. If we let Δx approach zero by assuming the values of a sequence whose limit is zero, then B assumes a sequence of positions $B_1, B_2, B_3, \cdots$. The secant lines of the sequence AB_1, $AB_2, AB_3, \cdots$ approach the line t which is tangent to the curve at A. The sequence of slopes of the secant lines AB_1, AB_2, AB_3, $\cdots$ has the slope of the tangent line as a limit. Hence the derivative $\lim_{\Delta x \to 0} \dfrac{\Delta f(x)}{\Delta x}$ is a measure of the slope of the tangent line to the curve $y = f(x)$ at any point $(x, f(x))$. We define the **slope of the graph** of $y = f(x)$ at any point $(x, f(x))$ as the slope of the tangent line to the curve $y = f(x)$ at the point.

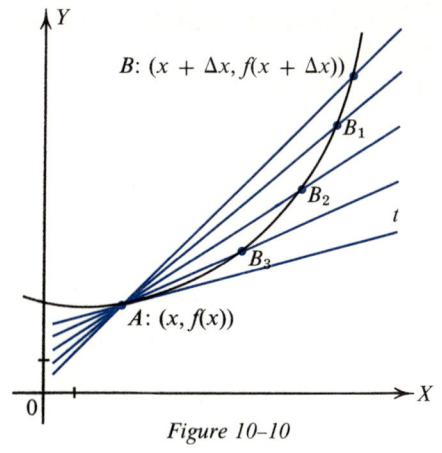

Figure 10-10

TEST YOURSELF

Find an expression for the average rate of change of each function over the interval stated:

1. $f(x) = x + 1$; $1 \leq x \leq 2$.
2. $f(x) = \dfrac{1}{3}x^3$; $2 \leq x \leq 4$.

Find the derivative, if it exists, for each function. Evaluate each derivative at $x = 3$:

3. $f(x) = x^3 + 4x$.
4. $f(x) = (3x + 1)^2$.

EXERCISES

Find an expression for the average rate of change of each function over the interval stated:

1. $f(x) = x^2$; $0 \leq x \leq 3$.
2. $f(x) = x^2 + 2x + 1$; $1 \leq x \leq 3$.

585

SEQUENCES, SERIES, AND LIMITS

In Exercises 3 through 10 find (a) an expression for the average rate of change of each function over any interval Δx; (b) the derivative of each function; (c) the value of the derivative at $x = 1$:

3. $f(x) = x + 3$.

4. $f(x) = \frac{1}{2}x^2$.

5. $f(x) = x^2 - 3x + 2$.

6. $f(x) = x^3 + 2x^2 + x - 3$.

7. $f(x) = x^5$.

8. $f(x) = (2x + 3)^3$.

9. $f(x) = \frac{1}{x}$.

10. $f(x) = \sqrt{x}$.

HINT: In Exercise 10 multiply $\Delta f(x)$ by $\dfrac{\sqrt{x + \Delta x} + \sqrt{x}}{\sqrt{x + \Delta x} + \sqrt{x}}$.

• • •

11. Find the equation of the tangent line to the graph of $y = x^2 - 4x + 1$ where $x = 3$.

12. Find the coordinates of the points on the graph of $y = x^3 - 3x + 2$ where the tangent line is parallel to the x-axis.

13. Find the points on the graph of $y = 3x - x^3$ where the inclination of the tangent line is 45°.

14. Prove that if $f(x) = k$ where k is a constant, then $f'(x) = 0$.

15. Prove that if $f(x) = x^n$, then $f'(x) = nx^{n-1}$.

16. Let $f(x) = 3x^2$, $g(x) = x^3$, and $h(x) = 3x^2 + x^3$. Verify that $h'(x) = f'(x) + g'(x)$.

In Exercises 17 and 18 let $f(x) = 3x^2$, $g(x) = x^3$, $h(x) = 3x^5$, and $j(x) = \dfrac{3}{x}$. Verify that:

17. $h'(x) = f(x) \times g'(x) + g(x) \times f'(x)$.

18. $j'(x) = \dfrac{g(x) \times f'(x) - f(x) \times g'(x)}{[g(x)]^2}$.

19. A function $f(x)$ has a *relative maximum* value at $x = x_0$ if there exists an interval $x_0 - \delta < x < x_0 + \delta$ such that the value of $f(x)$ is larger when $x = x_0$ than for any other value in the interval. Find a relative maximum value of $(3 + 2x - x^2)$ and graph the function.

20. A function $f(x)$ has a *relative minimum* value at $x = x_0$ if there exists an interval $x_0 - \delta < x < x_0 + \delta$ such that the value of $f(x)$ is smaller when $x = x_0$ than for any other value in the interval. Find a relative minimum value of $(x^2 - 3x + 5)$ and graph the function.

21. The height h in feet of an object above ground level at t seconds after it is shot straight up into the air is given by the formula $h = 1600t - 16t^2$. **(a)** Find the velocity and acceleration of the object at any time t. **(b)** At what time t does it reach its highest point above ground? **(c)** How high above ground is its highest point? **(d)** At what time t does it return to ground level?

SUMMARY OF CHAPTER 10

1. In this chapter you have studied limits of sequences of numbers and the application of such sequences in finding the sum of an infinite series, the area under the graph of a continuous function $f(x)$ over an interval $a \leq x \leq b$, the limit of a function at a specific value of x, and the derivative of a function for any given value of x. The area bounded by the x-axis, the lines $x = a$ and $x = b$, and the graph of a continuous function $f(x)$ where $0 \leq f(x)$ for $a \leq x \leq b$ may be approximated by the sum of the inner rectangles and also by the sum of the outer rectangles. In each case the line segment from $(a, 0)$ to $(b, 0)$ is divided into n equal subintervals which form the bases of the rectangles. (§ 10–1)

2. Sequences $\{a_n\}$ of numbers may be generated by functional expressions $f(n)$ and indicated by $\{f(n)\}$. When the first few terms of a sequence are given, the sequence may be continued by means of the method of differences. (§ 10–2)

3. A sequence of terms which approach zero is a null sequence. If for a sequence $\{a_n\}$ there exists a number a such that $\{a_n - a\}$ is a null sequence, then $\lim \{a_n\} = a$. (§§ 10–3 and 10–4)

4. If $\lim \{a_n\} = a$ and $\lim \{b_n\} = b$, then $\lim \{ka_n\} = ka$; $\lim \{a_n + b_n\} = a + b$; $\lim \{a_n - b_n\} = a - b$; $\lim \{a_n b_n\} = ab$; and, if $b \neq 0$, $\lim \left\{\dfrac{a_n}{b_n}\right\} = \dfrac{a}{b}$. (§ 10–5)

5. If any three of the numbers a, d, n, l, and S_n for a finite arithmetic series are known, we can find the other two. If any three of the numbers a, r, n, l, and S_n for a finite geometric series are known, we can find the other two. (§ 10–6)

6. An infinite series is convergent (has a sum S) if the limit of the sequence of partial sums exists; an infinite series is divergent if such a limit does not exist. This concept may be used to aid our understanding of infinite geometric series, nonterminating repeating decimals, and infinite power series. (§ 10–7)

7. The binomial theorem for $(a + b)^n$ with positive integral values of n may be extended to obtain a binomial series. (§ 10–8)

SEQUENCES, SERIES, AND LIMITS

8. The method of mathematical induction may be used to prove that some statements involving a variable n are true for all positive integral values of n. (§ 10–9)

9. The area bounded by the x-axis, the lines $x = a$ and $x = b$, and the graph of a continuous function $f(x)$ where $0 \leq f(x)$ for $a \leq x \leq b$ is equal to the limit as n increases of the sum of n inner rectangles on equal subintervals of the line segment from $(a, 0)$ to $(b, 0)$. Outer rectangles, and indeed any rectangle with height $f(x_j)$ where x_j is on the jth subinterval, may be used. (§ 10–10)

10. If a function $f(x)$ is continuous at $x = a$, then $\lim_{x \to a} f(x)$ exists and is equal to $f(a)$. (§ 10–11)

11. The average rate of change of a function $f(x)$ with respect to x over an interval Δx is $\dfrac{\Delta f(x)}{\Delta x}$; the instantaneous rate of change is $\lim_{\Delta x \to 0} \dfrac{\Delta f(x)}{\Delta x}$, if the limit exists. The instantaneous rate of change is also called the derivative. (§ 10–12)

12. The following words have been introduced or used extensively in this chapter:

area (§§ 10–1, 10–10)
arithmetic mean (§ 10–6)
arithmetic progression (§ 10–6)
arithmetic sequence (§ 10–6)
arithmetic series (§ 10–6)
average (§ 10–6)
average rate of change (§ 10–12)
binomial series (§ 10–8)
common difference (§ 10–6)
common ratio (§ 10–6)
continuous function (§ 10–11)
convergent series (§ 10–7)
derivative (§ 10–12)
divergent series (§ 10–7)
domination principle (§ 10–5)
finite sequence (§ 10–2)
finite series (§ 10–6)
generator (§ 10–2)
geometric mean (§ 10–6)
geometric progression (§ 10–6)
geometric sequence (§ 10–6)
geometric series (§ 10–6)

infinite geometric series (§ 10–7)
infinite sequence (§ 10–2)
infinite series (§ 10–7)
inner rectangle (§ 10–1)
instantaneous rate of change (§ 10–12)
limit (§§ 10–1, 10–4, and 10–11)
mathematical induction (§ 10–9)
mean proportional (§ 10–6)
method of differences (§ 10–2)
method of exhaustion (§ 10–1)
null sequence (§ 10–3)
ordinate (§ 10–1)
outer rectangle (§ 10–1)
partial fractions (§ 10–7)
partial sums (§ 10–7)
power series (§ 10–7)
rate of change (§ 10–12)
sequence (§ 10–2)
slope of a graph (§ 10–12)
sum of a series (§§ 10–6, 10–7)
summation symbol (§ 10–10)

KEYED PRACTICE ON CHAPTER 10

1. Use inner rectangles as in the method of exhaustion to approximate the area of the triangle bounded by the coordinate axes and the line $3x + 4y = 12$ when the line segment from (0, 0) to (4, 0) is divided into eight equal subintervals. (§ 10–1)

2. Find the first five terms of the sequence $\{n^2 + (-1)^n\}$. (§ 10–2)

3. Find the next five terms of the sequence $4, 7, 12, 19, 28, \cdots$. (§ 10–2)

4. Use $\epsilon = 0.01$ and find an N_ϵ such that $|a_n| < \epsilon$ for all $n > N_\epsilon$ for the sequence $\left\{\dfrac{2n - 5}{n^2}\right\}$. (§ 10–3)

5. Find: $\lim \left\{\dfrac{2n - 3}{3n + 2}\right\}$. (§ 10–4)

6. Find, if it exists, the $\lim \left\{\dfrac{n(n - 1)}{2n^2 + 5}\right\}$. (§ 10–5)

7. Determine whether the sequence $-2, 4, 10, \cdots$ is arithmetic or geometric, and find the seventh term. (§ 10–6)

8. Find the sum of the infinite geometric series $25, 5, 1, \cdots$. (§ 10–7)

9. Find the first five terms of the binomial series for $(1 - 2x)^{\frac{1}{3}}$. (§ 10–8)

10. Prove by mathematical induction that for every natural number n
$$2 + 2^2 + 2^3 + \cdots + 2^n = 2(2^n - 1).$$ (§ 10–9)

11. Evaluate: $\sum_{j=2}^{5} (j^2 - 1)$. (§ 10–10)

12. Find the area under the graph of $y = x^2 + 2$ over the interval $1 \leq x \leq 3$. (§ 10–10)

13. Find $\lim\limits_{x \to 3} \dfrac{x^2 - 9}{2x - 6}$. (§ 10–11)

14. Find an expression for the average rate of change of the function $y = x^2 - 2x + 5$ over the interval $1 \leq x \leq 3$. (§ 10–12)

15. Find the derivative of $f(x) = x^2 - x + 3$. (§ 10–12)

TESTS ON CHAPTER 10

A

1. Use inner rectangles as in the method of exhaustion to approximate the area bounded by the x-axis, the line $x = 2$, and the line $y = 4x$ when the line segment from (0, 0) to (2, 0) is divided into eight equal subintervals.

2. Find the first five terms of the sequence $\{2^n - n^2\}$.

3. Use $\epsilon = 0.01$ and find an N_ϵ such that $|a_n| < \epsilon$ for all $n > N_\epsilon$ for the sequence $\left\{\dfrac{n^2 - 1}{n^3 + 2}\right\}$.

SEQUENCES, SERIES, AND LIMITS

4. Find: $\lim \left\{ \dfrac{n!}{(n+2)!} \right\}$.

5. Determine whether the sequence 36, 12, 4, $\cdots$ is arithmetic or geometric and find the fifth term.

6. Find the sum of the infinite geometric series $18 + 6 + 2 + \cdots$.

7. Find the first five terms of the binomial series for $(1 - 3x)^{\frac{1}{2}}$.

8. Use a binomial series to find $\sqrt[6]{63}$ correct to two decimal places.

9. Evaluate $\displaystyle\sum_{j=2}^{6} (2j - 3)$.

10. Find $\displaystyle\lim_{x \to \pi} (x + \sin x)$.

B

1. Use outer rectangles to approximate the area bounded by the x-axis, the line $x = 2$, and the line $y = 4x$ when the line segment from $(0, 0)$ to $(2, 0)$ is divided into eight equal subintervals.

2. Find a generator for the sequence 5, 8, 11, 14, $\cdots$.

3. Use $\epsilon = 0.01$ and find an N_ϵ such that $|a_n| < \epsilon$ for all $n > N_\epsilon$ for the sequence $\left\{ \dfrac{5}{2^n} \right\}$.

4. Find $\lim \{f(n)\}$ when $f(n) = \dfrac{n^2 + n + 5}{5n^2 + 2n - 1}$.

5. Find the tenth term of the arithmetic sequence with third term 24 and eighth term 144.

6. Use a binomial series to find $\sqrt[3]{26}$ to two decimal places.

7. Prove by mathematical induction that for every natural number n we have $3 + 5 + 7 + \cdots + (2n + 1) = n(n + 2)$.

8. Find the area under the graph of $y = x^2 + 5$ over the interval $1 \le x \le 4$. Use $\displaystyle\sum_{j=1}^{n} j^2 = \dfrac{n(n+1)(2n+1)}{6}$.

9. Find $\displaystyle\lim_{x \to 2} \dfrac{x^2 + x - 6}{x - 2}$.

10. Find an expression for the derivative of $x^3 - 2x^2 + 7$ and evaluate the derivative at $x = 5$.

C

1. Use the method of differences and find the next five terms of the sequence 3, 10, 29, 66, 127, $\cdots$.

2. Determine whether or not $\{\log 10^{\frac{5}{n^2}}\}$ is a null sequence.

ANSWERS TO TEST YOURSELF EXERCISES

3. Find $\lim \left\{ \dfrac{\sin n}{n^2} \right\}$.

4. Determine whether the sequence $\dfrac{1}{6}, \dfrac{1}{4}, \dfrac{1}{3}, \cdots$ is arithmetic or geometric and find the twenty-third term.

5. Find $\sqrt[5]{240}$ correct to two decimal places.

6. Find the first five terms of an infinite geometric series with sum 9 and common ratio $-\dfrac{1}{3}$.

7. Prove by mathematical induction that for every natural number n the expression $x^{2n} - y^{2n}$ is divisible by $x + y$.

8. Find the area under the graph of $y = x^3 - 2x^2$ over the interval $1 \leq x \leq 4$. Use $\sum_{j=1}^{n} j^2 = \dfrac{n(n+1)(2n+1)}{6}$ and $\sum_{j=1}^{n} j^3 = \dfrac{n^2(n+1)^2}{4}$.

9. Find $\lim\limits_{x \to \pi} \dfrac{x}{\csc^2 x}$.

10. Find the derivative of $x^3 + x^2 - 3$ and evaluate the derivative at $x = 2$.

ANSWERS TO TEST YOURSELF EXERCISES

§ 10-1. **1.** $\dfrac{1}{2}$. **2.** $\dfrac{3}{4}$. **3.** $\dfrac{7}{8}$. **4.** $\dfrac{9}{10}$. **5.** (a) $\dfrac{1}{2}$; (b) $\dfrac{1}{4}$; (c) $\dfrac{1}{8}$; (d) $\dfrac{1}{10}$.

§ 10-2. **1.** 3, 9, 27, 81, 243. **6.** 25, 36, 49, 64.
2. 0, 6, 24, 60, 120. **7.** $a^{-2}, a^{-3}, a^{-4}, a^{-5}$.
3. 1, 2, 6, 24, 120. **8.** 27, 31, 35, 39.
4. $-1, 1, -1, 1, -1$. **9.** 28, 39, 52, 67.
5. 10, 12, 14, 16. **10.** 37, 67, 106, 154.

§ 10-3. **1.** (a) 50; (b) 5.
2. (a) $\{n^2 - 10^8\}$ is not a null sequence;
(b) $\{10^{2-n}\}$ is a null sequence.

§ 10-4. **1.** 2. **2.** The sequence has no limit. **3.** 2.
4. 3. **5.** The sequence has no limit. **6.** 0.

§ 10-5. **1.** 3. **2.** $\dfrac{2}{3}$. **3.** 0. **4.** The sequence has no limit. **5.** $a - 3b$.
6. $\dfrac{a}{b}$ if $b \neq 0$; the limit does not exist if $b = 0$.

591

SEQUENCES, SERIES, AND LIMITS

§ 10-6. **1.** $d = 3$; 14, 17, 20, 23. **2.** 119.
3. It is the thirty-second term. **4.** 9660.
5. $r = \sqrt{a}$; a^2, $a^2\sqrt{a}$, a^3, $a^3\sqrt{a}$. **6.** $a^6\sqrt{a}$.
7. 2188. **8.** $\dfrac{2186}{243}$.

§ 10-7. **1.** 16. **2.** $\dfrac{1250}{9}$. **3.** $\dfrac{4}{33}$. **4.** $\dfrac{7}{3}$.
5. $1; \dfrac{3}{2}; \dfrac{11}{6}; \dfrac{25}{12}$.
6. 1, 8, 27, 64, 125, 216, $\cdots$.
7. 1. **8.** $\sqrt{e} \approx 1.65$.

§ 10-8. **1.** $1 - \dfrac{3x}{2} + \dfrac{3x^2}{8} - \dfrac{x^3}{16}$.
2. $\dfrac{1}{8} - \dfrac{3x}{16} + \dfrac{3x^2}{16} - \dfrac{5x^3}{32}$. **3.** 5.03.

§ 10-9. **1.** When $n = 1$, $1 = \dfrac{1(2)}{2}$. If for $n = k$ we have

$$1 + 2 + 3 + \cdots + k = \dfrac{k(k + 1)}{2},$$

then for $n = k + 1$ we have

$$1 + 2 + 3 + \cdots + k + (k + 1) = \dfrac{k(k + 1)}{2} + (k + 1)$$

$$= \dfrac{k(k + 1) + 2(k + 1)}{2}$$

$$= \dfrac{(k + 1)[(k + 1) + 1]}{2}.$$

2. When $n = 1$, $1 \times 2 = \dfrac{1(2)(3)}{3}$. If for $n = k$ we have $1(2) + 2(3) + 3(4) + \cdots + k(k + 1) = \dfrac{k(k + 1)(k + 2)}{3}$, then for $n = k + 1$ we have

$$1(2) + 2(3) + 3(4) + \cdots + k(k + 1) + (k + 1)[(k + 1) + 1]$$

$$= \dfrac{k(k + 1)(k + 2)}{3} + (k + 1)[(k + 1) + 1]$$

$$= \dfrac{(k + 1)[(k + 1) + 1][(k + 1) + 2]}{3}.$$

3. When $n = 1$, $\dfrac{1}{1(2)} = \dfrac{1}{2}$. If for $n = k$ we have

$$\frac{1}{1(2)} + \frac{1}{2(3)} + \cdots + \frac{1}{k(k+1)} = \frac{k}{k+1}$$

then for $n = k + 1$ we have

$$\frac{1}{1(2)} + \frac{1}{2(3)} + \frac{1}{3(4)} + \cdots + \frac{1}{k(k+1)} + \frac{1}{(k+1)[(k+1)+1]}$$

$$= \frac{k}{k+1} + \frac{1}{(k+1)[(k+1)+1]} = \frac{k+1}{(k+1)+1}.$$

§ 10–10. **1.** $1^3 + 2^3 + 3^3 + 4^3 + 5^3$.
2. $5 - 6 + 7 - 8 + 9 - 10 + 11 - 12 + 13$.
3. $ar^0 + ar^1 + ar^2 + \cdots + ar^{n-1}$.
4. $\sum_{n=1}^{100} n$. **5.** $\sum_{n=3}^{17} n^2$. **6.** $\sum_{n=1}^{7} 2^n(-1)^{n-1} x_n$.
7. $\lim \dfrac{4}{n} \sum_{j=1}^{n} \left(\dfrac{4}{n}\right) j = 8$. **8.** $\lim \dfrac{1}{n} \sum_{j=1}^{n} \left[1 + j\left(\dfrac{1}{n}\right)\right]^2 = \dfrac{7}{3}$.

§ 10–11. **1.** 6. **2.** 12. **3.** 0.
4. $|f(x) - L| = |(x + 1) - 2| = |x - 1|$. Given any $\epsilon > 0$, take $\delta = \epsilon$; then for $|x - a| = |x - 1| < \delta$, $|f(x) - L| = |x - 1| < \epsilon$.

§ 10–12. **1.** $\dfrac{\Delta f(x)}{\Delta x} = 1$. **2.** $\dfrac{\Delta f(x)}{\Delta x} = \dfrac{28}{3}$.
3. $f'(x) = 3x^2 + 4$; $f'(3) = 31$.
4. $f'(x) = 18x + 6$; $f'(3) = 60$.

ANSWERS TO KEYED PRACTICE ON CHAPTER 10

1. $\dfrac{21}{4}$.

2. 0, 5, 8, 17, 24.

3. 39, 52, 67, 84, 103.

4. $N_\epsilon \geq 198$. Normally we would take $N_\epsilon \geq 200$ thereby avoiding superfluous calculations.

5. $\dfrac{2}{3}$.

6. $\dfrac{1}{2}$.

7. The sequence is arithmetic; $a_7 = 34$.

8. $\dfrac{125}{4}$.

9. $1 - \dfrac{2x}{3} - \dfrac{4x^2}{9} - \dfrac{40x^3}{81} - \dfrac{160x^4}{243}$.

10. When $n = 1$, $2 = 2$. If for $n = k$ we have
$$2 + 2^2 + 2^3 + \cdots + 2^k = 2(2^k - 1),$$
then for $n = k + 1$ we have
$$2 + 2^2 + 2^3 + \cdots + 2^k + 2^{k+1} = 2(2^k - 1) + 2^{k+1} = 2(2^{k+1} - 1).$$

11. 50.
12. $12\tfrac{2}{3}$.
13. 3.
14. $\dfrac{\Delta y}{\Delta x} = 2$.
15. $f'(x) = 2x - 1$.

Chapter 11

Vectors

§ 11-1 Numbers and vectors

Many physical objects have a property of *magnitude* associated with them. Whenever we speak of "how many" or "how much" we are talking about a magnitude. In order to discuss a magnitude of a physical object we must use a unit of measure for that type of magnitude (length, mass, area, volume, temperature, time, density, work, and so forth). In each case we think of a scale such as that in Figure 11-1.

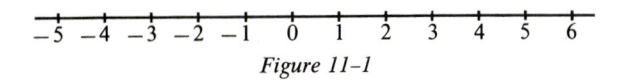

$$-5 \quad -4 \quad -3 \quad -2 \quad -1 \quad 0 \quad 1 \quad 2 \quad 3 \quad 4 \quad 5 \quad 6$$

Figure 11-1

Notice that any scale involves both a unit of measure and numbers. The numbers are called **scalars**. Since all points on a line can be associated with real numbers, all scalars are real numbers and are subject to the laws of ordinary algebra. In advanced mathematics courses the concept of scalar is extended to include complex numbers. However, we shall consider only real numbers as scalars.

Each magnitude of a physical object may be expressed as a real number of units relative to some convenient scale or unit of measure. The sum of the magnitudes of two similar quantities may be found by adding the numbers representing the magnitudes. For example, consider two time intervals, one of 2 hours and the other of 3 hours. Then the sum of these two time intervals is 5 hours. Consider also a man who spends $1.52 in one store and $2.31 in a second store. The total amount spent by the man in the two stores is $3.83.

There is also a class of physical quantities which possess the property of *direction* as well as magnitude. These quantities may not be combined by the ordinary laws of algebra. For example, suppose a man walks 2 miles east from a point A to a point B and then 3 miles north from the point B to a point C as in Figure 11-2. If we ask how far the man at C is from his starting point A, it would be incorrect to answer 5 miles. He walked

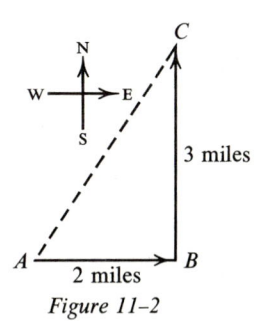

Figure 11-2

595

VECTORS

5 miles, but he is not 5 miles from his starting point. The two displacements A to B and B to C cannot be added in this fashion since displacements involve direction as well as magnitude.

Quantities which possess the property of direction as well as magnitude may be represented by directed line segments. We define any directed line segment to be a **vector**. Force, velocity, acceleration, and displacement are quantities which may be represented by vectors.

Since a vector is a directed line segment, it may be shown as an arrow such as that from A to B in Figure 11–3. The length of the directed line segment represents the magnitude of the vector according to the chosen arbitrary unit. The student should be careful to note that the line vector of Figure 11–3 may be on a line, on a plane, or in space.

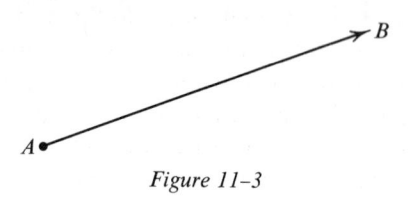

Figure 11–3

We use the notation $\overrightarrow{AB}$ for the vector represented in Figure 11–3. The point A is called the **origin** or **initial point** of $\overrightarrow{AB}$; the point B is called the **terminal point** of $\overrightarrow{AB}$. The notation $\overrightarrow{AB}$ is used here instead of the common notation $\overrightarrow{AB}$ since the latter has already been used for a ray. A vector has a finite magnitude (length); a ray does not. We denote the magnitude of $\overrightarrow{AB}$ by $|\overrightarrow{AB}|$. The magnitude of a vector is a scalar and is never negative.

We shall, for convenience, also use the notation $\vec{a}, \vec{b}, \vec{c}, \cdots$ for vectors and $|\vec{a}|, |\vec{b}|, |\vec{c}|, \cdots$ for their magnitudes. Whatever notation is used, it is necessary to distinguish between vectors and their magnitudes (scalars) since vectors and scalars satisfy different operations and algebraic laws.

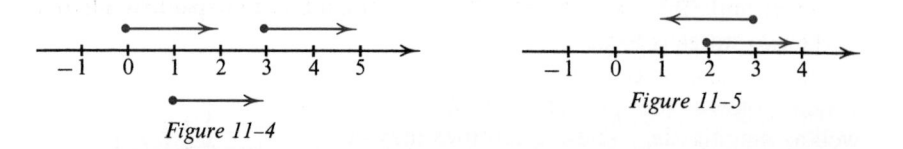

Figure 11–4

Figure 11–5

On a number line there are many ways of representing a signed number such as $+2$ in Figure 11–4. In each case $+2$ is represented by a directed line segment that is 2 units long and is directed in the positive sense. Each directed line segment is a vector. Any two of these vectors are *equal* since they have the same magnitude, are on the same line, and have the same (positive) sense. In Figure 11–5 two vectors are shown which are equal in

§ 11–1 NUMBERS AND VECTORS

magnitude but opposite in direction (or sense along the line). In general, two vectors are defined to be **equal** if and only if they have the same magnitude, are on the same or parallel lines, and have the same sense. In other words, two vectors are equal if they have the same magnitude and **direction.**

We have defined a vector to be a directed line segment. Any two line segments with the same directions and magnitudes are equal vectors. Some mathematicians prefer to define a vector as a class of all directed line segments with a given magnitude and direction. Then each directed line segment is merely one of many representations for a vector; there are equivalent representations for a given vector rather than equivalent vectors as we have defined them. This same situation arises in arithmetic where there are equivalent quotients of integers representing a given rational number rather than equivalent rational numbers. For example, $\frac{2}{3}, \frac{4}{6}, \frac{10}{15}$ are equivalent representations of the same rational number.

In mathematics a vector may be replaced by its equal at any time. Therefore the origins of vectors on a line, plane, or space are immaterial and only direction and magnitude need be considered. However in certain physical applications the origin (that is, the point of application) may need to be considered. If $\vec{a}$ and $\vec{b}$ are equal vectors as in Figure 11–6, we write $\vec{a} = \vec{b}$.

Each vector of magnitude 1 will be called a **unit vector.** A vector $\vec{a}$ will be defined as the **zero vector** or **null vector** $\vec{0}$ if $|\vec{a}| = 0$. We shall consider a null vector as having no direction. Thus its direction is undefined; its length is zero. The symbol $-\vec{a}$ will be used to represent a vector equal in magnitude to $\vec{a}$ but having the opposite direction, as illustrated in Figures 11–5 and 11–7.

Figure 11–6

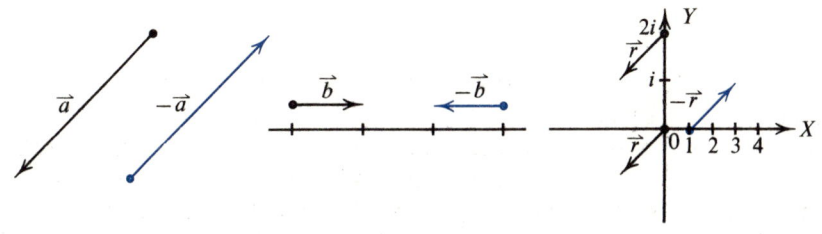

Figure 11–7

VECTORS

TEST YOURSELF

On a number line draw two vectors representing each of these numbers:

1. $+3$. **2.** -1. **3.** $-\pi$.

On a complex plane draw two vectors representing each of these numbers:

4. $3 + 4i$. **5.** i. **6.** $-1 + 2i$.

EXERCISES

On a number line draw two vectors representing each of these numbers:

1. $+1$. **3.** 2.1. **5.** $\pi/2$.
2. -2. **4.** 2π. **6.** $\sqrt{2}$.

On a complex plane draw two vectors representing each of these numbers:

7. $2 + i$. **8.** $1 - 2i$. **9.** $-2 + 0.5i$.

• • •

10. πi. **12.** $(1 - i)^2$. • **14.** $e^{\pi i}$.

11. $2 + \sqrt{-3}$. • **13.** $\sqrt{2 - \sqrt{3}}$. • **15.** $e^{\frac{\pi i}{2}}$.

• **16.** Describe **(a)** the magnitude and **(b)** the direction (in terms of the positive angle formed with the positive real axis) of each vector in Exercises 1 through 12.

§ 11-2 Addition and subtraction of vectors

Many centuries ago the law of vector addition was discovered empirically (that is, by observing many examples of it). The two displacements represented by $\overrightarrow{AB}$ and $\overrightarrow{BC}$ in Figure 11-2 have already been mentioned as vectors. In that problem we may observe that the result of adding these two displacements is the displacement from A to C. Hence, $\overrightarrow{AC} = \overrightarrow{AB} + \overrightarrow{BC}$.

Consideration of the displacement problem leads us to the following **law of vector addition:**

Given any two vectors $\vec{a}$ and $\vec{b}$, construct a vector $\vec{b'}$ equal to $\vec{b}$ and such that its origin coincides with the terminal point of $\vec{a}$. The vector $\vec{c}$ with the origin of $\vec{a}$ and the terminal point of $\vec{b'}$ is equal to the vector sum

§ 11-2 ADDITION AND SUBTRACTION OF VECTORS

$(\vec{a} + \vec{b})$. Notice that the vector $\vec{c}$ equal to $(\vec{a} + \vec{b})$ is completely determined;

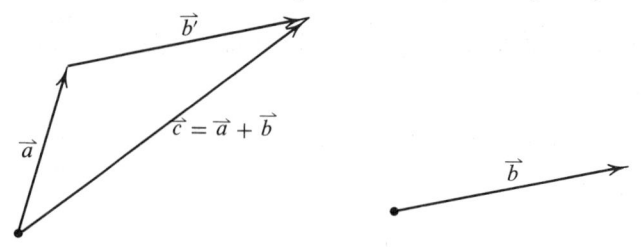

Figure 11-8

that is, the sum of two vectors is a *uniquely* determined vector.

The fundamental properties of the addition of real numbers also hold for the addition of vectors. For example,

$$\vec{a} + \vec{b} = \vec{b} + \vec{a}, \tag{1}$$

$$(\vec{a} + \vec{b}) + \vec{c} = \vec{a} + (\vec{b} + \vec{c}). \tag{2}$$

That is, (1) vectors satisfy the commutative law of addition, and (2) vectors satisfy the associative law of addition. These results are illustrated geometrically in Figures 11-9 and 11-10.

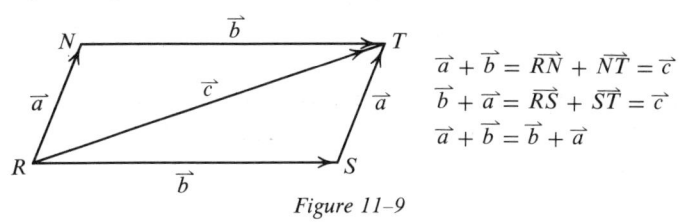

$$\vec{a} + \vec{b} = \vec{RN} + \vec{NT} = \vec{c}$$
$$\vec{b} + \vec{a} = \vec{RS} + \vec{ST} = \vec{c}$$
$$\vec{a} + \vec{b} = \vec{b} + \vec{a}$$

Figure 11-9

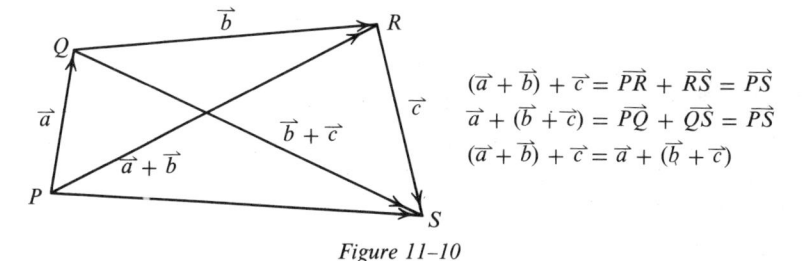

$$(\vec{a} + \vec{b}) + \vec{c} = \vec{PR} + \vec{RS} = \vec{PS}$$
$$\vec{a} + (\vec{b} + \vec{c}) = \vec{PQ} + \vec{QS} = \vec{PS}$$
$$(\vec{a} + \vec{b}) + \vec{c} = \vec{a} + (\vec{b} + \vec{c})$$

Figure 11-10

The vector law of addition is sometimes called the **triangle law** or the **parallelogram law of vectors.** The source of these terms is evident in Figures 11-8 and 11-9. If two vectors $\vec{a}$ and $\vec{b}$ are drawn from the same origin as in Figure 11-11, their difference $\vec{a} - \vec{b}$ is defined to be the vector extending from the terminal point of $\vec{b}$ to the terminal point of $\vec{a}$. In Figures

VECTORS

11-11 and 11-12, we see that $\vec{a} - \vec{b} = \vec{a} + (-\vec{b})$.

$\vec{a} = \vec{RT}, \vec{b} = \vec{RS}, \vec{a} - \vec{b} = \vec{ST}, -\vec{b} = \vec{SR};$
$\vec{ST} = \vec{SR} + \vec{RT}; \vec{a} - \vec{b} = (-\vec{b}) + \vec{a} = \vec{a} + (-\vec{b}).$

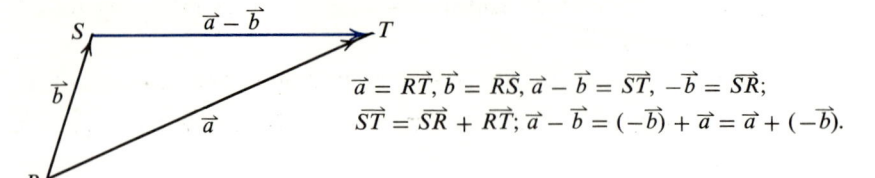

Figure 11-11

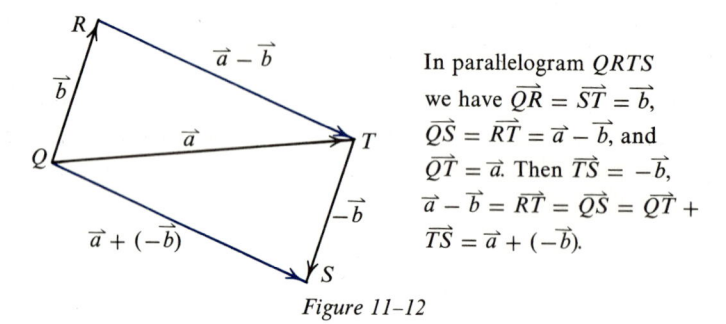

In parallelogram $QRTS$ we have $\vec{QR} = \vec{ST} = \vec{b}$, $\vec{QS} = \vec{RT} = \vec{a} - \vec{b}$, and $\vec{QT} = \vec{a}$. Then $\vec{TS} = -\vec{b}$, $\vec{a} - \vec{b} = \vec{RT} = \vec{QS} = \vec{QT} + \vec{TS} = \vec{a} + (-\vec{b})$.

Figure 11-12

TEST YOURSELF

1. Give a geometric illustration of the fact that $\vec{a} - (-\vec{b}) = \vec{a} + \vec{b}$.

2. Draw vectors from the center of a square to each vertex and explain why the sum of the four vectors is a zero vector.

EXERCISES

1. Explain why $\vec{AB} + \vec{BC} + \vec{CD} = \vec{AD}$ for any points A, B, C, and D.

2. Explain why $\vec{AB} + \vec{BC} + \vec{CA} = \vec{0}$ for any triangle ABC.

3. If $\vec{a}$ and $\vec{b}$ are vectors forming consecutive sides $\vec{AB}$ and $\vec{BC}$ of a parallelogram $ABCD$, find **(a)** the vectors forming the other two sides taken in order and **(b)** the vectors representing the diagonals.

• • •

4. Give a geometric illustration of the fact that $\vec{a} - (\vec{b} - \vec{c}) = (\vec{a} + \vec{c}) - \vec{b}$.

5. If $\vec{a}$ and $\vec{b}$ are vectors forming consecutive sides of a regular hexagon, find the vectors forming each of the other four sides taken in order.

§ 11-3 MULTIPLICATION OF A VECTOR BY A SCALAR

6. If $\vec{a}, \vec{b}, \vec{c}$, and $\vec{d}$ are vectors from a point O to the coplanar points A, B, C, and D respectively, and if $\vec{b} - \vec{a} = \vec{c} - \vec{d}$, explain why $ABCD$ must be a parallelogram.

7. If $\vec{a}$ and $\vec{b}$ are two vectors acting at an angle of 45° to each other, construct the vectors: (a) $2\vec{a}$, that is, $\vec{a} + \vec{a}$; (b) $\vec{a} + 2\vec{b}$; (c) $3\vec{a} - \vec{b}$; (d) $-2\vec{a} - 2\vec{b}$.

● **8.** Use the commutative and associative laws for vector addition to prove that $(\vec{a} + \vec{b}) + \vec{c} = (\vec{a} + \vec{c}) + \vec{b}$.

● **9.** From the center of a regular pentagon vectors are drawn to each of its vertices. Explain why the sum of the five vectors must be zero.

● **10.** The vectors $\vec{a}, \vec{b}$, and $\vec{c}$, have a common origin and form adjacent edges of a parallelepiped. Use a figure to show that the vector $(\vec{a} + \vec{b} + \vec{c})$ forms a diagonal of the parallelepiped.

● **11.** Give a geometric basis for each of these statements:

(a) $|\vec{a} + \vec{b}| \leq |\vec{a}| + |\vec{b}|$;
(b) $|\vec{a} - \vec{b}| \geq |\vec{a}| - |\vec{b}|$.

● **12.** Two forces of 50 pounds and 80 pounds respectively act at an angle of 60° on an object. Find to three significant digits the magnitude and direction of the vector sum.

● **13.** The wind drives a steamer east with a force which would give it a speed of 12 knots. The steamer's propeller is driving it southeast with a force which would give it a speed of 15 knots. Find the distance it will actually travel in an hour, and the direction of its course.

§ 11-3 Multiplication of a vector by a scalar

If we multiply a vector $\vec{a}$ by a real number m, the product $m\vec{a}$ is defined to be a vector parallel to $\vec{a}$ and with magnitude $|m|$ times the magnitude of $\vec{a}$;

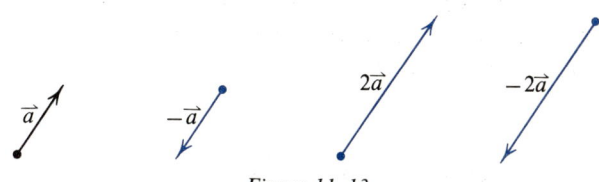

Figure 11-13

that is, $|m\vec{a}| = |m| |\vec{a}|$. If m is positive, the new vector $m\vec{a}$ is parallel to $\vec{a}$ and in the same sense; if m is negative, $m\vec{a}$ is parallel to $\vec{a}$ and in the op-

VECTORS

posite sense. Figure 11-13 shows the results of multiplying $\vec{a}$ by scalars -1, 2, and -2. From Figure 11-13 it can be seen that $-\vec{a}$ need not be considered as a new type of vector at all, but merely the product of the scalar -1 and the vector $\vec{a}$.

The multiplication of a vector by a scalar satisfies the distributive and associative laws:

$$(m + n)\vec{a} = m\vec{a} + n\vec{a}, \tag{3}$$

$$m(\vec{a} + \vec{b}) = m\vec{a} + m\vec{b}, \tag{4}$$

$$m(\vec{a} - \vec{b}) = m\vec{a} - m\vec{b}, \tag{5}$$

$$m(n\vec{a}) = (mn)\vec{a}. \tag{6}$$

Each of these laws may be illustrated geomtrically (Exercise 13).

If $|\vec{a}|$ and $|\vec{b}|$ are any two given real numbers both different from zero, then there exist real numbers m and n such that $|\vec{a}| = m|\vec{b}|$ and $|\vec{b}| = n|\vec{a}|$. Accordingly, if $\vec{a}$ and $\vec{b}$ are parallel vectors and neither vector is a zero vector, then for a suitable choice of sign for the scalar, each vector may be expressed as a scalar multiple of the other; that is, $\vec{a} = m\vec{b}$ and $\vec{b} = n\vec{a}$. We use this relation to prove that one vector is parallel to another. A vector $\vec{a}$ that is not a zero vector is **parallel** to a vector $\vec{b}$ that is not a zero vector if and only if $\vec{a}$ can be expressed as a scalar multiple of $\vec{b}$. Remember that we do not associate any direction with a zero vector and thus a zero vector cannot be parallel to any other vector.

Any two distinct points O and U determine a line, $\overleftrightarrow{OU}$; a line segment, $\overline{OU}$; two rays, $\overrightarrow{OU}$ and $\overrightarrow{UO}$; and two vectors $\overrightarrow{OU}$ and $\overrightarrow{UO}$. Each point P on the line has a coordinate p on the number scale for which O has coordinate 0 and U has coordinate 1; that is, $\overrightarrow{OP} = |p|\overrightarrow{OU}$ and therefore $|\overrightarrow{OP}| = |p||\overrightarrow{OU}|$. For any point P on $\overrightarrow{OU}$ we have $\overrightarrow{OP} = p\overrightarrow{OU}$. Thus the mid-point M of $\overline{OU}$ may be identified by the vector equation $\overrightarrow{OM} = \frac{1}{2}\overrightarrow{OU}$; the point Q two-thirds of the way from O to U may be identified by $\overrightarrow{OQ} = \frac{2}{3}\overrightarrow{OU}$; and so forth (Figure 11-14).

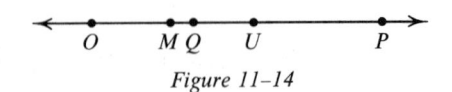

Figure 11-14

§ 11-3 MULTIPLICATION OF A VECTOR BY A SCALAR

The following properties of equations involving vectors correspond to common properties of equations involving only real numbers and are postulated so that they may be used in proofs. Note that they are actually the equality axioms; that is, properties of equations.

If $\vec{a} = \vec{b}$, then $\vec{a} + \vec{c} = \vec{b} + \vec{c}$. (7)

If $\vec{a} = \vec{b}$ and $\vec{c} = \vec{d}$, then $\vec{a} + \vec{c} = \vec{b} + \vec{d}$. (8)

If $\vec{a} = \vec{b}$ and $\vec{c} = \vec{d}$, then $\vec{a} - \vec{c} = \vec{b} - \vec{d}$. (9)

If $\vec{a} = \vec{b}$ and m is a scalar, then $m\vec{a} = m\vec{b}$. (10)

Example 1. Prove that the line segment joining the mid-points of any two sides of a triangle is parallel to the third side and is equal to one-half the length of the third side.

Let ABC represent any triangle. For the mid-point M of $\overline{CA}$ we have $\overrightarrow{CM} = \frac{1}{2}\overrightarrow{CA} = \overrightarrow{MA}$; for the mid-point N of $\overline{CB}$ we have $\overrightarrow{CN} = \frac{1}{2}\overrightarrow{CB} = \overrightarrow{NB}$ as in Figure 11-15. Then by the definition of subtraction

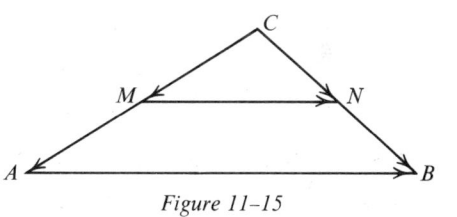

Figure 11-15

$$\overrightarrow{MN} = \overrightarrow{CN} - \overrightarrow{CM};$$

after replacing $\overrightarrow{CN}$ and $\overrightarrow{CM}$ by their equals, we have

$$\overrightarrow{MN} = \frac{1}{2}\overrightarrow{CB} - \frac{1}{2}\overrightarrow{CA};$$

and by the distributive law (5)

$$\overrightarrow{MN} = \frac{1}{2}(\overrightarrow{CB} - \overrightarrow{CA}).$$

However, $\overrightarrow{CB} - \overrightarrow{CA} = \overrightarrow{AB}$ by the definition of subtraction; so

$$\overrightarrow{MN} = \frac{1}{2}\overrightarrow{AB}.$$

In other words, $\overrightarrow{MN}$ is parallel to $\overrightarrow{AB}$ and $\overrightarrow{MN} = \frac{1}{2}\overrightarrow{AB}$.

VECTORS

Example 2. Prove that the diagonals of a parallelogram bisect each other.

Let $ABCD$ represent any parallelogram, and let M be the mid-point of $\overline{BD}$. As in Figure 11–16 $\overrightarrow{AD} = \overrightarrow{BC}$ since the opposite sides of a parallelogram are parallel and equal;

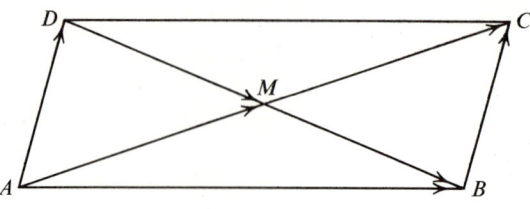

Figure 11–16

$\overrightarrow{DM} = \overrightarrow{MB}$ since M is the mid-point of line segment BD. Then

$$\overrightarrow{AM} = \overrightarrow{AD} + \overrightarrow{DM} = \overrightarrow{BC} + \overrightarrow{MB},$$
$$\overrightarrow{MC} = \overrightarrow{MB} + \overrightarrow{BC} = \overrightarrow{BC} + \overrightarrow{MB},$$

and $\overrightarrow{AM} = \overrightarrow{MC}.$

Therefore, $\overrightarrow{AM}$ is parallel to $\overrightarrow{MC}$; the points A, M, and C must be collinear; and M is the mid-point of the diagonal $\overline{AC}$.

TEST YOURSELF

1. Use the given vectors and construct $(3\vec{p} - 2\vec{q})$.

2. Parallelogram $ABCD$ is given with $\overrightarrow{AM} = \frac{1}{2}\overrightarrow{AB}$ and $\overrightarrow{DN} = \frac{1}{2}\overrightarrow{DC}$. Prove that $AMCN$ is a parallelogram.

EXERCISES

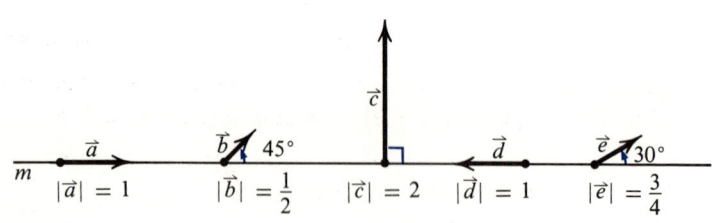

$|\vec{a}| = 1$ $\quad |\vec{b}| = \frac{1}{2}$ $\quad |\vec{c}| = 2$ $\quad |\vec{d}| = 1$ $\quad |\vec{e}| = \frac{3}{4}$

Copy the given vectors $\vec{a}$, $\vec{b}$, $\vec{c}$, $\vec{d}$, $\vec{e}$ and use them to construct by ruler and protractor (or compasses) each of the following vectors listed in Exercises 1 through 8:

1. $3\vec{b}$.
2. $2\vec{a} + \vec{c}$.
3. $2\vec{a} - \vec{d}$.
4. $3\vec{b} + 2\vec{c}$.

5. $\vec{a} - \vec{c} + 2\vec{b}$.

6. $2\vec{a} + \vec{c} - \frac{1}{2}\vec{e}$.

7. $2\vec{b} + \vec{d} - \vec{e}$.

8. $\vec{e} - 2\vec{b} - \vec{d}$.

• 9. Give an interpretation of $\dfrac{\vec{p}}{|\vec{p}|}$.

• 10. Explain why any vector is parallel to itself.

• 11. Prove that the median of a trapezoid is parallel to the bases and equals one-half their sum.

• 12. Prove that the line segment joining the mid-points of the two diagonals of a trapezoid is parallel to the bases and equal to one-half their difference.

• 13. Illustrate geometrically each of the laws (3), (4), (5), and (6).

§ 11-4 Linear functions

Consider a line t on which we choose a vector $\vec{a}$ as indicated in Figure 11-17. As mentioned in § 11-3 every vector on line t is some multiple

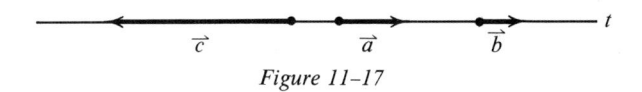

Figure 11-17

of $\vec{a}$ since every vector on t and different from the zero vector, is parallel to $\vec{a}$. For example, if $\vec{b}$ is a vector on t and in the same sense as $\vec{a}$ such that $|\vec{b}| = \frac{1}{2}|\vec{a}|$, then $\vec{b} = \frac{1}{2}\vec{a}$. Similarly, if $\vec{c}$ is a vector on t in the opposite sense to a such that $|\vec{c}| = 2|\vec{a}|$, then $\vec{c} = -2\vec{a}$. Both $\vec{b}$ and $\vec{c}$ are called linear functions of $\vec{a}$. In general, any expression such as $m_1\vec{a}_1 + m_2\vec{a}_2 + \cdots + m_n\vec{a}_n$ obtained by the addition of a set of scalar multiples of n vectors is called a **linear function** of those n vectors.

In Figure 11-18 the unit vector along the x-axis is $\vec{a}$ and the unit vector along the y-axis is $\vec{b}$. Any vector $\vec{c}$ in the xy-plane may be represented by $\overrightarrow{OP}$ for

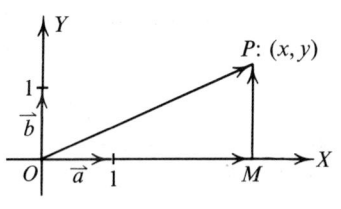

Figure 11-18

VECTORS

some point $P: (x, y)$. However, $\overrightarrow{OP} = \overrightarrow{OM} + \overrightarrow{MP}$, $\overrightarrow{OM} = x\vec{a}$, and $\overrightarrow{MP} = y\vec{b}$ where x and y are real numbers, that is, scalars. Thus $\overrightarrow{OP} = x\vec{a} + y\vec{b}$. In other words, any vector $\vec{c}$ in the xy-plane may be expressed as a linear function of the unit vectors along the x-axis and the y-axis. In general we have the following theorem:

Theorem 1. *If $\vec{a}$ and $\vec{b}$ are any two nonparallel, nonzero vectors on a plane and if $\vec{c}$ is any vector on that plane, then $\vec{c}$ may be expressed as a linear function of $\vec{a}$ and $\vec{b}$; that is, there exist scalars m and n such that $\vec{c} = m\vec{a} + n\vec{b}$.*

PROOF: If $\vec{c}$ is parallel to $\vec{a}$, then $\vec{c} = m\vec{a}$ and $n = 0$; if $\vec{c}$ is parallel to $\vec{b}$, then $\vec{c} = n\vec{b}$ and $m = 0$. If $\vec{c}$ is not parallel to either $\vec{a}$ or $\vec{b}$, then there exists a parallelogram $PQRS$ with $\vec{c}$ as its diagonal $\overrightarrow{PR}$ and with edges parallel to $\vec{a}$ and $\vec{b}$. Vectors parallel to $\vec{a}$ and $\vec{b}$ can be expressed as multiples of $\vec{a}$ and $\vec{b}$; suppose $\overrightarrow{PQ} = m\vec{a}$ and $\overrightarrow{QR} = n\vec{b}$. Then, as in Figure 11–19, $\vec{c} = m\vec{a} + n\vec{b}$, where m and n are scalars and $\vec{c}$ is a linear function of $\vec{a}$ and $\vec{b}$.

Figure 11–19

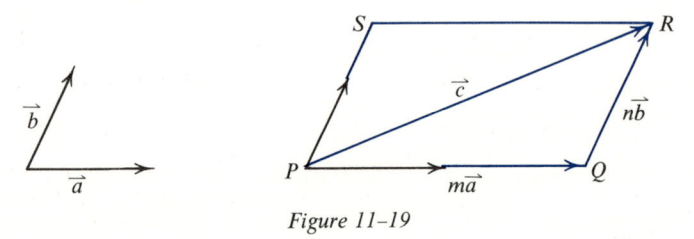

We next consider the conditions under which three vectors with a common origin have their terminal points on a line. Suppose that $\vec{a}$ and $\vec{b}$ have a common origin O. Let $\vec{c}$ be any vector whose origin is O and whose terminal point C lies on a line through the terminal points A and B of $\vec{a}$ and $\vec{b}$ as in Figure 11–20.

The vectors $\overrightarrow{BC}$, $\overrightarrow{BA}$, and $\overrightarrow{CA}$ are parallel vectors. Therefore, $\overrightarrow{BC} = m\overrightarrow{BA}$ for some scalar m and $\overrightarrow{CA} = n\overrightarrow{BA}$ for some scalar n.

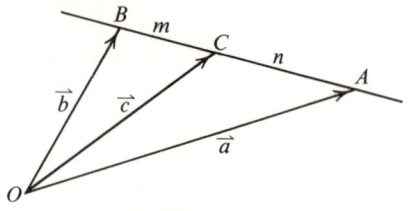

Figure 11–20

Since $\overrightarrow{BC} + \overrightarrow{CA} = \overrightarrow{BA}$, we have, after substituting, $m\overrightarrow{BA} + n\overrightarrow{BA} = (m+n)\overrightarrow{BA} = \overrightarrow{BA}$ and $m + n = 1$. In terms of the vectors $\tilde{a}$, $\tilde{b}$, and $\tilde{c}$, we have

$$\overrightarrow{BA} = \tilde{a} - \tilde{b};$$
$$\overrightarrow{BC} = m(\tilde{a} - \tilde{b});$$
$$\tilde{c} = \overrightarrow{OB} + \overrightarrow{BC} = \tilde{b} + m(\tilde{a} - \tilde{b}) = m\tilde{a} + (1-m)\tilde{b};$$

that is, $\tilde{c} = m\tilde{a} + n\tilde{b}$.

We have proved that if C is on the line AB, then $\tilde{c} = m\tilde{a} + n\tilde{b}$ where $m + n = 1$.

Conversely, if $\tilde{c} = m\tilde{a} + n\tilde{b}$ and $m + n = 1$, then the point C must lie on the line BA since this given equation may be written in each of these forms:

$$\tilde{c} = (1-n)\tilde{a} + n\tilde{b},$$
$$\tilde{c} - \tilde{a} = n(\tilde{b} - \tilde{a}).$$

Thus, $\overrightarrow{AC} = n\overrightarrow{AB}$; in other words, $\overrightarrow{AC}$ is parallel to $\overrightarrow{AB}$, then line segment AC lies along line segment AB, and the point C lies on line AB. We have proved the following theorem:

Theorem 2. *The end points A, B, and C of three vectors $\overrightarrow{OA}$, $\overrightarrow{OB}$, and $\overrightarrow{OC}$ are collinear if and only if $\overrightarrow{OC} = (1-n)\overrightarrow{OA} + n\overrightarrow{OB}$ for some scalar n.*

Several common theorems from geometry may be proved, as in the following examples. We use Theorem 2 and the fact that equations involving vectors have many of the properties of ordinary equations involving only scalars.

Example. Prove that the three medians of a triangle are concurrent at a point which is two-thirds of the distance from a vertex to the opposite side.

Let A', B', C' be the mid-points of sides $\overline{BC}$, $\overline{CA}$, and $\overline{AB}$ of triangle ABC, as in Figure 11–21.

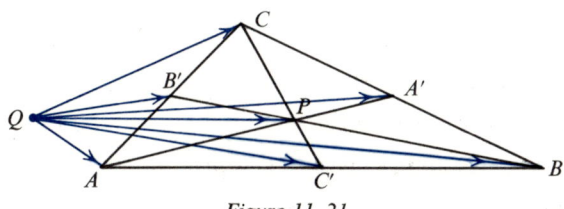

Figure 11–21

VECTORS

Let Q be any reference point. Then

$$\overrightarrow{QA'} = \frac{1}{2}\overrightarrow{QB} + \frac{1}{2}\overrightarrow{QC},$$

$$\overrightarrow{QB'} = \frac{1}{2}\overrightarrow{QA} + \frac{1}{2}\overrightarrow{QC},$$

and by subtraction $\overrightarrow{QA'} - \overrightarrow{QB'} = \frac{1}{2}\overrightarrow{QB} - \frac{1}{2}\overrightarrow{QA}$. If we add $\left(\overrightarrow{QB'} + \frac{1}{2}\overrightarrow{QA}\right)$ to both members of this equation, we have

$$\overrightarrow{QA'} + \frac{1}{2}\overrightarrow{QA} = \overrightarrow{QB'} + \frac{1}{2}\overrightarrow{QB}.$$

Each point on $\overleftrightarrow{AA'}$ is the terminal point of a vector $m\overrightarrow{QA'} + n\overrightarrow{QA}$ where $m + n = 1$. Each point on $\overleftrightarrow{BB'}$ is the terminal point of a vector $r\overrightarrow{QB'} + s\overrightarrow{QB}$ where $r + s = 1$.

The sum of the scalar coefficients in each member of the last vector equation is $\frac{3}{2}$. If we multiply both members by $\frac{2}{3}$, we obtain scalar coefficients whose sum is 1 in each member;

$$\frac{2}{3}\overrightarrow{QA'} + \frac{1}{3}\overrightarrow{QA} = \frac{2}{3}\overrightarrow{QB'} + \frac{1}{3}\overrightarrow{QB}.$$

This equation asserts that the point of $\overleftrightarrow{AA'}$ that is two-thirds of the distance from A to A' is the terminal point of the same vector as the point of $\overleftrightarrow{BB'}$ that is two-thirds of the distance from B to B'. In other words, $\overleftrightarrow{AA'}$ and $\overleftrightarrow{BB'}$ intersect at a point P that is two-thirds of the distance from A to A'.

We next consider the medians $\overline{CC'}$ and $\overline{AA'}$. Since their point of intersection must divide $\overline{AA'}$ in the ratio of 2:1 by the same argument as for $\overline{BB'}$, the median $\overline{CC'}$ passes through P and is divided in the same ratio.

TEST YOURSELF

1. Use the vectors identified in the given figure and express $\overrightarrow{OP}$ as a linear function of: **(a)** $\overrightarrow{OA}$ and $\overrightarrow{OB}$; **(b)** $\overrightarrow{OC}$ and $\overrightarrow{OD}$; **(c)** $\overrightarrow{OA}$ and $\overrightarrow{OD}$; **(d)** $\overrightarrow{OC}$ and $\overrightarrow{OB}$.

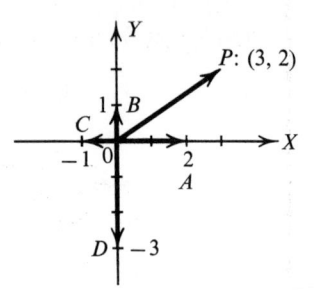

608

§ 11-4 LINEAR FUNCTIONS

2. Prove that the terminal points of the vectors $\overrightarrow{OB}$, $\overrightarrow{OA}$, and $\overrightarrow{OA} + \frac{1}{3}(\overrightarrow{OB} - \overrightarrow{OA})$ are collinear.

3. Prove that if $\overrightarrow{AM} + \overrightarrow{AM} = \overrightarrow{AB} + \overrightarrow{AC}$, then M is the mid-point of $\overline{BC}$.

EXERCISES

In Exercises 1 through 6 express each vector as a linear function of **(a)** $\overrightarrow{OA}$ and $\overrightarrow{OB}$, **(b)** $\overrightarrow{OC}$ and $\overrightarrow{OD}$, and **(c)** $\overrightarrow{OC}$ and $\overrightarrow{OS}$:

1. $\overrightarrow{OP}$.

2. $\overrightarrow{OQ}$.

3. $\overrightarrow{OR}$.

4. $\overrightarrow{OT}$.

5. $\overrightarrow{OS}$.

6. $\overrightarrow{OB}$.

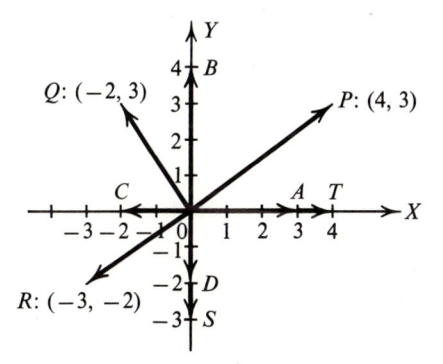

7. Identify $P, Q, A,$ and B as in Exercise 1 and express **(a)** $\overrightarrow{OA}$ and **(b)** $\overrightarrow{OB}$ as linear functions of $\overrightarrow{OP}$ and $\overrightarrow{OQ}$.

8. Let $\vec{a} = \overrightarrow{OA}, \vec{b} = \overrightarrow{OB}$, and $\vec{c} = \overrightarrow{OC}$ for $O: (0, 0), A: (11, 5), B: (4, -2)$, and $C: (7, 1)$. **(a)** Express $\vec{c}$ as a linear function of $\vec{a}$ and $\vec{b}$. **(b)** Use Theorem 2 to prove whether or not the points A, B, and C are collinear. **(c)** If the points are collinear, find the ratio of $\overline{AC}$ to $\overline{CB}$ and express this ratio in terms of the coefficients of $\vec{a}$ and $\vec{b}$ in (a).

9. Repeat Exercise 8 for $O: (0, 0), A: (-5, -6), B: (2, 1),$ and $C: (19, 18)$.

10. Repeat Exercise 8 for $O: (0, 0), A: (13, 0), B: (1, 12),$ and $C: (5, 7)$.

• • •

11. Use Theorem 2 and derive the formula $\overrightarrow{AM} = \frac{1}{2}\overrightarrow{AB} + \frac{1}{2}\overrightarrow{AC}$ for the mid-point M of $\overline{BC}$.

VECTORS

12. Prove: If M and N are mid-points of $\overline{AC}$ and $\overline{BD}$ respectively, then $\overrightarrow{AB} + \overrightarrow{AD} + \overrightarrow{CB} + \overrightarrow{CD} = 4\overrightarrow{MN}$.

13. Use Theorem 2 and prove that the line joining the mid-points of any two sides of a triangle is parallel to the third side and is equal to one-half the length of the third side.

14. Without using the results obtained or the methods used in Exercise 13 prove that the lines joining the mid-points of the sides of a skew quadrilateral (that is, a quadrilateral whose vertices are not all on the same plane) form a parallelogram.

15. Prove that the line joining a vertex of a parallelogram to the mid-point of an opposite side divides the diagonal in the ratio of 1:2.

● **16.** Prove that if points P_1, P_2, P_3 are collinear and are on the lines AB, BC, CA, respectively, determined by triangle ABC, then

$$\frac{\overline{AP_1}}{\overline{P_1B}} \times \frac{\overline{BP_2}}{\overline{P_2C}} \times \frac{\overline{CP_3}}{\overline{P_3A}} = 1.$$

§ 11-5 Rectangular cartesian coordinates

Any vector on a plane may be considered with reference to a rectangular coordinate system. For example, in § 11-4 we proved that any vector $\vec{c}$ on the xy-plane was equal to a vector $\overrightarrow{OP}$ with terminal point $P: (x, y)$ and may be expressed as a linear function $x\vec{a} + y\vec{b}$ of the unit vectors $\vec{a}$ and $\vec{b}$ along the x-axis and y-axis. We now introduce a set of rectangular cartesian coordinates for three-dimensional space in order to assist our discussion of vectors in space.

On a plane (Figure 11–18) we may use unit vectors $\vec{a}$ and $\vec{b}$ along two perpendicular lines (axes) and locate any point $P: (x, y)$ on that plane as the terminal point of a vector $\overrightarrow{OP}$ where O is the point of intersection of the axes and $\overrightarrow{OP} = x\vec{a} + y\vec{b}$. The unit vectors indicate both the units of length and the positive senses of measurements along the axes. The vector $x\vec{a}$ indicates the directed distance of the point P from the y-axis; the vector $y\vec{b}$ indicates the directed distance of the point P from the x-axis. Thus any point P and any vector $\overrightarrow{OP}$ on the xy-plane may be determined by the directed distances of the point P from two perpendicular lines.

In space we measure the distance of a point from a plane along a line perpendicular to the plane. We may determine any point P and any vector $\overrightarrow{OP}$ by the directed distances of P from three mutually perpendicular

§ 11-5 RECTANGULAR CARTESIAN COORDINATES

planes. Consider the xy-plane, yz-plane, and xz-plane as in § 1–7. Each of these planes is perpendicular to the other two. The pairs of planes intersect in three axes; the x-axis, y-axis, and z-axis as in Figure 11–22. The unit vectors along these axes are customarily called $\vec{i}, \vec{j}$, and $\vec{k}$ where $\vec{i}$ is the unit vector along the x-axis and should not be confused with the pure imaginary number i (that is, $\sqrt{-1}$), $\vec{j}$ is the unit vector along the y-axis, and $\vec{k}$ is the unit vector along the z-axis.

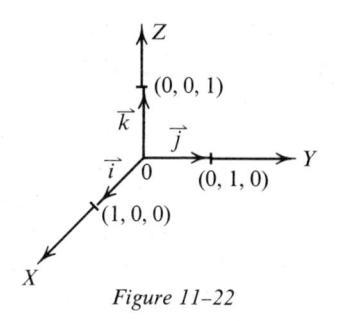

Figure 11–22

The three unit vectors are said to have a **right-handed orientation** if a right-handed screw when turned through the 90° angle from $\vec{i}$ to $\vec{j}$ would advance along the z-axis in the same sense as $\vec{k}$. We can also describe a coordinate system with a right-handed orientation (that is, a **right-handed system**) in terms of a person's right hand (Figure 11–23). Think of the thumb as pointing along the vector $\vec{i}$, the index finger as pointing along $\vec{j}$, and the next finger as pointing along $\vec{k}$. Thus in a right-handed coordinate system the thumb, index finger, and next finger of a person's right hand may be used to point in the positive senses along the x-axis, y-axis, and z-axis respectively.

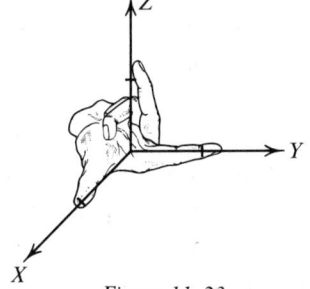

Figure 11–23

There also exist left-handed systems (Figure 11–24) in which the thumb, index finger, and next finger of a person's left hand may be used to point in the positive senses along the x-axis, y-axis, and z-axis. However, we shall use right-handed systems throughout our discussion of vectors.

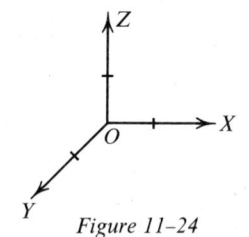

The common point of the three axes is the origin O of the coordinate system and is usually taken as the initial point of the three unit vectors.

Figure 11–24

Then these unit vectors $\vec{i}, \vec{j}, \vec{k}$ have terminal points (1, 0, 0), (0, 1, 0), and

611

VECTORS

(0, 0, 1) as in Figure 11–22. Any vector in space is equal to a vector $\overrightarrow{OP}$ with terminal point $P: (x, y, z)$. The vector $x\vec{i}$ indicates the directed distance of P from the yz-plane, the vector $y\vec{j}$ indicates the directed distance of P from the xz-plane, and the vector $z\vec{k}$ indicates the directed distance of P from the xy-plane. Thus any point P and any vector $\overrightarrow{OP}$, in space may be determined by the directed distances of the point P from three mutually perpendicular planes. The vector, $\overrightarrow{OP}$, is called the **position vector** of the point P.

The position vector of a point $P: (x_1, y_1, z_1)$ is shown in Figure 11–25.

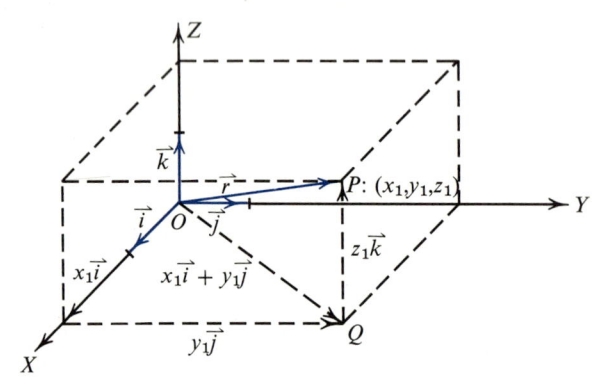

Figure 11–25

Note that $\overrightarrow{OP} = x_1\vec{i} + y_1\vec{j} + z_1\vec{k}$. Frequently the position vector is denoted by $\vec{r}$. In Figure 11–25, the position vector $\vec{r}$ appears as the diagonal of a rectangular parallelepiped whose edges have lengths $|x_1|$, $|y_1|$, and $|z_1|$. Hence the magnitude of $\vec{r}$ can be determined by applying the Theorem of Pythagoras twice: $\overline{OQ}^2 = x_1^2 + y_1^2$ and $\overline{OP}^2 = \overline{OQ}^2 + z_1^2$. Then, $|\vec{r}|$ is given by the relation

$$|\vec{r}| = \sqrt{x_1^2 + y_1^2 + z_1^2}.$$

The scalars x_1, y_1, and z_1 are sometimes called the **components** of $\vec{r}$ along the coordinate axes. Since only one rectangular parallelepiped can be constructed with edges equal to the components x_1, y_1, and z_1, two vectors are equal if and only if their components are equal.

The definition of the sum of two vectors (§ 11–2) can be proved in advanced courses to imply that the components of the sum of two vectors are equal to the sums of the like components of the vectors. That is, given two

§ 11-5 RECTANGULAR CARTESIAN COORDINATES

vectors $\vec{a}$ and $\vec{b}$ with components x_1, y_1, z_1 and x_2, y_2, z_2, the vector sum $(\vec{a} + \vec{b})$ has components $(x_1 + x_2), (y_1 + y_2),$ and $(z_1 + z_2)$. The proof follows from the properties of equations (§ 11–3). We add the members of the equations

$$\vec{a} = x_1\vec{i} + y_1\vec{j} + z_1\vec{k}$$
$$\vec{b} = x_2\vec{i} + y_2\vec{j} + z_2\vec{k},$$

and we use the properties of vectors and scalar multiples to express the sum in the form

$$\vec{a} + \vec{b} = (x_1 + x_2)\vec{i} + (y_1 + y_2)\vec{j} + (z_1 + z_2)\vec{k}.$$

Any difference $(\vec{a} - \vec{b})$ equals a sum $[\vec{a} + (-\vec{b})]$; therefore the components of the difference of two vectors are equal to the differences of the like components of the vectors. That is, for vectors $\vec{a}$ and $\vec{b}$ above,

$$\vec{a} - \vec{b} = \vec{a} + (-\vec{b}) = (x_1 - x_2)\vec{i} + (y_1 - y_2)\vec{j} + (z_1 - z_2)\vec{k}.$$

Example. Determine the position vector of the point $P: (3, -4, 2)$. Compute its magnitude. Determine a unit vector parallel to and in the direction of $\overrightarrow{OP}$.

> The position vector of the point $(3, -4, 2)$ is $(3\vec{i} - 4\vec{j} + 2\vec{k})$ which has magnitude $\sqrt{3^2 + (-4)^2 + 2^2}$; that is, $\sqrt{29}$. Any vector parallel to $\overrightarrow{OP}$ may be expressed as $t(3\vec{i} - 4\vec{j} + 2\vec{k})$ and has magnitude $t\sqrt{29}$ for some real number $t \neq 0$. The value of t such that this vector will have magnitude 1 is $\dfrac{1}{\sqrt{29}}$. If $t = \dfrac{1}{\sqrt{29}}$, the vector is $\dfrac{1}{\sqrt{29}}(3\vec{i} - 4\vec{j} + 2\vec{k})$ and may be expressed as
>
> $$\frac{3}{\sqrt{29}}\vec{i} - \frac{4}{\sqrt{29}}\vec{j} + \frac{2}{\sqrt{29}}\vec{k}.$$
>
> This vector has magnitude 1 and is a unit vector in the direction of the position vector of $(3, -4, 2)$.

TEST YOURSELF

The point $P: (2, -1, -2)$ is given:

1. Find the position vector $\overrightarrow{OP}$.
2. Find the magnitude of $\overrightarrow{OP}$.
3. Find a unit vector in the direction of $\overrightarrow{OP}$.

VECTORS

EXERCISES

Find for the given point: **(a)** *the position vector;* **(b)** *the magnitude of the position vector; and* **(c)** *a unit vector in the direction of the position vector:*

1. (2, 0, 0).
2. (2, −1, 0).
3. (3, 4, 5).
4. (3, 1, 4).
5. (2, −2, −1).
6. (−3, 1, 5).

Describe the location of the points (x, y, z) in space for which:

7. $x = y = 0$.
8. $z = 0$.
9. $x = 2$.
10. $x > 2$.
11. $x < 2$.
12. $|x| < 2$.
13. $|x| < 3$ and $|y| < 1$.
14. $|x| = 2$ and $|z| < 2$.
15. $|x| < 10$, $|y| < 10$, and $|z| < 10$.

• • •

In Exercises 16 and 17 prove that the given points are collinear:

16. P: (2, 5, 9), Q: (5, 5, 15), R: (3, 5, 11).
17. P: (1, −1, 2), Q: (0, 1, 1), R: (2, −3, 3).
18. If the position vectors of points A and B are $2\vec{i} - 3\vec{j} + \vec{k}$ and $\vec{i} + 5\vec{j} - 3\vec{k}$ respectively, find $\overrightarrow{AB}$.
19. Find the distance of P: (x_1, y_1, z_1) from the z-axis.
20. Where does the point P lie if $\overrightarrow{OP}$ is a unit vector?
• 21. Describe the location of P: (x_1, y_1, z_1) if $\overrightarrow{OP}$ is a unit vector and $0 \le z$.
• 22. Given vectors $\vec{r_1} = \vec{i} + \vec{j} - \vec{k}$ and $\vec{r_2} = 3\vec{i} - 2\vec{j} - \vec{k}$, prove that the line through their terminal points is parallel to the xy-plane.

§ 11–6 Division of a line segment in a given ratio

A point C is on a line AB if and only if $\overrightarrow{AC} = k\overrightarrow{AB}$ for some real number k. If $k = 0$, then $C = A$ (that is, C coincides with A); if $k = 1$, then $C = B$. In general, the values of k provide a coordinate for each point C with respect to A and B as in Figure 11–26. For each value of k we have

$$\overrightarrow{CB} = \overrightarrow{CA} + \overrightarrow{AB} = \overrightarrow{AB} - \overrightarrow{AC} = \overrightarrow{AB} - k\overrightarrow{AB} = (1 - k)\overrightarrow{AB}.$$

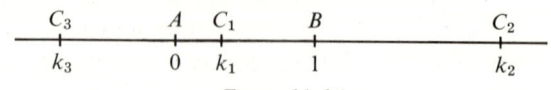

```
     C₃        A   C₁      B              C₂
     +         +   +       +              +
     k₃        0   k₁      1              k₂
```

Figure 11–26

§ 11-6 DIVISION OF A LINE SEGMENT IN A GIVEN RATIO

For any real number k we may find a point C on $\overrightarrow{AB}$ such that $\overrightarrow{AC} = k\overrightarrow{AB}$ and $\overrightarrow{CB} = (1-k)\overrightarrow{AB}$. It is customary to say that C divides the line segment AB in the ratio $k:(1-k)$. Note that the customary reference to a line segment AB is somewhat misleading since A must be taken as the initial point and the ratio may involve negative numbers; that is, involve directions as well as distances along the line. If C divides $\overline{AB}$ in the ratio $\frac{1}{3}:\frac{2}{3}$, then C divides $\overline{BA}$ in the ratio $\frac{2}{3}:\frac{1}{3}$; in other words, if C is one-third of the distance from A to B, then C is two-thirds of the distance from B to A.

Each point C on $\overleftrightarrow{AB}$ is either on $\overline{AB}$ or not on $\overline{AB}$. If C is on $\overline{AB}$, then $C = A$, $C = B$ or $\overrightarrow{AC} = k\overrightarrow{AB}$ where $0 < k < 1$ as in the case of C_1 in Figure 11-26. In this case $\overrightarrow{AC} = k\overrightarrow{AB}$, $\overrightarrow{CB} = (1-k)\overrightarrow{AB}$, $(1-k)\overrightarrow{AC} = k\overrightarrow{CB}$, and C is said to divide $\overline{AB}$ in the ratio $k:(1-k)$. This ratio $k:(1-k)$ may also be expressed as $n:m$ since if $k = \frac{n}{m+n}$, then $1 - k = \frac{m}{m+n}$ and $k:(1-k) = \frac{n}{m+n}:\frac{m}{m+n} = n:m$. Thus for any given $\overline{AB}$ and any two positive real numbers n and m, there exists a point C on $\overline{AB}$ such that $m\overrightarrow{AC} = n\overrightarrow{CB}$ and $\overrightarrow{AC}:\overrightarrow{CB} = n:m$.

If C is on $\overleftrightarrow{AB}$ and is not a point of $\overline{AB}$, then either $k > 1$ and C is on $\overrightarrow{AB}$ but not on $\overline{AB}$ or $k < 0$ and C is on $\overrightarrow{BA}$ but not on $\overline{AB}$. If $k > 1$, then $(1-k)$ is negative; $k:(1-k)$ is negative; $\frac{k}{1-k} < -1$ since $\frac{k}{k-1} > 1$; and thus $\frac{n}{m} < -1$. If $k < 0$, then $1 - k > 0$; $k:(1-k)$ is negative; $\frac{k}{1-k} > -1$ since $k > -1 + k$; and thus $-1 < \frac{n}{m} < 0$. These possibilities for k, m, and n are shown in Figure 11-27.

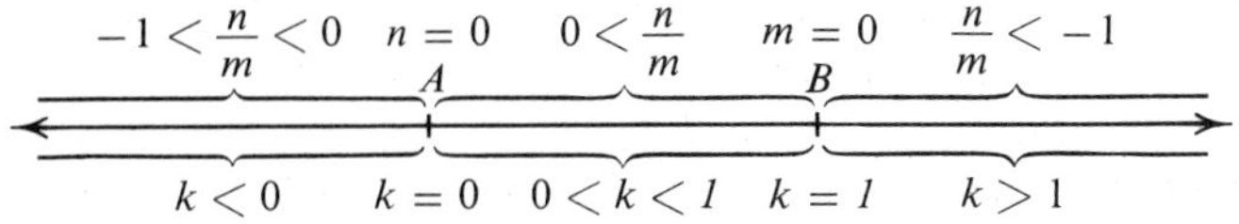

$$-1 < \frac{n}{m} < 0 \quad n = 0 \quad 0 < \frac{n}{m} \quad m = 0 \quad \frac{n}{m} < -1$$
$$\underbrace{}_{k<0} \underbrace{}_{A,\ k=0} \underbrace{}_{0<k<1} \underbrace{}_{B,\ k=1} \underbrace{}_{k>1}$$

Figure 11-27

Note that when C is on the line segment AB, we have $\overline{AC}:\overline{CB} = n:m$; when C is on the line AB but not on the line segment, we must write $\overline{AC}:\overline{CB} = |n|:|m|$ since one of the numbers n, m is negative. We distinguish between these two cases by saying that the line segment is divided

615

VECTORS

internally when C is a point, but not an end point, of the line segment; the line segment is divided **externally** when C is not a point of the line segment. It is customary to speak of a point C on $\vec{AB}$ as dividing $\overline{AB}$ in the ratio $n:m$ whether C is on $\overline{AB}$ or not and whether n and m are both positive or not. For any real numbers n and m there is one and only one point C on $\vec{AB}$ which divides $\overline{AB}$ in the ratio $n:m$. However, for any two positive numbers n and m there are two points C such that $\overline{AC}:\overline{CB} = n:m$; namely, the point C_1 which divides $\overline{AB}$ in the ratio $n:m$ and the point C_2 which divides $\overline{AB}$ in the ratio $-n:m$.

We now use coordinates as in § 11–5, and consider points $A: (x_1, y_1, z_1)$, $B: (x_2, y_2, z_2)$, and $C: (x, y, z)$. The position vectors of A, B, and C are given by the equations

$$\vec{a} = x_1\vec{i} + y_1\vec{j} + z_1\vec{k},$$
$$\vec{b} = x_2\vec{i} + y_2\vec{j} + z_2\vec{k},$$
$$\vec{c} = x\vec{i} + y\vec{j} + z\vec{k}.$$

The condition that C divide $\overline{AB}$ in the ratio of n to m is

$$x\vec{i} + y\vec{j} + z\vec{k} = \frac{m}{m+n}(x_1\vec{i} + y_1\vec{j} + z_1\vec{k}) + \frac{n}{m+n}(x_2\vec{i} + y_2\vec{j} + z_2\vec{k}).$$

The vectors in the right member of the equation may be added by adding their components. The vectors in the two members of the equation are equal if and only if their respective components are equal. Thus the condition that C divide $\overline{AB}$ in the ratio of n to m is given by the three equations

$$x = \frac{mx_1 + nx_2}{m+n}, \quad y = \frac{my_1 + ny_2}{m+n}, \quad z = \frac{mz_1 + nz_2}{m+n}. \qquad (11)$$

Example. Find the coordinates of the point C on the line segment AB for $A: (0, 1, -3)$ and $B: (-4, 5, 9)$ such that $\overline{AC}:\overline{CB} = 1:3$.

In the formula (11), $n = 1$ and $m = 3$. Thus

$$x = \frac{(3)(0) + (1)(-4)}{3 + 1} = -1,$$

$$y = \frac{(3)(1) + (1)(5)}{3 + 1} = 2,$$

$$z = \frac{(3)(-3) + (1)(9)}{3 + 1} = 0.$$

The point $(-1, 2, 0)$ divides the line segment AB in the ratio $1:3$.

§ 11-7 SCALAR PRODUCT

TEST YOURSELF

1. Find the mid-point of $\overline{AB}$ for A: $(1, -3, 7)$ and B: $(-5, 3, 1)$.
2. Find the coordinates of points C and D on the line segment AB in Exercise 1, such that $\overline{AC} = \overline{CD} = \overline{DB}$.

EXERCISES

Find the mid-point of $\overline{AB}$ for:

1. A: $(2, 5, -6)$ and B: $(6, 7, 2)$.
2. A: $(-11, 7, -13)$ and B: $(11, 7, 1)$.

Find the coordinates of points C and D on $\overline{AB}$ such that $\overline{AC} = \overline{CD} = \overline{DB}$ for:

3. A: $(3, -1, 4)$ and B: $(0, 2, -2)$.
4. A: $(7, 14, 11)$ and B: $(1, 2, -1)$.

• • •

In Exercises 5 through 8 find (a) the position vector and (b) the coordinates of the point C dividing $\overline{AB}$ in the given ratio where A: $(14, 5, -10)$ and B: $(-2, 1, 2)$.

5. $1:2$.   6. $2:3$.   7. $3:-1$.   8. $-2:1$.

• 9. If A: (x_1, y_1, z_1), B: (x_2, y_2, z_2) and C: (x_3, y_3, z_3) are the vertices of a triangle, find the coordinates of the centroid (the point of intersection of the medians) of triangle ABC in terms of the coordinates of A, B, and C.

§ 11-7 Scalar product

Physicists and engineers have defined "work" as a technical term. Suppose that a man moves an object from one place to another by exerting a steady "push" or "pull" on the object. For example, think of a person lifting an object or pulling a sled along the ground. The "push" or "pull" is called a **force**. A vector may be used to represent a force since it has both direction and magnitude. The magnitude of a force is measured in terms of units of weight such as pounds or grams.

When a constant force is used to move an object, the force is applied throughout the distance that the object moves. This distance is measured in terms of units of length such as feet or centimeters. The **work** done in moving an object is defined as the product of the magnitude of the force and the distance through which the force is applied. Work is measured in terms of units such as foot-pounds or gram-centimeters.

VECTORS

Example 1. Find the work done in lifting a fifty-pound bag of flour from the floor to a table top four feet above the floor.

> The bag can be held by a steady vertical pull of 50 pounds. A slightly larger force will raise the bag. We disregard the small additional pull necessary to cause the bag to rise and consider a vertical force of 50 pounds applied for 4 feet. The work done is 200 foot-pounds.

Frequently a force is exerted in one direction on an object and the object moves in another direction. For example, suppose that a man pulls a sled a distance d along the ground by exerting a force with magnitude F at an angle θ with the ground as in Figure 11–28.

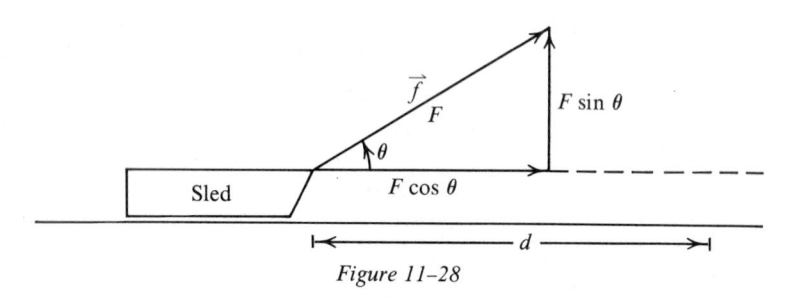

Figure 11–28

In the figure the force is represented as the vector $\vec{f}$ with magnitude F. The vector may be considered as the sum of two components. One component is parallel to the ground, has magnitude $F \cos \theta$, and tends to pull the sled along the ground. The other component is perpendicular to the ground, has magnitude $F \sin \theta$, and tends to lift the sled off the ground. The magnitude of the work done in moving the sled d units is $(F \cos \theta) \times d$.

Example 2. Find the work done using a force of 30 pounds applied at an angle of 45° to the horizontal to pull a sled a horizontal distance of 50 feet.

> Use Figure 11–28 with $F = 30$, $\theta = 45°$, and $d = 50$. The work done W is $(F \cos \theta) \times d$ foot-pounds.
>
> $$W = 30 (\cos 45°) \times 50 = 1500 \cos 45° = 1500 \frac{\sqrt{2}}{2}$$
>
> $= 750 \sqrt{2}$; that is, $750 \sqrt{2}$ foot-pounds.

Figure 11–28 may be replaced by a vector diagram with a force $\vec{f}$ and a displacement $\vec{d}$ as in Figure 11–29. Then $|\vec{f}| \cos \theta$ represents the magnitude of the projection of $\vec{f}$ onto $\vec{d}$. The work done in moving the sled $|\vec{d}|$ units is then $|\vec{d}| |\vec{f}| \cos \theta$.

§ 11-7 SCALAR PRODUCT

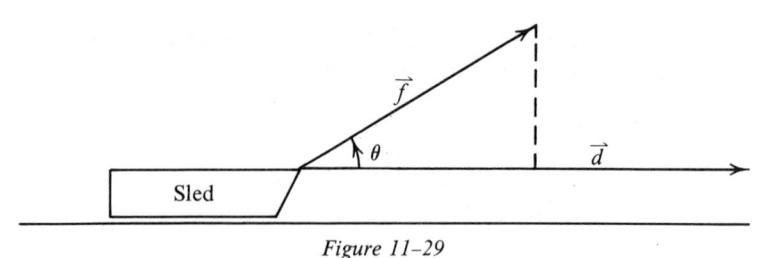

Figure 11-29

We use the identity

$$\vec{a} \cdot \vec{b} = |\vec{a}||\vec{b}| \cos \theta$$

to define the **scalar product** of any two given vectors $\vec{a}$ and $\vec{b}$ where θ stands for the angle determined by two vectors with a common origin and parallel to the given vectors. Any scalar product $\vec{a} \cdot \vec{b}$ (read "$\vec{a}$ dot $\vec{b}$") is a scalar and is often called the **dot product** of the given vectors. The dot is always used here as the operation symbol since we shall later define and use the symbol $\times$ for another type of product of vectors.

The work done pulling the sled in Figure 11-29 may now be written as $\vec{d} \cdot \vec{f}$. In general any scalar product $\vec{a} \cdot \vec{b}$ is numerically equal to the product of $|\vec{b}|$ and the magnitude of the projection of $\vec{a}$ onto $\vec{b}$. The magnitude of the projection is $\frac{1}{|\vec{b}|}(\vec{a} \cdot \vec{b})$ when for vectors with a common origin the projection is along $\vec{b}$; the magnitude is $-\frac{1}{|\vec{b}|}(\vec{a} \cdot \vec{b})$ when the projection is along $-\vec{b}$ (Figure 11-30). In any case the signed values of the projections are $\frac{1}{|\vec{b}|}(\vec{a} \cdot \vec{b})$.

$|\vec{OP}| = \frac{1}{|\vec{b}|}(\vec{a} \cdot \vec{b})$ $|\vec{OP}| = -\frac{1}{|\vec{b}|}(\vec{a} \cdot \vec{b})$

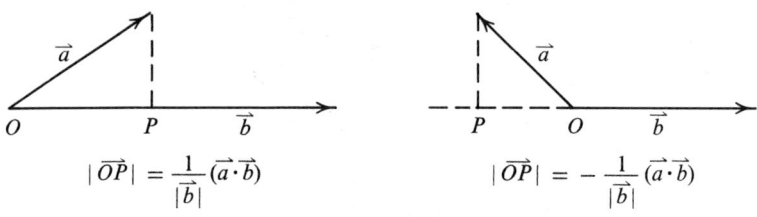

Figure 11-30

The proof that the scalar product of any two vectors is commutative may be stated as follows: $\cos \theta = \cos(-\theta)$ for any θ and in particular for the angle determined by the vectors $\vec{a}$ and $\vec{b}$; $\vec{a} \cdot \vec{b} = |\vec{a}||\vec{b}| \cos \theta = |\vec{b}||\vec{a}| \cos(-\theta) = \vec{b} \cdot \vec{a}$. The proofs of the following properties are left

619

VECTORS

as exercises (see A Exercises 4 through 8):

$$\vec{a} \cdot \vec{a} = |\vec{a}|^2. \tag{12}$$

$$\vec{a} \cdot (-\vec{a}) = -|\vec{a}|^2. \tag{13}$$

If $\vec{a}$ is perpendicular to $\vec{b}$, then $\vec{a} \cdot \vec{b} = 0.$ (14)

If $\vec{a} \cdot \vec{b} = 0$, then $|\vec{a}| = 0$, $|\vec{b}| = 0$, or $\vec{a}$ is perpendicular to $\vec{b}$. (15)

$$\vec{a} \cdot (\vec{b} + \vec{c}) = \vec{a} \cdot \vec{b} + \vec{a} \cdot \vec{c}. \tag{16}$$

We assume these properties and consider scalar products of vectors expressed in terms of their components parallel to coordinate axes (§ 11–5). By Property (12)

$$\vec{i} \cdot \vec{i} = 1, \quad \vec{j} \cdot \vec{j} = 1, \quad \text{and} \quad \vec{k} \cdot \vec{k} = 1.$$

By Property (14)

$$\vec{i} \cdot \vec{j} = \vec{j} \cdot \vec{i} = 0, \quad \vec{j} \cdot \vec{k} = \vec{k} \cdot \vec{j} = 0, \quad \text{and} \quad \vec{k} \cdot \vec{i} = \vec{i} \cdot \vec{k} = 0.$$

Then by the distributive law, Property (16), the scalar product of any two vectors

$$\vec{a} = x_1\vec{i} + y_1\vec{j} + z_1\vec{k} \quad \text{and} \quad \vec{b} = x_2\vec{i} + y_2\vec{j} + z_2\vec{k}$$

may be determined:

$$\vec{a} \cdot \vec{b} = (x_1\vec{i} + y_1\vec{j} + z_1\vec{k}) \cdot (x_2\vec{i} + y_2\vec{j} + z_2\vec{k});$$
$$\vec{a} \cdot \vec{b} = x_1x_2(\vec{i} \cdot \vec{i}) + x_1y_2(\vec{i} \cdot \vec{j}) + x_1z_2(\vec{i} \cdot \vec{k})$$
$$+ y_1x_2(\vec{j} \cdot \vec{i}) + y_1y_2(\vec{j} \cdot \vec{j}) + y_1z_2(\vec{j} \cdot \vec{k})$$
$$+ z_1x_2(\vec{k} \cdot \vec{i}) + z_1y_2(\vec{k} \cdot \vec{j}) + z_1z_2(\vec{k} \cdot \vec{k});$$

$$\vec{a} \cdot \vec{b} = x_1x_2 + y_1y_2 + z_1z_2. \tag{17}$$

Example 3. Find the vector projection of $\vec{a} = \vec{i} + 3\vec{j} + 4\vec{k}$ onto $\vec{b} = 10\vec{i} + 11\vec{j} - 2\vec{k}$. Also find the angle θ between the vectors.

The vector projection of $\vec{a}$ onto $\vec{b}$ is $|\vec{a}| \cos \theta$.

Since $\vec{a} \cdot \vec{b} = |\vec{a}| |\vec{b}| \cos \theta$,

$$|\vec{a}| \cos \theta = \frac{\vec{a} \cdot \vec{b}}{|\vec{b}|} = \frac{10 + 33 - 8}{\sqrt{10^2 + 11^2 + (-2)^2}} = \frac{35}{15} = \frac{7}{3}.$$

Since $|\vec{a}| \cos \theta = \frac{7}{3}$,

$$\cos \theta = \frac{7}{3|\vec{a}|} = \frac{7}{3\sqrt{1^2 + 3^2 + 4^2}} = \frac{7}{3\sqrt{26}};$$

therefore, $\theta = \text{Arc cos} \frac{7}{3\sqrt{26}} \approx 62° 46'$.

Example 4. Prove that $\vec{a}$ and $\vec{b}$ are perpendicular where $\vec{a} = 3\vec{i} - 2\vec{j} + \vec{k}$ and $\vec{b} = \vec{i} - 3\vec{k}$.

By Property (17), $\vec{a} \cdot \vec{b} = (3)(1) + (-2)(0) + (1)(-3) = 0$. Since neither $\vec{a}$ nor $\vec{b}$ is a null vector and $\vec{a} \cdot \vec{b} = 0$, it follows from Property (15) that $\vec{a}$ is perpendicular to $\vec{b}$.

The use of a scalar product to express the length of a line segment is developed in the set B of the exercises. In particular we may prove this formula (B, Exercise 3): If A and B have position vectors $\vec{a}$ and $\vec{b}$, then

$$\overline{AB}^2 = (\vec{b} - \vec{a}) \cdot (\vec{b} - \vec{a}). \tag{18}$$

Example 5. Prove that any angle inscribed in a semicircle is a right angle.

Consider a circle with center O, diameter $\overline{AB}$, and let C be any third point of the the circle.

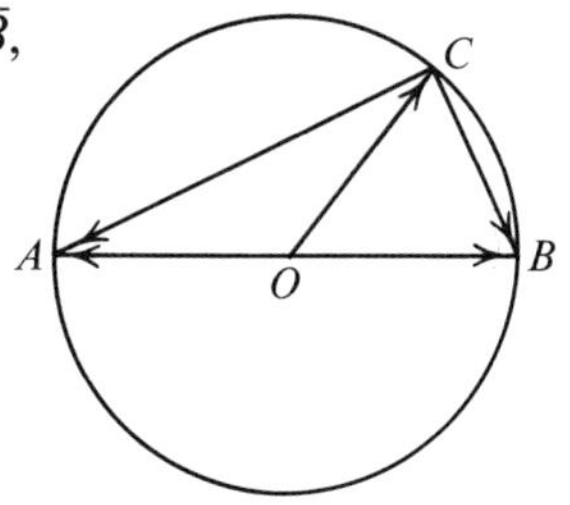

Then
$$\overrightarrow{CA} = \overrightarrow{OA} - \overrightarrow{OC},$$
$$\overrightarrow{CB} = \overrightarrow{OB} - \overrightarrow{OC},$$
$$\overrightarrow{OB} = -\overrightarrow{OA},$$
$$\overrightarrow{CB} = -\overrightarrow{OA} - \overrightarrow{OC};$$
$$\overrightarrow{CA} \cdot \overrightarrow{CB} = (\overrightarrow{OA} - \overrightarrow{OC}) \cdot (-\overrightarrow{OA} - \overrightarrow{OC})$$
$$= \overrightarrow{OA} \cdot (-\overrightarrow{OA}) - \overrightarrow{OA} \cdot \overrightarrow{OC} - \overrightarrow{OC} \cdot (-\overrightarrow{OA}) + \overrightarrow{OC} \cdot \overrightarrow{OC}$$
$$= |\overrightarrow{OA}||\overrightarrow{OA}|(-1) - \overrightarrow{OC} \cdot (\overrightarrow{OA} - \overrightarrow{OA}) + |\overrightarrow{OC}|^2$$
$$= -|\overrightarrow{OA}|^2 + |\overrightarrow{OC}|^2$$
$$= 0, \text{ since } |\overrightarrow{OA}| = |\overrightarrow{OC}|, \text{ the radius.}$$

Figure 11-31

Since C is a third point, the product of $|\overrightarrow{CA}|$ and $|\overrightarrow{CB}|$ is not zero. Therefore, since $\overrightarrow{CA} \cdot \overrightarrow{CB} = 0$, $\overrightarrow{CA}$ is perpendicular to $\overrightarrow{CB}$, Property (15).

VECTORS

TEST YOURSELF

1. Apply Property (17) to $\vec{a} \cdot \vec{a}$ to find the magnitude $|\vec{a}|$ when $\vec{a} = 3\vec{i} + \vec{j} - 2\vec{k}$.

2. Use the scalar product $\overrightarrow{CA} \cdot \overrightarrow{CB}$ to prove the Pythagorean Theorem for any right triangle ABC with the right angle at C.

EXERCISES

A

Find the magnitude of the position vector of each point:

1. $P: (2, 2, -1)$. 2. $R: (-3, 4, 1)$. 3. $S: (5, -2, 3)$.

Prove:

4. $\vec{a} \cdot \vec{a} = |\vec{a}|^2$.
5. $\vec{a} \cdot (-\vec{a}) = -|\vec{a}|^2$.
6. If $\vec{a}$ is perpendicular to $\vec{b}$, then $\vec{a} \cdot \vec{b} = 0$.
7. If $\vec{a} \cdot \vec{b} = 0$, then $|\vec{a}| = 0$, $|\vec{b}| = 0$, or $\vec{a}$ is perpendicular to $\vec{b}$.
8. $\vec{a} \cdot (\vec{b} + \vec{c}) = \vec{a} \cdot \vec{b} + \vec{a} \cdot \vec{c}$.

HINT: Use the accompanying figure and the fact that for any vectors $\vec{a}$, $\vec{b}$, and $\vec{c}$ the signed values $\frac{1}{|\vec{a}|}(\vec{a} \cdot \vec{b})$ and $\frac{1}{|\vec{a}|}(\vec{a} \cdot \vec{c})$ of the projections $\overline{PR}$ and $\overline{RS}$ may be added to obtain the signed value $\frac{1}{|\vec{a}|}[\vec{a} \cdot (\vec{b} + \vec{c})]$ of the projection $\overline{PS}$.

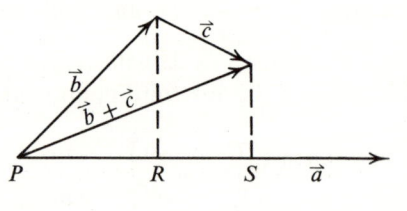

9. $(x_1\vec{i} + y_1\vec{j} + z_1\vec{k}) \cdot \vec{i} = x_1$.
10. The magnitude of $(x_1\vec{i} + y_1\vec{j} + z_1\vec{k})$ is $\sqrt{x_1^2 + y_1^2 + z_1^2}$.

• • •

11. $(\vec{i} + 4\vec{j} + 3\vec{k})$ and $(4\vec{i} + 2\vec{j} - 4\vec{k})$ are perpendicular.
12. $\overrightarrow{OA}$ is perpendicular to $\overrightarrow{BC}$ where $O: (0, 0, 0)$, $A: (2, 1, 1)$, $B: (3, 5, -1)$, and $C: (4, 3, -1)$.

§ 11-7 SCALAR PRODUCT

Find:

13. The cosine of the angle between $\vec{a}$ and $\vec{b}$ where $\vec{a} = 2\vec{i} - 3\vec{j} + \vec{k}$ and $\vec{b} = 3\vec{i} - \vec{j} - 2\vec{k}$.

14. The projection of $\vec{a}$ along $\vec{b}$ where $\vec{a} = 2\vec{i} - 3\vec{j} + \vec{k}$ and $\vec{b} = 3\vec{j} - 4\vec{k}$.

15. The magnitude of $\overrightarrow{AB}$ where $A: (2, -4, 7)$ and $B: (-2, 1, -3)$. Then find the unit vector having the same direction as $\overrightarrow{AB}$.

16. The distance from the point $P: (2, 5, 6)$ to the x-axis.

17. The conditions such that (a) $|\vec{r}_1 \cdot \vec{r}_2| \le |\vec{r}_1||\vec{r}_2|$; (b) $\vec{r}_1 \cdot \vec{r}_2 = |\vec{r}_1||\vec{r}_2|$; (c) $\vec{r}_1 \cdot \vec{r}_2 = -|\vec{r}_1||\vec{r}_2|$.

18. The distance from the point $P: (x, y, z)$ to each of the coordinate axes.

B

In Exercises 1 through 3 consider any two points $A: (x_1, y_1, z_1)$ and $B: (x_2, y_2, z_2)$ with position vectors $\vec{a}$ and $\vec{b}$:

1. Express $\overrightarrow{AB}$ in terms of (a) $\vec{a}$ and $\vec{b}$; (b) the components of $\vec{a}$ and $\vec{b}$.

2. Express the length of the line segment AB in terms of (a) $\vec{a}$ and $\vec{b}$; (b) the components of $\vec{a}$ and $\vec{b}$.

3. Prove that $\overrightarrow{AB}^2 = (\vec{b} - \vec{a}) \cdot (\vec{b} - \vec{a})$.

4. Find the length of each side of the triangle whose vertices are the points $A: (2, 0, -4)$, $B: (1, 3, 7)$, and $C: (5, -1, 0)$.

5. Use the scalar product to prove that the triangle with vertices at $A: (1, 3, -5)$, $B: (3, 4, -7)$, and $C: (2, 5, -3)$ is a right triangle.

6. Prove that the triangle with vertices at $P: (7, 3, 4)$, $Q: (1, 0, 6)$, and $R: (4, 5, -2)$ is a right isosceles triangle.

• • •

7. Find a point on the x-axis which is equidistant from the points $A: (2, 4, -3)$ and $B: (-3, 5, 1)$.

8. Find the condition on the coordinates $P: (x, y, z)$ imposed by the requirement that $\overrightarrow{AP}$ and $\overrightarrow{BP}$ be perpendicular where $A: (-a, 0, 0)$ and $B: (a, 0, 0)$.

9. Let $\vec{r}$ be the position vector of an arbitrary point $P: (x, y, z)$, and let $\vec{a}$ be a given vector. Interpret the equation $(\vec{r} - \vec{a}) \cdot \vec{a} = 0$.

10. Find the work done using a force of 50 pounds applied at an angle of 60° to the horizontal to pull a sled a horizontal distance of 20 feet.

623

VECTORS

11. Repeat Exercise 10 for a force of 225 pounds, an angle of 60°, and a horizontal distance of 80 feet.

Use scalar products to prove:
- **12.** The diagonals of a rhombus are perpendicular.
- **13.** The sum of the squares of the diagonals of a parallelogram is equal to the sum of the squares of the sides.
- **14.** In any right triangle the line segment joining the vertex of the right angle to the mid-point of the hypotenuse is equal to one-half the hypotenuse.

§ 11-8   Direction cosines

Any vector in space is equal to a vector $\vec{r}$ with initial point $O: (0, 0, 0)$ and some terminal point $P: (x, y, z)$. If $\overrightarrow{OP} \neq 0$, the vector $\overrightarrow{OP}$, and thus also the vector $\vec{r}$, has a direction which is uniquely determined by the angles XOP, YOP, and ZOP which $\overrightarrow{OP}$ forms with the unit vectors $\vec{i}, \vec{j}$, and $\vec{k}$ on the coordinate axes. By convention these angles are called α, β, and γ respectively, the **direction angles** of $\overrightarrow{OP}$. Since there is one and only one line through the end points of any nonzero vector, the direction angles of $\overrightarrow{OP}$ may also be used as direction angles of $\overrightarrow{OP}$.

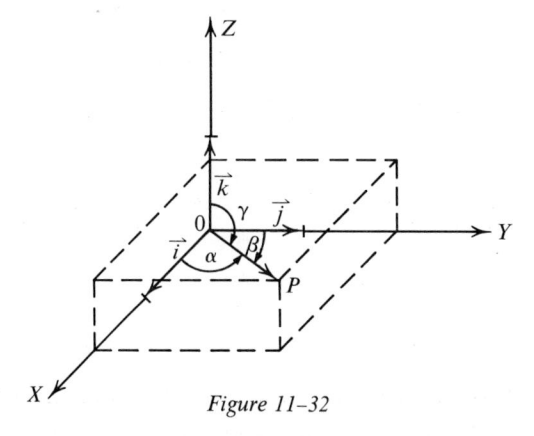

Figure 11–32

We may use scalar products to obtain the cosines of the direction angles of the position vector $\vec{r}$ of any point $P: (x, y, z) \neq (0, 0, 0)$:

$$\vec{r} \cdot \vec{i} = (x\vec{i} + y\vec{j} + z\vec{k}) \cdot \vec{i} = x$$
$$\vec{r} \cdot \vec{i} = |\vec{r}| |\vec{i}| \cos \alpha$$
$$\cos \alpha = \frac{\vec{r} \cdot \vec{i}}{|\vec{r}| |\vec{i}|} = \frac{x}{|\vec{r}|};$$

similarly

$$\cos \beta = \frac{y}{|\vec{r}|}; \quad \text{and} \quad \cos \gamma = \frac{z}{|\vec{r}|}.$$

The numbers $\cos \alpha$, $\cos \beta$, and $\cos \gamma$ are the **direction cosines** of $\vec{r}$ and also serve as direction cosines of the line OP through the origin.

Let $P_1: (x_1, y_1, z_1)$ be any point different from the origin. Then

$$|\vec{r}| = |\vec{OP_1}| = \sqrt{x_1^2 + y_1^2 + z_1^2}; \quad \cos \alpha = \frac{x_1}{\sqrt{x_1^2 + y_1^2 + z_1^2}},$$

$$\cos \beta = \frac{y_1}{\sqrt{x_1^2 + y_1^2 + z_1^2}}, \quad \cos \gamma = \frac{z_1}{\sqrt{x_1^2 + y_1^2 + z_1^2}},$$

$$\cos^2 \alpha + \cos^2 \beta + \cos^2 \gamma = \frac{x_1^2 + y_1^2 + z_1^2}{x_1^2 + y_1^2 + z_1^2} = 1.$$

We have proved that the sum of the squares of the direction cosines of any nonzero vector is 1. It is customary to designate the direction cosines of any vector, and thus a set of direction cosines for any line, by l, m, and n;

$$l = \cos \alpha, \quad m = \cos \beta, \quad n = \cos \gamma.$$

We have proved that for any set of direction cosines

$$l^2 + m^2 + n^2 = 1.$$

We have also proved that for any given point $P_1: (x_1, y_1, z_1)$ different from the origin

$$l = \frac{x_1}{\sqrt{x_1^2 + y_1^2 + z_1^2}}, \quad m = \frac{y_1}{\sqrt{x_1^2 + y_1^2 + z_1^2}},$$

$$n = \frac{z_1}{\sqrt{x_1^2 + y_1^2 + z_1^2}};$$

$$x_1 = |\vec{OP_1}|l, \quad y_1 = |\vec{OP_1}|m, \quad z_1 = |\vec{OP_1}|n.$$

We say that the coordinates of P_1 are proportional to the direction cosines of $\vec{OP_1}$ since

$$\frac{x_1}{l} = \frac{y_1}{m} = \frac{z_1}{n} = |\vec{OP_1}|.$$

If we draw the coordinates of any point $P_1: (x_1, y_1, z_1)$ different from the origin, we can find the direction cosines of $\vec{OP_1}$. If $P_2: (x_2, y_2, z_2)$ is any point different from the origin on the line OP_1, then the vectors $\vec{OP_1}$

VECTORS

and $\overrightarrow{OP_2}$ are parallel and $\overrightarrow{OP_2} = t\overrightarrow{OP_1}$ for some scalar t. In other words,

$$x_2\vec{i} + y_2\vec{j} + z_2\vec{k} = tx_1\vec{i} + ty_1\vec{j} + tz_1\vec{k}.$$

Let l_1, m_1, and n_1 be the direction cosines of $\overrightarrow{OP_1}$ and l_2, m_2, and n_2 be the direction cosines of $\overrightarrow{OP_2}$. Then

$$\begin{aligned} x_1 &= l_1|\overrightarrow{OP_1}|, & y_1 &= m_1|\overrightarrow{OP_1}|, & z_1 &= n_1|\overrightarrow{OP_1}|; \\ x_2 &= l_2|\overrightarrow{OP_2}|, & y_2 &= m_2|\overrightarrow{OP_2}|, & z_2 &= n_2|\overrightarrow{OP_2}|; \\ x_2 &= tx_1, & y_2 &= ty_1, & z_2 &= tz_1; \end{aligned}$$

the coordinates of P_1 and P_2 are proportional, that is,

$$\frac{x_2}{x_1} = \frac{y_2}{y_1} = \frac{z_2}{z_1} = t; \text{ also, } \frac{l_1|\overrightarrow{OP_1}|}{l_2|\overrightarrow{OP_2}|} = \frac{m_1|\overrightarrow{OP_1}|}{m_2|\overrightarrow{OP_2}|} = \frac{n_1|\overrightarrow{OP_1}|}{n_2|\overrightarrow{OP_2}|} = \frac{1}{t};$$

$$\frac{l_1}{l_2} = \frac{m_1}{m_2} = \frac{n_1}{n_2} = \frac{|\overrightarrow{OP_2}|}{t|\overrightarrow{OP_1}|}.$$

If $t > 0$, we have P_2 on $\overrightarrow{OP_1}$ and

$$l_1 = l_2, \quad m_1 = m_2, \quad n_1 = n_2;$$

if $t < 0$, we have P_2 on $-\overrightarrow{OP_1}$ and

$$l_1 = -l_2, \quad m_1 = -m_2, \quad n_1 = -n_2.$$

Thus two parallel vectors with the same sense have the same direction cosines; two parallel vectors with opposite senses have direction cosines which differ only in their signs. Since sense is not defined on a line, either l_1, m_1, n_1, or $-l_1, -m_1, -n_1$ may be used as direction cosines for the line OP_1.

The coordinates of P_1 may be used to find the direction cosines of $\overrightarrow{OP_1}$. Indeed, the coordinates of any point P_2 on $\overrightarrow{OP_1}$ may be so used. We have seen that the coordinates of P_1 and P_2 are proportional whenever P_2 is on $\overrightarrow{OP_1}$. Conversely, we know from similar figures that if the coordinates are proportional, then the points are collinear. Then since coordinates may be used to find direction cosines, we can use any set of numbers proportional to the coordinates of P_1 to find direction cosines for the line OP_1. Any such set of numbers is called a set of **direction numbers** for the line. Note for example that x_1, y_1, z_1 are direction numbers for $\overrightarrow{OP_1}$; $2x_1, 2y_1, 2z_1$ are direction numbers for $\overrightarrow{OP_1}$; and for any $t \neq 0$ tl_1, tm_1, tn_1 are

§ 11-8 DIRECTION COSINES

direction numbers for $\overleftrightarrow{OP_1}$. Whenever we list direction numbers, we shall assume that they are listed in the order of l, m, and n.

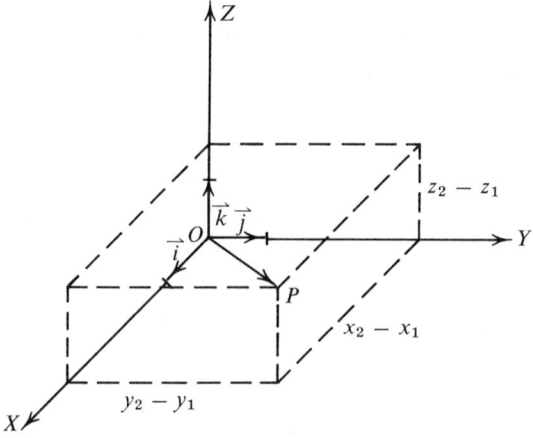

Figure 11-33

Direction numbers, and thus direction cosines, for any line P_1P_2 may be found by considering the vector $\overrightarrow{P_1P_2}$. Equal vectors have the same direction cosines; parallel lines have the same direction numbers. Consider $P_1: (x_1, y_1, z_1)$ and $P_2: (x_2, y_2, z_2)$. Then

$$\overrightarrow{P_1P_2} = (x_2 - x_1)\vec{i} + (y_2 - y_1)\vec{j} + (z_2 - z_1)\vec{k};$$

that is, $\overrightarrow{P_1P_2}$ is equal to the position vector of P: $(x_2 - x_1, y_2 - y_1, z_2 - z_1)$. Since $\overrightarrow{OP}$ has coordinates and thus direction numbers $x_2 - x_1$, $y_2 - y_1$, $z_2 - z_1$, the line P_1P_2 also has these three numbers as direction numbers.

Example. Given $A: (1, 5, -3)$ and $B: (-2, 1, 5)$, find the length of $\overline{AB}$, direction cosines for $\overline{AB}$, and four sets of direction numbers for $\overleftrightarrow{AB}$.

$\overline{AB}^2 = (-2 - 1)^2 + (1 - 5)^2 + (5 + 3)^2 = 9 + 16 + 64 = 89,$
$\overline{AB} = \sqrt{89}.$
$\overrightarrow{AB} = \overrightarrow{OP}$ where $P: (-3, -4, 8) = (-2 - 1, 1 - 5, 5 + 3).$
$\overrightarrow{AB}$ and $\overrightarrow{OP}$ have direction cosines $\dfrac{-3}{\sqrt{89}}, \dfrac{-4}{\sqrt{89}}, \dfrac{8}{\sqrt{89}}.$

Any set of numbers of the form $-3t$, $-4t$, $8t$ where $t \neq 0$ may be used as direction numbers for $\overleftrightarrow{AB}$; for example: $-3, -4, 8$; $3, 4, -8$; $6, 8, -16$; and $12, 16, -32$ may be used.

627

VECTORS

TEST YOURSELF

The points $A: (3, -2, 4)$ and $B: (5, -3, 2)$ are given. Find:

1. The length of the line segment AB.
2. Direction cosines for the vector $\overrightarrow{AB}$.
3. Four sets of direction numbers for the line AB.

EXERCISES

1. Find the direction cosines of $\overrightarrow{AB}$ for $A: (-4, -6, 2)$ and $B: (3, -6, 4)$.
2. Find three sets of direction numbers for $\overrightarrow{AB}$ in Exercise 1.
3. Find (a) a set of direction numbers, and (b) the direction cosines for $\overrightarrow{OP}$ where $P: (3, 4, 0)$.
4. Find direction cosines for the unit vectors on the coordinate axes (a) $\vec{i}$; (b) $\vec{j}$; (c) $\vec{k}$.

• • •

5. Find a set of direction cosines for a line with direction numbers 6, -3, and 2.
6. A line through $A: (1, -1, 2)$ has direction numbers 3, 2, and -1. (a) Find two other points on the line. (b) Use an arbitrary constant t and give general expressions for the coordinates of any point P on the line.
7. Use the scalar product $\vec{r}_1 \cdot \vec{r}_2$ and derive this formula for the cosine of the angle θ between the two vectors:

$$\cos \theta = l_1 l_2 + m_1 m_2 + n_1 n_2$$

where l_1, m_1, n_1 are the direction cosines of $\vec{r}_1$ and l_2, m_2, n_2 are the direction cosines of $\vec{r}_2$.

8. Use the formula in Exercise 7 and find an angle between two intersecting lines if one line has direction cosines $\frac{1}{2}, \frac{\sqrt{2}}{2}$, and $\frac{1}{2}$ and the other line has direction cosines $\frac{6}{7}, \frac{3}{7}$, and $\frac{-2}{7}$.

9. Use the formula in Exercise 7 and prove that any vector with direction numbers $-6, -3, -2$ is perpendicular to any vector with direction numbers $-2, 6, -3$.

10. As in Exercise 7 prove that two vectors are perpendicular if and only if $l_1 l_2 + m_1 m_2 + n_1 n_2 = 0$.

● 11. Explain this statement: The direction cosines of any vector $\overrightarrow{AB}$ are the negatives of the direction cosines of $\overrightarrow{BA}$ and either set of direction cosines may be used for $\overrightarrow{AB}$.

§ 11-9 Vector product

Let $\vec{a}'$ and $\vec{b}'$ be any two vectors. There exist equivalent vectors $\vec{a}$ and $\vec{b}$ with a common initial point O. There exist real numbers m and n different from zero such that $m\vec{a} + n\vec{b} = \vec{0}$ if and only if $\vec{a}$ and $\vec{b}$ lie on the same straight line. If $\vec{a}$ and $\vec{b}$ do *not* lie on the same line, they determine a plane and there is an angle θ with $\vec{a}$ on its initial side and $\vec{b}$ on its terminal side such that $0 < \theta < \pi$.

We next define a unit vector $\vec{n}$ perpendicular to the plane of $\vec{a}$ and $\vec{b}$ and oriented such that the vectors $\vec{a}$, $\vec{b}$, and $\vec{n}$ form a right-handed system (§ 11–5) in which the relative directions of $\vec{a}$, $\vec{b}$, and $\vec{n}$ correspond to those of $\vec{i}, \vec{j}$, and $\vec{k}$ respectively. The **vector product** of $\vec{a}$ and $\vec{b}$ is a vector $\vec{c}$ in the direction of $\vec{n}$ and with magnitude numerically equal to the area of a parallelogram with $\vec{a}$ and $\vec{b}$ as sides (Figure 11–34). We write $\vec{c} = \vec{a} \times \vec{b}$ (read "$\vec{a}$ cross $\vec{b}$") and sometimes call this the **cross product**.

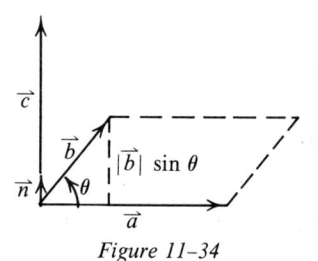

Figure 11-34

If we think of $\vec{a}$ as the base of the parallelogram in Figure 11–34, then the altitude is $|\vec{b}| \sin \theta$ and the area is $|\vec{a}||\vec{b}| \sin \theta$. Thus we have

$$\vec{c} = \vec{a} \times \vec{b} = (|\vec{a}||\vec{b}|\sin\theta)\vec{n}. \tag{19}$$

If $\vec{a}$ and $\vec{b}$ are on the same line, they do not determine a plane; and the interpretation in Figure 11–34 must be modified to allow us to think of the parallelogram as having area zero. With this idea in mind we may make use of (19) and define $\vec{a} \times \vec{b} = 0\vec{n} = \vec{0}$ whenever $\vec{a}$ and $\vec{b}$ are parallel.

The vector product is not commutative (TY Exercise 1), but it is distributive with respect to addition, that is,

$$\vec{a} \times (\vec{b} + \vec{c}) = \vec{a} \times \vec{b} + \vec{a} \times \vec{c}. \tag{20}$$

VECTORS

We assume this distributive property and leave its proof for more advanced courses. However, the scalar coefficient of the cross product of two vectors may be associated with either vector:

$$c(\vec{a} \times \vec{b}) = (c\vec{a}) \times \vec{b} = \vec{a} \times (c\vec{b}). \tag{21}$$

This can be proved easily (Exercises 3 and 4). We shall use these properties to determine the components of the cross product of two position vectors.

Theorem 3. *If* $\vec{a} = x_1\vec{i} + y_1\vec{j} + z_1\vec{k}$ *and* $\vec{b} = x_2\vec{i} + y_2\vec{j} + z_2\vec{k}$, *then* $\vec{a} \times \vec{b} = (y_1z_2 - y_2z_1)\vec{i} + (z_1x_2 - z_2x_1)\vec{j} + (x_1y_2 - x_2y_1)\vec{k}$.

PROOF: Notice that $\vec{i} \times \vec{j}$ is a vector of magnitude 1 along the positive z-axis; that is, $\vec{i} \times \vec{j} = \vec{k}$. Also $\vec{j} \times \vec{i}$ is a vector of magnitude 1 along the negative z-axis; that is, $\vec{j} \times \vec{i} = -\vec{k}$. Thus we note from the definition (19) that

$$\vec{i} \times \vec{j} = -\vec{j} \times \vec{i} = \vec{k},$$
$$\vec{j} \times \vec{k} = -\vec{k} \times \vec{j} = \vec{i},$$
$$\vec{k} \times \vec{i} = -\vec{i} \times \vec{k} = \vec{j}; \text{ and}$$
$$\vec{i} \times \vec{i} = \vec{0}, \quad \vec{j} \times \vec{j} = \vec{0}, \quad \vec{k} \times \vec{k} = \vec{0}.$$

Then from these results and the properties (20) and (21)

$$\vec{a} \times \vec{b} = (x_1\vec{i} + y_1\vec{j} + z_1\vec{k}) \times (x_2\vec{i} + y_2\vec{j} + z_2\vec{k})$$
$$\vec{a} \times \vec{b} = x_1x_2\vec{i} \times \vec{i} + x_1y_2\vec{i} \times \vec{j} + x_1z_2\vec{i} \times \vec{k}$$
$$+ y_1x_2\vec{j} \times \vec{i} + y_1y_2\vec{j} \times \vec{j} + y_1z_2\vec{j} \times \vec{k}$$
$$+ z_1x_2\vec{k} \times \vec{i} + z_1y_2\vec{k} \times \vec{j} + z_1z_2\vec{k} \times \vec{k}.$$
$$\vec{a} \times \vec{b} = \vec{0} + x_1y_2\vec{k} - x_1z_2\vec{j} - y_1x_2\vec{k} + \vec{0}$$
$$+ y_1z_2\vec{i} + z_1x_2\vec{j} - z_1y_2\vec{i} + \vec{0}$$
$$\vec{a} \times \vec{b} = (y_1z_2 - y_2z_1)\vec{i} + (z_1x_2 - z_2x_1)\vec{j} + (x_1y_2 - x_2y_1)\vec{k}.$$

We may write this equation using second order determinants as

$$\vec{a} \times \vec{b} = \begin{vmatrix} y_1 & z_1 \\ y_2 & z_2 \end{vmatrix}\vec{i} - \begin{vmatrix} x_1 & z_1 \\ x_2 & z_2 \end{vmatrix}\vec{j} + \begin{vmatrix} x_1 & y_1 \\ x_2 & y_2 \end{vmatrix}\vec{k}$$

or using a single third order determinant as

$$\vec{a} \times \vec{b} = \begin{vmatrix} \vec{i} & \vec{j} & \vec{k} \\ x_1 & y_1 & z_1 \\ x_2 & y_2 & z_2 \end{vmatrix}.$$

§ 11-9 VECTOR PRODUCT

Example 1. Find $\vec{a} \times \vec{b}$ if $\vec{a} = 2\vec{i} - 2\vec{j} - \vec{k}$ and $\vec{b} = \vec{i} + \vec{j} + \vec{k}$.

$$\vec{a} \times \vec{b} = \begin{vmatrix} \vec{i} & \vec{j} & \vec{k} \\ 2 & -2 & -1 \\ 1 & 1 & 1 \end{vmatrix} = -\vec{i} - 3\vec{j} + 4\vec{k}.$$

Example 2. Find a vector perpendicular to the line AB for $A: (1, 0, -1)$ and $B: (-1, 1, 0)$, and also perpendicular to the line CD for $C: (3, 1, -1)$ and $D: (4, 5, -2)$.

Consider $\overrightarrow{AB} = -2\vec{i} + \vec{j} + \vec{k}$ and $\overrightarrow{CD} = \vec{i} + 4\vec{j} - \vec{k}$. Since $\overrightarrow{AB} \times \overrightarrow{CD}$ is perpendicular to $\overrightarrow{AB}$ and $\overrightarrow{CD}$, it is perpendicular to lines AB and CD. Therefore,

$$\begin{vmatrix} \vec{i} & \vec{j} & \vec{k} \\ -2 & 1 & 1 \\ 1 & 4 & -1 \end{vmatrix}, \text{that is, } -5\vec{i} - \vec{j} - 9\vec{k},$$

or any multiple of this vector, is perpendicular to $\overrightarrow{AB}$ and to $\overrightarrow{CD}$.

The area in square units of any triangle ABC is equal to one-half the area of the parallelogram with $\overrightarrow{AB}$ and $\overrightarrow{AC}$ as adjacent sides. Thus the area of the triangle is $\frac{1}{2}|\overrightarrow{AB} \times \overrightarrow{AC}|$. If $\vec{a}, \vec{b},$ and $\vec{c}$ are the position vectors of $A, B,$ and C, the area may be expressed as $\frac{1}{2}|(\vec{b} - \vec{a}) \times (\vec{c} - \vec{a})|$.

Figure 11-35

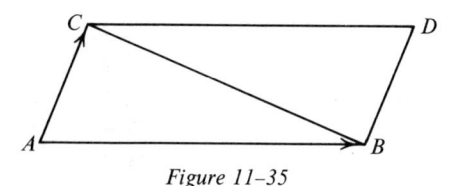

Example 3. Find the area of the triangle with $A: (1, -1, 2)$, $B: (2, 0, -1)$, and $C: (0, 2, 1)$ as vertices. Then find the angle at A.

Since $\overrightarrow{AB} = \vec{i} + \vec{j} - 3\vec{k}$ and $\overrightarrow{AC} = -\vec{i} + 3\vec{j} - \vec{k}$, then

$$\overrightarrow{AB} \times \overrightarrow{AC} = \begin{vmatrix} \vec{i} & \vec{j} & \vec{k} \\ 1 & 1 & -3 \\ -1 & 3 & -1 \end{vmatrix} = 8\vec{i} + 4\vec{j} + 4\vec{k};$$

$$\frac{1}{2}|\overrightarrow{AB} \times \overrightarrow{AC}| = \frac{1}{2}\sqrt{8^2 + 4^2 + 4^2} = 2\sqrt{6}.$$

Therefore, the area of a triangle ABC is $2\sqrt{6}$ square units.

VECTORS

Since $|\vec{AB} \times \vec{AC}| = 4\sqrt{6} = |\vec{AB}||\vec{AC}|\sin A$,

$$\sin A = \frac{4\sqrt{6}}{|\vec{AB}||\vec{AC}|}$$

$$= \frac{4\sqrt{6}}{\sqrt{1^2 + 1^2 + (-3)^2}\sqrt{(-1)^2 + 3^2 + (-1)^2}}$$

$$= \frac{4\sqrt{6}}{11}.$$

Therefore, angle $A = \text{Arc sin } \frac{4\sqrt{6}}{11}$ or approximately $62° \ 58'$.

TEST YOURSELF

1. Prove that $\vec{a} \times \vec{b} = -(\vec{b} \times \vec{a})$.
2. Prove that $(\vec{a} - \vec{b}) \times (\vec{a} + \vec{b}) = 2(\vec{a} \times \vec{b})$.
3. Simplify: $(2\vec{i} + 3\vec{j} + 4\vec{k}) \times (5\vec{i} - 2\vec{j} - 2\vec{k})$.

EXERCISES

In Exercises 1 through 5 prove each statement:

1. $\vec{a} \times \vec{a} = \vec{0}$.
2. If $\vec{a} \times \vec{b} = \vec{0}$, then $\vec{a} = \vec{0}$, $\vec{b} = \vec{0}$, or $\vec{a}$ and $\vec{b}$ are parallel.
3. $(c\vec{a}) \times \vec{b} = c(\vec{a} \times \vec{b})$ for $0 < c$.
4. $\vec{a} \times (c\vec{b}) = c(\vec{a} \times \vec{b})$ for $0 < c$.
5. If $|\vec{a}| \neq 0$, $\vec{b} \neq \vec{c}$, and $\vec{a} \times \vec{b} = \vec{a} \times \vec{c}$, then $\vec{a} \times (\vec{b} - \vec{c}) = \vec{0}$ and $\vec{a}$ is parallel to $\vec{b} - \vec{c}$.

6. Simplify: $(\vec{ai} - \vec{aj} + \vec{ak}) \times (-\vec{ai} + \vec{aj} - \vec{ak})$.
7. Find the area of the parallelogram formed by the two vectors $\vec{a} = 3\vec{i} + 2\vec{j}$ and $\vec{b} = 2\vec{j} - 4\vec{k}$.
8. Find the area of the triangle with vertices at $A: (0, 2, 1)$, $B: (0, 0, 2)$, and $C: (-1, 1, 1)$.

• • •

9. Find (a) the unit vector perpendicular to each of the vectors $2\vec{i} - \vec{j} + \vec{k}$ and $3\vec{i} + 4\vec{j} - \vec{k}$; and (b) the sine of the angle θ between these two given vectors.

10. The vectors $\vec{r}_1 = 3\vec{i} - 2\vec{j} + 6\vec{k}$ and $\vec{r}_2 = -4\vec{j} + 3\vec{k}$ are given. Find (a) $\vec{r}_1 \times \vec{r}_2$ and the area of the triangle which has $\vec{r}_1$ and $\vec{r}_2$ as sides; (b) the angle θ between the two given vectors; and (c) the projection of $\vec{r}_1$ upon $\vec{r}_2$.

11. Prove that the triangle with vertices at $A: (2, 4, 1)$, $B: (1, 2, -2)$, and $C: (5, 0, -2)$ is a right triangle and find its area.

12. Show that $|\vec{a} \times \vec{b}|^2 + |\vec{a} \cdot \vec{b}|^2 = |\vec{a}|^2 |\vec{b}|^2$.

13. Derive the law of sines for any triangle on a plane.

• 14. Derive the usual trigonometric formulas for $\cos(\theta - \phi)$ and $\sin(\theta - \phi)$.

HINT: Let $\vec{a}$ and $\vec{b}$ be unit vectors in the xy-plane and make angles θ and ϕ with the x-axis. Then find $\vec{a} \cdot \vec{b}$ and $\vec{b} \times \vec{a}$.

• 15. As in Exercise 14 derive the formulas for $\cos(\theta + \phi)$ and $\sin(\theta + \phi)$ letting $\vec{a}$ and $\vec{b}$ be unit vectors making angles of θ and $-\phi$ with the x-axis.

• 16. Prove that if vectors representing the diagonals of a parallelogram are used as sides of a new parallelogram, then the area of the new parallelogram is twice that of the original parallelogram.

§ 11-10 Equation of a plane

Planes may be determined in several ways. The vector equation of a plane is based upon the concept of a plane as the set of points on lines which are perpendicular to a given line m at a given point P of m. The line m is perpendicular to the plane, that is, the line is normal to the plane. Any vector parallel to m is also normal to the plane. Any plane may be determined by a point $P_0: (x_0, y_0, z_0)$ of the plane and a vector $\vec{n}$ which is normal to the plane (Figure 11–36). Note that it does not matter whether P_0 does or does not lie on $\vec{n}$.

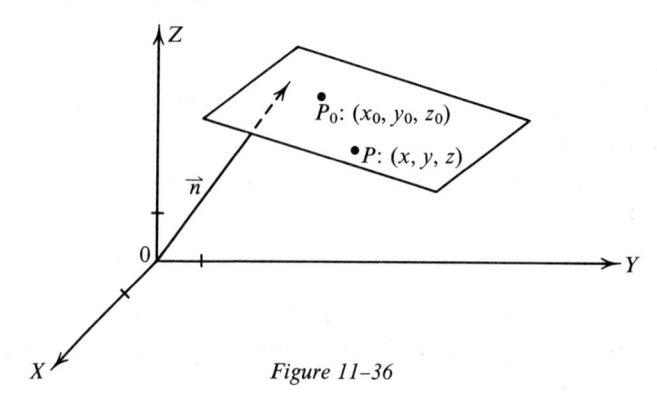

Figure 11–36

VECTORS

Let $P: (x, y, z)$ be a general point on the plane. Since $\overrightarrow{P_0P}$ is perpendicular to $\vec{n}$, $\overrightarrow{P_0P} \cdot \vec{n} = 0$. If $\vec{n} = a\vec{i} + b\vec{j} + c\vec{k}$, then the points (x, y, z) on the plane must satisfy the equations

$$a(x - x_0) + b(y - y_0) + c(z - z_0) = 0 \tag{22}$$

and

$$ax + by + cz + d = 0 \tag{23}$$

where the constant term d is equal to $-ax_0 - by_0 - cz_0$.

Equation (22) is used to find the equation of a plane through a given point (x_0, y_0, z_0). Both equations have the components a, b, and c of the normal vector as the coefficients of x, y, and z respectively. It is customary to call (23) "the equation" of the plane even though it may be written in other forms.

Example 1. Find the equation of the plane through $C: (3, 10, 1)$ and perpendicular to the line through $A: (6, -2, 2)$ and $B: (7, 4, 17)$.

Let $P: (x, y, z)$ be any point on the plane. Then

$\overrightarrow{AB} = \vec{i} + 6\vec{j} + 15\vec{k}$,
$\overrightarrow{CP} = (x - 3)\vec{i} + (y - 10)\vec{j} + (z - 1)\vec{k}$,
$\overrightarrow{AB} \cdot \overrightarrow{CP} = (x - 3) + 6(y - 10) + 15(z - 1) = 0$,
and $x + 6y + 15z - 78 = 0$.

Example 2. Find the equation of the plane which is parallel to the plane with equation $x - 2y + 6z + 17 = 0$ and passes through $P: (3, 2, -5)$.

The normal vector $\vec{i} - 2\vec{j} + 6\vec{k}$ may be used for any plane parallel to the given plane. Thus the desired equation has the form

$$x - 2y + 6z + d = 0.$$

The value of d may be found either by using the statement $d = -ax_0 - by_0 - cz_0$ as in (23) or by substituting the coordinates of P in the given equation since P is on the plane. In both cases $3 - 2(2) + 6(-5) + d = 0$ and $d = 31$.

Thus the equation of the plane is $x - 2y + 6z + 31 = 0$.

The vector form of the equation of the plane through three given non-collinear points may be determined directly from the coordinates of the points. Let $A: (x_1, y_1, z_1)$, $B: (x_2, y_2, z_2)$, and $C: (x_3, y_3, z_3)$ be the three given points. Let $P: (x, y, z)$ be a general point in the desired plane

§ 11-10 EQUATION OF A PLANE

Figure 11-37

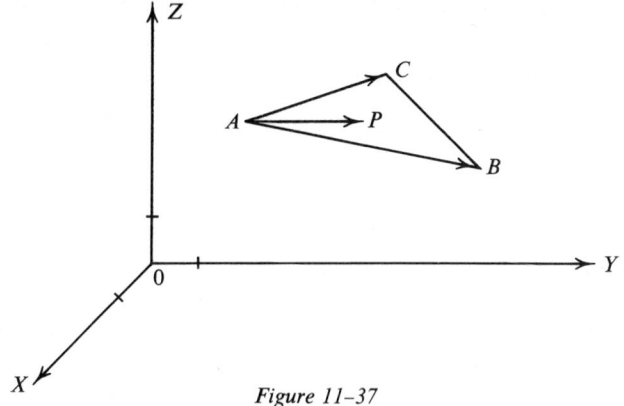

as shown in Figure 11-37. Since $\overrightarrow{AB} \times \overrightarrow{AC}$ is a vector perpendicular to the plane determined by $\overrightarrow{AB}$ and $\overrightarrow{AC}$, this vector product may be used as the vector normal to the plane. Then, since $\overrightarrow{AP}$ lies in the plane, the equation

$$\overrightarrow{AP} \cdot (\overrightarrow{AB} \times \overrightarrow{AC}) = 0$$

is a vector form of the equation of the plane through the three given points A, B, and C. The left member of this equation has the form $\vec{a} \cdot (\vec{b} \times \vec{c})$ and is called a **triple scalar product.**

The triple scalar product $\vec{a} \cdot (\vec{b} \times \vec{c})$, where $\vec{a} = a_1\vec{i} + a_2\vec{j} + a_3\vec{k}$, $\vec{b} = b_1\vec{i} + b_2\vec{j} + b_3\vec{k}$, and $\vec{c} = c_1\vec{i} + c_2\vec{j} + c_3\vec{k}$, may be expressed as a determinant. As in § 11-9

$$\vec{b} \times \vec{c} = \begin{vmatrix} \vec{i} & \vec{j} & \vec{k} \\ b_1 & b_2 & b_3 \\ c_1 & c_2 & c_3 \end{vmatrix};$$

$$\vec{b} \times \vec{c} = (b_2c_3 - b_3c_2)\vec{i} + (b_3c_1 - b_1c_3)\vec{j} + (b_1c_2 - b_2c_1)\vec{k}.$$

As in § 11-7

$$\vec{a} \cdot (\vec{b} \times \vec{c}) = a_1(b_2c_3 - b_3c_2) + a_2(b_3c_1 - b_1c_3) + a_3(b_1c_2 - b_2c_1).$$

Note that the expression for $\vec{a} \cdot (\vec{b} \times \vec{c})$ may be obtained from the expression for $\vec{b} \times \vec{c}$ by replacing $\vec{i}$ by a_1, $\vec{j}$ by a_2, and $\vec{k}$ by a_3. Thus

$$\vec{a} \cdot (\vec{b} \times \vec{c}) = \begin{vmatrix} a_1 & a_2 & a_3 \\ b_1 & b_2 & b_3 \\ c_1 & c_2 & c_3 \end{vmatrix}.$$

VECTORS

Thus the equation $\vec{AP} \cdot (\vec{AB} \times \vec{AC}) = 0$ where

$$\vec{AP} = (x - x_1)\vec{i} + (y - y_1)\vec{j} + (z - z_1)\vec{k},$$
$$\vec{AB} = (x_2 - x_1)\vec{i} + (y_2 - y_1)\vec{j} + (z_2 - z_1)\vec{k}, \text{ and}$$
$$\vec{AC} = (x_3 - x_1)\vec{i} + (y_3 - y_1)\vec{j} + (z_3 - z_1)\vec{k}$$

may be expressed in the form

$$\begin{vmatrix} x - x_1 & y - y_1 & z - z_1 \\ x_2 - x_1 & y_2 - y_1 & z_2 - z_1 \\ x_3 - x_1 & y_3 - y_1 & z_3 - z_1 \end{vmatrix} = 0. \tag{24}$$

Example 3. Find the equation of the plane through $A: (-1, 2, 3)$, $B: (-3, 1, 2)$, and $C: (-5, 4, 6)$.

$$\vec{AB} = -2\vec{i} - \vec{j} - \vec{k}; \quad \vec{AC} = -4\vec{i} + 2\vec{j} + 3\vec{k};$$
$$\vec{AP} = (x + 1)\vec{i} + (y - 2)\vec{j} + (z - 3)\vec{k};$$

$$\vec{AP} \cdot (\vec{AB} \times \vec{AC}) = \begin{vmatrix} (x+1) & (y-2) & (z-3) \\ -2 & -1 & -1 \\ -4 & 2 & 3 \end{vmatrix} = 0$$

$$(x+1)(-3+2) - (y-2)(-6-4) + (z-3)(-4-4) = 0$$
$$-(x+1) + 10(y-2) - 8(z-3) = 0$$
$$-x + 10y - 8z + 3 = 0$$
$$x - 10y + 8z - 3 = 0.$$

TEST YOURSELF

1. Find the equation of the plane through $P: (-2, 1, 2)$ and perpendicular to $\vec{OP}$.

2. Find the equation of the plane through $A: (2, 1, -3)$, $B: (1, -2, 0)$, and $C: (1, 1, 2)$.

EXERCISES

1. Determine the equation of the plane through $P: (-1, 1, 2)$ and perpendicular to $\vec{OP}$.

2. Determine the equation of the plane through $P: (4, 3, 7)$ and perpendicular to the line through $A: (0, 3, 2)$ and $B: (3, -5, 2)$.

3. Find the equation of the plane parallel to the plane $2x + 3y - z + 7 = 0$ and passing through the point $P: (4, -3, -6)$.

4. Find the equation of the plane parallel to the plane $3x - 2y + 7z - 6 = 0$ and passing through the point $P: (2, -6, 1)$.

• • •

5. Find the cosine of the angle θ between $\overrightarrow{AB}$, where $A: (2, 3, 5)$ and $B: (4, -1, 6)$, and the vector normal to the plane $2x - 6y + 3z - 4 = 0$.

6. Find the equations of the planes containing the faces of the tetrahedron whose vertices are $O: (0, 0, 0)$, $A: (0, 6, 0)$, $B: (4, 2, 0)$, and $C: (2, 2, 7)$.

7. What do you know about the plane $ax + by + cz + d = 0$ if $d = 0$? If $b = 0$? If $b = 0$ and $a = 0$? If $b = 0$ and $d = 0$?

8. State the conditions under which the equation $ax + by + cz + d = 0$ may be written in intercept form,

$$\frac{x}{e} + \frac{y}{f} + \frac{z}{g} = 1,$$

and identify the intercepts in terms of a, b, c, and d.

9. State what relation or relations must hold in each case among the coefficients of the equation of a plane $ax + by + cz + d = 0$ in order that:

(a) the plane have the intercept -3 on the x-axis;
(b) the plane have equal intercepts on the y- and z-axes;
(c) the plane have equal intercepts on all three axes;
(d) the plane be parallel to the plane whose equation is $5x + 2y - 3z + 12 = 0$;
(e) the plane be perpendicular to the vector $2\vec{i} + 5\vec{j} - 6\vec{k}$;
(f) the plane pass through the origin;
(g) the plane pass through the point $(3, 1, -2)$;
(h) the plane be parallel to the x-axis;
(i) the plane be parallel to the xy-plane.

§ 11-11 Equations of a line

There is one and only one line through a given point $P_0: (x_0, y_0, z_0)$ and parallel to a given vector $\vec{r}$. The condition that a point $P: (x, y, z)$ be on this line may be expressed as

$$\overrightarrow{P_0P} \times \vec{r} = \vec{0}$$

which is the **vector equation** of the line PP_0. This condition may also be expressed as in § 11-4 in the form

$$\overrightarrow{P_0P} = t\vec{r}$$

for some real number t.

VECTORS

If $\vec{r} = a\vec{i} + b\vec{j} + c\vec{k}$, we have the form

$$(x - x_0)\vec{i} + (y - y_0)\vec{j} + (z - z_0)\vec{k} = t(a\vec{i} + b\vec{j} + c\vec{k})$$

for a line through (x_0, y_0, z_0) with direction numbers a, b, and c. Each point on the line corresponds to a value of the *parameter t*. If we equate components of the vectors in the two members of the equation, we have

$$(x - x_0) = ta, \quad y - y_0 = tb, \quad z - z_0 = tc.$$

When these equations are written in the form

$$x = x_0 + ta, \quad y = y_0 + tb, \quad z = z_0 + tc, \quad (25)$$

they are called a set of **parametric equations** for the line PP_0.

If we solve each of the parametric equations for t and equate the expressions obtained, we have

$$\frac{x - x_0}{a} = \frac{y - y_0}{b} = \frac{z - z_0}{c}. \quad (26)$$

These equations are called a set of **symmetric equations** for a line through (x_0, y_0, z_0) with direction numbers a, b, and c. Whenever one or more of the direction numbers is zero, we use the parametric equations.

Example 1. Find a set of symmetric equations for the line through $A: (2, 2, 4)$ and $B: (8, 6\frac{1}{2}, 2\frac{1}{2})$.

The direction numbers may be taken as 6, $4\frac{1}{2}$, and $-1\frac{1}{2}$. They may also be taken as 12, 9, and -3 or as 4, 3, and -1. We may use the coordinates of A to obtain the symmetric equations

$$\frac{x - 2}{4} = \frac{y - 2}{3} = \frac{z - 4}{-1}.$$

Note that the coordinates of B could have been used to obtain equivalent equations

$$\frac{x - 8}{4} = \frac{y - 6\frac{1}{2}}{3} = \frac{z - 2\frac{1}{2}}{-1}.$$

Example 2. Find a set of symmetric equations for the line through $A: (2, 0, 1)$ and perpendicular to the plane with equation $3x + 2y - z = 3$.

Any line perpendicular to the given plane is parallel to the normal to the plane and thus has direction numbers 3, 2, and -1. By (26) the line through (2, 0, 1) with these direction numbers has symmetric equations

$$\frac{x-2}{3} = \frac{y}{2} = \frac{z-1}{-1}.$$

Example 3. Find a set of parametric equations for the line through $A: (4, 3, 5)$ and $B: (2, 3, 8)$.

The direction numbers for the line may be taken as 2, 0, and -3. If we use the coordinates of A, we have the parametric equations

$$x = 4 + 2t, \quad y = 3, \quad z = 5 - 3t.$$

If we use the coordinates of B, we have the equivalent equations in another parameter t'

$$x = 2 + 2t', \quad y = 3, \quad z = 8 - 3t'.$$

The line in Example 1 is the line of intersection of the planes with equations

$$\frac{x-2}{4} = \frac{y-2}{3} \quad \text{and} \quad \frac{x-2}{4} = \frac{z-4}{-1};$$

that is,

$$3x - 4y + 2 = 0 \quad \text{and} \quad x + 4z - 18 = 0.$$

This line may also be identified as the line of intersection of many other pairs of planes. The planes with equations

$$a_1 x + b_1 y + c_1 z + d_1 = 0$$
$$a_2 x + b_2 y + c_2 z + d_2 = 0$$

intersect if and only if their normal vectors are not parallel. In other words, the planes determine a line except when

$$a_1 \vec{i} + b_1 \vec{j} + c_1 \vec{k} = t(a_2 \vec{i} + b_2 \vec{j} + c_2 \vec{k})$$

for some constant t. After equating components and solving for t, this condition may be stated as

$$\frac{a_1}{a_2} = \frac{b_1}{b_2} = \frac{c_1}{c_2}.$$

Two planes are parallel if and only if the coefficients of x, y, and z in the equation of one plane are proportional to those coefficients in the equation of the other plane. Two planes determine a line if and only if the coefficients of the x-terms, the y-terms, and the z-terms are not respectively proportional. When a line is determined by two planes, we

VECTORS

use two points of the line to find a set of symmetric equations for the line. The points at which the line intersects the coordinate planes (that is, the **piercing points**) are usually the most convenient ones to find. To identify the piercing point in the xy-plane, we substitute $z = 0$ in the equations of the planes and solve the resulting equations in x and y simultaneously. To find the piercing points in the xz-plane and yz-plane we use $y = 0$ and $x = 0$ respectively.

Example 4. Find a set of symmetric equations for the line determined by the planes with equations $x - 2y + z = 2$ and $2x + y - 3z = 4$.

If $z = 0$, we have the equations

$$\begin{cases} x - 2y = 2 \\ 2x + y = 4 \end{cases}$$

with solution $x = 2$, $y = 0$. Thus the line pierces the xy-plane at $A: (2, 0, 0)$. If $x = 0$, we have

$$\begin{cases} -2y + z = 2 \\ y - 3z = 4 \end{cases}$$

with solution $y = -2$, $z = -2$. Thus the line pierces the yz-plane at $B: (0, -2, -2)$.

We could find, but do not need, the coordinates at which the line pierces the xz-plane. The components 2, 2, and 2 of $\overrightarrow{BA}$ may be used as direction numbers for the line. Then the coordinates of A may be used to obtain the symmetric equations

$$\frac{x-2}{2} = \frac{y}{2} = \frac{z}{2}.$$

Note that the line also has 1, 1, and 1 as direction numbers and has $\frac{1}{\sqrt{3}}, \frac{1}{\sqrt{3}},$ and $\frac{1}{\sqrt{3}}$ as direction cosines.

TEST YOURSELF

1. Find a set of symmetric equations for the line through $A: (-1, 2, 3)$ and $B: (2, 1, 0)$.
2. Find a set of parametric equations for the line through $P: (2, 4, 6)$ and $Q: (3, 4, 5)$.
3. Find a set of (a) direction numbers and (b) direction cosines for the line determined by the planes with equations

$$x - 2y + 3z = 6 \quad \text{and} \quad 2x + y - 4z = 2.$$

EXERCISES

1. Find a set of symmetric equations for the line through $A: (-1, 2, 4)$ and $B: (2, 1, 2)$.

2. Find a set of parametric equations for the line through $A: (3, 5, 1)$ and $B: (1, -2, 0)$.

3. Find a set of symmetric equations for the line passing through $A: (2, 1, 6)$ and having direction numbers 4, 3, and -2.

4. Find a set of symmetric equations for the line through $P: (4, 1, 2)$ and parallel to the line with equations $\dfrac{x-1}{3} = \dfrac{y}{5} = \dfrac{z-7}{-1}$.

5. Find a set of symmetric equations for the line through $P: (5, 1, 5)$ and parallel to vector $\vec{i} - \vec{j} + 3\vec{k}$.

• • •

6. Find a set of symmetric equations for the line through $A: (1, 1, 2)$ and perpendicular to the plane with equation $4x - 2y + 5z = 8$.

7. For the line with equations $x = 2 + t, y = 5 - 3t$, and $z = -1 + 4t$ find a set of direction numbers and locate three points on the line.

8. Find a set of parametric equations for the line through the origin and parallel to the line through the points $A: (-1, 1, 2)$ and $B: (3, 4, 0)$.

9. Find a set of **(a)** direction numbers and **(b)** symmetric equations for the line determined by the planes with equations $6x - 2y + z = 8$ and $2x + 4y - 3z = 1$.

10. Prove that the line determined by the planes with the equations $3x - 5y - z = 1$ and $4x - 3y + 6z = 5$ is parallel to the line determined by the planes with equations $x - y + z = 0$ and $4x - 7y - 2z = 6$.

11. Find a set of parametric equations for the line through $A: (2, -3, 2)$ and parallel to the line determined by the planes with equations $3x - 2y + 3z + 3 = 0$ and $x + y - 2z = 4$.

12. **(a)** Find a set of symmetric equations for the line which passes through $B: (2, -1, 3)$ and is parallel to the line determined by the planes with equations $x + y + z = 3$ and $x - y + 2z = 2$. **(b)** Find the equation of the plane through the given point and perpendicular to the given line.

• **13.** Prove that the direction of the line determined by the planes with equations $x + 5 = 3y$ and $4y = z + 9$ is perpendicular to the direction of the line determined by the planes with equations $x + z = 0$ and $x + 1 = y$.

VECTORS

● 14. Find the angle between the directions of the lines with the given equations:

(a) $\dfrac{x}{2} = \dfrac{y}{3} = \dfrac{z+6}{4}$; $\dfrac{x-3}{1} = \dfrac{y+6}{-2} = \dfrac{z}{1}$.

(b) $\dfrac{x+1}{1} = \dfrac{y}{2} = \dfrac{z-7}{2}$; $\dfrac{x-6}{-3} = \dfrac{y-2}{4} = \dfrac{z}{5}$.

● 15. Prove that the line determined by the planes with equations $a_1x + b_1y + c_1z = d_1$ and $a_2x + b_2y + c_2z = d_2$ has as a set of direction numbers

$$\begin{vmatrix} b_1 & c_1 \\ b_2 & c_2 \end{vmatrix}, \quad \begin{vmatrix} c_1 & a_1 \\ c_2 & a_2 \end{vmatrix}, \quad \begin{vmatrix} a_1 & b_1 \\ a_2 & b_2 \end{vmatrix}.$$

● 16. Repeat Exercise 9 using the results obtained in Exercise 15.

§ 11-12 Applications

Many applications of vectors have already been mentioned. In this section we shall consider the volume of a parallelepiped, the equation of a sphere, the equation of a plane tangent to a sphere, the angle between two planes, and the distance from a point to a plane.

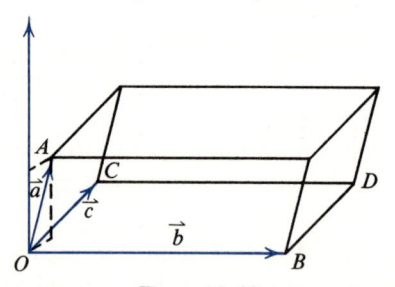

Figure 11-38

The area of parallelogram $OBDC$ in Figure 11-38 is $|\vec{b} \times \vec{c}|$ and the vector $\vec{b} \times \vec{c}$ is perpendicular to the plane OBC as in § 11-9. Let $\vec{v} = \dfrac{1}{|\vec{b} \times \vec{c}|}(\vec{b} \times \vec{c})$; that is, let $\vec{v}$ be a unit vector parallel to $\vec{b} \times \vec{c}$. Then $\vec{a} \cdot \vec{v}$ is equal to the projection of $\vec{a}$ onto $\vec{v}$ as in § 11-7 and thus to the altitude upon the base $OBDC$ of the parallelepiped in Figure 11-38. The **volume of the parallelepiped** is equal to the product of the altitude $\vec{a} \cdot \vec{v}$ and the area of the base $|\vec{b} \times \vec{c}|$. In other words, the volume in cubic units is represented by the triple scalar product

$$\vec{a} \cdot (\vec{b} \times \vec{c}) \tag{27}$$

and may be expressed by the determinant

$$\begin{vmatrix} a_1 & a_2 & a_3 \\ b_1 & b_2 & b_3 \\ c_1 & c_2 & c_3 \end{vmatrix}$$

involving the components of the vectors $\vec{a}$, $\vec{b}$, and $\vec{c}$ as in § 11–10.

If the three vectors $\vec{a}$, $\vec{b}$, $\vec{c}$ are coplanar, the parallelepiped is degenerate and has volume zero. We used this property in § 11–10 to obtain the equation $\vec{AP} \cdot (\vec{AB} \times \vec{AC}) = 0$ for the plane ABC as in Example 3 of that section.

Example 1. Find the volume of the parallelepiped whose edges are represented by $\vec{a}$, $\vec{b}$, and $\vec{c}$, where $\vec{a} = 2\vec{i} + 3\vec{j}$, $\vec{b} = \vec{i} + \vec{j} + 2\vec{k}$, and $\vec{c} = 4\vec{i} - \vec{k}$.

The volume of a parallelepiped is given by $\vec{a} \cdot (\vec{b} \times \vec{c})$.

$$\vec{a} \cdot (\vec{b} \times \vec{c}) = \begin{vmatrix} 2 & 3 & 0 \\ 1 & 1 & 2 \\ 4 & 0 & -1 \end{vmatrix} = -2 + 24 + 0 - 0 + 3 - 0 = 25.$$

The volume is 25 cubic units.

Each point $P: (x, y, z)$ on a sphere with center $C: (x_0, y_0, z_0)$ and radius r is at a distance r from C. In terms of the position vectors $\vec{p}$ and $\vec{c}$ (Figure 11–39) this condition may be expressed either as

$$|\vec{p} - \vec{c}| = r \tag{28}$$

or as

$$(\vec{p} - \vec{c}) \cdot (\vec{p} - \vec{c}) = r^2. \tag{29}$$

Either of these equations may be used as an **equation of the sphere**. Since $\vec{p} = x\vec{i} + y\vec{j} + z\vec{k}$ and $\vec{c} = x_0\vec{i} + y_0\vec{j} + z_0\vec{k}$, the equation of the sphere may also be written as

$$(x - x_0)^2 + (y - y_0)^2 + (z - z_0)^2 = r^2.$$

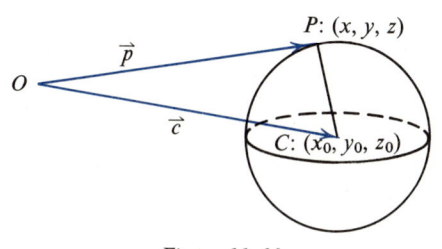

Figure 11–39

VECTORS

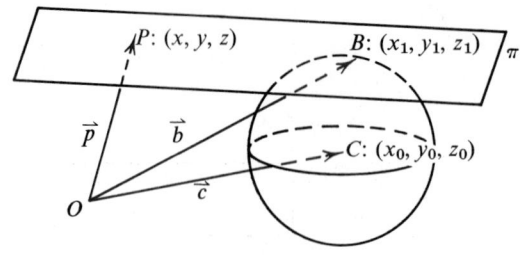

Figure 11–40

A plane π is tangent (Figure 11–40) at a point $B: (x_1, y_1, z_1)$ to a sphere with center $C: (x_0, y_0, z_0)$ if and only if for every point $P: (x, y, z)$ on the plane, $\overrightarrow{PB}$ is perpendicular to $\overrightarrow{BC}$. In other words, the points P such that $\overrightarrow{PB}$ is perpendicular to $\overrightarrow{BC}$ are the points of the **tangent plane** and thus the plane has the equation $\overrightarrow{PB} \cdot \overrightarrow{BC} = \mathbf{0}$; that is,

$$(\vec{b} - \vec{p}) \cdot (\vec{c} - \vec{b}) = \mathbf{0}. \tag{30}$$

Example 2. A sphere has equation $x^2 + y^2 + z^2 - 6x - 2y + 4z - 35 = 0$. Find the center of the sphere, its radius, and an equation of the plane that is tangent to the sphere at $B: (0, 3, 4)$.

The equation of the sphere may be written in the form

$$(x - 3)^2 + (y - 1)^2 + (z + 2)^2 = 49$$

which tells us that the center is at $C: (3, 1, -2)$ and the radius is 7. The point $B: (0, 3, 4)$ is on the sphere as expected.

Let $P: (x, y, z)$ be any point on the plane that is tangent to the sphere at B. Then

$$\overrightarrow{PB} = (0 - x)\vec{i} + (3 - y)\vec{j} + (4 - z)\vec{k},$$
$$\overrightarrow{BC} = (3 - 0)\vec{i} + (1 - 3)\vec{j} + (-2 - 4)\vec{k} = 3\vec{i} - 2\vec{j} - 6\vec{k},$$
$$\overrightarrow{PB} \cdot \overrightarrow{BC} = 3(0 - x) - 2(3 - y) - 6(4 - z) = 0$$
$$-3x - 6 + 2y - 24 + 6z = 0$$
$$-3x + 2y + 6z - 30 = 0.$$

This is an equation for the desired plane.

Any two intersecting lines form two pairs of supplementary plane angles. Any two intersecting planes form two pairs of supplementary dihedral angles. As in Figure 11–41 these dihedral angles are equal to the angles formed by the normals to the planes. In other words the **angles between any two planes** are equal to the angles between their normals.

§ 11–12 APPLICATIONS

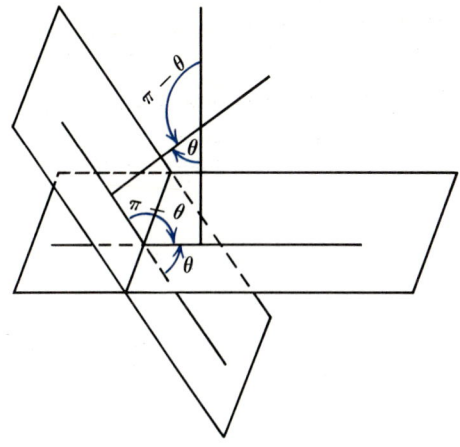

Figure 11–41

If the equations of the planes are

$$a_1x + b_1y + c_1z + d_1 = 0$$
$$a_2x + b_2y + c_2z + d_2 = 0,$$

then the normal vectors are

$$\vec{n_1} = a_1\vec{i} + b_1\vec{j} + c_1\vec{k}$$
$$\vec{n_2} = a_2\vec{i} + b_2\vec{j} + c_2\vec{k}.$$

The angle between these two vectors may be found by using their scalar product:

$$\vec{n_1} \cdot \vec{n_2} = |\vec{n_1}||\vec{n_2}| \cos \theta,$$

$$\cos \theta = \pm \frac{\vec{n_1} \cdot \vec{n_2}}{|\vec{n_1}||\vec{n_2}|} = \pm \frac{a_1a_2 + b_1b_2 + c_1c_2}{\sqrt{a_1^2 + b_1^2 + c_1^2}\sqrt{a_2^2 + b_2^2 + c_2^2}}. \quad (31)$$

The + and − signs are both considered in order to obtain the two supplementary angles formed by the normal lines. Thus the condition for the planes to be perpendicular is the same as for the normals to be perpendicular and may be stated in any one of these forms:

$$\cos \theta = 0, \qquad \vec{n_1} \cdot \vec{n_2} = 0, \qquad a_1a_2 + b_1b_2 + c_1c_2 = 0.$$

The condition for the planes to be parallel is the same as for the normals to be parallel and may be stated in any one of these forms in which t is

645

VECTORS

some scalar:

$$\cos\theta = \pm 1, \quad \vec{n_1} = t\vec{n_2}, \quad \frac{a_1}{a_2} = \frac{b_1}{b_2} = \frac{c_1}{c_2} = t.$$

Example 3. Find the cosines of the angles between the planes with equations $2x + 2y - z = 3$ and $3x - 2y + 6z = 14$.

The normal vectors are $\vec{n_1} = 2\vec{i} + 2\vec{j} - \vec{k}$ and $\vec{n_2} = 3\vec{i} - 2\vec{j} + 6\vec{k}$. Then $|\vec{n_1}| = \sqrt{4 + 4 + 1} = 3$; and $|\vec{n_2}| = \sqrt{9 + 4 + 36} = 7$. From this we obtain

$$\cos\theta = \pm \frac{(2)(3) + (2)(-2) + (-1)(6)}{(3)(7)} = \pm \frac{4}{21}.$$

The distance from a point P to a line m is defined to be the shortest distance from P to a point of m and is measured along the line through P and perpendicular to m. If P is on m, the distance is zero.

The distance from a point P to a plane π is defined to be the shortest distance from P to a point of π and is measured along the line through P and perpendicular to π. Let the equation of the plane be $ax + by + cz + d = 0$,

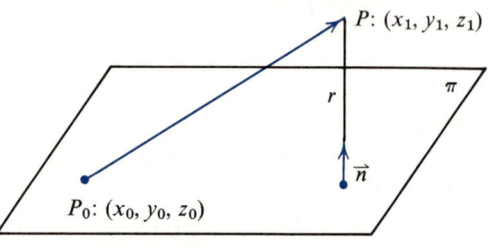

Figure 11–42

and let $P: (x_1, y_1, z_1)$ be any point in space. In order to determine the shortest distance r from P to the plane, choose any point $P_0: (x_0, y_0, z_0)$ on the plane and find the length of the projection of $\overrightarrow{P_0P}$ on a vector $\vec{n}$ which is perpendicular to the plane where $\vec{n} = a\vec{i} + b\vec{j} + c\vec{k}$. Then, as in § 11–7,

$$r = \frac{|\overrightarrow{P_0P} \cdot \vec{n}|}{\sqrt{a^2 + b^2 + c^2}};$$

$$\begin{aligned}\overrightarrow{P_0P} \cdot \vec{n} &= [(x_1 - x_0)\vec{i} + (y_1 - y_0)\vec{j} + (z_1 - z_0)\vec{k}] \cdot (a\vec{i} + b\vec{j} + c\vec{k}) \\ &= a(x_1 - x_0) + b(y_1 - y_0) + c(z_1 - z_0) \\ &= ax_1 + by_1 + cz_1 - (ax_0 + by_0 + cz_0) \\ &= ax_1 + by_1 + cz_1 + d\end{aligned}$$

where $d = -(ax_0 + by_0 + cz_0)$ since P_0 is a point of the plane. Then

$$r = \left|\frac{ax_1 + by_1 + cz_1 + d}{\sqrt{a^2 + b^2 + c^2}}\right|. \tag{32}$$

Example 4. Find the distance from the point $P: (2, -1, 5)$ to the plane with equation $2x + 2y - z - 3 = 0$.

$$r = \left|\frac{2(2) + 2(-1) + (-1)(5) - 3}{\sqrt{2^2 + 2^2 + 1^2}}\right| = \left|\frac{-6}{3}\right| = 2.$$

Vectors may be used to solve many problems in geometry. Other applications may be found in practically all subjects where extensive use is made of mathematics. Sometimes the vector methods are easier than other methods, sometimes they are harder. A major advantage of the vector methods arises from the fact that the procedures, and often the equations, for three dimensional problems are precisely the same as for two dimensional problems. For example, the vector equation of a sphere is the same as the vector equation of a circle; the vector equation of a plane tangent to a sphere at a given point is the same as the vector equation of a line tangent to a circle at a given point. The basic elementary uses of vectors have been considered in this chapter.

TEST YOURSELF

1. Find an equation of the sphere with center at $C: (2, -1, 3)$ and radius 7.
2. Find an equation of the plane that is tangent at $B: (4, -2, 6)$ to the sphere with center $C: (1, 0, 0)$.
3. Prove that the planes with equations $2x + 2y - z = 3$ and $x - 2y - 2z = 1$ are perpendicular.
4. Find the distance from the point $P: (7, -3, 2)$ to the plane with equation $3x + 2y - 6z + 4 = 0$.

EXERCISES

1. Find an equation of the sphere with center $C: (0, 4, -1)$ and radius 3.
2. Find an equation of the plane that is tangent at $B: (4, 2, 9)$ to a sphere with center $C: (2, -1, 3)$.
3. Find the center and radius of the sphere with equation

$$x^2 + y^2 + z^2 - 4x - 6y + 2z - 11 = 0.$$

4. Find an equation of the plane which is tangent at $B: (0, 2, 8)$ to the sphere with equation $x^2 + y^2 + z^2 - 2x + 4y = 76$.
5. Find an equation of the plane which is tangent at $B: (1, 2, -2)$ to the sphere with equation $x^2 + y^2 + z^2 = 9$.
6. Find a general equation of the plane which is tangent at $B: (x_1, y_1, z_1)$ to a sphere with equation $x^2 + y^2 + z^2 = a^2$.

VECTORS

7. Prove that the planes with equations $x + 2y - 3z - 7 = 0$ and $5x + 10y - 15z + 2 = 0$ are parallel.

8. Prove that the planes with equations $2x - 3y + 5z + 2 = 0$ and $5x - 2z + 7 = 0$ are perpendicular.

9. Find the value of C for which the planes with equations $3x - 4y + Cz = 0$ and $2x - 3y + 6z - 1 = 0$ are perpendicular.

10. Find the distance from the point $P: (-3, 2, -1)$ to the plane with equation $-2x + y - 2z + 3 = 0$.

11. Find the distance from the point $P: (2, 0, -5)$ to the plane with equation $x + y + 2z = 4$.

12. Find the volume of the parallelepiped with edges $\vec{a}$, $\vec{b}$, and $\vec{c}$ where
$$\vec{a} = \vec{i} + 2\vec{j} + \vec{k}, \quad \vec{b} = 2\vec{i} + \vec{j}, \quad \text{and} \quad \vec{c} = 3\vec{i} - 4\vec{j} - 5\vec{k}.$$

• • •

13. Find an equation of the sphere having $A: (-4, 5, 1)$ and $B: (4, 7, 1)$ as end points of a diameter.

14. Find the acute angle between the planes with equations $2x - y + 2z - 10 = 0$ and $4x + y + z - 7 = 0$.

15. Find the cosine of the obtuse angle between the planes with equations $3x + 4y = 16$ and $4y - 2z = 5$.

16. Find the distance between the parallel planes with equations $3x - 2y + z + 4 = 0$ and $3x - 2y + z - 13 = 0$.

17. Prove that the distance between two parallel planes with equations $a_1 x + b_1 y + c_1 z + d_1 = 0$ and $a_1 x + b_1 y + c_1 z + d_2 = 0$ is equal to
$$\left| \frac{-d_2 + d_1}{\sqrt{a_1^2 + b_1^2 + c_1^2}} \right|.$$

18. Determine d so that the distance from $P: (1, 0, 1)$ to the plane with equation $4x + y - 8z + d = 0$ is 2.

• **19.** Find an equation of the sphere through $O: (0, 0, 0)$, $A: (1, 0, 0)$, $B: (0, 4, 0)$, and $C: (-1, 2, 1)$.

• **20.** Find the volume of the tetrahedron with vertices $A: (0, -1, 3)$, $B: (3, 2, 1)$, $C: (1, -1, 2)$, and $D: (2, 3, 1)$.

• **21.** Prove that the volume V in cubic units of a tetrahedron with vertices at (x_1, y_1, z_1), (x_2, y_2, z_2), (x_3, y_3, z_3), and (x_4, y_4, z_4) can be expressed in the form

$$V = \pm \frac{1}{6} \begin{vmatrix} x_1 & y_1 & z_1 & 1 \\ x_2 & y_2 & z_2 & 1 \\ x_3 & y_3 & z_3 & 1 \\ x_4 & y_4 & z_4 & 1 \end{vmatrix}$$

SUMMARY OF CHAPTER 11

1. In this chapter you have studied the use of vectors in algebra, geometry, and applied problems. You have learned that any number has magnitude (absolute value) and is called a scalar; any vector has both magnitude and direction. Any real number n may be represented either by a point P with a coordinate on a number line or by a vector $\overrightarrow{OP}$ where O is the origin. Any complex number $a + bi$ may be represented on a complex plane either by a point $P: (a, b)$ or by a vector $\overrightarrow{OP}$ where O is the origin. (§ 11–1)

2. Any two vectors have a unique vector as their sum under the law of vector addition. The addition of vectors is commutative and associative: (§ 11–2)

$$\vec{a} + \vec{b} = \vec{b} + \vec{a}, \tag{1}$$

$$(\vec{a} + \vec{b}) + \vec{c} = \vec{a} + (\vec{b} + \vec{c}). \tag{2}$$

3. Multiplication of a vector by a scalar satisfies the distributive and associative laws: (§ 11–3)

$$(m + n)\vec{a} = m\vec{a} + n\vec{a}, \tag{3}$$

$$m(\vec{a} + \vec{b}) = m\vec{a} + m\vec{b}, \tag{4}$$

$$m(\vec{a} - \vec{b}) = m\vec{a} - m\vec{b}, \tag{5}$$

$$m(n\vec{a}) = (mn)\vec{a}. \tag{6}$$

4. Vector equations have many of the properties of ordinary equations: (§ 11–3)

$$\text{If } \vec{a} = \vec{b}, \text{ then } \vec{a} + \vec{c} = \vec{b} + \vec{c}. \tag{7}$$

$$\text{If } \vec{a} = \vec{b} \text{ and } \vec{c} = \vec{d}, \text{ then } \vec{a} + \vec{c} = \vec{b} + \vec{d}. \tag{8}$$

$$\text{If } \vec{a} = \vec{b} \text{ and } \vec{c} = \vec{d}, \text{ then } \vec{a} - \vec{c} = \vec{b} - \vec{d}. \tag{9}$$

$$\text{If } \vec{a} = \vec{b} \text{ and } m \text{ is a scalar, then } m\vec{a} = m\vec{b}. \tag{10}$$

5. Any vector $\vec{c}$ that is coplanar with two nonparallel, nonzero vectors $\vec{a}$ and $\vec{b}$ may be expressed as $\vec{c} = m\vec{a} + n\vec{b}$ for some scalars m and n (Theorem 1). The end points A, B, and C of three vectors $\overrightarrow{OA}$, $\overrightarrow{OB}$, and

VECTORS

$\overrightarrow{OC}$ are collinear if and only if $\overrightarrow{OC} = (1 - n)\overrightarrow{OA} + n\overrightarrow{OB}$ for some scalar n (Theorem 2). (§ 11-4)

6. Any vector on a plane or in space may be considered with reference to a rectangular coordinate system. If $\overrightarrow{OP} = x\vec{i} + y\vec{j} + z\vec{k}$, then $|\overrightarrow{OP}| = \sqrt{x^2 + y^2 + z^2}$. (§ 11-5)

7. If A, B, and C have position vectors $\vec{a}$, $\vec{b}$, and $\vec{c}$ where

$$\vec{a} = x_1\vec{i} + y_1\vec{j} + z_1\vec{k},$$
$$\vec{b} = x_2\vec{i} + y_2\vec{j} + z_2\vec{k},$$
$$\vec{c} = x_3\vec{i} + y_3\vec{j} + z_3\vec{k},$$

then C divides $\overline{AB}$ in the ratio of n to m if and only if

$$x = \frac{mx_1 + nx_2}{m + n}, \quad y = \frac{my_1 + ny_2}{m + n}, \quad z = \frac{mz_1 + nz_2}{m + n}. \quad (\S\ 11\text{-}6) \quad (11)$$

8. The scalar (dot) product $\vec{a} \cdot \vec{b}$ of two vectors $\vec{a}$ and $\vec{b}$ may be defined as $|\vec{a}||\vec{b}|\cos\theta$ where θ stands for the angle formed by two vectors with a common origin and parallel to the given vectors. Scalar products have these properties:

$$\vec{a} \cdot \vec{a} = |\vec{a}|^2. \tag{12}$$

$$\vec{a} \cdot (-\vec{a}) = -|\vec{a}|^2. \tag{13}$$

If $\vec{a}$ is perpendicular to $\vec{b}$, then $\vec{a} \cdot \vec{b} = 0$. $\tag{14}$

If $\vec{a} \cdot \vec{b} = 0$, then $|\vec{a}| = 0$, $|\vec{b}| = 0$, or $\vec{a}$ is

perpendicular to $\vec{b}$. $\tag{15}$

$$\vec{a} \cdot (\vec{b} + \vec{c}) = \vec{a} \cdot \vec{b} + \vec{a} \cdot \vec{c}. \tag{16}$$

If $\vec{a} = x_1\vec{i} + y_1\vec{j} + z_1\vec{k}$ and $\vec{b} = x_2\vec{i} + y_2\vec{j} + z_2\vec{k}$, then

$$\vec{a} \cdot \vec{b} = x_1x_2 + y_1y_2 + z_1z_2. \tag{17}$$

If A and B have position vectors $\vec{a}$ and $\vec{b}$, then

$$\overline{AB}^2 = (\vec{b} - \vec{a}) \cdot (\vec{b} - \vec{a}). \tag{18}$$

The vector projection of any given nonzero vector $\vec{a}$ onto any given nonzero vector $\vec{b}$ is $\dfrac{\vec{a} \cdot \vec{b}}{|\vec{b}|}$. Scalar products may be used to study forces, work, projection of line segments, and several types of geometric problems. (§ 11–7)

9. Directions in space may be identified in terms of direction angles α, β, and γ; in terms of direction cosines l, m, and n; and in terms of direction numbers. (§ 11–8)

10. The vector (cross) product $\vec{a} \times \vec{b}$ of two vectors may be defined by the equation

$$\vec{a} \times \vec{b} = (|\vec{a}||\vec{b}|\sin\theta)\vec{n} \tag{19}$$

where θ stands for the angle formed by two vectors with a common origin and parallel to the given vectors. If $\sin\theta = 0$, then $\vec{a} \times \vec{b} = \vec{0}$; if $\sin\theta \neq 0$, then the vector $\vec{n}$ is taken as the unit vector perpendicular to the plane of $\vec{a}$ and $\vec{b}$ and such that the vectors $\vec{a}$, $\vec{b}$, and $\vec{n}$ form a right-handed system. Vector products are not commutative but do have these properties:

$$\vec{a} \times (\vec{b} + \vec{c}) = \vec{a} \times \vec{b} + \vec{a} \times \vec{c}, \tag{20}$$

$$c(\vec{a} \times \vec{b}) = (c\vec{a}) \times \vec{b} = \vec{a} \times (c\vec{b}). \tag{21}$$

If $\vec{a} = x_1\vec{i} + y_1\vec{j} + z_1\vec{k}$ and $\vec{b} = x_2\vec{i} + y_2\vec{j} + z_2\vec{k}$, then

$$\vec{a} \times \vec{b} = (y_1z_2 - y_2z_1)\vec{i} + (z_1x_2 - z_2x_1)\vec{j} + (x_1y_2 - x_2y_1)\vec{k}$$

$$= \begin{vmatrix} \vec{i} & \vec{j} & \vec{k} \\ x_1 & y_1 & z_1 \\ x_2 & y_2 & z_2 \end{vmatrix}.$$

Vector products may be used to study several types of geometric problems. (§ 11–9)

11. The equation of a plane through $P: (x, y, z)$ and perpendicular to the vector $a\vec{i} + b\vec{j} + c\vec{k}$ may be expressed in either of these ways:

$$a(x - x_0) + b(y - y_0) + c(z - z_0) = 0, \tag{22}$$

$$ax + by + cz + d = 0. \tag{23}$$

The equation of the plane through three given noncollinear points $A: (x_1, y_1, z_1)$, $B: (x_2, y_2, z_2)$, and $C: (x_3, y_3, z_3)$ may be expressed using a triple scalar product as

$$\overrightarrow{AP} \cdot (\overrightarrow{AB} \times \overrightarrow{AC}) = 0$$

VECTORS

or in the form

$$\begin{vmatrix} x - x_1 & y - y_1 & z - z_1 \\ x_2 - x_1 & y_2 - y_1 & z_2 - z_1 \\ x_3 - x_1 & y_3 - y_1 & z_3 - z_1 \end{vmatrix} = 0. \quad (\S\ 11\text{--}10) \tag{24}$$

12. The line through a given point P_0: (x_0, y_0, z_0) and parallel to a given vector $\vec{r}$ with direction numbers a, b, and c may be expressed in each of these ways:

$$\overrightarrow{P_0P} \times \vec{r} = \vec{0},$$

$$x = x_0 + ta, \quad y = y_0 + tb, \quad z = z_0 + tc, \tag{25}$$

$$\frac{x - x_0}{a} = \frac{y - y_0}{b} = \frac{z - z_0}{c}. \tag{26}$$

The equations (25) are called parametric equations since the constant t serves as a parameter; the equations (26) are called symmetric equations. (§ 11–11)

13. The volume of a parallelepiped with edges represented by $\vec{a}$, $\vec{b}$, and $\vec{c}$ is

$$\vec{a} \cdot (\vec{b} \times \vec{c}). \quad (\S\ 11\text{--}12) \tag{27}$$

14. The equation of a sphere with radius r and center C where C has position vector $\vec{c}$ may be expressed in either of these ways:

$$|\vec{p} - \vec{c}| = r, \tag{28}$$

$$(\vec{p} - \vec{c}) \cdot (\vec{p} - \vec{c}) = r^2. \tag{29}$$

The plane that is tangent to this sphere at a point B with position vector $\vec{b}$ has equation

$$(\vec{b} - \vec{p}) \cdot (\vec{c} - \vec{b}) = 0. \quad (\S\ 11\text{--}12) \tag{30}$$

15. The angle θ between two planes with equations

$$a_1 x + b_1 y + c_1 z + d_1 = 0$$
$$a_2 x + b_2 y + c_2 z + d_2 = 0$$

is given by the equation

$$\cos \theta = \pm \frac{a_1 a_2 + b_1 b_2 + c_1 c_2}{\sqrt{a_1^2 + b_1^2 + c_1^2}\ \sqrt{a_2^2 + b_2^2 + c_2^2}}. \quad (\S\ 11\text{--}12) \tag{31}$$

16. The distance r from a point $P: (x_1, y_1, z_1)$ to a plane with equation $ax + by + cz + d = 0$ is given by the equation

$$r = \left| \frac{ax_1 + by_1 + cz_1 + d}{\sqrt{a^2 + b^2 + c^2}} \right|. \quad (\S\ 11-12) \tag{32}$$

17. The following words have been introduced or used extensively in this chapter:

component (§ 11–5)
cross product (§ 11–9)
direction (§ 11–1)
direction angles (§ 11–8)
direction cosines (§ 11–8)
direction numbers (§ 11–8)
divided externally (§ 11–6)
divided internally (§ 11–6)
dot product (§ 11–7)
equal (§ 11–1)
force (§ 11–7)
initial point (§ 11–1)
left-handed system (§ 11–5)
linear function (§ 11–4)
magnitude (§ 11–1)
null vector (§ 11–1)

parallel (§ 11–3)
parallelogram law (§ 11–2)
parameter (§ 11–11)
piercing points (§ 11–11)
position vector (§ 11–5)
right-handed system (§ 11–5)
scalar (§ 11–1)
scalar product (§ 11–7)
terminal point (§ 11–1)
triangle law (§ 11–2)
triple scalar product (§ 11–10)
vector (§ 11–1)
vector product (§ 11–9)
work (§ 11–7)
zero vector (§ 11–1)

KEYED PRACTICE ON CHAPTER 11

1. On a complex plane draw two vectors representing: (a) $2 - i$; (b) $e^{2\pi i}$. (§ 11–1)

2. Consider a regular hexagon $ABCDEF$ and let $\overrightarrow{AB} = \vec{p}$, $\overrightarrow{BC} = \vec{q}$, and $\overrightarrow{CD} = \vec{r}$. Express in terms of $\vec{p}$, $\vec{q}$, and $\vec{r}$: (a) $\overrightarrow{AC}$; (b) $\overrightarrow{DE}$; (c) $\overrightarrow{EF}$; (d) $\overrightarrow{FA}$; (e) $\overrightarrow{AD}$; (f) $\overrightarrow{AE}$; (g) $\overrightarrow{FB}$. (§ 11–2).

3. Given any two nonparallel vectors $\vec{a}$ and $\vec{b}$: (a) construct $\vec{a} - \vec{b}$ and $2\vec{b} - 2\vec{a}$; (b) prove that the two vectors constructed are parallel. (§ 11–3)

4. Consider $A: (2, -5)$ and $B: (-4, 3)$ on a coordinate plane with origin O. Express as a linear function of $\overrightarrow{OA}$ and $\overrightarrow{OB}$: (a) the vector $\overrightarrow{OC}$ where C is the mid-point of $\overline{AB}$; (b) the vector $\overrightarrow{OP}$ where $P: (5, 5)$. (§ 11–4)

5. Given $P: (3, 1, -5)$ find: (a) $\overrightarrow{OP}$; (b) $|\overrightarrow{OP}|$; (c) a unit vector in the direction of $\overrightarrow{OP}$. (§ 11–5)

VECTORS

6. If the point C on $\overline{AB}$ is such that $\overline{AC}:\overline{CB} = 3:1$ where $A:(2, -1, 7)$ and $B:(10, -5, -1)$, find: (a) the position vector of C; (b) the coordinates of C. (§ 11–6)

7. Find the work done using a force of 80 pounds applied at an angle of 30° to the horizontal to pull a sled a horizontal distance of 25 feet. (§ 11–7)

8. Find $(x_1\vec{i} + y_1\vec{j} + z_1\vec{k}) \cdot (2\vec{i} - 3\vec{j})$. (§ 11–7)

9. Given $A:(2, 6, -2)$ and $B:(-1, 2, 6)$, find: (a) the length of $\overline{AB}$; (b) direction cosines for $\overline{AB}$; (c) four sets of direction numbers for $\overline{AB}$. (§ 11–8)

10. Given any triangle ABC, let $\overline{AB} = \vec{p}$ and $\overline{BC} = \vec{q}$. Then (a) express the area of the triangle in terms of $\vec{p}$ and $\vec{q}$; (b) find the area if $\vec{p} = \vec{i} - 2\vec{j} + \vec{k}$ and $\vec{q} = 2\vec{i} + \vec{j} - \vec{k}$. (§ 11–9)

11. Find an equation of the plane through $A:(2, -5, 7)$ and perpendicular to the line through $B:(2, 4, -3)$ and $C:(0, 1, 4)$. (§ 11–10)

12. Find for the line through $P:(1, 5, -3)$ and $Q:(2, -1, 4)$ a set of: (a) direction numbers; (b) direction cosines; (c) parametric equations. (§ 11–11)

13. Find an equation of the plane which is tangent at $(1, -2, 2)$ to the sphere with equation $x^2 + y^2 + z^2 = 9$. (§ 11–12)

TESTS ON CHAPTER 11

A

1. On a number line draw two vectors representing -5.

2. Consider a quadrilateral $ABCD$ and let $\overline{AB} = \vec{p}$, $\overline{BC} = \vec{q}$, and $\overline{AD} = \vec{r}$. Express in terms of $\vec{p}$, $\vec{q}$, and $\vec{r}$: (a) $\overline{CA}$; (b) $\overline{CD}$; (c) $\overline{DB}$.

3. Given $O:(0, 0)$, $A:(3, 1)$, $B:(7, -5)$, and $C:(-10, 4)$, express $\overline{OC}$ as a linear function of $\overline{OA}$ and $\overline{OB}$.

4. Given $P:(4, 2, -4)$ find: (a) $\overline{OP}$; (b) $|\overline{OP}|$; (c) a unit vector in the direction of $\overline{OP}$.

5. Find (a) the position vector; and (b) the coordinates of the point C on $\overline{AB}$ such that $\overline{AC}:\overline{CB} = 2:3$ where $A:(-1, 7, 11)$ and $B:(4, -3, -4)$.

6. Find the cosine of an angle determined by vectors $3\vec{i} + 2\vec{j} + \vec{k}$ and $4\vec{i} - 3\vec{k}$.

7. Find a set of direction cosines for a line with direction numbers 2, -3, 5.

8. (a) Express in terms of vectors; and (b) find the area of the triangle with vertices at A: $(1, 2, -5)$, B: $(2, -1, 0)$, and C: $(-3, 2, 1)$.

9. Find an equation of the plane through P: $(2, -3, 7)$ and perpendicular to the line with equations

$$x = 5 + 2t, \quad y = 7 - 5t, \quad z = -2 + 4t.$$

10. Find the distance from the point P: $(1, 4, -3)$ to the plane with equation $2x - 3y + 6z - 7 = 0$.

B

1. On a complex plane draw two vectors representing $3 + 2i$.

2. Consider a quadrilateral $ABCD$ and let $\vec{AB} = \vec{p}$, $\vec{AC} = \vec{q}$, and $\vec{DC} = \vec{r}$. Express in terms of $\vec{p}$, $\vec{q}$, and $\vec{r}$: (a) $\vec{BC}$; (b) $\vec{AD}$; (c) $\vec{BD}$.

3. Use a property of vectors to prove that the points P: $(1, 3, -5)$, Q: $(4, 1, -1)$, and R: $(7, -1, 3)$ are collinear.

4. Find (a) the position vector; and (b) the coordinates of the point C on $\vec{AB}$ but not on $\overline{AB}$ such that $\overline{AC}:\overline{CB} = 3:1$ where A: $(-3, 5, 7)$ and B: $(6, -1, 1)$.

5. Prove that $\vec{a}$ and $\vec{b}$ are perpendicular where $\vec{a} = 6\vec{i} + 5\vec{j} - 2\vec{k}$ and $\vec{b} = 4\vec{i} + 12\vec{k}$.

6. A line through A: $(2, -1, 5)$ has direction numbers $3, -1$, and 5. Explain whether or not $(8, -3, -15)$ is on the line.

7. Find an equation of the plane through P: $(11, 2, -5)$ and perpendicular to the line $\dfrac{x-1}{3} = \dfrac{y+3}{4} = \dfrac{z-5}{-2}$.

8. Find a set of parametric equations for the line through R: $(2, -11, 15)$ and S: $(-5, 6, 21)$.

9. Find the volume of the parallelepiped whose edges are represented by the vectors $3\vec{i} - 5\vec{j} + \vec{k}$, $\vec{i} + \vec{j} - 3\vec{k}$, and $2\vec{i} + 3\vec{k}$.

10. Find an equation of the plane which is tangent to the sphere with equation $x^2 + y^2 + z^2 - 2x + 4y = 14$ at $(2, 1, -3)$.

C

1. On a complex plane draw two vectors representing $2e^{\pi i}$.

2. Consider a pentagon $ABCDE$ and let $\vec{AB} = \vec{n}$, $\vec{AC} = \vec{p}$, $\vec{EC} = \vec{q}$, and $\vec{DE} = \vec{r}$. Express in terms of $\vec{n}, \vec{p}, \vec{q}$, and $\vec{r}$: (a) $\vec{BC}$; (b) $\vec{CD}$; (c) $\vec{AE}$; (d) $\vec{BD}$; (e) $\vec{BE}$.

VECTORS

3. Use a property of vectors to prove that the points $P: (7, -3, 4)$, $Q: (5, 1, -3)$, and $R: (3, 5, -10)$ are collinear.

4. Note that $\overline{AC} = |\overrightarrow{AC}|$ and find **(a)** the position vectors; and **(b)** the coordinates of all points C on $\overleftrightarrow{AB}$ such that $\overline{AC}:\overline{CB} = 2:3$ where $A: (13, 1, -7)$ and $B: (-2, 16, 3)$.

5. Use direction numbers to explain whether or not the points $A: (2, -4, 7)$, $B: (8, -6, 17)$, and $C: (-1, -3, 3)$ are collinear.

6. Express an equation of the plane through $A: (2, 1, 5)$, $B: (-1, 3, 2)$, and $C: (5, 0, 1)$ **(a)** as a vector equation; **(b)** in the form $ax + by + cz + d = 0$.

7. Find a set of parametric equations for the line through the origin and parallel to the line through the points $A: (5, -2, 7)$ and $B: (3, 4, -1)$.

8. Find a set of **(a)** direction numbers; and **(b)** symmetric equations for the line determined by the planes with equations $2x - 3y + 2z = 4$ and $x + 2y - z = 7$.

9. Determine d so that the distance from $P: (-1, 0, 1)$ to the plane with equation $4x - y + 8z + d = 0$ is 2.

10. Find the volume of the parallelepiped with edges represented by the vectors $2\vec{i} - 3\vec{j} + \vec{k}, \vec{i} + 2\vec{j} - \vec{k}$, and $\vec{i} - 2\vec{j} + \vec{k}$.

ANSWERS TO TEST YOURSELF EXERCISES

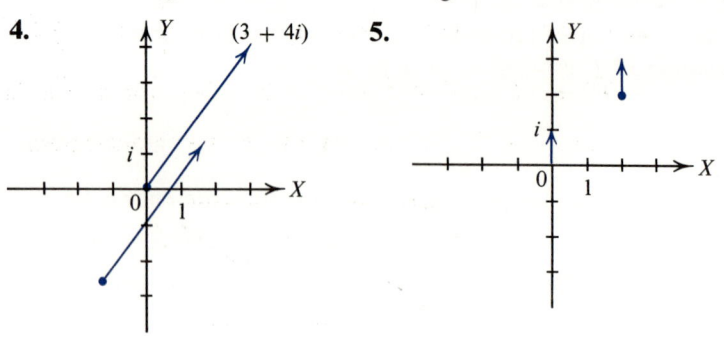

§ 11-1. 1. Any vector three units long and directed in the positive sense is satisfactory.

2. Any vector one unit long and directed in the negative sense is satisfactory.

3. Any vector approximately 3.14 units long and directed in the negative sense is satisfactory.

4.

5.

ANSWERS TO TEST YOURSELF EXERCISES

6.

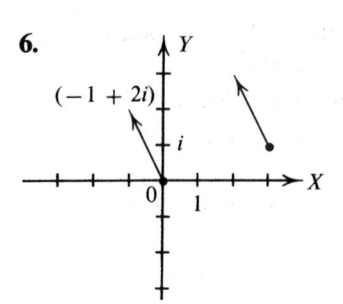

In each of the Exercises 4 through 6 any vector having the magnitude and direction of the vectors shown is satisfactory.

§ 11-2. 1.

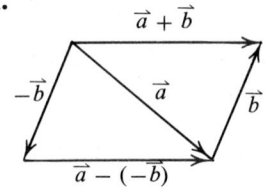

2.
$$\vec{a} + (-\vec{a}) = \vec{0},$$ 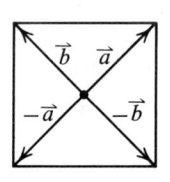
$$\vec{b} + (-\vec{b}) = \vec{0},$$
$$\vec{a} + (-\vec{a}) + \vec{b} + (-\vec{b}) = \vec{0}.$$

§ 11-3. 1.

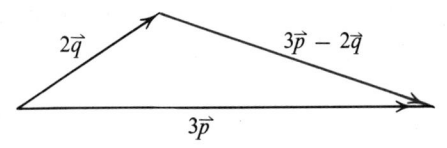

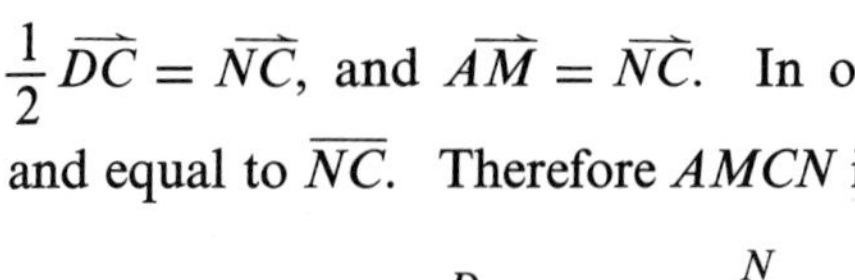

2. In parallelogram $ABCD$ $\overrightarrow{AB} = \overrightarrow{DC}$, $\frac{1}{2}\overrightarrow{AB} = \frac{1}{2}\overrightarrow{DC}$, $\overrightarrow{DN} = \frac{1}{2}\overrightarrow{DC} = \overrightarrow{NC}$, and $\overrightarrow{AM} = \overrightarrow{NC}$. In other words, $\overrightarrow{AM}$ is parallel and equal to $\overrightarrow{NC}$. Therefore $AMCN$ is a parallelogram.

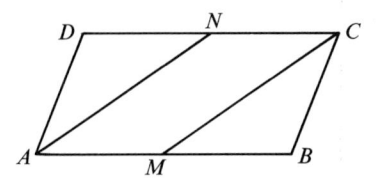

657

VECTORS

§ 11-4. 1. (a) $\overrightarrow{OP} = \frac{3}{2}\overrightarrow{OA} + 2\overrightarrow{OB}$. (b) $\overrightarrow{OP} = -3\overrightarrow{OC} - \frac{2}{3}\overrightarrow{OD}$.
(c) $\overrightarrow{OP} = \frac{3}{2}\overrightarrow{OA} - \frac{2}{3}\overrightarrow{OD}$. (d) $\overrightarrow{OP} = -3\overrightarrow{OC} + 2\overrightarrow{OB}$.

2. $\overrightarrow{OA} + \frac{1}{3}(\overrightarrow{OB} - \overrightarrow{OA}) = \overrightarrow{OA} + \frac{1}{3}\overrightarrow{OB} - \frac{1}{3}\overrightarrow{OA} = \frac{1}{3}\overrightarrow{OB} + \frac{2}{3}\overrightarrow{OA}$;
therefore by Theorem 2, $\overrightarrow{OA} + \frac{1}{3}(\overrightarrow{OB} - \overrightarrow{OA})$ lies on $\overline{AB}$.

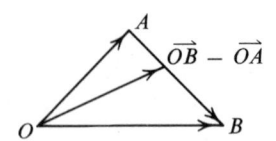

3. $\overrightarrow{AM} + \overrightarrow{AM} = \overrightarrow{AB} + \overrightarrow{AC}$; $2\overrightarrow{AM} = \overrightarrow{AB} + \overrightarrow{AC}$; $\overrightarrow{AM} = \frac{1}{2}\overrightarrow{AB} + \frac{1}{2}\overrightarrow{AC}$; therefore by Theorem 2, M is the mid-point of $\overline{BC}$.

§ 11-5. 1. $2\vec{i} - \vec{j} - 2\vec{k}$. **2. 3.** $\frac{2}{3}\vec{i} - \frac{1}{3}\vec{j} - \frac{2}{3}\vec{k}$.

§ 11-6. 1. $(-2, 0, 4)$. **2.** $C: (-1, -1, 5)$; $D: (-3, 1, 3)$.

§ 11-7. 1. $\sqrt{14}$.

2. Consider right triangle ABC with $\angle C = 90°$. Then 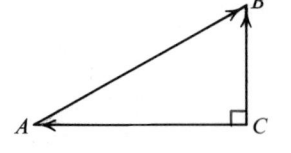
$\overrightarrow{AB} = \overrightarrow{CB} - \overrightarrow{CA}$;
$\overrightarrow{AB} \cdot \overrightarrow{AB} = (\overrightarrow{CB} - \overrightarrow{CA}) \cdot (\overrightarrow{CB} - \overrightarrow{CA})$
$= \overrightarrow{CB} \cdot \overrightarrow{CB} - 2\overrightarrow{CA} \cdot \overrightarrow{CB} + \overrightarrow{CA} \cdot \overrightarrow{CA}$,
$|\overrightarrow{AB}|^2 = |\overrightarrow{CB}|^2 - 0 + |\overrightarrow{CA}|^2 = |\overrightarrow{CB}|^2 + |\overrightarrow{CA}|^2$.

§ 11-8. 1. 3 units. **2.** $\frac{2}{3}, -\frac{1}{3}, -\frac{2}{3}$. **3.** $2, -1, -2$; $-2, 1, 2$; $4, -2, -4$; $-6, 3, 6$; any set of numbers of the form $2t, -t, -2t$, where any real number $t \neq 0$ is satisfactory.

§ 11-9. 1. Let $\vec{a} \times \vec{b} = (|\vec{a}||\vec{b}| \sin \theta)\vec{n}$. Then, just as $\vec{i} \times \vec{j} = \vec{k}$ and $\vec{j} \times \vec{i} = -\vec{k}$, $\vec{b} \times \vec{a} = (|\vec{a}||\vec{b}| \sin \theta)(-\vec{n}) = -(\vec{a} \times \vec{b})$.

ANSWERS TO KEYED PRACTICE ON CHAPTER 11

2. $(\vec{a} - \vec{b}) \times (\vec{a} + \vec{b}) = (\vec{a} - \vec{b}) \times \vec{a} + (\vec{a} - \vec{b}) \times \vec{b}$
$= -\vec{a} \times (\vec{a} - \vec{b}) - \vec{b} \times (\vec{a} - \vec{b})$
$= -(\vec{a} \times \vec{a}) + \vec{a} \times \vec{b} - (\vec{b} \times \vec{a}) + \vec{b} \times \vec{b}$
$= \vec{0} + \vec{a} \times \vec{b} + \vec{a} \times \vec{b} + \vec{0}$
$= 2(\vec{a} \times \vec{b})$.

3. $2\vec{i} + 24\vec{j} - 19\vec{k}$.

§ 11-10. **1.** $2x - y - 2z + 9 = 0$. **2.** $15x - 2y + 3z - 19 = 0$.

§ 11-11. **1.** $\dfrac{x+1}{3t} = \dfrac{y-2}{-t} = \dfrac{z-3}{-3t}$ or $\dfrac{x-2}{3t} = \dfrac{y-1}{-t} = \dfrac{z}{-3t}$ for any real number $t \neq 0$. **2.** $x = 2 + t_1, y = 4, z = 6 - t_1$; or $x = 3 + t_2, y = 4, z = 5 - t_2$ for any real number $t_i \neq 0$. **3.** (a) 1, 2, 1 or any set of numbers of the form $t, 2t, t$ for any real number $t \neq 0$.
(b) $\dfrac{1}{\sqrt{6}}, \dfrac{2}{\sqrt{6}}, \dfrac{1}{\sqrt{6}}$; or $-\dfrac{1}{\sqrt{6}}, -\dfrac{2}{\sqrt{6}}, -\dfrac{1}{\sqrt{6}}$.

§ 11-12. **1.** $x^2 + y^2 + z^2 - 4x + 2y - 6z - 35 = 0$.
2. $3x - 2y + 6z - 52 = 0$. **3.** Let the normals to the given planes be $\vec{n_1} = 2\vec{i} + 2\vec{j} - \vec{k}$ and $\vec{n_2} = \vec{i} - 2\vec{j} - 2\vec{k}$ respectively. Then $\vec{n_1} \cdot \vec{n_2} = 0$, therefore the planes are perpendicular. **4.** 1.

ANSWERS TO KEYED PRACTICE ON CHAPTER 11

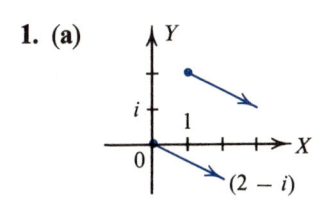

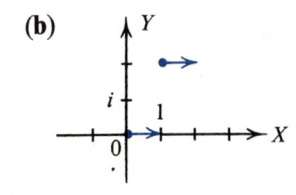

1. (a) [graph showing vector from i on Y-axis to $(2-i)$]

(b) [graph showing horizontal vector at height i]

$e^{2\pi i} = \cos 2\pi + i \sin 2\pi$
$= 1 + 0i = 1$.

There are any number of equivalent vectors for each of these.

2. (a) $\vec{AC} = \vec{p} + \vec{q}$; (b) $\vec{DE} = -\vec{p}$; (c) $\vec{EF} = -\vec{q}$; (d) $\vec{FA} = -\vec{r}$; (e) $\vec{AD} = 2\vec{q}$; (f) $\vec{AE} = \vec{q} + \vec{r}$; (g) $\vec{FB} = \vec{p} - \vec{r}$. Note that since $\vec{p} + \vec{r} = \vec{q}$, the given vector expressions are not unique.

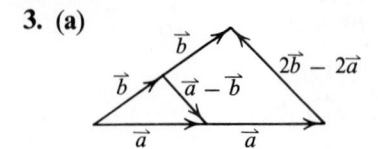

VECTORS

3. (a)

(b) $-2(-\vec{b} + \vec{a}) = -2(\vec{a} - \vec{b})$; since $2\vec{b} - 2\vec{a}$ may be written as a scalar multiple of $\vec{a} - \vec{b}$, $2\vec{b} - 2\vec{a}$ is parallel to $\vec{a} - \vec{b}$.

4. (a) $\vec{OC} = \frac{1}{2}\vec{OA} + \frac{1}{2}\vec{OB}$; **(b)** $\vec{OP} = -\frac{5}{2}\vec{OA} - \frac{5}{2}\vec{OB}$.

5. (a) $\vec{OP} = 3\vec{i} + \vec{j} - 5\vec{k}$; **(b)** $\sqrt{35}$; **(c)** $\frac{3}{\sqrt{35}}\vec{i} + \frac{1}{\sqrt{35}}\vec{j} - \frac{5}{\sqrt{35}}\vec{k}$.

6. (a) $\vec{OC} = 8\vec{i} - 4\vec{j} + \vec{k}$; **(b)** $(8, -4, 1)$.

7. $1000\sqrt{3}$ foot-pounds.

8. $2x_1 - 3y_1$.

9. (a) $\sqrt{89}$ units; **(b)** $-\frac{3}{\sqrt{89}}, -\frac{4}{\sqrt{89}}, \frac{8}{\sqrt{89}}$; **(c)** any set of numbers of the form $-3t, -4t, 8t$ where $t \neq 0$ is any real number.

10. (a) Area $\triangle ABC = \frac{1}{2}|\vec{p} \times \vec{q}|$; **(b)** $\frac{1}{2}\sqrt{35}$.

11. $2x + 3y - 7z + 60 = 0$.

12. (a) A set of numbers of the form $t, -6t, 7t$ for any real number $t \neq 0$;
(b) $\frac{1}{\sqrt{86}}, -\frac{6}{\sqrt{86}}, \frac{7}{\sqrt{86}}$; **(c)** $x = 1 + t_1, y = 5 - 6t_1, z = -3 + 7t_1$; or $x = 2 + t_2, y = -1 - 6t_2, z = 4 + 7t_2$, for any real number $t_i \neq 0$.

13. $x - 2y + 2z - 9 = 0$.

Chapter 12

The Algebra of Matrices

§ 12-1 Matrices

Matrices were introduced in § 7–3 as rectangular arrays. In Example 1 of § 7–3 the system of linear equations

$$\begin{cases} x + y = 3 \\ 3x - 2y = 4 \end{cases}$$

was represented by the matrix

$$\begin{pmatrix} 1 & 1 & 3 \\ 3 & -2 & 4 \end{pmatrix}$$

and solved by matrices. Each row of the matrix corresponds to an equation; each column corresponds to a variable or the constant terms. In Example 1 of § 7–4 a matrix of three rows and four columns was used to solve a system of three linear equations in three variables; in Example 2 of § 7–4 a matrix of five rows and six columns was used to solve a system of five linear equations in five variables.

In general, any rectangular array of real numbers is a **real matrix.** Unless otherwise stated we shall consider only real matrices.

Matrices are usually designated either by capital letters $A, B, C, \cdots$ or in terms of their elements $a_{ij}, b_{ij}, c_{ij}, \cdots$. If A is a real matrix of m rows and n columns, then

$$A = \begin{pmatrix} a_{11} & a_{12} & \cdots & a_{1n} \\ a_{21} & a_{22} & \cdots & a_{2n} \\ \cdots & \cdots & \cdots & \cdots \\ a_{m1} & a_{m2} & \cdots & a_{mn} \end{pmatrix}$$

and we may denote this matrix in several ways including

$$A = ((a_{ij})), \quad 1 \leq i \leq m, \quad 1 \leq j \leq n.$$

The real numbers $a_{i1}, a_{i2}, a_{i3}, \cdots, a_{in}$ are the elements of the ith row. The real numbers $a_{1j}, a_{2j}, a_{3j}, \cdots, a_{mj}$ are the elements of the jth column. The element a_{ij} is the element located on the ith row and on the jth column. In the symbol a_{ij} the subscript i is the **row index,** the subscript j is the **column index,** and the row index always precedes the column index.

THE ALGEBRA OF MATRICES

A matrix of m rows and n columns is called a matrix of **order** m by n, or $m \times n$. A matrix for which the number n of rows is equal to the number of columns is called a **square matrix** of order n. Any two matrices of the same order are said to be **conformable for addition**.

Example 1. Construct a square matrix of order 3 where $a_{ij} = i - j$.

Under the condition that $a_{ij} = i - j$,

$$a_{11} = 1 - 1 = 0, \quad a_{12} = 1 - 2 = -1, \quad a_{13} = 1 - 3 = -2,$$
$$a_{21} = 2 - 1 = 1, \quad a_{22} = 2 - 2 = 0, \quad a_{23} = 2 - 3 = -1,$$
$$a_{31} = 3 - 1 = 2, \quad a_{32} = 3 - 2 = 1, \quad a_{33} = 3 - 3 = 0.$$

Hence the desired matrix is

$$\begin{pmatrix} 0 & -1 & -2 \\ 1 & 0 & -1 \\ 2 & 1 & 0 \end{pmatrix}.$$

Any position vector $\overrightarrow{OP} = x_1\vec{i} + y_1\vec{j} + z_1\vec{k}$ (§ 11-5) may be represented by a 1×3 matrix $(x_1 \ y_1 \ z_1)$. The definitions for equal matrices, sums of matrices, and multiplication of a matrix by a scalar (number) are the same as for vectors. Two vectors are equal if and only if their corresponding components are equal; if

$$x_1\vec{i} + y_1\vec{j} + z_1\vec{k} = 2\vec{i} - 3\vec{j} + 5\vec{k},$$

then $(x_1 \ y_1 \ z_1) = (2 \ -3 \ 5)$ and $x_1 = 2, y_1 = -3, z_1 = 5$. In general two matrices A and B are said to be **equal** if and only if they are of the same order and $a_{ij} = b_{ij}$ for all pairs (i, j) under the equivalence relation for the set of elements from which the elements of the matrix are selected. The equivalence will generally be the "equals" for real numbers.

Example 2. Determine which of the following pairs of matrices are equal:

(a) $\begin{pmatrix} 2 & 1 \\ 3 & 0 \end{pmatrix}$ and $\begin{pmatrix} 2 & 1 & 6 \\ 3 & 0 & 2 \end{pmatrix}$; (b) $\begin{pmatrix} 1 \\ 2 \\ 3 \end{pmatrix}$ and $\begin{pmatrix} 1 \\ 4 \\ 9 \end{pmatrix}$;

(c) $\begin{pmatrix} 3 & -1 \\ 0 & -2 \end{pmatrix}$ and $\begin{pmatrix} 3 & -1 \\ 0 & -2 \end{pmatrix}$; (d) $\begin{pmatrix} 4 & -3 \\ 1 & -2 \\ 0 & 2 \end{pmatrix}$ and $\begin{pmatrix} 3 & -3 \\ 1 & -2 \\ 2 & 2 \end{pmatrix}$.

The pair of matrices in (a) cannot be equal since they are not of the same order. The pairs of matrices in (b) and (d) are not equal, although they are of the same order, since not all of their corresponding elements are equal. The pair of matrices in (c) are equal.

§ 12-1 MATRICES

The sum of two vectors is a vector whose components are the sums of the corresponding components of the given vectors; for example,

$$(2\vec{i} + 3\vec{j} - \vec{k}) + (3\vec{i} - \vec{j} + 5\vec{k}) = 5\vec{i} + 2\vec{j} + 4\vec{k}$$

and thus

$$(2 \ \ 3 \ \ -1) + (3 \ \ -1 \ \ 5) = (5 \ \ 2 \ \ 4).$$

In general, the sum of two m by n matrices, A and B, is another m by n matrix C such that each element c_{ij} of C is the sum of the corresponding elements a_{ij} and b_{ij} of A and B respectively; in other words, $A + B = C$ if and only if $a_{ij} + b_{ij} = c_{ij}$ for all pairs of integers (i, j) where $1 \leq i \leq m$ and $1 \leq j \leq n$.

Example 3. Find the sum of matrices A and B where

$$A = \begin{pmatrix} 2 & 0 & 3 \\ -1 & 1 & 0 \end{pmatrix}; B = \begin{pmatrix} -1 & 2 & 6 \\ 3 & -4 & 0 \end{pmatrix}.$$

$$A + B = \begin{pmatrix} 2 + (-1) & 0 + 2 & 3 + 6 \\ -1 + 3 & 1 + (-4) & 0 + 0 \end{pmatrix} = \begin{pmatrix} 1 & 2 & 9 \\ 2 & -3 & 0 \end{pmatrix}.$$

For any given positive integers m and n the set of real matrices of order m by n forms a commutative group under addition (Exercise 11). For example, the addition of matrices is commutative since $a_{ij} + b_{ij} = b_{ij} + a_{ij}$ for all pairs (i, j). The identity element under addition is the **zero matrix** 0 (also called the **null matrix**) with $a_{ij} = 0$ for all pairs (i, j).

The product of any number (scalar) k and any vector is a vector which may be obtained by multiplying each component of the given vector by the scalar; for example,

$$2(2\vec{i} + 3\vec{j} - \vec{k}) = 4\vec{i} + 6\vec{j} - 2\vec{k}$$

and thus

$$2 \times (2 \ \ 3 \ \ -1) = (4 \ \ 6 \ \ -2).$$

In general, the product of any scalar k and any matrix A with elements a_{ij} is a matrix kA with elements ka_{ij} for all pairs (i, j). Since $ka_{ij} = (a_{ij})k$, $kA = Ak$.

Example 4. Find the product of the scalar 3 and matrix A where

$$A = \begin{pmatrix} 2 & 1 \\ -1 & 3 \\ 0 & -4 \end{pmatrix}.$$

THE ALGEBRA OF MATRICES

$$3A = 3\begin{pmatrix} 2 & 1 \\ -1 & 3 \\ 0 & -4 \end{pmatrix} = \begin{pmatrix} 3(2) & 3(1) \\ 3(-1) & 3(3) \\ 3(0) & 3(-4) \end{pmatrix} = \begin{pmatrix} 6 & 3 \\ -3 & 9 \\ 0 & -12 \end{pmatrix}.$$

Linear combinations of matrices such as $sA + tB$ where s and t are scalars may be considered whenever A and B are matrices of the same order. The following properties may be proved from the definitions that we have introduced:

$$sA + tA = (s + t)A;$$
$$(st)A = s(tA) = t(sA) = stA;$$

and for any two matrices of the same order

$$k(A + B) = kA + kB.$$

For any matrix B we define $-B$ as $(-1)B$. Then $B + (-B) = 0$ (Exercise 9) and we define $A - B = A + (-B)$ for any two matrices A and B of the same order.

TEST YOURSELF

1. Construct a 2 by 3 matrix $((a_{ij}))$ such that $a_{ij} = i^2 + j$.
2. Given $A = \begin{pmatrix} 2 & 0 \\ 1 & 3 \end{pmatrix}$, find (a) $3A$; (b) $-A$; (c) $0A$.
3. Given $A = \begin{pmatrix} 1 & 0 & 1 \\ -1 & 2 & 3 \end{pmatrix}$ and $B = \begin{pmatrix} 2 & -1 & 0 \\ 1 & -4 & 3 \end{pmatrix}$, find (a) $A + B$; (b) $2A + 3B$.
4. List the elements of $((a_{ij}))$ for which $i = j$ when

$$((a_{ij})) = \begin{pmatrix} 4 & 3 & 2 \\ 1 & 0 & 1 \\ 0 & 2 & -1 \end{pmatrix}.$$

EXERCISES

1. In the matrix $((a_{ij}))$ describe the location of the elements (a) with a given subscript i; (b) with a given subscript j.
2. Construct a 3 by 4 matrix $((a_{ij}))$ where $a_{ij} = 2i - j$ for all pairs (i, j).
3. Find $2((a_{ij}))$ for the matrix obtained in Exercise 2.
4. Given $A = \begin{pmatrix} 1 & 2 & -1 \\ 2 & 3 & 0 \end{pmatrix}$ and $B = \begin{pmatrix} 2 & -6 & 5 \\ 3 & 7 & 1 \end{pmatrix}$, find (a) $A + B$; (b) $A + 2B$; (c) $A - B$.

664

§ 12-2 MULTIPLICATION OF MATRICES

5. Find: $\begin{pmatrix} \sin^2\theta & \sec^2\theta \\ -\sin^2\theta & \tan^2\theta \end{pmatrix} + \begin{pmatrix} \cos^2\theta & -\tan^2\theta \\ 1 & 1 \end{pmatrix}$.

• • •

6. Verify the associative law of addition for the matrices

$$A = \begin{pmatrix} 1 & 3 & -1 \\ 0 & 2 & -1 \end{pmatrix}, B = \begin{pmatrix} 1 & 0 & 2 \\ 0 & 5 & 4 \end{pmatrix}, \text{ and } C = \begin{pmatrix} 6 & -3 & 0 \\ 4 & 2 & -1 \end{pmatrix}.$$

7. Solve for the elements a_{ij}:

$$\begin{pmatrix} 3 & -6 \\ 5 & 7 \end{pmatrix} + \begin{pmatrix} a_{11} & a_{12} \\ a_{21} & a_{22} \end{pmatrix} = \begin{pmatrix} 0 & 2 \\ 6 & -4 \end{pmatrix}.$$

8. Find the inverse under addition for the matrix:

(a) $\begin{pmatrix} 1 & 5 \\ 2 & 7 \end{pmatrix}$; (b) $\begin{pmatrix} 1 & 2 & -3 \\ -2 & 5 & -7 \end{pmatrix}$; (c) $\begin{pmatrix} 0 & -3 & 4 & -1 \\ 1 & 0 & 5 & 2 \end{pmatrix}$.

9. Prove that for every m by n matrix B, $B + (-B) = 0$.
10. Prove that every m by n matrix $((a_{ij}))$ has an inverse under addition.
11. Prove that for any given positive integers m and n the set of real matrices of order m by n forms a commutative group under addition.
• 12. Extend the corresponding definitions for equations (§ 7-3) and define (a) linearly dependent matrices; (b) linearly independent matrices.

§ 12-2 Multiplication of matrices

Products of vectors were defined in two different ways; scalar products in § 11-7 and vector products in § 11-9. There were useful applications of each type of product. Only one product of matrices will be considered and it does not correspond to either of the products of vectors. Rather it has evolved from the study of systems of equations (§ 7-3) and particularly the use of systems of equations to represent transformations such as translations and rotations (§ 7-6).

Consider a system of linear equations such as

$$\begin{cases} 3x - 2y + z = 9 \\ 2x + y - 2z = 1 \\ x + y - z = 0. \end{cases} \qquad (1)$$

A unique solution of this system, if one exists, may be found by matrices (§ 7-4). Such a process places an emphasis upon the values of the coefficients. Consider the following method of representing the equations (1):

$$\begin{pmatrix} 3 & -2 & 1 \\ 2 & 1 & -2 \\ 1 & 1 & -1 \end{pmatrix} \begin{pmatrix} x \\ y \\ z \end{pmatrix} = \begin{pmatrix} 9 \\ 1 \\ 0 \end{pmatrix}. \qquad (2)$$

665

THE ALGEBRA OF MATRICES

By detaching the coefficients, we are able to display both the coefficients and the variables in matrix form, as well as the constants. Historically, it was the search for such a concise notation for a system of linear equations that led algebraists, particularly the English mathematician Cayley, to the discovery of matrices. Cayley regarded the 3 by 3 matrix of coefficients as an operator acting upon the column matrix of variables x, y, z in such a way as to produce the column matrix representing the constants in the linear system.

The multiplication of matrices is defined so that the statements (1) and (2) are equivalent. If we were to multiply the elements of the first row of the coefficient matrix in (2) by the elements of the column matrix of variables, element by element in order, and sum the products, we would obtain

$$(3)(x) + (-2)(y) + (1)(z); \text{ that is, } 3x - 2y + z.$$

The result is equal to the element 9 on the first row of the one column matrix on the right. Similarly, if we sum the products of the elements on the second row of the coefficient matrix by those of the column matrix of variables taken in order, we would obtain $2x + y - 2z$ which is equal to the element 1 on the second row of the one column matrix on the right. For the third row we obtain $x + y - z$ which is equal to the element 0 on the third row of the one column matrix on the right.

These products may be expressed individually as

$$\begin{pmatrix} 3 & -2 & 1 \end{pmatrix} \begin{pmatrix} x \\ y \\ z \end{pmatrix} = (3x - 2y + z);$$

$$\begin{pmatrix} 2 & 1 & -2 \end{pmatrix} \begin{pmatrix} x \\ y \\ z \end{pmatrix} = (2x + y - 2z); \qquad (3)$$

$$\begin{pmatrix} 1 & 1 & -1 \end{pmatrix} \begin{pmatrix} x \\ y \\ z \end{pmatrix} = (x + y - z)$$

where each right member is a matrix of one row and one column. The product of the matrices in the left member of (2) may be expressed as

$$\begin{pmatrix} 3 & -2 & 1 \\ 2 & 1 & -2 \\ 1 & 1 & -1 \end{pmatrix} \begin{pmatrix} x \\ y \\ z \end{pmatrix} = \begin{pmatrix} 3x - 2y + z \\ 2x + y - 2z \\ x + y - z \end{pmatrix} \qquad (4)$$

and the matrix equation (2) then has the form
$$\begin{pmatrix} 3x - 2y + z \\ 2x + y - 2z \\ x + y - z \end{pmatrix} = \begin{pmatrix} 9 \\ 1 \\ 0 \end{pmatrix}$$
which by the definition of the equality of matrices is equivalent to the system (1).

Notice that in the matrix equations (3) the product of a 1 by 3 matrix and a 3 by 1 matrix is a 1 by 1 matrix; in the matrix equation (4) the product of a 3 by 3 matrix and a 3 by 1 matrix is a 3 by 1 matrix. In each case the product AB of matrices A and B is a matrix; the element on the first row and first column of AB is the sum of the products of the elements on the first row of the matrix A and the elements taken in order on the first column of the matrix B; in general, the element on the ith row and first column of AB is the sum of the products on the ith row of the matrix A and the elements taken in order on the first column of the matrix B. In each case the matching of the elements on a row of the matrix A with the elements on a column of the matrix B requires that the number of columns of A must equal the number of rows of B. In other words, we can define the product AB of two matrices A and B if and only if A has order m by n and B has order n by t for some positive integers m, n, and t; that is, if and only if the matrices A and B are **conformable for multiplication**. Notice that whenever the elements on a row of a matrix A are multiplied by the elements on a column of a matrix B, the addition of products is the same as in the scalar product of two vectors (§ 11–7).

Let A be any m by n matrix $((a_{ij}))$ where $1 \leq i \leq m$ and $1 \leq j \leq n$; let B be any n by t matrix $((b_{ij}))$ where $1 \leq i \leq n$ and $1 \leq j \leq t$. The product AB of the two matrices in the order given is defined to be the matrix $((c_{ij}))$ where $((c_{ij})) = ((a_{i1}b_{1j} + a_{i2}b_{2j} + \cdots + a_{in}b_{nj}))$ and $1 \leq i \leq m$, $1 \leq j \leq t$. Notice that the **product** BA can be defined only if $m = t$. Even when $m = t$ the product matrices AB and BA are usually different; thus matrix multiplication is, in general, not commutative.

Example 1. Find the products AB and BA, if they exist, where
$$A = \begin{pmatrix} 1 & 5 \\ -1 & 3 \end{pmatrix} \quad \text{and} \quad B = \begin{pmatrix} -3 & 1 & 0 \\ 2 & 4 & -2 \end{pmatrix}.$$

The matrix A is a 2 by 2 matrix; B is a 2 by 3 matrix. Therefore the product AB exists and has order 2 by 3; the product BA of a 2 by 3 and a 2 by 2 matrix in that order does not exist.

The product AB has elements c_{ij} where $c_{ij} = a_{i1}b_{1j} + a_{i2}b_{2j}$. Each of these elements should be visualized as the sum of the products of the

THE ALGEBRA OF MATRICES

elements a_{ik} on a row of A and the elements b_{kj} on a column of B:

$$c_{11} = \begin{pmatrix} 1 & 5 \end{pmatrix} \begin{pmatrix} -3 \\ 2 \end{pmatrix} = (1)(-3) + (5)(2) = 7;$$

$$c_{12} = \begin{pmatrix} 1 & 5 \end{pmatrix} \begin{pmatrix} 1 \\ 4 \end{pmatrix} = (1)(1) + (5)(4) = 21;$$

$$c_{13} = \begin{pmatrix} 1 & 5 \end{pmatrix} \begin{pmatrix} 0 \\ -2 \end{pmatrix} = (1)(0) + (5)(-2) = -10;$$

$$c_{21} = \begin{pmatrix} -1 & 3 \end{pmatrix} \begin{pmatrix} -3 \\ 2 \end{pmatrix} = (-1)(-3) + (3)(2) = 9;$$

$$c_{22} = \begin{pmatrix} -1 & 3 \end{pmatrix} \begin{pmatrix} 1 \\ 4 \end{pmatrix} = (-1)(1) + (3)(4) = 11;$$

$$c_{23} = \begin{pmatrix} -1 & 3 \end{pmatrix} \begin{pmatrix} 0 \\ -2 \end{pmatrix} = (-1)(0) + (3)(-2) = -6.$$

Then

$$AB = \begin{pmatrix} 7 & 21 & -10 \\ 9 & 11 & -6 \end{pmatrix}.$$

Example 2. Find AB and BA, if they exist, where

$$A = \begin{pmatrix} 2 & 1 \end{pmatrix} \text{ and } B = \begin{pmatrix} -2 \\ 3 \end{pmatrix}.$$

Since A is of order 1 by 2 and B is of order 2 by 1, the matrices are conformable for multiplication regardless of the order in which they are considered. Hence the products AB and BA both exist:

$$AB = \begin{pmatrix} 2 & 1 \end{pmatrix} \begin{pmatrix} -2 \\ 3 \end{pmatrix} = (2 \times (-2) + 1 \times (3)) = (-4 + 3) = (-1);$$

$$BA = \begin{pmatrix} -2 \\ 3 \end{pmatrix} \begin{pmatrix} 2 & 1 \end{pmatrix} = \begin{pmatrix} (-2)(2) & (-2)(1) \\ (3)(2) & (3)(1) \end{pmatrix} = \begin{pmatrix} -4 & -2 \\ 6 & 3 \end{pmatrix}.$$

Notice that AB is a 1 by 1 matrix; BA is a 2 by 2 matrix.

While matrix multiplication is not commutative, two other familiar properties of the algebra of numbers are properties of matrix multiplication. It can be proved that the multiplication of matrices is distributive with respect to addition:

$$A(B + C) = AB + AC; \qquad (A + B)C = AC + BC.$$

It can also be proved that the multiplication of matrices is associative:

$$(AB)C = A(BC).$$

§ 12-2 MULTIPLICATION OF MATRICES

Example 3. Verify that $(AB)C = A(BC)$ where

$$A = \begin{pmatrix} 2 & 0 & -1 \\ -1 & 1 & 3 \end{pmatrix}, B = \begin{pmatrix} 1 & 2 \\ 0 & 1 \\ -1 & 2 \end{pmatrix}, \text{ and } C = \begin{pmatrix} 0 & 3 \\ 1 & 2 \end{pmatrix}.$$

$$AB = \begin{pmatrix} 2 & 0 & -1 \\ -1 & 1 & 3 \end{pmatrix}\begin{pmatrix} 1 & 2 \\ 0 & 1 \\ -1 & 2 \end{pmatrix} = \begin{pmatrix} 3 & 2 \\ -4 & 5 \end{pmatrix};$$

$$(AB)C = \begin{pmatrix} 3 & 2 \\ -4 & 5 \end{pmatrix}\begin{pmatrix} 0 & 3 \\ 1 & 2 \end{pmatrix} = \begin{pmatrix} 2 & 13 \\ 5 & -2 \end{pmatrix};$$

$$BC = \begin{pmatrix} 1 & 2 \\ 0 & 1 \\ -1 & 2 \end{pmatrix}\begin{pmatrix} 0 & 3 \\ 1 & 2 \end{pmatrix} = \begin{pmatrix} 2 & 7 \\ 1 & 2 \\ 2 & 1 \end{pmatrix};$$

$$A(BC) = \begin{pmatrix} 2 & 0 & -1 \\ -1 & 1 & 3 \end{pmatrix}\begin{pmatrix} 2 & 7 \\ 1 & 2 \\ 2 & 1 \end{pmatrix} = \begin{pmatrix} 2 & 13 \\ 5 & -2 \end{pmatrix} = (AB)C.$$

In addition to lacking the commutative property of multiplication, the algebra of matrices differs from the algebra of numbers in that if $AB = 0$, it does not necessarily follow that either $A = 0$, $B = 0$, or both equal zero. For example, consider the matrices

$$A = \begin{pmatrix} 1 & 0 \\ 0 & 0 \end{pmatrix} \text{ and } B = \begin{pmatrix} 0 & 0 \\ 0 & 1 \end{pmatrix}$$

where $AB = 0$, but neither A nor B are null matrices.

Any square matrix A has a determinant $|A|$. The value of any determinant of order two was defined in § 7-3; the value of any determinant of order three was defined in § 7-4. In general, any real matrix is a rectangular array of real numbers; the determinant of any square real matrix may be defined (§ 12-5) and is a real number. For example, if

$$A = \begin{pmatrix} 1 & 2 \\ 5 & 7 \end{pmatrix}, \text{ then } |A| = \begin{vmatrix} 1 & 2 \\ 5 & 7 \end{vmatrix} = 7 - 10 = -3.$$

TEST YOURSELF

1. Find AB and BA, if they exist, where

$$A = \begin{pmatrix} 2 & 1 \\ 4 & 3 \end{pmatrix} \text{ and } B = \begin{pmatrix} 2 & -3 & 5 \\ 6 & 2 & 4 \end{pmatrix}.$$

THE ALGEBRA OF MATRICES

2. Find $A(BC)$ for $A = \begin{pmatrix} 1 & 2 \\ 3 & 0 \end{pmatrix}$, $B = \begin{pmatrix} 2 & -1 \\ 4 & 2 \end{pmatrix}$, and $C = \begin{pmatrix} 1 & 0 \\ -1 & 1 \end{pmatrix}$; then verify the associative property $A(BC) = (AB)C$ of multiplication of matrices.

3. Find $A(B + C)$ for the matrices of Exercise 2 and verify the distributive property $A(B + C) = AB + AC$ of matrix multiplication with respect to addition.

4. If the orders of matrices A, B, C, and D are 2 by 3, 3 by 3, 2 by 5, and 5 by 3, respectively, identify all of the possible products involving two of these matrices.

EXERCISES

Given $A = \begin{pmatrix} 1 & 0 \\ 0 & 1 \end{pmatrix}$, $B = \begin{pmatrix} 3 & 5 \\ 1 & 2 \end{pmatrix}$, $C = \begin{pmatrix} 2 & -5 \\ -1 & 3 \end{pmatrix}$, $D = \begin{pmatrix} 2 & 1 \\ -3 & 4 \end{pmatrix}$,

$E = \begin{pmatrix} 3 & 0 \\ 0 & 3 \end{pmatrix}$, $F = \begin{pmatrix} 5 & 0 \\ 0 & 2 \end{pmatrix}$, $G = \begin{pmatrix} 2 & 1 & 4 \\ 3 & 1 & -2 \end{pmatrix}$, and $H = \begin{pmatrix} 5 & 3 & -1 \\ 2 & 0 & 4 \end{pmatrix}$, find,

in Exercises 1 through 12, the indicated products if they exist:

1. BD.
2. AG.
3. BC.
4. CB.
5. EB.
6. BE.
7. FG.
8. HF.
9. CF.
10. DG.
11. GA.
12. GH.

13. If the orders of matrices Q, R, S, and T are 1 by 3, 3 by 4, 2 by 3, and 3 by 1 respectively, identify all of the possible products involving two of these matrices.

14. Find $A(BC)$ and $(AB)C$ and verify that the product of matrices is associative when

$$A = \begin{pmatrix} 1 & 1 & -1 \\ 2 & 0 & 3 \\ 1 & 2 & -1 \end{pmatrix}, B = \begin{pmatrix} 1 & 2 \\ 3 & 0 \\ -1 & 4 \end{pmatrix}, \text{ and } C = \begin{pmatrix} 1 & 2 & 0 & -3 \\ 1 & 2 & 4 & 1 \end{pmatrix}.$$

15. Find $A(B + C)$ and $AB + AC$ and verify that the multiplication of matrices is distributive with respect to addition when

$$A = \begin{pmatrix} 1 & 2 \\ 0 & -3 \\ 2 & 1 \end{pmatrix}, B = \begin{pmatrix} 3 & -2 \\ -1 & 4 \end{pmatrix}, \text{ and } C = \begin{pmatrix} -2 & 2 \\ 1 & -3 \end{pmatrix}.$$

• • •

16. Given $A = \begin{pmatrix} 2 & 1 \\ -2 & 3 \end{pmatrix}$ and $B = \begin{pmatrix} 1 & -1 \\ 0 & 2 \end{pmatrix}$, show that

$$(A + B)(A + B) = A^2 + AB + BA + B^2 \neq A^2 + 2AB + B^2.$$

Explain why the inequality holds.

§ 12-3 SPECIAL MATRICES

17. If A and B are square matrices of the same order, determine the necessary conditions that $(A + B)(A - B) = A^2 - B^2$.

18. Under what condition is the product of two rectangular matrices that are not square matrices a square matrix?

19. Prove that $|AB| = |A| \times |B|$ for any two square matrices A and B of order two; that is, the determinant of the product is equal to the product of the determinants.

• **20.** Find a square matrix A of order two such that

$$A \begin{pmatrix} 4 & 1 \\ 2 & 3 \end{pmatrix} = \begin{pmatrix} 4 & 1 \\ 2 & 3 \end{pmatrix} A.$$

Explain how A may be any one of an infinite set of matrices.

• **21.** Determine whether or not the matrices $\begin{pmatrix} -1 & 0 \\ 0 & 1 \end{pmatrix}$ and $\begin{pmatrix} 1 & 0 \\ 0 & 1 \end{pmatrix}$ form a group under multiplication.

• **22.** The matrices of the set $\begin{pmatrix} 1 & 0 \\ 0 & 1 \end{pmatrix}$, $\begin{pmatrix} 0 & 1 \\ -1 & 0 \end{pmatrix}$, $\begin{pmatrix} 0 & -1 \\ 1 & 0 \end{pmatrix}$, $\begin{pmatrix} -1 & 0 \\ 0 & -1 \end{pmatrix}$, $\begin{pmatrix} i & 0 \\ 0 & -i \end{pmatrix}$, $\begin{pmatrix} -i & 0 \\ 0 & i \end{pmatrix}$, $\begin{pmatrix} 0 & -i \\ -i & 0 \end{pmatrix}$, $\begin{pmatrix} 0 & i \\ i & 0 \end{pmatrix}$ where $i^2 = -1$ are the *Pauli matrices*; they are used in the study of electron spin in quantum mechanics. Identify the matrices as $\{A, B, C, \cdots, H\}$, assume that they satisfy the associative law for multiplication, and prove that the set forms a group under multiplication.

§ 12-3 Special matrices

Matrices are used extensively in both pure and applied mathematics. Accordingly many special types of matrices which have special uses have been given special names.

The elements a_{ii} of any square matrix of order n form the **main diagonal** (or **principal diagonal**) of the matrix and are called the **diagonal elements** of the matrix. If all elements, except possibly the diagonal elements, of a square matrix are equal to zero, the matrix is a **diagonal matrix**. For example,

$$\begin{pmatrix} 2 & 0 \\ 0 & 3 \end{pmatrix}, \begin{pmatrix} 1 & 0 & 0 \\ 0 & -1 & 0 \\ 0 & 0 & 0 \end{pmatrix}, \text{ and } \begin{pmatrix} 2 & 0 & 0 \\ 0 & 2 & 0 \\ 0 & 0 & 2 \end{pmatrix}$$

are diagonal matrices. If all the diagonal elements of a diagonal matrix of order n are equal, the matrix is called a **scalar matrix** of order n. The last example of a diagonal matrix is a scalar matrix. The name scalar matrix arises from the fact that whenever the two matrices are conformable

THE ALGEBRA OF MATRICES

for multiplication, multiplcation of a matrix by a scalar matrix with diagonal elements k is equivalent to multiplication by the scalar k.

Example 1. Prove that for square matrices of order 2 multiplication by the scalar matrix $\begin{pmatrix} k & 0 \\ 0 & k \end{pmatrix}$ is equivalent to multiplication by the scalar k.

Let $A = \begin{pmatrix} a & b \\ c & d \end{pmatrix}$ be any square matrix of order 2. Then

$$\begin{pmatrix} k & 0 \\ 0 & k \end{pmatrix}\begin{pmatrix} a & b \\ c & d \end{pmatrix} = \begin{pmatrix} ka & kb \\ kc & kd \end{pmatrix} = kA;$$

$$\begin{pmatrix} a & b \\ c & d \end{pmatrix}\begin{pmatrix} k & 0 \\ 0 & k \end{pmatrix} = \begin{pmatrix} ak & bk \\ ck & dk \end{pmatrix} = \begin{pmatrix} ka & kb \\ kc & kd \end{pmatrix} = kA.$$

A scalar matrix with diagonal elements 1 is called an **identity matrix**. The matrices

$$\begin{pmatrix} 1 & 0 \\ 0 & 1 \end{pmatrix}, \begin{pmatrix} 1 & 0 & 0 \\ 0 & 1 & 0 \\ 0 & 0 & 1 \end{pmatrix}, \begin{pmatrix} 1 & 0 & 0 & 0 \\ 0 & 1 & 0 & 0 \\ 0 & 0 & 1 & 0 \\ 0 & 0 & 0 & 1 \end{pmatrix}$$

are all identity matrices. For any matrix A of order n the identity matrix I of order n has the properties

$$AI = IA = A$$

of the identity element for multiplication. If a matrix B has order m by n, then *premultiplication* by the identity matrix of order m gives $IB = B$ and *postmultiplication* by the identity matrix of order n gives $BI = B$.

Consider any m by n matrix $A = ((a_{ij}))$. We may obtain an n by m matrix $((a_{ji}))$ by interchanging the rows and columns of A; the new matrix is called the **transpose** of A and is denoted by A^T. For example, each of these matrices is the transpose of the other

$$\begin{pmatrix} 1 & 3 & 0 \\ 2 & 5 & 7 \end{pmatrix}, \begin{pmatrix} 1 & 2 \\ 3 & 5 \\ 0 & 7 \end{pmatrix}.$$

Notice that the first row of the matrix of order 2 by 3 becomes the first column of the transpose of that matrix; the second row of a matrix becomes the second column of the transpose of that matrix. When this is done, the first, second, and third columns of the given matrix become the first, second, and third rows of the transpose of the matrix. Accordingly, we think of obtaining the transpose as interchanging the rows and columns of the matrix.

§ 12-3 SPECIAL MATRICES

Each of the following statements may be proved, at least in more advanced courses, as a theorem for any matrix A and its transpose A^T, any matrix B and its transpose B^T, and any scalar k:

(i) $(A^T)^T = A$;
(ii) $(kA)^T = kA^T$;
(iii) $(A + B)^T = A^T + B^T$;
(iv) $(AB)^T = B^T A^T$.

Examples of these statements will be considered in the exercises.

A matrix A such that $A = A^T$ is called a **symmetric matrix**. In other words, a matrix $((a_{ij}))$ is symmetric if $a_{ij} = a_{ji}$ for all pairs (i, j). The matrix

$$\begin{pmatrix} 2 & 0 & -4 \\ 0 & 3 & 2 \\ -4 & 2 & -1 \end{pmatrix}$$

is a symmetric matrix of order 3. Any diagonal matrix is a symmetric matrix. Symmetric matrices play an important role in many branches of mathematics, physics, and other subjects.

A matrix A such that $A = -A^T$ is called a **skew-symmetric matrix**. In other words, a matrix $((a_{ij}))$ is skew-symmetric if $a_{ij} = -a_{ji}$ for all pairs (i, j). The matrix

$$\begin{pmatrix} 0 & -4 & 1 \\ 4 & 0 & -5 \\ -1 & 5 & 0 \end{pmatrix}$$

is a skew-symmetric matrix of order 3. Notice that each diagonal element a_{ii} of a skew-symmetric matrix must be zero since $a_{ii} = -a_{ii}$ if and only if $a_{ii} = 0$. Notice also that any symmetric or skew-symmetric matrix must be a square matrix ($m = n$) since the m by n matrix A is equal to its transpose or the negative of its transpose (both of which are n by m matrices) and only matrices of the same order can be equal.

Example 2. Determine which of the following matrices are (a) symmetric; (b) skew-symmetric: $A = \begin{pmatrix} 2 & 0 \\ 0 & 1 \end{pmatrix}$, $B = \begin{pmatrix} 3 & -4 \\ -4 & 1 \end{pmatrix}$, $C = \begin{pmatrix} 2 & -3 \\ 3 & 5 \end{pmatrix}$,

$D = \begin{pmatrix} 0 & 1 \\ -1 & 0 \end{pmatrix}$, $E = \begin{pmatrix} 2 & 1 & 3 \\ -1 & 3 & 0 \end{pmatrix}$, $F = (2)$, $G = \begin{pmatrix} 0 & 2 & 3 \\ -2 & 0 & -1 \\ -3 & 1 & 0 \end{pmatrix}$,

$H = \begin{pmatrix} 0 & 2 \\ 0 & 0 \end{pmatrix}$.

673

THE ALGEBRA OF MATRICES

(a) Matrices A, B, and F are symmetric matrices.
(b) Matrices D and G are skew-symmetric matrices. Matrices C, E, and H are neither symmetric nor skew-symmetric matrices.

Example 3. Assume the properties of the transpose of a matrix and prove that (a) the sum of any square matrix and its transpose is symmetric; (b) the difference of any square matrix and its transpose is skew-symmetric.

(a) Let A be any square matrix and let $B = A + A^T$. We need to prove that $B = B^T$:

$$B^T = (A + A^T)^T$$
$$= A^T + (A^T)^T, \text{ by the third property of transposes;}$$
$$= A^T + A, \text{ by the first property of transposes;}$$
$$= A + A^T = B$$

[handwritten: $A + A^T =$ symmetric]

since the addition of matrices is commutative (§ 12–1).

(b) Let A be any square matrix and let $B = A - A^T$. We need to prove that $B = -B^T$:

$$-B^T = -[A + (-A^T)]^T$$
$$= -[A + (-A)^T]^T, \text{ by the second property of transposes;}$$
$$= -[A^T + ((-A)^T)^T], \text{ by the third property of transposes;}$$
$$= -[A^T + (-A)], \text{ by the first property of transposes;}$$
$$= -[(-A) + A^T], \text{ since addition is commutative;}$$
$$= A + (-A^T), \text{ since multiplication by a scalar is distributive}$$
$$\qquad \text{with respect to addition;}$$
$$= A - A^T = B.$$

Example 4. Find the sum of the matrix A and its transpose if

$$A = \begin{pmatrix} 3 & 2 & 0 \\ 1 & 1 & 4 \\ 5 & 2 & 3 \end{pmatrix}.$$

$$A^T = \begin{pmatrix} 3 & 1 & 5 \\ 2 & 1 & 2 \\ 0 & 4 & 3 \end{pmatrix};$$

$$A + A^T = \begin{pmatrix} 3+3 & 2+1 & 0+5 \\ 1+2 & 1+1 & 4+2 \\ 5+0 & 2+4 & 3+3 \end{pmatrix} = \begin{pmatrix} 6 & 3 & 5 \\ 3 & 2 & 6 \\ 5 & 6 & 6 \end{pmatrix}.$$

Note that the sum is a symmetric matrix as should be expected from part (a) of Example 3.

The two parts of Example 3 enable us to express any given square matrix A as the sum of a symmetric matrix and a skew-symmetric matrix.

674

§ 12-3 SPECIAL MATRICES

The matrix $A + A^T$ and therefore the matrix $\frac{1}{2}(A + A^T)$ is symmetric; the matrix $A - A^T$ and therefore the matrix $\frac{1}{2}(A - A^T)$ is skew-symmetric; and

$$A = \frac{1}{2}(A + A^T) + \frac{1}{2}(A - A^T).$$

If the elements of the matrix A are a_{ij}, then the elements of A^T are a_{ji}; the elements of $\frac{1}{2}(A + A^T)$ are $\frac{1}{2}(a_{ij} + a_{ji})$; and the elements of $\frac{1}{2}(A - A^T)$ are $\frac{1}{2}(a_{ij} - a_{ji})$.

Example 5. Find a symmetric matrix and a skew-symmetric matrix whose sum is the matrix A where

$$A = \begin{pmatrix} 3 & 2 & -1 \\ -4 & 1 & 5 \\ -3 & 1 & -2 \end{pmatrix}.$$

$$A^T = \begin{pmatrix} 3 & -4 & -3 \\ 2 & 1 & 1 \\ -1 & 5 & -2 \end{pmatrix}.$$

The symmetric matrix may be obtained as

$$\frac{1}{2}(A + A^T) = \frac{1}{2}\begin{pmatrix} 6 & -2 & -4 \\ -2 & 2 & 6 \\ -4 & 6 & -4 \end{pmatrix} = \begin{pmatrix} 3 & -1 & -2 \\ -1 & 1 & 3 \\ -2 & 3 & -2 \end{pmatrix}.$$

The skew-symmetric matrix may be obtained as

$$\frac{1}{2}(A - A^T) = \frac{1}{2}\begin{pmatrix} 0 & 6 & 2 \\ -6 & 0 & 4 \\ -2 & -4 & 0 \end{pmatrix} = \begin{pmatrix} 0 & 3 & 1 \\ -3 & 0 & 2 \\ -1 & -2 & 0 \end{pmatrix}.$$

Notice that the sum of these two matrices is A.

TEST YOURSELF

1. Determine which of the following matrices are (a) symmetric; (b) skew-symmetric:

$$A = \begin{pmatrix} -3 & 1 \\ 1 & -2 \end{pmatrix}, B = \begin{pmatrix} 0 & 5 \\ -5 & 0 \end{pmatrix}, C = \begin{pmatrix} 0 & 5 \\ 2 & 0 \end{pmatrix}, D = (5).$$

THE ALGEBRA OF MATRICES

2. Find: $\begin{pmatrix} 3 & 0 \\ 0 & 3 \end{pmatrix} \begin{pmatrix} 7 & 2 & 3 & 4 \\ 1 & 5 & 1 & 2 \end{pmatrix}$.

3. Find A^T for $A = \begin{pmatrix} 7 & 2 & 1 \\ 3 & 2 & 4 \end{pmatrix}$.

4. Express $\begin{pmatrix} 2 & 5 & 1 \\ -3 & 0 & 3 \\ -1 & 1 & 2 \end{pmatrix}$ as the sum of a symmetric and a skew-symmetric matrix.

EXERCISES

1. Determine which of the following matrices are (a) symmetric; (b) skew-symmetric: $A = \begin{pmatrix} 3 & 1 & 2 \\ 3 & 2 & 3 \\ 2 & 1 & 4 \end{pmatrix}$, $B = \begin{pmatrix} 0 & 5 & -2 \\ -5 & 0 & 1 \\ 2 & -1 & 0 \end{pmatrix}$,

$C = \begin{pmatrix} 1 & 1 & 1 \\ 1 & 1 & 1 \\ 1 & 1 & 1 \end{pmatrix}$, $D = \begin{pmatrix} 1 & 2 & 3 \\ -1 & 0 & 4 \end{pmatrix}$, $E = \begin{pmatrix} 0 & 3 \\ -3 & 2 \end{pmatrix}$,

$F = (0)$, $G = \begin{pmatrix} 2 & 3 \\ 3 & 1 \end{pmatrix}$, $H = \begin{pmatrix} 1 \\ 2 \end{pmatrix}$.

2. Find the transpose of each of the matrices given in Exercise 1.

3. Express $\begin{pmatrix} 3 & -1 & 0 \\ 4 & 2 & 1 \\ -2 & 3 & 1 \end{pmatrix}$ as the sum of a symmetric and a skew-symmetric matrix.

In Exercises 4 through 7 use the matrices A and B given in Exercise 1 and verify that:

4. $(A^T)^T = A$.
5. $(kA)^T = kA^T$ for any scalar k.
6. $(A + B)^T = A^T + B^T$.
7. $(AB)^T = B^T A^T$.

• • •

8. (a) Construct a 3 by 3 matrix $((\delta_{ij}))$ where the *Kronecker delta* $\delta_{ij} = 0$ when $i \neq j$ and $\delta_{ij} = 1$ when $i = j$. (b) Name the corresponding n by n matrix.

9. Determine the maximum possible number of distinct elements in any symmetric matrix of order n.

§ 12-4 SPECIAL COMPLEX MATRICES

10. Determine the effect of premultiplication and postmultiplication of a square matrix of order 3 by a diagonal matrix of order 3. Generalize your result for matrices of any order.

11. Prove that the product of two diagonal matrices of the same order is commutative for order (a) 2; (b) 3; (c) n.

12. Prove that the square of a skew-symmetric matrix is a symmetric matrix for order (a) 2; (b) 3.

13. Use an identity matrix for 1 and a null matrix for zero; then prove that the matrix $A = \begin{pmatrix} 3 & 1 \\ 2 & 2 \end{pmatrix}$ satisfies the equation $\begin{vmatrix} 3-x & 1 \\ 2 & 2-x \end{vmatrix} = 0$ if x is replaced by the matrix A.

14. As in Exercise 13 prove that the matrix $\begin{pmatrix} 2 & -1 \\ 0 & 5 \end{pmatrix}$ satisfies the equation $\begin{vmatrix} 4 & x-6 \\ 1-x & 1 \end{vmatrix} = 0$.

• 15. As in Exercise 13 prove that the matrix $\begin{pmatrix} -1 & 3 \\ 2 & 1 \end{pmatrix}$ satisfies the equation $\begin{vmatrix} x & 0 & 1 \\ -2 & x & 2 \\ 3 & x+1 & x \end{vmatrix} = -16$.

§ 12-4 Special complex matrices

A matrix with complex numbers as elements is a **complex matrix**. Any complex number $a + bi$ has a complex conjugate $a - bi$ (§ 6-7). If $z = a + bi$, then $\bar{z} = a - bi$. The **conjugate** of a matrix A with elements a_{ij} is the matrix $\bar{A}$ with elements $\overline{a_{ij}}$. Each of the following matrices is the conjugate of the other

$$\begin{pmatrix} 2+3i & 5i \\ 7 & 1-i \end{pmatrix}, \quad \begin{pmatrix} 2-3i & -5i \\ 7 & 1+i \end{pmatrix}.$$

The transpose of the conjugate of a matrix A (that is, $(\bar{A})^\mathsf{T}$) is the same as the conjugate of the transpose of the matrix (that is, $\overline{A^\mathsf{T}}$) and is the **transposed conjugate** A^* of the given matrix. Each of the following matrices is the transposed conjugate of the other

$$\begin{pmatrix} 2+3i & 5i \\ 7 & 1-i \end{pmatrix}, \quad \begin{pmatrix} 2-3i & 7 \\ -5i & 1+i \end{pmatrix}.$$

If a matrix A is equal to its conjugate, then $A = \bar{A}$; each element $a_{ij} = \overline{a_{ij}}$; each element is therefore a real number and the matrix is a real matrix. If a matrix A is equal to its transposed conjugate, then $A = A^*$;

THE ALGEBRA OF MATRICES

each element $a_{ij} = \overline{a_{ji}}$; and the matrix is called a **Hermitian matrix**. Hermitian matrices are common in abstract algebra and the theory of atomic physics.

Example. Prove that A is a Hermitian matrix when

$$A = \begin{pmatrix} 3 & 2+i \\ 2-i & 5 \end{pmatrix}.$$

$$\overline{A} = \begin{pmatrix} 3 & 2-i \\ 2+i & 5 \end{pmatrix};$$

$$A^* = \overline{A}^\mathsf{T} = \begin{pmatrix} 3 & 2+i \\ 2-i & 5 \end{pmatrix} = A.$$

If A is a real symmetric matrix, then for all pairs (i, j) we have $a_{ij} = a_{ji}$ and $a_{ji} = \overline{a_{ji}}$; therefore $a_{ij} = \overline{a_{ji}}$ and A is a Hermitian matrix. Thus when only real matrices are considered, the terms "symmetric" and "Hermitian" are synonymous. As might be expected, skew-symmetric real matrices are a special case of **skew-Hermitian matrices** defined by $A = -A^*$; that is, $a_{ij} = -\overline{a_{ji}}$ for all pairs (i, j). Some of the properties of Hermitian and skew-Hermitian matrices are developed in the exercises.

TEST YOURSELF

1. If $A = \begin{pmatrix} 2 & 7-3i \\ 3+i & 3 \end{pmatrix}$, find (a) $\overline{A}$; (b) A^*.

2. Determine which of the following matrices are (a) Hermitian; (b) skew-Hermitian:

$$A = \begin{pmatrix} 1 & 2-3i \\ 2+3i & 2 \end{pmatrix}, \quad B = \begin{pmatrix} i & 2 \\ -2 & -i \end{pmatrix}, \quad C = \begin{pmatrix} 0 & i \\ -i & 0 \end{pmatrix}.$$

3. Prove that each diagonal element of a skew-Hermitian matrix is either zero or a pure imaginary number.

EXERCISES

In Exercises 1 through 4 find (a) $\overline{A}$ and (b) A^* where A equals:

1. $\begin{pmatrix} 2+i & 3-i \\ 5i & -2 \end{pmatrix}.$

2. $\begin{pmatrix} 3 & 3+i \\ 3-i & -3 \end{pmatrix}.$

3. $\begin{pmatrix} -i & 5+2i \\ -5+2i & 2i \end{pmatrix}.$

4. $\begin{pmatrix} 0 & 2 \\ -2 & 0 \end{pmatrix}.$

5. Which of the matrices in Exercises 1 through 4 are Hermitian?

6. Which of the matrices in Exercises 1 through 4 are skew-Hermitian?

Show that for any square complex matrix A:

7. $(\overline{\overline{A}}) = A$.   **8.** $\overline{(A + B)} = \overline{A} + \overline{B}$.

• • •

9. $(A^*)^* = A$.   **11.** $\overline{(AB)} = \overline{A} \times \overline{B}$.
10. $(A + B)^* = A^* + B^*$.   **12.** $(AB)^* = B^*A^*$.

Prove that for complex matrices:

13. The sum of any square matrix and its transposed conjugate is a Hermitian matrix.

14. Any difference of a square matrix and its transposed conjugate is a skew-Hermitian matrix.

• **15.** Any square matrix may be expressed as the sum of a Hermitian matrix and a skew-Hermitian matrix.

• **16.** Any Hermitian matrix may be expressed as a sum $A + Bi$ where A is real and symmetric, B is real and skew-symmetric, and $i^2 = -1$.

§ 12-5   Rank of a matrix

We now return to a primary consideration of real matrices even though most of the discussion applies to complex matrices. The rank of a 2 by 3 matrix was defined in § 7-3. In order to define the rank of any matrix we need to consider the submatrices of any matrix and the determinant of any square matrix.

If any row is deleted from an m by n matrix where $m > 1$, an $(m - 1)$ by n matrix remains; if any column is deleted from an m by n matrix where $n > 1$, an m by $(n - 1)$ matrix remains. Any given matrix or any matrix obtained by deleting one or more columns and/or rows from the given matrix is called a **submatrix** of the given matrix.

Example 1. Find all the submatrices of the matrix $\begin{pmatrix} 1 & 0 & 2 \\ 4 & 3 & 8 \end{pmatrix}$.

$\begin{pmatrix} 1 & 0 & 2 \\ 4 & 3 & 8 \end{pmatrix}, \begin{pmatrix} 1 & 0 \\ 4 & 3 \end{pmatrix}, \begin{pmatrix} 1 & 2 \\ 4 & 8 \end{pmatrix}, \begin{pmatrix} 0 & 2 \\ 3 & 8 \end{pmatrix}, \begin{pmatrix} 1 \\ 4 \end{pmatrix}, \begin{pmatrix} 0 \\ 3 \end{pmatrix}, \begin{pmatrix} 2 \\ 8 \end{pmatrix},$

$(1\ 0\ 2), (4\ 3\ 8), (1\ 0), (1\ 2), (0\ 2), (4\ 3), (4\ 8), (3\ 8), (1),$
$(0), (2), (4), (3), (8)$.

Any square real matrix A has an associated real number called its *determinant* and denoted by $|A|$. This notation does *not* imply absolute value. Determinants of order 3, 2, and 1 were considered in §§ 7-3 and 7-4.

679

THE ALGEBRA OF MATRICES

Example 2. Find the determinant of each square submatrix of $\begin{pmatrix} 1 & 0 & 2 \\ 4 & 3 & 8 \end{pmatrix}$.

As in Example 1 the square submatrices of order two are

$$\begin{pmatrix} 1 & 0 \\ 4 & 3 \end{pmatrix}, \begin{pmatrix} 1 & 2 \\ 4 & 8 \end{pmatrix}, \begin{pmatrix} 0 & 2 \\ 3 & 8 \end{pmatrix}$$

with determinants 3, 0, and -6 respectively; the square submatrices of order one are

(1), (0), (2), (4), (3), (8)

with determinants 1, 0, 2, 4, 3, and 8 respectively.

The determinant of a square matrix of order n may be defined in terms of the cofactors of the elements a_{ij}. Let A be any real square matrix of order n with elements a_{ij}. The **cofactor** A_{ij} of a_{ij} is a real number and is $(-1)^{i+j}$ times the determinant of the submatrix of order $(n-1)$ which is obtained by deleting the ith row and the jth column from the matrix A. For example, if

$$A = \begin{pmatrix} a_{11} & a_{12} \\ a_{21} & a_{22} \end{pmatrix}$$

then

$$A_{11} = (-1)^{1+1}a_{22} = a_{22}; \quad A_{12} = (-1)^{1+2}a_{21} = -a_{21};$$
$$A_{21} = (-1)^{2+1}a_{12} = -a_{12}; \quad A_{22} = (-1)^{2+2}a_{11} = a_{11}.$$

Notice that the determinant of A is $a_{11}a_{22} - a_{12}a_{21}$ and may be expressed in any one of these forms:

$$a_{11}A_{11} + a_{12}A_{12}; \quad a_{11}A_{11} + a_{21}A_{21};$$
$$a_{21}A_{21} + a_{22}A_{22}; \quad a_{12}A_{12} + a_{22}A_{22}.$$

We assume (and leave the proof for a more advanced course) that this pattern holds for any square matrix A: the determinant $|A|$ of any square matrix A may be expressed as the algebraic sum of the products of the elements on any line (i.e., row or column) of the matrix and their cofactors. Then for a square matrix A of order three with elements a_{ij} the expansion of $|A|$ in terms of the elements on the first row is

$$|A| = a_{11}A_{11} + a_{12}A_{12} + a_{13}A_{13};$$

the expansion in terms of the elements on the second column is

$$|A| = a_{12}A_{12} + a_{22}A_{22} + a_{32}A_{32}.$$

§ 12-5 RANK OF A MATRIX

This procedure for expanding the determinant of any square matrix in terms of the elements on any row or column and their cofactors enables us to express the determinant of any square matrix of order n in terms of determinants of square matrices of order $(n - 1)$; to express the determinants of square matrices of order $(n - 1)$ in terms of determinants of square matrices of order $(n - 2)$; and so forth until we reach determinants of square matrices of order 3 or 2 which we can evaluate conveniently.

Two basic transformations (steps) were used in § 7-3 in working with matrices:

(i) Multiply each element of a row by a constant different from zero.

(ii) Replace each element of a row by the sum of itself and a constant multiple of the corresponding element on another row.

The first of these transformations multiplies the determinant of the matrix by the constant since the determinant may be expanded in terms of the elements of the row under consideration and each term of that expansion will be multiplied by that constant. This enables us to remove any common factor of the elements of a row of a determinant and use it as a coefficient of the new determinant. For example,

$$\begin{vmatrix} 2 & 6 \\ 1 & 5 \end{vmatrix} = 2 \begin{vmatrix} 1 & 3 \\ 1 & 5 \end{vmatrix}.$$

In more advanced courses it is proved, but we assume, that the second transformation does not change the determinant of the matrix (that is, the real number associated with the matrix). We also assume that when only the determinant of the matrix is being considered, these two transformations may be used on either rows or columns of the matrix; that is, on any **line** of the matrix. Thus any determinant is equivalent to the expression obtained when:

(i) A factor of any line (row or column) is removed and used as a coefficient of the new determinant.

(ii) Each element of a row is replaced by the sum of itself and a constant multiple of the corresponding element on another row; or each element of a column is replaced by the sum of itself and a constant multiple of the corresponding element on another column.

Example 3. Find the determinant of the matrix

$$\begin{pmatrix} 1 & 2 & 0 & 4 & 5 \\ 2 & 1 & 5 & 7 & 11 \\ 1 & 3 & 2 & 9 & 6 \\ 0 & 1 & 0 & 0 & 1 \\ 3 & 6 & 1 & 10 & 15 \end{pmatrix}.$$

THE ALGEBRA OF MATRICES

The elements on the fourth row are $a_{41} = 0, a_{42} = 1, a_{43} = 0, a_{44} = 0$, and $a_{45} = 1$. The expansion of the determinant in terms of the elements of the fourth row is

$$a_{41}A_{41} + a_{42}A_{42} + a_{43}A_{43} + a_{44}A_{44} + a_{45}A_{45}$$

which becomes $A_{42} + A_{45}$. Since $(-1)^{4+2} = 1$ and $(-1)^{4+5} = -1$,

$$A_{42} = \begin{vmatrix} 1 & 0 & 4 & 5 \\ 2 & 5 & 7 & 11 \\ 1 & 2 & 9 & 6 \\ 3 & 1 & 10 & 15 \end{vmatrix} ; A_{45} = - \begin{vmatrix} 1 & 2 & 0 & 4 \\ 2 & 1 & 5 & 7 \\ 1 & 3 & 2 & 9 \\ 3 & 6 & 1 & 10 \end{vmatrix}.$$

We could continue by expanding each of these determinants in terms of the elements on the first row and thereby replace each determinant by an algebraic sum of third order determinants. However, it is usually much easier to apply the transformations based upon those used in §§ 7–3 and 7–4 until all but one element on a row or column is zero before expanding the determinant in terms of that row or column. We illustrate this by starting the solution of the example over again and replacing each element of the fifth column by itself minus the corresponding element of the second column. Then the determinant of the given matrix is the same as the determinant of the matrix

$$\begin{pmatrix} 1 & 2 & 0 & 4 & 3 \\ 2 & 1 & 5 & 7 & 10 \\ 1 & 3 & 2 & 9 & 3 \\ 0 & 1 & 0 & 0 & 0 \\ 3 & 6 & 1 & 10 & 9 \end{pmatrix}.$$

When the determinant of this matrix is expanded in terms of the elements of the fourth row, the only term different from zero is $a_{42}A_{42}$. Since $a_{42} = 1$ and $(-1)^{4+2} = 1$, the desired determinant has the same value as the determinant

$$\begin{vmatrix} 1 & 0 & 4 & 3 \\ 2 & 5 & 7 & 10 \\ 1 & 2 & 9 & 3 \\ 3 & 1 & 10 & 9 \end{vmatrix}.$$

We now subtract four times the first column from the third, subtract three times the first column from the fourth, expand in terms of the elements on the first row, and then expand in terms of the elements on the

§ 12-5 RANK OF A MATRIX

new third column:

$$\begin{vmatrix} 1 & 0 & 0 & 0 \\ 2 & 5 & -1 & 4 \\ 1 & 2 & 5 & 0 \\ 3 & 1 & -2 & 0 \end{vmatrix} = \begin{vmatrix} 5 & -1 & 4 \\ 2 & 5 & 0 \\ 1 & -2 & 0 \end{vmatrix} = 4 \begin{vmatrix} 2 & 5 \\ 1 & -2 \end{vmatrix} = 4(-4-5) = -36.$$

The **rank** of a matrix is the order of the submatrix of largest possible order such that the determinant of the submatrix is different from zero. If the determinant of a square matrix of order n is different from zero, then the rank of the matrix is n. If the determinant of the matrix is zero, then if there exists a square submatrix of order $(n-1)$ with determinant different from zero, the rank is $(n-1)$. If all the submatrices of order $(n-1)$ have zero determinants, we consider the square submatrices of order $(n-2)$, and so forth. If the matrix has any element different from zero, the rank is at least 1; if every element of the matrix is zero, the rank is 0.

Example 4. Find the rank of the matrix

$$\begin{pmatrix} 1 & 0 & 2 & 3 \\ 2 & 1 & 0 & 1 \\ 4 & 1 & 4 & 7 \end{pmatrix}.$$

The given matrix has four square submatrices of order 3 which could be identified and checked as to the values of their determinants. However, it is usually easier to work with the given matrix and thereby to prepare at one time to check all four determinants. We subtract the second row from the third and obtain

$$\begin{pmatrix} 1 & 0 & 2 & 3 \\ 2 & 1 & 0 & 1 \\ 2 & 0 & 4 & 6 \end{pmatrix}.$$

Next we subtract twice the first row from the third:

$$\begin{pmatrix} 1 & 0 & 2 & 3 \\ 2 & 1 & 0 & 1 \\ 0 & 0 & 0 & 0 \end{pmatrix}.$$

It is now clear that every third order submatrix of this matrix will have a row of zeros and, since the determinant may be expanded in terms of the row of zeros, will have determinant zero. Each of the submatrices of the second order using the elements of the first two rows of the matrix has determinant different from zero. Thus the given matrix has rank 2 since at least one submatrix of the second order has determinant different from zero.

683

THE ALGEBRA OF MATRICES

As in Example 4, the two transformations used to evaluate determinants may be used for matrices and do not affect the rank of the matrix.

The statements involving ranks of matrices in § 7–3 may now be extended to include systems of linear equations involving n variables. As before we consider the matrix of the coefficients and the **augmented matrix** obtained by including the column of constant terms with the matrix of the coefficients. Any system of linear equations has a solution if and only if the rank of the coefficient matrix is equal to the rank of the augmented matrix. If a system of n equations in m variables has a unique solution, the rank is equal to the number of variables and the value of each variable in that solution may be expressed by Cramer's Rule (§ 7–4) as a quotient of determinants. The determinant of the matrix of the coefficients of m linearly independent equations serves as the denominator; the determinant of the matrix obtained by replacing in the matrix of the coefficients the column of the coefficients of the variable being solved for by the column of constant terms serves as the numerator.

Example 5. Use Cramer's Rule and solve for y in the system

$$\begin{cases} x + y - z + w = 3 \\ y + z + w = 0 \\ x \quad\quad - z - w = 4 \\ 2x - y \quad\quad + w = -3. \end{cases}$$

By Cramer's Rule

$$y = \frac{\begin{vmatrix} 1 & 3 & -1 & 1 \\ 0 & 0 & 1 & 1 \\ 1 & 4 & -1 & -1 \\ 2 & -3 & 0 & 1 \end{vmatrix}}{\begin{vmatrix} 1 & 1 & -1 & 1 \\ 0 & 1 & 1 & 1 \\ 1 & 0 & -1 & -1 \\ 2 & -1 & 0 & 1 \end{vmatrix}} = \frac{\begin{vmatrix} 1 & 3 & -1 & 1 \\ 0 & 0 & 1 & 1 \\ 0 & 1 & 0 & -2 \\ 0 & -9 & 2 & -1 \end{vmatrix}}{\begin{vmatrix} 1 & 1 & -1 & 1 \\ 0 & 1 & 1 & 1 \\ 0 & -1 & 0 & -2 \\ 0 & -3 & 2 & -1 \end{vmatrix}} = \frac{\begin{vmatrix} 0 & 1 & 1 \\ 1 & 0 & -2 \\ -9 & 2 & -1 \end{vmatrix}}{\begin{vmatrix} 1 & 1 & 1 \\ -1 & 0 & -2 \\ -3 & 2 & -1 \end{vmatrix}}$$

$$= \frac{\begin{vmatrix} 0 & 1 & 0 \\ 1 & 0 & -2 \\ -9 & 2 & -3 \end{vmatrix}}{\begin{vmatrix} 1 & 1 & -1 \\ -1 & 0 & 0 \\ -3 & 2 & 5 \end{vmatrix}} = \frac{-\begin{vmatrix} 1 & -2 \\ -9 & -3 \end{vmatrix}}{\begin{vmatrix} 1 & -1 \\ 2 & 5 \end{vmatrix}} = \frac{-(-3 - 18)}{5 + 2} = \frac{21}{7} = 3.$$

§ 12-5 RANK OF A MATRIX

TEST YOURSELF

1. Find all of the submatrices of the matrix $\begin{pmatrix} 2 & 1 & 3 \\ 0 & 4 & 6 \end{pmatrix}$.

2. Find the rank of the matrix given in Exercise 1.

3. Find the determinant of the matrix $\begin{pmatrix} 5 & 1 & 3 & 7 \\ 2 & 0 & 2 & 5 \\ 0 & 3 & 1 & 4 \\ 1 & 0 & 2 & 3 \end{pmatrix}$.

EXERCISES

1. Find all of the submatrices of the matrix $\begin{pmatrix} 5 & 1 & 3 \\ 2 & 4 & 12 \end{pmatrix}$.

2. Find the determinant of each square submatrix of the matrix given in Exercise 1.

3. What is the rank of the matrix given in Exercise 1?

Find the rank of each matrix:

4. $\begin{pmatrix} 1 & 2 & 4 \\ 2 & 4 & 8 \\ 3 & 5 & 7 \end{pmatrix}$.   5. $\begin{pmatrix} 2 & 6 & 4 & 5 \\ 1 & 3 & 3 & 7 \\ 0 & 0 & 2 & 5 \end{pmatrix}$.

Find the determinant of each matrix:

6. $\begin{pmatrix} 1 & 2 & 3 & 4 & 0 \\ 0 & 1 & 2 & 0 & 3 \\ 2 & 5 & 6 & 9 & 1 \\ 1 & 3 & 4 & 5 & 2 \\ 1 & 1 & 0 & 0 & 1 \end{pmatrix}$.   7. $\begin{pmatrix} 2 & 1 & 0 & 6 & 3 \\ 0 & 2 & -1 & 5 & 2 \\ 1 & 1 & 0 & 1 & 3 \\ 2 & 0 & 0 & 2 & 1 \\ 0 & 2 & 0 & 2 & 5 \end{pmatrix}$.

Use Cramer's Rule and solve for z:

8. $\begin{cases} x - y + 2z = -1 \\ x + 2y = 5 \\ 2x - z = 2. \end{cases}$ 9. $\begin{cases} x + y + z + w = 8 \\ x - y - w = -2 \\ y + z + 2w = 9 \\ x + 2z = 6. \end{cases}$

• • •

Simplify and then expand each determinant as a function of the variables:

10. $\begin{vmatrix} x-1 & y+2 \\ 1 & -2 \end{vmatrix}$.   11. $\begin{vmatrix} x & y & z \\ 1 & 2 & 0 \\ 0 & 2 & -1 \end{vmatrix}$.

THE ALGEBRA OF MATRICES

12. $\begin{vmatrix} x & y & z & 1 \\ 1 & 0 & 2 & 1 \\ 0 & 1 & 2 & 1 \\ 1 & 2 & 0 & 0 \end{vmatrix}$.

13. $\begin{vmatrix} x & y & z \\ x+1 & y-2 & z+3 \\ 2 & 0 & 1 \end{vmatrix}$.

14. $\begin{vmatrix} x+1 & y & z+4 \\ 2 & 0 & 3 \\ -1 & 0 & 1 \end{vmatrix}$.

• 15. $\begin{vmatrix} 2x & y-2 & z+1 & 3 \\ x & 1 & 0 & 2 \\ 2 & 5 & 6 & 3 \\ 2 & 2 & 7 & 1 \end{vmatrix}$.

§ 12-6 Inverse of a matrix

The additive inverse of a real number n is $-n$ since $n + (-n) = 0$ where 0 is the identity element for addition. The additive inverse of an m by n matrix A with elements a_{ij} is the matrix $-A$ with elements $-a_{ij}$ and the property that $A + (-A)$ is the m by n zero matrix.

In this section we are primarily concerned with multiplicative inverses. The multiplicative inverse of a real number $n \neq 0$ is its reciprocal $\dfrac{1}{n}$ since $n \times \dfrac{1}{n} = 1$ where 1 is the identity element for multiplication. Any square matrix A of order m has a diagonal matrix I of order m with $a_{ii} = 1$ as its identity matrix; as in § 12–3

$$AI = IA = A.$$

We assume that I is the only matrix with this property; that is, if $AB = A$, then $B = I$; if $CA = A$, then $C = I$.

We first prove that if a square matrix A has a multiplicative inverse A^{-1} such that $A^{-1}A = I$, then $AA^{-1} = I$; that is, if a square matrix has a left multiplicative inverse, it also has a right multiplicative inverse. The steps of the proof make use of the facts that both members of a matrix equation may be multiplied on the left (that is, use premultiplication) by the same matrix; the multiplication of matrices is associative; and the properties of I may be used:

$$A^{-1}A = I$$
$$A(A^{-1}A) = AI$$
$$(AA^{-1})A = AI$$
$$(AA^{-1})A = A$$
$$AA^{-1} = I.$$

Thus if A^{-1} is a left inverse of A, it is also the right inverse.

We next prove that if a square matrix A has a multiplicative inverse A^{-1}, that inverse is unique. Suppose $A^{-1}A = I$ and also $BA = I$. Then

$$A^{-1}A = BA$$

§ 12-6 INVERSE OF A MATRIX

$$(A^{-1}A)A^{-1} = (BA)A^{-1}$$
$$A^{-1}(AA^{-1}) = B(AA^{-1})$$
$$A^{-1}I = BI$$
$$A^{-1} = B.$$

In other words, if a matrix has a multiplicative inverse, that inverse is unique.

Not every square matrix has a multiplicative inverse. For example the matrix $\begin{pmatrix} 1 & 0 \\ 0 & 0 \end{pmatrix}$ does not have a multiplicative inverse. If $\begin{pmatrix} a & b \\ c & d \end{pmatrix}$ were the inverse of $\begin{pmatrix} 1 & 0 \\ 0 & 0 \end{pmatrix}$, then we would have

$$\begin{pmatrix} a & b \\ c & d \end{pmatrix}\begin{pmatrix} 1 & 0 \\ 0 & 0 \end{pmatrix} = \begin{pmatrix} 1 & 0 \\ 0 & 1 \end{pmatrix}$$

and therefore

$$\begin{pmatrix} a & 0 \\ c & 0 \end{pmatrix} = \begin{pmatrix} 1 & 0 \\ 0 & 1 \end{pmatrix}.$$

However, since two matrices are equal if and only if their corresponding elements are equal and since 0 can never equal 1, no values of a, b, c, and d exist which satisfy this matrix equation. Notice that the determinant of the given matrix was zero. In general, any square matrix with determinant zero is called a **singular matrix**; any square matrix with determinant different from zero is a **nonsingular matrix**. We assume (even though it may be proved in more advanced courses) that a square matrix has a multiplicative inverse if and only if the given matrix is nonsingular; that is, if and only if the determinant of the given matrix is different from zero. In other words, a square matrix of order n has a multiplicative inverse if and only if it has rank n.

Example 1. Find the multiplicative inverse, if it exists, of $\begin{pmatrix} 2 & 3 \\ 1 & 2 \end{pmatrix}$.

The matrix $\begin{pmatrix} 2 & 3 \\ 1 & 2 \end{pmatrix}$ has an inverse $\begin{pmatrix} a & b \\ c & d \end{pmatrix}$ since its determinant 4 − 3 is not equal to zero. We need

$$\begin{pmatrix} a & b \\ c & d \end{pmatrix}\begin{pmatrix} 2 & 3 \\ 1 & 2 \end{pmatrix} = \begin{pmatrix} 1 & 0 \\ 0 & 1 \end{pmatrix};$$

$$\begin{pmatrix} 2a + b & 3a + 2b \\ 2c + d & 3c + 2d \end{pmatrix} = \begin{pmatrix} 1 & 0 \\ 0 & 1 \end{pmatrix}.$$

687

THE ALGEBRA OF MATRICES

We solve these pairs of simultaneous equations

$$\begin{cases} 2a + b = 1 \\ 3a + 2b = 0, \end{cases} \quad \begin{cases} 2c + d = 0 \\ 3c + 2d = 1, \end{cases}$$

and obtain $a = 2$, $b = -3$, $c = -1$, and $d = 2$. Hence the multiplicative inverse of $\begin{pmatrix} 2 & 3 \\ 1 & 2 \end{pmatrix}$ is $\begin{pmatrix} 2 & -3 \\ -1 & 2 \end{pmatrix}$.

Example 2. Find the general form of the multiplicative inverse of the general square matrix of order two $\begin{pmatrix} a & b \\ c & d \end{pmatrix}$ with determinant $ad - bc \neq 0$.

Let the multiplicative inverse of $\begin{pmatrix} a & b \\ c & d \end{pmatrix}$ be represented by $\begin{pmatrix} w & x \\ y & z \end{pmatrix}$.
Then

$$\begin{pmatrix} w & x \\ y & z \end{pmatrix} \begin{pmatrix} a & b \\ c & d \end{pmatrix} = \begin{pmatrix} 1 & 0 \\ 0 & 1 \end{pmatrix};$$

$$\begin{pmatrix} aw + cx & bw + dx \\ ay + cz & by + dz \end{pmatrix} = \begin{pmatrix} 1 & 0 \\ 0 & 1 \end{pmatrix};$$

$$\begin{cases} aw + cx = 1 \\ bw + dx = 0, \end{cases} \quad \begin{cases} ay + cz = 0 \\ by + dz = 1. \end{cases}$$

Since $ad - bc \neq 0$, the solutions of these pairs of equations may be found by Cramer's Rule:

$$w = \frac{\begin{vmatrix} 1 & c \\ 0 & d \end{vmatrix}}{\begin{vmatrix} a & c \\ b & d \end{vmatrix}} = \frac{d}{ad - bc}, \qquad x = \frac{\begin{vmatrix} a & 1 \\ b & 0 \end{vmatrix}}{\begin{vmatrix} a & c \\ b & d \end{vmatrix}} = \frac{-b}{ad - bc},$$

$$y = \frac{\begin{vmatrix} 0 & c \\ 1 & d \end{vmatrix}}{\begin{vmatrix} a & c \\ b & d \end{vmatrix}} = \frac{-c}{ad - bc}, \qquad z = \frac{\begin{vmatrix} a & 0 \\ b & 1 \end{vmatrix}}{\begin{vmatrix} a & c \\ b & d \end{vmatrix}} = \frac{a}{ad - bc}.$$

Hence the inverse of $\begin{pmatrix} a & b \\ c & d \end{pmatrix}$ is $\begin{pmatrix} \dfrac{d}{ad - bc} & \dfrac{-b}{ad - bc} \\ \dfrac{-c}{ad - bc} & \dfrac{a}{ad - bc} \end{pmatrix}$.

The method of Example 2 is impractical for finding the inverses of square matrices of higher order. We can find the inverses of nonsingular square

§ 12-6 INVERSE OF A MATRIX

matrices directly. The following method can be proved in more advanced courses: The inverse of any square matrix A with determinant $|A| \neq 0$ may be expressed as the product of $\dfrac{1}{|A|}$ and the transpose of the matrix obtained by replacing each element by its cofactor in the matrix A. Consider, for example, $A = \begin{pmatrix} a & b \\ c & d \end{pmatrix}$ with $|A| = ad - bc \neq 0$ as in Example 2. Notice that in $\begin{pmatrix} a & b \\ c & d \end{pmatrix}$ the cofactor of a is d, the cofactor of b is $-c$, the cofactor of c is $-b$, and the cofactor of d is a. Therefore the matrix of the cofactors (§ 12–5) is $\begin{pmatrix} d & -c \\ -b & a \end{pmatrix}$. The transpose (§ 12–3) of the matrix of the cofactors is $\begin{pmatrix} d & -b \\ -c & a \end{pmatrix}$. Then the inverse of the given matrix is $\dfrac{1}{|A|} \begin{pmatrix} d & -b \\ -c & a \end{pmatrix}$ which, as in (§ 12–1), may also be expressed in the form given in Example 2.

Example 3. Find the multiplicative inverse of A if

$$A = \begin{pmatrix} 7 & -3 & -3 \\ -2 & 2 & 0 \\ -1 & 0 & 1 \end{pmatrix}.$$

We first evaluate $|A|$ to determine if A^{-1} exists. The expansion by minors of the elements on the third row is

$$|A| = (-1)\begin{vmatrix} -3 & -3 \\ 2 & 0 \end{vmatrix} + (1)\begin{vmatrix} 7 & -3 \\ -2 & 2 \end{vmatrix} = -6 + 8 = 2.$$

Since $|A| \neq 0$, A^{-1} exists. The cofactors A_{ij} of the elements a_{ij} of A are:

$$A_{11} = \begin{vmatrix} 2 & 0 \\ 0 & 1 \end{vmatrix} = 2;\ A_{12} = -\begin{vmatrix} -2 & 0 \\ -1 & 1 \end{vmatrix} = 2;\ A_{13} = \begin{vmatrix} -2 & 2 \\ -1 & 0 \end{vmatrix} = 2;$$

$$A_{21} = -\begin{vmatrix} -3 & -3 \\ 0 & 1 \end{vmatrix} = 3;\ A_{22} = \begin{vmatrix} 7 & -3 \\ -1 & 1 \end{vmatrix} = 4;$$

$$A_{23} = -\begin{vmatrix} 7 & -3 \\ -1 & 0 \end{vmatrix} = 3;\ A_{31} = \begin{vmatrix} -3 & -3 \\ 2 & 0 \end{vmatrix} = 6;$$

$$A_{32} = -\begin{vmatrix} 7 & -3 \\ -2 & 0 \end{vmatrix} = 6;\ A_{33} = \begin{vmatrix} 7 & -3 \\ -2 & 2 \end{vmatrix} = 8.$$

689

THE ALGEBRA OF MATRICES

When each element of A is replaced by its cofactor we have the matrix

$$\begin{pmatrix} 2 & 2 & 2 \\ 3 & 4 & 3 \\ 6 & 6 & 8 \end{pmatrix} \text{ with transpose } \begin{pmatrix} 2 & 3 & 6 \\ 2 & 4 & 6 \\ 2 & 3 & 8 \end{pmatrix}.$$

The product of the transpose of the matrix of cofactors and $\dfrac{1}{|A|}$ (that is, $\dfrac{1}{2}$) represents the inverse of A:

$$A^{-1} = \frac{1}{2} \begin{pmatrix} 2 & 3 & 6 \\ 2 & 4 & 6 \\ 2 & 3 & 8 \end{pmatrix} = \begin{pmatrix} 1 & \frac{3}{2} & 3 \\ 1 & 2 & 3 \\ 1 & \frac{3}{2} & 4 \end{pmatrix}.$$

This representation of A^{-1} may be checked as follows:

$$\begin{pmatrix} 1 & \frac{3}{2} & 3 \\ 1 & 2 & 3 \\ 1 & \frac{3}{2} & 4 \end{pmatrix} \begin{pmatrix} 7 & -3 & -3 \\ -2 & 2 & 0 \\ -1 & 0 & 1 \end{pmatrix} = \begin{pmatrix} 1 & 0 & 0 \\ 0 & 1 & 0 \\ 0 & 0 & 1 \end{pmatrix}.$$

Example 4. Solve the system of simultaneous equations $\begin{cases} 4x + y = 1 \\ 2x - y = 5 \end{cases}$ using the inverse of the matrix of the coefficients.

The given system of equations may be expressed as a single matrix equation:

$$\begin{pmatrix} 4 & 1 \\ 2 & -1 \end{pmatrix} \begin{pmatrix} x \\ y \end{pmatrix} = \begin{pmatrix} 1 \\ 5 \end{pmatrix}.$$

The matrix of the coefficients is $\begin{pmatrix} 4 & 1 \\ 2 & -1 \end{pmatrix}$, has determinant -6, and therefore has an inverse. As in Example 2, the inverse is

$$-\frac{1}{6} \begin{pmatrix} -1 & -1 \\ -2 & 4 \end{pmatrix}; \text{ that is, } \begin{pmatrix} \frac{1}{6} & \frac{1}{6} \\ \frac{1}{3} & -\frac{2}{3} \end{pmatrix}.$$

We multiply both sides of the

§ 12-6 INVERSE OF A MATRIX

matrix equation for the given system of equations by the inverse of the matrix of the coefficients and obtain

$$\begin{pmatrix} \frac{1}{6} & \frac{1}{6} \\ \frac{1}{3} & -\frac{2}{3} \end{pmatrix} \begin{pmatrix} 4 & 1 \\ 2 & -1 \end{pmatrix} \begin{pmatrix} x \\ y \end{pmatrix} = \begin{pmatrix} \frac{1}{6} & \frac{1}{6} \\ \frac{1}{3} & -\frac{2}{3} \end{pmatrix} \begin{pmatrix} 1 \\ 5 \end{pmatrix}$$

$$\begin{pmatrix} 1 & 0 \\ 0 & 1 \end{pmatrix} \begin{pmatrix} x \\ y \end{pmatrix} = \begin{pmatrix} 1 \\ -3 \end{pmatrix}$$

$$\begin{pmatrix} x \\ y \end{pmatrix} = \begin{pmatrix} 1 \\ -3 \end{pmatrix}.$$

Hence the solution of the given system of simultaneous equations is $x = 1$ and $y = -3$.

Notice that the inverse of the matrix of the coefficients may be found by inspection and thus all of the details that we have considered may be reduced to

$$\begin{pmatrix} x \\ y \end{pmatrix} = \begin{pmatrix} \frac{-1}{-6} & \frac{-1}{-6} \\ \frac{-2}{-6} & \frac{4}{-6} \end{pmatrix} \begin{pmatrix} 1 \\ 5 \end{pmatrix} = \begin{pmatrix} 1 \\ -3 \end{pmatrix}.$$

TEST YOURSELF

Determine the inverse of each matrix, if possible:

1. $\begin{pmatrix} 2 & 1 \\ 4 & 3 \end{pmatrix}$.

2. $\begin{pmatrix} 9 & 3 \\ 2 & 1 \end{pmatrix}$.

3. $\begin{pmatrix} 3 & -2 \\ 0 & 0 \end{pmatrix}$.

4. $\begin{pmatrix} m & n \\ r & s \end{pmatrix}$, if $\begin{vmatrix} m & n \\ r & s \end{vmatrix} \neq 0$.

5. $\begin{pmatrix} x^2 & 1 \\ 0 & x \end{pmatrix}$, if $x \neq 0$.

6. $\begin{pmatrix} 0 & 1 & 3 \\ -2 & 3 & 9 \\ 1 & -2 & -5 \end{pmatrix}$.

Use the inverse of the matrix of the coefficients to find the solution set for each system of equations:

7. $\begin{cases} x + y = -1 \\ 2x - y = 7. \end{cases}$

8. $\begin{cases} x + 3y = 5 \\ 2x - y = 3. \end{cases}$

691

THE ALGEBRA OF MATRICES

EXERCISES

Determine the inverse of each matrix, if possible:

1. $\begin{pmatrix} 8 & 5 \\ 12 & 8 \end{pmatrix}$.

2. $\begin{pmatrix} 5 & 3 \\ 2 & 1 \end{pmatrix}$.

3. $\begin{pmatrix} 3 & 6 \\ -1 & -2 \end{pmatrix}$.

4. $\begin{pmatrix} a & b \\ -b & a \end{pmatrix}$, if $ab \neq 0$.

5. $\begin{pmatrix} \cos \theta & \sin \theta \\ -\sin \theta & \cos \theta \end{pmatrix}$.

6. $\begin{pmatrix} t^2 & 1 \\ -t^3 & t \end{pmatrix}$, if $t \neq 0$.

7. $\begin{pmatrix} 3 & 0 & 0 \\ 0 & 4 & 0 \\ 0 & 0 & 2 \end{pmatrix}$.

8. $\begin{pmatrix} 2 & 1 & 1 \\ 2 & 0 & 2 \\ 0 & 1 & -3 \end{pmatrix}$.

In Exercises 9 and 10 use the inverse of the matrix of the coefficients to find the solution set for each system of equations:

9. $\begin{cases} 2x + y = 1 \\ 4x + 3y = 3. \end{cases}$

10. $\begin{cases} ax + a^2 y = 3 \\ x - ay = -\dfrac{1}{a}; a \neq 0. \end{cases}$

11. Prove that if A is a nonsingular matrix and $AB = AC$, then $B = C$.

• • •

12. Consider a matrix $A = \begin{pmatrix} w & z \\ -\bar{z} & \bar{w} \end{pmatrix}$ where w and z are complex numbers with conjugates $\bar{w}$ and $\bar{z}$ respectively and $w\bar{w} + z\bar{z} \neq 0$. Find A^{-1}.

13. Assume that the associative law for multiplication holds for matrix multiplication and prove that the set of matrices

$$\begin{pmatrix} 1 & 0 \\ 0 & 1 \end{pmatrix}, \begin{pmatrix} -1 & 0 \\ 0 & -1 \end{pmatrix}, \begin{pmatrix} 0 & 1 \\ -1 & 0 \end{pmatrix}, \begin{pmatrix} 0 & -1 \\ 1 & 0 \end{pmatrix}$$

forms a commutative group under matrix multiplication.

14. Assume that the associative law for multiplication holds for matrix multiplication and prove that the set of nonsingular matrices of any given order n forms a group under matrix multiplication.

15. Prove that the transpose of A^{-1} equals the inverse of $A^\top$ for nonsingular matrices A of order two.

16. Verify the results of Exercise 15 for the matrix $\begin{pmatrix} 8 & 5 \\ 12 & 8 \end{pmatrix}$.

17. Prove that $(A^{-1})^{-1} = A$.
18. Prove that $(AB)^{-1} = B^{-1}A^{-1}$.

19. Verify the results of Exercise 18 for the matrices $A = \begin{pmatrix} 2 & 1 \\ 4 & -3 \end{pmatrix}$ and $B = \begin{pmatrix} 1 & -5 \\ -2 & 3 \end{pmatrix}$.

§ 12-7 Systems of matrices

The principle properties of the integers may be summarized by saying that the set of integers forms an integral domain (§ 6–5). Similarly, the set of rational numbers forms a field. In each case the operations of addition and multiplication and the equivalence relation = are also parts of the mathematical system (§ 6–1).

The set of square matrices of any given order n under the operations of matrix addition and matrix multiplication forms another important abstract mathematical system, called a ring. A **ring** is a mathematical system which is a commutative group under addition and in which multiplication is closed, associative, and distributive with respect to addition. The distinction between a ring and an integral domain (§ 6–5) is that an integral domain must include a multiplicative identity element, must be commutative under multiplication, and must not have zero divisors while these properties are not required for a ring.

The existence of zero divisors in the algebra of matrices is shown by the following examples:

$$\begin{pmatrix} 1 & 3 \\ 2 & 6 \end{pmatrix} \begin{pmatrix} -3 & 12 \\ 1 & -4 \end{pmatrix} = \begin{pmatrix} 0 & 0 \\ 0 & 0 \end{pmatrix};$$

$$\begin{pmatrix} 3 & 0 & 2 \\ 1 & 0 & 5 \\ 7 & 0 & 6 \end{pmatrix} \begin{pmatrix} 0 & 0 & 0 \\ 5 & 7 & 11 \\ 0 & 0 & 0 \end{pmatrix} = \begin{pmatrix} 0 & 0 & 0 \\ 0 & 0 & 0 \\ 0 & 0 & 0 \end{pmatrix}.$$

For any given order n it is possible to find pairs of square matrices which are not zero matrices but which have a zero matrix as their product in a specified order. For example, as in the case of the matrix of order three, we may make all elements of the second column of the first matrix zero, all elements that are not on the second row of the second matrix zero, and use any nonzero elements that we like to complete the matrices. Accordingly, the set of square real matrices of order n cannot form an integral domain for any value of $n > 1$.

Example 1. Prove that the set S of square real matrices of order two forms a commutative group under matrix addition.

We must show that the set S is closed under addition, includes an additive identity element, includes the inverse of each element of S, and that the addition of elements of S is associative and commutative.

THE ALGEBRA OF MATRICES

Let $\begin{pmatrix} a & b \\ c & d \end{pmatrix}$ and $\begin{pmatrix} e & f \\ g & h \end{pmatrix}$ be any two elements of S.

Then $\begin{pmatrix} a & b \\ c & d \end{pmatrix} + \begin{pmatrix} e & f \\ g & h \end{pmatrix} = \begin{pmatrix} a+e & b+f \\ c+g & d+h \end{pmatrix}$ which is an element of S;

the matrix $\begin{pmatrix} 0 & 0 \\ 0 & 0 \end{pmatrix}$ is an element of S and is the additive identity element; each element $\begin{pmatrix} a & b \\ c & d \end{pmatrix}$ has an additive inverse $\begin{pmatrix} -a & -b \\ -c & -d \end{pmatrix}$.

The addition of elements of S is associative since for any three elements of S we have from the properties of real numbers

$$\begin{pmatrix} a & b \\ c & d \end{pmatrix} + \left(\begin{pmatrix} e & f \\ g & h \end{pmatrix} + \begin{pmatrix} r & s \\ t & u \end{pmatrix}\right) = \begin{pmatrix} a & b \\ c & d \end{pmatrix} + \begin{pmatrix} e+r & f+s \\ g+t & h+u \end{pmatrix}$$

$$= \begin{pmatrix} a+(e+r) & b+(f+s) \\ c+(g+t) & d+(h+u) \end{pmatrix} = \begin{pmatrix} (a+e)+r & (b+f)+s \\ (c+g)+t & (d+h)+u \end{pmatrix}$$

$$= \begin{pmatrix} a+e & b+f \\ c+g & d+h \end{pmatrix} + \begin{pmatrix} r & s \\ t & u \end{pmatrix}$$

$$= \left(\begin{pmatrix} a & b \\ c & d \end{pmatrix} + \begin{pmatrix} e & f \\ g & h \end{pmatrix}\right) + \begin{pmatrix} r & s \\ t & u \end{pmatrix}.$$

The addition of elements of S is commutative since for any two elements of S we have from the properties of real numbers

$$\begin{pmatrix} a & b \\ c & d \end{pmatrix} + \begin{pmatrix} e & f \\ g & h \end{pmatrix} = \begin{pmatrix} a+e & b+f \\ c+g & d+h \end{pmatrix}$$

$$= \begin{pmatrix} e+a & f+b \\ g+c & h+d \end{pmatrix} = \begin{pmatrix} e & f \\ g & h \end{pmatrix} + \begin{pmatrix} a & b \\ c & d \end{pmatrix}.$$

Thus the set S of square real matrices of order two forms a commutative group under matrix addition.

Example 2. Prove that the set S of square real matrices of order two forms a ring.

The set S forms a commutative group under matrix addition (Example 1). It remains to prove that the set is closed under matrix multiplication, that multiplication is associative, and that multiplication is distributive with respect to addition.

Let $\begin{pmatrix} a & b \\ c & d \end{pmatrix}$ and $\begin{pmatrix} e & f \\ g & h \end{pmatrix}$ be any two elements of S.

Then $\begin{pmatrix} a & b \\ c & d \end{pmatrix}\begin{pmatrix} e & f \\ g & h \end{pmatrix} = \begin{pmatrix} ae+bg & af+bh \\ ce+dg & cf+dh \end{pmatrix}$ which is an element of S and therefore the set S is closed under matrix multiplication.

§ 12-7 SYSTEMS OF MATRICES

Our proof that the multiplication of elements of S is associative makes extensive use of the properties of real numbers. We take any three elements A, B, C of S and show that $A(BC)$ and $(AB)C$ are equal to the same matrix and thus to each other as follows:

$$\begin{pmatrix} a & b \\ c & d \end{pmatrix} \left(\begin{pmatrix} e & f \\ g & h \end{pmatrix} \begin{pmatrix} j & k \\ m & n \end{pmatrix} \right) = \begin{pmatrix} a & b \\ c & d \end{pmatrix} \begin{pmatrix} ej + fm & ek + fn \\ gj + hm & gk + hn \end{pmatrix}$$

$$= \begin{pmatrix} aej + afm + bgj + bhm & aek + afn + bgk + bhn \\ cej + cfm + dgj + dhm & cek + cfn + dgk + dhn \end{pmatrix};$$

$$\left(\begin{pmatrix} a & b \\ c & d \end{pmatrix} \begin{pmatrix} e & f \\ g & h \end{pmatrix} \right) \begin{pmatrix} j & k \\ m & n \end{pmatrix} = \begin{pmatrix} ae + bg & af + bh \\ ce + dg & cf + dh \end{pmatrix} \begin{pmatrix} j & k \\ m & n \end{pmatrix}$$

$$= \begin{pmatrix} aej + bgj + afm + bhm & aek + bgk + afn + bhn \\ cej + dgj + cfm + dhm & cek + dgk + cfn + dhn \end{pmatrix}.$$

Since the matrices which were obtained as products are equal, matrix multiplication of elements of S is associative.

Finally, we need to prove that multiplication is distributive with respect to addition. Since multiplication is not commutative, two cases need to be considered:

$$A(B + C) = AB + AC; \quad (B + C)A = BA + CA.$$

We prove only the first of these two cases and leave the second one as an exercise (Exercise 15). In the following proof we take any three elements of S and prove that $A(B + C)$ and $AB + AC$ are equal to the same matrix and thus to each other:

$$\begin{pmatrix} a & b \\ c & d \end{pmatrix} \left(\begin{pmatrix} e & f \\ g & h \end{pmatrix} + \begin{pmatrix} j & k \\ m & n \end{pmatrix} \right) = \begin{pmatrix} a & b \\ c & d \end{pmatrix} \begin{pmatrix} e + j & f + k \\ g + m & h + n \end{pmatrix}$$

$$= \begin{pmatrix} ae + aj + bg + bm & af + ak + bh + bn \\ ce + cj + dg + dm & cf + ck + dh + dn \end{pmatrix};$$

$$\begin{pmatrix} a & b \\ c & d \end{pmatrix} \begin{pmatrix} e & f \\ g & h \end{pmatrix} + \begin{pmatrix} a & b \\ c & d \end{pmatrix} \begin{pmatrix} j & k \\ m & n \end{pmatrix}$$

$$= \begin{pmatrix} ae + bg & af + bh \\ ce + dg & cf + dh \end{pmatrix} + \begin{pmatrix} aj + bm & ak + bn \\ cj + dm & ck + dn \end{pmatrix}$$

$$= \begin{pmatrix} ae + aj + bg + bm & af + ak + bh + bn \\ ce + cj + dg + dm & cf + ck + dh + dn \end{pmatrix}.$$

Therefore $A(B + C) = AB + AC$; and the set S of square real matrices of order two satisfies all of the properties of a ring and thus forms a ring.

The concept of a ring is important in many algebraic topics. We shall digress slightly from our discussion of matrices to illustrate properties of a ring for other sets of elements.

THE ALGEBRA OF MATRICES

Example 3. Determine whether the set E of even integers forms a ring under ordinary addition and multiplication with equality as the equivalence relation.

$$E = \{\cdots, -4, -2, 0, 2, 4, 6, \cdots\}.$$

The set E is closed under addition and multiplication; the additive identity element 0 is a member of the set; each even integer has an even integer as its additive inverse (negative). The remaining desired properties (associativity and commutativity of addition, associativity of multiplication, distributivity of multiplication with respect to addition) hold for all integers and in particular for all even integers. Thus the set E forms a ring as specified.

A ring for which the commutative property of multiplication holds is called a **commutative ring**. Since the multiplication of any two even integers is commutative, the set E is an example of a commutative ring. Since the multiplication of matrices is, in general, not commutative, the set of square real matrices of order two does not form a commutative ring.

Throughout our study of mathematics we have been concerned with different notations and ways of representing various numbers. One basis for the importance of square real matrices of order two is that these matrices may represent either real or complex numbers. Whenever two sets of elements may be placed in one-to-one correspondence such that sums and products in the two systems correspond, the two sets are said to be **isomorphic**. For example, the matrices $\begin{pmatrix} x & 0 \\ 0 & x \end{pmatrix}$ may be used in the same manner as the real numbers x (Example 4); the matrices $\begin{pmatrix} x & y \\ -y & x \end{pmatrix}$ may be used in the same manner as the complex numbers $x + yi$ (Example 5).

Example 4. Prove that the set of real matrices $\begin{pmatrix} x & 0 \\ 0 & x \end{pmatrix}$ is isomorphic to the set of real numbers x.

We write the correspondence as $\begin{pmatrix} x & 0 \\ 0 & x \end{pmatrix} \leftrightarrow x$.

If $\begin{pmatrix} a & 0 \\ 0 & a \end{pmatrix} \leftrightarrow a$ and $\begin{pmatrix} b & 0 \\ 0 & b \end{pmatrix} \leftrightarrow b$, then

$$\begin{pmatrix} a & 0 \\ 0 & a \end{pmatrix} + \begin{pmatrix} b & 0 \\ 0 & b \end{pmatrix} = \begin{pmatrix} a+b & 0 \\ 0 & a+b \end{pmatrix} \leftrightarrow a+b;$$

$$\begin{pmatrix} a & 0 \\ 0 & a \end{pmatrix}\begin{pmatrix} b & 0 \\ 0 & b \end{pmatrix} = \begin{pmatrix} ab & 0 \\ 0 & ab \end{pmatrix} \leftrightarrow ab.$$

Then the set of matrices $\begin{pmatrix} x & 0 \\ 0 & x \end{pmatrix}$ is isomorphic to the set of real numbers x.

Example 5. Prove that the set of real matrices $\begin{pmatrix} x & y \\ -y & x \end{pmatrix}$ is isomorphic to the set of complex numbers $x + yi$.

Let $\begin{pmatrix} a & b \\ -b & a \end{pmatrix} \leftrightarrow a + bi$ and $\begin{pmatrix} c & d \\ -d & c \end{pmatrix} \leftrightarrow c + di$.

Then $(a + bi) + (c + di) = (a + c) + (b + d)i$,

$$\begin{pmatrix} a & b \\ -b & a \end{pmatrix} + \begin{pmatrix} c & d \\ -d & c \end{pmatrix} = \begin{pmatrix} a + c & b + d \\ -(b + d) & a + c \end{pmatrix},$$

$$\begin{pmatrix} a + c & b + d \\ -(b + d) & a + c \end{pmatrix} \leftrightarrow (a + c) + (b + d)i;$$

and therefore

$$\begin{pmatrix} a & b \\ -b & a \end{pmatrix} + \begin{pmatrix} c & d \\ -d & c \end{pmatrix} \leftrightarrow (a + bi) + (c + di),$$

which demonstrates that the correspondence is preserved under addition; $(a + bi) \times (c + di) = (ac - bd) + (ad + bc)i$,

$$\begin{pmatrix} a & b \\ -b & a \end{pmatrix}\begin{pmatrix} c & d \\ -d & c \end{pmatrix} = \begin{pmatrix} ac - bd & ad + bc \\ -(ad + bc) & ac - bd \end{pmatrix},$$

$$\begin{pmatrix} ac - bd & ad + bc \\ -(ad + bc) & ac - bd \end{pmatrix} \leftrightarrow (ac - bd) + (ad + bc)i,$$

and therefore

$$\begin{pmatrix} a & b \\ -b & a \end{pmatrix}\begin{pmatrix} c & d \\ -d & c \end{pmatrix} \leftrightarrow (a + bi) \times (c + di),$$

which demonstrates that the correspondence is preserved under multiplication.

Notice that under the isomorphism described in Example 5 we have for any real numbers a and b:

$$a + bi \leftrightarrow \begin{pmatrix} a & b \\ -b & a \end{pmatrix}$$

$$a - bi = a + (-b)i \leftrightarrow \begin{pmatrix} a & -b \\ b & a \end{pmatrix}.$$

THE ALGEBRA OF MATRICES

Example 6. Represent each complex number by a matrix, perform the indicated operation, and verify that the matrix result corresponds to the desired result in $a + bi$ form: (a) $i \times i$; (b) $(2 + 3i) \times (5 - 2i)$.

Under the isomorphism of Example 5, $\begin{pmatrix} x & y \\ -y & x \end{pmatrix} \leftrightarrow x + yi$.

Therefore $\begin{pmatrix} 0 & 1 \\ -1 & 0 \end{pmatrix} \leftrightarrow i$, $\begin{pmatrix} 2 & 3 \\ -3 & 2 \end{pmatrix} \leftrightarrow 2 + 3i$, and $\begin{pmatrix} 5 & -2 \\ 2 & 5 \end{pmatrix} \leftrightarrow 5 - 2i$.

(a) $i \times i = -1$; $\begin{pmatrix} 0 & 1 \\ -1 & 0 \end{pmatrix}\begin{pmatrix} 0 & 1 \\ -1 & 0 \end{pmatrix} = \begin{pmatrix} -1 & 0 \\ 0 & -1 \end{pmatrix} \leftrightarrow -1$.

(b) $(2 + 3i) \times (5 - 2i) = [(2)(5) - (3)(-2)] + [(2)(-2) + (3)(5)]i$
$= 16 + 11i$;

$\begin{pmatrix} 2 & 3 \\ -3 & 2 \end{pmatrix}\begin{pmatrix} 5 & -2 \\ 2 & 5 \end{pmatrix} = \begin{pmatrix} 16 & 11 \\ -11 & 16 \end{pmatrix} \leftrightarrow 16 + 11i$.

Many other interesting and important mathematical systems are isomorphic to sets of matrices of some type. For this reason the algebra of matrices has become a very important algebra for mathematicians and people who make extensive use of mathematics.

TEST YOURSELF

Determine which of the following sets of elements under the given operations form **(a)** *rings;* **(b)** *commutative rings:*

1. The set of odd integers under ordinary addition and multiplication.
2. The modulo 4 system under modular addition and multiplication.
3. The matrices $\begin{pmatrix} 1 & 0 \\ 0 & 1 \end{pmatrix}$ and $\begin{pmatrix} -1 & 0 \\ 0 & -1 \end{pmatrix}$ under matrix addition and multiplication.

Represent each complex number by a matrix, perform the indicated operation, and verify that the matrix result corresponds to the desired result in $a + bi$ form:

4. $(3 + i) + (6 - 2i)$.
5. $(5 + 4i) - (3 + 4i)$.
6. $(2 + i) \times i$.
7. $(4 + 2i) \times (4 - 2i)$.

EXERCISES

Determine which of the following sets of elements under the given operations form **(a)** *rings;* **(b)** *commutative rings:*

1. The set of integral multiples of 7 under ordinary addition and multiplication.

§ 12-7 SYSTEMS OF MATRICES

2. The set of numbers of the form $a + b\sqrt{3}$ where a and b are integers under ordinary addition and multiplication.
3. The set $\{-1, 0, 1\}$ under ordinary addition and multiplication.
4. The modulo 6 system under modular addition and multiplication.
5. The set of matrices $\begin{pmatrix} k & 0 \\ 0 & 0 \end{pmatrix}$ where k may be any real number under matrix addition and multiplication.
6. The set of square matrices of order two whose elements are even integers under matrix addition and multiplication.

In Exercises 7 through 12 represent each complex number by a matrix, perform the indicated operations, and verify that the matrix result corresponds to the desired result in $a + bi$ form:

7. $2 + (2 - i)$.
8. $(-3 + i) + (3 - i)$.
9. $(7 + 3i) - (4 - 2i)$.
10. $(-2 - i) \times (3 + 4i)$.
11. $i \times (5 - i)$.
12. $(6 - 3i) \times (-1 - 5i)$.

• • •

13. Show that the reciprocal of the complex number $a + bi$ corresponds to the inverse of the matrix $\begin{pmatrix} a & b \\ -b & a \end{pmatrix}$.

14. Use the results of Exercise 13 to evaluate $(3 + i) \div (2 - i)$ when the complex numbers are written in matrix form.

15. Prove that for any square real matrices of order two $(B + C)A = BA + CA$.

16. Determine if the set of nonsingular matrices of order two forms an integral domain under matrix addition and multiplication. State reasons for your answer.

Consider the set S of nonsingular matrices of order two. We define an operation $\odot$ on the set S such that if $A, B \in S$, $A \odot B = AB - BA$. In Exercises 17 through 19 prove the indicated properties of S under $\odot$:

17. $A \odot B = -(B \odot A)$.
18. $A \odot A = 0$.
19. $A \odot I = 0$.

In Exercises 20 through 23 give an example of two nonzero matrices of the specified order which have a zero matrix as their product:

20. Order three.
21. Order four.
22. Order five.
23. Order seven.

• 24. Prove that any complex number $x + yi$ can be expressed in the form $xI + yJ$ where I and J are square real matrices of order two and determinant 1.

699

THE ALGEBRA OF MATRICES

§ 12–8 Translations

Translations and rotations were introduced in § 7–6 and used extensively in Chapter 7 to transform the coordinate system so that the equation of a particular curve would assume a more convenient form. In Chapter 7 the transformations were represented by systems of linear equations. We now consider the representation of the transformations by matrix equations. As in § 12–2, any system of linear equations may be represented by a single equation involving matrices; that is, by a single matrix equation. In this section we use matrix equations to represent translations; in § 12–9 we shall use matrix equations to represent rotations; in § 12–10 we shall consider other types of transformations.

A translation of the x- and y-axes on a coordinate plane so that the lines $x = h$ and $y = k$ become the new x'- and y'-axes was observed in § 7–6 to assign coordinates (x', y') to each point (x, y) where

$$\begin{cases} x' = x - h \\ y' = y - k. \end{cases}$$

Similarly, a translation of the coordinate planes in space so that the planes $x = h$, $y = k$, and $z = n$ become the new $y'z'$-, $x'z'$-, and $x'y'$-planes was observed in § 7–6 to assign coordinates (x', y', z') to each point (x, y, z) where

$$\begin{cases} x' = x - h \\ y' = y - k \\ z' = z - n. \end{cases}$$

Whenever we found the equation of a given curve with reference to the new coordinate system, we used the systems of equations

$$\begin{cases} x = x' + h \\ y = y' + k; \end{cases} \tag{5}$$

$$\begin{cases} x = x' + h \\ y = y' + k \\ z = z' + n. \end{cases} \tag{6}$$

The systems of equations (5) and (6) may now be derived using vectors (Chapter 11). Let the origin of the original coordinate system be O, the origin of the new coordinate system be O', and consider any point P. The vector equation

$$\overrightarrow{OP} = \overrightarrow{OO'} + \overrightarrow{O'P} \tag{7}$$

holds for points on a plane and also for points in space. On a plane we may consider the points as $O: (0, 0)$, $O': (h, k)$, $P: (x, y)$ with reference to the x- and y-axes; $P: (x', y')$ with reference to the x'- and y'-axes. Then $\overrightarrow{OP} = x\vec{i} + y\vec{j}$; $\overrightarrow{OO'} = h\vec{i} + k\vec{j}$; $\overrightarrow{O'P} = x'\vec{i} + y'\vec{j}$. Notice that the same unit vectors $\vec{i}$ and $\vec{j}$ may be used for both sets of axes. The equation (7) may then be expressed as

$$x\vec{i} + y\vec{j} = (h\vec{i} + k\vec{j}) + (x'\vec{i} + y'\vec{j}),$$
$$x\vec{i} + y\vec{j} = (x' + h)\vec{i} + (y' + k)\vec{j}$$

which is equivalent to the system of equations (5). In space we consider the points as $O: (0, 0, 0)$, $O': (h, m, n)$, $P: (x, y, z)$ with reference to the given coordinate system, $P: (x', y', z')$ with reference to the new coordinate system. Then $\overrightarrow{OP} = x\vec{i} + y\vec{j} + z\vec{k}$, $\overrightarrow{OO'} = h\vec{i} + m\vec{j} + n\vec{k}$, $\overrightarrow{O'P} = x'\vec{i} + y'\vec{j} + z'\vec{k}$. The equation (7) may then be expressed as

$$x\vec{i} + y\vec{j} + z\vec{k} = (h\vec{i} + m\vec{j} + n\vec{k}) + (x'\vec{i} + y'\vec{j} + z'\vec{k}),$$
$$x\vec{i} + y\vec{j} + z\vec{k} = (x' + h)\vec{i} + (y' + m)\vec{j} + (z' + n)\vec{k}$$

which is equivalent to the system of equations (6).

The transformations (5) and (6) are both special cases of linear transformations. For example, the transformation (5) is a special case of the general **linear transformation of two variables**

$$\begin{cases} x = a_{11}x' + a_{12}y' + a_{13} \\ y = a_{21}x' + a_{22}y' + a_{23} \end{cases} \tag{8}$$

where the a_{ij} are constants and $a_{11}a_{22} - a_{12}a_{21} \neq 0$. The transformation (6) is a special case of the general **linear transformation of three variables**

$$\begin{cases} x = a_{11}x' + a_{12}y' + a_{13}z' + a_{14} \\ y = a_{21}x' + a_{22}y' + a_{23}z' + a_{24} \\ z = a_{31}x' + a_{32}y' + a_{33}z' + a_{34} \end{cases} \tag{9}$$

where the a_{ij} are constants and the determinant

$$\begin{vmatrix} a_{11} & a_{12} & a_{13} \\ a_{21} & a_{22} & a_{23} \\ a_{31} & a_{32} & a_{33} \end{vmatrix} \neq 0.$$

In each case the condition that the determinant of the coefficients be different from zero is necessary so that each system of equations can be solved for the primed variables in terms of the unprimed variables (§ 12–6). This is equivalent to the condition that the transformation have an inverse.

In order to express the system of equations (8) by a matrix equation, we must have a matrix representation for coordinates of points which is con-

THE ALGEBRA OF MATRICES

formable for multiplication to the matrix

$$\begin{pmatrix} a_{11} & a_{12} & a_{13} \\ a_{21} & a_{22} & a_{23} \end{pmatrix}$$

of the system of equations (8). Accordingly points on a plane must be represented by a matrix which has either three rows or three columns. It is customary to use a 3 by 1 matrix:

$$\begin{pmatrix} x \\ y \\ 1 \end{pmatrix} \leftrightarrow (x, y).$$

This is equivalent to using a triple $(x, y, 1)$ to represent each point (x, y). There is obviously a one-to-one correspondence between the set of coordinates (x, y) and the set of coordinates $(x, y, 1)$ for points on a plane. When we wish to distinguish between these two systems of coordinates, we call (x, y) **nonhomogeneous coordinates,** and we call (x_k, y_k, k) **homogeneous coordinates** of which this representation $(x, y, 1)$ is the special case which we shall use in this chapter. The system of equations (8) is equivalent to the matrix equation

$$\begin{pmatrix} x \\ y \\ 1 \end{pmatrix} = \begin{pmatrix} a_{11}x' + a_{12}y' + a_{13} \\ a_{21}x' + a_{22}y' + a_{23} \\ 1 \end{pmatrix}$$

and since

$$\begin{pmatrix} a_{11} & a_{12} & a_{13} \\ a_{21} & a_{22} & a_{23} \\ 0 & 0 & 1 \end{pmatrix} \begin{pmatrix} x' \\ y' \\ 1 \end{pmatrix} = \begin{pmatrix} a_{11}x' + a_{12}y' + a_{13} \\ a_{21}x' + a_{22}y' + a_{23} \\ 1 \end{pmatrix},$$

the system of equations (8) may be represented by the matrix equation

$$\begin{pmatrix} x \\ y \\ 1 \end{pmatrix} = \begin{pmatrix} a_{11} & a_{12} & a_{13} \\ a_{21} & a_{22} & a_{23} \\ 0 & 0 & 1 \end{pmatrix} \begin{pmatrix} x' \\ y' \\ 1 \end{pmatrix}$$

in terms of the homogeneous coordinates of the points on a plane. Notice that when a triple of numbers such as (6, 2, 1) is given, we must specify whether these are homogeneous coordinates of a point on a coordinate plane or nonhomogeneous coordinates of a point in a coordinate space.

The system of equations (5) is equivalent to the matrix equation

$$\begin{pmatrix} x \\ y \\ 1 \end{pmatrix} = \begin{pmatrix} x' + h \\ y' + k \\ 1 \end{pmatrix}$$

§ 12-8 TRANSLATIONS

and since
$$\begin{pmatrix} 1 & 0 & h \\ 0 & 1 & k \\ 0 & 0 & 1 \end{pmatrix} \begin{pmatrix} x' \\ y' \\ 1 \end{pmatrix} = \begin{pmatrix} x' + h \\ y' + k \\ 1 \end{pmatrix},$$
the system of equations (5) may be represented by the matrix equation
$$\begin{pmatrix} x \\ y \\ 1 \end{pmatrix} = \begin{pmatrix} 1 & 0 & h \\ 0 & 1 & k \\ 0 & 0 & 1 \end{pmatrix} \begin{pmatrix} x' \\ y' \\ 1 \end{pmatrix}$$
in terms of the homogeneous coordinates of the points on a plane. These equations represent the change in the coordinates (x, y) of a point P when the coordinate axes are translated so that the origin is mapped onto (h, k). When we solve for the new coordinates, the matrix equation is
$$\begin{pmatrix} x' \\ y' \\ 1 \end{pmatrix} = \begin{pmatrix} 1 & 0 & -h \\ 0 & 1 & -k \\ 0 & 0 & 1 \end{pmatrix} \begin{pmatrix} x \\ y \\ 1 \end{pmatrix}. \tag{10}$$
Notice that the matrices
$$\begin{pmatrix} 1 & 0 & h \\ 0 & 1 & k \\ 0 & 0 & 1 \end{pmatrix} \text{ and } \begin{pmatrix} 1 & 0 & -h \\ 0 & 1 & -k \\ 0 & 0 & 1 \end{pmatrix}$$
each have determinant 1 and are multiplicative inverses since
$$\begin{pmatrix} 1 & 0 & h \\ 0 & 1 & k \\ 0 & 0 & 1 \end{pmatrix} \begin{pmatrix} 1 & 0 & -h \\ 0 & 1 & -k \\ 0 & 0 & 1 \end{pmatrix} = \begin{pmatrix} 1 & 0 & 0 \\ 0 & 1 & 0 \\ 0 & 0 & 1 \end{pmatrix}.$$

Example 1. Find the new coordinates of $P: (5, 3)$ after a translation of the coordinate axes so that the new origin is at $(2, -5)$ in the original system. Use **(a)** the equations of the translation; **(b)** matrices.

(a) Since the new origin is at $(2, -5)$, $(2, -5) = (h, k)$; $h = 2$, $k = -5$. The equations (5) become
$$\begin{cases} x = x' + 2 \\ y = y' - 5 \end{cases} \text{ and thus } \begin{cases} x' = x - 2 \\ y' = y + 5. \end{cases}$$
Then $P: (5, 3)$ has new coordinates $(5 - 2, 3 + 5)$; that is, $(3, 8)$.

(b) As in (a) we have $h = 2$ and $k = -5$. When $(x, y) = (5, 3)$ in the equation (10), we have
$$\begin{pmatrix} x' \\ y' \\ 1 \end{pmatrix} = \begin{pmatrix} 1 & 0 & -2 \\ 0 & 1 & 5 \\ 0 & 0 & 1 \end{pmatrix} \begin{pmatrix} 5 \\ 3 \\ 1 \end{pmatrix} = \begin{pmatrix} 3 \\ 8 \\ 1 \end{pmatrix}$$
where the new homogeneous coordinates of P are $(3, 8, 1)$ and the new nonhomogeneous coordinates are $(3, 8)$.

THE ALGEBRA OF MATRICES

The system of equations (5) and the equation (10) are both concerned with the new coordinates (x', y') of a point $P: (x, y)$ when the coordinate axes are translated so that the new origin is at (h, k) in the original system. In § 7–6 we observed that any transformation of coordinates might also be visualized as a mapping of points (x, y) onto points (x', y') where (x, y) and (x', y') both refer to the same coordinates axes. The translation which maps each point (x, y) onto a point $(x + h, y + k)$ maps the origin onto (h, k) and has the equation

$$\begin{pmatrix} x' \\ y' \\ 1 \end{pmatrix} = \begin{pmatrix} 1 & 0 & h \\ 0 & 1 & k \\ 0 & 0 & 1 \end{pmatrix} \begin{pmatrix} x \\ y \\ 1 \end{pmatrix}. \tag{11}$$

Notice that the matrix

$$\begin{pmatrix} 1 & 0 & h \\ 0 & 1 & k \\ 0 & 0 & 1 \end{pmatrix}$$

used in this equation is the multiplicative inverse of the matrix used in the equation (10).

The mapping of points (x, y) onto points $(x + h, y + k)$ is a translation of the coordinate plane onto itself such that $(0, 0)$ is mapped onto (h, k). Each point $(x + h, y + k)$ is the **image** of a point (x, y). Whenever we speak of a translation (11) of a plane onto itself (as contrasted with a translation of the coordinate axes), we shall mean a mapping of the form (x, y) onto $(x + h, y + k)$.

Example 2. Find a matrix equation for the mapping of points (x, y) onto points (x', y') under a translation such that the origin is mapped onto $(-3, 7)$.

Since $(0, 0)$ is mapped onto $(-3, 7)$, $h = -3$, $k = 7$, and the matrix equation (11) has the form

$$\begin{pmatrix} x' \\ y' \\ 1 \end{pmatrix} = \begin{pmatrix} 1 & 0 & -3 \\ 0 & 1 & 7 \\ 0 & 0 & 1 \end{pmatrix} \begin{pmatrix} x \\ y \\ 1 \end{pmatrix}.$$

In order to express the system of equations (9) by a matrix equation, we use homogeneous coordinates $(x, y, z, 1)$ instead of the nonhomogeneous coordinates (x, y, z) for points in a coordinate space. The system of equations (9) is equivalent to the matrix equation

$$\begin{pmatrix} x \\ y \\ z \\ 1 \end{pmatrix} = \begin{pmatrix} a_{11} & a_{12} & a_{13} & a_{14} \\ a_{21} & a_{22} & a_{23} & a_{24} \\ a_{31} & a_{32} & a_{33} & a_{34} \\ 0 & 0 & 0 & 1 \end{pmatrix} \begin{pmatrix} x' \\ y' \\ z' \\ 1 \end{pmatrix};$$

the system of equations (6) is equivalent to the matrix equation

$$\begin{pmatrix} x \\ y \\ z \\ 1 \end{pmatrix} = \begin{pmatrix} 1 & 0 & 0 & h \\ 0 & 1 & 0 & k \\ 0 & 0 & 1 & n \\ 0 & 0 & 0 & 1 \end{pmatrix} \begin{pmatrix} x' \\ y' \\ z' \\ 1 \end{pmatrix}$$

in terms of the homogeneous coordinates of points in space. As in the case of a translation on a plane, the matrix of the translation of the points (x, y, z) onto points (x', y', z') such that the origin is mapped onto (h, k, n) is

$$\begin{pmatrix} x' \\ y' \\ z' \\ 1 \end{pmatrix} = \begin{pmatrix} 1 & 0 & 0 & h \\ 0 & 1 & 0 & k \\ 0 & 0 & 1 & n \\ 0 & 0 & 0 & 1 \end{pmatrix} \begin{pmatrix} x \\ y \\ z \\ 1 \end{pmatrix}.$$

When we speak of a translation of coordinate space (as contrasted with coordinate axes), we mean this transformation.

Example 3. Find the image of $P: (2, -3, 4)$ under a translation of the coordinate space so that the origin is mapped onto $(5, 3, -2)$.

The point $P: (2, -3, 4)$ has homogeneous coordinates $(2, -3, 4, 1)$; $(5, 3, -2) = (h, k, n), h = 5, k = 3, n = -2$;

$$\begin{pmatrix} x' \\ y' \\ z' \\ 1 \end{pmatrix} = \begin{pmatrix} 1 & 0 & 0 & 5 \\ 0 & 1 & 0 & 3 \\ 0 & 0 & 1 & -2 \\ 0 & 0 & 0 & 1 \end{pmatrix} \begin{pmatrix} 2 \\ -3 \\ 4 \\ 1 \end{pmatrix} = \begin{pmatrix} 7 \\ 0 \\ 2 \\ 1 \end{pmatrix}$$

The point $P: (2, -3, 4)$ has image point $(7, 0, 2)$.

TEST YOURSELF

1. Find homogeneous coordinates for the points with nonhomogeneous coordinates: (a) $(2, 3)$; (b) $(1, -2)$; (c) $(0, 0)$.
2. Find nonhomogeneous coordinates for the points with homogeneous coordinates: (a) $(4, 1, 1)$; (b) $(3, -2, 1)$; (c) $(0, 1, 1)$.
3. Find homogeneous coordinates for the points with nonhomogeneous coordinates: (a) $(1, 0, 3)$; (b) $(2, 4, 0)$; (c) $(0, 1, 1)$.
4. Find nonhomogeneous coordinates for the points with homogeneous coordinates: (a) $(1, 2, 3, 1)$; (b) $(0, 1, 1, 1)$; (c) $(0, 0, 3, 1)$.
5. Find a matrix equation for a translation of the coordinate plane onto itself such that the origin is mapped onto $(-2, 4)$.
6. Find the image of $(1, 5)$ under the translation in Exercise 5.

THE ALGEBRA OF MATRICES

ORAL EXERCISES

Find homogeneous coordinates for the points with nonhomogeneous coordinates:

1. (3, 7).
2. (2, 6).
3. (−2, 0).
4. (0, 3).
5. (−5, 11).
6. (−1, 1).
7. (2, 3, 5).
8. (1, 0, 2).
9. (−1, 2, 1).
10. (5, −2, −1).
11. (2, 0, 0).
12. (0, −5, 0).

Find nonhomogeneous coordinates for the points with homogeneous coordinates:

13. (2, 0, 1).
14. (1, 1, 1).
15. (5, 2, 1).
16. (−1, 2, 1).
17. (−2, −7, 1).
18. (0, 0, 1).
19. (2, 5, −1, 1).
20. (1, 0, 0, 1).
21. (0, 0, 2, 1).
22. (1, −5, −3, 1).
23. (−2, 1, 5, 1).
24. (−2, −3, 1, 1).

EXERCISES

Find a matrix equation for a translation of the coordinate plane onto itself such that the origin is mapped onto:

1. (5, 2).
2. (−3, 1).
3. (2, −7).

Find the image of each point under the translation in **(a)** *Exercise 1;* **(b)** *Exercise 2;* **(c)** *Exercise 3:*

4. (1, 3).
5. (−3, 2).
6. (−6, −1).

Use a matrix equation to find the image point of P: (−2, 3, 7) under a translation of coordinate space so that the origin is mapped onto:

7. (1, 3, 0).
8. (−2, 5, 1).
9. (2, −3, −7).

• • •

In Exercises 10 through 13 prove that:

10. The product of any two matrices for translations of a coordinate plane onto itself is a matrix for a translation.

11. The multiplication of two matrices for translations of a coordinate plane onto itself is commutative.

12. The multiplication of matrices for translations of a coordinate plane onto itself is associative.

13. The set of matrices for translations of a coordinate plane onto itself forms a commutative group under matrix multiplication.

14. Determine a matrix equation for the translation of a coordinate plane onto itself such that: (a) (2, 5) is mapped onto (6, 8); (b) (1, −2) is mapped onto (−3, 4); (c) (−2, 5) is mapped onto (6, −1).
• 15. Any geometric property that is not altered by a particular transformation is said to be *invariant* with respect to that transformation. Prove that the distance between two points on a coordinate plane is invariant under any translation of the plane onto itself.

§ 12-9 Rotations

A rotation about the origin through an angle θ of the x- and y-axes on a coordinate plane was used in § 7-6 to assign coordinates (x', y') to each point (x, y) where

$$\begin{cases} x' = x \cos \theta + y \sin \theta \\ y' = -x \sin \theta + y \cos \theta; \end{cases}$$

that is,

$$\begin{pmatrix} x' \\ y' \\ 1 \end{pmatrix} = \begin{pmatrix} \cos \theta & \sin \theta & 0 \\ -\sin \theta & \cos \theta & 0 \\ 0 & 0 & 1 \end{pmatrix} \begin{pmatrix} x \\ y \\ 1 \end{pmatrix}. \tag{12}$$

This is the matrix equation for the change of the coordinates of each point (x, y) when the coordinate axes are rotated about the origin through an angle θ.

Example 1. Determine the new coordinates of the point $P: (5, \sqrt{3})$ if the axes are rotated 60° about the origin.

Since the angle of rotation θ is 60°, $\sin \theta = \dfrac{\sqrt{3}}{2}$ and $\cos \theta = \dfrac{1}{2}$.

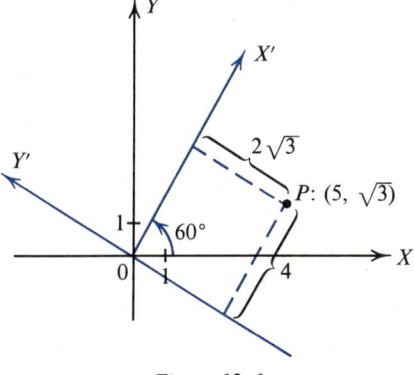

Figure 12-1

THE ALGEBRA OF MATRICES

The matrix equation (12) becomes

$$\begin{pmatrix} x' \\ y' \\ 1 \end{pmatrix} = \begin{pmatrix} \frac{1}{2} & \frac{\sqrt{3}}{2} & 0 \\ -\frac{\sqrt{3}}{2} & \frac{1}{2} & 0 \\ 0 & 0 & 1 \end{pmatrix} \begin{pmatrix} x \\ y \\ 1 \end{pmatrix}$$

and the image of $(5, \sqrt{3})$ is $(4, -2\sqrt{3})$ since

$$\begin{pmatrix} x' \\ y' \\ 1 \end{pmatrix} = \begin{pmatrix} \frac{1}{2} & \frac{\sqrt{3}}{2} & 0 \\ -\frac{\sqrt{3}}{2} & \frac{1}{2} & 0 \\ 0 & 0 & 1 \end{pmatrix} \begin{pmatrix} 5 \\ \sqrt{3} \\ 1 \end{pmatrix} = \begin{pmatrix} 4 \\ -2\sqrt{3} \\ 1 \end{pmatrix}.$$

The equation (12) may be solved for (x, y) as in § 12–6 by premultiplying both members of the equation by the inverse of the matrix for a rotation of the coordinate axes about the origin through an angle θ; that is, by the matrix for a rotation through an angle $-\theta$:

$$\begin{pmatrix} \cos(-\theta) & \sin(-\theta) & 0 \\ -\sin(-\theta) & \cos(-\theta) & 0 \\ 0 & 0 & 1 \end{pmatrix} \begin{pmatrix} \cos\theta & \sin\theta & 0 \\ -\sin\theta & \cos\theta & 0 \\ 0 & 0 & 1 \end{pmatrix} = \begin{pmatrix} 1 & 0 & 0 \\ 0 & 1 & 0 \\ 0 & 0 & 1 \end{pmatrix}.$$

Since $\cos(-\theta) = \cos\theta$, $\sin(-\theta) = -\sin\theta$, and $\sin^2\theta + \cos^2\theta = 1$, we have

$$\begin{pmatrix} x \\ y \\ 1 \end{pmatrix} = \begin{pmatrix} \cos\theta & -\sin\theta & 0 \\ \sin\theta & \cos\theta & 0 \\ 0 & 0 & 1 \end{pmatrix} \begin{pmatrix} x' \\ y' \\ 1 \end{pmatrix}. \qquad (13)$$

Example 2. Find the new equation of the line $\sqrt{2}x + \sqrt{2}y + 5 = 0$ if the axes are rotated $45°$ about the origin.

Since the angle of rotation θ is $45°$, $\sin\theta = \frac{\sqrt{2}}{2}$ and $\cos\theta = \frac{\sqrt{2}}{2}$.

The matrix equation (13) becomes

$$\begin{pmatrix} x \\ y \\ 1 \end{pmatrix} = \begin{pmatrix} \frac{\sqrt{2}}{2} & -\frac{\sqrt{2}}{2} & 0 \\ \frac{\sqrt{2}}{2} & \frac{\sqrt{2}}{2} & 0 \\ 0 & 0 & 1 \end{pmatrix} \begin{pmatrix} x' \\ y' \\ 1 \end{pmatrix};$$

§ 12-9 ROTATIONS

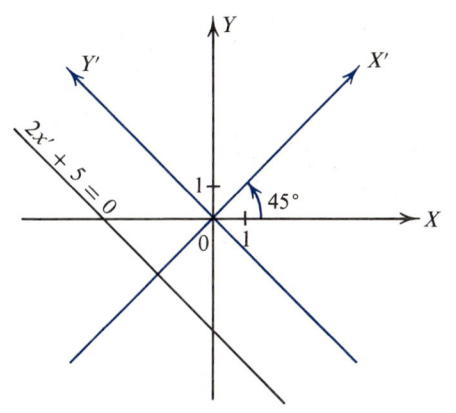

Figure 12-2

$$x = \frac{\sqrt{2}}{2}x' - \frac{\sqrt{2}}{2}y'; \quad y = \frac{\sqrt{2}}{2}x' + \frac{\sqrt{2}}{2}y';$$

and the given equation

$$\sqrt{2}x + \sqrt{2}y + 5 = 0$$

becomes

$$\sqrt{2}\left(\frac{\sqrt{2}}{2}x' - \frac{\sqrt{2}}{2}y'\right) + \sqrt{2}\left(\frac{\sqrt{2}}{2}x' + \frac{\sqrt{2}}{2}y'\right) + 5 = 0$$
$$x' - y' + x' + y' + 5 = 0$$
$$2x' + 5 = 0.$$

The equations (12) and (13) are both concerned with the new coordinates (x', y') of a point $P: (x, y)$ when the coordinate axes are rotated about the origin through an angle θ. We are also concerned with rotations which map points (x, y) onto points (x', y') under a rotation of the plane about the origin through an angle θ. As in the case of translations, the matrix equation for this rotation of the coordinate plane involves the multiplicative inverse of the matrix used in the equation (12). Thus the equation is

$$\begin{pmatrix} x' \\ y' \\ 1 \end{pmatrix} = \begin{pmatrix} \cos\theta & -\sin\theta & 0 \\ \sin\theta & \cos\theta & 0 \\ 0 & 0 & 1 \end{pmatrix} \begin{pmatrix} x \\ y \\ 1 \end{pmatrix}. \qquad (14)$$

Whenever we speak of a rotation of the plane (as contrasted with a rotation of the coordinate axes) about the origin, we shall mean a transformation of this type.

THE ALGEBRA OF MATRICES

Under the rotation of the plane (14) the origin (0, 0) corresponds to itself. Any point which corresponds to itself under a transformation is called a **fixed point** of the transformation. Notice that under a translation (10) in which $(h, k) \neq (0, 0)$ there are no fixed points; that is, each point (x, y) is mapped into a different point.

If a translation T_1 is followed by a translation T_2, the result is a translation (Exercise 10 of § 12–8).

If a rotation R_1 of points (x, y) about the origin is followed by a rotation R_2 of points about the origin, the result is a rotation of points about the origin:

$$\begin{pmatrix} x' \\ y' \\ 1 \end{pmatrix} = \begin{pmatrix} \cos \theta_1 & -\sin \theta_1 & 0 \\ \sin \theta_1 & \cos \theta_1 & 0 \\ 0 & 0 & 1 \end{pmatrix} \begin{pmatrix} x \\ y \\ 1 \end{pmatrix}$$

$$\begin{pmatrix} x'' \\ y'' \\ 1 \end{pmatrix} = \begin{pmatrix} \cos \theta_2 & -\sin \theta_2 & 0 \\ \sin \theta_2 & \cos \theta_2 & 0 \\ 0 & 0 & 1 \end{pmatrix} \begin{pmatrix} x' \\ y' \\ 1 \end{pmatrix}$$

$$\begin{pmatrix} x'' \\ y'' \\ 1 \end{pmatrix} = \begin{pmatrix} \cos \theta_2 & -\sin \theta_2 & 0 \\ \sin \theta_2 & \cos \theta_2 & 0 \\ 0 & 0 & 1 \end{pmatrix} \begin{pmatrix} \cos \theta_1 & -\sin \theta_1 & 0 \\ \sin \theta_1 & \cos \theta^1 & 0 \\ 0 & 0 & 1 \end{pmatrix} \begin{pmatrix} x \\ y \\ 1 \end{pmatrix}$$

$$\begin{pmatrix} x'' \\ y'' \\ 1 \end{pmatrix} = \begin{pmatrix} \cos (\theta_2 + \theta_1) & -\sin (\theta_2 + \theta_1) & 0 \\ \sin (\theta_2 + \theta_1) & \cos (\theta_2 + \theta_1) & 0 \\ 0 & 0 & 1 \end{pmatrix} \begin{pmatrix} x \\ y \\ 1 \end{pmatrix}.$$

Consider the result of following a rotation of points (x, y) about the origin by a translation of these points:

$$\begin{pmatrix} x' \\ y' \\ 1 \end{pmatrix} = \begin{pmatrix} \cos \theta & -\sin \theta & 0 \\ \sin \theta & \cos \theta & 0 \\ 0 & 0 & 1 \end{pmatrix} \begin{pmatrix} x \\ y \\ 1 \end{pmatrix}$$

$$\begin{pmatrix} x'' \\ y'' \\ 1 \end{pmatrix} = \begin{pmatrix} 1 & 0 & h \\ 0 & 1 & k \\ 0 & 0 & 1 \end{pmatrix} \begin{pmatrix} x' \\ y' \\ 1 \end{pmatrix}$$

$$\begin{pmatrix} x'' \\ y'' \\ 1 \end{pmatrix} = \begin{pmatrix} 1 & 0 & h \\ 0 & 1 & k \\ 0 & 0 & 1 \end{pmatrix} \begin{pmatrix} \cos \theta & -\sin \theta & 0 \\ \sin \theta & \cos \theta & 0 \\ 0 & 0 & 1 \end{pmatrix} \begin{pmatrix} x \\ y \\ 1 \end{pmatrix}$$

$$\begin{pmatrix} x'' \\ y'' \\ 1 \end{pmatrix} = \begin{pmatrix} \cos \theta & -\sin \theta & h \\ \sin \theta & \cos \theta & k \\ 0 & 0 & 1 \end{pmatrix} \begin{pmatrix} x \\ y \\ 1 \end{pmatrix} \quad (15)$$

$$\begin{cases} x'' = x \cos \theta - y \sin \theta + h \\ y'' = x \sin \theta + y \cos \theta + k. \end{cases}$$

§ 12-9 ROTATIONS

The transformation (15) of points (x, y) is neither a translation nor a rotation; it is a special case of the set of rigid motions (§ 12–10). Notice that in all three of the cases we have just considered, products of matrices may be used to find a matrix for the transformation obtained by following one transformation with another. In each case if a transformation T_1 of points is followed by a transformation T_2 of points, the matrices are multiplied in the order $T_2 T_1$.

In § 12–8 we considered matrices (10) for a translation of the coordinate axes and also matrices (11) for a translation of the points of a coordinate plane with reference to a given set of axes. In this section we have considered matrices (12) for the rotation of the coordinate axes about the origin and also matrices (14) for the rotation of the points of the plane about the origin. We now consider examples of these cases being careful to distinguish between transformations of the coordinate system and transformations of the plane onto itself with reference to a fixed coordinate system.

Example 3. Find a matrix equation for the transformation obtained by rotating the coordinate axes 90° about the origin and then translating the x'- and y'-axes so that $(0, 0)$ is mapped onto $(0, 3)$ with reference to the x'- and y'-axes.

Since the angle of rotation is 90°, $\sin \theta = 1$ and $\cos \theta = 0$. The matrix equation (12) becomes

$$\begin{pmatrix} x' \\ y' \\ 1 \end{pmatrix} = \begin{pmatrix} 0 & 1 & 0 \\ -1 & 0 & 0 \\ 0 & 0 & 1 \end{pmatrix} \begin{pmatrix} x \\ y \\ 1 \end{pmatrix}.$$

Since $(0, 0)$ is to be mapped onto $(0, 3)$ in the $x'y'$-plane,

$$\begin{pmatrix} x'' \\ y'' \\ 1 \end{pmatrix} = \begin{pmatrix} 1 & 0 & 0 \\ 0 & 1 & -3 \\ 0 & 0 & 1 \end{pmatrix} \begin{pmatrix} x' \\ y' \\ 1 \end{pmatrix}$$

as in § 12–8. Then

$$\begin{pmatrix} x'' \\ y'' \\ 1 \end{pmatrix} = \begin{pmatrix} 1 & 0 & 0 \\ 0 & 1 & -3 \\ 0 & 0 & 1 \end{pmatrix} \begin{pmatrix} 0 & 1 & 0 \\ -1 & 0 & 0 \\ 0 & 0 & 1 \end{pmatrix} \begin{pmatrix} x \\ y \\ 1 \end{pmatrix}$$

$$\begin{pmatrix} x'' \\ y'' \\ 1 \end{pmatrix} = \begin{pmatrix} 0 & 1 & 0 \\ -1 & 0 & -3 \\ 0 & 0 & 1 \end{pmatrix} \begin{pmatrix} x \\ y \\ 1 \end{pmatrix}.$$

THE ALGEBRA OF MATRICES

Example 4. Find a matrix equation for the transformation obtained by translating the coordinate axes so that (0, 0) is mapped onto (0, 3) and then rotating the x'- and y'-axes 90° about their origin.

The matrices for the transformations are the same as in Example 3. The matrix equations of the transformations are:

$$\begin{pmatrix} x' \\ y' \\ 1 \end{pmatrix} = \begin{pmatrix} 1 & 0 & 0 \\ 0 & 1 & -3 \\ 0 & 0 & 1 \end{pmatrix} \begin{pmatrix} x \\ y \\ 1 \end{pmatrix}$$

$$\begin{pmatrix} x'' \\ y'' \\ 1 \end{pmatrix} = \begin{pmatrix} 0 & 1 & 0 \\ -1 & 0 & 0 \\ 0 & 0 & 1 \end{pmatrix} \begin{pmatrix} x' \\ y' \\ 1 \end{pmatrix}$$

$$\begin{pmatrix} x'' \\ y'' \\ 1 \end{pmatrix} = \begin{pmatrix} 0 & 1 & 0 \\ -1 & 0 & 0 \\ 0 & 0 & 1 \end{pmatrix} \begin{pmatrix} 1 & 0 & 0 \\ 0 & 1 & -3 \\ 0 & 0 & 1 \end{pmatrix} \begin{pmatrix} x \\ y \\ 1 \end{pmatrix}$$

$$\begin{pmatrix} x'' \\ y'' \\ 1 \end{pmatrix} = \begin{pmatrix} 0 & 1 & -3 \\ -1 & 0 & 0 \\ 0 & 0 & 1 \end{pmatrix} \begin{pmatrix} x \\ y \\ 1 \end{pmatrix}.$$

The multiplication of matrices is in general not commutative and the result obtained in Example 3

$$\begin{cases} x'' = y \\ y'' = -x - 3 \end{cases}$$

is different from the result obtained in Example 4

$$\begin{cases} x'' = y - 3 \\ y'' = -x. \end{cases}$$

This difference can be explained by considering the transformation with respect to the original coordinate axes in each case. In Example 3 the point (0, 3) with reference to the x'- and y'-axes has coordinates $(-3, 0)$ with reference to the x- and y-axes. Thus in Example 3 a 90° rotation of the axes about (0, 0) was followed by a translation of the axes so that (0, 0) was mapped onto $(-3, 0)$ with reference to the x- and y-axes. In Example 4 the origin of the x'- and y'-axes has coordinates (0, 3) with reference to the x- and y-axes. Thus in Example 4 a translation so that (0, 0) was mapped onto (0, 3) was followed by a 90° rotation of the axes about the point with coordinates (0, 3) with reference to the x- and y-axes. Notice that Example 4 provides an illustration of rotating the coordinate axes about a point (r, s) which is different from the origin: first translate the coordinate axes so that (0, 0) is mapped onto (r, s); then rotate the coordinate axes about the new origin.

§ 12–9 ROTATIONS

TEST YOURSELF

Use the matrix equation of the transformation to determine the new coordinates of the given point if the axes are rotated about the origin through an angle θ:

1. $P: (2, \sqrt{3}); \theta = 30°$. **2.** $P: (\sqrt{3}, -1); \theta = -60°$.

Find the matrix of the transformation obtained when:

3. The transformation in Exercise 1 is followed by the transformation in Exercise 2.

4. The transformation in Exercise 2 is followed by a translation which maps the origin onto the point with coordinates (1, 3) with reference to the x'- and y'-axes.

EXERCISES

Use the matrix equation of the transformation to determine the new coordinates of the given point if the axes are rotated about the origin through an angle θ:

1. $P: (3, -2); \theta = 270°$. **3.** $P: (\sqrt{3}, 1); \theta = 60°$.
2. $P: (1, 1); \theta = 45°$. **4.** $P: (1, 2); \theta = -210°$.

In Exercises 5 through 8 find the matrix of the transformation obtained when:

5. The transformation in Exercise 1 is followed by the transformation in Exercise 3.

6. The transformation in Exercise 1 is followed by the transformation in Exercise 4.

7. The transformation in Exercise 2 is followed by a translation of the axes which maps the origin onto the point with coordinates $(2, -3)$ with reference to the x'- and y'-axes.

8. A translation of the axes which maps the origin onto (3, 5) is followed by the transformation in Exercise 3 with reference to the x'- and y'-axes.

• • •

9. Determine whether or not the matrix on the right may represent a rotation of the coordinate axes about the origin. Explain your answer.

$$\begin{pmatrix} \dfrac{1}{\sqrt{2}} & -\dfrac{1}{\sqrt{2}} & 0 \\ -\dfrac{1}{\sqrt{2}} & \dfrac{1}{\sqrt{2}} & 0 \\ 0 & 0 & 1 \end{pmatrix}$$

THE ALGEBRA OF MATRICES

10. Find the new coordinates of the point (3, 4) if the coordinate axes are translated so that the origin is mapped onto the point with coordinates (2, −3) and this transformation is followed by a 60° rotation of the new axes about their origin.

11. Find the new coordinates of the point (3, 4) if the coordinate axes are rotated 60° about the origin and then the x'- and y'-axes are translated so that their origin is mapped onto the point with coordinates (2, −3) with reference to the x'- and y'-axes.

12. Prove that multiplication of matrices for rotations of a coordinate plane about the origin is **(a)** commutative; **(b)** associative.

13. Prove that the set of matrices for rotations of a coordinate plane about the origin forms a commutative group under matrix multiplication.

• **14.** Determine a matrix equation for a transformation of the coordinate plane onto itself such that the point (5, 2) is mapped onto (−2, 5) and the point (3, −1) is mapped onto (1, 3).

• **15.** Prove that the distance between two points on a coordinate plane is invariant under any rotation of the plane about the origin.

§ 12–10 Rigid motions and dilations

Translations (§ 12–8) and rotations (§ 12–9) are special cases of *rigid motions,* that is, transformations of the coordinate plane (or space) onto itself which preserve lengths of line segments and measures of angles. If two plane figures correspond under a rigid motion, then they are congruent; that is, the lengths of corresponding line segments are equal, corresponding angles are equal, and the areas of corresponding regions of the figures are equal. If two space figures correspond under rigid motion, then they are congruent; that is, corresponding line segments, plane angles and dihedral angles taken in the same order, areas of regions, and volumes are equal. Briefly, two figures correspond under a rigid motion if and only if they have the same size and shape. Euclidean geometry is often defined as the study of properties which remain **invariant** (unchanged) when figures correspond under rigid motions.

Any point (x, y) is symmetric to $(x, -y)$ with respect to the x-axis. The transformation of the xy-plane onto itself such that each point (x, y) corresponds to the point $(x, -y)$ is a **reflection** in the x-axis, has equations

$$\begin{cases} x' = x \\ y' = -y, \end{cases}$$

and has matrix equation

$$\begin{pmatrix} x' \\ y' \\ 1 \end{pmatrix} = \begin{pmatrix} 1 & 0 & 0 \\ 0 & -1 & 0 \\ 0 & 0 & 1 \end{pmatrix} \begin{pmatrix} x \\ y \\ 1 \end{pmatrix}. \tag{16}$$

§ 12-10   RIGID MOTIONS AND DILATIONS

The equations $\begin{cases} x' = -x \\ y' = y \end{cases}$ of a reflection in the y-axis may be obtained by rotating the coordinate axes 90° about the origin so that the x'-axis corresponds to the y-axis, reflecting in the x'-axis, and then rotating the coordinate axes back to their original position so that the new coordinates are expressed in the same system as the given coordinates. Any point (x, y) is symmetric to (−x, y) with respect to the y-axis. Thus the equations of a reflection of the coordinate plane in the y-axis are

$$\begin{cases} x' = -x \\ y' = y \end{cases}$$

and the matrix equation is

$$\begin{pmatrix} x' \\ y' \\ 1 \end{pmatrix} = \begin{pmatrix} -1 & 0 & 0 \\ 0 & 1 & 0 \\ 0 & 0 & 1 \end{pmatrix} \begin{pmatrix} x \\ y \\ 1 \end{pmatrix}. \tag{17}$$

We may rotate the x- and y-axes 90° about the origin using the matrix equation (12) from § 12–9 with $\theta = 90°$, $\sin \theta = 1$, $\cos \theta = 0$;

$$\begin{pmatrix} x' \\ y' \\ 1 \end{pmatrix} = \begin{pmatrix} 0 & 1 & 0 \\ -1 & 0 & 0 \\ 0 & 0 & 1 \end{pmatrix} \begin{pmatrix} x \\ y \\ 1 \end{pmatrix}.$$

Then we use the equation (16) to reflect the x'y'-plane in the x'-axis;

$$\begin{pmatrix} x'' \\ y'' \\ 1 \end{pmatrix} = \begin{pmatrix} 1 & 0 & 0 \\ 0 & -1 & 0 \\ 0 & 0 & 1 \end{pmatrix} \begin{pmatrix} x' \\ y' \\ 1 \end{pmatrix}$$

$$= \begin{pmatrix} 1 & 0 & 0 \\ 0 & -1 & 0 \\ 0 & 0 & 1 \end{pmatrix} \begin{pmatrix} 0 & 1 & 0 \\ -1 & 0 & 0 \\ 0 & 0 & 1 \end{pmatrix} \begin{pmatrix} x \\ y \\ 1 \end{pmatrix} = \begin{pmatrix} 0 & 1 & 0 \\ 1 & 0 & 0 \\ 0 & 0 & 1 \end{pmatrix} \begin{pmatrix} x \\ y \\ 1 \end{pmatrix}.$$

Finally, we rotate the x'- and y'-axes −90° about the origin using the equation (12) with $\theta = -90°$, $\sin \theta = -1$, $\cos \theta = 0$;

$$\begin{pmatrix} x''' \\ y''' \\ 1 \end{pmatrix} = \begin{pmatrix} 0 & -1 & 0 \\ 1 & 0 & 0 \\ 0 & 0 & 1 \end{pmatrix} \begin{pmatrix} x'' \\ y'' \\ 1 \end{pmatrix}$$

$$= \begin{pmatrix} 0 & -1 & 0 \\ 1 & 0 & 0 \\ 0 & 0 & 1 \end{pmatrix} \begin{pmatrix} 0 & 1 & 0 \\ 1 & 0 & 0 \\ 0 & 0 & 1 \end{pmatrix} \begin{pmatrix} x \\ y \\ 1 \end{pmatrix} = \begin{pmatrix} -1 & 0 & 0 \\ 0 & 1 & 0 \\ 0 & 0 & 1 \end{pmatrix} \begin{pmatrix} x \\ y \\ 1 \end{pmatrix}.$$

This result is consistent with the equation (17). In general, if A is the matrix of the transformation of the x-axis onto the line t, R is the matrix for a reflection in the x-axis, and X is a one-column matrix for a point;

THE ALGEBRA OF MATRICES

then a reflection in the line t may be expressed in the form

$$X' = (A^{-1}RA)X. \tag{18}$$

Consider the line $y = x$. The mapping of (x, y) onto (y, x) with equation

$$\begin{pmatrix} x' \\ y' \\ 1 \end{pmatrix} = \begin{pmatrix} 0 & 1 & 0 \\ 1 & 0 & 0 \\ 0 & 0 & 1 \end{pmatrix} \begin{pmatrix} x \\ y \\ 1 \end{pmatrix} \tag{19}$$

is a reflection in the line $y = x$. However, let us test our general theory:

$$X = \begin{pmatrix} x \\ y \\ 1 \end{pmatrix}; \quad R = \begin{pmatrix} 1 & 0 & 0 \\ 0 & -1 & 0 \\ 0 & 0 & 1 \end{pmatrix}$$

from (16); A represents a rotation of the coordinate axes about the origin through $45°$, $\sin 45° = \frac{\sqrt{2}}{2}$, $\cos 45° = \frac{\sqrt{2}}{2}$, and from the equation (12) in § 12–9

$$A = \begin{pmatrix} \frac{\sqrt{2}}{2} & \frac{\sqrt{2}}{2} & 0 \\ -\frac{\sqrt{2}}{2} & \frac{\sqrt{2}}{2} & 0 \\ 0 & 0 & 1 \end{pmatrix};$$

A^{-1} represents a rotation of the coordinate axes about the origin through $-45°$, $\sin(-45°) = -\frac{\sqrt{2}}{2}$, $\cos(-45°) = \frac{\sqrt{2}}{2}$,

$$A^{-1} = \begin{pmatrix} \frac{\sqrt{2}}{2} & -\frac{\sqrt{2}}{2} & 0 \\ \frac{\sqrt{2}}{2} & \frac{\sqrt{2}}{2} & 0 \\ 0 & 0 & 1 \end{pmatrix}.$$

The equation (18) may be expressed using the associative property of matrix multiplication as

$$\begin{pmatrix} x' \\ y' \\ 1 \end{pmatrix} = \begin{pmatrix} \frac{\sqrt{2}}{2} & -\frac{\sqrt{2}}{2} & 0 \\ \frac{\sqrt{2}}{2} & \frac{\sqrt{2}}{2} & 0 \\ 0 & 0 & 1 \end{pmatrix} \begin{pmatrix} 1 & 0 & 0 \\ 0 & -1 & 0 \\ 0 & 0 & 1 \end{pmatrix} \begin{pmatrix} \frac{\sqrt{2}}{2} & \frac{\sqrt{2}}{2} & 0 \\ -\frac{\sqrt{2}}{2} & \frac{\sqrt{2}}{2} & 0 \\ 0 & 0 & 1 \end{pmatrix} \begin{pmatrix} x \\ y \\ 1 \end{pmatrix}$$

§ 12–10 RIGID MOTIONS AND DILATIONS

$$\begin{pmatrix} x' \\ y' \\ 1 \end{pmatrix} = \begin{pmatrix} \frac{\sqrt{2}}{2} & \frac{\sqrt{2}}{2} & 0 \\ \frac{\sqrt{2}}{2} & -\frac{\sqrt{2}}{2} & 0 \\ 0 & 0 & 1 \end{pmatrix} \begin{pmatrix} \frac{\sqrt{2}}{2} & \frac{\sqrt{2}}{2} & 0 \\ -\frac{\sqrt{2}}{2} & \frac{\sqrt{2}}{2} & 0 \\ 0 & 0 & 1 \end{pmatrix} \begin{pmatrix} x \\ y \\ 1 \end{pmatrix}$$

$$\begin{pmatrix} x' \\ y' \\ 1 \end{pmatrix} = \begin{pmatrix} 0 & 1 & 0 \\ 1 & 0 & 0 \\ 0 & 0 & 1 \end{pmatrix} \begin{pmatrix} x \\ y \\ 1 \end{pmatrix}$$

which is consistent with the equation (19).

In general, any line t on a coordinate plane either has an equation of the form $x = c$ or has an equation of the form $y = mx + b$. If the line t has an equation of the form $x = c$, we may transform the coordinate axes so that the x'-axis coincides with the line t by translating the axes so that the origin is mapped onto $(c, 0)$ and then rotating the coordinate axes about the new origin through 90°. If the line t has an equation of the form $y = mx + b$, we may transform the coordinate axes so that the x'-axis coincides with the line t by translating the axes so that the origin is mapped onto $(0, b)$ and then rotating the coordinate axes about the new origin through an angle θ where $\tan \theta = m$; that is, use $\sin \theta = \dfrac{m}{\sqrt{1 + m^2}}$ and $\cos \theta = \dfrac{1}{\sqrt{1 + m^2}}$. Thus translations (§ 12–8) and rotations (§ 12–9) may be used to transform the coordinate axes so that the x'-axis coincides with any given line t. Then the transformation (16) may be used to reflect the plane in the x'-axis, and the x'- and y'-axes may be transformed into the x- and y-axes. This process is summarized in the equation (18) and may be used to obtain a matrix equation for the reflection of the coordinate plane in any given line t.

It is interesting to note, although the proof will be left for more advanced courses, that the result of reflecting the coordinate plane in each of two lines which intersect at a point Q and form an angle θ is a rotation of the plane about the point Q through an angle 2θ; the result of reflecting the coordinate plane in a line t and then in a line m which is parallel to t and at a distance d from t is a translation of the coordinate plane a distance $2d$ in a direction from t to m and perpendicular to t.

The set of **rigid motions** may be defined as the set of reflections, rotations, and translations of a plane onto itself.

The transformation of the coordinate plane onto itself such that

$$\begin{cases} x' = 2x \\ y' = 2y \end{cases}$$

717

THE ALGEBRA OF MATRICES

maps each point $P: (x, y)$ onto a point $P': (2x, 2y)$ such that $\overrightarrow{OP'} = 2\overrightarrow{OP}$. In a sense the transformation *dilates* the plane about the origin. For any real number $k \neq 1$ the matrix equation

$$\begin{pmatrix} x' \\ y' \\ 1 \end{pmatrix} = \begin{pmatrix} k & 0 & 0 \\ 0 & k & 0 \\ 0 & 0 & 1 \end{pmatrix} \begin{pmatrix} x \\ y \\ 1 \end{pmatrix} \qquad (20)$$

represents a **dilation** of the plane about the origin. Each point P is mapped onto a point P' such that $\overrightarrow{OP'} = k\overrightarrow{OP}$. If $|k| > 1$, the dilation represents a "stretching"; if $0 < |k| < 1$, the dilation represents a "compression." If $k = -1$, the dilation is a reflection in the origin. If $k < 0$, the "stretching" or "compression" is followed by a reflection in the origin. Dilations are very important in several areas of mathematics including the study of statistics and are often called **stretching transformations.**

Example 1. Describe the effect of the dilation $\begin{pmatrix} 2 & 0 & 0 \\ 0 & 2 & 0 \\ 0 & 0 & 1 \end{pmatrix}$

(a) upon the circle $x^2 + y^2 = 16$;

(b) upon the xy-plane.

The dilation may be expressed as

$$\begin{pmatrix} x' \\ y' \\ 1 \end{pmatrix} = \begin{pmatrix} 2 & 0 & 0 \\ 0 & 2 & 0 \\ 0 & 0 & 1 \end{pmatrix} \begin{pmatrix} x \\ y \\ 1 \end{pmatrix};$$

that is, $x' = 2x$ and $y' = 2y$. Then $x = \dfrac{x'}{2}$ and $y = \dfrac{y'}{2}$.

(a) The circle $x^2 + y^2 = 16$ is transformed into the circle $\dfrac{x'^2}{4} + \dfrac{y'^2}{4} = 16$; that is, $x^2 + y^2 = 64$, the circle with center at the origin and radius 8.

(b) Each point (x, y) is mapped onto the point $(2x, 2y)$; that is, each point P is mapped onto a point P' such that $\overrightarrow{OP'} = 2\overrightarrow{OP}$.

In general, each dilation (20) maps each point P onto a point P' such that $\overrightarrow{OP'} = k\overrightarrow{OP}$; maps line segments AB onto line segments $A'B'$ such that $\overline{A'B'} = |k|\overline{AB}$; maps triangles ABC onto similar triangles $A'B'C'$ with ratio of similitude $|k|$; and, indeed, maps all geometric figures onto similar geometric figures with ratio of similitude $|k|$. Thus lengths of line segments are multiplied by $|k|$, and areas are multiplied by k^2. Dilations and rigid motions are used in the study of similar and congruent figures in geometry. The dilations preserve the shapes of figures; the rigid motions preserve the shapes and sizes of figures.

There are also other types of transformations of the coordinate plane onto itself which may be represented by matrices and which have many applications in mathematics. One specific type is considered in Example 2; several others are considered in the exercises.

Example 2. Describe the effect of the transformation $\begin{pmatrix} 3 & 0 & 0 \\ 0 & 1 & 0 \\ 0 & 0 & 1 \end{pmatrix}$ upon the circle $x^2 + y^2 = 16$.

The transformation may be expressed as

$$\begin{pmatrix} x' \\ y' \\ 1 \end{pmatrix} = \begin{pmatrix} 3 & 0 & 0 \\ 0 & 1 & 0 \\ 0 & 0 & 1 \end{pmatrix} \begin{pmatrix} x \\ y \\ 1 \end{pmatrix};$$

that is, $x' = 3x$ and $y' = y$. Then $x = \frac{x'}{3}$, $y = y'$, and the circle $x^2 + y^2 = 16$ is transformed into the ellipse $\frac{x'^2}{9} + y'^2 = 16$; that is, $\frac{x^2}{144} + \frac{y^2}{16} = 1$.

TEST YOURSELF

In Exercises 1 and 2 describe the effect upon the coordinate plane of the transformation of the plane onto itself with the given matrix:

1. $\begin{pmatrix} -1 & 0 & 0 \\ 0 & -1 & 0 \\ 0 & 0 & 1 \end{pmatrix}$.   2. $\begin{pmatrix} 0 & 2 & 0 \\ 2 & 0 & 0 \\ 0 & 0 & 1 \end{pmatrix}$.

3. Describe the effect upon the locus $3x + 2y = 6$ of the transformation $\begin{pmatrix} 3 & 0 & 0 \\ 0 & 3 & 0 \\ 0 & 0 & 1 \end{pmatrix}$.

4. Prove that the product of a reflection in the x-axis and a reflection in the y-axis is a rotation of the plane 180° about the origin.

THE ALGEBRA OF MATRICES

EXERCISES

Describe the effect upon the coordinate plane of the transformation of the plane onto itself with the given matrix:

1. $\begin{pmatrix} 4 & 0 & 0 \\ 0 & 4 & 0 \\ 0 & 0 & 1 \end{pmatrix}$.

2. $\begin{pmatrix} -3 & 0 & 0 \\ 0 & -3 & 0 \\ 0 & 0 & 1 \end{pmatrix}$.

3. $\begin{pmatrix} 2 & 0 & 0 \\ 0 & -2 & 0 \\ 0 & 0 & 1 \end{pmatrix}$.

4. $\begin{pmatrix} 1 & -1 & 0 \\ -1 & 0 & 0 \\ 0 & 0 & 1 \end{pmatrix}$.

5. $\begin{pmatrix} 2 & 0 & 0 \\ 0 & 1 & 0 \\ 0 & 0 & 1 \end{pmatrix}$.

6. $\begin{pmatrix} 0 & 1 & 0 \\ 2 & 0 & 0 \\ 0 & 0 & 1 \end{pmatrix}$.

In Exercises 7 through 12 describe the effect of the transformation of the coordinate plane onto itself with the given matrix upon the graph of the given equation:

7. $\begin{pmatrix} 2 & 0 & 0 \\ 0 & 2 & 0 \\ 0 & 0 & 1 \end{pmatrix}$; $x^2 + (y-1)^2 = 9$.

8. $\begin{pmatrix} 3 & 0 & 0 \\ 0 & 2 & 0 \\ 0 & 0 & 1 \end{pmatrix}$; $\dfrac{x^2}{4} + \dfrac{y^2}{9} = 1$.

9. $\begin{pmatrix} b & 0 & 0 \\ 0 & a & 0 \\ 0 & 0 & 1 \end{pmatrix}$; $\dfrac{x^2}{a^2} + \dfrac{y^2}{b^2} = 1$.

10. $\begin{pmatrix} 2 & 0 & 0 \\ 0 & -1 & 0 \\ 0 & 0 & 1 \end{pmatrix}$; $3x + 2y = 6$.

11. $\begin{pmatrix} \frac{1}{2} & 0 & 0 \\ 0 & \frac{1}{3} & 0 \\ 0 & 0 & 1 \end{pmatrix}$; $3x + 2y = 6$.

12. $\begin{pmatrix} \frac{1}{a} & 0 & 0 \\ 0 & \frac{1}{b} & 0 \\ 0 & 0 & 1 \end{pmatrix}$; $bx + ay = ab$.

13. Find the matrix for a dilation which maps the points of the circle $x^2 + y^2 = 1$ onto the circle (a) $x^2 + y^2 = 9$; (b) $x^2 + y^2 = 0.25$.

14. Find a matrix for a transformation of the plane onto itself which maps the points of the circle $x^2 + y^2 = 1$ onto the ellipse (a) $4x^2 + 9y^2 = 36$; (b) $x^2 + 16y^2 = 16$.

In Exercises 15 through 17 prove that:

15. If a reflection in the x-axis is followed by a reflection in the line $y = x$, the result is a rotation of the plane about the origin through 90°.

16. If a reflection in the line $y = x$ is followed by a reflection in the x-axis, the result is a rotation of the plane about the origin through $-90°$.

• • •

17. The distance between any two points (x_1, y_1) and (x_2, y_2) is invariant under a reflection in (a) the x-axis; (b) the y-axis; (c) the line $y = x$.

• 18. The transformation of the form

$$\begin{pmatrix} x' \\ y' \\ 1 \end{pmatrix} = \begin{pmatrix} 1 & 0 & 0 \\ k & 1 & 0 \\ 0 & 0 & 1 \end{pmatrix} \begin{pmatrix} x \\ y \\ 1 \end{pmatrix}$$

represents a "shearing" parallel to the y-axis. Use $k = 2$ and graph the rectangle with vertices (0, 0), (3, 0), (3, 1), (0, 1) and its image under the transformation on the same coordinate plane.

• 19. Give the equation and identify the curve which is the image of the circle with center at the origin and radius equal to 3 under the transformation $\begin{pmatrix} 1 & 0 & 0 \\ 2 & 1 & 0 \\ 0 & 0 & 1 \end{pmatrix}$.

• 20. Consider the transformation $\begin{pmatrix} 1 & 0 & 0 \\ 3 & 1 & 0 \\ 0 & 0 & 1 \end{pmatrix}$ and the line $3x + y = 6$.

Find the equation of the image of the line under the transformation, and check the equation by finding the points which correspond under the transformation to three points of the given line.

• 21. Find a matrix which maps the point (1, 2) onto (7, -1), (4, -3) onto (6, 7), and (0, 0) onto (0, 0).

SUMMARY OF CHAPTER 12

1. In this chapter we have studied the algebra of matrices. A rectangular array of real numbers forms a real matrix. The set of real matrices of order m by n forms a commutative group under addition. (§ 12-1)

721

THE ALGEBRA OF MATRICES

2. The product AB of any m by n matrix A and any n by t matrix B is an m by t matrix. The multiplication of matrices is associative but not in general commutative. (§ 12–2)

3. Diagonal, scalar, symmetric, and skew-symmetric matrices have useful special properties. (§ 12–3)

4. Conjugate, transposed conjugate, Hermitian, and skew-Hermitian complex matrices have useful special properties. (§ 12–4)

5. The rank of any matrix and the determinant of any square matrix may be determined. If a system of n linear equations in m variables has a unique solution, then the rank of the matrix of the coefficients and of the augmented matrix is m and the system may be solved by Cramer's Rule. (§ 12–5)

6. Any square nonsingular matrix has a unique multiplicative inverse. (§ 12–6)

7. The set of square real matrices of any given order n forms a ring. The set of real matrices $\begin{pmatrix} x & 0 \\ 0 & x \end{pmatrix}$ is isomorphic to the set of real numbers x. The set of real matrices $\begin{pmatrix} x & y \\ -y & x \end{pmatrix}$ is isomorphic to the set of complex numbers $x + yi$. (§ 12–7)

8. On a coordinate plane translations of coordinate axes and translations of the set of points (x, y) with reference to given coordinate axes may be represented by matrices. (§ 12–8)

9. On a coordinate plane rotations of coordinate axes and rotations of the set of points (x, y) with reference to given coordinate axes may be represented by matrices. (§ 12–9)

10. The transformations of Euclidean geometry (rigid motions) may be defined as the set of translations, rotations, and reflections of a plane onto itself. (§ 12–10)

11. The following words have been introduced or used extensively in this chapter:

augmented matrix (§ 12–5)
column index (§ 12–1)
complex matrix (§ 12–4)
conformable for addition (§ 12–1)
conformable for multiplication (§ 12–2)
conjugate (§ 12–4)
Cramer's Rule (§ 12–5)
determinant (§§ 12–2, 12–5)
diagonal elements (§ 12–3)

diagonal matrix (§ 12–3)
dilation (§ 12–10)
equal matrices (§ 12–1)
fixed point (§ 12–9)
Hermitian matrix (§ 12–4)
homogeneous coordinates (§ 12–8)
identity matrix (§ 12–3)
image (§ 12–8)
invariant (§ 12–10)
isomorphic (§ 12–7)

KEYED PRACTICE ON CHAPTER 12

linear transformation (§ 12–8)
main diagonal (§ 12–3)
multiplicative inverse (§ 12–6)
nonhomogeneous coordinates
 (§ 12–8)
nonsingular matrix (§ 12–6)
null matrix (§ 12–1)
order (§ 12–1)
postmultiplication (§ 12–3)
premultiplication (§ 12–3)
principal diagonal (§ 12–3)
product (§ 12–2)
rank (§ 12–5)
real matrix (§ 12–1)
reflection (§ 12–10)
rigid motion (§ 12–10)

ring (§ 12–7)
rotation (§ 12–9)
row index (§ 12–1)
scalar matrix (§ 12–3)
singular matrix (§ 12–6)
skew-Hermitian matrix (§ 12–4)
skew-symmetric matrix (§ 12–3)
square matrix (§ 12–1)
stretching transformation (§ 12–10)
submatrix (§ 12–5)
sum (§ 12–1)
symmetric matrix (§ 12–3)
translation (§ 12–8)
transpose (§ 12–3)
transposed conjugate (§ 12–4)
zero matrix (§ 12–1)

KEYED PRACTICE ON CHAPTER 12

1. Find $2A - B$ where

$$A = \begin{pmatrix} 2 & -1 & 3 \\ 1 & 4 & -2 \\ 0 & 0 & 1 \end{pmatrix} \text{ and } B = \begin{pmatrix} 3 & 2 & 1 \\ -1 & 2 & -5 \\ 0 & -1 & 0 \end{pmatrix}. \quad (§ 12\text{–}1)$$

2. Use A and B from Exercise 1 and find AB. (§ 12–2)

3. Express $\begin{pmatrix} 2 & 1 & -3 \\ 0 & 2 & 4 \\ 3 & 5 & 1 \end{pmatrix}$ as the sum of a symmetric and a skew-symmetric matrix. (§ 12–3)

4. If $A = \begin{pmatrix} 1+i & 2 \\ 3i & 4-i \end{pmatrix}$, find (a) $\bar{A}$; (b) A^*. (§ 12–4)

5. Find the rank of the matrix given in Exercise 3. (§ 12–5)

6. Find the multiplicative inverse for the matrix A in Exercise 1. (§ 12–6)

7. Use a real matrix to represent
 (a) $-4 + 2i$; (b) $5 - i$; (c) $(-4 + 2i)(5 - i)$. (§ 12–7)

8. State the matrix equation for the translation of a coordinate plane onto itself such that $(1, 3)$ is mapped onto $(-2, 5)$. (§ 12–8)

9. Find a matrix equation for the transformation obtained by rotating the coordinate axes 300° about the origin. (§ 12–9)

THE ALGEBRA OF MATRICES

10. Describe the effect of the transformation of the coordinate plane onto itself with matrix $\begin{pmatrix} 0.5 & 0 & 0 \\ 0 & 0.2 & 0 \\ 0 & 0 & 1 \end{pmatrix}$ upon the line with equation $2x + 5y = 3$. (§ 12–10)

TESTS ON CHAPTER 12

A

1. Find $A + 2B$ where

$$A = \begin{pmatrix} 3 & 1 & -1 \\ 2 & -2 & 5 \\ 5 & -1 & 0 \end{pmatrix} \text{ and } B = \begin{pmatrix} 1 & 2 & 2 \\ -1 & 2 & -3 \\ 2 & 3 & 4 \end{pmatrix}.$$

2. Use A and B from Exercise 1 and find AB.

3. Find $A^\top$ for $A = \begin{pmatrix} 1 & -2 & 5 \\ 3 & 0 & 6 \end{pmatrix}$.

4. If $A = \begin{pmatrix} 2i & 3-i \\ 3+i & 5 \end{pmatrix}$, find (a) $\overline{A}$; (b) A^*.

5. Find the rank of the matrix A in Exercise 1.
6. Find the multiplicative inverse of the matrix B in Exercise 1.
7. Use a real matrix to represent
   (a) $7 - 3i$; (b) $1 + 5i$; (c) $(7 - 3i)(1 + 5i)$.
8. State the matrix equation for the translation of a coordinate plane onto itself such that the origin is mapped onto $(3, -2)$.
9. Find a matrix equation for the transformation obtained by rotating the coordinate axes $330°$ about the origin.
10. Describe the effect of the transformation of the coordinate plane onto itself with matrix $\begin{pmatrix} 3 & 0 & 0 \\ 0 & 3 & 0 \\ 0 & 0 & 1 \end{pmatrix}$ upon the graph of $x^2 + y^2 - 2x = 3$.

B

1. Find the inverse under addition for

$$\begin{pmatrix} 1 & 0 & 3 & -2 \\ 2 & -5 & 1 & 4 \end{pmatrix}.$$

2. Find AB where $A = \begin{pmatrix} 2 & 1 \\ -1 & 3 \end{pmatrix}$ and B is the matrix given in Exercise 1.

724

ANSWERS TO KEYED PRACTICE ON CHAPTER 12

1. $\begin{pmatrix} 1 & -4 & 5 \\ 3 & 6 & 1 \\ 0 & 1 & 2 \end{pmatrix}$.

2. $\begin{pmatrix} 7 & -1 & 7 \\ -1 & 12 & -19 \\ 0 & -1 & 0 \end{pmatrix}$.

3. $\begin{pmatrix} 2 & 1 & -3 \\ 0 & 2 & 4 \\ 3 & 5 & 1 \end{pmatrix} = \begin{pmatrix} 2 & \frac{1}{2} & 0 \\ \frac{1}{2} & 2 & \frac{9}{2} \\ 0 & \frac{9}{2} & 1 \end{pmatrix} + \begin{pmatrix} 0 & \frac{1}{2} & -3 \\ -\frac{1}{2} & 0 & -\frac{1}{2} \\ 3 & \frac{1}{2} & 0 \end{pmatrix}$.

4. (a) $\begin{pmatrix} 1-i & 2 \\ -3i & 4+i \end{pmatrix}$; (b) $\begin{pmatrix} 1-i & -3i \\ 2 & 4+i \end{pmatrix}$.

5. 3.

6. $\begin{pmatrix} \frac{4}{9} & \frac{1}{9} & -\frac{10}{9} \\ -\frac{1}{9} & \frac{2}{9} & \frac{7}{9} \\ 0 & 0 & 1 \end{pmatrix}$.

7. (a) $\begin{pmatrix} -4 & 2 \\ -2 & -4 \end{pmatrix}$; (b) $\begin{pmatrix} 5 & -1 \\ 1 & 5 \end{pmatrix}$; (c) $\begin{pmatrix} -18 & 14 \\ -14 & -18 \end{pmatrix}$.

8. $\begin{pmatrix} x' \\ y' \\ 1 \end{pmatrix} = \begin{pmatrix} 1 & 0 & -3 \\ 0 & 1 & 2 \\ 0 & 0 & 1 \end{pmatrix} \begin{pmatrix} x \\ y \\ 1 \end{pmatrix}$.

9. $\begin{pmatrix} x' \\ y' \\ 1 \end{pmatrix} = \begin{pmatrix} \frac{1}{2} & -\frac{\sqrt{3}}{2} & 0 \\ \frac{\sqrt{3}}{2} & \frac{1}{2} & 0 \\ 0 & 0 & 1 \end{pmatrix} \begin{pmatrix} x \\ y \\ 1 \end{pmatrix}$.

10. The line $2x + 5y = 3$ is mapped onto the line $4x + 25y = 3$.

TABLE I. LOGARITHMS OF NUMBERS
Table of Mantissas

No.	0	1	2	3	4	5	6	7	8	9
10	0000	0043	0086	0128	0170	0212	0253	0294	0334	0374
11	0414	0453	0492	0531	0569	0607	0645	0682	0719	0755
12	0792	0828	0864	0899	0934	0969	1004	1038	1072	1106
13	1139	1173	1206	1239	1271	1303	1335	1367	1399	1430
14	1461	1492	1523	1553	1584	1614	1644	1673	1703	1732
15	1761	1790	1818	1847	1875	1903	1931	1959	1987	2014
16	2041	2068	2095	2122	2148	2175	2201	2227	2253	2279
17	2304	2330	2355	2380	2405	2430	2455	2480	2504	2529
18	2553	2577	2601	2625	2648	2672	2695	2718	2742	2765
19	2788	2810	2833	2856	2878	2900	2923	2945	2967	2989
20	3010	3032	3054	3075	3096	3118	3139	3160	3181	3201
21	3222	3243	3263	3284	3304	3324	3345	3365	3385	3404
22	3424	3444	3464	3483	3502	3522	3541	3560	3579	3598
23	3617	3636	3655	3674	3692	3711	3729	3747	3766	3784
24	3802	3820	3838	3856	3874	3892	3909	3927	3945	3962
25	3979	3997	4014	4031	4048	4065	4082	4099	4116	4133
26	4150	4166	4183	4200	4216	4232	4249	4265	4281	4298
27	4314	4330	4346	4362	4378	4393	4409	4425	4440	4456
28	4472	4487	4502	4518	4533	4548	4564	4579	4594	4609
29	4624	4639	4654	4669	4683	4698	4713	4728	4742	4757
30	4771	4786	4800	4814	4829	4843	4857	4871	4886	4900
31	4914	4928	4942	4955	4969	4983	4997	5011	5024	5038
32	5051	5065	5079	5092	5105	5119	5132	5145	5159	5172
33	5185	5198	5211	5224	5237	5250	5263	5276	5289	5302
34	5315	5328	5340	5353	5366	5378	5391	5403	5416	5428
35	5441	5453	5465	5478	5490	5502	5514	5527	5539	5551
36	5563	5575	5587	5599	5611	5623	5635	5647	5658	5670
37	5682	5694	5705	5717	5729	5740	5752	5763	5775	5786
38	5798	5809	5821	5832	5843	5855	5866	5877	5888	5899
39	5911	5922	5933	5944	5955	5966	5977	5988	5999	6010
40	6021	6031	6042	6053	6064	6075	6085	6096	6107	6117
41	6128	6138	6149	6160	6170	6180	6191	6201	6212	6222
42	6232	6243	6253	6263	6274	6284	6294	6304	6314	6325
43	6335	6345	6355	6365	6375	6385	6395	6405	6415	6425
44	6435	6444	6454	6464	6474	6484	6493	6503	6513	6522
45	6532	6542	6551	6561	6571	6580	6590	6599	6609	6618
46	6628	6637	6646	6656	6665	6675	6684	6693	6702	6712
47	6721	6730	6739	6749	6758	6767	6776	6785	6794	6803
48	6812	6821	6830	6839	6848	6857	6866	6875	6884	6893
49	6902	6911	6920	6928	6937	6946	6955	6964	6972	6981
50	6990	6998	7007	7016	7024	7033	7042	7050	7059	7067
51	7076	7084	7093	7101	7110	7118	7126	7135	7143	7152
52	7160	7168	7177	7185	7193	7202	7210	7218	7226	7235
53	7243	7251	7259	7267	7275	7284	7292	7300	7308	7316
54	7324	7332	7340	7348	7356	7364	7372	7380	7388	7396

TABLE I. LOGARITHMS OF NUMBERS
Table of Mantissas

No.	0	1	2	3	4	5	6	7	8	9
55	7404	7412	7419	7427	7435	7443	7451	7459	7466	7474
56	7482	7490	7497	7505	7513	7520	7528	7536	7543	7551
57	7559	7566	7574	7582	7589	7597	7604	7612	7619	7627
58	7634	7642	7649	7657	7664	7672	7679	7686	7694	7701
59	7709	7716	7723	7731	7738	7745	7752	7760	7767	7774
60	7782	7789	7796	7803	7810	7818	7825	7832	7839	7846
61	7853	7860	7868	7875	7882	7889	7896	7903	7910	7917
62	7924	7931	7938	7945	7952	7959	7966	7973	7980	7987
63	7993	8000	8007	8014	8021	8028	8035	8041	8048	8055
64	8062	8069	8075	8082	8089	8096	8102	8109	8116	8122
65	8129	8136	8142	8149	8156	8162	8169	8176	8182	8189
66	8195	8202	8209	8215	8222	8228	8235	8241	8248	8254
67	8261	8267	8274	8280	8287	8293	8299	8306	8312	8319
68	8325	8331	8338	8344	8351	8357	8363	8370	8376	8382
69	8388	8395	8401	8407	8414	8420	8426	8432	8439	8445
70	8451	8457	8463	8470	8476	8482	8488	8494	8500	8506
71	8513	8519	8525	8531	8537	8543	8549	8555	8561	8567
72	8573	8579	8585	8591	8597	8603	8609	8615	8621	8627
73	8633	8639	8645	8651	8657	8663	8669	8675	8681	8686
74	8692	8698	8704	8710	8716	8722	8727	8733	8739	8745
75	8751	8756	8762	8768	8774	8779	8785	8791	8797	8802
76	8808	8814	8820	8825	8831	8837	8842	8848	8854	8859
77	8865	8871	8876	8882	8887	8893	8899	8904	8910	8915
78	8921	8927	8932	8938	8943	8949	8954	8960	8965	8971
79	8976	8982	8987	8993	8998	9004	9009	9015	9020	9025
80	9031	9036	9042	9047	9053	9058	9063	9069	9074	9079
81	9085	9090	9096	9101	9106	9112	9117	9122	9128	9133
82	9138	9143	9149	9154	9159	9165	9170	9175	9180	9186
83	9191	9196	9201	9206	9212	9217	9222	9227	9232	9238
84	9243	9248	9253	9258	9263	9269	9274	9279	9284	9289
85	9294	9299	9304	9309	9315	9320	9325	9330	9335	9340
86	9345	9350	9355	9360	9365	9370	9375	9380	9385	9390
87	9395	9400	9405	9410	9415	9420	9425	9430	9435	9440
88	9445	9450	9455	9460	9465	9469	9474	9479	9484	9489
89	9494	9499	9504	9509	9513	9518	9523	9528	9533	9538
90	9542	9547	9552	9557	9562	9566	9571	9576	9581	9586
91	9590	9595	9600	9605	9609	9614	9619	9624	9628	9633
92	9638	9643	9647	9652	9657	9661	9666	9671	9675	9680
93	9685	9689	9694	9699	9703	9708	9713	9717	9722	9727
94	9731	9736	9741	9745	9750	9754	9759	9763	9768	9773
95	9777	9782	9786	9791	9795	9800	9805	9809	9814	9818
96	9823	9827	9832	9836	9841	9845	9850	9854	9859	9863
97	9868	9872	9877	9881	9886	9890	9894	9899	9903	9908
98	9912	9917	9921	9926	9930	9934	9939	9943	9948	9952
99	9956	9961	9965	9969	9974	9978	9983	9987	9991	9996

TABLE II. VALUES OF CIRCULAR FUNCTIONS

θ	$\mathrm{Sin}\,\theta$	$\mathrm{Cos}\,\theta$	$\mathrm{Tan}\,\theta$	$\mathrm{Cot}\,\theta$	
0° 00′	0.0000	1.0000	0.0000	----	90° 00′
10	0.0029	1.0000	0.0029	343.77	50
20	0.0058	1.0000	0.0058	171.89	40
30	0.0087	1.0000	0.0087	114.59	30
40	0.0116	0.9999	0.0116	85.940	20
50	0.0145	0.9999	0.0145	68.750	10
1° 00′	0.0175	0.9998	0.0175	57.290	89° 00′
10	0.0204	0.9998	0.0204	49.104	50
20	0.0233	0.9997	0.0233	42.964	40
30	0.0262	0.9997	0.0262	38.188	30
40	0.0291	0.9996	0.0291	34.368	20
50	0.0320	0.9995	0.0320	31.242	10
2° 00′	0.0349	0.9994	0.0349	28.636	88° 00′
10	0.0378	0.9993	0.0378	26.432	50
20	0.0407	0.9992	0.0407	24.542	40
30	0.0436	0.9990	0.0437	22.904	30
40	0.0465	0.9989	0.0466	21.470	20
50	0.0494	0.9988	0.0495	20.206	10
3° 00′	0.0523	0.9986	0.0524	19.081	87° 00′
10	0.0552	0.9985	0.0553	18.075	50
20	0.0581	0.9983	0.0582	17.169	40
30	0.0610	0.9981	0.0612	16.350	30
40	0.0640	0.9980	0.0641	15.605	20
50	0.0669	0.9978	0.0670	14.924	10
4° 00′	0.0698	0.9976	0.0699	14.301	86° 00′
10	0.0727	0.9974	0.0729	13.727	50
20	0.0756	0.9971	0.0758	13.197	40
30	0.0785	0.9969	0.0787	12.706	30
40	0.0814	0.9967	0.0816	12.251	20
50	0.0843	0.9964	0.0846	11.826	10
5° 00′	0.0872	0.9962	0.0875	11.430	85° 00′
10	0.0901	0.9959	0.0904	11.059	50
20	0.0929	0.9957	0.0934	10.712	40
30	0.0958	0.9954	0.0963	10.385	30
40	0.0987	0.9951	0.0992	10.078	20
50	0.1016	0.9948	0.1022	9.7882	10
6° 00′	0.1045	0.9945	0.1051	9.5144	84° 00′
10	0.1074	0.9942	0.1080	9.2553	50
20	0.1103	0.9939	0.1110	9.0098	40
30	0.1132	0.9936	0.1139	8.7769	30
40	0.1161	0.9932	0.1169	8.5555	20
50	0.1190	0.9929	0.1198	8.3450	10
7° 00′	0.1219	0.9925	0.1228	8.1443	83° 00′
10	0.1248	0.9922	0.1257	7.9530	50
20	0.1276	0.9918	0.1287	7.7704	40
30	0.1305	0.9914	0.1317	7.5958	30
	$\mathrm{Cos}\,\theta$	$\mathrm{Sin}\,\theta$	$\mathrm{Cot}\,\theta$	$\mathrm{Tan}\,\theta$	θ

TABLE II. VALUES OF CIRCULAR FUNCTIONS

θ	Sin θ	Cos θ	Tan θ	Cot θ	
7° 30′	0.1305	0.9914	0.1317	7.5958	82° 30′
40	0.1334	0.9911	0.1346	7.4287	20
50	0.1363	0.9907	0.1376	7.2687	10
8° 00′	0.1392	0.9903	0.1405	7.1154	82° 00′
10	0.1421	0.9899	0.1435	6.9682	50
20	0.1449	0.9894	0.1465	6.8269	40
30	0.1478	0.9890	0.1495	6.6912	30
40	0.1507	0.9886	0.1524	6.5606	20
50	0.1536	0.9881	0.1554	6.4348	10
9° 00′	0.1564	0.9877	0.1584	6.3138	81° 00′
10	0.1593	0.9872	0.1614	6.1970	50
20	0.1622	0.9868	0.1644	6.0844	40
30	0.1650	0.9863	0.1673	5.9758	30
40	0.1679	0.9858	0.1703	5.8708	20
50	0.1708	0.9853	0.1733	5.7694	10
10° 00′	0.1736	0.9848	0.1763	5.6713	80° 00′
10	0.1765	0.9843	0.1793	5.5764	50
20	0.1794	0.9838	0.1823	5.4845	40
30	0.1822	0.9833	0.1853	5.3955	30
40	0.1851	0.9827	0.1883	5.3093	20
50	0.1880	0.9822	0.1914	5.2257	10
11° 00′	0.1908	0.9816	0.1944	5.1446	79° 00′
10	0.1937	0.9811	0.1974	5.0658	50
20	0.1965	0.9805	0.2004	4.9894	40
30	0.1994	0.9799	0.2035	4.9152	30
40	0.2022	0.9793	0.2065	4.8430	20
50	0.2051	0.9787	0.2095	4.7729	10
12° 00′	0.2079	0.9781	0.2126	4.7046	78° 00′
10	0.2108	0.9775	0.2156	4.6382	50
20	0.2136	0.9769	0.2186	4.5736	40
30	0.2164	0.9763	0.2217	4.5107	30
40	0.2193	0.9757	0.2247	4.4494	20
50	0.2221	0.9750	0.2278	4.3897	10
13° 00′	0.2250	0.9744	0.2309	4.3315	77° 00′
10	0.2278	0.9737	0.2339	4.2747	50
20	0.2306	0.9730	0.2370	4.2193	40
30	0.2334	0.9724	0.2401	4.1653	30
40	0.2363	0.9717	0.2432	4.1126	20
50	0.2391	0.9710	0.2462	4.0611	10
14° 00′	0.2419	0.9703	0.2493	4.0108	76° 00′
10	0.2447	0.9696	0.2524	3.9617	50
20	0.2476	0.9689	0.2555	3.9136	40
30	0.2504	0.9681	0.2586	3.8667	30
40	0.2532	0.9674	0.2617	3.8208	20
50	0.2560	0.9667	0.2648	3.7760	10
15° 00′	0.2588	0.9659	0.2679	3.7321	75° 00′
	Cos θ	Sin θ	Cot θ	Tan θ	θ

TABLE II. VALUES OF CIRCULAR FUNCTIONS

θ	Sin θ	Cos θ	Tan θ	Cot θ	
15° 00′	0.2588	0.9659	0.2679	3.7321	75° 00′
10	0.2616	0.9652	0.2711	3.6891	50
20	0.2644	0.9644	0.2742	3.6470	40
30	0.2672	0.9636	0.2773	3.6059	30
40	0.2700	0.9628	0.2805	3.5656	20
50	0.2728	0.9621	0.2836	3.5261	10
16° 00′	0.2756	0.9613	0.2867	3.4874	74° 00′
10	0.2784	0.9605	0.2899	3.4495	50
20	0.2812	0.9596	0.2931	3.4124	40
30	0.2840	0.9588	0.2962	3.3759	30
40	0.2868	0.9580	0.2994	3.3402	20
50	0.2896	0.9572	0.3026	3.3052	10
17° 00′	0.2924	0.9563	0.3057	3.2709	73° 00′
10	0.2952	0.9555	0.3089	3.2371	50
20	0.2979	0.9546	0.3121	3.2041	40
30	0.3007	0.9537	0.3153	3.1716	30
40	0.3035	0.9528	0.3185	3.1397	20
50	0.3062	0.9520	0.3217	3.1084	10
18° 00′	0.3090	0.9511	0.3249	3.0777	72° 00′
10	0.3118	0.9502	0.3281	3.0475	50
20	0.3145	0.9492	0.3314	3.0178	40
30	0.3173	0.9483	0.3346	2.9887	30
40	0.3201	0.9474	0.3378	2.9600	20
50	0.3228	0.9465	0.3411	2.9319	10
19° 00′	0.3256	0.9455	0.3443	2.9042	71° 00′
10	0.3283	0.9446	0.3476	2.8770	50
20	0.3311	0.9436	0.3508	2.8502	40
30	0.3338	0.9426	0.3541	2.8239	30
40	0.3365	0.9417	0.3574	2.7980	20
50	0.3393	0.9407	0.3607	2.7725	10
20° 00′	0.3420	0.9397	0.3640	2.7475	70° 00′
10	0.3448	0.9387	0.3673	2.7228	50
20	0.3475	0.9377	0.3706	2.6985	40
30	0.3502	0.9367	0.3739	2.6746	30
40	0.3529	0.9356	0.3772	2.6511	20
50	0.3557	0.9346	0.3805	2.6279	10
21° 00′	0.3584	0.9336	0.3839	2.6051	69° 00′
10	0.3611	0.9325	0.3872	2.5826	50
20	0.3638	0.9315	0.3906	2.5605	40
30	0.3665	0.9304	0.3939	2.5386	30
40	0.3692	0.9293	0.3973	2.5172	20
50	0.3719	0.9283	0.4006	2.4960	10
22° 00′	0.3746	0.9272	0.4040	2.4751	68° 00′
10	0.3773	0.9261	0.4074	2.4545	50
20	0.3800	0.9250	0.4108	2.4342	40
30	0.3827	0.9239	0.4142	2.4142	30
	Cos θ	Sin θ	Cot θ	Tan θ	θ

TABLE II. VALUES OF CIRCULAR FUNCTIONS

θ	$\operatorname{Sin} \theta$	$\operatorname{Cos} \theta$	$\operatorname{Tan} \theta$	$\operatorname{Cot} \theta$	
22° 30'	0.3827	0.9239	0.4142	2.4142	**67°** 30'
40	0.3854	0.9228	0.4176	2.3945	20
50	0.3881	0.9216	0.4210	2.3750	10
23° 00'	0.3907	0.9205	0.4245	2.3559	**67°** 00'
10	0.3934	0.9194	0.4279	2.3369	50
20	0.3961	0.9182	0.4314	2.3183	40
30	0.3987	0.9171	0.4348	2.2998	30
40	0.4014	0.9159	0.4383	2.2817	20
50	0.4041	0.9147	0.4417	2.2637	10
24° 00'	0.4067	0.9135	0.4452	2.2460	**66°** 00'
10	0.4094	0.9124	0.4487	2.2286	50
20	0.4120	0.9112	0.4522	2.2113	40
30	0.4147	0.9100	0.4557	2.1943	30
40	0.4173	0.9088	0.4592	2.1775	20
50	0.4200	0.9075	0.4628	2.1609	10
25° 00'	0.4226	0.9063	0.4663	2.1445	**65°** 00'
10	0.4253	0.9051	0.4699	2.1283	50
20	0.4279	0.9038	0.4734	2.1123	40
30	0.4305	0.9026	0.4770	2.0965	30
40	0.4331	0.9013	0.4806	2.0809	20
50	0.4358	0.9001	0.4841	2.0655	10
26° 00'	0.4384	0.8988	0.4877	2.0503	**64°** 00'
10	0.4410	0.8975	0.4913	2.0353	50
20	0.4436	0.8962	0.4950	2.0204	40
30	0.4462	0.8949	0.4986	2.0057	30
40	0.4488	0.8936	0.5022	1.9912	20
50	0.4514	0.8923	0.5059	1.9768	10
27° 00'	0.4540	0.8910	0.5095	1.9626	**63°** 00'
10	0.4566	0.8897	0.5132	1.9486	50
20	0.4592	0.8884	0.5169	1.9347	40
30	0.4617	0.8870	0.5206	1.9210	30
40	0.4643	0.8857	0.5243	1.9074	20
50	0.4669	0.8843	0.5280	1.8940	10
28° 00'	0.4695	0.8829	0.5317	1.8807	**62°** 00'
10	0.4720	0.8816	0.5354	1.8676	50
20	0.4746	0.8802	0.5392	1.8546	40
30	0.4772	0.8788	0.5430	1.8418	30
40	0.4797	0.8774	0.5467	1.8291	20
50	0.4823	0.8760	0.5505	1.8165	10
29° 00'	0.4848	0.8746	0.5543	1.8040	**61°** 00'
10	0.4874	0.8732	0.5581	1.7917	50
20	0.4899	0.8718	0.5619	1.7796	40
30	0.4924	0.8704	0.5658	1.7675	30
40	0.4950	0.8689	0.5696	1.7556	20
50	0.4975	0.8675	0.5735	1.7437	10
30° 00'	0.5000	0.8660	0.5774	1.7321	**60°** 00'
	$\operatorname{Cos} \theta$	$\operatorname{Sin} \theta$	$\operatorname{Cot} \theta$	$\operatorname{Tan} \theta$	θ

TABLE II. VALUES OF CIRCULAR FUNCTIONS

θ	Sin θ	Cos θ	Tan θ	Cot θ	
30° 00′	0.5000	0.8660	0.5774	1.7321	**60°** 00′
10	0.5025	0.8646	0.5812	1.7205	50
20	0.5050	0.8631	0.5851	1.7090	40
30	0.5075	0.8616	0.5890	1.6977	30
40	0.5100	0.8601	0.5930	1.6864	20
50	0.5125	0.8587	0.5969	1.6753	10
31° 00′	0.5150	0.8572	0.6009	1.6643	**59°** 00′
10	0.5175	0.8557	0.6048	1.6534	50
20	0.5200	0.8542	0.6088	1.6426	40
30	0.5225	0.8526	0.6128	1.6319	30
40	0.5250	0.8511	0.6168	1.6212	20
50	0.5275	0.8496	0.6208	1.6107	10
32° 00′	0.5299	0.8480	0.6249	1.6003	**58°** 00′
10	0.5324	0.8465	0.6289	1.5900	50
20	0.5348	0.8450	0.6330	1.5798	40
30	0.5373	0.8434	0.6371	1.5697	30
40	0.5398	0.8418	0.6412	1.5597	20
50	0.5422	0.8403	0.6453	1.5497	10
33° 00′	0.5446	0.8387	0.6494	1.5399	**57°** 00′
10	0.5471	0.8371	0.6536	1.5301	50
20	0.5495	0.8355	0.6577	1.5204	40
30	0.5519	0.8339	0.6619	1.5108	30
40	0.5544	0.8323	0.6661	1.5013	20
50	0.5568	0.8307	0.6703	1.4919	10
34° 00′	0.5592	0.8290	0.6745	1.4826	**56°** 00′
10	0.5616	0.8274	0.6787	1.4733	50
20	0.5640	0.8258	0.6830	1.4641	40
30	0.5664	0.8241	0.6873	1.4550	30
40	0.5688	0.8225	0.6916	1.4460	20
50	0.5712	0.8208	0.6959	1.4370	10
35° 00′	0.5736	0.8192	0.7002	1.4281	**55°** 00′
10	0.5760	0.8175	0.7046	1.4193	50
20	0.5783	0.8158	0.7089	1.4106	40
30	0.5807	0.8141	0.7133	1.4019	30
40	0.5831	0.8124	0.7177	1.3934	20
50	0.5854	0.8107	0.7221	1.3848	10
36° 00′	0.5878	0.8090	0.7265	1.3764	**54°** 00′
10	0.5901	0.8073	0.7310	1.3680	50
20	0.5925	0.8056	0.7355	1.3597	40
30	0.5948	0.8039	0.7400	1.3514	30
40	0.5972	0.8021	0.7445	1.3432	20
50	0.5995	0.8004	0.7490	1.3351	10
37° 00′	0.6018	0.7986	0.7536	1.3270	**53°** 00′
10	0.6041	0.7969	0.7581	1.3190	50
20	0.6065	0.7951	0.7627	1.3111	40
30	0.6088	0.7934	0.7673	1.3032	30
	Cos θ	Sin θ	Cot θ	Tan θ	θ

TABLE II. VALUES OF CIRCULAR FUNCTIONS

θ	$\sin\theta$	$\cos\theta$	$\tan\theta$	$\cot\theta$	
37° 30′	0.6088	0.7934	0.7673	1.3032	**52°** 30′
40	0.6111	0.7916	0.7720	1.2954	20
50	0.6134	0.7898	0.7766	1.2876	10
38° 00′	0.6157	0.7880	0.7813	1.2799	**52°** 00′
10	0.6180	0.7862	0.7860	1.2723	50
20	0.6202	0.7844	0.7907	1.2647	40
30	0.6225	0.7826	0.7954	1.2572	30
40	0.6248	0.7808	0.8002	1.2497	20
50	0.6271	0.7790	0.8050	1.2423	10
39° 00′	0.6293	0.7771	0.8098	1.2349	**51°** 00′
10	0.6316	0.7753	0.8146	1.2276	50
20	0.6338	0.7735	0.8195	1.2203	40
30	0.6361	0.7716	0.8243	1.2131	30
40	0.6383	0.7698	0.8292	1.2059	20
50	0.6406	0.7679	0.8342	1.1988	10
40° 00′	0.6428	0.7660	0.8391	1.1918	**50°** 00′
10	0.6450	0.7642	0.8441	1.1847	50
20	0.6472	0.7623	0.8491	1.1778	40
30	0.6494	0.7604	0.8541	1.1708	30
40	0.6517	0.7585	0.8591	1.1640	20
50	0.6539	0.7566	0.8642	1.1571	10
41° 00′	0.6561	0.7547	0.8693	1.1504	**49°** 00′
10	0.6583	0.7528	0.8744	1.1436	50
20	0.6604	0.7509	0.8796	1.1369	40
30	0.6626	0.7490	0.8847	1.1303	30
40	0.6648	0.7470	0.8899	1.1237	20
50	0.6670	0.7451	0.8952	1.1171	10
42° 00′	0.6691	0.7431	0.9004	1.1106	**48°** 00′
10	0.6713	0.7412	0.9057	1.1041	50
20	0.6734	0.7392	0.9110	1.0977	40
30	0.6756	0.7373	0.9163	1.0913	30
40	0.6777	0.7353	0.9217	1.0850	20
50	0.6799	0.7333	0.9271	1.0786	10
43° 00′	0.6820	0.7314	0.9325	1.0724	**47°** 00′
10	0.6841	0.7294	0.9380	1.0661	50
20	0.6862	0.7274	0.9435	1.0599	40
30	0.6884	0.7254	0.9490	1.0538	30
40	0.6905	0.7234	0.9545	1.0477	20
50	0.6926	0.7214	0.9601	1.0416	10
44° 00′	0.6947	0.7193	0.9657	1.0355	**46°** 00′
10	0.6967	0.7173	0.9713	1.0295	50
20	0.6988	0.7153	0.9770	1.0235	40
30	0.7009	0.7133	0.9827	1.0176	30
40	0.7030	0.7112	0.9884	1.0117	20
50	0.7050	0.7092	0.9942	1.0058	10
45° 00′	0.7071	0.7071	1.0000	1.0000	**45°** 00′
	$\cos\theta$	$\sin\theta$	$\cot\theta$	$\tan\theta$	θ

TABLE III. LOGARITHMS OF CIRCULAR FUNCTIONS

θ	Log Sin θ	Log Cos θ	Log Tan θ	Log Cot θ	
0° 0' 10 20 30 40 50	---- 7.4637 7.7648 7.9408 8.0658 8.1627	0.0000 0.0000 0.0000 0.0000 0.0000 0.0000	---- 7.4637 7.7648 7.9409 8.0658 8.1627	---- 2.5363 2.2352 2.0591 1.9342 1.8373	90° 0' 50 40 30 20 10
1° 0' 10 20 30 40 50	8.2419 8.3088 8.3668 8.4179 8.4637 8.5050	9.9999 9.9999 9.9999 9.9999 9.9998 9.9998	8.2419 8.3089 8.3669 8.4181 8.4638 8.5053	1.7581 1.6911 1.6331 1.5819 1.5362 1.4947	89° 0' 50 40 30 20 10
2° 0' 10 20 30 40 50	8.5428 8.5776 8.6097 8.6397 8.6677 8.6940	9.9997 9.9997 9.9996 9.9996 9.9995 9.9995	8.5431 8.5779 8.6101 8.6401 8.6682 8.6945	1.4569 1.4221 1.3899 1.3599 1.3318 1.3055	88° 0' 50 40 30 20 10
3° 0' 10 20 30 40 50	8.7188 8.7423 8.7645 8.7857 8.8059 8.8251	9.9994 9.9993 9.9993 9.9992 9.9991 9.9990	8.7194 8.7429 8.7652 8.7865 8.8067 8.8261	1.2806 1.2571 1.2348 1.2135 1.1933 1.1739	87° 0' 50 40 30 20 10
4° 0' 10 20 30 40 50	8.8436 8.8613 8.8783 8.8946 8.9104 8.9256	9.9989 9.9989 9.9988 9.9987 9.9986 9.9985	8.8446 8.8624 8.8795 8.8960 8.9118 8.9272	1.1554 1.1376 1.1205 1.1040 1.0882 1.0728	86° 0' 50 40 30 20 10
5° 0' 10 20 30 40 50	8.9403 8.9545 8.9682 8.9816 8.9945 9.0070	9.9983 9.9982 9.9981 9.9980 9.9979 9.9977	8.9420 8.9563 8.9701 8.9836 8.9966 9.0093	1.0580 1.0437 1.0299 1.0164 1.0034 0.9907	85° 0' 50 40 30 20 10
6° 0' 10 20 30 40 50	9.0192 9.0311 9.0426 9.0539 9.0648 9.0755	9.9976 9.9975 9.9973 9.9972 9.9971 9.9969	9.0216 9.0336 9.0453 9.0567 9.0678 9.0786	0.9784 0.9664 0.9547 0.9433 0.9322 0.9214	84° 0' 50 40 30 20 10
7° 0' 10 20 30	9.0859 9.0961 9.1060 9.1157	9.9968 9.9966 9.9964 9.9963	9.0891 9.0995 9.1096 9.1194	0.9109 0.9005 0.8904 0.8806	83° 0' 50 40 30
	Log Cos θ	Log Sin θ	Log Cot θ	Log Tan θ	θ

TABLE III. LOGARITHMS OF CIRCULAR FUNCTIONS

θ	Log Sin θ	Log Cos θ	Log Tan θ	Log Cot θ	
7° 30′	9.1157	9.9963	9.1194	0.8806	82° 30′
40	9.1252	9.9961	9.1291	0.8709	20
50	9.1345	9.9959	9.1385	0.8615	10
8° 0′	9.1436	9.9958	9.1478	0.8522	82° 0′
10	9.1525	9.9956	9.1569	0.8431	50
20	9.1612	9.9954	9.1658	0.8342	40
30	9.1697	9.9952	9.1745	0.8255	30
40	9.1781	9.9950	9.1831	0.8169	20
50	9.1863	9.9948	9.1915	0.8085	10
9° 0′	9.1943	9.9946	9.1997	0.8003	81° 0′
10	9.2022	9.9944	9.2078	0.7922	50
20	9.2100	9.9942	9.2158	0.7842	40
30	9.2176	9.9940	9.2236	0.7764	30
40	9.2251	9.9938	9.2313	9.7687	20
50	9.2324	9.9936	9.2389	0.7611	10
10° 0′	9.2397	9.9934	9.2463	0.7537	80° 0′
10	9.2468	9.9931	9.2536	0.7464	50
20	9.2538	9.9929	9.2609	0.7391	40
30	9.2606	9.9927	9.2680	0.7320	30
40	9.2674	9.9924	9.2750	0.7250	20
50	9.2740	9.9922	9.2819	0.7181	10
11° 0′	9.2806	9.9919	9.2887	0.7113	79° 0′
10	9.2870	9.9917	9.2953	0.7047	50
20	9.2934	9.9914	9.3020	0.6980	40
30	9.2997	9.9912	9.3085	0.6915	30
40	9.3058	9.9909	9.3149	0.6851	20
50	9.3119	9.9907	9.3212	0.6788	10
12° 0′	9.3179	9.9904	9.3275	0.6725	78° 0′
10	9.3238	9.9901	9.3336	0.6664	50
20	9.3296	9.9899	9.3397	0.6603	40
30	9.3353	9.9896	9.3458	0.6542	30
40	9.3410	9.9893	9.3517	0.6483	20
50	9.3466	9.9890	9.3576	0.6424	10
13° 0′	9.3521	9.9887	9.3634	0.6366	77° 0′
10	9.3575	9.9884	9.3691	0.6309	50
20	9.3629	9.9881	9.3748	0.6252	40
30	9.3682	9.9878	9.3804	0.6196	30
40	9.3734	9.9875	9.3859	0.6141	20
50	9.3786	9.9872	9.3914	0.6086	10
14° 0′	9.3837	9.9869	9.3968	0.6032	76° 0′
10	9.3887	9.9866	9.4021	0.5979	50
20	9.3937	9.9863	9.4074	0.5926	40
30	9.3986	9.9859	9.4127	0.5873	30
40	9.4035	9.9856	9.4178	0.5822	20
50	9.4083	9.9853	9.4230	0.5770	10
15° 0′	9.4130	9.9849	9.4281	0.5719	75° 0′
	Log Cos θ	Log Sin θ	Log Cot θ	Log Tan θ	θ

TABLE III. LOGARITHMS OF CIRCULAR FUNCTIONS

θ	Log Sin θ	Log Cos θ	Log Tan θ	Log Cot θ	
15° 0′	9.4130	9.9849	9.4281	0.5719	75° 0′
10	9.4177	9.9846	9.4331	0.5669	50
20	9.4223	9.9843	9.4381	0.5619	40
30	9.4269	9.9839	9.4430	0.5570	30
40	9.4314	9.9836	9.4479	0.5521	20
50	9.4359	9.9832	9.4527	0.5473	10
16° 0′	9.4403	9.9828	9.4575	0.5425	74° 0′
10	9.4447	9.9825	9.4622	0.5378	50
20	9.4491	9.9821	9.4669	0.5331	40
30	9.4533	9.9817	9.4716	0.5284	30
40	9.4576	9.9814	9.4762	0.5238	20
50	9.4618	9.9810	9.4808	0.5192	10
17° 0′	9.4659	9.9806	9.4853	0.5147	73° 0′
10	9.4700	9.9802	9.4898	0.5102	50
20	9.4741	9.9798	9.4943	0.5057	40
30	9.4781	9.9794	9.4987	0.5013	30
40	9.4821	9.9790	9.5031	0.4969	20
50	9.4861	9.9786	9.5075	0.4925	10
18° 0′	9.4900	9.9782	9.5118	0.4882	72° 0′
10	9.4939	9.9778	9.5161	0.4839	50
20	9.4977	9.9774	9.5203	0.4797	40
30	9.5015	9.9770	9.5245	0.4755	30
40	9.5052	9.9765	9.5287	0.4713	20
50	9.5090	9.9761	9.5329	0.4671	10
19° 0′	9.5126	9.9757	9.5370	0.4630	71° 0′
10	9.5163	9.9752	9.5411	0.4589	50
20	9.5199	9.9748	9.5451	0.4549	40
30	9.5235	9.9743	9.5491	0.4509	30
40	9.5270	9.9739	9.5531	0.4469	20
50	9.5306	9.9734	9.5571	0.4429	10
20° 0′	9.5341	9.9730	9.5611	0.4389	70° 0′
10	9.5375	9.9725	9.5650	0.4350	50
20	9.5409	9.9721	9.5689	0.4311	40
30	9.5443	9.9716	9.5727	0.4273	30
40	9.5477	9.9711	9.5766	0.4234	20
50	9.5510	9.9706	9.5804	0.4196	10
21° 0′	9.5543	9.9702	9.5842	0.4158	69° 0′
10	9.5576	9.9697	9.5879	0.4121	50
20	9.5609	9.9692	9.5917	0.4083	40
30	9.5641	9.9687	9.5954	0.4046	30
40	9.5673	9.9682	9.5991	0.4009	20
50	9.5704	9.9677	9.6028	0.3972	10
22° 0′	9.5736	9.9672	9.6064	0.3936	68° 0′
10	9.5767	9.9667	9.6100	0.3900	50
20	9.5798	9.9661	9.6136	0.3864	40
30	9.5828	9.9656	9.6172	0.3828	30
	Log Cos θ	Log Sin θ	Log Cot θ	Log Tan θ	θ

TABLE III. LOGARITHMS OF CIRCULAR FUNCTIONS

θ	Log Sin θ	Log Cos θ	Log Tan θ	Log Cot θ	
22° 30′	9.5828	9.9656	9.6172	0.3828	67° 30′
40	9.5859	9.9651	9.6208	0.3792	20
50	9.5889	9.9646	9.6243	0.3757	10
23° 0′	9.5919	9.9640	9.6279	0.3721	67° 0′
10	9.5948	9.9635	9.6314	0.3686	50
20	9.5978	9.9629	9.6348	0.3652	40
30	9.6007	9.9624	9.6383	0.3617	30
40	9.6036	9.9618	9.6417	0.3583	20
50	9.6065	9.9613	9.6452	0.3548	10
24° 0′	9.6093	9.9607	9.6486	0.3514	66° 0′
10	9.6121	9.9602	9.6520	0.3480	50
20	9.6149	9.9596	9.6553	0.3447	40
30	9.6177	9.9590	9.6587	0.3413	30
40	9.6205	9.9584	9.6620	0.3380	20
50	9.6232	9.9579	9.6654	0.3346	10
25° 0′	9.6259	9.9573	9.6687	0.3313	65° 0′
10	9.6286	9.9567	9.6720	0.3280	50
20	9.6313	9.9561	9.6752	0.3248	40
30	9.6340	9.9555	9.6785	0.3215	30
40	9.6366	9.9549	9.6817	0.3183	20
50	9.6392	9.9543	9.6850	0.3150	10
26° 0′	9.6418	9.9537	9.6882	0.3118	64° 0′
10	9.6444	9.9530	9.6914	0.3086	50
20	9.6470	9.9524	9.6946	0.3054	40
30	9.6495	9.9518	9.6977	0.3023	30
40	9.6521	9.9512	9.7009	0.2991	20
50	9.6546	9.9505	9.7040	0.2960	10
27° 0′	9.6570	9.9499	9.7072	0.2928	63° 0′
10	9.6595	9.9492	9.7103	0.2897	50
20	9.6620	9.9486	9.7134	0.2866	40
30	9.6644	9.9479	9.7165	0.2835	30
40	9.6668	9.9473	9.7196	0.2804	20
50	9.6692	9.9466	9.7226	0.2774	10
28° 0′	9.6716	9.9459	9.7257	0.2743	62° 0′
10	9.6740	9.9453	9.7287	0.2713	50
20	9.6763	9.9446	9.7317	0.2683	40
30	9.6787	9.9439	9.7348	0.2652	30
40	9.6810	9.9432	9.7378	0.2622	20
50	9.6833	9.9425	9.7408	0.2592	10
29° 0′	9.6856	9.9418	9.7438	0.2562	61° 0′
10	9.6878	9.9411	9.7467	0.2533	50
20	9.6901	9.9404	9.7497	0.2503	40
30	9.6923	9.9397	9.7526	0.2474	30
40	9.6946	9.9390	9.7556	0.2444	20
50	9.6968	9.9383	9.7585	0.2415	10
30° 0′	9.6990	9.9375	9.7614	0.2386	60° 0′
	Log Cos θ	Log Sin θ	Log Cot θ	Log Tan θ	θ

TABLE III. LOGARITHMS OF CIRCULAR FUNCTIONS

θ	Log Sin θ	Log Cos θ	Log Tan θ	Log Cot θ	
30° 0'	9.6990	9.9375	9.7614	0.2386	**60°** 0'
10	9.7012	9.9368	9.7644	0.2356	50
20	9.7033	9.9361	9.7673	0.2327	40
30	9.7055	9.9353	9.7701	0.2299	30
40	9.7076	9.9346	9.7730	0.2270	20
50	9.7097	9.9338	9.7759	0.2241	10
31° 0'	9.7118	9.9331	9.7788	0.2212	**59°** 0'
10	9.7139	9.9323	9.7816	0.2184	50
20	9.7160	9.9315	9.7845	0.2155	40
30	9.7181	9.9308	9.7873	0.2127	30
40	9.7201	9.9300	9.7902	0.2098	20
50	9.7222	9.9292	9.7930	0.2070	10
32° 0'	9.7242	9.9284	9.7958	0.2042	**58°** 0'
10	9.7262	9.9276	9.7986	0.2014	50
20	9.7282	9.9268	9.8014	0.1986	40
30	9.7302	9.9260	9.8042	0.1958	30
40	9.7322	9.9252	9.8070	0.1930	20
50	9.7342	9.9244	9.8097	0.1903	10
33° 0'	9.7361	9.9236	9.8125	0.1875	**57°** 0'
10	9.7380	9.9228	9.8153	0.1847	50
20	9.7400	9.9219	9.8180	0.1820	40
30	9.7419	9.9211	9.8208	0.1792	30
40	9.7438	9.9203	9.8235	0.1765	20
50	9.7457	9.9194	9.8263	0.1737	10
34° 0'	9.7476	9.9186	9.8290	0.1710	**56°** 0'
10	9.7494	9.9177	9.8317	0.1683	50
20	9.7513	9.9169	9.8344	0.1656	40
30	9.7531	9.9160	9.8371	0.1629	30
40	9.7550	9.9151	9.8398	0.1602	20
50	9.7568	9.9142	9.8425	0.1575	10
35° 0'	9.7586	9.9134	9.8452	0.1548	**55°** 0'
10	9.7604	9.9125	9.8479	0.1521	50
20	9.7622	9.9116	9.8506	0.1494	40
30	9.7640	9.9107	9.8533	0.1467	30
40	9.7657	9.9098	9.8559	0.1441	20
50	9.7675	9.9089	9.8586	0.1414	10
36° 0'	9.7692	9.9080	9.8613	0.1387	**54°** 0'
10	9.7710	9.9070	9.8639	0.1361	50
20	9.7727	9.9061	9.8666	0.1334	40
30	9.7744	9.9052	9.8692	0.1308	30
40	9.7761	9.9042	9.8718	0.1282	20
50	9.7778	9.9033	9.8745	0.1255	10
37° 0'	9.7795	9.9023	9.8771	0.1229	**53°** 0'
10	9.7811	9.9014	9.8797	0.1203	50
20	9.7828	9.9004	9.8824	0.1176	40
30	9.7844	9.8995	9.8850	0.1150	30
	Log Cos θ	Log Sin θ	Log Cot θ	Log Tan θ	θ

TABLE III. LOGARITHMS OF CIRCULAR FUNCTIONS

θ	Log Sin θ	Log Cos θ	Log Tan θ	Log Cot θ	
37° 30′	9.7844	9.8995	9.8850	0.1150	52° 30′
40	9.7861	9.8985	9.8876	0.1124	20
50	9.7877	9.8975	9.8902	0.1098	10
38° 0′	9.7893	9.8965	9.8928	0.1072	52° 0′
10	9.7910	9.8955	9.8954	0.1046	50
20	9.7926	9.8945	9.8980	0.1020	40
30	9.7941	9.8935	9.9006	0.0994	30
40	9.7957	9.8925	9.9032	0.0968	20
50	9.7973	9.8915	9.9058	0.0942	10
39° 0′	9.7989	9.8905	9.9084	0.0916	51° 0′
10	9.8004	9.8895	9.9110	0.0890	50
20	9.8020	9.8884	9.9135	0.0865	40
30	9.8035	9.8874	9.9161	0.0839	30
40	9.8050	9.8864	9.9187	0.0813	20
50	9.8066	9.8853	9.9212	0.0788	10
40° 0′	9.8081	9.8843	9.9238	0.0762	50° 0′
10	9.8096	9.8832	9.9264	0.0736	50
20	9.8111	9.8821	9.9289	0.0711	40
30	9.8125	9.8810	9.9315	0.0685	30
40	9.8140	9.8800	9.9341	0.0659	20
50	9.8155	9.8789	9.9366	0.0634	10
41° 0′	9.8169	9.8778	9.9392	0.0608	49° 0′
10	9.8184	9.8767	9.9417	0.0583	50
20	9.8198	9.8756	9.9443	0.0557	40
30	9.8213	9.8745	9.9468	0.0532	30
40	9.8227	9.8733	9.9494	0.0506	20
50	9.8241	9.8722	9.9519	0.0481	10
42° 0′	9.8255	9.8711	9.9544	0.0456	48° 0′
10	9.8269	9.8699	9.9570	0.0430	50
20	9.8283	9.8688	9.9595	0.0405	40
30	9.8297	9.8676	9.9621	0.0379	30
40	9.8311	9.8665	9.9646	0.0354	20
50	9.8324	9.8653	9.9671	0.0329	10
43° 0′	9.8338	9.8641	9.9697	0.0303	47° 0′
10	9.8351	9.8629	9.9722	0.0278	50
20	9.8365	9.8618	9.9747	0.0253	40
30	9.8378	9.8606	9.9772	0.0228	30
40	9.8391	9.8594	9.9798	0.0202	20
50	9.8405	9.8582	9.9823	0.0177	10
44° 0′	9.8418	9.8569	9.9848	0.0152	46° 0′
10	9.8431	9.8557	9.9874	0.0126	50
20	9.8444	9.8545	9.9899	0.0101	40
30	9.8457	9.8532	9.9924	0.0076	30
40	9.8469	9.8520	9.9949	0.0051	20
50	9.8482	9.8507	9.9975	0.0025	10
45° 0′	9.8495	9.8495	0.0000	0.0000	45° 0′
	Log Cos θ	Log Sin θ	Log Cot θ	Log Tan θ	θ

TABLE IV. SQUARE ROOTS AND CUBE ROOTS, 1–200

NO.	SQUARE ROOT	CUBE ROOT	NO.	SQUARE ROOT	CUBE ROOT	NO.	SQUARE ROOT	CUBE ROOT	NO.	SQUARE ROOT	CUBE ROOT
1	1.000	1.000	51	7.141	3.708	101	10.050	4.657	151	12.288	5.325
2	1.414	1.260	52	7.211	3.733	102	10.100	4.672	152	12.329	5.337
3	1.732	1.442	53	7.280	3.756	103	10.149	4.688	153	12.369	5.348
4	2.000	1.587	54	7.348	3.780	104	10.198	4.703	154	12.410	5.360
5	2.236	1.710	55	7.416	3.803	105	10.247	4.718	155	12.450	5.372
6	2.449	1.817	56	7.483	3.826	106	10.296	4.733	156	12.490	5.383
7	2.646	1.913	57	7.550	3.849	107	10.344	4.747	157	12.530	5.395
8	2.828	2.000	58	7.616	3.871	108	10.392	4.762	158	12.570	5.406
9	3.000	2.080	59	7.681	3.893	109	10.440	4.777	159	12.610	5.418
10	3.162	2.154	60	7.746	3.915	110	10.488	4.791	160	12.649	5.429
11	3.317	2.224	61	7.810	3.936	111	10.536	4.806	161	12.689	5.440
12	3.464	2.289	62	7.874	3.958	112	10.583	4.820	162	12.728	5.451
13	3.606	2.351	63	7.937	3.979	113	10.630	4.835	163	12.767	5.463
14	3.742	2.410	64	8.000	4.000	114	10.677	4.849	164	12.806	5.474
15	3.873	2.466	65	8.062	4.021	115	10.724	4.863	165	12.845	5.485
16	4.000	2.520	66	8.124	4.041	116	10.770	4.877	166	12.884	5.496
17	4.123	2.571	67	8.185	4.062	117	10.817	4.891	167	12.923	5.507
18	4.243	2.621	68	8.246	4.082	118	10.863	4.905	168	12.961	5.518
19	4.359	2.668	69	8.307	4.102	119	10.909	4.919	169	13.000	5.529
20	4.472	2.714	70	8.367	4.121	120	10.954	4.932	170	13.038	5.540
21	4.583	2.759	71	8.426	4.141	121	11.000	4.946	171	13.077	5.550
22	4.690	2.802	72	8.485	4.160	122	11.045	4.960	172	13.115	5.561
23	4.796	2.844	73	8.544	4.179	123	11.091	4.973	173	13.153	5.572
24	4.899	2.884	74	8.602	4.198	124	11.136	4.987	174	13.191	5.583
25	5.000	2.924	75	8.660	4.217	125	11.180	5.000	175	13.229	5.593
26	5.099	2.962	76	8.718	4.236	126	11.225	5.013	176	13.267	5.604
27	5.196	3.000	77	8.775	4.254	127	11.269	5.027	177	13.304	5.615
28	5.292	3.037	78	8.832	4.273	128	11.314	5.040	178	13.342	5.625
29	5.385	3.072	79	8.888	4.291	129	11.358	5.053	179	13.379	5.636
30	5.477	3.107	80	8.944	4.309	130	11.402	5.066	180	13.416	5.646
31	5.568	3.141	81	9.000	4.327	131	11.446	5.079	181	13.454	5.657
32	5.657	3.175	82	9.055	4.344	132	11.489	5.092	182	13.491	5.667
33	5.745	3.208	83	9.110	4.362	133	11.533	5.104	183	13.528	5.677
34	5.831	3.240	84	9.165	4.380	134	11.576	5.117	184	13.565	5.688
35	5.916	3.271	85	9.220	4.397	135	11.619	5.130	185	13.601	5.698
36	6.000	3.302	86	9.274	4.414	136	11.662	5.143	186	13.638	5.708
37	6.083	3.332	87	9.327	4.431	137	11.705	5.155	187	13.675	5.718
38	6.164	3.362	88	9.381	4.448	138	11.747	5.168	188	13.711	5.729
39	6.245	3.391	89	9.434	4.465	139	11.790	5.180	189	13.748	5.739
40	6.325	3.420	90	9.487	4.481	140	11.832	5.192	190	13.784	5.749
41	6.403	3.448	91	9.539	4.498	141	11.874	5.205	191	13.820	5.759
42	6.481	3.476	92	9.592	4.514	142	11.916	5.217	192	13.856	5.769
43	6.557	3.503	93	9.644	4.531	143	11.958	5.229	193	13.892	5.779
44	6.633	3.530	94	9.695	4.547	144	12.000	5.241	194	13.928	5.789
45	6.708	3.557	95	9.747	4.563	145	12.042	5.254	195	13.964	5.799
46	6.782	3.583	96	9.798	4.579	146	12.083	5.266	196	14.000	5.809
47	6.856	3.609	97	9.849	4.595	147	12.124	5.278	197	14.036	5.819
48	6.928	3.634	98	9.899	4.610	148	12.166	5.290	198	14.071	5.828
49	7.000	3.659	99	9.950	4.626	149	12.207	5.302	199	14.107	5.838
50	7.071	3.684	100	10.000	4.642	150	12.247	5.313	200	14.142	5.848

TABLE IV. SQUARE ROOTS AND CUBE ROOTS, 201–400

NO.	SQUARE ROOT	CUBE ROOT	NO.	SQUARE ROOT	CUBE ROOT	NO.	SQUARE ROOT	CUBE ROOT	NO.	SQUARE ROOT	CUBE ROOT
201	14.177	5.858	251	15.843	6.308	301	17.349	6.702	351	18.735	7.054
202	14.213	5.867	252	15.875	6.316	302	17.378	6.709	352	18.762	7.061
203	14.248	5.877	253	15.906	6.325	303	17.407	6.717	353	18.788	7.067
204	14.283	5.887	254	15.937	6.333	304	17.436	6.724	354	18.815	7.074
205	14.318	5.896	255	15.969	6.341	305	17.464	6.731	355	18.841	7.081
206	14.353	5.906	256	16.000	6.350	306	17.493	6.739	356	18.868	7.087
207	14.387	5.915	257	16.031	6.358	307	17.521	6.746	357	18.894	7.094
208	14.422	5.925	258	16.062	6.366	308	17.550	6.753	358	18.921	7.101
209	14.457	5.934	259	16.093	6.374	309	17.578	6.761	359	18.947	7.107
210	14.491	5.944	**260**	16.125	6.383	**310**	17.607	6.768	**360**	18.974	7.114
211	14.526	5.953	261	16.155	6.391	311	17.635	6.775	361	19.000	7.120
212	14.560	5.963	262	16.186	6.399	312	17.664	6.782	362	19.026	7.127
213	14.595	5.972	263	16.217	6.407	313	17.692	6.790	363	19.053	7.133
214	14.629	5.981	264	16.248	6.415	314	17.720	6.797	364	19.079	7.140
215	14.663	5.991	265	16.279	6.423	315	17.748	6.804	365	19.105	7.147
216	14.697	6.000	266	16.310	6.431	316	17.776	6.811	366	19.131	7.153
217	14.731	6.009	267	16.340	6.439	317	17.804	6.818	367	19.157	7.160
218	14.765	6.018	268	16.371	6.447	318	17.833	6.826	368	19.183	7.166
219	14.799	6.028	269	16.401	6.455	319	17.861	6.833	369	19.209	7.173
220	14.832	6.037	**270**	16.432	6.463	**320**	17.889	6.840	**370**	19.235	7.179
221	14.866	6.046	271	16.462	6.471	321	17.917	6.847	371	19.261	7.186
222	14.900	6.055	272	16.492	6.479	322	17.944	6.854	372	19.287	7.192
223	14.933	6.064	273	16.523	6.487	323	17.972	6.861	373	19.313	7.198
224	14.967	6.073	274	16.553	6.495	324	18.000	6.868	374	19.339	7.205
225	15.000	6.082	275	16.583	6.503	325	18.028	6.875	375	19.365	7.211
226	15.033	6.091	276	16.613	6.511	326	18.056	6.882	376	19.391	7.218
227	15.067	6.100	277	16.643	6.519	327	18.083	6.889	377	19.416	7.224
228	15.100	6.109	278	16.673	6.527	328	18.111	6.896	378	19.442	7.230
229	15.133	6.118	279	16.703	6.534	329	18.138	6.903	379	19.468	7.237
230	15.166	6.127	**280**	16.733	6.542	**330**	18.166	6.910	**380**	19.494	7.243
231	15.199	6.136	281	16.763	6.550	331	18.193	6.917	381	19.519	7.250
232	15.232	6.145	282	16.793	6.558	332	18.221	6.924	382	19.545	7.256
233	15.264	6.153	283	16.823	6.565	333	18.248	6.931	383	19.570	7.262
234	15.297	6.162	284	16.852	6.573	334	18.276	6.938	384	19.596	7.268
235	15.330	6.171	285	16.882	6.581	335	18.303	6.945	385	19.621	7.275
236	15.362	6.180	286	16.912	6.589	336	18.330	6.952	386	19.647	7.281
237	15.395	6.188	287	16.941	6.596	337	18.358	6.959	387	19.672	7.287
238	15.427	6.197	288	16.971	6.604	338	18.385	6.966	388	19.698	7.294
239	15.460	6.206	289	17.000	6.611	339	18.412	6.973	389	19.723	7.300
240	15.492	6.214	**290**	17.029	6.619	**340**	18.439	6.980	**390**	19.748	7.306
241	15.524	6.223	291	17.059	6.627	341	18.466	6.986	391	19.774	7.312
242	15.556	6.232	292	17.088	6.634	342	18.493	6.993	392	19.799	7.319
243	15.588	6.240	293	17.117	6.642	343	18.520	7.000	393	19.824	7.325
244	15.621	6.249	294	17.146	6.649	344	18.547	7.007	394	19.849	7.331
245	15.652	6.257	295	17.176	6.657	345	18.574	7.014	395	19.875	7.337
246	15.684	6.266	296	17.205	6.664	346	18.601	7.020	396	19.900	7.343
247	15.716	6.274	297	17.234	6.672	347	18.628	7.027	397	19.925	7.350
248	15.748	6.283	298	17.263	6.679	348	18.655	7.034	398	19.950	7.356
249	15.780	6.291	299	17.292	6.687	349	18.682	7.041	399	19.975	7.362
250	15.811	6.300	**300**	17.321	6.694	**350**	18.708	7.047	**400**	20.000	7.368

TABLE IV. SQUARE ROOTS AND CUBE ROOTS, 401–600

NO.	SQUARE ROOT	CUBE ROOT	NO.	SQUARE ROOT	CUBE ROOT	NO.	SQUARE ROOT	CUBE ROOT	NO.	SQUARE ROOT	CUBE ROOT
401	20.025	7.374	451	21.237	7.669	501	22.383	7.942	551	23.473	8.198
402	20.050	7.380	452	21.260	7.674	502	22.405	7.948	552	23.495	8.203
403	20.075	7.386	453	21.284	7.680	503	22.428	7.953	553	23.516	8.208
404	20.100	7.393	454	21.307	7.686	504	22.450	7.958	554	23.537	8.213
405	20.125	7.399	455	21.331	7.691	505	22.472	7.963	555	23.558	8.218
406	20.149	7.405	456	21.354	7.697	506	22.494	7.969	556	23.580	8.223
407	20.174	7.411	457	21.378	7.703	507	22.517	7.974	557	23.601	8.228
408	20.199	7.417	458	21.401	7.708	508	22.539	7.979	558	23.622	8.233
409	20.224	7.423	459	21.424	7.714	509	22.561	7.984	559	23.643	8.238
410	20.248	7.429	**460**	21.448	7.719	**510**	22.583	7.990	**560**	23.664	8.243
411	20.273	7.435	461	21.471	7.725	511	22.605	7.995	561	23.685	8.247
412	20.298	7.441	462	21.494	7.731	512	22.627	8.000	562	23.707	8.252
413	20.322	7.447	463	21.517	7.736	513	22.650	8.005	563	23.728	8.257
414	20.347	7.453	464	21.541	7.742	514	22.672	8.010	564	23.749	8.262
415	20.372	7.459	465	21.564	7.747	515	22.694	8.016	565	23.770	8.267
416	20.396	7.465	466	21.587	7.753	516	22.716	8.021	566	23.791	8.272
417	20.421	7.471	467	21.610	7.758	517	22.738	8.026	567	23.812	8.277
418	20.445	7.477	468	21.633	7.764	518	22.760	8.031	568	23.833	8.282
419	20.469	7.483	469	21.656	7.769	519	22.782	8.036	569	23.854	8.286
420	20.494	7.489	**470**	21.679	7.775	**520**	22.804	8.041	**570**	23.875	8.291
421	20.518	7.495	471	21.703	7.780	521	22.825	8.047	571	23.896	8.296
422	20.543	7.501	472	21.726	7.786	522	22.847	8.052	572	23.917	8.301
423	20.567	7.507	473	21.749	7.791	523	22.869	8.057	573	23.937	8.306
424	20.591	7.513	474	21.772	7.797	524	22.891	8.062	574	23.958	8.311
425	20.616	7.518	475	21.794	7.802	525	22.913	8.067	575	23.979	8.316
426	20.640	7.524	476	21.817	7.808	526	22.935	8.072	576	24.000	8.320
427	20.664	7.530	477	21.840	7.813	527	22.956	8.077	577	24.021	8.325
428	20.688	7.536	478	21.863	7.819	528	22.978	8.082	578	24.042	8.330
429	20.712	7.542	479	21.886	7.824	529	23.000	8.088	579	24.062	8.335
430	20.736	7.548	**480**	21.909	7.830	**530**	23.022	8.093	**580**	24.083	8.340
431	20.761	7.554	481	21.932	7.835	531	23.043	8.098	581	24.104	8.344
432	20.785	7.560	482	21.954	7.841	532	23.065	8.103	582	24.125	8.349
433	20.809	7.565	483	21.977	7.846	533	23.087	8.108	583	24.145	8.354
434	20.833	7.571	484	22.000	7.851	534	23.108	8.113	584	24.166	8.359
435	20.857	7.577	485	22.023	7.857	535	23.130	8.118	585	24.187	8.363
436	20.881	7.583	486	22.045	7.862	536	23.152	8.123	586	24.207	8.368
437	20.905	7.589	487	22.068	7.868	537	23.173	8.128	587	24.228	8.373
438	20.928	7.594	488	22.091	7.873	538	23.195	8.133	588	24.249	8.378
439	20.952	7.600	489	22.113	7.878	539	23.216	8.138	589	24.269	8.382
440	20.976	7.606	**490**	22.136	7.884	**540**	23.238	8.143	**590**	24.290	8.387
441	21.000	7.612	491	22.159	7.889	541	23.259	8.148	591	24.310	8.392
442	21.024	7.617	492	22.181	7.894	542	23.281	8.153	592	24.331	8.397
443	21.048	7.623	493	22.204	7.900	543	23.302	8.158	593	24.352	8.401
444	21.071	7.629	494	22.226	7.905	544	23.324	8.163	594	24.372	8.406
445	21.095	7.635	495	22.249	7.910	545	23.345	8.168	595	24.393	8.411
446	21.119	7.640	496	22.271	7.916	546	23.367	8.173	596	24.413	8.416
447	21.142	7.646	497	22.293	7.921	547	23.388	8.178	597	24.434	8.420
448	21.166	7.652	498	22.316	7.926	548	23.409	8.183	598	24.454	8.425
449	21.190	7.657	499	22.338	7.932	549	23.431	8.188	599	24.474	8.430
450	21.213	7.663	**500**	22.361	7.937	**550**	23.452	8.193	**600**	24.495	8.434

TABLE IV. SQUARE ROOTS AND CUBE ROOTS, 601–800

NO.	SQUARE ROOT	CUBE ROOT	NO.	SQUARE ROOT	CUBE ROOT	NO.	SQUARE ROOT	CUBE ROOT	NO.	SQUARE ROOT	CUBE ROOT
601	24.515	8.439	651	25.515	8.667	701	26.476	8.883	751	27.404	9.090
602	24.536	8.444	652	25.534	8.671	702	26.495	8.887	752	27.423	9.094
603	24.556	8.448	653	25.554	8.676	703	26.514	8.892	753	27.441	9.098
604	24.576	8.453	654	25.573	8.680	704	26.533	8.896	754	27.459	9.102
605	24.597	8.458	655	25.593	8.685	705	26.552	8.900	755	27.477	9.106
606	24.617	8.462	656	25.612	8.689	706	26.571	8.904	756	27.495	9.110
607	24.637	8.467	657	25.632	8.693	707	26.589	8.909	757	27.514	9.114
608	24.658	8.472	658	25.652	8.698	708	26.608	8.913	758	27.532	9.118
609	24.678	8.476	659	25.671	8.702	709	26.627	8.917	759	27.550	9.122
610	24.698	8.481	660	25.690	8.707	710	26.646	8.921	760	27.568	9.126
611	24.718	8.486	661	25.710	8.711	711	26.665	8.925	761	27.586	9.130
612	24.739	8.490	662	25.729	8.715	712	26.683	8.929	762	27.604	9.134
613	24.759	8.495	663	25.749	8.720	713	26.702	8.934	763	27.622	9.138
614	24.779	8.499	664	25.768	8.724	714	26.721	8.938	764	27.641	9.142
615	24.799	8.504	665	25.788	8.729	715	26.740	8.942	765	27.659	9.146
616	24.819	8.509	666	25.807	8.733	716	26.758	8.946	766	27.677	9.150
617	24.839	8.513	667	25.826	8.737	717	26.777	8.950	767	27.695	9.154
618	24.860	8.518	668	25.846	8.742	718	26.796	8.955	768	27.713	9.158
619	24.880	8.522	669	25.865	8.746	719	26.814	8.959	769	27.731	9.162
620	24.900	8.527	670	25.884	8.750	720	26.833	8.963	770	27.749	9.166
621	24.920	8.532	671	25.904	8.755	721	26.851	8.967	771	27.767	9.170
622	24.940	8.536	672	25.923	8.759	722	26.870	8.971	772	27.785	9.174
623	24.960	8.541	673	25.942	8.763	723	26.889	8.975	773	27.803	9.178
624	24.980	8.545	674	25.962	8.768	724	26.907	8.979	774	27.821	9.182
625	25.000	8.550	675	25.981	8.772	725	26.926	8.984	775	27.839	9.185
626	25.020	8.554	676	26.000	8.776	726	26.944	8.988	776	27.857	9.189
627	25.040	8.559	677	26.019	8.781	727	26.963	8.992	777	27.875	9.193
628	25.060	8.564	678	26.038	8.785	728	26.981	8.996	778	27.893	9.197
629	25.080	8.568	679	26.058	8.789	729	27.000	9.000	779	27.911	9.201
630	25.100	8.573	680	26.077	8.794	730	27.019	9.004	780	27.928	9.205
631	25.120	8.577	681	29.096	8.798	731	27.037	9.008	781	27.946	9.209
632	25.140	8.582	682	26.115	8.802	732	27.056	9.012	782	27.964	9.213
633	25.159	8.586	683	26.134	8.807	733	27.074	9.016	783	27.982	9.217
634	25.179	8.591	684	26.153	8.811	734	27.092	9.021	784	28.000	9.221
635	25.199	8.595	685	26.173	8.815	735	27.111	9.025	785	28.018	9.225
636	25.219	8.600	686	26.192	8.819	736	27.129	9.029	786	28.036	9.229
637	25.239	8.604	687	26.211	8.824	737	27.148	9.033	787	28.054	9.233
638	25.259	8.609	688	26.230	8.828	738	27.166	9.037	788	28.071	9.237
639	25.278	8.613	689	26.249	8.832	739	27.185	9.041	789	28.089	9.240
640	25.298	8.618	690	26.268	8.837	740	27.203	9.045	790	28.107	9.244
641	25.318	8.622	691	26.287	8.841	741	27.221	9.049	791	28.125	9.248
642	25.338	8.627	692	26.306	8.845	742	27.240	9.053	792	28.142	9.252
643	25.357	8.631	693	26.325	8.849	743	27.258	9.057	793	28.160	9.256
644	25.377	8.636	694	26.344	8.854	744	27.276	9.061	794	28.178	9.260
645	25.397	8.640	695	26.363	8.858	745	27.295	9.065	795	28.196	9.264
646	25.417	8.645	696	26.382	8.862	746	27.313	9.069	796	28.213	9.268
647	25.436	8.649	697	26.401	8.866	747	27.331	9.073	797	28.231	9.272
648	25.456	8.653	698	26.420	8.871	748	27.350	9.078	798	28.249	9.275
649	25.475	8.658	699	26.439	8.875	749	27.368	9.082	799	28.267	9.279
650	25.495	8.662	700	26.458	8.879	750	27.386	9.086	800	28.284	9.283

TABLE IV. SQUARE ROOTS AND CUBE ROOTS, 801–1000

NO.	SQUARE ROOT	CUBE ROOT	NO.	SQUARE ROOT	CUBE ROOT	NO.	SQUARE ROOT	CUBE ROOT	NO.	SQUARE ROOT	CUBE ROOT
801	28.302	9.287	851	29.172	9.476	901	30.017	9.658	951	30.838	9.834
802	28.320	9.291	852	29.189	9.480	902	30.033	9.662	952	30.854	9.837
803	28.337	9.295	853	29.206	9.484	903	30.050	9.666	953	30.871	9.841
804	28.355	9.299	854	29.223	9.488	904	30.067	9.669	954	30.887	9.844
805	28.373	9.302	855	29.240	9.491	905	30.083	9.673	955	30.903	9.848
806	28.390	9.306	856	29.257	9.495	906	30.100	9.676	956	30.919	9.851
807	28.408	9.310	857	29.275	9.499	907	30.116	9.680	957	30.935	9.855
808	28.425	9.314	858	29.292	9.502	908	30.133	9.683	958	30.952	9.858
809	28.443	9.318	859	29.309	9.506	909	30.150	9.687	959	30.968	9.861
810	28.460	9.322	860	29.326	9.510	910	30.166	9.691	960	30.984	9.865
811	28.478	9.326	861	29.343	9.513	911	30.183	9.694	961	31.000	9.868
812	28.496	9.329	862	29.360	9.517	912	30.199	9.698	962	31.016	9.872
813	28.513	9.333	863	29.377	9.521	913	30.216	9.701	963	31.032	9.875
814	28.531	9.337	864	29.394	9.524	914	30.232	9.705	964	31.048	9.879
815	28.548	9.341	865	29.411	9.528	915	30.249	9.708	965	31.064	9.882
816	28.566	9.345	866	29.428	9.532	916	30.265	9.712	966	31.081	9.885
817	28.583	9.348	867	29.445	9.535	917	30.282	9.715	967	31.097	9.889
818	28.601	9.352	868	29.462	9.539	918	30.299	9.719	968	31.113	9.892
819	28.618	9.356	869	29.479	9.543	919	30.315	9.722	969	31.129	9.896
820	28.636	9.360	870	29.496	9.546	920	30.332	9.726	970	31.145	9.889
821	28.653	9.364	871	29.513	9.550	921	30.348	9.729	971	31.161	9.902
822	28.671	9.368	872	29.530	9.554	922	30.364	9.733	972	31.177	9.906
823	28.688	9.371	873	29.547	9.557	923	30.381	9.736	973	31.193	9.909
824	28.705	9.375	874	29.563	9.561	924	30.397	9.740	974	31.209	9.913
825	28.723	9.379	875	29.580	9.565	925	30.414	9.743	975	31.225	9.916
826	28.740	9.383	876	29.597	9.568	926	30.430	9.747	976	31.241	9.919
827	28.758	9.386	877	29.614	9.572	927	30.447	9.750	977	31.257	9.923
828	28.775	9.390	878	29.631	9.576	928	30.463	9.754	978	31.273	9.926
829	28.792	9.394	879	29.648	9.579	929	30.479	9.758	979	31.289	9.930
830	28.810	9.398	880	29.665	9.583	930	30.496	9.761	980	31.305	9.933
831	28.827	9.402	881	29.682	9.586	931	30.512	9.764	981	31.321	9.936
832	28.844	9.405	882	29.698	9.590	932	30.529	9.768	982	31.337	9.940
833	28.862	9.409	883	29.715	9.594	933	30.545	9.771	983	31.353	9.943
834	28.879	9.413	884	29.732	9.597	934	30.561	9.775	984	31.369	9.946
835	28.896	9.417	885	29.749	9.601	935	30.578	9.778	985	31.385	9.950
836	28.914	9.420	886	29.766	9.605	936	30.594	9.782	986	31.401	9.953
837	28.931	9.424	887	29.783	9.608	937	30.610	9.785	987	31.417	9.956
838	28.948	9.428	888	29.799	9.612	938	30.627	9.789	988	31.432	9.960
839	28.966	9.432	889	29.816	9.615	939	30.643	9.792	989	31.448	9.963
840	28.983	9.435	890	29.833	9.619	940	30.659	9.796	990	31.464	9.967
841	29.000	9.439	891	29.850	9.623	941	30.676	9.799	991	31.480	9.970
842	29.017	9.443	892	29.866	9.626	942	30.692	9.803	992	31.496	9.973
843	29.034	9.447	893	29.883	9.630	943	30.708	9.806	993	31.512	9.977
844	29.052	9.450	894	29.900	9.633	944	30.725	9.810	994	31.528	9.980
845	29.069	9.454	895	29.917	9.637	945	30.741	9.813	995	31.544	9.983
846	29.086	9.458	896	29.933	9.641	946	30.757	9.817	996	31.559	9.987
847	29.103	9.462	897	29.950	9.644	947	30.773	9.820	997	31.575	9.990
848	29.120	9.465	898	29.967	9.648	948	30.790	9.824	998	31.591	9.993
849	29.138	9.469	899	29.983	9.651	949	30.806	9.827	999	31.607	9.997
850	29.155	9.473	900	30.000	9.655	950	30.822	9.830	1000	31.623	10.000

Index

Abscissa, 19
Absolute value, 13, 305
  of a function, 490
Accuracy, 101
Addition law of probability, 76
Algebra, laws of, 6
  of sets, 6
Altitude of a solid, 126
Ambiguous case, 224
Amplitude, 169, 305
Angles, acute, 149
  between two planes, 644
  dihedral, 113
  face, 120
  negative, 159
  of depression, 219
  of elevation, 219
  of inclination, 328
  plane, 113
  polyhedral, 120
  positive, 153
  quadrantal, 158
  reference, 154
  trihedral, 120
Angular measurement, 97, 113
Apothem, 125
Approximate computations, 100, 101
Approximate numbers, 100
Arc cosecant, 185
Arc cosine, 179
Arc cotangent, 182
Arc secant, 184
Arc sine, 178
Arc tangent, 182
Area, 118, 124, 233
  Hero's formula for, 124, 234
  lateral, 126
  measurement, 98
  of a regular polygon, 125
  of a triangle, 233, 631
  total, 126
  under a graph, 572
Argand plane, 304
Argument, 305
Arrangement, 45
Associative laws, 6, 265
  for addition, 272, 288
  for multiplication, 272, 288
Assumed statements, 262

Asymmetric, 265
Asymptote, horizontal, 461
  multiplicity of an, 458
  of a hyperbola, 385
  vertical, 458
Average, 550
Axioms, 262
Axis of, a hyperbola, conjugate, 384
  a hyperbola, transverse, 384
  a parabola, 372
  an ellipse, major, 378
  an ellipse, minor, 378
  imaginaries, 304
  reals, 304
  revolution, 136
  symmetry, 33, 367

Base of, a logarithmic function, 479
  a solid, 122, 125
Bernoulli, density function, 508
  experiment, 508
  random variable, 508
Binary operation, 5, 261
Binomial, density function, 508
  random variable, 508
    mean of a, 510
    variance of a, 510
  series, 564
  theorem, 61
Bounds, 533

Cardinal number, 8
Cartesian, coordinates, 19, 610
  equation, 488
  plane, 19
  product, 19
  set, 19
Cavalieri's theorem, 134
Center of, a hyperbola, 383
  an ellipse, 377
  any regular polygon, 125
  symmetry, 367, 418
Centroid, 136
Chebyshev's Theorem, 501
Circle, 24, 364, 389, 392
  exterior point of a, 370
  interior point of a, 370
  standard form of equation of a, 365

749

INDEX

Closure, 11, 261, 265, 274, 288, 300
Coefficients, 327, 415
   relation to roots of a polynomial equation, 450
Cofactor, 680
Cofunctions, 209
Collinear points, 607
Combinations, 45, 55
   notations for, 57
Commutative laws, 6
   for addition, 272, 288
   for multiplication, 272, 288
Complement of a set, 5
Complementary event, 77
Complementation, 5
Complex numbers, 298
   conjugate, 299, 437
   in exponential form, 306
   in polar form, 306
   in rectangular form, 298
   in trigonometric form, 305
   products and quotients of, 308
   representations of, 303
Complex plane, 304
Conditional probability, 80
Cone, frustum of a, 127
   oblique circular, 127
   right circular, 126
   slant height of a, 127
Congruence classes of integers, 290
Congruent figures, 128
Conic sections, 392
   degenerate, 393
Conical surface, 120
Conjugate complex numbers, 299
Consistent, 263, 342
Constant, 327
   of proportionality, 403
Continuous function, 578
Conversion factors, 97
Coordinate plane, 19
Coordinate systems, left-handed, 611
   right-handed, 611
Coordinates, 12, 610
   cylindrical, 190
   homogeneous, 702
   nonhomogeneous, 702
   plane, 19
   polar, 187
Coplanar lines, 105

Cosecant, 149, 154, 205
   graph of, 173
Cosine, 149, 154, 205
   graph of, 166
Cotangent, 149, 154, 205
   graph of, 171
Counter-example, 261
Cramer's Rule, 353, 684
Cube, 121
Curve, 118
   closed, 118
   open, 118
   simple, 118
Cylinder, oblique circular, 126
   right circular, 126
Cylindrical, coordinates, 190
   surface, 119

Decimal, infinite, 293
   nonrepeating infinite, 294
   nonterminating, 293
   repeating infinite, 294
   terminating, 296
Defined over a set, 261
Degree of a, polynomial, 416
   power function, 473
   term, 415
De Moivre's theorem, 313
De Morgan's laws, 11
Derivative, 584
Descartes' Rule of Signs, 435
Determinant, 345
   of a matrix, 679
   of the coefficients, 345
   rank of a, 346
   second order, 345
   third order, 351
Determined, a triangle is, 217
Die, (dice), 67
Difference, 278, 549
Differences, method of, 536
Dihedral angle, 113
Dilation, 718
Direction, 597
   angles, 624
   cosines, 625
   numbers, 626
Directrix, 119
   of a parabola, 371
Discrete set, 518

INDEX

Discriminant, 357
Disjoint sets, 5
Distance, 22
  between two figures, 105
  formulas, 23, 26, 109
  of a point from a figure, 105
  of a point from a line, 104
  of a point from a plane, 105
Distributive laws, 7, 273, 288
Domain, 16, 29, 178, 385
  of a logarithmic function, 479
  of a polynomial, 417
  of a power function, 476
  of an exponential function, 477
Domination principle, 547
Double-angle formulas, 238

Edge of a, dihedral angle, 113
  half-plane, 113
  polyhedron, 121
  tetrahedron, 125
Element, generating a surface, 126
  of a matrix, 340
  of a sequence, 534
  of a set, 1
Ellipse, 377, 391, 392
  center of an, 377
  eccentricity of an, 379
  exterior point of an, 379
  focal width of an, 378
  foci of an, 377
  interior point of an, 380
  latera recta of an, 378
  major axis of an, 378
  minor axis of an, 378
  standard form of equation of an, 379
  vertices of an, 377
Empty set, 2
End point, of a half-line, 113
Enumeration, fundamental principle of, 47
Equation(s), 16, 488
  Cartesian, 488
  conditional, 16
  depressed, 423
  exponential, 483
  identity, 16
  impossible, 16
  involving circular functions, 245

  linear, in several variables, 348
  in x and y, 333
  intercept form, 330
  point-slope form, 329
  slope-intercept form, 329
  two-point form, 329
  linearly dependent, 342
  linearly independent, 343
  logarithmic, 483
  of a line, 329, 637
  of a plane, 633
  of a sphere, 365, 643
  parametric, 488
  polynomial, 423
  systems of, 338
  vector, 637
Equations of a line, parametric, 638
  symmetric, 638
Equivalence relation, 259
Events, 67
  complementary, 77
  exhaustive, 87
  independent, 84
  mutually exclusive, 76
Exhaustion, method of, 531
Expectation, mathematical, 88, 497
Exterior point of, a circle, 370
  a hyperbola, 386
  a parabola, 362
  a polygon, 118
  an ellipse, 379
Faces, of a dihedral angle, 113
  of a tetrahedron, 125
Factor Theorem, 422
Factorial notation, 48
Failure, 68
Fair game, 89
Family of graphs, 358
Fermat, Pierre, 66
Field, 289
Finite, group, 267
  sequence, 535
  series, 549
    arithmetic, 550
    geometric, 552
  set, 1
Focal width of, a hyperbola, 384
  a parabola, 373
  an ellipse, 378

INDEX

Focus of, a hyperbola, 382
  a parabola, 371
  an ellipse, 377
Force, 617
Fractions, partial, 558
Frustum of, a cone, 127
  a pyramid, 127
Functions, 35, 178
  absolute value, 490
  Bernoulli density, 508
  binomial density, 508
  circular, 153, 160, 163, 209, 213
    undefined, 158
  even, 417
  exponential, 477
  greatest integer, 491
  hyperbolic cosine, 482
  hyperbolic sine, 482
  hypergeometric density, 515
  linear, of n vectors, 605
    of x, 36, 333
    of x and y, 333
  logarithmic, 479
    common, 481
    natural, 481
  multinomial density, 514
  odd, 418
  periodic, 166, 245
  Poisson density, 517
  power, 473
    of degree n, 473
  probability, 68
    density, 493
    distribution, 504
  quadratic, 355
  rational, 457
    defined, 457
    undefined, 457
  set, 68
  trigonometric, 149
  uniform density, 513
  wrapping, 115
Fundamental Theorem of Algebra, 431

Generator of a sequence, 534
Geometric figures, 104, 118
  solids, 121
Graphing, 495
  by composition of ordinates, 175
  special methods of, 174

Graphs of, a point, 12, 19
  a statement, 16
  linear relations, 333
  secants and cosecants, 173
  sines and cosines, 161, 166
  tangents and cotangents, 171
Great circle of a sphere, 127
Groups, 266
  commutative, 267
  finite, 267
  infinite, 267

Half-angle formulas, 238
Half-lines, 113
Half-planes, 113, 335
Hero's formula, 124, 234
Hyperbola, 382, 391, 392
  asymptotes of a, 385
  center of a, 383
  conjugate axis of a, 384
  equilateral, 394
  exterior points of a, 386
  focal width of a, 384
  foci of a, 382
  interior points of a, 386
  latera recta of a, 384
  rectangular, 394
  standard form of equation of a, 386
  transverse axis of a, 384
  vertices of a, 384
Hypergeometric density function, 515
Hypotenuse, 147

Idempotent law, 7
Identities, 16, 206, 240
Identity elements, 266
  additive, 7, 288
  multiplicative, 7, 288
Inconsistent, 263, 342
Independent events, 84
Inequality, absolute, 16
  conditional, 16
  false statement of, 16
  linear, in x and y, 336
  polynomial, 454
  symbols, 12
Infinite, decimal, 293
  group, 267
  sequence, 535
  series, 556
  set, 2

Initial side, 153
Inner rectangles, 531
Integers, 12, 272, 273, 278
 congruence classes of, 290
 relatively prime, 441
Integral domains, 288
Interior point of, a circle, 370
 a hyperbola, 386
 a parabola, 362
 a polygon, 118
 an ellipse, 380
Interpolation, 213
Intersection of sets, 5, 17
Intransitive, 265
Inverse, additive, 277, 288
 elements, 266
 multiplicative, 284
 of a matrix, 686
 of cosecant, 184
 of cosine, 178
 of cotangent, 182
 of secant, 184
 of sine, 178
 of tangent, 182
 relations, 31
Irrational numbers, 13, 294
Irreflexive, 265
Isomorphic, 696
Iteration process, 462

Kronecker delta, 676

Lateral surface, 126
Lattice, 20, 46
 point, 20
Latus rectum of, a hyperbola, 384
 a parabola, 373
 an ellipse, 378
Law of cosines, 229
Law of sines, 223
 ambiguous case, 224
Law of tangents, 231
Law of vector addition, 598
Limit, 533
 of a function, 576
 of a sequence of numbers, 541
Line, 104, 118
 broken, 118
 parametric equations of a, 638
 symmetric equations of a, 638
 vector equation of a, 637

Line segment, 104
 division into a given ratio of a, 111, 614
 externally, 616
 internally, 616
Line values of circular functions, 163
Linear expressions, 327, 333, 398
Linear measurement, 97, 104
Linear transformation, of three variables, 701
 of two variables, 701
Listing method, 1
Location principle, 446
Logarithm, 481
Lower bound of roots of an equation, 448

Mathematical expectation, 88
 of a random variable, 497
Mathematical induction, 566
Mathematical probability, 67
Mathematical system, 262
Matrices, conformable for addition, 662
 conformable for multiplication, 667
 equal, 662
 Pauli, 671
 postmultiplication of, 672
 premultiplication of, 672
 product of, 667
 systems of, 693
Matrix, 340, 661
 augmented, 346, 684
 column index of a, 661
 column of a, 340
 complex, 677
 conjugate of a, 677
 determinant of a, 679
 diagonal, 671
 diagonal element of a, 671
 element of a, 340, 661
  cofactor of an, 680
 Hermitian, 678
 identity, 672
 inverse of a, 686
 line of a, 681
 main diagonal of a, 671
 nonsingular, 687
 null, 663
 of the coefficients, 346
 order of a, 662

INDEX

principal diagonal of a, 671
rank of a, 346, 683
real, 661
row index of a, 661
row of a, 340
scalar, 671
singular, 687
skew-Hermitian, 678
skew-symmetric, 673
square, 662
submatrix of a, 679
symmetric, 673
transpose of a, 672
transposed conjugate of a, 677
zero, 663
Maximum point, 356
relative, 586
Mean, 497
arithmetic, 550
geometric, 551
of a binomial random variable, 510
proportional, 551
Median, 504
Member of a set, 1
Membership, 1
Mid-point formulas, 110
Midsection, 131
Minimum point, 356
relative, 586
Mode, 504
Model, 263
Modulo m, 290
Modulus, 305
Multinomial density function, 514
Multiple-angle formulas, 237, 238
Multiplication law of probability, 83
Multiplicity of, a root, 433, 458
an asymptote, 458
an element in a permutation, 52
Mutually exclusive events, 76

Nappes, 120
n-**ary operation,** 261
Natural numbers, 11
Negative, integer, 278
of a number, 277
Nonnegative, 26
Nonreflexive, 265
Nonsymmetric, 265
Nontransitive, 265
Null sequence, 539

Null set, 2
Number line, 12
Number system, 291
Numbers, as distances, 22
cardinal, 8
complex, 298
imaginary, mixed, 298
pure, 298
integers, 12, 273
irrational, 13, 294
natural, 11
nonnegative, 26
rational, 13, 281, 441
real, 13, 293
Numeral, 16

Odds, 78
Operations, 261
binary, 5, 261
unary, 5, 260
with sets, 4
Order, 12
algebraic, 13
numerical, 13
of a matrix, 662
relations, 12, 259, 273
is equal to, 12
is greater than, 12
is less than, 12
Ordered pairs, 19, 333
Ordinate, 19, 175, 531
Origin, 12
Outer rectangles, 533

Pappus, theorems of, 136, 137
Parabola, 356, 371, 391, 392
axis of a, 372
directrix of a, 371
exterior point of a, 362
focal width of a, 373
focus of a, 371
interior point of a, 362
latus rectum of a, 373
standard form of equation of a, 373, 374
vertex of a, 372
Parameter, 21, 488
Partial fractions, 558
Pascal, Blaise, 66
Pascal's triangle, 60

754

INDEX

Period of a function, 167
Periodic functions, 166
Permutations, 45, 48, 52
  circular, 53
  linear, 53
  special, 51
  symbols for, 50
Phase, 167
Piercing point, 640
Plane, angle, 113
  equation of a, 633
  figure, 118
  section, 124, 131
Point, 118
  of a sample space, 67
Poisson density function, 517
Polar coordinates, 187, 193
Polygon, 118
  convex, 118
  exterior of a, 118
  interior of a, 118
  regular, 124
Polyhedral angle, 120
  face angle of a, 120
Polyhedron, 121
  convex, 122
  diagonal of a, 121
  diagonal of a face of a, 121
Polynomial, 415
  binomial, 415
  complex, 416
  cubic, 416
  degree of a, 416
  domain of a, 417
  equation, 423
  expression, 415
  in x, 415
  inequality, 454
  monomial, 415
  nested form of a, 430
  of higher degree, 416
  quartic, 416
  rational, 416
  real, 416
  trinomial, 415
Positive integer, 278
Postulate, 262
  of Finite Induction, 566
Powers of x, descending, 416
Precision, 99
Principal values, 179, 182, 184

Prism, 122
  oblique, 122
  rectangular, 125
  right, 122
Prismatoid, 122
  bases of a, 122
  lateral edges of a, 122
Prismoid, 122
Prismoidal formula, 131
Probability, *a priori*, 71
  addition law of, 76
  bar chart, 495
  conditional, 80
  density function, 493
  distribution function, 504
  empirical, 69
  for continuous variables, 518
  function, 68, 493
  histogram, 495
  mathematical, 67
  measure, 494
  multiplication law of, 83
  statistical, 69
Product formulas, 243
Progression, arithmetic, 549
  geometric, 551
Proportion, 402
Proportional, 128
Pyramid, 122
  base of a, 122
Pythagorean relations, 206

Quadratic, equation, 398
  expressions in two variables, 389, 398
  functions of one variable, 355
  real, 355
Quotient, 284
  of complex numbers, 310

Radian, 115
Radius, of the inscribed circle of a triangle, 234
Random selection, 66
Random variable, 493, 508
  mathematical expectation of a, 497
  mean of a, 497, 510
  standard deviation of a, 500
  variance of a, 499, 510

INDEX

Range, 29, 178, 385
  of a logarithmic function, 479
  of a power function, 476
  of an exponential function, 477
Rate of change, average, 582
  instantaneous, 584
Ratio, 402
  of similitude, 128
  trigonometric, 149
Rational functions, 457
Rational numbers, 13, 281
  improper, 285
  in lowest terms, 441
  in reduced form, 441
  proper, 285
Ray, 104
Real numbers, 13, 293
Reciprocal, 284
  relations, 205
Rectangular prism, 125
Rectangular region, 4
Recursion formula, 512
Reference angle, 154
Reflection, 714
Reflexive, 260
Relation, defined over, 259
Relations, 28, 178, 265
  equivalence, 259
  inverse, 31
  linear, 333
  order, 259, 273
  Pythagorean, 206
  reciprocal, 205
  reflexive, 35, 260
  symmetric, 35, 260
  systems of, 395
  transitive, 260
Remainder Theorem, 421
Ring, 693
  commutative, 696
Root, 338, 357, 423, 448, 457
  double, 433
  extraneous, 484
  isolation of a, 445
  multiple, 433
  multiplicity of a, 433, 458
  of a rational function, 457
  $\sqrt[r]{N}$, 462
  rational, 439
  relation to coefficients, 450
  simple, 433
  triple, 433

Roster method, 1
Rotation, 368, 707
Rounded off, 102
Rule of Signs, Descartes', 435

Sample point, 67
Sample space, 67, 71
  fundamental, 74
Scalar, 595
  multiplication of a vector by a, 601
Scientific notation, 101
Secant, 149, 154, 205
  graph of a, 173
Semi-perimeter, 234
Sequence, 13, 534
  arithmetic, 549
    common difference of an, 549
  finite, 535
  geometric, 551
    common ratio of a, 551
  infinite, 535
  null, 539
Series, binomial, 564
  finite, 549
    arithmetic, 550
    geometric, 552
    sum of a, 549
  infinite, 556
    convergent, 557
    divergent, 557
    nth partial sum of an, 556
    sum of an, 557
  power, 560
Set, cardinal number of a, 8
  closed, 11
  elements of a, 1
  empty, 2
  finite, 1
  function, 68
  infinite, 2
  members of a, 1
  null, 2
  of ordered pairs, 19
  solution, 2
  truth, 2
  universal, 2
Set-builder notation, 2
Sets, algebra of, 6
  disjoint, 5
  equal, 2
  isomorphic, 696
  operations with, 4

INDEX

Side, adjacent, 148
   of a plane angle, 113
   opposite, 148
Significant digits, 101
Similar, figures, 128
   triangles, 147
Simple curve, 118
Simplifying a trigonometric expression, 210
Simultaneous equations, 338
   solution by matrices, 349
Sine, 149, 154, 205
   graph of a, 166
Skew lines, 105
Slant height, of a cone, 127
   of a cylinder, 126
Slope of a graph, 585
Slope of a line, 327
Solids, 121
   of revolution, 136
Solution set, 2, 17, 338, 423
Space figure, 118
Sphere, 24, 365
   equation of a, 643
   great circle of a, 127
   small circle of a, 128
   zone of a, 128
Standard deviation, 500
Standard form, 365, 367
Standard position, 153
Statements, 16
   classification of, 16
   equations, 16
   inequalities, 16
Straight line test, 35
Subsets, 2
   proper, 2
Success, 68
Summation symbol, 569
   index of a, 569
Surface, 118
Symmetric, 260
   with respect to a line m, 366
   with respect to a point M, 367
   with respect to the origin, 366
   with respect to the x-axis, 366
   with respect to the y-axis, 366
Symmetry, 33
   axis of, 33, 367
   center of, 367, 418
Synthetic division, 426

Systems, consistent, 342
   equivalent, 339
   inconsistent, 342
   of equations, 338
   of linear relations, 338
   of linearly dependent equations, 342
   of linearly independent equations, 343
   of relations, 395

Tangent, 149, 154, 205
   graph of a, 171
   of half-angles, 236
   plane, 644
Term(s), 415
   coefficient of a, 415
   degree of a, 415
   literal part of a, 415
   numerical coefficient of a, 415
   of a sequence, 534
   similar, 415
Terminal side, 153
Ternary operation, 261
Tetrahedron, 125
Three-dimensional figure, 118
Torus, 136
Transformation, 365, 701
   dilation, 718
   fixed point of a, 710
   image of a point under a, 704
   invariant property under a, 707, 714
   reflection, 714
   rigid motion, 714, 717
   rotation, 368, 707
   shearing, 721
   stretching, 718
   translation, 365, 700
Transitive, 260
Translation, 365, 700
Tree diagram, 46
Triangles, oblique, 217
   right, 147, 217
   similar, 147
   solution of oblique, 223, 229, 231
   solution of right, 217
   solution of special, 151
Trigonometric functions, 149
Trigonometric ratios, 149
Trigonometry, 149
Trihedral angle, 120

INDEX

Truncated, cone, 127
   cylinder, 127
   prism, 127
   pyramid, 127
Truth set, 2

Unary operation, 5, 260
Uniform density function, 513
Union of sets, 5, 17
Unit circle, 115, 163
Unit, imaginary, 298
Unit point, 22
Units of measure, 97
Unity, 285, 288
Universe, 2
Upper bound of roots of an equation, 448

Variable, 16, 493, 508
   continuous, 518
   dependent, 29
   discrete, 518
   domain of a, 16
   independent, 29
   random, 493
   real, 16
Variance, 499
   of a binomial random variable, 510
Variation, 402
   direct, 403
   in signs, 435
   inverse, 403
   joint, 403
Vector, 104, 596
   addition, 598
   components of a, 612
   direction angles of a, 624
   direction cosines of a, 625
   direction numbers of a, 626
   direction of a, 597
   equation of a line, 637
   equation of a plane, 633
   initial point of a, 596
   magnitude of a, 595
   multiplication by a scalar, 601
   null, 597
   origin of a, 596
   position, 612
   terminal point of a, 596
   unit, 597
   zero, 597
Vectors, cross product of, 629
   dot product of, 619
   equal, 597
   linear function of, 605
   parallel, 602
   parallelogram law of, 599
   perpendicular, 620
   right-handed orientation of unit, 611
   scalar product of, 619
   triangle law of, 599
   triple scalar product of, 635
   vector product of, 629
Venn diagram, 5
Vertex of, a cone, 126
   a parabola, 372
   a plane angle, 113
   a pyramid, 126
   a trihedral angle, 120
Vertices of, a hyperbola, 384
   a polyhedron, 121
   a tetrahedron, 125
   an ellipse, 377
Volume, 118, 130
   measurement of, 98
   of a parallelepiped, 642

Well-defined, operations, 261
   sets, 1
Work, 617
Wrapping function, 115

x**-axis,** 19
x**-coordinate,** 19
x**-intercept,** 330, 356

y**-axis,** 19
y**-coordinate,** 19
y**-intercept,** 329, 356

Zero, 278, 288
   divisors, 288
   of a function, 356
0!, 49
Zone of a sphere, 128
   of one base, 128